14th INTERNATIONAL SYMPOSIUM ON
PROCESS SYSTEMS ENGINEERING

VOLUME 2

COMPUTER-AIDED CHEMICAL ENGINEERING, 49

14ᵗʰ INTERNATIONAL SYMPOSIUM ON PROCESS SYSTEMS ENGINEERING

VOLUME 2

Edited by

Yoshiyuki Yamashita
Professor and Chair of Department of Chemical Engineering
Tokyo University of Agriculture and Technology (TUAT), Tokyo, Japan
yama_pse@cc.tuat.ac.jp

Manabu Kano
Professor, Department of Systems Science
Kyoto University, Kyoto, Japan
manabu@human.sys.i.kyoto-u.ac.jp

ELSEVIER

Amsterdam – Boston – Heidelberg – London – New York – Oxford
Paris – San Diego – San Francisco – Singapore – Sydney – Tokyo

Elsevier
Radarweg 29, PO Box 211, 1000 AE Amsterdam, Netherlands
The Boulevard, Langford Lane, Kidlington, Oxford OX5 1GB, UK
50 Hampshire Street, 5th Floor, Cambridge, MA 02139, USA

Notices
Knowledge and best practice in this field are constantly changing. As new research and experience
broaden our understanding, changes in research methods, professional practices, or medical treatment
may become necessary.

Practitioners and researchers must always rely on their own experience and knowledge in evaluating
and using any information, methods, compounds, or experiments described herein. In using such
information or methods they should be mindful of their own safety and the safety of others, including
parties for whom they have a professional responsibility.

To the fullest extent of the law, neither the Publisher nor the authors, contributors, or editors, assume
any liability for any injury and/or damage to persons or property as a matter of products liability,
negligence or otherwise, or from any use or operation of any methods, products, instructions, or ideas
contained in the material herein.

British Library Cataloguing in Publication Data
A catalogue record for this book is available from the British Library

Library of Congress Cataloging-in-Publication Data
A catalog record for this book is available from the Library of Congress

ISBN (Volume 2): 978-0-443-18725-4
ISBN (Set) :   978-0-323-85159-6
ISSN: 1570-7946

For information on all Elsevier publications visit our
website at https://www.elsevier.com/

  Working together
to grow libraries in
developing countries

ELSEVIER   Book Aid International

www.elsevier.com • www.bookaid.org

Publisher: Susan Dennis
Acquisition Editor: Anita Koch
Editorial Project Manager: Lena Sparks
Production Project Manager: Paul Prasad Chandramohan
Designer: Greg Harris

Typeset by STRAIVE

Contents

Contributed Papers: Modeling, Analysis, and Simulation

Contributed Papers: Optimization Methods and Computational Tools

Contributed Papers: Process Monitoring and Safety

Contributed Papers: Cyber-Physical Systems and Security

Proceedings of the 14th International Symposium on Process Systems Engineering – PSE 2021+
June 19-23, 2022, Kyoto, Japan © 2022 Elsevier B.V. All rights reserved.
http://dx.doi.org/10.1016/B978-0-323-85159-6.50135-4

A combinatorial tool for monitoring flocculation processes: Using non-invasive measurements and hybrid deep learning assisted modelling

Nima Nazemzadeh[a], Josep Serra Olivé[a], Rasmus Fjorbak Nielsen[a], Krist V. Gernaey[a], Martin P. Andersson[b], Seyed Soheil Mansouri[a,*]

[a] Process and Systems Engineering Centre (PROSYS), Department of Chemical and Biochemical Engineering, Technical University of Denmark, Søltofts Plads, Building 228A, 2800 Kgs. Lyngby, Denmark

[b] Combustion and Harmful Emission Control Centre (CHEC), Department of Chemical and Biochemical Engineering, Technical University of Denmark, Søltofts Plads, Building 228A, 2800 Kgs, Lyngby, Denmark

seso@kt.dtu.dk

Abstract

Particulate processes have a wide range of applications in many different industries, from wastewater treatment to the pharmaceutical industry. Despite their extensive applications, control and monitoring of chemical and biochemical processes that contain solid particles are challenging due to the lack of fundamental understanding of the process mechanism and the limited availability of real-time process data. In this study, a hybrid multiscale framework is introduced for flocculation processes as a particulate process, and it is validated against experimental data resulting from the flocculation of silica particles. The variations of the particle size distribution are imposed by varying the pH in different experimental batches. In this study, an integrated hybrid deep learning approach combining deep learning with first principles is implemented to predict the future state of the process. The first-principles model combines a population balance model with surface properties of the particles calculated with computational chemistry, while the deep learning model is a deep neural network.

Keywords: Hybrid modelling, flocculation, interactions, multiscale modelling.

1. Introduction

The flocculation process consists of the separation of solid particles from a liquid medium by the aggregation of two or more particles that collide and cluster as an aggregate/agglomerate. In the flocculation process, the stability of the suspension is influenced by parameters, as the particle properties (charge, morphology, characteristics), properties of the flocculant (concentration, type) or properties of the media (pH, ionic strength). Previous studies have investigated the correlation between media conditions and polyelectrolyte (PE) properties. For example, a low charge density is a limiting factor for polyelectrolyte adsorption and retention. Nevertheless, lower ionic strength results in a decreasing surface charge, which can also decrease the flocculation efficiency of the flocculant. Adsorption can be controlled by the addition of salt (ionic strength) in the PE solution (Scheepers et al., 2021).

In this context, the industry could benefit from the development of a model to predict the optimum flocculant dosage in a particular system. However, specifically in the case of the flocculation process, a hybrid multiscale model can facilitate obtaining more precise predictions of the future state of the process by integrating the physical understanding of the process phenomena with the underlying features of the data. In this case, deep learning models can be used to develop correlations between states of the process that cannot be explained by the available first-principles models.

In this study, the first-principles models are implementations of a population balance model with surface charge properties that are derived from computational methods in chemistry, and the deep learning model is an architecture of deep neural networks (DNNs). These two models are integrated as such that the parameters that are difficult to measure or estimate are being estimated by the DNN and the predictions of the future state of the process are carried out by the first-principles model.

2. Modelling framework

A hybrid multiscale framework is developed based on earlier work (Nazemzadeh et al., 2021a; Nielsen et al., 2020). The inputs for the neural network will be the data collected from the experiments including pH, polymer dosage, particle morphology. Then the neural network will be trained to estimate the kinetic parameters by determining underlying correlations among the process state variables. However, the first-principles model is a discretized population balance model (PBM) with computational and theoretical chemistry models. The PBM is the component that predicts the particle size evolution with the assistance of the parameters estimated from DNN and the surface properties determined from computational and theoretical chemistry models.

The computational chemistry models are employed to calculate the surface charge density, surface potential, and solid-liquid interfacial energy of the particles vs. medium conditions (pH, ionic strength) by using a mean-field model (Andersson et al., 2020). The theoretical chemistry model used in this study is based on the DLVO theory (Yotsumoto and Yoon, 1993). The theory is named after the four scientists (Derjaguin, Landau, Verwey, and Overbeek) that developed the concept. It uses theoretical chemistry approaches to quantify the interaction energy among particles in a system. The implementation of this theory on a silica particle flocculation was demonstrated earlier (Nazemzadeh et al., 2021b). However, in this study, a computational chemistry approach is used rather than a completely theoretical approach to determine the surface interaction among particles. This potentially leads to a more accurate prediction of the surface properties.

In this study, the flocculation process is considered as the combination of aggregation, where particles interact with each other to form bigger particles, and the breakage phenomenon, where flocs break to form smaller sized particles. However, solving the partial integro-differential equation describing the PBM numerically is not trivial, and different methods have been proposed. In this study, the PBM is solved using a discretization method, where the PSD is distributed in size bins where flocs with similar sizes are grouped, to estimate the variation rate of the aggregates during the process (Kumar and Ramkrishna, 1996). The discretized PBM is represented in Eq. (1):

$$\frac{dN_i}{dt} = \sum_{j,k}^{j \geq k} \left(1 - \frac{1}{2}\delta_{j,k}\right)\eta_i\alpha_{j,k}\beta_{j,k}N_jN_k - N_i\sum_k \alpha_{i,k}\beta_{i,k}N_k + \sum_{j \geq i}\gamma_{j,i}S_jN_j - S_iN_i \qquad (1)$$

$$v_{i-1} \leq (v_j + v_k) \leq v_{i+1}$$

Where N_i is the concentration of aggregates in the size bin i, $\delta_{j,k}$ is the Dirac delta function to avoid calculating collision of the same size particles twice, η is a proportional coefficient assigning the fraction of the floc v_i from the aggregate $(v_j + v_k)$, α is the collision efficiency, β is the collision frequency of two aggregates, γ represents the breakage distribution function, and S is the breakage rate of the flocs.

The hybrid model framework is represented in Figure 1. This modelling framework is developed based on the previous work (Nazemzadeh et al., 2021a; Nielsen et al., 2020), which integrates computational chemistry calculations within the population balance model to more accurately estimate the kinetic parameters. The output of the neural network will be the unknown parameters of the population balance model that cannot be explained with the first-principles model. The population balance model evaluates the particle size evolution through time based on the kinetic rates, the data collected from experiments, and complementary non-observable information estimating the interaction energies from computational chemistry approaches. It must be noted that the framework is structured such that density functional theory is carried out in the outer loop of the hybrid model. To evaluate the deviation of the predictions from experimental data an L1norm loss function is defined, which determines the absolute differences between the model-based predictions and the experimental data.

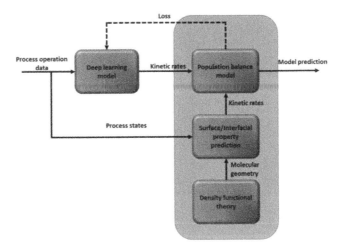

Figure 1: An overview of the hybrid multiscale framework

3. Application example

The proposed hybrid model framework is demonstrated through a laboratory-scale flocculation with silica particles in water, a common model system for flocculation. The particle size distribution is monitored within different batches by monitoring pH as the key process variable. The material and methods are fully described in (Nazemzadeh et al., 2021a). According to previous experiments, pH must be kept between 2 and 3, as this corresponds to the point of zero charge (PZC) (Barisik et al., 2014), overcoming the repulsion forces between particles with the same charge. This is also illustrated by our computational chemistry calculation (mean-field model) in Figure 2. The particles are neutral within the claimed PZC and above that range, the particles are negatively charged. It must be noted that particles with a diameter above 500 nm have extremely close surface (Barisik et al., 2014) charge density as the calculations are only done for nanoparticles with a diameter of 500 nm.

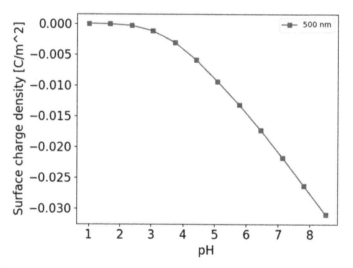

Figure 2: Surface charge density of nanoparticles with a diameter of 500 nm

The experiments have been carried out in 9 batches, two of those show agglomeration of silica and the rest shows breakage. The data is split into three datasets. One training dataset, which consists of one agglomeration batch and four breakage batches, while two batches (different from the training set) are left for validation. Moreover, in order to evaluate the model performance, the second agglomeration batch and one breakage batch are left in the test dataset. The model predictions for agglomeration and breakage batches in the test set are illustrated in Figure 3. The model is trained for 400 epochs and it can roughly predict the dynamics of the flocculation process for both agglomeration and breakage phenomena. The predictions can be improved by training the model for more than 400 epochs. To compare it with the models developed in (Nazemzadeh et al., 2021a; Nielsen et al., 2020) a further uncertainty analysis can be carried out similar to the one developed by (Nielsen et al., 2021) to analyse the performance of each model more in detail.

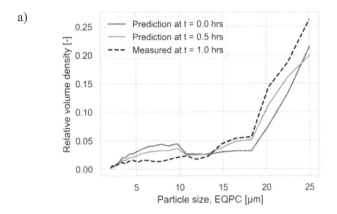

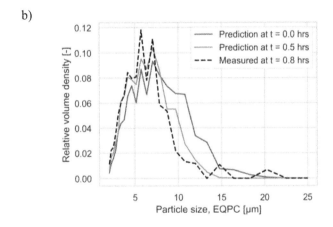

Figure 3: model predictions of a) agglomeration, and b) breakage batches

4. Conclusions

In this study, a hybrid multiscale framework has been developed to predict the dynamics of a laboratory-scale flocculation of silica particles. The hybrid multiscale model has the advantage of employing the data at non-observable scale to assisting the prediction of the dynamics of the process. The framework allows of using computational and theoretical chemistry models to predict surface properties of the colloidal silica particles based on the medium conditions. Hence, these properties are used in the hybrid model to estimate the kinetic parameters of the flocculation process. It is also planned to use this framework for predicting the dynamics of a polymeric flocculation process.

5. Acknowledgements

We would like to thank Novozymes A/S and Greater Copenhagen Food Innovation program (CPH-FOOD) for co-financing this research, and for their support during this project.

References

Andersson, M.P., Hassenkam, T., Matthiesen, J., Nikolajsen, L., Okhrimenko, D. V., Dobberschütz, S., Stipp, S.L.S., 2020. First-principles prediction of surface wetting. Langmuir. https://doi.org/10.1021/acs.langmuir.0c01241

Barisik, M., Atalay, S., Beskok, A., Qian, S., 2014. Size dependent surface charge properties of silica nanoparticles. J. Phys. Chem. C 118, 1836–1842. https://doi.org/10.1021/jp410536n

Kumar, S., Ramkrishna, D., 1996. On the solution of population balance equations by discretization-I. A fixed pivot technique. Chem. Eng. Sci. 51, 1311–1332.

Nazemzadeh, N., Malanca, A.A., Nielsen, R.F., Gernaey, K. V., Andersson, M.P., Mansouri, S.S., 2021a. Integration of first-principle models and machine learning in a modeling framework: An application to flocculation. Chem. Eng. Sci. 245, 116864. https://doi.org/10.1016/j.ces.2021.116864

Nazemzadeh, N., Nielsen, R.F., Gernaey, K. V., Mansouri, S.S., Andersson, M.P., 2021b. Implementation of first-principles surface interactions in a hybrid machine learning assisted modelling of flocculation, Computer Aided Chemical Engineering. Elsevier Masson SAS. https://doi.org/10.1016/B978-0-323-88506-5.50132-7

Nielsen, R.F., Nazemzadeh, N., Andersson, M.P., Gernaey, K. V., Mansouri, S.S., 2021. An uncertainty-aware hybrid modelling approach using probabilistic machine learning, Computer Aided Chemical Engineering. Elsevier Masson SAS. https://doi.org/10.1016/B978-0-323-88506-5.50094-2

Nielsen, R.F., Nazemzadeh, N., Sillesen, L.W., Andersson, M.P., Gernaey, K. V., Mansouri, S.S., 2020. Hybrid machine learning assisted modelling framework for particle processes. Comput. Chem. Eng. 140. https://doi.org/10.1016/j.compchemeng.2020.106916

Scheepers, D., Chatillon, B., Borneman, Z., Nijmeijer, K., 2021. Influence of charge density and ionic strength on diallyldimethylammonium chloride (DADMAC)-based polyelectrolyte multilayer membrane formation. J. Memb. Sci. 617. https://doi.org/10.1016/j.memsci.2020.118619

Yotsumoto, H., Yoon, R.H., 1993. Application of extended DLVO theory. II. Stability of silica suspensions. J. Colloid Interface Sci. https://doi.org/10.1006/jcis.1993.1206

Proceedings of the 14th International Symposium on Process Systems Engineering – PSE 2021+
June 19-23, 2022, Kyoto, Japan © 2022 Elsevier B.V. All rights reserved.
http://dx.doi.org/10.1016/B978-0-323-85159-6.50136-6

Optimal Design of Experiments Based on Artificial Neural Network Classifiers for Fast Kinetic Model Recognition

Enrico Sangoi[a,b], Marco Quaglio[a], Fabrizio Bezzo[b], Federico Galvanin[a*]

[a]Department of Chemical Engineering, University College London, Torrington Place, WC1E 7JE London, United Kingdom
[b]CAPE-lab (Computer-Aided Process Engineering Laboratory), Department of Industrial Engineering, University of Padova, 35131 Padova PD, Italy
f.galvanin@ucl.ac.uk

Abstract

Developing mathematical models for the description of reaction kinetics is fundamental for process design, control and optimisation. The problem of model discrimination among a set of candidate models is not trivial, and recently a new and complementary approach based on artificial neural networks (ANNs) for kinetic model recognition was proposed. This paper extends the ANNs-based model identification approach by defining an optimal design of experiment procedure, whose performance is assessed through a simulated case study. The proposed design of experiments method allows to reduce the number of experiments to be conducted while increasing the ability of the artificial neural network in recognising the proper kinetic model structure.

Keywords: optimal design of experiments, kinetic model identification, ANN classifiers.

1. Introduction

The mathematical description of the phenomena occurring in reacting systems is crucial to evaluate the progress of chemical reactions occurring in the reactor, which is a central aspect in reactor design, control and optimisation. The first step in modelling reaction kinetics is the definition of candidate models based on preliminary experimental evidence and hypothesis about the underlying reaction mechanism.

The subsequent step in the modelling procedure is to determine among the candidate models the most suitable one for describing the chemical system, i.e. to perform the model discrimination. Asprey and Macchietto (2000) presented a standard model building approach including model discrimination, which can be summarised in the following steps: i) structural identiability analysis of each model; ii) regression of model parameters on experimental data; iii) evaluation of the quality of fit; iv) application of the chosen model selection criterion; v) if required, design and perform new experiments, then iteration from step (ii). When new experiments must be performed, experimental conditions are typically designed through a mathematical optimisation to maximise their information content. Different approaches can be employed for designing optimally informative experiments, such as model-based design of experiments (MBDoE) (Chen and Asprey, 2003) or probabilistic approaches based on Bayesian statistics or Monte Carlo methods. One limitation of standard MBDoE-driven model building strategies is that these methods may even lead to the rejection of the "exact" model if the identifiability requirements are not satisfied in step (i) of the procedure. These reasons motivate the research for an alternative approach to the kinetic model discrimination and design of experiments problem. Quaglio et al. (2020) looked at the problem of selecting a kinetic model among a set of candidate ones from a completely different perspective, applying artificial neural network (ANN) classifiers for a fast recognition of the kinetic model structure of reacting systems from the experimental evidence provided. The idea behind the ANN-based approach is to train the ANN classifier (Zou et al., 2009) with in-silico generated data for each model from the set of rival kinetic models, so that the trained ANN would determine the kinetic model based on the input concentration measurements. A key aspect of this approach is that it does not require the fitting of kinetic parameters; parameter uncertainty is included during the dataset generation step. The method proved to be satisfactory, particularly when the noise on the measured values is low, and within this framework the modelling time is expected to decrease. However, the approach was characterised by a fixed design of the experiments, which can lead to poorly informative experiments.

The research here presented extends Quaglio et al. (2020) work by defining a procedure for optimal experimental design coupled to the ANN-based classifier for fast kinetic model recognition. Classical MBDoE approaches are not suitable for the direct integration of the ANN approach, because the kinetic models are not used for experimental data fitting and making predictions; therefore a new criterion for optimally designing experiments has been formulated. The new approach is tested on a simulated case study related to the identification of kinetic models in a batch reaction system.

2. Proposed framework and methods

Chemical reacting system are typically described by nonlinear dynamic models. In this work, the N_m possible models are formulated as systems of differential and algebraic equations in the form

$$\begin{cases} \mathbf{f}_l(\dot{\mathbf{x}}_l(t), \mathbf{x}_l(t), \mathbf{u}(t), \boldsymbol{\theta}_l, t) = 0 \\ \hat{\mathbf{y}}_l(t) = \mathbf{g}_l(\mathbf{x}_l(t)) \end{cases} \quad \forall \, l \in \{1, \dots, N_m\} \tag{1}$$

where $\mathbf{x}$ is the vector of N_x state variables, $\dot{\mathbf{x}}$ is the derivative of the state variables, the vector $\mathbf{u}$ represents the array of N_u input variables, $\boldsymbol{\theta}$ is the N_θ-dimensional vector of model parameters, t is the variable time, $\hat{\mathbf{y}}$ is N_y-dimensional vector of measured output variables that are function of the state variables, and subscript $l = 1, \dots, N_m$ stands for the l-th candidate model. In the ANN model recognition framework, the ANN is trained and then employed to determine among the N_m models the most suitable one for describing the reacting system behaviour.

The aim is to enhance the ANN ability in associating the right model label to the input data, which are affected by the choice of the experimental conditions. To optimise the experimental design, the objective function to be maximised is the ANN accuracy on the testing dataset is defined in Eq. 2 as the percentage of correctly classified model structures where Ψ_{test} is the testing dataset, the dataset elements are the experimental data array $\mathbf{n}_i$ and the respective model label l_i, while $\hat{l}_i$ is the label predicted by the ANN.

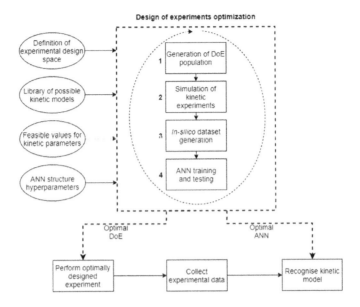

Figure 1 Block diagram representation of the proposed procedure for design of experiments optimisation coupled to ANN-based kinetic model recognition.

$$\text{Acc}_{\Psi_{\text{test}}} = \frac{\left|\{i \in \{1, \dots, N_{\Psi_{\text{test}}}\} \text{ s.t. } (\mathbf{n}_i, l_i) \in \Psi_{\text{test}} \wedge \hat{l}_i = l_i\}\right|}{\left|\{i \in \{1, \dots, N_{\Psi_{\text{test}}}\} \text{ s.t. } (\mathbf{n}_i, l_i) \in \Psi_{\text{test}}\}\right|} \cdot 100\% \qquad (2)$$

The proposed procedure is illustrated in Figure 1. The procedure starts with the definition of all the inputs that must be fed to the optimiser, which are:

- The library of the rival kinetic model structures.
- A list of feasible values of the kinetic parameters for each candidate model. Parameters values are bounded and are said feasible if they satisfy constraints on the conversion and selectivity of chemical species when simulating the experiments.
- The number of experiments to be optimised and the space of experimental conditions, i.e. which experimental variables can be manipulated and their range of variability.
- The ANN structure: the number of layers, the number of nodes at each layer, the activation functions and all the other ANN hyperparameters.

Afterwards, the optimisation of the experimental design is performed, coupled to the training of ANNs. The discussion about the DoE optimisation step, represented in Figure 1 by the dashed box, addresses two aspects.

i)   How the objective function is evaluated for a certain experimental design.

The objective function has to be evaluated many times for each experimental design proposed within the DoE optimiser iterations. The procedure to assess the ANN accuracy for a particular DoE choice involves the following sequential steps:

1. An experimental design is chosen within the experimental design space.
2. The respective experimental campaign is simulated in-silico for each model and for each set of feasible parameter values.

3. Simulated measurements of species concentration $\mathbf{n}_i$ are collected and organised to build a labelled dataset Ψ, where each element of the dataset is associated to the kinetic model used for its generation l_i. An error factor is added to the simulated measurements to mimic real experimental circumstances.
4. The ANN is trained and tested in the classification of the kinetic model structures based on the experimental evidence provided. The ANN accuracy (Eq. 2) is evaluated at this step.

ii) The choice of the algorithm for optimising the DoE.

The accuracy of ANN predictions on the test set is the metric used to evaluate the goodness of the experimental design: the higher the test-accuracy, the better the DoE. Since this metric is affected by intrinsic randomness in the neural network training process, a direct search method has been employed to deal with the optimisation problem. In particular, the differential evolution algorithm (Storn and Price, 1997) is chosen, a population-based algorithm inspired by the evolutionary theory. Once the algorithm converges to a solution, it provides as an output the optimal DoE and the respective ANN, i.e. the most accurate one at recognising the right kinetic model structure. In the final step of the proposed procedure, the optimally determined conditions are applied to the real system. Experimental data are collected and fed to the trained ANN, obtaining as output a measure of how likely each model is to describe the chemical system under investigation.

3. Case study description

The proposed methodology was tested on an in-silico simulated case study, considering an isothermal batch reactor where 3 species (A, B, C) react in the liquid phase.

$$A \xrightarrow{r_1} B ; \qquad A \xrightarrow{r_2} C ; \qquad B \xrightarrow{r_3} C \tag{2}$$

The set of equations describing the evolution of the system, assuming constant volume for the liquid mixture in the batch reactor, is given by Eq. 3, where C_i (mol/m^3) indicate the concentration of species i, namely the state variables of the system, r_j (mol/m^{3}s) is the rate of reaction j, and v_{ij} (-) represents the stoichiometric coefficient of species i in the reaction j.

$$\frac{dC_i}{dt} = \sum_{j=1}^{N_r} v_{ij} r_j \quad \forall\, i = A, B, C \tag{3}$$

$$k_j = A_j e^{-E_{a,j}/RT} \quad \forall j = 1,2,3 \tag{4}$$

Kinetic models are formulated assuming that reactions can occur either in series or parallel, and reactions rates were modelled with first or second order power-law expressions. Moreover, Arrhenius-type kinetic factors are assumed (Eq. 4) for evaluating the reaction rates, characterised by two parameters: pre-exponential factor A_j and activation energy $E_{a,j}$. Therefore, a total of 8 rival kinetic model structures are formulated, as summarised in Table 1.

Table 1 Power-law rate expression for the candidate kinetic models. Models with label l=1,...,4 consider a series mechanism, while models l=5,...,8 consider a parallel mechanism.

	Series				Parallel			
Label:	1	2	3	4	5	6	7	8
r_1	$k_1 \cdot C_A$	$k_1 \cdot C_A$	$k_1 \cdot C_A^2$	$k_1 \cdot C_A^2$	$k_1 \cdot C_A$	$k_1 \cdot C_A$	$k_1 \cdot C_A^2$	$k_1 \cdot C_A^2$
r_2	$k_2 \cdot 0$	$k_2 \cdot 0$	$k_2 \cdot 0$	$k_2 \cdot 0$	$k_2 \cdot C_A$	$k_2 \cdot C_A^2$	$k_2 \cdot C_A$	$k_2 \cdot C_A^2$
r_3	$k_3 \cdot C_B$	$k_3 \cdot C_B^2$	$k_3 \cdot C_B$	$k_3 \cdot C_B^2$	$k_3 \cdot 0$	$k_3 \cdot 0$	$k_3 \cdot 0$	$k_3 \cdot 0$

The dataset Ψ is generated starting from 125 sets of feasible parameters for each model structure, therefore Ψ includes 1000 elements $(\mathbf{n}_i, l_i)$. The dataset is split into training-validation-testing sets on a 60-20-20 basis for ANN training, validation and testing.

In this case study, the experimental error is generated from a normal distribution with zero mean and constant variance σ^2, assuming three different noise levels: $\sigma=1$ mol/m^3, $\sigma=4$ mol/m^3, $\sigma=10.00$ mol/m^3.

The experimental variables manipulated when designing the experiments, and their upper and lower bounds, are: i) initial concentration of reactant A (0-250 mol/m^3), ii) sampling times (50-350 s), and iii) temperature in the isothermal reactor (520-720 K).

As underlined in section 2 of this paper, also the hyperparameters defining the ANN architecture must be provided as an input. Quaglio et al. (2020) work is used as the starting point to retrieve the ANN hyperparameters for this case study:

- one hidden layer with 100 nodes and rectified linear unit activation function,
- 8 nodes in the output layer characterised by softmax activation function,
- the optimiser is adaptive moment estimation (Adam), (Kingma and Ba, 2014).

Before employing the optimisation algorithm on the case study, it is worth conducting some preliminary study to examine whether the experimental design affects the ANN accuracy and to identify potential regions of the design space where to expect optimal experimental conditions. A sensitivity analysis has been carried out to this purpose.

The optimisation is conducted considering three different scenarios of simulated experimental noise on concentration measurements and for each scenario the DoE optimisation is repeated with i) different number of experiments; ii) different number of samples, to determine the minimum amount of experimental effort required from the ANN to reach the highest accuracy.

4. Results

As far as the ANN test-accuracy is concern, the results are extremely promising, as shown in Figure 2a. These results refer to the DoE optimisation of experiments characterised by just one sample per batch, which indeed is even more remarkable. Very high accuracy in the ANN predictions is achieved even in the case of extremely noisy measurements with a limited number of optimally designed experiments. In particular, with four optimally designed batches a 100 % accuracy is reached in the low noise scenario, while in the medium noise case a 95 % accuracy is reached. In the scenario characterised by high noise, still, 90 % accuracy is achieved with just five optimally designed experiments. Figure 2b shows the sensitivity of ANN accuracy to temperature and initial concentration of species A in the high noise scenario, compared to the optimisation result for a single experiment with a single sample collected after t=100 s. Figure 2b suggests that optimal conditions for model discrimination are characterised by high initial concentration of reactant A ($C_{A,0}$) and a medium range temperature around 630K.

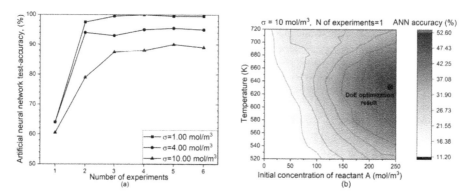

Figure 2 (a) ANN accuracy obtained from the optimal design of experiments for variable number of experiments: comparison between the three experimental noise scenarios. (b) Contour plot of the ANN accuracy as a function of design variables for σ =10 mol/m^3, fixed sampling time t = 100 s.

The high value obtained for $C_{A,0}$ can be due to the hypothesis of constant σ. Under this assumption, the relative error is lower when the concentration measurement is higher. In the scenario described for Figure 2b, the CPU time required for the DoE optimisation was 1376 s (approx. 23 minutes), carried out on an Intel Core i5-7200U processor with 8GB RAM workstation.

5. Conclusions

This study allowed to define a new method for optimal design of experiments that can be coupled with the ANN-based methodology for kinetic model recognition. Optimally designed experiments lead to a significant improvement in terms of ANN accuracy, thus paving the way towards ANN-based DoE methods for the recognition of kinetic models in complex reaction networks. Preliminary results show that kinetic model structures can be identified with limited experimental effort also in the presence of high noise level on the measurements. Future works will include the application to real chemical systems to test the reliability of the methods and the comparison in terms of time required and experimental campaign costs with classical model discrimination approaches.

References

S.P. Asprey and S. Macchietto, 2000, Statistical Tools for Optimal Dynamic Model Building, Computers & Chemical Engineering, 24, 1261-1267

B.H. Chen and S.P. Asprey, 2003, On the Design of Optimally Informative Dynamic Experiments for Model Discrimination in Multiresponse Nonlinear Situations, Industrial & Engineering Chemistry Research, 42, 7, 1379-1390

D.P. Kingma and J. Ba, 2014, Adam: A Method for Stochastic Optimization

M. Quaglio, L. Roberts, M.S. Bin Japaar, E.S. Fraga, V. Dua, F. Galvanin, 2020, An Artificial Neural Network Approach to Recognise Kinetic Models from Experimental Data, Computers & Chemical Engineering, 135, 106759

R. Storn and K. Price, 1997, Differential Evolution – A Simple and Efficient Heuristic for Global Optimization over Continuous Spaces, Journal of Global Optimization, 11, 4, 341-359

J. Zou, Y. Han and SS. So, 2009, Overview of Artificial Neural Networks, Artificial Neural Networks: Methods and Applications, ed. David J. Livingstone, Totowa NJ, Humana Press, 15-23

Proceedings of the 14th International Symposium on Process Systems Engineering – PSE 2021+
June 19-23, 2022, Kyoto, Japan © 2022 Elsevier B.V. All rights reserved.
http://dx.doi.org/10.1016/B978-0-323-85159-6.50137-8

Modelling of the rice bran protein extraction using response surface methodology

Mohd Sharizan Md Sarip[a*], Felicia Kang Suet Lyna[a], Mohd Rizuan Mansor[a], Ken-Ichiro Sotowa[b]

[a]*Faculty of Chemical Engineering Technology, Universiti Malaysia Perlis, Kompleks Pusat Pengajian Jejawi 3, Universiti Malaysia Perlis (UniMAP), 02600 Arau, Perlis , Malaysia*
[b]*Department of Chemical Engineering, Kyoto University, Kyotodaigau-Katsura, Nishikyo-ku, Kyoto-shi Kyoto 615-8510,Japan.*

sharizan@unimap.edu.my

Abstract

Rice bran is a natural by-product that is produced by the rice milling process in the rice industry. In this study, the modelling of the protein extraction from rice bran using Soni-auto hybrid method was evaluate via response surface methodology (RSM). Soni-auto hybrid method are the combination of the autoclaving extraction followed by sonication process. The experimental design for this process was performed using Response Surface Methodology (RSM) with Central Composite Design (CCD) model in Design Expert software. Three variables parameters namely solvent to sample ratio from 1:20 to 1:40, sonication temperature from 40 to 60°C and 20 to 40 minutes was evaluated. The response variable in this study are protein concentration. A highly accurate empirical quadratic response model for protein concentration was developed for three independent variable with adjusted R-squared value for the model was 0.8933. Two parameters; temperature and feed-to-solvent ratio give a significant effect ($p<0.05$) on protein concentration. Meanwhile, extraction times are not given the significant on this response. The model will be used to obtain the optimum condition for the process.

Keywords: Modelling, rice bran protein, response surface methodology.

1. Introduction

In the rice industry, the large amount of rice bran produced through rice milling process is often considered as waste. These rice brans are either being thrown away or sell at a very cheap price as animal feed or fertilizer (Gul et al., 2015). The under-utilization of rice bran is due to the high amount of free fatty acid in the rice bran due to the reaction of the lipase enzyme in the rice bran. Patil et al. (2016) stated that within hours large amount of free fatty acid can be produced in the rice bran and the amount can reach 5 to 7% within the first 24 hours of storage. Nutritionists have considered rice bran with more than 5% of free fatty acid are unsuitable for human consumption (Patil et al., 2016). Moreover, rice bran contains fiber and phytate which are extensively associated or bounded to the proteins makes the separation of protein from these components difficult to achieve. Therefore, various extraction techniques such as alkaline extraction, enzymatic extraction and physical extraction were used to extract the protein from the rice bran fibers and at the same time inhibit the lipase activity in the rice bran (Bhat and Riar, 2017). In this study, Soni-auto hybrid method was utilized for the protein extraction from the rice bran. Three main extraction parameter namely sonicator temperature, extraction time dan solvent to sample ratio was studied as the independent variable. The modelling for this process was done through response surface methodology using central composite design (CCD) model to obtain the best multivariable equation to represent the proses. Besides that, the significant effect of this parameter toward protein concentration was determine based on analysis of variance (ANOVA) analysis.

2. Methodology

2.1 Raw material

Rice bran was collected from Kilang Beras BERNAS Sdn Bhd, Perlis, Malaysia. It was heated in a microwave oven at 850 W for 3 minutes and stored at 4 to 5°C prior to each experimental run (Pandey and Shrivastava, 2018).

2.2 Soni-auto hybrid extraction method

Soni-auto hybrid method are the combination of the autoclaving extraction followed by sonication process. 5 g of rice bran was added into a conical flask and followed by 100 ml of distilled water for feed to solvent ratio of 1:20 g:ml. Then, the sample mixture was autoclaved at 121°C for 20 minutes. After that, the autoclaved rice bran solution was left to cool down to room temperature. Finally, the mixture of rice bran was sonicated by using the sonicator bath (Model: WUC-D22H, Germany). Throughout the sonication process, the ultrasonic frequency was maintained at 70% with temperature range between 40°C to 60°C and extraction time between 20 to 40 minutes After sonication, the rice bran mixture was centrifuged at 4000 rpm for 30 minutes at 25°C. Then, volume of the supernatant was measured. The absorbance of supernatant from each extraction method was measured using the UV-Vis spectrophotometer (Shimadzu, Model: UV-1800, Japan) to determine protein concentration in the rice bran solution. The procedures were repeated three times for all the parameters.

2.3 Response surface methodology (RSM)

In this study, response surface methodology (RSM) with Central Composite Design (CCD) model was utilized to model the extraction of rice bran protein using Soni-auto hybrid. The target response that needed to achieve was the maximum level of protein concentration in the rice bran solution. Therefore, the influence of the three parameters; time, temperature and feed-to-solvent ratio on the protein concentration was investigated. The factors and response as defined in CCD model is shown in Table 1. Design Expert V10.0.7 software was used as statistical tool for this purpose.

Table 1: List of numeric factors and response defined in Central Composite Design (CCD) model

Numeric Factors	Name	Units	Minimum	Maximum
A	Temperature	°C	40	60
B	Extraction time	Minutes	20	40
C	Feed : Solvent Ratio	g:ml	1:20	1: 60
Response				
R1	Protein Concentration	mg/ml		

3. Results and discussion

Based on the response surface methodology (RSM) with Central Composite Design (CCD) model, 20 runs of experiment was done with different operating conditions was evaluated as shown in Table 2. The condition was generated through design of experiment (DOE) procedure using Design Expert V10.0.7 software.

Table 2: Experimental data based on CCD model for protein extraction from rice bran

Run	A Temperature (°C)	B Extraction Time (minutes)	C Feed: Solvent Ratio (g:ml)	R1 Protein Concentration (mg/ml)
1	50	30	40	17.588
2	56	36	52	14.014
3	50	30	40	17.418
4	50	30	40	17.502
5	50	30	40	17.287
6	44	36	52	14.881
7	44	24	52	14.894
8	56	24	28	15.898
9	50	30	60	13.129
10	50	40	40	16.876
11	56	24	52	13.978
12	50	30	40	17.012
13	40	30	40	15.218
14	50	30	20	14.375
15	56	36	28	15.796
16	50	20	40	16.614
17	50	30	40	16.998
18	60	30	40	15.008
19	44	36	28	16.598
20	44	24	28	16.499

3.1 Model selection

Table 3 shows the model summary statistics for protein concentration, R1. In this section, predicted residual sum of squares (PRESS) value was taken into consideration for the selection of model. PRESS is a measure of how a particular model fits each design point. The coefficients for the model were calculated without the first design point. This model was used to predict the first point and then the new residual was calculated for this point. This was done for each data point and then the squared residuals were summed. In this case, the quadratic polynomial model has the lowest predicted residual sum of squares (PRESS) at 11.42 compared to all other models which are not aliased. In addition, adjusted R^2 values are also used in determining the type of polynomial that is suitable to represent the model. From table 3, other than the cubic model that was aliased, the quadratic polynomial model was observed to have the highest adjusted R^2 value of 0.9046 compared to the linear and 2FI models that have adjusted R^2 value of only 0.0510 and -

0.1671 respectively. Therefore, from the model summary statistics, the quadratic polynomial model with high adjusted R^2 and low PRESS values was chosen to represent the model of study. The predicted R-square value indicates how well a regression model predicts response values; while the adjusted R-square (Adj. R^2) indicates the descriptive power of the regression models while including the diverse numbers of variables (Che Sulaiman et al., 2017).

Table 3 : Model summary statistics for protein concentration

Source	Standard Deviation	R-Squared	Adjusted R-Squared	Predicted R-Squared	PRESS
Linear	1.32	0.2009	0.0510	-0.2031	42.06
2FI	1.47	0.2015	-0.1671	-0.7254	60.32
Quadratic	**0.42**	**0.9498**	**0.9046**	**0.6734**	**11.42**
Cubic	0.29	0.9857	0.9546	-0.2082	42.24

Based on the Table 3, the difference between adjusted R-Squared and predicted R-Squared of 0.2312 are high for quadratic model. The differences of this value more than 0.2 are not considered to be a reasonable agreement (Tesfay et al.,2020). Therefore, the analysis of variance (ANOVA) was performed for the quadratic model as tabulated in Table 4. In general, values of "Prob>F" less than 0.0500 indicate the model terms are significant based on 95 % confidence level. In this case, A, C, A^2 and C^2 are significant model as shown in Table 4. If there are many insignificant model terms, model reduction can be done to improve the model and produce the reasonable agreement model.

Table 4 : Analysis of variance (ANOVA) results for quadratic model

Source		F Value	p-value Prob>F	Observation
Model		21.02	<0.0001	Significant
A-	Temperature	5.22	0.0453	Significant
B-	Extraction Time	0.088	0.7722	Insignificant
C-	Feed: Solvent	34.69	0.0002	Significant
AB		0.016	0.9005	Insignificant
AC		0.10	0.7551	Insignificant
BC		4.813E-4	0.9829	Insignificant
A^2		42.80	<0.0001	Significant
B^2		1.73	0.2180	Insignificant
C^2		118.85	<0.0001	Significant

Based on Table 4, it was found out that B^2, BC, AC and AB are in insignificant but only B^2 model term is removed to improve the model. This is because BC, AC and AB terms are required to support the polynomial equation hierarchy in data fitting based on trial-and-error model reduction process. The results for reduced quadratic model are shown in table 5.

Table 5 : Analysis of variance (ANOVA) results for reduced quadratic model

Source	Sum of Squares	Df*	Mean Square	F Value	p-value Prob>F
Model	32.90	8	4.11	21.97	<0.0001
A- Temperature	0.92	1	0.92	4.90	0.0489
B- Extraction Time	0.016	1	0.016	0.083	0.7786
C- Feed : Solvent	6.09	1	6.09	32.53	0.0001
AB	2.888E-3	1	2.888E-3	0.015	0.9034
AC	0.018	1	0.018	0.096	0.7620
BC	8.450E-5	1	8.450E-5	4.514E-4	0.9834
A^2	7.29	1	7.29	38.94	<0.0001
C^2	20.57	1	20.57	109.90	<0.0001
Residual	2.06	11	0.19		
Standard Deviation	0.43		R-Squared		0.9411
Mean	15.88		Adjusted R-Squared		0.8983
C.V. %	2.72		Predicted R-Squared		0.7049
PRESS	10.32		Adeq Precision		15.651
-2 Log Likelihood	11.29		BIC		38.25

*degree of freedom

The quadratic model with f value (0, 8) = 21.97 and p <0.0001 implies the model has significant effect on the response. It also indicates that only 0.01% chance that the F-value occurs due to noise. Therefore, the overall model has a significant effect in determining the protein concentration within the experimental ranges.

Based on this result, the feed-to-solvent ratio and temperature had significant effect on protein concentration with f value (1,8) = 32.52, p = 0.0001 and f value (1,8) = 4.90, p = 0.0489, respectively. In contrast, the extraction time for sonication do not exhibit significant effects on the protein concentration as it has a low f value (1,8) = 0.083 with p = 0.7786.

As a conclusion, a final equation of the quadratic polynomial model was established to represent the process as shown in eq. 1. The adjusted R-squared value for the model was 0.8933 while predicted R-squared value was 0.7049. The differences of this value are less than 0.2 and it considered to be a reasonable agreement.

$$R1 = 17.17 - 0.26A + 0.034B - 0.67C - 0.019AB - 0.047\,AC + 0.00325BC - 0.71A^2 - 1.19C^2 \tag{1}$$

Where,	R1	= Protein Concentration (mg/ml)
	A	= Temperature
	B	= Extraction time
	C	= Feed: Solvent ratio

Based on the equation, the validation of model is conducted to evaluate the uncertainty of this model by comparing the experiment data with predicted value. The experiment was conducted at temperature of 50°C, feed to solvent ratio set at 1:40 and extraction time of 30 minutes. The analysis is shown in table 6.

Table 6 : Model validation with experimental data.

Response (R1)	Experimental data		Predicted value (mg/ml)	Error AARD[2] (%)
	Average (mg/ml)	AAD[1] (mg/ml)		
Protein concentration	16.995	0.137	17.174	1.053

[1] AAD - Absolute average deviation $= \frac{1}{n}\sum_{m=1}^{n}|Y_m - Y_{average}|$, where n= 3, no of experiment repeated.

[2] AARD - Absolute average relative deviation $= (\frac{Y_{experiment} - Y_{predicted}}{Y_{experiment}}) x\ 100$.

4. Conclusions

As a conclusion, the quadratic model was successfully being developed for protein extraction process from rice bran using Soni-auto hybrid extraction method with adjusted R-squared value of 0.8933 and predicted R-squared value of 0.7049. The model has the f value (0, 8) = 21.97 and p <0.0001 which implies it has significant effect on the response. Two parameters namely feed-to-solvent ratio and temperature are observed to give the significant effect on protein concentration with f value (1,8) = 32.52, p = 0.0001 and f value (1,8) = 4.90, p = 0.0489, respectively. In contrast, the extraction time for sonication not given the significant effects on the protein concentration with f value (1,8) = 0.083 with p = 0.7786. The empirical model develop in this study will be used to obtain optimum condition.

Acknowledgement

The financial support provided by the Ministry of Higher Education Malaysia through Fundamental Research Grant Scheme reference no: FRGS/1/2018/TK02/UNIMAP/02/3 was acknowledged.

References

K.Gul, B.Yousuf, A.K.Singh, P.Singh and A.A.Wani, 2015, Rice bran: Nutritional values and its emerging potential for development of functional food—A review. Bioact. Carbohydr. Diet. Fibre, 6,1, 24-30.

S.S. Patil, A.Kar, and D. Mohapatra, 2016, Stabilization of rice bran using microwave: Process optimization and storage studies, Food Bioprod. Process, 99, 204-211.

F.M. Bhat and C.S. Riar, 2017, Extraction, identification and assessment of antioxidative compounds of bran extracts of traditional rice cultivars: An analytical approach, Food Chem., 237, 264-274.

I.S. Che Sulaiman, M.Basri, H.R. Fard Masoumi, W.J. Chee, S.E. Ashari and M. Ismail, 2017, Effects of temperature, time, and solvent ratio on the extraction of phenolic compounds and the anti-radical activity of Clinacanthus nutans Lindau leaves by response surface methodology, Chem. Cent. J., 11, 1, 54-54.

D.Tesfay, S.Abrha, Z.Yilma, G.Woldu, & F.Molla, 2020, Preparation, Optimization, and Evaluation of Epichlorohydrin Cross-Linked Enset (Ensete ventricosum (Welw.) Cheeseman) Starch as Drug Release Sustaining Excipient in Microsphere Formulation, Biomed Res. Int., 2020, 1-19.

Proceedings of the 14th International Symposium on Process Systems Engineering – PSE 2021+
June 19-23, 2022, Kyoto, Japan © 2022 Elsevier B.V. All rights reserved.
http://dx.doi.org/10.1016/B978-0-323-85159-6.50138-X

Weibull Reliability Regression Model for Prediction of Bearing Remaining Useful Life

Jun-Jie Lai, Shih-Jie Pan, Chong-Wei Ong, Cheng-Liang Chen[*]
Department of Chemical engineering, National Taiwan University, No. 1, Section 4, Roosevelt Rd, Da'an District, Taipei City, 106319, Taiwan
[*]CCL@ntu.edu.tw

Abstract

In this work, a scenario-based approach that uses multiple Weibull Accelerated Failure Time Regression (WAFTR) models is proposed to predict the remaining useful life (RUL) of a benchmark bearing. The external features such as operational load and rotatory speed of the bearing are used to categorize the operational scenarios and a scenario-based WAFTR model is identified for each operational scenario by using the internal features extracted from the sampled horizontal and vertical vibration data. Therein, the Weibull parameters in each WAFTR model are expressed either in exponential or in linear form of these internal and external operational features. By using the mean squared error (MSE) as the performance measure of the prediction model, it is found that the proposed multiple WAFTR models approach can predict the RUL within 20% error.

Keywords: Bearing, Weibull distribution, Remaining Useful Life (RUL), Reliability function

1. Background

Rotation equipment such as motors, compressors are largely used in chemical plants. How to avoid those equipment damage is an importance task for field engineers. Engineers would check some indicators such as the temperature change or vibration amplitude to identify the health condition of the machine. Remaining useful life (RUL) is an estimate of the time that an item or component can function normally. Normally, the health condition of a machine will be worse with time goes by. Thus, maintenance and replacement are needed. In a plant, although earlier maintenance can prevent machines from broken, the more unnecessary cost has to pay. However, if the maintenance is too late, the machine may be broken and cause casualties. The accurate RUL prediction provides a suitable moment for replacement actions and keeps a safe environment for workers.

In 2012, the Institution of Electric, Electrical, and Engineering (IEEE) launched a challenge to the world (Patrick Nectoux et al (2012)). IEEE provided 17 bearing vibration datasets: six of them are the start-to-failure datasets, of which the whole vibration condition is from beginning to failure. The rest of them is the testing dataset, of which the vibration condition is not given fully. The purpose of this challenge is to let the engineers around the world predict the remaining useful life (RUL) for the bearing. There are two sensors detected the vibration acceleration connected with the bearing in the horizontal and vertical directions. These two sensors would take action every 10 seconds. Each time they would collect 2,560 data points in 0.1 seconds. Moreover, this experiment provided three different operating conditions by controlling the rotation speed and the force conducted on the bearing. Although the experimental data provided includes the horizontal and vertical data, most of the researchers in this field would only use the horizontal data, such as Mao at al. (2018) and Guo et al. (2017), to name a few, the horizontal and vertical data together will affect the prediction accuracy. However, it is believed that the vertical data can still give us important information despite its fluctuation. In this work, both the horizontal and vertical data is used to build an RUL prediction model to enhance the prediction accuracy.

2. Methodology

2.1. Weibull reliability model

Kundu et al. (2019) proposed using the Weibull distribution function to describe the machine failure probability density with time, such as depicted in Eq. (1). The Weilbull reliability function can be derived from the Weilbull distribution function, as shown in equation (2).

$$f(t) = \frac{\beta}{\eta} \left(\frac{t - \gamma}{\eta} \right)^{\beta-1} e^{-(\frac{t-\gamma}{\eta})^\beta} \tag{1}$$

$$R(t) = 1 - \int_0^t f(s)ds = \int_t^\infty f(s)ds = e^{-(\frac{t}{\eta})^\beta} \tag{2}$$

Different types of machine failure can be described by tuning the three parameters in the Weilbull reliability function. Among these three tuning parameters, β is the shape parameter that would determine the type of failure, η is the scale parameter that would determine that machine's life span, and γ is the location parameter that determines at what time the machine starts to fail. It is assumed that the machine starts to break at the beginning, which means that γ can be set as zero. In a normal degradation process, the magnitude of β should greater than 1, and the magnitude of η should be similar to the total life span. When the operating time is closed to the failure time, the reliability of the machine is deemed to be closed to zero. It is assumed that the reliability is 0.01 at the failure time. Eq. (3) shows the relationship of the present time, t, and the RUL.

$$t + \text{RUL}(t) = t_{\text{failure}} \tag{3}$$

By plunging Eq. (3) into Eq. (2), the main prediction model is derived in Eq. (4).

$$\text{RUL}(t) = \eta \times [-\ln(0.01)]^{\frac{1}{\beta}} - t \tag{4}$$

Time t is the primary factor that affects the reliability. However, there are some other aging factors contributing to the decreasing reliability. Some parameters can be controlled by the operators, like the applied load, and the rotary speed. The other internal aging parameters are features revealed by the machine like temperature, vibration magnitude. In Kundu's work, the two parameters β and η can be replaced by the bearing's features, where the η is expressed as an exponential expansion such as Eq. (5) shown.

$$\eta = \exp\left(a_0 + \sum_{n=1}^N a_n I_n + \sum_{m=1}^M b_m E_m \right) \tag{5}$$

I_n and E_m are the internal and external parameters, respectively, and a_n and b_m are the coefficients of the aging parameters. In this work, β are also a parameter that would change as time goes by. As the result, β can also be expressed as an exponential expansion as shown in Eq. (6). Furthermore, the performance of using linear expansion is investigated for both β and η as shown in Eq. (7) and Eq. (8).

$$\beta = \exp\left(c_0 + \sum_{n=1}^{N} c_n I_n + \sum_{m=1}^{M} d_m E_m \right) \tag{6}$$

$$\eta = \left(a_0 + \sum_{n=1}^{N} a_n I_n + \sum_{m=1}^{M} b_m E_m \right) \tag{7}$$

$$\beta = \left(c_0 + \sum_{n=1}^{N} c_n I_n + \sum_{m=1}^{M} d_m E_m \right) \tag{8}$$

2.2. Features

It is found that only horizontal dataset is used for model building in most of the previous studies. However, it is believed that the vertical datasets still contain important information, so both the horizontal and vertical datasets are took into concern. Moreover, the net vibration magnitude is also an important indicator for the RUL prediction. Thus, the "Scalar dataset" is calculated by Eq. (9):

$$\text{Scalar}(t) = \sqrt{\text{Horizontal}(t)^2 + \text{Vertical}(t)^2} \tag{9}$$

By now, there are three types of datasets: the horizontal, the vertical, and the scalar. Because all of these contain much noise, the frequency-domain features are used as our main inputs for RUL prediction.

The horizontal dataset 1_1 is illustrated as shown in Figure 1. The Discrete Fourier Transform (DFT) is conducted to three types of raw data. Next, the frequency-domain features are normalized to highlight the magnitude ratio of frequency-domain features at each observation. This normalized value is also called the frequency signal energy. Instead of using the specific frequency as our model feature, we prefer to use a zone of the frequency. Thus, the whole frequency span is divided into 16 zones, (0 Hz – 800 Hz), (800 Hz – 1,600 Hz), (1,600 Hz – 2,400 Hz)… (12,000 Hz – 12,800 Hz). The principal component analysis (PCA) is conducted to these 16 frequency-domain features. Three principal components are extracted as the internal parameters. Furthermore, because using the frequency-domain features is possible to lose information, one time-domain internal parameter, the standard deviation, is picked. The standard deviation has high monotonicity. It would be seen as a health indicator for prediction.

$$\text{Std} = \sqrt{\sum_{n=1}^{N} \frac{(x - \mu)^2}{N}} \tag{10}$$

Combined with the standard deviation, 12 features are extracted form three types of raw data (the horizontal, vertical, scalar data) in each dataset. These 12 internal parameters and the 2 external parameters (force load, rotatory speed) will be plugged into the prediction model.

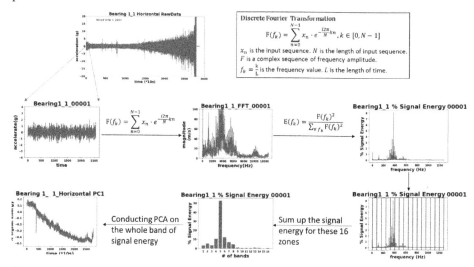

Figure 1 Frequency-domain features extraction with DFT and PCA

2.3. Target

The target of the model, in our case, is accurate prediction of the actual remaining useful life (RUL). The target will be used either in the regression part or in the testing part. It is assumed that the RUL is decreased linearly to zero at the failure time in our case. One can easily use the formula to get our RUL since the IEEE has given all the failure times.

3. Result and Discussion

3.1. Regression pre-process

Before building the prediction model, it is necessary to take a look at the raw data. The data provided by IEEE 2012 challenge is the real experimental data, so some datasets may include too much noise in building the prediction model. The datasets 1_2, 2_3, 2_5, 2_7, and 3_2 are excluded because they contain large fluctuation in the middle of the process. Also, the mean squared error (MSE) of the life percentage as shown in Eq. (11) is introduced. The value of MSE can show the precision of the prediction.

$$\text{MSE} = \frac{1}{N} \sum_{n=1}^{N} \left(\frac{\text{RUL}_{\text{prediction}}(n)}{\text{Total Life}} - \frac{\text{RUL}_{\text{actual}}(n)}{\text{Total Life}} \right)^2 \tag{11}$$

In this way, regardless of any case, the MSE will give the same value, which is 0.04, when the prediction RUL is just at the tolerance boundary. After defining the MSE, one can just use the MSE to describe the accuracy of the prediction model.

3.2. Model selection

In section *2.1.*, two types of expansion of β and η are combined in the model. The adequacy of these models are evaluated by checking the MSE values. The whole datasets are used to regress the model coefficients. All the simulations are done in the Python environment. The Python 3.9.4 script has the package to solve the non-linear regression.

It is found that the model with exponential β and linear η is the best because it brings the smallest MSE value.

During the prediction model process, it is critical to determine the training sets and testing sets. As there are three operating conditions, it is reasonable to pick at least one dataset from each operating condition. Also, the 1_1, 2_1, 2_2, and 3_1 are the start-to-failure datasets, which means that those datasets should have more information than the others. However, the prediction result is not good enough as shown in Table 1. The MSE values of 1_4, 1_5, and 1_7 are larger than 0.04, which means that the predicted RUL is out of the tolerance zone.

Table 1   The MSE testing result by prediction model trained with 1_1, 2_1, 2_2, and 3_1

Testing set	1_3	1_4	1_5	1_6	1_7	2_4	2_6	3_3
MSE	0.032	0.280	1.192	0.021	0.045	0.010	0.003	0.035

It is suspected that regressing the model with different operating conditions would decrease the accuracy. Moreover, the datasets from the same operating condition may not consistent enough. As the result, an analysis in done to check the relationship between each dataset. In this analysis, each dataset itself is used as the regression dataset to build the local model. The MSE value can be used in this analysis since it can represent how similar the datasets are. By test the other datasets with the local model, we can build an MSE map as shown in Figure 2. The blank parts mean that the testing set is the same as the training set. The dot parts mean that the MSE value is lower than 0.04. The other gray parts mean the MSE value is larger than 0.04.

| | Testing | | | | | | | | | | | |
Training	1_1	1_3	1_4	1_5	1_6	1_7	2_1	2_2	2_4	2_6	3_1	3_3
1_1	8.01E-19	3.25E-02	1.93E+00	1.91E-02	2.10E-02	5.80E-02	6.24E+00	8.90E+00	1.03E+01	1.23E+01	1.38E+01	2.06E+01
1_3	2.33E-02	4.06E-18	1.05E+00	1.27E-03	8.89E-04	2.64E-03	7.29E+00	1.01E+01	1.14E+01	1.37E+01	4.64E+00	7.28E+00
1_4	3.38E-01	2.56E-01	3.70E-17	2.74E-01	2.71E-01	2.31E-01	2.07E+22	6.19E+21	3.84E+22	3.62E+21	inf	inf
1_5	1.48E-02	1.33E-03	1.21E+00	3.81E-19	3.57E-05	8.15E-03	2.42E+00	3.73E+00	4.48E+00	5.48E+00	6.20E+00	1.13E+01
1_6	1.60E-02	9.42E-04	1.18E+00	3.68E-05	9.81E-19	7.00E-03	2.72E+00	4.12E+00	4.91E+00	5.99E+00	1.38E+01	2.12E+01
1_7	3.06E-02	8.81E-04	1.17E+00	1.06E-04	1.40E-04	4.97E-14	2.55E+00	4.31E+00	4.50E+00	6.08E+00	1.60E+01	2.11E+01
2_1	4.54E-01	3.78E-01	4.83E-02	3.95E-01	3.92E-01	3.54E-01	5.59E-15	2.05E-02	4.54E-02	8.99E-02	6.58E-01	1.36E+00
2_2	5.07E-01	4.34E-01	1.00E-01	4.55E-01	4.53E-01	3.91E-01	1.46E-02	1.60E-13	3.90E-03	1.93E-02	3.39E-01	8.29E-01
2_4	6.21E-01	4.65E-01	1.75E-01	4.79E-01	4.77E-01	4.41E-01	3.04E-02	2.98E-03	9.03E-14	5.49E-03	2.63E-01	7.06E-01
2_6	5.75E-01	5.11E-01	1.79E-01	5.26E-01	5.24E-01	4.89E-01	5.31E-02	1.45E-02	4.43E-03	5.64E-19	1.35E-01	3.88E-01
3_1	7.70E-01	7.33E-01	4.78E-01	7.26E-01	7.34E-01	7.07E-01	2.62E-01	1.90E-01	1.57E-01	1.25E-01	5.96E-19	3.50E-02
3_3	7.06E-01	6.56E-01	3.89E-01	6.73E-01	6.74E-01	6.17E-01	2.69E-01	2.09E-01	1.78E-01	1.44E-01	2.21E-02	3.52E-14

Figure 2   MSE map that represents how similar each dataset is.

As the MSE map shows, except for 1_4, all the MSE values are nice when we test the datasets from the same operating condition. Thus, 1_4 is seen as an abnormal. By checking the MSE map, we aim to pick one dataset from each operating condition. In condition 1, 1_3, 1_5, 1_6, and 1_7 do have suitable MSE values. Taking any one of them as one of the training sets is acceptable. In condition 2, both 2_2 and 2_4 are suitable. In condition 3, both 3_1 and 3_3 are suitable. Finally, we find that taking 1_5, 2_2, 3_3 as the training sets can bring the smallest MSE value when predicting either the whole datasets or the other testing datasets. Thus, these three datasets are set to be our training sets.

3.3. Single model to multiple models

Although the model trained with 1_5, 2_2, 3_3 brings precise prediction, β and η will lose their physical meaning when the value of them is checked. Take 1_1 as an example, the value of β is around 0.34 and the value of η is around 27.7. It is suspected that regressing with the datasets from different operating conditions is more likely to let the parameters optimized in an extreme situation. To solve this problem, it is intended to build one specific model for each specific operating conditions instead of building a single model to be responsible for the RUL prediction over whole operating conditions. 1_5, 2_2, and 3_3 are used to build three prediction models. The MSE results is shown in Table 2. And the magnitude of β and η will be settled in the scale of a normal degradation process.

Table 2   The MSE testing result by prediction model trained with 1_5, 2_2, and 3_3

Testing set	1_1	1_3	1_6	1_7	2_1	2_4	2_6	3_1
MSE	1.47E-02	1.37E-03	3.76E-05	8.15E-03	1.57E-02	3.75E-03	1.88E-02	2.47E-02

4. Conclusions

This work aims at establishing the Weibull Accelerated Failure Time Regression (WAFTR) models to predict the remaining useful life (RUL) of a benchmark bearing. The external features such as bearing load and rotary speed are used to categorize the local WAFTR model and then the internal features extracted from the frequency characteristics of sampled vibration data are used to adjust the scenario-based model parameters. In building the Weibull models, it is found that the parameter β expressed as exponential expansion and the parameter η expressed as linear expansion is the best choice to reflux the complex relationship between the RUL and operational features. By applying the multiple WAFTR models, the RUL prediction error is within 20% for all testing cases.

References

P. Kundu, A. K. Darpe, M. S. Kulkarni, 2019, Weibull accelerated failure time regression model for remaining useful life prediction of bearing working under multiple operating conditions, Mechanical Systems and Signal Processing, Volume 134.

W. Mao, J. He, J. Tang, Y. Li, 2018, Predicting Remaining Useful Life of Rolling Bearings Based on Deep Feature Representation and Long Short-Term Memory Neural Network, Advances in Mechanical Engineering, Volume 10.

P. Nectoux, R. Gouriveau, K. Medjaher, E. Ramasso, B. Chebel-Morello, N. Zerhouni, C. Varnier, 2012, PRONOSTIA: An experimental platform for bearingsaccelerated degradation tests, IEEE Int.

L. Guo, N. Li, F. Jia, Y. Lei, J. Lin, 2017. A recurrent neural network based health indicator for remaining useful life prediction of bearings, Neurocomputing, Volume 240, Pages 98-109.

Proceedings of the 14th International Symposium on Process Systems Engineering – PSE 2021+
June 19-23, 2022, Kyoto, Japan © 2022 Elsevier B.V. All rights reserved.
http://dx.doi.org/10.1016/B978-0-323-85159-6.50139-1

Supporting Hyperparameter Optimization in Adaptive Sampling Methods

Joschka Winz[a*], Florian Fromme[a], Sebastian Engell[a]

[a] *Process Dynamics and Operations Group, Department of Biochemical and Chemical Engineering, Technische Universität Dortmund, Emil-Figge Str. 70, 44227 Dortmund, Germany*
joschka.winz@tu-dortmund.de

Abstract

Surrogate models can be used to reduce the computational load when a simulation model is computationally costly to evaluate. This is the case if sophisticated thermodynamic models are integrated as e.g. the Perturbed-Chain Statistical Associating Fluid Theory (PC-SAFT) equation of state. When constructing surrogate models, the question of how to choose the training set arises. Recent research showed that promising results were obtained using adaptive or sequential sampling methods. In these approaches, the surrogate model predictions are used to identify additional promising sample locations. The results depend on the structure of the surrogate model, i.e. the choice of the hyperparameters. It is in general a tedious task to choose hyperparameters by trial and error, and a set of hyperparameters that is suitable in the initial phase may not be adequate anymore when the size of the training set increases significantly. Therefore, we here propose a methodology to incorporate hyperparameter optimization (HPO) into the adaptive sampling workflow. As this comes with a significant effort, HPO is only performed when it promises improvements.

Keywords: surrogate modeling, adaptive sampling, gray-box modeling, hyperparameter optimization, machine learning

1. Introduction

For an accurate description of complex phase equilibria in chemical process simulation and optimization, modern thermodynamic models like the Perturbed-Chain Statistical Associating Fluid Theory (PC SAFT) should be used. When applying such models, the issue of the high computational cost caused by evaluating the phase equilibria arises. To overcome this issue, surrogate models can be applied to approximate the predictions of the complex thermodynamic models. Surrogate models are black-box models that can describe arbitrary relationships while being computationally cheap to evaluate. An overview of different surrogate model types is given in McBride and Sundmacher (2019). Recent applications include the development of biorefineries (Mountraki et al., 2020) and assisting in the optimization of chemical processes (Janus et al., 2020).

The process of creating a training set to fit a surrogate model to data is denoted as sampling. Recent work showed that adaptive sampling can be used to improve the accuracy of the surrogate model, see Nentwich et al. (2019) and Winz et al. (2021).

One important issue in the application of surrogate models is the choice of a suitable surrogate model structure. In a real scenario, there is only limited knowledge about the original functional relationship that the surrogate model must approximate, and determining the structure of the surrogate model structure and the parameters of the training procedure is a complex task. This issue is further complicated when during the application of adaptive sampling methods additional samples are collected. Some surrogate model types may be suitable for a small initial training set, but not provide enough flexibility for a large training set in later iterations. So there is a need for a methodology to on the one hand automatically determine a suitable model structure for a specific data set and on the other hand detect when during the adaptive sampling it is necessary to adapt the model structure.

In the following, we describe such a methodology. In section 2, we introduce an example to which the methodology is applied. Section 3 entails the description of the developed methodology for simultaneous adaptive sampling and adaptation of the model structure, and in section 4 the results of the application of this method to the use case are presented.

2. Hydroformylation

The considered use case is the design of a process to conduct the hydroformylation of 1-dodecene in a thermomorphic solvent system, see Nentwich et al. (2019) for further details. In this process, a liquid phase reaction is conducted using an expensive homogeneous Rhodium-based catalyst. To minimize the loss of the catalyst, the solvent system is set up in a specific way. At elevated temperatures the mixture is homogeneous and the reaction can be performed with little transport limitations. After cooling down the reaction medium, two liquid phases form, which enables the separation of the mixture using a decanter and the recycling of the catalyst in the polar phase.

The intricate thermodynamic phase behavior of the reaction mixture can be accurately modeled using the equation of state PC-SAFT (Schäfer et al., 2012). But due to the high computational cost involved in solving the PC-SAFT equations, the fugacity coefficients are approximated by a surrogate model as described in the next sections. As a quaternary component system is considered and the temperature has a strong influence on the miscibility, the four fugacity coefficients are a function of four inputs each.

3. Methodology

3.1. Surrogate model types

In this work, different types of surrogate models are considered. Surrogate models can be classified with respect to several aspects. A property that is especially relevant in this context is parametricity. In parametric methods, the functional form of the response surface is fixed before the training. In non-parametric methods, the functional form is determined during the training, which typically leads to inherent scaling of the model complexity with the training data size (James et al., 2013). To cover both categories of models, in this work both Gaussian process regression (GPR) models, as an example of a non-parametric method, and parametric artificial neural network (ANN) models are applied.

For the GPR models, the considered hyperparameters are the types of basis and kernel functions. For the ANN models, these are the numbers of layers and nodes in each layer. The training of the ANN is done using the Levenberg-Marquardt algorithm with early stopping after six iterations of non-decreasing validation errors.

3.2. Adaptive sampling methodology

Adaptive sampling methods are used to select sets of samples such that accurate surrogate models are be obtained when they are fitted to the samples. In this work, the adaptive sampling methodology described in Nentwich et al. (2019) is applied.

A key element of sampling methods is to introduce a measure of how promising it is to evaluate a new sample and to add it to the sample set. This measure is commonly denoted as η_j. Here it is computed as the weighted mean of the scaled Jackknife variance $\hat{\sigma}_j{}^2$ and the scaled nearest neighbor distance d_j.

$$\eta_j = \alpha \frac{\hat{\sigma}_j{}^2}{\max_j \hat{\sigma}_j{}^2} + (1 - \alpha) \frac{d_j}{\max_j d_j} \tag{1}$$

The weighting factor α reflects the trade-off between exploration and exploitation. To ensure appropriate surrogate model predictions which are necessary for reliably computing η_j, the hyperparameters of the model have to be chosen carefully.

3.3. Hyperparameter optimization

The task of automatically determining hyperparameters of machine learning models and methods has attracted much interest in the last years. Recently, Bayesian optimization has become popular. In Bayesian optimization, a GPR surrogate of the cost function is constructed and used to define an acquisition function that is utilized to identify promising inputs by considering both the predicted value of the cost function and the estimated uncertainty. A commonly used acquisition function is the expected improvement (EI). A variant, where the EI relative to the expected evaluation time is optimized, is proposed by Snoek et al. (2012). This tends to favor sets of hyperparameters that lead to a low evaluation time. In general, this procedure is time-consuming as the surrogate model has to be trained multiple times. Thus, the next section deals with determining when the HPO is promising.

3.4. Supporting hyperparameter optimization

As the HPO routine is computationally costly to perform, it is impractical to apply it in every iteration of the adaptive sampling process. Therefore, in this section we describe a criterion to determine when the current set of hyperparameters is not likely to lead to sufficient progress. Its combination with adaptive sampling is shown in Algorithm 1.

As can be seen in Algorithm 1, two main elements are added to the adaptive sampling procedure, the hyperparameter optimization itself and a method to evaluate whether the hyperparameter optimization is promising. For this evaluation, we propose to adapt the slope ratio criterion proposed by Nuchitprasittichai and Cremaschi (2013) using the relative progress, RP.

$$\text{RP}_i = \left| \left(\frac{\text{CVE}_{i-1}}{\text{CVE}_i} - 1 \right) (n_i - n_{i-1})^{-1} \right| \tag{2}$$

As can be seen in (2), RP is computed from the cross-validation error in iteration , CVE_i, and the number of samples in iteration i, n_i. This is motivated by the idea that if the errors in one iteration and in the next one are similar, the progress is small, while large progress is observed if the error is reduced by a significant factor. This is different from the criterion proposed in previous work (Nuchitprasittichai and Cremaschi, 2013), where the absolute difference of the errors is considered. This modification is done here to consider a large relative change of the error as significant even if the absolute error is small, as it commonly occurs in later iterations of the algorithm.

As this ratio tends to give noisy results, a smoothening is performed by applying an exponential fit to the data points of $\{n_i\}, \{\text{RP}_i\}$ that were gathered since the last HPO was performed, whenever there are at least minCVEs = 4 error values available. An optimization of hyperparameters is conducted if there is not sufficient progress, i.e. at the sample size where the exponential fit reaches a minimum threshold ϵ.

Data: Initial training input and output sets X and Y
Conduct hyperparameter optimization using X and Y to obtain an initial set of hyperparameters $\{\lambda_i\}$
Initialize the set of cross-validation errors CVEs $\leftarrow \emptyset$
while stopping criterion not met **do**
    Train surrogate models with hyperparameters $\{\lambda_i\}$
    Update the set of cross-validation errors CVEs $\leftarrow$ CVEs $\cup$ CVE
    if number of elements in CVEs $>$ minCVEs **do**
        Compute $\{RP_i\}$ from CVEs (see eq. (2)) and perform an exponential fit for $\{n_i\}, \{RP_i\}$
        if number of samples where exponential fit meets threshold ϵ < number of samples in X **do**
            Conduct hyperparameter optimization using X and Y to give a new set of hyperparameters $\{\lambda_i\}$
            Reset the set of cross-validation errors CVEs $\leftarrow$ CVE
            Train surrogate models with the new hyperparameters $\{\lambda_i\}$
        end
    end
    Adaptive sampling using trained surrogate models to update sample sets $X \leftarrow X \cup X_{new}, Y \leftarrow Y \cup Y_{new}$
end

Algorithm 1: Inclusion of hyperparameter optimization in adaptive sampling

4. Results

4.1. Hyperparameter dependency

A first investigation is conducted to answer the question of how strongly the prediction capabilities of the considered surrogate models depend on the choice of the hyperparameters. For this, three training sets of varying sizes with 50, 500, and 5000 training examples each were created twice using Latin hypercube sampling. One set was used for the optimization of the hyperparameters, and the other one for the evaluation of the performance of the surrogate models. These sets were created by evaluating the fugacity coefficient of the liquid phase with PC-SAFT for different combinations of temperature and composition (a relationship with 4 inputs and 4 outputs).

A hyperparameter optimization was performed using each of the three sets of different sizes performing 50 iterations using the EI acquisition function. The optimized hyperparameter sets were used to create surrogate models based on different sets also containing 50, 500, and 5000 training examples. The resulting performance is shown in Figure 1 in terms of the normalized RMSE computed on a separate test set of 964120 samples. In this figure, it can be seen that for GPR models all sets of hyperparameters perform similarly on any training set size, as expected for a non-parametric model. On the other hand, for ANN surrogate models there is a strong dependency on the model structure. The model where the hyperparameters were optimized for 50 samples does not perform well when being trained on a set of 5000 samples and vice versa.

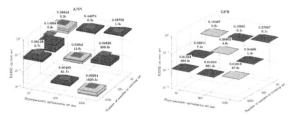

Figure 1: Normalized test set error of different surrogate models for hyperparameters optimized for different sizes of the training sets. The top numbers denote the mean value, the bottom numbers are the mean computation times of training on a standard desktop PC

4.2. Combination of adaptive sampling and hyperparameter optimization

As shown, the ANN surrogate models are sensitive to the choice of the hyperparameters. Thus, the adaptive sampling loop from (Nentwich et al., 2019) was extended with the described supporting hyperparameter optimization. The adaptive sampling was initially conducted only performing an HPO at the first iteration to analyze the chosen criterion for re-optimization as shown below.

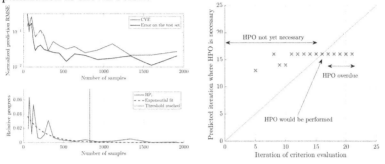

Figure 2: Left, top: Error-values over numbers of samples. Left, bottom: Improvement criterion and exponential fit. Right: Predicted iteration of need for HPO at different adaptive sampling iterations as crosses, identity line as a dashed line

In this figure in the left upper part, the trajectory of the error on the test set and the CVE are presented over the iterations of the adaptive sampling. In the bottom part, the RP criterion values, as well as the exponential fit, are shown. Using the criterion, a HPO should be performed after 924 samples have been collected as shown by the dotted line denoting where the criterion reaches the threshold of 0.001. On the right-hand side, it is shown for which iteration the criterion is fulfilled, with the criterion being evaluated at different stages of the adaptive sampling. It can be seen that after the 11th adaptive sampling iteration the RP criterion consistently predicts the HPO to become necessary in iteration 17. This holds true also for later iterations, where the HPO eventually becomes overdue. This shows the robustness of the methodology and confirms the assumption, that the RP values can be smoothened with an exponential fit.

After validation, the methodology was applied by performing adaptive sampling and HPO, when the RP criterion is met. The results of this procedure are shown in Figure 3.

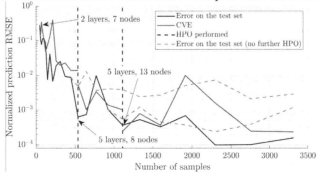

Figure 3: Adaptive sampling in combination with supporting hyperparameter optimization, the hyperparameters are visible as annotations. The dashed lines show the evolution of the error for the test set when the hyperparameters were kept constant.

It can be seen from Figure 3 that when using adaptive sampling with hyperparameter optimization, the model structure is adapted twice, once after 642 samples have been collected and then once again for a sample set of 1109 samples, which leads to a significant decrease in the test set error, compared to the case, where no HPO was performed.

5. Conclusion

In this work, a novel methodology for combining hyperparameter optimization and adaptive sampling is presented and applied to the approximation of the liquid phase fugacity coefficients obtained by PC-SAFT in a quaternary thermomorphic solvent system. The methodology is based on evaluating the slope of the cross-validation error to detect when the accuracy of the surrogate models is not increasing sufficiently anymore. The manual (re-)setting of the hyperparameters, which is a tedious and error-prone task, is avoided and replaced by an automatic procedure. The presented results show the necessity of hyperparameter re-optimization and the successful application of the automatic procedure.

6. Acknowledgment

This research has been supported by the project "KI-Inkubator-Labore in der Prozessindustrie - KEEN", funded by the Bundesministerium für Wirtschaft und Energie (BMWi) under grant number 01MK20014T. This support is gratefully acknowledged.

References

G. James, F. Witten, T. Hastie, R. Tibshirani, 2013, An Introduction to Statistical Learning, Springer New York

T. Janus, A. Luebbers, S. Engell, 2020, Neural Networks for Surrogate-assisted Evolutionary optimization of Chemical Processes, in Proc. 2020 IEEE Congress on Evolutionary Computation (CEC), pp. 1–8

K. McBride, K. Sundmacher, 2019, Overview of Surrogate Modeling in Chemical Process Engineering, Chemie-Ingenieur-Technik, Vol. 91, Issue 3, pp. 228–239

A. D. Mountraki, B. Benjelloun-Mlayah, A. C. Kokossis, 2020, A Surrogate Modeling Approach for the Development of Biorefineries. Frontiers in Chemical Engineering, 2:568196

C. Nentwich, J. Winz, S. Engell, 2019, Surrogate Modeling of Fugacity Coefficients Using Adaptive Sampling. Industrial and Engineering Chemistry Research, Vol. 58, Issue 40, pp. 18703–18716

A. Nuchitprasittichai, S. Cremaschi, 2013, An algorithm to determine sample sizes for optimization with artificial neural networks, AIChE Journal, Vol. 59, Issue 3, pp. 805–812

E. Schäfer, Y. Brunsch, G. Sadowski, A. Behr, 2012, Hydroformylation of 1-dodecene in the thermomorphic solvent system dimethylformamide/decane. Phase behavior-reaction performance-catalyst recycling, Industrial and Engineering Chemistry Research, Vol. 51, Issue 31, pp. 10296–10306

J. Snoek, H. Larochelle, R. P. Adams, 2012, Practical Bayesian optimization of machine learning algorithms, Advances in Neural Information Processing Systems, Vol. 4, pp. 2951–2959

J. Winz, C. Nentwich, S. Engell, 2021, Surrogate Modeling of Thermodynamic Equilibria: Applications, Sampling and Optimization, Chemie-Ingenieur-Technik

Proceedings of the 14th International Symposium on Process Systems Engineering – PSE 2021+
June 19-23, 2022, Kyoto, Japan © 2022 Elsevier B.V. All rights reserved.
http://dx.doi.org/10.1016/B978-0-323-85159-6.50140-8

Optimal Catalyst-Reactor Design for Load-Flexible CO_2 Methanation by Multi-Period Design Optimization

Ronny T. Zimmermann[a], Jens Bremer[b], Kai Sundmacher[a,b,*]

[a]*Otto von Guericke University Magdeburg, Chair for Process Systems Engineering, Universitätsplatz 2, 39106 Magdeburg, Germany*
[b]*Max Planck Institute Magdeburg, Department Process Systems Engineering, Sandtorstraße 1, 39106 Magdeburg, Germany*
sundmacher@mpi-magdeburg.mpg.de

Abstract

Fixed-bed reactors employed within Power-to-X technologies are expected to be subject to volatile process feeds, in order to minimize intermediate buffer or storage systems. In this context, catalyst particles with an inert shell have proven suitable to prevent reactor runaway and severe temperature excursion at various loads and during load-changes, while still allowing for high reactor space-time yields. The aim of this work is to determine how much active catalyst mass can be saved by multi-period design optimization of methanation reactors with one, two, and infinite fixed-bed segments. Our results show that the amount of active mass, which can be saved with a single fixed-bed segment, is negligible. If more than one fixed-bed segment is considered, up to 45.2 % can be saved at the expense of a more complex dynamic reactor behavior. In the worst case, severe temperature excursions during transient scenarios might occur, which is not the case, if only a single fixed-bed segment is considered.

Keywords: Multi-Period Design Optimization, Load-Flexible Fixed-Bed Reactor, Dynamic Reactor Operation, Carbon Dioxide Methanation

1. Introduction

Fixed-bed reactors are commonly employed to carry out heterogeneously catalysed gas-phase reactions. As they are often the central process unit, their optimal operation and design has been investigated for decades. Special attention is often paid to heat management, as many reactions are highly exothermic. With respect to the increase in volatile process feeds (e.g., due to renewable energies), load-flexible operation of fixed-bed reactors is expected to become increasingly important (Bremer and Sundmacher, 2019). Consequently, the employed reactors must not only operate reliably in one steady state, but in many as well as in the transitions between the steady states. Otherwise, severe temperature excursions could deactivate the catalyst or even destroy the reactor material.

The design of the employed catalyst particles has a significant impact on the dynamic behaviour of fixed-bed reactors. Core-shell catalyst particles consisting of an active core and an inert shell ('egg-yolk' catalyst particles) exhibit favourable properties in this context (Zimmermann et al., 2020). In our recent work, we compare such catalyst particles to ordinary fixed-bed dilution, exemplified for carbon dioxide methanation (Zimmermann et al., 2022). In both cases, industry scale fixed-bed reactors with one, two, and infinitely many segments in axial direction are considered.

We conclude, that fixed-beds consisting of core-shell catalyst particles are favourable for load-flexible reactor operation compared to ordinary fixed-bed dilution. The reason for this can be seen in Fig. 1. Whereas ordinary fixed-bed dilution decreases the effective reaction rate by a constant factor over the whole temperature range, core-shell catalyst particles of the 'egg-yolk' type decrease the effective reaction rate selectively at high temperatures, where the diffusion through the inert shell is rate-determining. In consequence, much higher effective reaction rates are obtained towards the reactor outlet, where no reduction of the heat release rate is necessary. This results in higher space-time yield and lower pressure loss.

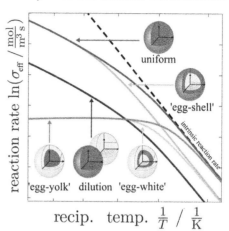

If the catalyst particles are operating in the regime of diffusion limitation by the inert shell, the active mass in the centre of the catalyst particles does not contribute to the conversion of reactants. However, as the active mass often consists of precious noble metals, it should be located within the particles only

Figure 1: Schematic comparison of the effective reaction rates of different catalyst particle concepts and ordinary fixed-bed dilution in Arrhenius plots.

where needed, in order to save investment costs. In this work, we extend the discussed procedure to include catalyst particles, which consist of an inert core and an inert shell with a layer of catalytically active mass in between (a.k.a. 'egg-white' catalyst particles), as seen in Fig. 1. We aim to minimize the amount of active mass needed, while ensuring a high space-time yield and the compliance of conversion and temperature bounds within the entire reactor.

2. Fixed-Bed Reactor and Catalyst Particle Model

A pseudo-homogeneous fixed-bed reactor model is employed. In addition to the carbon dioxide conversion X and radially averaged temperature T, the fixed-bed's centre temperature $\widehat{T}_C$ is approximated by the correlation of Dixon (1996). The reaction kinetic model of Koschany et al. (2016), which considers no side reactions, is used to describe the methanation reaction kinetics. Further details on the remaining constitutive equations are given by Zimmermann et al. (2022).

$$\varepsilon_R \frac{\partial X}{\partial t} = -u \frac{\partial X}{\partial z} + \frac{M_{CO_2}}{\rho \, y_{CO_2,in}} \left(1 - \varepsilon_R\right) r_{\text{eff}} \tag{1}$$

$$(\rho c_p)_{\text{eff}} \frac{\partial T}{\partial t} = -u_{\text{in}} \, \rho_{\text{in}} c_p \frac{\partial T}{\partial z} +$$
$$\frac{\partial}{\partial z} \left[\Lambda_{\text{ax}} \frac{\partial T}{\partial z} \right] - \frac{4 \, U}{D} \left(T - T_{\text{cool}} \right) - H_{\text{r}} \left(1 - \varepsilon_R \right) r_{\text{eff}} \tag{2}$$

The effective reaction rate of the catalyst particles is calculated according to

$$\frac{1}{\eta} = (1+\delta)^{n+1}\left[\frac{\Phi}{\tanh(\gamma\Phi)} + \frac{\Phi^2}{\mathrm{Bi_{ext}}(1+\delta)^n} + \frac{\Phi^2}{\mathrm{Bi_{int}}}\right] \qquad (3)$$

$$\eta = \frac{r_{\mathrm{eff}}}{r_{\mathrm{int}}}, \qquad \Phi = \frac{R_{\mathrm{core}}}{n+1}\sqrt{\frac{\sigma(c_{\mathrm{bulk}})}{\mathfrak{D}_{\mathrm{core}}(c_{\mathrm{bulk}} - c_{\mathrm{bulk,eq}})}}, \qquad \mathrm{Bi_{ext}} = \frac{\mathfrak{D}_{\mathrm{core}}(n+1)}{\beta R_{\mathrm{core}}}$$

$$\mathrm{Bi_{int}} = \frac{\mathfrak{D}_{\mathrm{core}}R_{\mathrm{core}}^{n-1}\Psi(n+1)}{\mathfrak{D}_{\mathrm{shell}}}, \qquad \gamma = \frac{R_{\mathrm{core}}^{n+1} - R_0^{n+1}}{R_{\mathrm{core}}^{n+1}}, \qquad \delta = \frac{R_{\mathrm{shell}} - R_{\mathrm{core}}}{R_{\mathrm{core}}}$$

$$(4)$$

This equation is derived by extending the procedure given by Zimmermann et al. (2022) and is an explicit analytical approximation of the effectiveness factor for a single reaction. It considers the influence of an inert core with radius R_0 in the dimensionless group γ, and the inert shell with radius R_{shell} in the dimensionless group δ.

3. Multi-Period Design Optimization

Multi-period design optimizations, as proposed by Grossmann and Sargent (1979), are performed by employing the pseudo-homogeneous reactor model. Three periods of equal temporal length and carbon dioxide loads of 0.5 t/h, 1.0 t/h, and 1.5 t/h are considered. The operating variables consist of the inlet pressure, velocity, and temperature as well as the coolant temperature and wall heat transfer coefficient. The inlet feed is always a stoichiometric mixture of pure carbon dioxide and hydrogen. The design variables are the reactor's tube length, diameter, and number, together with the catalyst particle diameter, shell porosity, pore diameter, and thickness, as well as radius of the inert core. In each state, the temperature in the centre of the fixed-bed must never exceed 750 K, and the conversion at the outlet of the reactor must be at least 95 %. The remaining constraints are given by Zimmermann et al. (2022).

The amount of catalyst, which can be saved by employing catalyst particles with an inert core is determined in two steps. First, the time-average methane space-time yield is maximized, considering a fully active core. In the second step, the amount of active mass in the reactor is minimized, while at least 99 % of the first steps space-time yield has to be achieved. Each of the steps is performed with one, two, and infinite segments, which can consist of different catalyst loadings. Details on the numerical solution strategy and the used solvers are given by Zimmermann et al. (2022).

Subsequently, dynamic load-change simulations are performed, by switching between the optimal operating parameters of the respective cases. Additionally, a start-up and a shutdown are investigated. The initial conditions for the start-up are given as $X_0 = 0$ % and $T_0 = 300$ K. For the shut-down, T_{in} and T_{cool} are reduced to 300 K.

4. Results

4.1. Multi-Period Design Optimization

The results of the multi-period design optimization are shown in Fig. 2 and in Tab. 1. The optimal steady states of the first step are identical to those discussed in detail by Zimmermann et al. (2022) and serve as reference. In summary, the optimal reactor is designed such that the maximum heat transfer to the coolant is realized and the length is determined by the residence time required to achieve 95 % reactant conversion in each case. The latter is the main factor for the differing time-average space-time yields.

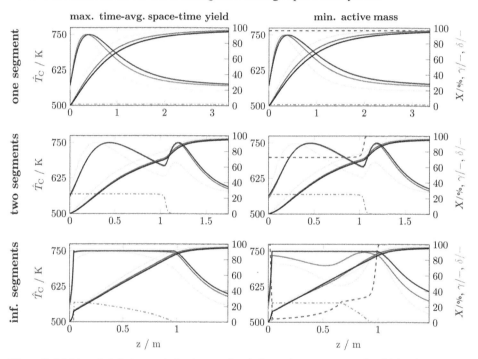

Figure 2: Multi-period design optimization results, darker colours correspond to higher loads (0.5 t/h, 1.0 t/h, and 1.5 t/h).

Table 1: Results of all multi-period design optimizations, respective objective function values in bold.

objective func.	max. time-average STY (step 1, reference cases)			min. active mass (step 2)		
fixed-bed segments	1	2	Inf.	1	2	Inf.
STY / kg m^{-3} s^{-1}	**0.3850**	**0.7440**	**0.8773**	0.3811 (-1%)	0.7366 (-1%)	0.8771 (-0%)
m_{act} / kg	215.1	82.2	77.3	**211.1** (-2%)	**73.95** (-10%)	**42.3** (-45%)

Compared to these results, reactors with minimized active mass show very similar trends, especially if one or two segments are considered. In the case of a single fixed-bed segment, almost no potential for removing active mass from the centre of the catalyst particles is available. This is because it is only suitable to save active mass in the particle cores in the regime of mass transfer limitation, since no reactants enter the interior of the particles in this case. However, this happens only at high temperatures near the reactor inlet. At low temperatures near the reactor outlet, the inert core acts as fixed-bed dilution (Fig. 1) and consequently longer reactors would be necessary to achieve the lower conversion constraint of 95%, which would lead to a significant drop of reactor space-time compared to the reactor with maximum time-average space-time yield.

Consequently, more potential to save active mass exists for the two-segment reactor. Only in first segment close to the reactor inlet, an inert shell is used to limit the effective reaction rate in order to stay within the temperature limit. Consequently, the core of the catalyst particles is chosen to be inert. As a large part of the reactants has been consumed in the first segment, no restriction of the effective reaction rate is necessary in the second segment. Thus, the optimizer prefers uniform catalyst particles, as these exhibit the highest effective reaction rate of all particle designs considered in this work. This results in a reduction of the required active mass by 10.0 %.

The results of the reactor with infinite segments confirm this trend in shape of singular arcs for the inert core and inert shell radii. Additionally, a segment of uniform catalyst is introduced directly at the reactor inlet, to increase the reactor temperature and thus the reaction rate. This case yields the maximum potential of active mass reduction, which is 45.2 %.

4.2. Dynamic Load-Change Simulations

Although all steady-states shown in the previous section convey to the upper temperature limit of 750 K, severe temperature excursions might still occur during dynamic transitions. Thus, dynamic load-change simulations have been performed as shown in Fig. 3.

All cases show a fast start-up behaviour and the ignited steady-states are achieved in less than two minutes. The one- and two-segment reactors with maximized space-time yields also show smooth transitions between the optimal sets of operating parameters. The same is true for their counterparts with minimized active mass, although slight oscillations can be observed after load-

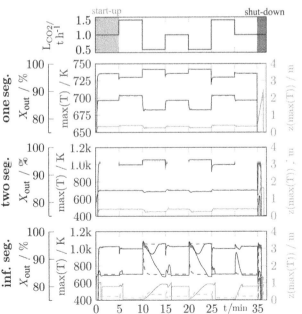

Figure 3: Dynamic load-change simulations, dashed lines show the results of reactors with maximized time-average space-time yield and solid lines show the results of reactors with minimized active mass. Please note the differing scales.

changes. In the cases with infinite segments, the reactors with maximized time-averaged space-time yield exhibit a travelling hot-spot, whenever the load is reduced. This is even more pronounced for the reactor with minimized active mass. In addition, such reactors also show temperature excursions when the load is increased.

During the shut-down, all reactors with more than one fixed-bed segment show pronounced temperature excursions. The reason for this is the high amount of inert mass of the segments close to the reactor inlet, which cool down quickly. Consequently, high amounts of reactants encounter the hot segments with high amounts of active mass towards the reactor outlet. As the catalyst particles in these segments also do not exhibit an inert shell, a steep increase in temperature is observed. The reactors with just one segment contain catalyst particles with an inert shell along the whole length, and thus no temperature excursions are observed.

5. Conclusions

The introduction of catalyst particles with an inert core offers the possibility to reduce expensive active mass in fixed-bed reactors on the one hand, but also reduces the effective reaction rate of the catalyst particles in the kinetically limited regime on the other. Thus, the reactor space-time yield might drop, such that an inert particle core is only purposeful at fixed-bed locations, where the reactants are not present in the particle core, which is the case in the regime of mass transport limitation. In consequence, only minimal potential is available for reducing the active mass if one fixed-bed segment and high space-time yield are aimed for, but this case offers fast and save transition during load-changes. Up to 45.2 % of active mass can be saved if more than one segment is considered. However, in these cases active mass is in direct contact with the surrounding gas phase, leading to the risk of severe temperature excursions during load-changes.

6. Acknowledgment

This research work was conducted within the DFG Priority Program SPP2080 'Catalysts and reactors under dynamic conditions for energy storage and conversion' and was funded by the Deutsche Forschungsgemeinschaft (DFG, German Research Foundation) - 406914011 (Gefördert durch die Deutsche Forschungsgemeinschaft (DFG) - 406914011.). Ronny Zimmermann is also affiliated with the International Max Planck Research School (IMPRS) for Advanced Methods in Process and Systems Engineering, Magdeburg, Germany.

References

J. Bremer, K. Sundmacher, 2019. Operation range extension via hot-spot control for catalytic CO_2 methanation reactors. Reaction Chemistry & Engineering 4 (6), 1019–1037.

A. G. Dixon, 1996. An improved equation for the overall heat transfer coefficient in packed beds. Chemical Engineering and Processing: Process Intensification 35 (5), 323–331.

I. E. Grossmann, R. W. H. Sargent, 1979. Optimum design of multipurpose chemical plants. Industrial & Engineering Chemistry Process Design and Development 18 (2), 343–348.

F. Koschany, D. Schlereth, O. Hinrichsen, 2016. On the kinetics of the methanation of carbon dioxide on coprecipitated $NiAl(O)_x$. Applied Catalysis B: Environmental 181, 504–516.

R. T. Zimmermann, J. Bremer, K. Sundmacher, 2020. Optimal catalyst particle design for flexible fixed-bed CO_2 methanation reactors. Chemical Engineering Journal 387, 123704.

R. T. Zimmermann, J. Bremer, K. Sundmacher, 2022. Load-flexible fixed-bed reactors by multi-period design optimization. Chemical Engineering Journal 425, 130771.

Proceedings of the 14th International Symposium on Process Systems Engineering – PSE 2021+
June 19-23, 2022, Kyoto, Japan © 2022 Elsevier B.V. All rights reserved.
http://dx.doi.org/10.1016/B978-0-323-85159-6.50141-X

Data-Driven Modeling of Long-Term Performance Degradation in Solid Oxide Electrolyzer Cell System

Mina Naeini[a], James S. Cotton[b], Thomas A. Adams II[a]*

[a]*Department of Chemical Engineering, McMaster University, Hamilton, ON, L8S 4L7, Canada*
[b]*Department of Mechanical Engineering, McMaster University, Hamilton, ON, L8S 4L7, Canada*

tadams@mcmaster.ca

Abstract

One key challenge of Solid Oxide Electrolyzer Cell (SOEC) systems is degradation over long periods of time. Degradation decreases efficiency by increasing the electrical energy required for H_2 production. This paper presents the first step in managing long-term degradation in SOEC systems. In this work, the first data-driven dynamic model for the prediction of performance degradation in SOECs as a function of humidity, operating temperature, and current density was developed. The model was trained using experimental data from multiple data sets in the literature under various conditions. The model showed good agreement with validation data over 7000 h operation. One key finding is that the data show there are three distinct time regimes in which degradation behaviour is qualitatively different. This is likely due to different degradation phenomena, although the specific phenomena have not yet been isolated. This is significant for PSE applications because operators can choose to vary the operating conditions over time in order to predict, account for, or minimize the effects of long-term degradation.

Keywords: SOEC; Performance Degradation; Data-Driven Model; Operating Condition.

1. Background

When baseload power facilities or renewable sources of intermittent power are used for electricity generation, excess electricity may be produced during low demand hours. Producing surplus electricity can impose additional costs to electricity systems as it should be either curtailed or sold at a low price. Therefore, there is a great need for reliable energy storage systems at low demand hours. SOEC is a promising technology for energy storage that can utilize the excess electricity from the grid to electrolyze steam and generate hydrogen. H_2 is a clean, useful source of energy with high energy content per weight unit. The produced H_2 can be compressed and stored in cylinders for various purposes, supplied to stationary power generators such as fuel cells to produce electricity, or injected into the existing natural gas network to lower carbon intensity. SOECs are Solid Oxide Fuel Cells (SOFCs) which are operated in reverse. Indeed, the same technology can either generate electricity via some exothermic electrochemical reactions (SOFC mode) when supplied with fuel and air, or it can electrolyze water and produce H_2 through endothermic electrochemical reactions (SOEC mode), when supplied with steam and electricity. SOFCs and SOECs feature several advantages over some existing power generation technologies and electrolyzer systems such as high efficiency, low noise, and reduced greenhouse gas (GHG) emissions. However, this technology suffers the drawback of significant long-term degradation under normal operating conditions. This issue has been a barrier for commercialization of SOFCs and SOECs and has limited their application in the industry (Zaccaria et al., 2015). In our prior work, we were able to successfully overcome this problem for SOFCs specifically by constructing a mathematical model for dynamic simulation of the long-term performance drop in SOFC systems (Naeini et al., 2021). Using this model in a techno-economic analysis (TEA) enabled us to determine the optimal capacity and corresponding optimal dynamic operational trajectories of SOFCs that make them more cost-competitive with traditional power generation, by managing their long-term degradation and increasing their useful lifetime (Naeini et al., 2021). This was possible because the individual mechanisms that cause SOFC degradation are known, and thus first principles could be considered directly in the model.

Since the electrochemical reactions and degradation mechanisms in SOFCs are different from those in SOECs, the model developed for degradation in SOFCs cannot be used to predict degradation in SOECs. As such, a dynamic model should be constructed for simulation of long-term performance degradation in SOECs. This is essential for identifying optimal sizing and operating strategies of SOEC systems for a cost-effective energy storage over an extended lifetime, with controlled degradation. Our broad literature survey revealed that a dynamic degradation-based model for SOECs is lacking in the open literature. Also, the mechanisms of degradation phenomena in electrolysis mode are not well known, which prevents us from developing a first-principles model. However, there have been number of experiments investigating impacts of operating conditions on SOEC performance degradation. Hoerlein et al.'s (2018) experiments in particular showed the impacts of current density, humidity, and operating temperature on voltage and ohmic resistance of 20 SOECs over 1000 h of operation. This is a good, representative dataset that contains acceptable ranges of operating parameters as it includes current density ranging from 0 to 1.5 A/cm^2, humidity varying from 40 % to 80 %, and temperature from 750 to 850 °C. This dataset is used in the current work to develop a data-driven model for degradation of SOEC.

2. Modeling strategy

The following information shows that the time evolution of SOEC's ohmic resistance can be used to calculate SOEC degradation. SOECs produce H$_2$ at a constant rate as long as the current density supplied to the cell is constant (Eq.(1)).

$$r_{H_2} = \frac{i}{nF} \tag{1}$$

where r_{H_2} is the rate of H$_2$ production, i, n, and F are the current density, moles of electrons involved in the electrolysis electrochemical reactions, and Faraday constant, respectively. The ohmic resistance of SOECs increases over time due to degradation. According to Ohm's law (Eq.(2)), the voltage of the SOEC and therefore the energy required to produce a constant amount of H$_2$ increase with its degradation (Eq.(3)).

$$V = R\,i \tag{2}$$

$$P = R\,i^2 = V\,i \tag{3}$$

In these equations R, V, and P represent the SOEC's ohmic resistance, voltage, and power, respectively. The magnitude of resistance increase depends on the operating conditions. Therefore, a model that predicts time evolution of resistance as a function of current density, humidity, and temperature will allow us to quantify performance degradation in the SOEC. Data from figure 1 is used in the present work to develop a model for SOEC degradation. Given in the y-axis of these plots is ΔR_{ohm} which shows the ohmic resistance increase with respect to the initial ohmic resistance of the cells.

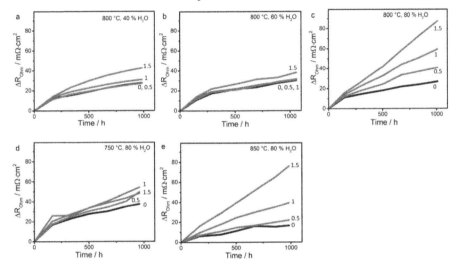

Figure 1. Time evolution of ohmic resistance of SOECs at various current densities from 0 to 1.5 A/cm² and a) 800°C and 40% humidity, b) 800°C and 60% humidity, c) 800°C and 80% humidity, d) 750°C and 80% humidity, and e) 850°C and 80% humidity. Original data from (Hoerlein et al.).

The data show an unstable behavior in some SOECs during the first 200 h of operation, where the resistance, voltage, and other parameters do not follow a reproducible or consistent trajectory from run to run. This behavior is known as cell conditioning or transition period and cannot be modelled since it does not conform to any known pattern (Sohal; Hubert). However, the data show that the cumulative degradation of the cell at the 200h mark does correlate well with temperature, humidity, and current density, even though the trajectory in getting there does not. We removed the first 200 h from the training data and as a result the developed model applies only beyond 200 h. It should also be noted that even though Hoerlein et al.'s (2018) data includes voltage trajectories of SOECs, voltage is not used for building the SOEC model in this study. The reason is that when there is not any current in the external circuit, i.e. the open circuit voltage condition (OCV), the voltage remains constant and as a result it is not a good state variable for predicting degradation of SOECs.

ALAMO (Automated Learning of Algebraic Models) was used to develop the data-driven model. This software employs a machine learning approach to learn accurate and simple algebraic models from the training dataset (Wilson and Sahinidis). ALAMO models are typically linear combinations of nonlinear transformations of the input variables. The software uses an optimization approach to find not only the best fit of model parameters, but the selection of the basis functions themselves. This avoids overfitting and helps choose basis functions that best characterize the data.

2.1. Development of the linear model from 200h to 2500h

First, a partial model was developed based on Hoerlein et al's (2018) dataset (which has data out to 1000h), shown in Eq. (4).

$$R_{t'} = R_0 + \underline{0.019\ TH + 7.290\ Hi} + [0.033\ Ht' + 0.017\ it'] \tag{4}$$

where t' is time since 200h (h), $R_{t'}$ is ohmic resistance at t' (mΩ.cm^2), R_0 is resistance of virginal SOEC at time 0h (mΩ.cm^2), T is temperature (°C), and H is humidity of the fuel feed expressed as mole fraction of water. Eq.(4) includes two time-independent (underlined) and two time-dependent (enclosed in square brackets) terms. Underlined terms show the change in resistance from R0 within the first 200h. While time-dependent terms show the increase in resistance from 200h and onward. Since the data for the first 200h were removed from training data, the model cannot indicate time evolution of resistance within this period. Instead, it quantifies the total change in resistance from R0 within the first 200h. As can be seen, given a constant molar humidity and current density, ohmic resistance of SOEC increases linearly with time for at least 1000h, and so we refer to this model as the "linear model". This is in agreement with number of other studies that reported linear trend in time for SOEC degradation at fixed operating conditions (Hauch; Hubert; Trofimenko et al.). These studies all consider operation for 2500h or less. Eq.(4) was fit with R^2=0.94 across the training datasets considered up to 1000h. Rapid transients may have impacts which are not considered in the model.

2.2. Validation of the linear model out to 2500 h

In order to ensure validity of the developed model for predicting performance degradation in SOECs under given operating conditions, Tietz et al.'s (2013) experimental data – which was not considered in building the model – was used to compare with the model. In Tietz et al. (2013) an SOEC was operated at 778±6°C out to 7600h, supplied with current density of 1A/cm^2, and 80% humidity. We calculated the SOEC's ohmic resistance trajectory using Eq. (4) and then its voltage trajectory using Eq. (2) under the given condition. The results, given in Figure 2, indicate capability of this linear model to simulate performance deterioration in SOECs for the first 2500 h of operation (R^2=0.87). After 2500h, it becomes more apparent that the SOEC degrades sub-linearly and the degradation rate decreases. We note that most studies that conclude that degradation rates are linear, such as Hauch et al. (2006), Hubert et al. (2018), and Trofimenko et al. (2017) do not run the experiments long enough to experience this inflection point around 2500h.

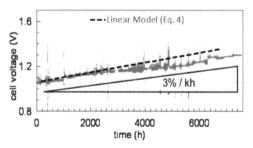

Figure 2. Results of the developed model for SOEC performance degradation compared to experimental data from (Tietz et al.).The dashed line is our model, drawn on top of a modified version of the original figure reproduced from that work.

2.3. Sublinear model out to 7000 h

The model was modified to reflect the sublinear nature of the degradation by adding a power term to the time component, and fitting the exponent to Tietz et al.'s data. The basis functions and their parameters were unmodified from Eq. 4. The sublinear model is given in Eq.(5), in which degradation is sublinear to the order of 0.97, and $R^2=0.95$ for Tietz et al.'s data out to 7000h.

$$R_{t'} = R_0 + 0.019\,T + 7.290Hi + (0.033H + 0.017i)(t')^{0.97} \tag{5}$$

A comparison between the linear model, sublinear model, and experimental data is provided in Figure 3. As can be seen, the original and modified models are almost equally good for simulation of short-term operation. But for the long-term operation, sublinear model is significantly better than the linear one.

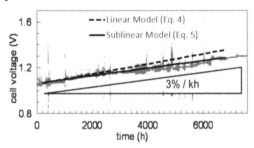

Figure 3. Results of the linear and sublinear models for long-term performance degradation in SOEC compared to experimental data from (Tietz et al.). Figure modified from the original.

3. Discussion and Future Work

One key finding is the sublinear nature of the degradation rate, but this is supported only by one data set since most experiments in the open literature are not conducted for long enough in order to see this trend. Additional research is needed to validate this sublinear characteristic. However, sublinear behavior makes sense, as in practice SOECs can be used for many years. If the degradation rate was truly linear such that long-term degradation continued at the same rate as in the first 1000h, the amount of degradation would be much higher than what is actually experienced in practice. For example, comparing extrapolating the sublinear (Eq. (5)) and linear (Eq. (4)) models out to 10 years, the linear model would predict a required voltage of 30% higher than the sublinear model. This will make a significant difference in design and operation of large-scale systems. Using either the linear or sublinear model, as well as Eq.(2) and Eq.(3), one can calculate voltage of SOECs and the required power supply for producing a specific amount of H_2 at different points of operating time considering the degradation. This will enable system designers to find the optimal capacity and operation strategy of SOEC system for an economical energy storage with reduced degradation rate. As such, a TEA will be performed on SOEC systems as the future work. The findings will improve cost-effectiveness of this technology and will help its commercialization.

4. Conclusions

This paper presented a data-driven model constructed from experimental data derived from the literature for prediction of the performance deterioration in SOEC. To the best of authors' knowledge, this is the first dynamic model for simulation of the SOEC degradation under different operating conditions with high accuracy across a range of cell conditions. This model, developed using ALAMO, is a composition of nonlinear functions of operating parameters namely humidity, temperature, and current density. The model was well-validated using many training and testing sets for the first 2500h of operation, but the extension to 7000h requires additional validation. Both the linear (Eq 4) and sublinear (Eq 5) models work equally well for those first 2500h but the linear model breaks down afterward. The results indicated that the rate of SOEC degradation depends on the humidity and current density, and decays sublinearly in the long-term.

References

Hauch, Anne. "Performance and Durability of Solid Oxide Electrolysis Cells." *ECS Meeting Abstracts*, vol. 37, no. October, 2006, doi:10.1149/ma2006-01/24/842.

Hoerlein, M. P., et al. "A Parameter Study of Solid Oxide Electrolysis Cell Degradation: Microstructural Changes of the Fuel Electrode." *Electrochimica Acta Journal*, vol. 276, 2018, pp. 162–75, doi:10.1016/j.electacta.2018.04.170.

Hubert, M. "Durability of Solid Oxide Cells: An Experimental and Modelling Investigation Based on Synchrotron X-Ray Nano-Tomography Characterization." *PhD Thesis*, 2018.

Naeini, Mina, Haoxiang Lai, et al. "A Mathematical Model for Prediction of Long-Term Degradation Effects in Solid Oxide Fuel Cells." *Industrial and Engineering Chemistry Research*, vol. 60, no. 3, 2021, pp. 1326–40, doi:10.1021/acs.iecr.0c05302.

Naeini, Mina, James S. Cotton, et al. *Economically Optimal Sizing and Operation Strategy for Solid Oxide Fuel Cells to Effectively Manage Long Term Degradation*. 2021.

Sohal, Manohar S. *Degradation in Solid Oxide Cells During High Temperature Electrolysis*. 2009.

Tietz, F., et al. "Degradation Phenomena in a Solid Oxide Electrolysis Cell after 9000 h of Operation." *Journal of Power Sources*, vol. 223, Elsevier B.V, 2013, pp. 129–35, doi:10.1016/j.jpowsour.2012.09.061.

Trofimenko, Nikolai, et al. "Optimization of ESC Performance for Co-Electrolysis Operation." *ECS Transactions*, vol. 78, no. 1, 2017, pp. 3025–37, doi:10.1149/07801.3025ecst.

Wilson, Zachary T., and Nikolaos V. Sahinidis. "The ALAMO Approach to Machine Learning." *Computers & Chemical Engineering*, vol. 106, Pergamon, Nov. 2017, pp. 785–95, doi:10.1016/J.COMPCHEMENG.2017.02.010.

Zaccaria, Valentina, et al. "A Real-Time Degradation Model for Hardware in the Loop." *Proceedings of ASME Turbo Expo 2015: Turbine Technical Conference and Exposition GT2015*, 2015, pp. 1–8.

Proceedings of the 14th International Symposium on Process Systems Engineering – PSE 2021+
June 19-23, 2022, Kyoto, Japan © 2022 Elsevier B.V. All rights reserved.
http://dx.doi.org/10.1016/B978-0-323-85159-6.50142-1

Modeling and Optimal Design of Pressure Swing Adsorber for Carbon Dioxide and Hydrogen Separation from Industrial Waste Gas

Toji Kakiuchi[a] , Tomoyuki Yajima[a] ,Nobuyuki Shigaki[b], Yoshiaki Kawajiri[a*]

[a]*Department of Materials Process Engineering, Nagoya University, Aichi 464-8603, JAPAN*
[b]*Steel Research Laboratory, JFE Steel Corporation, 1 Kokan-cho, Fukuyama, JAPAN*
kawajiri@nagoya-u.jp

Abstract

Recently, carbon dioxide capture utilization and storage (CCUS) is gaining attention as a way to reduce carbon dioxide emissions. Blast furnace gas (BFG) in the steel industry is one of the major sources of carbon dioxide (CO_2) emissions, which has the potential to be a hydrogen (H_2) source by water gas shift reaction to. In this work, we pursue simultaneous purification of H_2 and CO_2 from reformed BFG by pressure swing adsorption (PSA). A mathematical model of newly designed PSA for simultaneous separation of CO_2 and H_2 is developed from experimental results. After fitting to the experimental results to the model, we were able to reproduce the purity and recovery of the recovered gas with an error of about 5 %. The model was also used to perform multi-objective optimization of the PSA process. From the Pareto solutions, the relationship between energy consumption and throughput is analyzed. In addition, it was confirmed that there is an operation condition that can increase the purity of carbon dioxide and throughput while suppressing the decrease of purity and recovery of hydrogen.

Keywords: Pressure Swing Adsorption; Modeling; Dynamics; Optimization.

1. Introduction

Due to rising concentration of carbon dioxide in the atmosphere, global warming is posing a serious threat. To deal with this issue, Carbon Dioxide Capture, Storage and Utilization (CCUS), a technological concept to capture carbon dioxide from flue gas from power plants and steel mills, etc. to use it as a resource, or to inject it into the ground and seawater, has been attracting attention. It is estimated that CCUS could reduce 20% of worldwide carbon dioxide (CO_2) emission in 2008, which has substantial potential[1]. In particular, blast furnace gas in the steel industry is one of the major sources of carbon dioxide emissions, and the application of CCUS to this source is expected[2].

One of the promising techniques for capturing CO_2 is Pressure Swing Adsorption (PSA). PSA has been used in many applications of large-scale gas separation[3]. However, power consumption and energy cost must be reduced substantially for successful CCUS implementation[4]. A study reported that the estimated cost is $72-114 to capture and store a ton of carbon dioxide, most of which is spent to capture CO_2[5]. It is expected that this cost should be reduced to approximately $18 [3].

Blast furnace gas (BFG) contains not only CO_2 at high concentration, but also carbon monoxide and a small amount of hydrogen. BFG has the potential to be a hydrogen source by steam reforming. The production of methane and methanol, promising products of CO_2 utilization in CCUS, can be produced from carbon dioxide and hydrogen (H_2) included in the reformed BFG. To realize this CCUS approach, simultaneous capture of

CO_2 and H_2 from BFG after reforming is expected. However, the process of capturing both gases at the same time remains a challenge. For example, multiple PSA units designed by Air Products and Chemicals, Inc. may increase the total capital cost[6]. Other PSAs that separate these two components at the same time also tend to require high hydrogen concentrations in the feed gas, and only a few studies have considered dilute hydrogen [7].

This work pursues simultaneous purification of H_2 and CO_2 from reformed BFG by a novel PSA process. A mathematical model is developed from experimental results. Using the model, multi-objective optimization of the PSA process is performed, where the Pareto solutions provides insights into the relationship between energy consumption and throughput.

2. Process description

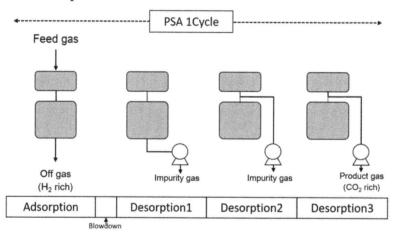

Figure 1 Operation of PSA for multiple separation

Figure 1 shows the operation of the newly designed PSA for CO_2 and H_2 multiple gas separation. The process consists of 2 tandem columns, which allows separation of two gas components within one cycle. Reformed BFG from a water gas shift reactor is supplied as the feed gas. In the Adsorption step, the off-gas is collected, which is rich in the component that adsorbs onto the adsorbent most weakly. In the following two steps, Desorption 1 and Desorption 2, a vacuum pump withdraws impurity gas, mainly N_2, from the upper and lower column, respectively. Finally, CO_2 is withdrawn from the upper column in the last desorption step through the gas fraction line, fractionated at the delivery side of the vacuum pump.

To demonstrate this novel operation, a laboratory-scale PSA experiment was conducted. Figure 2 and Table 1 show the experimental conditions and setup

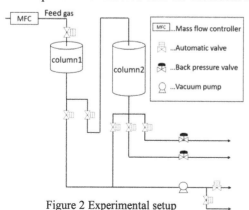

Figure 2 Experimental setup

of this 2-column PSA. Zeolite 13X was employed as adsorbent in both columns. In this setup, the flow rate of the feed gas was controlled by mass flow controller. The adsorption pressure was controlled by a back pressure valve, and the desorption pressure was manipulated by a vacuum pump.

Table 1 Experimental condition

Condition	Value	Condition	Value
Adsorbent	Zeolite13X	Feed gas composition [%]	N_2:40, CO_2:37 H_2:23
Pellet diameter [mm]	1.5	Feed gas temperature [K]	298.15
Height of column [mm]	Upper:60 Lower:200	Cycle time [s/cycle]	100
Weight of adsorbent [g]	Upper:57 Lower:190	Pressure at the bottom of column [kPa]	Adsorption: 151 Desorption: 6
Column inner diameter [mm]	42	Feed gas flow rate [NL/min]	3.0

3. Mathematical model

A model was constructed that consists of mass and energy balance equations, Langmuir isotherms, and mass transfer rate assuming linear driving force[8]. Boundary conditions for each operation stage were also employed from the ones in a previous study[8].

3.1. Model fitting

To fit the model to the experimental data, we employ the formulation of Tikhonov regularization[9]. The model parameters were estimated using equation (1) as the objective function.

$$\min_{\theta} \sum_{j=1}^{3} \sum_{i=1}^{N_{Comp}} \left(Flow_{i,j,Model} - Flow_{i,j,exp}\right)^2 + \rho \sum_{i=1}^{N_{Comp}} \left(\frac{\theta_{opt,i} - \theta_{lit,i}}{\theta_{lit,i}}\right)^2 \tag{1}$$

N_{Comp} is the number of component, with $N_{Comp} = 3$; θ is the vector of parameters to be estimated; *Flow* [NL/min] is the flow rate from the column; ρ [-] is the regularization coefficient; subscripts i and j are for gas components and steps shown in Figure 1, respectively; *Model* and *exp* denote calculated and experimental value; and *opt* and *lit* denote optimized and literature parameter values, respectively. The isotherm equation is given by the Langmuir model, and the mass transfer between the gas and adsorbent phases is described by the linear driving force model:

$$q_i^* = \frac{q_{eq,i} K_i P_i}{1 + \sum_{i=1}^{n} K_i P_i} \tag{2}$$

$$K_i = K_{1_i} \exp\left(1000 K_{2_i}\left(\frac{1}{T} - \frac{1}{250}\right)\right) \tag{3}$$

$$q_i = \frac{15 D_e}{R_p^{\ 2}}(q^* - q_i) \tag{4}$$

where $q_{eq,i}$ [mol/kg], q_i^* [mol/kg] and q_i [mol/kg] are saturation adsorption capacity, equilibrium adsorption amount, and adsorption amount, respectively; K_1 [1/Pa] and K_2 [K] are affinity constants; P_i [kPa] is partial pressure; De [m²/s] is the diffusion coefficient; R_p [m] is the particle radius of adsorbent; and T [K] is temperature. The parameter vector θ is defined as defined as $\theta = [K_1, K_2, De]^T$.

3.2. Process optimization

Feed gas inflow rate and energy consumption are strongly associated with efficiency. The objective function for process optimization is formulated as in Equation (5) and (6).

$$\max_{u} \frac{\sum_{i=1}^{N_{Comp}} Feed_i}{t_{cy}(L_1 + L_2)} - M\varepsilon_1 - M\varepsilon_2 \tag{5}$$

where $Feed$ [mol/m²] is the total molar volume of gas that enters the PSA; t_{cy} [s] is the cycle time; L_1 and L_2 [m] are the height of column1 and column2; ε_1 and ε_2 [-] are tolerance variables to enforce a cyclic steady state; M is the penalty constant set to 5000; u is a vector of decision variables, defined as $u = [P_{ad}, P_{de}, tcy, L_1, L_2, F]^T$; P_{ad} and P_{de} [kPa] are the pressure of adsorption and desorption step; F [NL/min] is the feed flow rate.

$$\min_{u} E = \frac{\dfrac{work_{ad}}{\eta_{blower}} + \dfrac{work_{de}}{\eta_{pump}}}{Product} \tag{6}$$

E [kJ/mol] is the energy consumption for a unit mole of recovered gas; $work_{ad}$ and $work_{de}$ [kJ] are the work of adsorption and desorption step; η_{blower} and η_{pump} [-] are the efficiency of blower and pump; $Product$ [mol] is the total molar volume of recovered CO_2 and H_2. Finally, the product purity and recovery must be at least $Pur_{min,i}$ and $Rec_{min,i}$, respectively:

$$Purity_i \geqq Pur_{min,i} \tag{7}$$

$$Recovery_i \geqq Rec_{min,i} \tag{8}$$

where i = H_2, CO_2. In this study, the optimization formulation and solution approach in Ko et al. [8] was employed.

4. Results and Discussion

4.1. Model fitting

Table 2 Experimental values and model fitting of purity and recovery

	$Purity_{CO2}$	$Recovery_{CO2}$	$Purity_{H2}$	$Recovery_{H2}$
Experiment	0.894	0.718	0.534	0.752
Model	0.823	0.758	0.532	0.758

Table 2 shows the model fitting for the experiment. It can be seen that both of the purity and recovery of CO_2 have an error of about 5 % compared to the experimental results, while hydrogen reproduces the experimental results well. While further reducing the value of ρ in Equation (1) would allow the parameter values to deviate from literature and reduce the model error, overfitting and parameter values that are physically inconsistent must be avoided. A potential reason for the model mismatch is the isotherm model in Equation (2), which has substantial influence on the desorption gas flow rate in Desorption1, 2 and 3.

4.2. Optimization Results

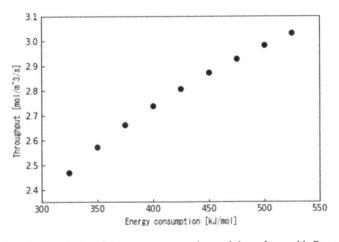

Figure 3 Pareto optimal solutions for energy consumption and throughput with $Pur_{min,CO2} - 0.99$, $Rec_{min,CO2} = 0.90$, $Pur_{min,H2} = 0.60$, $Rec_{min,H2} = 0.70$ in Equation (7) and (8).

Figure 3 shows the energy consumption and throughput, showing the trade-off between throughput and energy consumption for a unit mole of recovered CO_2 and H_2. All of the optimal solutions reach the lower bound of the constraints shown in Chapter 3. It can be confirmed that as the energy consumption increases, the impact on the throughput decreases. According to this graph, the higher energy consumption is, the smaller increment of throughput.

Comparing the experimental and optimized performance in Table 3, it is confirmed that better operating conditions can be found by the optimization, where the product constraints, Equation (7) and (8), are adjusted to the experimental data. In the optimal solution, the throughput is increased by approximately 20 %, and CO_2 purity and CO_2 recovery are both higher, while H_2 recovery and H_2 purity are same and the energy consumption is slightly lower.

Table 3 Comparison of experimental and optimized performance. The optimization was performed with the following conditions to match the experimental results: $Pur_{min,CO2} = 0.894$, $Rec_{min,CO2} = 0.718$, $Pur_{min,H2} = 0.534$, $Rec_{min,H2} = 0.752$ in Equation (7) and (8).

	experiment	optimization		experiment	optimization
Energy Consumption E [kJ/mol]	468	461	Throughput [mol/m³/s]	3.064	3.65
$Purity_{CO2}$	0.894	0.983	$Recovery_{CO2}$	0.718	0.877
$Purity_{H2}$	0.534	0.534	$Recovery_{H2}$	0.752	0.752

5. Conclusions

In this study, we developed a mathematical model of the newly designed PSA for simultaneous gas separation of CO_2 and H_2, and optimized the process to improve the performance. The model was fitted to experimental results by Tikhonov regularization to consider literature data. Furthermore, the analysis by multi-objective optimization enabled trade-off analysis of process performance and identification of new operating conditions. Future study aims to reduce model error, and analyze the influence of constraints for product purity and recovery.

Acknowledgement

This article is based on results obtained from a project, JPNP16002, commissioned by the New Energy and Industrial Technology Development Organization (NEDO).

References

1. International Energy Agency. (2008) Energy technology perspectives. Paris: International Energy Agency
2. Shigaki, N., Mogi, Y., Haraoka, T., and Sumi, I. (2018). Reduction of electric power consumption in CO2-PSA with zeolite 13X adsorbent. *Energies*, *11*(4), 1–21.
3. Saima H., Mogi Y., and Haraoka T.: JFE Tech. Rep. 2014, 19, 133.
4. Saima, H., Mogi, Y., and Haraoka, T. (2013). Development of PSA system for the recovery of carbon dioxide and carbon monoxide from blast furnace gas in steel works. *Energy Procedia*, *37*(19), 7152–7159.
5. Hasan, M. M. F., First, E. L., Boukouvala, F., and Floudas, C. A. (2015). A multi-scale framework for CO_2 capture, utilization, and sequestration: CCUS and CCU. *Computers and Chemical Engineering*, *81*, 2–21.
6. Sircar, S. (1993). Recent trends in pressure swing adsorption: Production of multiple products from a multicomponent feed gas. Gas Separation and Purification, 7(2), 69–73.
7. Streb, A., Hefti, M., Gazzani, M., and Mazzotti, M. (2019). Novel Adsorption Process for Co-Production of Hydrogen and CO_2 from a Multicomponent Stream. *Industrial and Engineering Chemistry Research*, *58*(37), 17489–17506.
8. Ko, D., Siriwardane, R., and Biegler, L. T. (2005). Optimization of pressure swing adsorption and fractionated vacuum pressure swing adsorption processes for CO_2 capture. *Industrial and Engineering Chemistry Research*, *44*(21), 8084–8094.
9. Suzuki, K., Harada, H., Sato, K., Okada, K., Tsuruta, M., Yajima, T., and Kawajiri, Y. (2021). Utilization of operation data for parameter estimation of simulated moving bed chromatography. *Journal of Advanced Manufacturing and Processing*, e10103

Proceedings of the 14th International Symposium on Process Systems Engineering – PSE 2021+
June 19-23, 2022, Kyoto, Japan © 2022 Elsevier B.V. All rights reserved.
http://dx.doi.org/10.1016/B978-0-323-85159-6.50143-3

Membrane Characterization with Model-Based Design of Experiments

Xinhong Liu[a], Jialu Wang[a], Jonathan A. Ouimet[a], William A. Phillip[a], Alexander W. Dowling[a*]

[a] *Department of Chemical and Biomolecular Engineering, University of Notre Dame, Notre Dame, IN 46556, USA*
adowling@nd.edu

Abstract

Membrane characterization provides essential information for the scale-up, design, and optimization of new separation systems. We recently proposed the diafiltration apparatus for high-throughput analysis (DATA), which enables a 5-times reduction in the time, energy, and the number of experiments necessary to characterize membrane transport properties. This paper applies formal model-based design of experiments (MBDoE) techniques to further analyse and optimize DATA. For example, the eigenvalues and eigenvectors of the Fisher Information Matrix (FIM) show dynamic diafiltration experiments improve parameter identifiability by 3 orders of magnitude compared to traditional filtration experiments. Moreover, continuous retentate conductivity measurements in DATA improve A-, D-, E-, and ME-optimal MBDoE criteria by between 6 % and 32 %. Using these criteria, we identify pressure and initial concentrations conditions that maximize parameter precision and remove correlations.

Keywords: Membranes, Design of experiments, Parameter Estimation, Dynamic Modelling, Diafiltration

1. Introduction

Membrane processes have shown promise for addressing the critical needs for sustainability and energy efficiency. Recent material design to achieve separations of similar-sized molecules has evolved in the directions of precisely controlling the nanostructure of membranes and identifying chemical functionalities which accentuate desired transport properties (Hoffman and Phillip, 2020; Sadeghi et al., 2018). A detailed understanding of the underlying thermodynamic and transport phenomena can elucidate the molecular interactions and mechanisms that affect the macroscopic transport properties of the membrane (Geise et al., 2014; Yaroshchuk et al., 2018). Motivated by this need, the development of membrane characterization techniques that explore the dependency of membrane performance on feed conditions can greatly accelerate the development of materials (Ghosh et al., 2000). In addition, membrane characterization that elucidates underlying mechanisms provides essential information for scale-up, design, and optimization, facilitating the development of separations.

Design of Experiments (DoE) methods optimize computational and physical experiments to maximize the information gain and to minimize time and resource costs. Classical 'black-box' (a.k.a. factorial, response surface) DoE approaches, which decide the best design by the input-output relationship, does not (directly) incorporate membrane science knowledge; in contrast, model-based DoE (MBDoE) leverages high-fidelity models constructed from underlying physical principles that describe the experimental system (Franceschini and Macchietto, 2008). The information collected from experiments can be applied to discriminate between scientific hypotheses, posed as mathematical models, and to improve the precision of parameter estimation. However, to date, MBDoE has not been applied to membrane characterization techniques.

Guided by data analytics, Ouimet et al. (2021) developed a diafiltration apparatus for high-throughput analysis (DATA) to address the limitations of current membrane characterization methods, e.g., time-consuming experimental campaigns and parameter non-identifiability. In this paper, we use MBDOE and FIM-based analysis to mathematically quantify the improvements reported by Ouimet et al. (2021) and further refine the experimental conditions needed in DATA to characterize membrane transport properties and discriminate between possible transport mechanisms.

2. Mathematical model, materials, and methods

In the dynamic diafiltration experiments described by Ouimet et al. (2021), a concentrated diafiltrate is continuously injected into a stirred cell under applied pressure, permeate is collected in several scintillation vials with the mass of the sample vial, m_v, permeate concentration, c_v, and retentate concentration in the stirred cell, c_f, measured. Using these measurements, three model parameters - hydraulic permeability, L_p, the solute permeability coefficient, B that correspond to the membrane transport properties, and the reflection coefficient, σ, that depends on the thermodynamics of the membrane-solution interface - are estimated via weighted least-square nonlinear regression (Eq. (1) where $\theta = \{L_p, B, \sigma\}$). These parameters are related to the volumetric flux of water, J_w, and the molar flux of the solute, J_s, across the membrane in Eq. (2).

$$\hat{\theta} = \arg\min_{\theta} \sum_i w_{m_{v,i}}(m_{v,i} - \hat{m}_{v,i})^2 + \sum_j w_{c_{v,j}}(c_{v,j} - \hat{c}_{v,j})^2$$
$$+ \sum_k w_{c_{f,k}}(c_{f,k} - \hat{c}_{f,k})^2 \tag{1}$$

$$J_w = L_p(\Delta P - \sigma \Delta \pi), \quad J_s = B\Delta c \tag{2}$$

The diafiltration apparatus, the differential-algebraic equations (DAEs) model, the data, and the regressed parameters values, i.e., $L_p = 3.90$ L·m^{-2}·h^{-1}·bar^{-1}, $B = 0.29$ μm·s^{-1} and $\sigma = 1$ are described by Ouimet et al. (2021). Three key design decisions, the diafiltrate concentration, c_d, the initial feed concentration, $c_f(0)$, and the applied pressure, ΔP may be optimized to maximize the precision of the estimated parameters from dynamic diafiltration experiments.

3. Fisher Information Matrix (FIM)

The Fisher Information Matrix (FIM), $\mathbf{M}$, measures the information content of measurements and is defined as the inverse of the posterior covariance matrix $\mathbf{V}$, Eq. (4), ignoring the prior information (Franceschini and Macchietto, 2008). Here, $v_{m,rs}$ is the rsth element of the $N_y \times N_y$ inverse matrix of measurements error. $\mathbf{J}_r$ is the sensitivity matrix of output y_r sampled at times t_s and evaluated at nominal parameters values $\hat{\theta}$ and specified experimental design conditions ϕ.

$$\mathbf{M} = \left[\mathbf{V}(\hat{\boldsymbol{\theta}}, \boldsymbol{\phi})\right]^{-1} = \sum_{r=1}^{N_y} \sum_{s=1}^{N_y} v_{m,rs}^{-1} \mathbf{J}_r^T \mathbf{J}_s , \qquad \mathbf{J}_r = \begin{bmatrix} \frac{\partial y_r}{\partial \hat{\theta}_1}\Big|_{t_1} & \cdots & \frac{\partial y_r}{\partial \hat{\theta}_m}\Big|_{t_1} \\ \vdots & \ddots & \vdots \\ \frac{\partial y_r}{\partial \hat{\theta}_1}\Big|_{t_n} & \cdots & \frac{\partial y_r}{\partial \hat{\theta}_m}\Big|_{t_n} \end{bmatrix} \qquad (3)$$

MBDoE techniques increases parameter precision by minimising a metric of $\mathbf{V}$ or equivalently maximizing a metric of $\mathbf{M}$. A-, D-, E-optimal experimental designs correspond to minimising the trace, the determinant, and the maximum eigenvalue of $\mathbf{V}$, respectively (or maximizing the trace, the determinant, and the maximum eigenvalue of $\mathbf{M}$). The determinant and trace of the covariance matrix $\mathbf{V}$ can be interpreted as the volume of the covariance ellipsoid under feasible experimental conditions, while the maximum eigenvalue represents the size of the major axis, minimizing them reduces model parameter uncertainty. Additionally, the modified E-optimal (ME-) criterion minimizing the condition number of $\mathbf{M}$ which is defined as the ratio of the largest to the smallest eigenvalues, removes the correlation of parameters.

4. Results and discussions

4.1. Diafiltration experiment enables identification of all model parameters

Table 1 compares the FIMs and their eigen decompositions for experiments in both filtration (F) and diafiltration (D) modes as reported by Ouimet et al. (2021). The analysis of each mode considers one experiment with continuous data collection from the inline conductivity probe (M1) and one experiment encompassing only the initial and final retentate measurements (M2). The elements of the FIMs are one order of magnitude larger for diafiltration (D) than filtration (F) experiments. This shows diafiltration experiments contains more useful information to infer the model parameters. Moreover, analysing the eigenvalues and eigenvectors indicates which parameter can be precisely estimated through experimental design. For example, the minimum eigenvalue of filtration (F) M1 is 4.93E+05; the corresponding eigenvector is predominantly in the direction of model parameter σ. Under the same mode, the largest eigenvalue, 4.71E+09, corresponds the eigenvector in the direction of L_p. This difference, 4 orders of magnitude, indicates that a filtration experiment alone is unable to precisely estimate σ. In contrast, for diafiltration (D) mode, the eigenvalues whose corresponding eigenvectors in the direction of σ, 8.53E+10 in M1 and 8.18E+10 in M2, become the largest ones. Moreover, the smallest eigenvalues for diafiltration mode are 2.17E+08 (M1) and 1.96E+08 (M2), which are 3 orders of magnitude larger than the smallest eigenvalues for filtration mode. This difference indicates that diafiltration experiments are better suited to precisely estimate all three model parameters. Both findings are consistent with the sensitivity analysis results from Ouimet et al. (2021).

4.2. Additional retentate measurements improve parameter precision

Ouimet et al. (2021) show that measuring the retentate concentration is necessary to identify a converging set of parameters. We now use MBDoE to quantify the information content of the additional measurements. Recall M1 in Table 1 considers inline conductivity probe measurements for the retentate whereas M2 omits these measurements and only considers initial and final retentate measurements. Table 1 shows elements and eigenvalues of FIMs of M1 are always larger than M2, which shows the additional data increases the precision of the estimated parameters for both modes. Furthermore, for diafiltration, Table 2 shows 6 % and 32 % reduction in terms of the volume of the confidence ellipsoid from A-, D-optimal criteria, respectively, 11 % reduction in terms of the uncertainty of the least confident parameter (B) from E-optimal, and 6% improvement in the ME-optimal criterion which measures parameter correlation. Similarly, Table 2 also shows 8 %, 17 %, and 2 % improvements from A-, D-, E-optimal criteria, respectively, in filtration experiments. However, the 6 % worsening of the ME-optimal criterion, indicates collecting additional data in filtration mode increases the correlation of the estimated parameters.

Table 1. FIM, eigenvalues and eigenvectors of FIM are calculated in both filtration (F) mode and diafiltration (D) mode. Model M1 includes inline conductivity probe measurements while models M2 includes only the initial and final retentate measurements.

Mode	Model	FIM (×1e9)			Eigenvalues	Eigenvectors		
		L_p	B	σ		L_p	B	σ
F	M1	4.67	-0.01	-0.40	4.93E+05	-8.57E-02	-8.50E-03	-9.96E-01
		-0.01	0.02	0.00	1.74E+07	1.80E-03	1.00E+00	-8.70E-03
		-0.40	0.00	0.04	4.71E+09	-9.96E-01	2.60E-03	8.57E-02
	M2	4.34	0.01	-0.37	4.85E+05	8.60E-02	3.30E-03	9.96E-01
		0.01	0.02	0.00	1.63E+07	2.00E-03	-1.00E+00	3.20E-03
		-0.37	0.00	0.03	4.37E+09	-9.96E-01	-1.70E-03	8.60E-02
D	M1	20.85	3.09	-20.62	2.17E+08	-1.46E-01	-9.47E-01	-2.88E-01
		3.09	5.56	-19.14	1.45E+10	9.41E-01	-2.23E-01	2.56E-01
		-20.62	-19.14	73.61	8.53E+10	-3.07E-01	-2.33E-01	9.23E-01
	M2	17.78	3.00	-18.36	1.96E+08	-1.41E-01	-9.47E-01	-2.89E-01
		3.00	5.57	-19.03	1.27E+10	9.50E-01	-2.11E-01	2.29E-01
		-18.36	-19.03	71.38	8.18E+10	-2.78E-01	-2.43E-01	9.29E-01

Table 2. DoE optimality criteria for models M1 and improvement of using M1 instead of M2.

Mode	Model	Functions of FIM			
		A-optimal	D-optimal	E-optimal	ME-optimal
		Trace	Determinant	Minimal eigenvalue	Condition number
F	M1 Improvement	4.73E+09 8%↑	4.04E+22 17%↑	4.93E+05 2%↑	9551 6%↑
	M2	4.38E+09	3.45E+22	4.85E+05	9002
D	M1 Improvement	1.00E+11 6%↑	2.69E+29 32%↑	2.17E+08 11%↑	393 6%↓
	M2	9.47E+10	2.03E+29	1.96E+08	418

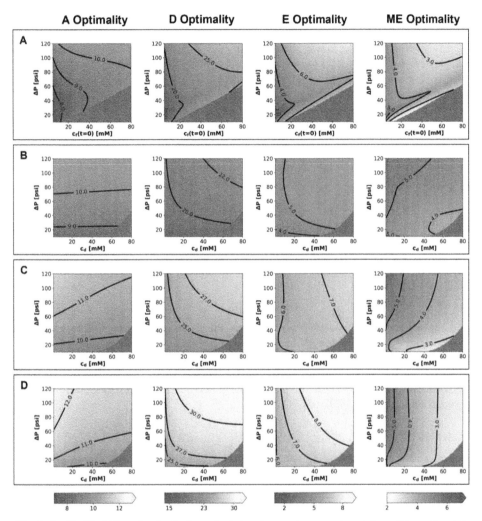

Fig. 1. A-, D-, E-, ME-optimal criteria evaluated under varying experimental conditions. Panel A shows filtration experiment (with 8 vials collected) predictions for varying initial feed concentration and applied pressure. Panels B, C, D examine the diafiltration experiment with 1, 5 and 10 vials collected, respectively, for the diafiltrate concentration and applied pressure.

4.3. MBDoE optimizes DATA system

We now use A-, D-, E-, and ME-optimality criteria to inform the applied pressure, initial retentate or diafiltrate concentrations (experimental design decisions) necessary to identify all parameters in filtration and diafiltration. Fig. 2A. examines filtration experiment at varying initial feed concentration $c_f(t = 0)$ and applied pressure ΔP with 8 vials collected. Fig. 2B, 2C, and 2D examine diafiltration experiments at varying diafiltrate concentration c_d with 1, 5, and 10 vial collected, respectively. The gray regions correspond to physically impossible operating conditions where the water flux is equal to or less than zero. The contour lines show the $\log_{10}$-transformed values of every criterion. Comparing Fig. 2C to 2A, the lighter color and larger contour values for A-, D-, E-optimality metrics indicates that the diafiltration experiments with 5 vial collections contains more information than the filtration experiment with 8 vial collections. Moreover, higher applied pressures maximize A-, D-, and E-optimal metrics. However, based on ME-optimality, low applied pressure is desired in diafiltration experiment with 5 or fewer vial collections to remove the correlation among parameters. Increasing to 10 vial collections in diafiltration, shown in Fig. 2D, resolves the trade-off between parameter precision (A and D) and removing correlations (ME). Thus, with 10 vial collections, diafiltration experiments with a feed concentration of 5 mM KCl should be performed with a diafiltrate concentration greater than 50 mM KCl and an applied pressure at least 45 psi to identify all parameters with an order of magnitude of improvement in precision over filtration experiments.

5. Conclusions

In this paper, we apply MBDoE analyses to quantify the information gain in a recently proposed diafiltration apparatus for high-throughput analysis (DATA) for membrane characterization. In the future, MBDoE can be used to discriminate possible phenomena and mechanisms within complex multi-component systems and optimize diafiltration experiments with more degrees of freedom (e.g., time-varying applied pressure).

Acknowledgements

We appreciatively acknowledge support from the National Science Foundation (NSF) through the Advanced Manufacturing Program (Award Number: 1932206) and the CAREER Program (Award Number: CBET-1941596). J.W. gratefully acknowledges support from the Carbon Capture Simulation for Industry Impact (CCSI^2), funded through the U.S. DOE office of Fossil Energy by the Lawrence Berkeley National Laboratory through contract# DE-AC02-05CH11231.

References

G. Franceschini and S. Macchietto, 2008, Model-based design of experiments for parameter precision: State of the art, Chemical engineering science, 63, 19, 4846-4872, 10.1016/j.ces.2007.11.034

G.M. Geise, D.R. Paul and B.D. Freeman, 2014, Fundamental water and salt transport properties of polymeric materials, Progress in polymer science, 39, 1, 1-42, 10.1016/j.progpolymsci.2013.07.001

R. Ghosh and Z. Cui, 2000, Analysis of protein transport and polarization through membranes using pulsed sample injection technique, Journal of membrane science, 175, 1, 75-84, 10.1016/s0376-7388(00)00397-5

J.R. Hoffman and W.A. Phillip, 2020, 100th anniversary of macromolecular science viewpoint: Integrated membrane systems, ACS Macro Lett, 9, 9, 1267-1279, 10.1021/acsmacrolett.0c00482

J.A. Ouimet, X. Liu, D.J. Brown, E.A. Eugene, T. Popps, Z.W. Muetzel, A.W. Dowling and W.A. Phillip, Data: Diafiltration apparatus for high-throughput analysis, Journal of membrane science, 10.1016/j.memsci.2021.119743

I. Sadeghi, P. Kaner and A. Asatekin, 2018, Controlling and expanding the selectivity of filtration membranes, Chem. Mater, 30, 21, 7328-7354, 10.1021/acs.chemmater.8b03334

A. Yaroshchuk, M.L. Bruening and E. Zholkovskiy, 2019, Modelling nanofiltration of electrolyte solutions, Adv Colloid Interface Sci, 268, C, 39-63, 10.1016/j.cis.2019.03.004

Proceedings of the 14th International Symposium on Process Systems Engineering – PSE 2021+
June 19-23, 2022, Kyoto, Japan © 2022 Elsevier B.V. All rights reserved.
http://dx.doi.org/10.1016/B978-0-323-85159-6.50144-5

Systematic Modelling of Distillation Columns based on Topologies and Ontologies

Robert Pujan[a,b*], Philipp Sengupta[a], Heinz A. Preisig[b]

[a]DBFZ Deutsches Biomasseforschungszentrum gemeinnützige GmbH, Torgauer Straße 116, 04347 Leipzig, Germany
[b]NTNU Norwegian University of Science and Technology, Høgskoleringen 5, 7491 Trondheim, Norway
robert.pujan@dbfz.de

Abstract

This contribution proposes a systematic modelling approach for tray distillation columns. Abstracting the distillation column into a network of the underlying, essential processes introduces a model topology. The topology is equipped with a centrally-established ontology that is a collection of fundamental principles and definitions describing the processes' nature. This systematic approach minimises modelling errors, enables rapid model design, and significantly lowers the entry threshold for non-expert modellers.

This study provides a holistic model that is, in contrast to common distillation models, applicable to steady-state as well as dynamic process conditions. The model's design and mathematical formalism are described, followed by a discussion of the model capabilities including model fitting and evaluation of the simulation results against experimental data as well as a commercial flowsheeting package.

Keywords: process modelling, simulation, topology, ontology, methodology

1. Motivation

Distillation is probably the most widespread industrial process for the separation of liquid mixtures. Accordingly, design, optimisation and process control are required for the exploration and testing of a myriad of various, differing process scales, operational domains and mixtures. Experimental studies may have been the conventional approach in process engineering for the better part of the 20th century, but they are expensive, time-consuming and limited in their viability. Process simulations, on the other hand, are executed in computers and thus not limited by physical constraints. The fast development of computing rapidly enhanced the capabilities of numerical simulation, thus moving the centre of process engineering progressively away from lab facilities towards modelling suites. The increasing need for model implementations places a high demand on the modellers, thereby prompting a growing interest in more effective model generation methods that incorporate the expertise from different scientific domains like physics, chemistry, biology and engineering. Providing the modeller with customisable compound models equipped with multi-disciplinary expert knowledge is thus a critical undertaking for process engineering in general and distillation applications in particular.

Applying the modelling method established by Preisig (2014), this study proposes a systematic modelling approach for distillation model design. First, an exemplary tray distillation process is graphically abstracted through a topology. Due to the established links between the topology and a physics ontology, the modeller-specified capacities inherently provide the model's fundamental mathematical abstraction. This study showcases the capabilities and reliability of the resulting compound model by validating the simulation results against experimental data as well as the results of commercially available flowsheeting software.

2. Structural model design

The processes we observe are intrinsically composed of various sub-processes on multiple scales. Modelling has thus to include both, the identification of the physical processes involved, and the adaptation of the mathematical formalisms to the systems' nature and application.

Topologies appear to be particularly convenient for model design since they are easily translated into matrix algebra and applied to multiple scales. A topology is the graphical abstraction of a process as a graph network of nodes representing finite-volume capacities and arcs that are flows of extensive quantities driven by gradients in intensive properties. Our methodology limits the topology design to basic entities, provides a maths description for each entity, and associates the entities to the graphical objects used to establish the topologies. This approach enables the rapid design of rigorous, holistic models that are also easily customisable and minimised in the amount of potential, modeller-caused errors. Furthermore, the topology structure enables the process depiction in both, steady-state as well as dynamic operation.

Figure 1 presents the topology for tray distillation columns that was applied in this study. For an in-depth description of topology symbols and terminology, please see Pujan & Preisig (2022). A column outfitted with n trays is fed a fluid mixture by the reservoir F on feed tray n_F. On every tray, part of the stage's liquid phase L_i is dripping down to tray $i + 1$ while other parts evaporate into the gas phase G_i, subsequently rising up to tray $i - 1$. While ascending, the vapour passes both an empty column space S_n as well as the cavities of the tray T_i. The condenser C at the column's head cools down the arriving vapour G_0, forming the condensate L_0 that is, according to the specified reflux ratio, partially dripping back to the column's first tray and partially drained as distillate D. The column bottom is heated by H, thus evaporating parts of the boiler's liquid L_{n+1}, while the bottom product B is continuously drained at a certain rate. In steady-state (on the left of Figure 1), each tray's liquid and vapour capacities are in thermodynamic equilibrium and without any time-dependencies, thus depicted as point capacities (black dots). Under dynamic conditions, for example during start-up and shut-down, these volumes change over time, both in extensive quantities as well as intensive properties. If considering distributional effects in them to be negligible, the phases appear as lumped capacities (circles) in terms of mass and heat distribution (central topology of Figure 1).

As described in detail by Pujan & Preisig (2020), the pressure distribution in dynamic processes can only be assessed employing a model split. This split results in a dynamic model for the observable mass and heat flows and an event-dynamic model (on the right of Figure 1) for the supposedly immediate pressure distribution.

The graphical topology structure is accessed by mathematical modelling through the so-called incidence matrix $\underline{\underline{F}}$ that is a structural matrix that can be sub-divided into $\underline{\underline{F}}_m$, $\underline{\underline{F}}_q$, and $\underline{\underline{F}}_w$ specific for mass, heat and work transport (Pujan & Preisig, 2022).

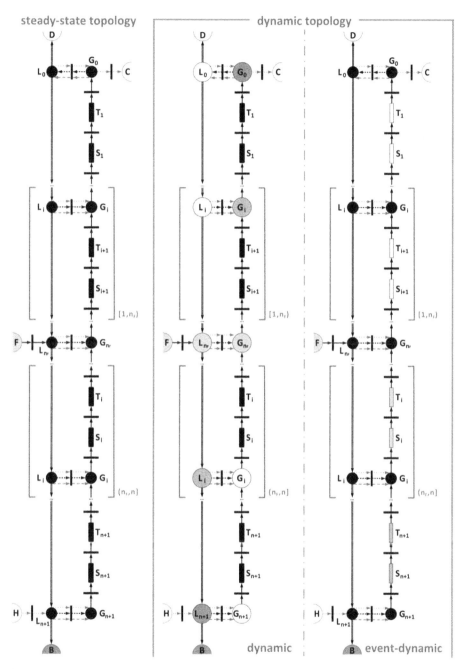

Figure 1: Topologies for a tray distillation column in steady-state (left) and dynamic process conditions (middle: dynamic mass and heat distribution; right: event-dynamic pressure distribution)

3. Mathematical model design

The model's mathematical behaviour is extracted from a centrally established equation ontology. The term ontology encompasses the entirety of fundamental concepts, definitions and relations taken from the application-specific scientific roots. Ontologies are a means of abstraction and concentrating information, promoting a more systematic approach to model design (Preisig, 2012).

Table 1 shows the fundamental equation ontology for the physical domain of tray distillation columns. Vectors and matrices are depicted as $\underline{x}$ and $\underline{\underline{x}}$, respectively. The decorator $\dot{x}$ represents an accumulation and $\hat{x}$ a flow. The grey-marked variables have to be specified further for the model initiation. These specifications typically are:

- assumptions and preset values, like the nullification of the system's change in kinetic and potential energy $\dot{K}$ and $\dot{P}$, and the gravitational acceleration g,
- initial conditions x_0,
- plant dimensions such as liquid and weir heights h_L and h_W, diameters d, weir length s_W, and weir drain coefficient C_W,
- thermodynamic values from databases or external estimators, like the specific enthalpy h_i, density ρ_i, molar mass M_i, and transport coefficients for heat k_i^q and mass k_i^d for substance i,
- and further ontology equations, e.g. for temperature T, volume-specific interphase area a, and frictional pressure drop Δp^f.

4. Results and discussion

The model was initiated for the distillation of the binary mixture water-methanol and the steady-state results were validated against the experimental data by Kazameas et al. (2015) and Morinaga & Yao (1965), as well as simulation results derived from the flowsheeting package Aspen Plus®. Unfortunately, at the time of this publication, no sufficient data set was available for the validation of the model's dynamic capabilities.

Below the feed tray (feed stage marked with a circle), the initial simulation results in Figure 2 show a notably increased deviation from the experimentally determined molar fractions. Whereas the flowsheeting results seem to better match the experiments below the feed, our model seems more appropriate above. This performance was significantly improved through a simple model fitting, including only thermodynamic estimation parameters and the Murphree tray efficiency.

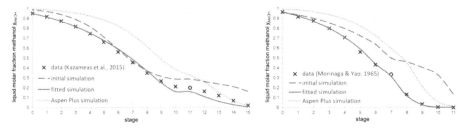

Figure 2: Comparing simulation results to Kazameas et al. (2015) and Morinaga & Yao (1965)

Table 1: Physics equation ontology for tray distillation columns

---

Integrals

Substance

$$\underline{n} = \int_0^\tau \underline{\dot{n}}_t \mathrm{dt} + \underline{n}_0 \tag{1}$$

Energy

$$\underline{E} = \int_0^\tau \underline{\dot{E}}_t \mathrm{dt} + \underline{E}_0 \tag{2}$$

Balances

Substance conservation

$$\underline{\dot{n}} = \underline{\underline{F}}_m \, \widehat{\underline{n}} \tag{3}$$

Energy conservation

$$\underline{\dot{E}} = \underline{\dot{U}} + \underline{\dot{K}} + \underline{\dot{P}} \tag{4}$$

Internal energy conservation

$$\underline{\dot{U}} = \underline{\underline{F}}_m \left[\widehat{\underline{U}} + \widehat{\underline{K}} + \widehat{\underline{P}} + \widehat{\underline{w}}^v + \widehat{\underline{w}}^f \right] + \underline{\underline{F}}_w \, \widehat{\underline{w}} + \underline{\underline{F}}_q \, \widehat{\underline{q}} \tag{5}$$

Transport terms

Mass flow

$$\widehat{\underline{m}} = \sum \widehat{\underline{m}}_i \tag{6}$$

Mass component flow

$$\widehat{\underline{m}}_i = \underline{\underline{M}}_i \, \widehat{\underline{n}}_i \tag{7}$$

Substance flow

$$\widehat{\underline{n}} = \sum \widehat{\underline{n}}_i \tag{8}$$

Molar flow of i (convection)

$$\widehat{\underline{n}}_i = \underline{c}_i \, \widehat{\underline{V}} \tag{9}$$

Molar flow of i (diffusion)

$$\widehat{\underline{n}}_i = -\underline{k}_i^d \, \underline{\underline{a}} \, \underline{\underline{F}}_m^{\mathrm{T}} \, \underline{c}_i \tag{10}$$

Internal energy flow

$$\widehat{\underline{U}} = \widehat{\underline{H}} - \widehat{\underline{w}}^v \tag{11}$$

Kinetic energy flow

$$\widehat{\underline{K}} = {}^1\!/_2 \, \widehat{\underline{m}} \, v^2 \tag{12}$$

Potential energy flow

$$\widehat{\underline{P}} = \underline{h} \, \widehat{\underline{m}} \, g \tag{13}$$

Volume work flow

$$\widehat{\underline{w}}^v = \underline{p} \, \widehat{\underline{V}} \tag{14}$$

Friction work flow

$$\widehat{\underline{w}}^f = \underline{\Delta p}^f \, \widehat{\underline{V}} \tag{15}$$

System volumetric work

$$\widehat{\underline{w}} = \underline{p} \, \underline{\dot{V}} \tag{16}$$

Heat flow (conduction)

$$\widehat{\underline{q}} = -\underline{k}^q \, \underline{\underline{A}} \, \underline{\underline{s}}^{-1} \, \underline{\underline{F}}_q^{\mathrm{T}} \, \underline{T} \tag{17}$$

Enthalpy flow

$$\widehat{\underline{H}} = \sum \widehat{\underline{H}}_i \tag{18}$$

Enthalpy component flow

$$\widehat{\underline{H}}_i = \underline{h}_i \, \widehat{\underline{m}}_i \tag{19}$$

Volume flow

$$\widehat{\underline{V}} = \underline{\underline{A}} \, \underline{v} \tag{20}$$

Volume flow (weir)

$$\widehat{\underline{V}} = {}^2\!/_3 \, \underline{C}_w \, \underline{s}_w \sqrt{2g} \left(\underline{h}_L - \underline{h}_w \right)^{1.5} \tag{21}$$

State variable transformations

Cylindrical cross-section

$$\underline{A} = {}^\pi\!/_4 \, \underline{d}^2 \tag{22}$$

Molar concentration

$$\underline{c}_i = \underline{n}_i \, \underline{V}^{-1} \tag{23}$$

Substance component

$$\underline{\chi}_i = \underline{n}_i \, \underline{n}^{-1} \tag{24}$$

Mass fraction

$$\underline{\omega}_i = \underline{m}_i \, \underline{m}^{-1} \tag{25}$$

Figure 3 compares the simulation results to the temperature profile recorded by Kazameas et al. (2015). The model shows a better (unfitted) performance than Aspen Plus®, however, the significant different shapes of experimental and simulation results hypothesise measurement errors in the experiment. As the dashed curve indicates, assuming constant pressure does not perceptibly alter the model's temperature profile under steady-state conditions.

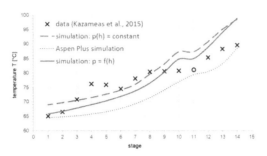

Figure 3: Stage temperatures T compared to Kazameas et al. (2015)

5. Conclusions

As this paper shows, ontology-imposed topology model designs are a fast and reliable method for modelling distillation columns. The presented model will be implemented in the compound model library of the modelling suite ProMo, which is currently in development at the NTNU (Elve & Preisig, 2019; Preisig, 2020). The software automatically selects the required ontology equations and generates executable program code, thus enabling rapid custom distillation model design. Future work will add models and ontology equations specific for packed and divided-wall distillation columns as well.

Acknowledgements

This study was created as part of the research projects Bio4Fuels (Norwegian Centre for Environment-friendly Energy Research (FME), project 257622), MarketPlace (Horizon 2020, project 760173), and VIPCOAT (Horizon 2020, project 952903).

References

A. Elve & H.A. Preisig, 2019, From ontology to executable program code, Computers & Chemical Engineering, 122, 383-394

C.G. Kazameas, K.N. Keller & W.L. Luyben, 2015, A Comprehensive Real-World Distillation Experiment, Chemical Engineering Education, 49 (3), 131-140

T. Morinaga & H. Yao, 1965, Regelung einer Destillationskolonne für ein binäres Gemisch, at-Automatisierungstechnik, 13 (1-12), 543-546

H.A. Preisig, 2012, Thinking Ontologies, Computer Aided Chemical Engineering, 31, 1682-1686

H.A. Preisig, 2014, Visual Modelling, Computer Aided Chemical Engineering, 34, 729-734

H.A. Preisig, 2020, ProMo – A multi-disciplinary process modelling suite, Computer Aided Chemical Engineering, 48, 571-576

R. Pujan & H.A. Preisig, 2020, Systematic Modelling of Flow and Pressure Distribution in a Complex Tank, Computer Aided Chemical Engineering, 48, 1945-1950

R. Pujan & H.A. Preisig, 2022, Systematic Modelling of Flow and Pressure Distribution in a Complex Tank, Computers & Chemical Engineering, 157, 107608

Proceedings of the 14th International Symposium on Process Systems Engineering – PSE 2021+
June 19-23, 2022, Kyoto, Japan © 2022 Elsevier B.V. All rights reserved.
http://dx.doi.org/10.1016/B978-0-323-85159-6.50145-7

Sensitivity Analysis of an Electrospray Dehumidification System

David Young[a], Yasuhiro Shoji[a], Maliha Yel Mahi[b], Mike Ellis[c], Selen Cremaschi[a*], Lorenzo Cremaschi[b]

[a]*Department of Chemical Engineering, Auburn University, Auburn, AL 36849, USA*
[b]*Department of Mechanical Engineering, Auburn University, Auburn, AL 36849, USA*
[c]*Advanced Cooling Technologies, Inc. (ACT), Lancaster, PA 17601, USA*
selen-cremaschi@auburn.edu

Abstract

Electrically enhanced condensation achieved by an electrospray system can enhance dehumidification in HVAC applications if successfully scaled up. The first step towards scale-up is identifying critical design and operating parameters that significantly impact dehumidification for the electrospray system. Sensitivity analysis is one approach for identifying critical parameters. This paper presents a methodology that can efficiently perform quantitative sensitivity analysis on a computationally expensive high fidelity simulation model, which is a computational fluid dynamics (CFD) model of the electrospray system. The methodology employs surrogate modeling and Sobol sensitivity analysis. We estimate the main and total effect Sobol sensitivity indices of four operating parameters of the electrospray system. The results reveal that the most important parameter is the size of the sprayed droplets, followed by the volumetric flow rate of the bulk air and injected water in the system. The water injection velocity of the spray was found to have little to no impact on dehumidification.

Keywords: CFD; Sensitivity Analysis; Surrogate-modelling; ALAMO; PRESTO

1. Introduction

Dielectrophoresis is a well-documented phenomenon, with the first study coining the name in 1951 (Pohl, 1951). The phenomenon refers to the force imparted on a dielectric particle from a nonhomogenous electric field. Dielectrophoresis has been used in various applications, e.g., from cell separation (Henslee et al., 2011) to nanowire assembly (Collet et al., 2015). One more promising application is in heating, ventilation, and air conditioning (HVAC) systems. For an HVAC application, water condensation in the air can be enhanced by dielectrophoresis by spraying electrically charged droplets into the air, reducing the energy consumption of conventional HVAC systems.

Electrically enhanced condensation uses highly charged water droplets injected in the moist air. The droplets become electric seeds that attract polar water vapor molecules to their surfaces and promote condensation. The growth of the charged droplets depletes the vapor phase near a droplet, while dielectrophoresis flow and diffusion compensate for this depletion. Dielectrophoresis flow involves surrounding vapor at a distance of about 10 to 100 nm for droplets charged by an electrospray compared to ~2 nm for a single electron charge in a droplet. As vapor molecules collapse on the surface of the droplets, their initial electrical charge decreases due to the neutralization of the ions.

An electrically enhanced dehumidification system thus far has only been demonstrated in laboratory-scale studies (Higashiyama and Kamada, 2017). One challenge that hinders its large-scale application is the lack of knowledge on critical design and operating parameters that significantly impact the dehumidification rate. This work addresses this challenge by efficiently developing an approach to identify the critical parameters. The approach utilizes a CFD model of the electrospray system within a duct, surrogate modeling, and Sobol sensitivity analysis. The CFD model includes a particle-laden flow, where the dielectrophoresis flow is modeled within the mass transfer between the two phases (Section 2). We develop a surrogate model that links the dehumidification rate to select CFD model parameters (Section 3) and perform Sobol sensitivity analysis (Section 3) on the surrogate model to identify the critical parameters (Section 4).

2. Electrospray System Computational Fluid Dynamics (CFD) Model

The CFD model was built using open-source CFD simulation software OpenFOAM v8. We modified the sprayFoam solver to add an electro-condensation model, which includes the thermal and transport equations for water vapor dielectrophoresis condensation at the interface of electrically charged liquid droplets. SprayFoam is a numerical solver that takes the Eulerian-Lagrangian approach to simulate dispersed particle-laden flow. The Euler method was used to model the continuous phase, bulk airflow as dry air and water vapor mixture. The Lagrangian approach was used to model the dispersed phase, the electrically charged water droplets from the spray. The water vapor was modeled as a component of the bulk air, transported by both diffusion and convection. The governing equations for the moist airflow were the conservation of continuity, momentum, species, energy, and the equation of state in the laminar flow regime. Droplets in the spray were subjected to several physical phenomena, including coalescence and drag effects. Two-way coupling was introduced in the numerical study to establish the interaction between the two phases (air and water droplet). Source terms calculated in the sub-models using the Lagrangian approach were introduced into gas phase equations in the Eulerian approach to represent the interaction between Euler and Lagrangian methods. The water molecules placed in a gradient electric field experienced a force that moved them toward the charged droplets.

2.1. *Particle-Laden Gas Using Eulerian Method*

Eqn. 1 reflects the conservation of mass for the gas phase,

$$\frac{\partial \rho}{\partial t} + \nabla \cdot (\rho U) = \dot{\rho}_s \tag{1}$$

where ρ is the density of air, t is time, U is the velocity, and $\dot{\rho}_s$ is a source term defined only for the water vapor. It is calculated using the water vapor condensation into liquid droplets. Mass transport for individual species in the gas phase is given in Eqs. 2 - 4,

$$\frac{\partial \rho Y_i}{\partial t} = \nabla \cdot (\mu_L \nabla Y_i) = \dot{\rho}_s^i \tag{2}$$

$$\dot{\rho}_s = \sum_i \dot{\rho}_s^i \tag{3}$$

where, Y_i is the mass fraction for the i-th gas species ($i = H_2O$, O_2, N_2) in the bulk air, and μ_L is the laminar viscosity.

$$\frac{\partial \rho U}{\partial t} + \nabla \cdot (\rho U U) = -\nabla P + \nabla \cdot (\mu_L \nabla U) + \nabla \cdot [\text{dev}(\mu_L (\nabla U)^T)] + \rho g + F_S \qquad (4)$$

In Eq. 4, ∇P is the pressure gradient, g is the acceleration due to gravity, F_S is the the resultant force induced by the charged water droplets due to drag force and gravity force.

2.2. *Spray Charged Droplets Using Lagrangian Method*

The dispersed charged spray droplets were solved using the Lagrangian particle tracking method. The approach assumes that spray injection consists of different droplet parcels, and each parcel consists of many spherical droplets sharing the same location, diameter, velocity, and temperature. Newton's second law describes the charged droplet motion. The driving forces for the charged droplets are drag force from the surrounding air, the electrostatic force, and gravity force. These forces link droplet mass (m_D) and velocity (U_{inj}) to droplet density (ρ_d), and diameter (d_{inj}).

2.3. *Droplet Electro-Condensation Model*

With the dielectrophoresis effects, the saturated vapor pressure can be evaluated by the modified Kelvin-Thomson (MKT) model as described in Eqn. (1) of Morcelli and Cremaschi (2021). This equation provides the oversaturation pressure ratio, (P_{sat}/P_{sat}^{flat}) where, P_{sat} is the saturated vapor pressure near the surface of the droplet and P_{sat}^{flat} is the saturated water vapor pressure above a flat surface at temperature T. The oversaturation ratio is calculated, as the electric charge on the droplet increases the differences between the vapor pressure of the water droplet and bulk air. If the bulk air vapor pressure is higher, droplets grow. For the present study, the temperature T was constant at $20°C$ for both moist airflow and droplets. For the MKT model, the droplets were kept fixed to the maximum electric charge (q_e), dictated by the Rayleigh limit, Eq.5,

$$q_e = 8\pi\sqrt{\varepsilon_0 \sigma R^3} \qquad (5)$$

Where R is the instantaneous water droplet radius. The oversaturation ratio, was determined from MKT model and a mass transfer from the water vapor to the droplet surface occurred. A prerequisite condition of oversaturation ratio less than 1 was introduced to limit the droplet growth via diffusion for realistic cases. The dielectrophoretic force sustain the vapor flow towards the droplet surface even if the diffusion transport diminishes due to the equality of the pressures near the droplet surface and far away from the droplet. The mass transfer due to electrically enhanced condensation is calculated using Eq. 6.

$$\frac{dm_D}{dt} = -4\pi R^2 \frac{dR}{dt} \rho_d \qquad (6)$$

Here $\frac{dR}{dt}$ is the constant droplet growth rate, estimated using data from Abe and Kameda (2003) and Morcelli and Cremaschi (2021).

3. Surrogate-based Sobol Sensitivity Analysis

Sensitivity analysis (SA) identifies parameters that significantly impact the output of interest for a model. We employed Sobol SA (Sobol, 2001) to investigate the sensitivity of the dehumidification rate in the duct, estimated by the CFD model, to select operating parameters of the electrospray system. Sobol SA is a global method that quantifies the effect of each variable and its interactions with other variables on the model output by decomposing the output variance. These effects are quantified using main-effect and total Sobol indices and show the true sensitivity of the outputs with a high degree of accuracy. However, obtaining stable Sobol index estimates may be computationally expensive as it may require a large number of model evaluations (Tian, 2013). A surrogate model-based Sobol SA is proposed to overcome this issue, considering a single run of the CFD simulation for electrospray system in the duct takes, on average, seven days (wall time) on an Intel E5-2660, 20 core 2.6 GHz node.

The surrogate-based Sobol SA is performed to determine the impact of four operating parameters on dehumidification. The parameters are injected water flowrate ($\dot{V}_{inj}$), the injected water droplet size (d_{inj}), the injected water velocity (U_{inj}), and the bulk air flowrate ($\dot{V}_{air}$). The potential operating ranges for these parameters are listed in Table 1.

Table 1 Potential operating ranges for the four parameters considered for sensitivity analysis

Parameter	Upper bound	Lower bound	Unit
U_{inj}	2.73×10^{-2}	2.73×10^{-1}	[m/s]
d_{inj}	15	100	[m]
$\dot{V}_{inj}$	0.1	50	[μL/min]
$\dot{V}_{air}$	0.5	5	[ft^3/min]

The surrogate-based SA starts by running the CFD simulation at selected parameter values to compute the corresponding output, dehumidification. The parameter values for the CFD runs are selected according to Saltelli's (2002) method. We collected 78 unique input/output pairs by running the CFD simulation.

Next, an appropriate surrogate modeling technique is selected to represent the input-output relationship. Previous analysis revealed that the data characteristics and the application (surface approximation or optimization) are essential for selecting the correct surrogate modeling technique (Williams and Cremaschi, 2021). To determine the correct modeling technique, we employed PRESTO, Predictive REcommendations of Surrogate models To Optimize (Williams et al., 2022), which recommended automated learning of algebraic models (ALAMO) (Cozad et al., 2014) as the technique to best represent the data out of eight potential surrogate modeling approaches. We trained a surrogate model using ALAMO and the input-output pairs and employed it to estimate the Sobol indices following Saltelli's (2002) method.

4. Results

The maximum number of terms allowed during training a surrogate model should be determined *a priori* when using ALAMO. The allowed basis functions were $sin(x)$, $cos(x)$, $exp(x)$, $\ln(x)$, Gaussian radial basis function, polynomials up to third power, and pairwise combination of variables, both linear and quadratic. We employed 4-fold cross-validation (Burman, 1989) with 30 Monte Carlo replications using a 75 % to 25 % training to testing split to determine the maximum number of terms. Fig. 1 (A) includes a plot of the root mean square error (RMSE) for the training and test data sets vs. the maximum number of terms. We used 20 terms to train the ALAMO model used in the SA based on the beginning of an upward trend of the testing RMSE. The dehumidification rate predictions of the ALAMO model are plotted against the values calculated by the CDF model in Fig. 1(B). The plot also includes the RMSE of the trained model with the model output normalized to the range of the data.

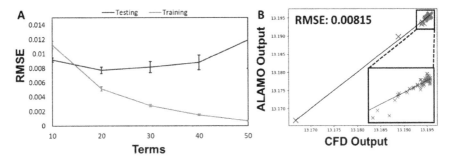

Figure 1 A) RMSE of training and testing data for term number determination of ALAMO model and B) parity plot of the trained ALAMO model versus the CFD output.

The main-effect and total Sobol indices are estimated using the ALAMO model. A plot of how the index values and their confidence intervals change as the number of model evaluations increases is given in Fig. 2. The number of model evaluations, N, are increased according to $N = n(2D + 2)$ where D is the input dimension, and $n = 2^x$ ($x \in \mathbb{Z}^+$) is the number of Sobol sequence samples to satisfy the convergence properties of the Sobol sequence. For this study, $x \in [1,15]$.

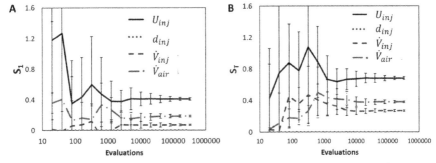

Figure 2 A) Main-effect and B) Total Sobol indices estimated using the ALAMO model

Fig. 2A is a plot of the main effect indices, and Fig. 2B total effect indices. As can be seen from Fig. 2, the droplet diameter, d_{inj}, is the most impactful parameter and the injection velocity, U_{inj}, the least with a negligible contribution to the variation of outlet humidity for the system considering the main-effect and total Sobol indices. The bulk air flowrate, $\dot{V}_{air}$, has the second-highest contribution for both the main effect and the total Sobol indices, while the injected water flowrate, $\dot{V}_{inj}$, shows to have the third most contribution. The droplet diameter impacts the number of droplets for condensation to occur within the system, driving the overall reduction in humidity. The air flowrate determines the droplet residence time in the duct, controlling the time allowed for condensation to occur on each droplet. When the injected water flowrate is considered on its own, it has little impact on dehumidification (Fig. 2A). However, when its interactions with the other parameters are considered, its impact increases (Fig. 2B). The primary interaction contributing to its increased impact is with the droplet diameter. For higher injection rates with smaller droplet diameters, many droplets are injected, enhancing condensation.

5. Conclusions and Future Work

We introduce a computationally-efficient surrogate-model-based sensitivity analysis (SA) approach to identify the critical parameters of a CFD model. The approach combines accurate surrogate modeling and Sobol SA. We applied the approach to a CFD model of an electrospray system designed for enhanced dehumidification of moist air in a duct. The results indicate that the dehumidification rate was most sensitive to the diameter of the charged water droplets injected into the duct. Our analysis also revealed that the number of CFD model evaluations to estimate stable Sobol indices is temporally intractable without employing the proposed approach for this system. The SA results will be used to construct an experimental matrix for a scale-up study of the electrospray system for maximizing dehumidification.

6. Acknowledgments

This work is supported by the U.S. DOE Office of Energy Efficiency and Renewable Energy (EERE) under Building Technologies Program Award Number DE-EE0009161.

References

Abe, K., Kameda, M., 2003. Condensation on droplets in moist air by heterogeneous nucleation. Comput. FLUID Dyn. J. 12, 295–308.

Burman, P., 1989. A comparative study of ordinary cross-validation, v-fold cross-validation and the repeated learning-testing methods. Biometrika 76, 503–514.

Collet, M., Salomon, S., Klein, N.Y., Seichepine, F., Vieu, C., Nicu, L., Larrieu, G., 2015. Large-scale assembly of single nanowires through capillary-assisted dielectrophoresis. Adv. Mater. 27, 1268–1273.

Cozad, A., Sahinidis, N. V, Miller, D.C., 2014. Learning surrogate models for simulation-based optimization. AIChE J. 60, 2211–2227. https://doi.org/https://doi.org/10.1002/aic.14418

Henslee, E.A., Sano, M.B., Rojas, A.D., Schmelz, E.M., Davalos, R. V, 2011. Selective concentration of human cancer cells using contactless dielectrophoresis. Electrophoresis 32, 2523–2529.

Higashiyama, Y., Kamada, M., 2017. Dehumidification using negative corona discharge from a water droplet, in: Proceedings of the Annual Meeting of the Electrostatics of America, Ottawa, ON, Canada. pp. 13–15.

Morcelli, S., Cremaschi, L., 2021. Analysis of Electro-static Assisted Air Dehumidification Processes.

Pohl, H.A., 1951. The Motion and Precipitation of Suspensoids in Divergent Electric Fields. J. Appl. Phys. 22, 869–871. https://doi.org/10.1063/1.1700065

Sobol, I.M., 2001. Global sensitivity indices for nonlinear mathematical models and their Monte Carlo estimates. Math. Comput. Simul. 55, 271–280.

Tian, W., 2013. A review of sensitivity analysis methods in building energy analysis. Renew. Sustain. energy Rev. 20, 411–419.

Williams, B., Cremaschi, S., 2021. Selection of surrogate modeling techniques for surface approximation and surrogate-based optimization. Chem. Eng. Res. Des. 170, 76–89.

Williams, B., Otashu, J., Leyland, S., Eden, M.R., Cremaschi, S., 2022. PRESTO: Predictive REcommendation of Surrogate models To approximate and Optimize. Chem. Eng. Sci. 249, 117360. https://doi.org/https://doi.org/10.1016/j.ces.2021.117360

Proceedings of the 14th International Symposium on Process Systems Engineering – PSE 2021+
June 19-23, 2022, Kyoto, Japan © 2022 Elsevier B.V. All rights reserved.
http://dx.doi.org/10.1016/B978-0-323-85159-6.50146-9

Rigorous modelling for comparing batch and flow syntheses of a drug substance using heterogeneous hydrogenation

Junu Kim[a], Hironori Yonekura[b], Takeaki Watanabe[b], Satoshi Yoshikawa[b], Hayao Nakanishi[b], Sara Badr[a], Hirokazu Sugiyama[a*]

[a]*Department of Chemical System Engineering, The University of Tokyo, 7-3-1, Hongo, Bunkyo-ku, Tokyo, 113-8656, JAPAN*
[b]*Production Technology Department, Shionogi Pharma Co., Ltd., 2-5-1, Mishima, Settsu-Shi, Osaka, 566-0022, JAPAN*
sugiyama@chemsys.t.u-tokyo.ac.jp

Abstract

This work presents the simulation-based comparison of batch and flow syntheses of a drug substance. The target reaction is heterogeneous hydrogenation which is the most widely used reduction method in pharmaceutical synthesis. We developed rigorous physical models of batch and flow syntheses considering the decrease in catalyst activity due to poisoning. Sensitivity analysis of reaction rate constant and viscosity was performed. The reaction rate constant had an effect on the conversion of both batch and flow syntheses. On the other hand, the impact of viscosity on conversion was greater in flow synthesis than in batch synthesis. This result suggests the importance of careful selection of operational conditions when changing from batch to flow synthesis as optimal conditions might differ between them.

Keywords: Flow chemistry; Drug Substance; Physical modelling; Viscosity; Sensitivity

1. Introduction

There have been significant advances in the application of flow synthesis in drug substance production. Bogdan et al. (2009) reported the synthesis of ibuprofen, a widely used painkiller. Other studies include an anti-malaria drug (Lévesque and Seeberger, 2012); olanzapine, an atypical antipsychotic (Hartwig et al., 2013) and rolipram, an anti-inflammatory drug (Tsubogo et al., 2015).

With progress in flow synthesis research, the question remains whether the novel technology proves to be more beneficial than the conventional batch technology. Few studies report specifically on the comparison of drug substance synthesis. Pedersen et al. (2018) redesigned the synthetic routes of melitracen, an antidepressant using flow synthesis, and compared it with the conventional synthetic routes in batch. However, simulation-based investigation in this field is still in infancy despite the need for it due to expensive experimental costs. Therefore, this work presents the simulation-based comparison of batch and flow syntheses for an actual drug substance using heterogeneous hydrogenation. Multi-objective comparison of batch and flow syntheses were performed in the previous work (Kim et al., 2022). Here, the impact of reaction rate and viscosity on batch and flow syntheses are investigated.

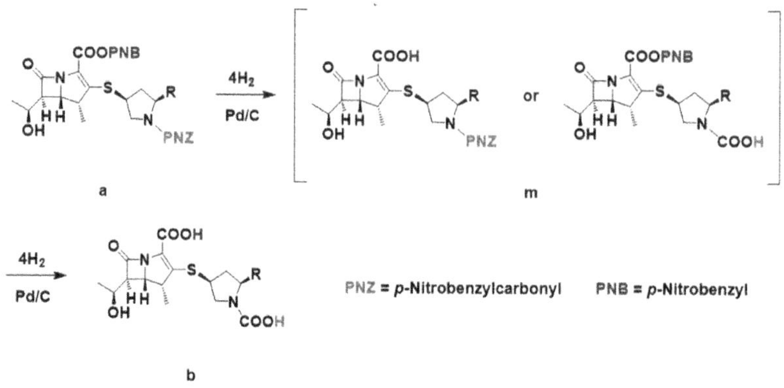

Figure 1. Target reaction scheme (modified from Kim et al. (2022))

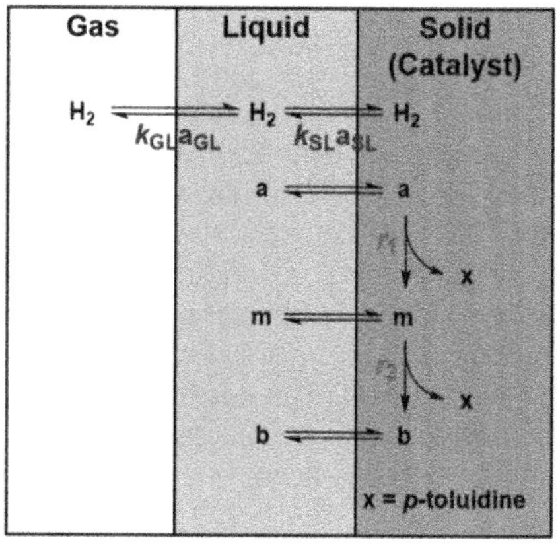

Figure 2. Mass transfer and reactions in gas/liquid/solid phases (modified from Kim et al., (2022))

2. Materials and methods

2.1. Target reaction

Figure 1 shows the target reaction, heterogeneous hydrogenation. The figure was modified based on the previous work (Kim, et al., 2022). The reaction scheme is the part of the synthetic route of an antibiotic active pharmaceutical ingredient, doripenem. In the hydrogenation, compound **a** is reduced to give intermediate **b** in the presence of the hydrogen gas and Pd/C catalyst. During this process, *p*-toluidine is produced as byproduct **x**, which causes the poisoning of the catalyst. In the model, **m** was assumed as intermediate of the hydrogenation reaction, which refers to compounds having either of the two protecting groups remaining. In the original reaction scheme (Kim, et al., 2022), compound **b** undergoes decarboxylation reaction, where the product decomposes into various byproducts. Here, only the hydrogenation part was considered as the comparison of the conversion of **a** is the focus of this work.

2.2. Model assumptions

Figure 2 shows the overview of the mass transfer and reactions. The figure was modified based on the previous study (Kim, et al., 2022). In the model, the same reaction mechanisms and parameters are assumed in batch and flow syntheses. The mass balance in the liquid and solid phases are considered. The energy balance was neglected in this work because batch experiments did not show significant temperature changes. The hydrogenation reaction was modelled based on the Langmuir–Hinshelwood (LH) mechanism.

2.3. Model equations for batch synthesis

The mass balance equations of liquid and solid phases in batch synthesis were defined as:

$$\frac{dC_{i,L}}{dt} = k_{GL}a_{GL}\left(C_{i,L}^* - C_{i,L}\right) - k_{SL}a_{SL}\left(C_{i,L} - C_{i,S}\right) \tag{1}$$

$$\frac{dC_{i,L}}{dt} = k_{SL}a_{SL}\left(C_{i,L} - C_{i,S}\right) + v_{i,j}r_1\alpha_{act}^2 + v_{i,j}r_2\alpha_{act}^2 \tag{2}$$

where $C_{i,L}$ [mol m^{-3}] and $C_{i,S}$ are the concentrations of compound i (H$_2$, **a**, **m**, **b**, **x**) in the liquid and solid phases, respectively, t [s] is time, k_{GL} [m s^{-1}] is the gas-liquid mass transfer coefficient, a_{GL} [m^{-1}] is the specific gas-liquid contact area, $C_{i,L}^*$ [mol m^{-3}] is the saturation concentration of i, k_{SL} [m s^{-1}] is the solid-liquid mass transfer coefficient, a_{SL} [m^{-1}] is the specific solid-liquid contact area, $v_{i,j}$ [–] is the stoichiometric coefficient, r_1 [mol m^{-3} s^{-1}] and r_2 [mol m^{-3} s^{-1}] are the reaction rates for the first and second steps of hydrogenation, respectively, and α_{act} [–] is the activity coefficient of the catalyst. The values for mass transfer between the gas and liquid phases in batch synthesis ($k_{GL}a_{GL}$) were estimated by catalogue data (e.g., Satake MultiMix Corporation, 2021) for the actual batch reactor in use. The values for mass transfer between the solid and liquid phases (k_{SL}, a_{SL}) were estimated using the following equations (Sano et al., 1974):

$$k_{SL} = \frac{ShD_i}{d_p} \tag{3}$$

$$Sh = 2 + 0.4Re_L^{1/4}Sc^{1/3} \tag{4}$$

$$a_{SL} = \frac{6m_S\rho_S}{d_p m_L \rho_L} \tag{5}$$

where Sh [–] is the Sherwood number, D_i [m^2 s^{-1}] is the diffusion coefficient of compound i in the liquid phase, Re_L [–] is the particle Reynolds number in the liquid phase, Sc [–] is the Schmidt number, m_S [kg] is the catalyst mass, ρ_S [kg m^{-3}] is the density of the catalyst, d_p [m] is the particle diameter, m_L [kg] is the liquid mass and ρ_L [kg m^{-3}] is the density of the liquid. The reaction rates of hydrogenation were modelled by using the following equations:

$$r_1 = \rho_{cat}k_1 \frac{K_{H_2}K_a C_{H_2,S}C_{a,S}}{(1 + K_{H_2}C_{H_2,S} + K_a C_{a,S} + K_m C_{m,S} + K_b C_{b,S} + K_x C_{x,S} + K_c C_{c,S})^2} \tag{6}$$

$$r_2 = \rho_{cat}k_1 \frac{K_{H_2}K_m C_{H_2,S}C_{m,S}}{(1 + K_{H_2}C_{H_2,S} + K_a C_{a,S} + K_m C_{m,S} + K_b C_{b,S} + K_x C_{x,S} + K_c C_{c,S})^2} \tag{7}$$

where ρ_{cat} [kg m^{-3}] is the bulk density of the catalyst, k_1 [mol kg^{-1} s^{-1}] is the reaction rate constant of hydrogenation and K_i [mol^{-1}] is the adsorption coefficient of compound *i.* The change in catalyst activity was calculated by the following equation (Kilpiö et al., 2012):

$$\frac{d\alpha_{act}}{dt} = \frac{-\alpha_{act}k_p K_x C_{x,S}}{\left(1 + K_{H_2} C_{H_2,S} + K_a C_{a,S} + K_m C_{m,S} + K_b C_{b,S} + K_x C_{x,S} + K_c C_{c,S}\right)} \tag{8}$$

where k_p [s^{-1}] is the poisoning rate constant. Eqs. (6)–(8) were used in the flow synthesis as well.

2.4. Model equations for flow synthesis

The mass balance of liquid and solid phases in flow synthesis are defined as:

$$\frac{\partial C_{i,L}}{\partial t} = -\frac{u_L}{\varepsilon_L}\frac{\partial C_{i,L}}{\partial l} + D_i \frac{\partial^2 C_{i,L}}{\partial l^2} + \frac{1}{\varepsilon_L} k_{GL} a_{GL}\left(C_{i,L}^* - C_{i,L}\right)$$
$$- \frac{1}{\varepsilon_L} k_{SL} a_{SL}(C_{i,L} - C_{i,S}) \tag{9}$$

$$\frac{\partial C_{i,S}}{\partial t} = \frac{1}{\varepsilon_S} k_{SL} a_{SL}\left(C_{i,L} - C_{i,S}\right) + v_{i,j} r_1 \alpha_{act}^2 + v_{i,j} r_2 \alpha_{act}^2 \tag{10}$$

where u_L [m s^{-1}] is the superficial liquid velocity, ε_L [–] is the liquid holdup and l [m] represents the location in the reactor, and ε_s [–] is the solid holdup. The values for mass transfer between the gas and liquid phases ($k_{GL} a_{GL}$) were estimated by the following equation (Kilpiö et al., 2012):

$$\frac{k_{GL} a_{GL} d_p^2}{D_{H_2}\left(1 - \frac{\varepsilon_L}{\varepsilon_P}\right)} = 2\theta^{0.2} Re_L^{0.73} Re_G^{0.2} Sc^{0.5} \left(\frac{d_p}{d_{pipe}}\right)^{0.2} \tag{11}$$

where ε_P [–] is the porosity of the reactor, θ [–] is the surface shape factor for the particle (specified as 2.0 for a sphere according to Kilpiö et al., 2012), Re_G [–] is the particle Reynolds number in the gas phase and d_{pipe} [m] is the diameter of the reactor. The values for mass transfer between the liquid and solid phases (k_{SL}, a_{SL}) were estimated by the following equations (Burghardt et al., 1995).

$$Sh = 2 + 1.1 Re_L^{0.6} Sc^{1/3} \tag{12}$$

$$a_{SL} = \frac{6}{d_p}(1 - \varepsilon_P) \tag{13}$$

3. Results and discussion

3.1. Conversion of raw materials

The conversion of batch synthesis was defined as:

$$conv = (1 - \frac{C_{a,L}(t_{batch})}{C_{a,L}(0)}) \times 100 \tag{14}$$

where t_{batch} [min] is the batch reaction time and $C_{a,L}(0)$ is the initial concentration of **a**. In this work, $t_{batch} = 60$ min. The conversion of flow synthesis was defined as:

$$conv = (1 - \frac{\sum_{t_0}^{t_1} C_{a,L}(t) \cdot v_L \cdot \Delta t}{C_{a,L}(0) \cdot v_L \cdot (t_1 - t_0)}) \times 100 \tag{15}$$

where $C_{a,L}(0)$ is the concentration of **a** at the inlet, v_L [cm³ min⁻¹] is the volumetric flow rate of the liquid phase and Δt is the time interval for the calculation output (set as 1 min in the simulation). The parameters t_0 [min] and t_1 [min] represent the beginning and the end of production using flow synthesis (start-up and shut-down were excluded).

3.2. Sensitivity analysis of reaction rate constant and viscosity

Sensitivity analysis was performed to investigate the impact of the hydrogenation reaction rate constant and viscosity on the conversion in batch and flow syntheses. The parameters were changed under the following ranges.

$$k_1 \in \{5, 10, \cdots, 100\}$$

$$\eta_{solvent} \in \{0.2, 0.25, \cdots, 2.0\}$$

Here, $\eta_{solvent}$ [mPa s] is the viscosity of the solvent. Figure 3 shows the conversion of **a**. The reaction rate constant affects the conversion of both batch and flow. It showed less impact in flow synthesis, especially with smaller viscosity values. This is because almost 100% of conversion was obtained even under small reaction rate constant values. On the other hand, the viscosity showed a greater impact on the conversion of flow compared to batch. The viscosity affects the mass transfer between phases (gas-liquid and liquid-solid), and it has less impact in batch synthesis because mass transfer in batch is sufficient even with larger viscosity values.

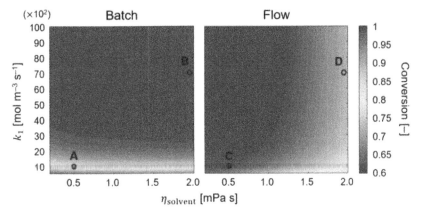

Figure 3. Conversion in batch and flow syntheses

Table 1. Parameter values and conversion at four conditions

Condition	$\eta_{solvent}$ [mPa s]	k_1 [10^2 mol m⁻³ s⁻¹]	Conversion [–]
A	0.5	10	0.83
B	1.95	70	1.00
C	0.5	10	0.99
D	1.95	70	0.90

The results suggest that the optimal condition may differ between batch and flow synthesis, and could result in a need for extra flow experiments at all relevant conditions when changing from batch to flow synthesis. For example, the optimal operation was obtained at condition B (Figure 3) in batch synthesis, which shows 17% higher conversion than the condition A (Table 1). However, condition C shows 9% higher conversion than condition D in flow synthesis. Further investigation of the impact of other parameters such as solvent density could contribute to reducing the number of or avoiding extra experiments needed for the change from batch to flow.

4. Conclusions and outlook

Sensitivity analysis was performed to compare the impact of reaction rate constant and viscosity in batch and flow syntheses. Reaction rate constant influenced the conversion of both batch and flow syntheses. Viscosity showed much greater impact on the conversion of flow than that of batch. The differences in optimal condition between batch and flow hinder the direct transfer of process experiences between the different production modes. Thus, dedicated experiments are required to optimize production in flow synthesis. Extensive simulation of flow synthesis incorporating the effects of other parameters could help lower the expected experimental load.

References

A.R. Bogdan, S.L. Poe, D.C. Kubis, S.J. Broadwater, D.T. McQuade, 2009. The continuous-flow synthesis of ibuprofen. Angew. Chem., Int. Ed. 48, 8547–8550.

A. Burghardt, G. Bartelmus, M. Jaroszyński, A. Kołodziej, 1995. Hydrodynamics and mass transfer in a three-phase fixed-bed reactor with cocurrent gas-liquid downflow. Chem. Eng. J. Biochem. Eng. J. 58, 83–99.

J. Hartwig, S. Ceylan, L. Kupracz, L. Coutable, A. Kirschning, 2013. Heating under high-frequency inductive conditions: Application to the continuous synthesis of the neurolepticum olanzapine (Zyprexa). Angew. Chem., Int. Ed. 52, 9813–9817.

J. Kim, H. Yonekura, T. Watanabe, S. Yoshikawa, H. Nakanishi, S. Badr, H. Sugiyama, 2022, Model-based comparison of batch and flow syntheses of an active pharmaceutical ingredient using heterogeneous hydrogenation, Comput. Chem. Eng., 156, 107541.

T. Kilpiö, P. Mäki-Arvela, M. Rönnholm, V. Sifontes, J. Wärnå, T. Salmi, 2012. Modeling of a three-phase continuously operating isothermal packed-bed reactor: Kinetics, mass-transfer, and dispersion effects in the hydrogenation of citral. Ind. Eng. Chem. Res. 51, 8858–8866.

F. Lévesque, P.H. Seeberger, 2012. Continuous-flow synthesis of the anti-malaria drug artemisinin. Angew. Chem., Int. Ed. 51, 1706–1709.

M.J. Pedersen, T. Skovby, M.J. Mealy, K. Dam-Johansen, S. Kiil, 2018. Redesign of a Grignard-based active pharmaceutical ingredient (API) batch synthesis to a flow process for the preparation of melitracen HCl. Org. Proc. Res. Dev. 22, 228–235.

Y. Sano, N. Yamaguchi, T. Adachi, 1974. Mass transfer coefficients for suspended particles in agitated vessels and bubble columns. J. Chem. Eng. Jpn., 7 (4) 255–261.

Satake MultiMix Corporation, https://www.satake.co.jp/product/catalog/download/data/17_ impeller.pdf (accessed November 5, 2021)

T. Tsubogo, H. Oyamada, S. Kobayashi, 2015. Multistep continuous-flow synthesis of (R)- and (S)-rolipram using heterogeneous catalysts. Nature 520, 329–332.

Proceedings of the 14th International Symposium on Process Systems Engineering – PSE 2021+
June 19-23, 2022, Kyoto, Japan © 2022 Elsevier B.V. All rights reserved.
http://dx.doi.org/10.1016/B978-0-323-85159-6.50147-0

Assessment on the heat integration potential for different pressure thermally coupled distillation structures

J. Rafael Alcántara-Avila[a]*, Rodrigo Tinoco Saenz[a,b]

[a]*Department of Chemical Engineering, Kyoto University, Katsura Campus Nishikyo-ku, Kyoto 615-8510, Japan*
[b]*Sales del Istmo, S.A de C.V. Grupo CYDSA. Complejo industrial Pajaritos, Coatzacoalcos, 96400, México*
jrafael@cheme.kyoto-u.ac.jp

Abstract

This work presents a comparison of several distillation structures that can attain energy and cost savings. The Different Pressure Thermally Coupled Distillation (DPTCD) was studied to increase its energy-savings potential by exploiting heat integration among stages. Therefore, a Mixed-Integer Linear Programming (MILP) problem was proposed and solved to find heat-integrated distillation column (HIDiC) structures that can improve energy and cost savings of DPTCD. The separation of a closed-boiling point mixture was taken as a case study. The HIDiC slightly outperformed DPTCD in energy and cost terms.

Keywords: Process Synthesis, MILP, DPTCD, HIDiC, Heat Integration

1. Introduction

Distillation is the most widely used technique to separate liquid mixtures. However, it uses large amounts of energy because it boils liquid streams. Typically, more than half of the process heat distributed to a plant is dedicated to supplying heat in distillation columns' reboilers (Caballero and Grossmann, 2013). To improve energy efficiency in distillation processes, several alternatives, including heat integration and thermal coupling, have been proposed. Heat integration between hot streams and cold streams has been widely used in the Chemical Industry.

Different Pressure Thermally Coupled distillation (DPTCD) has been proposed as an energy-saving distillation alternative for the separation of close-boiling point mixtures (Liu *et al.*, 2017) and in reactive distillation (Li *et al.*, 2015). DPTCD claims that heat integration between the top vapor of a high-pressure rectifying column and the bottom liquid of a low-pressure stripping column reduces the energy requirements in comparison with its conventional counterpart. The Vapor Recompression Column (VRC) can also realize condenser-reboiler heat integration by compressing the top vapor stream leaving the column. Finally, the Heat Integrated Distillation Column (HIDiC) can also realize condenser-reboiler heat integration. However, it also exploits the idea of realizing heat integration among stages in the rectifying and stripping columns. This work compares the economic and energy performance of DPTCD, VRD, and HIDiC. The economic criterion is assessed by minimizing the total annual cost (TAC), while the energy requirement criterion is assessed by minimizing energy consumption.

2. Problem Statement

The HIDiC structure is expected to be the most promising alternative to reduce the energy consumption in the chemical plants because outstanding energy savings up to 60% in comparison with its conventional distillation counterparts have been obtained theoretically and experimentally in pilot plants (Matsuda, Iwakabe and Nakaiwa, 2012). However, the typical HIDiC structure (i.e., concentric arrangement of inner and outer tubes) has presented operating issues such as difficult maintenance, HIDiC structures with few heat integrations have been proposed (Wakabayashi and Hasebe, 2013, 2015).

The simulation of DPTCD and VRC alternatives is straightforward because the only heat integration is between the condenser and reboiler. However, the simulation and optimization of the HIDiC structure is more challenging because the following questions must be answered: (1) how many heat integrations are needed? and (2) what is the best amount of heat transferred at the chosen locations?

This work adopts a synthesis methodology for the generation of near-optimal HIDIC structures where the stages in a high-pressure rectifying column are regarded as heat sources, and the stages in a low-pressure stripping column are regarded as heat sinks. The synthesis problem is represented by a superstructure in which all possible heat integrations are explicitly included. Finally, the superstructure is formulated as a mixed-integer linear programming (MILP) problem that successively combines process simulation and optimization (Alcantara-Avila, 2019; Herrera Velázquez *et al.*, 2021).

In this work, the synthesis problem for the heat integration among stages in a HIDiC structure is formulated based on the following assumptions:

1. The top pressure in each section is given in advance, and the pressure drop is considered (i.e., 75 kPa per stage).
2. The feed composition and product specifications are given in advance.
3. The feed and products are saturated liquids.
4. Only one stage in the high-pressure column (i.e., rectifying section) can supply heat to only one stage in the low-pressure column (i.e., stripping section).
5. Only one stage in the low-pressure column (i.e., stripping section) can receive heat from only one stage in the high-pressure column (i.e., rectifying section).
6. The minimum temperature difference value that enables heat integration is given in advance.
7. The compressor type and efficiency are given in advance.
8. The process is at the steady-state.
9. Vapor-liquid equilibrium is reached in each distillation stage.
10. Utility costs per unit amount of heating and cooling are given in advance.

The synthesis problem is represented by the superstructure in Figure 1. *REC* and *STR* are the sets of stages in the rectifying and stripping sections. *LC* and *HC* are the light and heavy component(s), respectively. The arrows connecting stages of different sections represent the heat transfer between stages.

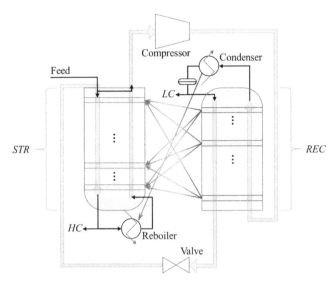

Figure 1. Superstructure representation

3. Mathematical formulation

The superstructure in Figure 1 can be reformulated as the optimization problem represented by Eq. (1). The detailed optimization model can be found in Herrera Velázquez *et al.*, (2021).

$$UC = \sum_{\substack{i \in REC \\ j \in CU}} Q_{i,j}^{hx} C_j^{cool} + \sum_{\substack{i \in HU \\ j \in STR}} C_i^{heat} Q_{i,j}^{hx} + W C^{elec} \tag{1}$$

s.t.

✳ Heat balance at each stage

✳ Heat balance in the condenser, reboiler, and compressor

✳ Heat integration feasibility

✳ Work, condenser and reboiler duty estimation

where UC is the utility cost, CU and HU are the set of cooling and heating utilities, respectively. $Q_{i,j}^{hx}$ is the heat exchange between a heat source i and a heat sink j. C_j^{cool} and C_i^{heat} is the cooling and heating cost of utilities per unit amount of heat. W is the compressor work duty and C^{elec} is the electricity cost.

The optimization variables are the pressure ratio between the rectifying and stripping sections (PR), the heat removed at a stage in the rectifying section (Q_i), the heat removed at a stage in the stripping section (Q_j), the location of a heat integration ($Y_{i,j}^{hx}$), and the number of heat integrations (N^{hx}), respectively. $Y_{i,j}^{hx}$ is an integer variable that becomes one if heat integration is realized between stages i and j while it becomes zero otherwise. Therefore, the optimization problem can be solved as an MILP problem.

The stage-by-stage material balance, thermodynamic relationships, and summation restrictions are considered in the process simulation Aspen Plus V11. The iterative execution of simulations and optimizations result in the optimal HIDiC structure when the convergence criterion in Eq. (2) is met.

$$\sqrt{\sum_{i \in REC} \left(T_{i,s} - T_{i,s-1}\right)^2 + \sum_{j \in STR} \left(T_{j,s} - T_{j,s-1}\right)^2} \leq (NR + NS)\varphi \tag{2}$$

where T is the temperature of stage i and j at an iteration s. NR and NS are the number of stages in the rectifying and stripping sections of the HIDiC structure, and φ is the tolerance for the termination criterion, which is a small value (e. g., 0.01).

4. Case Study: n-butanol/isobutanol separation

The separation of a close-boiling point mixture of n-butanol and isobutanol studied by Liu *et al.*, (2017) is taken as a case study to compare economic and energy criteria for the DPTCD, VRC, and HIDiC structures. The key ideas in this comparison are to know the true energy-saving potential of DPTCD and to know if HIDiC can outperform DPTCD.

Table 1. shows the parameters used in the optimization problem.

Parameter	Value
Cooling cost (C_j^{cool}) [\$/GJ]	0.354
Heating cost (C_i^{heat}) [\$/GJ]	7.720
Electricity cost (C^{elec}) [\$/GJ]	16.81
Payback time [yr]	5
Overall heat transfer coefficient [BTU/h F ft^2]	
Condenser:	190
Heat exchanger / Reboiler:	175
Big-M parameter (M) [-]	250
Minimum Temperature difference (ΔT_{min}) [F]	18

The total annual cost (TAC) was calculated using the Marshall & Swift index for 2020 (i.e., 2171.6). The TAC was calculated according to Eq. (3)

$$\min TAC = OC * \text{AOH} + \frac{\left[C_{\text{shell}} + C_{\text{tray}} + C_{\text{comp}} + \sum_{\substack{i \in HS \\ j \in CS}} C_{hex_{i,j}}\right]}{\text{PBP}} \tag{3}$$

where $i \in HS$ is the set of heating streams ($HS = REC \cup HU$), $j \in CS$ is the set of cooling streams ($CS = STR \cup CU$), C_{shell}, C_{tray}, C_{comp}, and $C_{hex_{i,j}}$ is the cost of the column shell, trays, compressor, and heat exchangers. AOH and PBP are the annual operation hours (i.e., 8000 h/y) and the payback time (i.e., 5 years), respectively.

5. Results and Discussions

Table 2 shows the results of the conventional distillation column (CD), VRC, DPTCD, and HIDiD structures after executing the optimization problem in Section 3. It is worthy of keeping in mind that even the solution of the MILP needs to determine the following questions: 1) how many heat integrations does the optimal result have, and 2) what is the maximum amount of heat integrated at stages. Table 2 shows the simulation and optimization results, while Table 3 summarizes the energy and cost savings.

Table 2. TAC results for the different distillation structures

	CD*	VRC*	DPTCD*	HIDiC
Heating [$/y]	542,169	---	---	23,072
Cooling [$/y]	25,554	4,187	3,300	3,856
Electricity [$/y]	---	165,934	137,710	104,147
Operating Cost [$/y]	567,723	170,120	141,009	131,075
Condenser [$]	211,959	79,699	55,954	64,231
Reboiler [$]	456,595	---	---	42,009
Heat Exchangers [$]	---	761,662	522,257	656,844
Column [$]	1,327,953	1,327,953	1,360,239	1,519,093
Tray [$]	156,973	156,973	133,271	151,423
Compressor [$]	---	1,903,129	1,633,325	1,298,955
Equipment Cost [$/y]	2,153,479	4,229,415	3,705,045	3,732,554
TAC [$/y]	998,419	1,016,003	882,018	877,586

*Adapted from the simulation results in Liu *et al.*, (2017).

Table 3. Energy and cost savings comparison for the different distillation structures

	CD	VRC	DPTCD	HIDiC
Energy Consumption [kW]	2438.5	935.7	776.5	691.1
Energy savings [%]	0.0	61.6	68.2	71.7
TAC savings [%]	0.0	-1.8	11.7	12.1

The energy consumption was calculated according to Eq. (4) as the summation the energy from heating utilities and the electricity used in the compressor

$$\text{Energy consumption} = \sum_{\substack{i \in HU \\ j \in STR}} Q_{i,j}^{hx} + 2.73W \qquad (3)$$

From the results in Tables 2 and 3, it can be seen that in terms of energy consumption, the HIDiC uses less energy because it operates at a compression ratio smaller than that of DPTCD (2.0 and 2.6, respectively) despite HIDiC needs steam at the bottom reboiler in the stripping section. Although HIDiC needs energy, electricity, and compressor costs less than DPTCD, it increases the column, trays, and heat exchangers cost.

Therefore, overall, DPTCD and HIDiC have similar TAC, but there is a trade-off between energy consumption and equipment cost. This same behavior has been presented in previous works when compressors are included in the synthesis and optimization of distillation sequences (Cabrera-Ruiz *et al.*, 2012; J. Alcántara-Avila, Kano and Hasebe, 2012; J. R. Alcántara-Avila, Kano and Hasebe, 2012). The HIDiC structure had one heat integration between stage 9 in the rectifying section and the reboiler in the stripping section.

6. Conclusions

This work presented a comparison between several distillation structures that can realize heat integration between a condenser and reboiler as well as among stages in different column sections. When one heat integration was done, the HIDiC structure attained energy and cost savings higher than DPTCD. Although the HIDiC and DPTCD can have very similar performances, there is a trade-off between these alternatives.

References

Alcántara-Avila, J., Kano, M. and Hasebe, S. (2012) 'Environmental and economic optimization of distillation structures to produce anhydrous ethanol', *Computer Aided Chemical Engineering*.

Alcantara-Avila, J. R. (2019) 'Optimization methodologies for intensified distillation processes with flexible heat integration networks', in Gomez Castro, F. I. and Segovia-Hernández, J. G. (eds) *Process Intensification: Design Methodologies*. 1st edn. Berlin: De Gruyter, pp. 181–209.

Alcántara-Avila, J. R., Kano, M. and Hasebe, S. (2012) 'Multiobjective optimization for synthesizing compressor-aided distillation sequences with heat integration', *Industrial and Engineering Chemistry Research*, 51(17), pp. 5911–5921.

Caballero, J. A. and Grossmann, I. E. (2013) 'Synthesis of Complex Thermally Coupled Distillation Systems Including Divided Wall Columns', *AIChE Journal*, 59(4), pp. 1139–1159.

Cabrera-Ruiz, J. *et al.* (2012) 'Optimal dynamic controllability in compressor-aided distillation schemes using stochastic algorithms', *Computer Aided Chemical Engineering*.

Herrera Velázquez, J. J. *et al.* (2021) 'Hybrid two-step optimization of internally heat-integrated distillation columns', *Journal of the Taiwan Institute of Chemical Engineers*. In press.

Li, L. *et al.* (2015) 'Design and Control of Different Pressure Thermally Coupled Reactive Distillation for Methyl Acetate Hydrolysis', *Industrial and Engineering Chemistry Research*, 54(49), pp. 12342–12353.

Liu, L. *et al.* (2017) 'Simulation and optimization of different pressure thermally coupled distillation for separating a close-boiling mixture of n-butanol and isobutanol', *Applied Petrochemical Research*. Springer Berlin Heidelberg, 7(2–4), pp. 143–150.

Matsuda, K., Iwakabe, K. and Nakaiwa, M. (2012) 'Recent advances in internally Heat-integrated distillation columns (HIDiC) for sustainable development', *Journal of Chemical Engineering of Japan*, 45(6), pp. 363–372.

Wakabayashi, T. and Hasebe, S. (2013) 'Reversible distillation curve and operating locus as criteria for appropriate of HIDiC', *Kagaku Kogaku Ronbunshu*, 39(6), pp. 493–502.

Wakabayashi, T. and Hasebe, S. (2015) 'Higher Energy Saving with New Heat Integration Arrangement in Heat-Integrated Distillation Column', *AIChE Journal*, 61(10), pp. 3479–2488.

Proceedings of the 14th International Symposium on Process Systems Engineering – PSE 2021+
June 19-23, 2022, Kyoto, Japan © 2022 Elsevier B.V. All rights reserved.
http://dx.doi.org/10.1016/B978-0-323-85159-6.50148-2

Python platform for Tennessee Eastman Process

Chengyu HAN, Shiping HUANG, and Wei SUN*

College of Chemical Engineering, Beijing University of Chemical Technology, Beijing 100029, CHINA.
sunwei@mail.buct.edu.cn

Abstract

Tennessee Eastman process (TEP) is a widely used test benchmark in the field of process monitoring and process control. A complete chemical plant is simulated, which can provide a large amount of process data as DCS (Distributed Control System), and people can introduce various faults artificially as case studies in their research. original TEP program was written in FORTRAN. Ricker used f2c (Fortran to C) program to convert Fortran code to C code, and wrote a mex function to connect TEP to MATLAB. Users can run the TEP process graphically and view the curves of variables. The graphical interface of MATLAB/Simulink is easy to use, but it takes a lot of glue code to set up TEP's parameters and run simulations in other programming languages. In addition, the fault adding logic of TEP is put in the code written in C language, which prevents the fault from being added dynamically at the expected time.

In order to make better use of the TEP process and make it convenient for people to use it, a method of calling TEP through python instead of MATLAB is proposed. Through the interaction between python's C-API and TEP's C program, all the functions of TEP are exported. The stop time of running open-loop simulation is consistent with the result of MATLAB, and the relative error between the modified program running results and the data generated by the original TEP program with open-loop is less than 10^{-6}. Ricker developed a Simplified TEP (S-TEP), and kept only one tank reactor with two phases. In the same way, the method of connecting S-TEP with python is proposed. Then the C library with python interface is bundled into a python package. This allows users to install all programs needed to run S-TEP, and only one python package needs to install through the python package manager without configuring the C language compilation environment, which greatly facilitates the use of S-TEP. A GUI interface was added to the modified S-TEP program to make it easier for people to use.

Keywords: Process Monitoring; Fault detection; Tennessee Eastman Process; Process models; Process simulators.

1. Introduction

Modern chemical industry is large in scale and high in complexity, which runs a multivariable control system. With the upgrading of chemical processes and the use of new reaction equipment, the chemical process has become more and more complex and highly nonlinear. Large-scale complex systems will produce a large amount of process data. Although more information from the process can be collected, the amount of data provided by existing distributed control system (DCS) is quite tremendous, which makes it hard for operators or engineers to evaluate the effectiveness of the process only by observing process data. Especially when a fault occurs, it is more difficult to find the real cause of the fault from overwhelming information provided by DCS and solve it quickly.

In order to ensure that the process operations meet the performance specifications, faults in the process need to be detected, diagnosed and eliminated. These tasks are related to process monitoring, more specifically, it is data-driven process monitoring. Benefited from proper process monitoring, downtime is minimized, safety of plant operations is improved, and production costs is reduced. With the increase of the number of instruments in the plant, the amount of data available for monitoring and troubleshooting is also increasing.

Data-driven methods require a large amount of process data, including data under normal working conditions and data in case of failure. For the stable operation of the chemical process, most of the time is in normal state. Faults only occur in unusual situations, and the operator will try to shorten the duration of faults as much as possible. Factories will not provide its process data for data security or confidentiality. Therefore, it is difficult to extract the fault state data from the actual chemical process.

Downs and Vogel (1993) presented the Tennessee Eastman Challenge in their paper. This process is also known as Tennessee Eastman Process (TEP). TEC is based on a real industrial process and consists of a set of FORTRAN subroutines. Running these subroutines can obtain instrumental information in a process like DCS. Furthermore, by introducing faults manually, we can capture process data in case of faults. TEP has been used to research and evaluate many aspects, such as process monitoring algorithms, control system design, optimization algorithms. Many authors have used it to demonstrate their procedures for the design of control systems (Ricker, 1995; Ricker and Lee, 1995; Ricker, 1996; Larsson and Skogestad, 2001).

Bathelt and Ricker (2015) have studied the underlying computer code of the well-known TEP model. A bug was found in the original TEP. The causes of bug are discussed in this paper and a solution in terms of a modified code is presented. Furthermore, some additional changes are discussed, widening the usability of the simulation model. This improvement to the TEP has improved TEP, but the current TEP is still difficult to extend programmatically. Martin-Villalba and Guodong Shao (2018) presented the development of two different Modelica libraries, TE-process and TE-Simplified. Using Modelica is an important attempt to improve the programmability of TEP, which proves that TEP does not completely rely on MATLAB. However, the modelling language used by Modelica is not very popular, and there are not many packages related to statistical algorithms, so we tried to use other languages to replace MATLAB, and after some comparison we finally chose python to encapsulate the TEP code.

2. Different versions of TEP

Ignoring the control part and considering only the core process simulation part, there are many versions of the TEP. The most important versions are: the original TEP, the simplified version of the TEP and the latest version of the TEP.

2.1. Original TEP

The TEP was created by the Eastman Chemical Company to provide a realistic industrial process for evaluating process control and monitoring methods. The testing process is based on a simulation of an actual industrial process, in which components, dynamics and operating conditions are modified due to patent reasons. This process is well suited for a wide variety of studies including both plant-wide control and multivariable control problems. FORTRAN code representing the process is available from Downs and Vogel (1993), but they have chosen not to publish the model equations. Instead, they provide a flowsheet, a steady-state material balance, and a qualitative description of the key process characteristics. The process is nonlinear and open-loop unstable. Without control, it reaches shutdown limits within an hour, even for very small disturbances.

All codes are written in FORTRAN 77 in a fixed format. According to the notes in the source code, MEX interface only supports the MATLAB version 3.x and 4.x, and cannot be used with the new version of MATLAB at present. Only FORTRAN source files and MEX interface codes are provided, and no control codes of MATLAB are provided. All symbols in the FORTRAN code are capitalized, and there is no space or indentation between statements. This version of the code is the original TEC code, and is often used as the basis for improvements in other versions, but it can neither be compiled nor read because of its long history and incomplete code. Therefore, papers will use the dataset that comes with the original TEP directly instead of running the program to generate a new dataset. If not specified in papers, the TEP dataset usually refers to the dataset accompanying this version.

2.2. Simplified TEP

Ricker (1995) proposed the Simplified Tennessee Eastman Challenge (S-TEP) which is a simplification of the TEP model, with only one process unit and eight state variables. The process consists of a single vessel that represents a combination of the reactor and separation system in the original TE process. The process unit has two input flows and two output flow. The S-TEP model is also a well-known benchmark process. It is a multi-input multi-output, nonlinear system, open-loop unstable, and contains fast and slow dynamics.

FORTRAN77 with fixed format is used in the code of process simulation. The control part of the code is written by MATLAB, but only supports MATLAB version 3.x or 4.x. Therefore, the S-TEP code needs to be updated to use.

2.3. The Newest TEP

With the update of MATLAB and the improvement of the complexity of TEP control system, a bug was found in the original process simulation code: when using different integration methods or different integration steps, the results of process simulation are inconsistent. After detailed debugging, the problem lies in the generation of random numbers. Different integrators need different convergence times, which leads to different calls of random number generators, which makes the generated random numbers different, and finally leads to inconsistent process simulation results. Bathelt and Ricker (2015) implemented a new random number generation method to fix this problem. Furthermore, some additional changes are discussed, widening the usability of the simulation model.

The core process simulation part is written in C language, and the control part is written in MATLAB/Simulink. The tested code can run on MATLAB 2014~2020. C language can be recompiled by MSVC 2017 compiler. The work in this article is also based on this version.

2.4. Possible way to improve TEP

At present, TEP mainly uses FORTRAN, C and MATLAB. The core part of process simulation is written in FORTRAN and C languages, which runs well and is rarely modified. Most of the modifications are in the MATLAB. MATLAB is used to call the process simulation, integrate the process variables and implement control system. Using TEP to generate data requires using graphical user interface, adjusting parameters, setting the running time length, then clicking the Run button, waiting for the simulation to be completed, and finally manually exporting the required data sets. If you need data for multiple faults, you need to manually repeat the above steps several times. Using MATLAB script some of the above steps can be completed automatically to a certain extent, but the copyright and toolbox package of MATLAB somehow limited TEP revision. Python or R is usually used in statistical study of data processing. Among the above languages, Python has the most mature data science ecology, and many data-driven algorithms can be used directly. Therefore, we chose Python as a substitute for MATLAB, so that data generation and post-processing can be carried out in one language. The advantage of doing this is to improve the usability of TEP, and to make TEP more widely used.

3. Connect TEP to Python

3.1. System Architecture

The architecture of the 2015 modified version of TEP is shown on the left side of Figure 1. The core module is written in C and the interface is exported for MATLAB through a wrapper of S-functions. The control logic is written in MATLAB, and the input of parameters and the output of results are performed in MATALB.

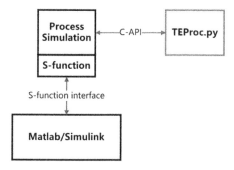

Figure 1 Original and modified TEP architecture diagram

Such an architecture involves encapsulating the details of the process simulation, and the control logic can be modified in MATALB, which is very convenient for researchers in the control field. However, for the field of process monitoring, the control methods of the system are generally not modified, and researchers are more concerned with the introduction of faults, the superposition of noise, and the input of parameters and output of results. The generation and export of the dataset is performed manually in MATLAB's GUI, and the processing of the data and application of the algorithm is performed in python. These can be partially automated in MATLAB, and a more desirable situation would be to use one language to perform these operations as well.

To solve the problem of interaction between TEP and other languages, we propose to use python to call the core modules directly, without MATLAB. The overall architecture is shown on the right side of the figure, where the python wrapper script calls the modules of TEP by using C-API directly, and the control logic is moved to the python script. We use the ctypes module in python standard library to wrap constants, variables, and structures from C code into python, and then define the prototypes of the functions in python. Once the correct C compiled shared library is loaded, the corresponding C functions can be called in python.

3.2. Precision Comparison

To verify that the accuracy of the TEP process simulation does not degrade after switching from MATLAB to python. We used the open-loop TEP model without control system as a test, compared the stopping time of the original TEP and the python wrapped TEP, and calculated the deviation of each process variable. Additional noise was added to the output of the TEP, so we calculated the relative error of the 50 state variables in the TEP. As shown in Figure 2, the relative errors of component A in vapor phase of reactor are within acceptable limits (less than 10^{-6}). This indicates that the same accuracy can be achieved by using python to call the TEP core module directly as by using MATLAB to call the TEP.

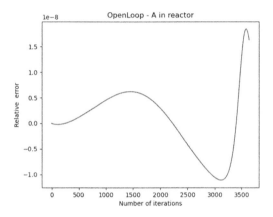

Figure 2 Errors in TEP.py vs. TEP-2015

3.3. GUI for S-TEP

The TEP process is complex and requires many variables to be wrapped. After verifying the feasibility of calling TEP in python, we used the S-TEP process as an example, wrapped the code using the same method, and created a graphical user interface (GUI) for ease of use. The GUI for model parameter setting is shown in Figure 3.

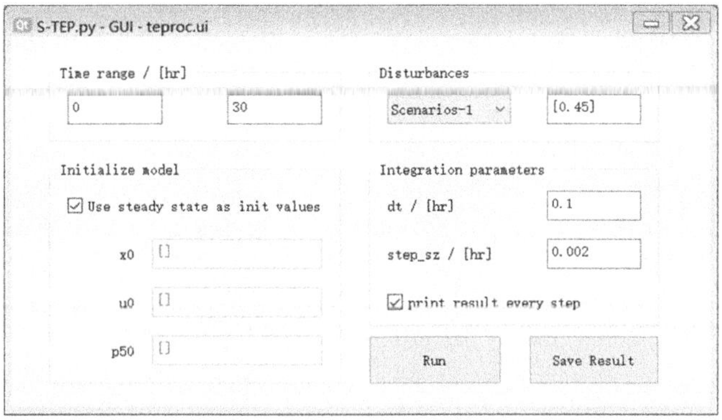

Figure 3 GUI for S-TEP.py

4. Conclusions

The existing TEP still can be further improved, such as the need to compile before use, the use of commercial software MATLAB/Simulink, the lack of standardization of process, and the weak repeatability of process simulation, etc. This paper proposes a method to connect C code in python through C-API, and successfully use python to call the core code of TEP directly. And it achieves the same accuracy as the original TEP in the open-loop test without control system. A GUI interface of the modified S-TEP program has been added to make it easier for people to use. Then a package of S-TEP process has been made by using modern scripting language Python and new object-oriented programming technology. A standardized S-TEP can promote the use of S-TEP, and make all kinds of research based on S-TEP comparable.

Next step, the original control logic of S-TEP will be transplanted into python, which will prove that python can substitute for Simulink. When the output accuracy of the python S-TEP program with control logic reaches an acceptable range, and the bundled S-TEP python module will be uploaded to the python package hosting website for everyone to use.

References

A. Bathelt, N. L. Ricker, M. Jelali, 2015, Revision of the Tennessee Eastman Process Model, IFAC-PapersOnLine, 9th IFAC Symposium on Advanced Control of Chemical Processes ADCHEM 2015, 48, 309-314.

J. J. Downs, E. F. Vogel, 1993, A plant-wide industrial process control problem, Computers & Chemical Engineering, Industrial challenge problems in process control, 17, 245-255.

A. Kroll, H. Schulte, 2014, Benchmark problems for nonlinear system identification and control using Soft Computing methods: Need and overview, Applied Soft Computing, 25, 496-513.

T. Larsson, K. Hestetun, E. Hovland, S. Skogestad, 2001, Self-Optimizing Control of a Large-Scale Plant: The Tennessee Eastman Process, Ind. Eng. Chem. Res., 40, 4889-4901.

C. Martin-Villalba, A. Urquia, G. Shao, 2018, Implementations of the Tennessee Eastman Process in Modelica, IFAC-PapersOnLine, 9th Vienna International Conference on Mathematical Modelling, 51, 619-624.

T. J. McAvoy, N. Ye, 1994, Base control for the Tennessee Eastman problem, Computers & Chemical Engineering, An International Journal of Computer Applications in Chemical Engineering, 18, 383-413.

N. L. Ricker, 1993, Model predictive control of a continuous, nonlinear, two-phase reactor, Journal of Process Control, 3, 109-123.

N. L. Ricker, 1995, Optimal steady-state operation of the Tennessee Eastman challenge process, Computers & Chemical Engineering, 19, 949-959.

N. L. Ricker, J. H. Lee, 1995, Nonlinear model predictive control of the Tennessee Eastman challenge process, Computers & Chemical Engineering, 19, 961-981.

N. L. Ricker, 1996, Decentralized control of the Tennessee Eastman Challenge Process, Journal of Process Control, 6, 205-221.

N. L. Ricker, 1995, Tennessee eastman challenge archive, URL: http://depts.washington.edu/control/LARRY/TE/download.html.

Proceedings of the 14th International Symposium on Process Systems Engineering – PSE 2021+
June 19-23, 2022, Kyoto, Japan © 2022 Elsevier B.V. All rights reserved.
http://dx.doi.org/10.1016/B978-0-323-85159-6.50149-4

Computational Modeling of Lube-Oil Flows in Pipelines to Study the Efficacy of Flushing Operations

Swapana S. Jerpoth, Robert P. Hesketh, C. Stewart Slater, Mariano J. Savelski, Kirti M. Yenkie*

Department of Chemical Engineering, Rowan University, Glassboro, NJ-08028, USA.
yenkie@rowan.edu

Abstract

Lube-oil industries use a complex network of pipelines for transporting thousands of high-value finished products successively in batches throughout the production plant. Each lube-oil is unique in regard to its properties, and its integrity is extremely crucial. Therefore, during a changeover operation, the lines are flushed using a high-value finished product of the current batch that is desired to be processed. The existing flushing operation typically rely on a trial-and-error procedure, resulting in the downgrading of the finished product. Moreover, it leads to enormous economic losses to the industries. In response to this problem, this work presents an approach for modeling and optimizing the flushing operation by employing first-principles and optimal control strategies. We model the flushing operation by integrating the Kendall and Monroe viscosity blending equations with time-dependent component balance equations for lube-oil pipelines. The models developed are validated against the data collected from well-designed flush-study experiments, and a good agreement is observed. We generate theoretical optimal flowrate profiles and provide insights for designing and controlling the flushing operation.

Keywords: lube-oil pipelines, flushing, optimization, optimal control

1. Introduction

In the lube-oil process industries, pipelines are considered the safest and most cost-effective mode of transportation. Therefore, complex pipeline networks are widely used for the transfer of lube-oils during various phases of manufacturing. A single network of pipelines is used for processing over thousands of different product blends. Product quality is extremely crucial to the lube-oil industries because even the slightest amount of contamination can reduce their market value and desired functionality. Hence, to ensure the integrity of every product and avoid contamination due to product mixing, pipelines are flushed between every changeover operation. The traditional flushing techniques involve the use of a finished product of the new batch for cleaning the residual oil from the previous batch. A finished product is used for flushing because using a different cleaner such as water or other oil-based fluid adds further contamination possibilities. Hence the existing flushing technique leads to the downgrading of the high-value finished product, is labor-intensive, primarily depends on a trial-and-error basis, and adds to long operational downtime. Moreover, it leads to economic losses exceeding over $1M/year and renders the product commercially unviable in the worst-case scenario. However, by integrating chemical engineering principles with process optimization techniques, the operation can be conducted more efficiently (Cafaro et al. 2015). The optimized operation could save the industry over a million dollars per annum as well as minimize material and energy consumption footprint.

Product composition must be within specifications required by the purchaser, as the systems in which these products are used (automotive engines, turbines, gears etc.) are extremely sensitive to contamination. During transportation of lube-oil in a batch changeover, a formerly processed oil mixes with the oil that is desired to be processed next. It results in the creation of a mixed oil at the interface of the two batches. The mixed oil does not match in specification to either of the two batches, hence it is classified as downgraded oil/commingled oil, and is unsuitable for the intended end-use consumer. The knowledge of physical property of the mixture is used as a quality indicator to predict whether the desired purity level of the current product batch is attained. One of the most important physical property of lube oils is viscosity. In commercial lube oil industries, samples are collected at the end of a flush period and tested for their viscosity to confirm the quality specifications prior to final packaging. This is a labour-intensive test, and results in operational downtime, which can be minimized via predictive modeling and optimization for effective flushing operation.

2. Optimal Control Problems and Applications

The flushing operation involves controlling a dynamic system, i.e., the system that evolves with time. Optimal control theory is a branch of mathematics that finds optimal ways to control dynamic systems (Sethi 2019). Here, the system refers to the pipeline flushing operation. The way of controlling the state of our system is through the oil flow rate in the flushing operation. Hence, our control variable is the flush oil flow rate. We achieve the theoretical optimal flow rate profile and report insights for designing and controlling the flushing operation. Optimal control deals with the properties of control functions, such that these functions, when inserted in differential equations, give a solution that minimizes or maximizes a performance index. In engineering applications, the control function is an intended outcome denoted in a mathematical form. The differential equations describe the dynamic response of the mechanism to be controlled and depend on the control strategy employed. The evaluation of the time-dependent operating profiles, in terms of the control variable, is used for optimizing the process performance (Yenkie and Diwekar 2012). In this work, our developed optimal control problem for predicting the optimal flushing policies is solved by using the Pontryagin's maximum principle.

3. Viscosity Blending Equations

To model the flushing operation, it is important to calculate the viscosity of the mixture of the two oils. Viscosity blending equations or mixing rules are widely used in the lubricant industries to calculate the viscosity of the mixture of lube oils (Roegiers and Zhmud 2011). One of the best-known viscosity blending equations was proposed by Kendall and Monroe (1917) (represented by equation (1)). It relies on the power law and calculates blend viscosity as the cubic-root average of the component viscosities. This equation also gives us an understanding of the mass fraction of the individual components of the blend. Through this equation, we would predict how the blend viscosity attains the desired specifications of the new oil with time.

$$\mu_{AB}^{1/3} = x_A \, \mu_A^{1/3} + x_B \, \mu_B^{1/3} \tag{1}$$

where: μ_{AB}- viscosity of blend A and B; μ_A and μ_B- viscosities of lubricants A and B;

x_A and x_B - mass fractions of lubricants A and B

Based on these fundamentals, we model the flushing operation by combining the Kendall-Monroe equation with the component balance equations for the lube oil transportation pipelines. The developed models were compared against the experimental data, and a good agreement was observed. The comparison graphs for two different products are shown in Figure 1. A comparison for thirty such changeover operations was analysed. This confirms that our developed models hold value in representing the lube oil pipeline system.

4. Modeling the Flushing Operation

Based on the fundamental first-principles, the component balance equations for the lube oil transportation pipelines are represented by equations (2) and (3). The assumptions made while developing the component balance equations are as follows: The densities of the lube oil A & B is approximately the same. Furthermore, prior to flushing the pipeline with lube oil B, it is completely filled with lube oil A.

$$\frac{dx_A}{dt} = -\frac{x_A Q}{A_C L} \tag{2}$$

$$\frac{dx_B}{dt} = \frac{x_A Q}{A_C L} \tag{3}$$

where: Q- volumetric flowrate of lubricant B; A_C - cross-sectional area; L- pipe length

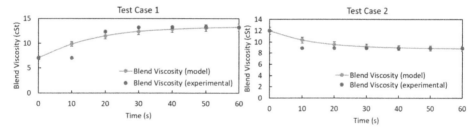

Figure 1. Validation of First Principle Mathematical Models against Experimental Data

5. Solution Methodology

Our objective is to have the pipeline completely free of the old lube oil A and just filled with the pure lube oil B. Mathematically, our objective can be formulated as minimization of the difference between the viscosity of the blend (time-dependent) and the viscosity of lube oil B (constant) at the final flush time. In other terms, the objective is to maximize the negative of the difference in viscosities of the blend and the lube oil B, as shown in equation (4).

$$\text{Max J} = -[\mu_{AB}(t_{final}) - \mu_B]^2 \tag{4}$$

The state of our system is controlled through the flow rate of lube oil B. Hence, the variable Q represents the control variable of the system. The process performance is determined by attaining the desired viscosity of lube oil B. Given the values of the state variables x_i [*where* $x_i = (x_A, x_B, \mu_{AB})$] and the control variable Q at time t, the differential equations (2), (3), and (5) specify the instantaneous rate of change in the state variables. Equation (5) is obtained by differentiating equation (1) w.r.t time and substituting equation (2) and (3) in it.

$$\frac{d\mu_{AB}}{dt} = 3\mu_B^{2/3} x_A{}^3 \frac{Q}{A_C L} [1 - \mu_A^{1/3}] + 6x_A{}^2 x_B \frac{Q}{A_C L} [\mu_A^{1/3}\mu_B^{2/3} - \mu_A^{2/3}\mu_B^{1/3}] +$$
$$3\mu_B^{2/3} x_A x_B \frac{Q}{A_C L} [\mu_B^{1/3} x_B - 2\mu_A^{1/3}] \tag{5}$$

The application of the Pontryagin's maximum principle involves the introduction of additional variables known as adjoint variables and reformulation of the objective as a Hamiltonian function. Three adjoint variables 'z_i', corresponding to each of the state variables result in three more adjoint differential equations as shown in equation (7), and the Hamiltonian must satisfy equation (8). The initial values of the state, and control variable, and model parameters are: $x_A = 1$, $x_B = 0$, $\mu_{AB} = 12$cSt, $Q = 0.007$ (m^3/s), $\mu_A = 12$ cSt, $\mu_B = 8.7$cSt, $A_C = 0.019$m^2, $L = 6.1$m

$$\frac{dx_i}{dt} = f(x_i, Q, t) \tag{6}$$

$$\frac{dz_i}{dt} = -\sum_{j=1}^{3} z_j \frac{\partial f_j}{\partial x_i} \tag{7}$$

$$H = \sum_{i=1}^{3} z_j f(x_i, Q, t) \tag{8}$$

The system results in a two-point boundary value problem since we have initial conditions for the state variables, $x_i(t_0) = [1\ 0\ \mu_A]$, and final conditions for the adjoint variables, $z_i(t_f) = [0\ 0\ -1]$. Furthermore, the total flush time is 60 seconds. For evaluating the Hamiltonian derivative, we use an analytical method proposed by Benavides and Diwekar (2013), which introduces an additional variable θ_i corresponding to each state variable and Φ_i corresponding to each adjoint variable.

$$\theta_i = \frac{dx_i}{dQ} \& \Phi_i = \frac{dz_i}{dQ} \tag{9}$$

$$\frac{d(dx_i/dt)}{dQ} = \frac{d(dx_i/dQ)}{dt} = \frac{d\theta_i}{dt} \tag{10}$$

$$\frac{d(dz_i/dt)}{dQ} = \frac{d(dz_i/dQ)}{dt} = \frac{d\Phi_i}{dt} \tag{11}$$

$$\frac{dH}{dQ} = \sum_{i=1}^{3} \left(\frac{dH}{dx_i}\right)\left(\frac{dx_i}{dQ}\right) + \sum_{i=1}^{3} \left(\frac{dH}{dz_i}\right)\left(\frac{dz_i}{dQ}\right) \tag{12}$$

The solution algorithm shown in Figure 2 starts with the initial guess of flowrate $Q(t)$. Next, state equations are solved for the interval of t_0 to t_f using forward integration then, the adjoint equations are solved using backward integration. Next, the optimal control variable $Q(t)$ is obtained by finding the extremum of the Hamiltonian at each time step, using the optimality condition of $[|dH/dQ|] <$ tolerance. If the optimality condition is not satisfied, the flowrate $Q(t)$ is updated using the gradient, such that the updated flowrate profile improves the objective function.

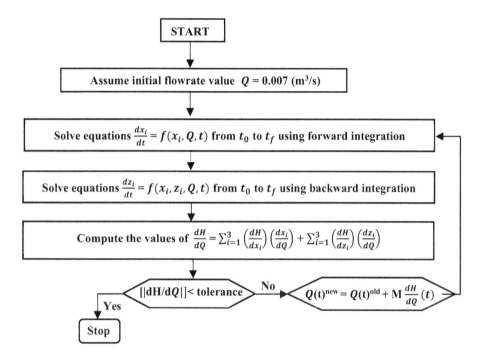

Figure 3. Flowchart of Solution Technique Using Maximum Principle Approach

6.   Results and Discussions

The profiles for the derivative of Hamiltonian with respect to the control variable 'Q' is shown in Figure 4(a). It can be seen that the value of dH/dQ decreases with every iteration. The final iteration value lies within the given tolerance limit hence, we conclude the flowrate to be optimal and the corresponding flowrate profile 'Q (flow)' is shown in Figure 4(b). The variation of the state variables with respect to time is shown in Figure 5. The desired viscosity value for the lube oil B was 8.9 cSt and was attained at approximately 40 s.

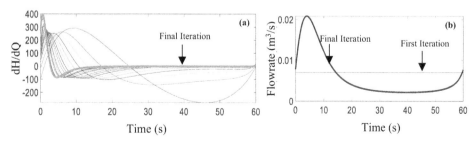

Figure 4. (a) Profiles of Hamiltonian Gradients for All Iterations (b) Profile of Control Variable (Flowrate) for Final Iteration

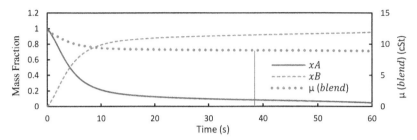

Figure 5. Variation of State Variables $[x_A, x_B, \mu_{AB}]$ with Time

7. Conclusion

In this work, the flushing operation of the lube-oil transportation pipelines was modelled by integrating the Kendall-Monroe mixing rule with component balance equations. Optimal control theory was employed in the form of the Pontryagin's maximum principle for solving the optimal flushing flowrate prediction problem. The results indicated that the optimal flushing time was 40 seconds with a modified flowrate profile. Thus, our solution approach will provide a platform for strategically optimizing the flushing operation in the lube-oil transportation pipelines and will eliminate long operational downtimes, product downgrade, and economic losses.

References

Benavides, Pahola T., and Urmila Diwekar. 2013. "Studying Various Optimal Control Problems in Biodiesel Production in a Batch Reactor under Uncertainty." *Fuel* 103 (January): 585–92. https://doi.org/10.1016/j.fuel.2012.06.089.

Cafaro, Vanina G., Diego C. Cafaro, Carlos A. Méndez, and Jaime Cerdá. 2015. "Optimization Model for the Detailed Scheduling of Multi-Source Pipelines." *Computers & Industrial Engineering* 88 (October): 395–409. https://doi.org/10.1016/j.cie.2015.07.022.

Kendall, James, and Kenneth Potter Monroe. 1917. "The Viscosity of Liquids. II. The Viscosity-Composition Curve for Ideal Liquid Mixtures." *Journal of the American Chemical Society* 39 (9): 1787–1802. https://doi.org/10.1021/ja02254a001.

Roegiers, Michel, and Boris Zhmud. 2011. "Property Blending Relationships for Binary Mixtures of Mineral Oil and Elektrionised Vegetable Oil: Viscosity, Solvent Power, and Seal Compatibility Index." *Lubrication Science* 23 (6): 263–78. https://doi.org/10.1002/ls.154.

Sethi, Suresh P. 2019. *Optimal Control Theory: Applications to Management Science and Economics.* Cham: Springer International Publishing. https://doi.org/10.1007/978-3-319-98237-3.

Yenkie, Kirti M., and Urmila Diwekar. 2012. "Stochastic Optimal Control of Seeded Batch Crystallizer Applying the Ito Process." *Industrial & Engineering Chemistry Research,* June, 120604103933002. https://doi.org/10.1021/ie300491v.

Proceedings of the 14th International Symposium on Process Systems Engineering – PSE 2021+
June 19-23, 2022, Kyoto, Japan © 2022 Elsevier B.V. All rights reserved.
http://dx.doi.org/10.1016/B978-0-323-85159-6.50150-0

Comparison of ammonia synthesis plants of different scale with a dynamic model

Laron Burrows, George Bollas[*]

Department of Chemical & Biomolecular Engineering, University of Connecticut, 191 Auditorium Road, Unit 3222, Storrs, CT 06269, USA.
geroge.bollas@uconn.edu

Abstract

Distributed ammonia production has received a lot of attention as a means of converting stranded fossil resources to a valuable product or for energy storage. However, little attention is given to the potentially problematic pairing of a process sensitive to disturbances with a feedstock variable in rate and composition. The purpose of this work is to explore the stability of a small-scale ammonia production system and thus the viability of distributed ammonia production with processes and chemistries similar to those of large-scale plants. A state-of-the-art large-scale ammonia production system is modelled in Aspen Plus® and converted to a flow driven model in Aspen Dynamics® to serve as a reference model. The reference model is then scaled down to 10% of its original capacity using constant length to diameter ratios for the reactors, and both models are subjected to disturbances in reactor temperature, reactor feed flow rate, and natural gas feed. In the small-scale model, a 5% pulse in the natural gas flow rate is shown to cause 100 °C swings in reactor temperature and 550 kmol/h swings in reactor flow rate, while the reference model remains stable. We conclude with an outlook of the need of decoupled ammonia synthesis pathways that allow for independent control of the extent of reactions and therefore their heat generation or consumption.

Keywords: Distributed Chemical Manufacturing, Ammonia Production, Haber-Bosch

1. Introduction

In recent years, there has been an increasing interest in the concept of using distributed ammonia production systems to convert stranded resources such as wind, biomass, and natural gas into ammonia-based fertilizers for local markets (Arora et al., 2016). Using stranded resources as a feedstock has the advantages of proximity to local markets, low acquisition costs and, in the case of wind, being available in a virtually infinite supply (Allman and Daoutidis, 2016). However, commingled with these advantages are disadvantages of the variable quality, intermittency, and volatility associated with distributed resources. While some chemical manufacturing processes are resilient enough to withstand volatile feedstocks, there is sufficient evidence to suggest that ammonia production processes may not be robust and stable to handle variability and disturbances in the process boundaries (Morud and Skogestad, 1998).

Distributed ammonia production proposals generally attempt to replicate the Haber-Bosch process at small scale, fed by a stranded resource, despite evidence that small changes in the Haber-Bosch process conditions can lead to system failures (Morud and Skogestad, 1998; Gullberg, 2018). Although considerable attention is being given to assessing the economic feasibility (Arora et al., 2016), optimal location (Allman and

Daoutidis, 2016), and coproduction options for distributed ammonia production systems (Andersson and Lundgren, 2014), little is being done to assess the difficulty in pairing of a temperamental process with a sporadic feedstock at a small scale.

Simulations are a powerful tool for assessing the feasibility of a proposed process and are the primary method used to evaluate distributed ammonia production proposals. Ammonia synthesis reactors exhibit multiple steady states and may move between steady states if perturbed (Morud and Skogestad, 1998), thus necessitating the need for dynamic as well as steady state simulations to accurately assess the feasibility of new process concepts. Nevertheless, the literature is a medley of distributed ammonia production proposals done at steady state without regard for process dynamics, stability and robustness to uncertainty. Arora et al. (2016) and Andersson and Lundgren (2014) investigated the techno-economic potential of a distributed ammonia production process fed by biomass at steady state using reactors modelled as Gibbs reactors, without studying the potential for process instabilities. Conversely, Gullberg (2018) studied the instability of a small-scale ammonia reactor in a steady state and dynamic simulation and showed that small changes in reactor feed temperature, pressure, or flow can induce oscillatory behavior and instability. Gullberg's study concluded with a control structure to reduce the oscillatory behavior brought on by process changes; however, the reactor was studied in isolation and the effects of feedstock changes upstream of the reactor were not evaluated. To date, scant attention has been paid to the potential of process instability jeopardizing distributed ammonia production proposals; thus, motivating this study into the effects of feedstock variation on the process stability of a small-scale ammonia production system.

In this study, a state-of-the-art ammonia production system fed by stranded natural gas was modelled in Aspen Plus® with the capacity of 1300 tNH$_3$/d and validated against industrial data to serve as a reference model. The reference model was then scaled down to 130 tNH$_3$/d using standard scaling principles for the reactors and heat exchangers. Both models were then converted to dynamic models in Aspen Dynamics® and subjected to disturbances in reactor feed temperature, reactor feed flow and natural gas flow. The study concludes with a stability comparison at each scale.

2. Methodology

2.1. Model Description

Figure 1 shows the block diagram of the model used in this work segmented into the following three sections: synthesis gas generation, gas purification, and ammonia synthesis. Unit operations in the synthesis gas generation and gas purification sections of the model were adapted from the ammonia plant model (Aspen Technology, 2008) and amine absorber model (Aspen Technology, 2013) included in the Aspen Plus® software examples respectively. The ammonia synthesis model was adapted from Morud and Skogestad (1998) using a kinetic model for a modern catalyst, and a 3-bed adiabatic plug flow reactor system with intermediate quench. The pressure drop across each bed is calculated by the Ergun equation and heat transfer to the catalyst is allowed with a catalyst heat capacity of 1100 J/kg-K and bulk density of 2200 kg/m^3.

The process modelled begins with the combustion of a split stream of natural gas to produce steam and preheat the feed to the primary reformer to 700 °C. The primary reformer is fed with a steam-to-carbon ratio of 3/1 at 2.5 MPa to steam-reform methane and produce hydrogen. The products of the primary reformer are sent to the secondary reformer where air is introduced to combust natural gas in an autothermal reformer design. The products of the secondary reformer are then cooled to 450 °C using the process feed water before entering the water gas shift reactors (high temperature shift, HTS and low temperature shift, LTS). Next, the process gas is fed to the gas purification section, where CO_2 is removed using an amine absorber adapted from the model developed by Aspen Technology (2013). Downstream the absorber, the process gas is passed through the methanator to remove unreacted CO and CO_2 from the process stream and convert it to CH_4 before being compressed to 21 MPa and fed to the ammonia reactor loop at a H_2/N_2 ratio of 3/1 at 250 °C. Finally, the products of the ammonia reactor are cooled to -10 °C to recover ammonia as a liquid product and the unreacted H_2 and N_2 is recycled to the reactor to increase NH_3 yield.

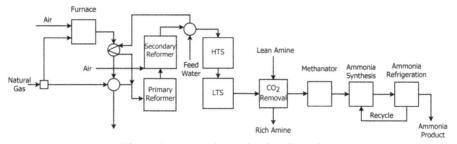

Figure 1. Ammonia production flow sheet.

2.2. Model Validation and Downscaling

The reference model was validated in three steps: first, individual components were validated against literature data; then, the ammonia loop was validated in a dynamic environment; and finally, the full model was validated against data from similar-sized plants. After the reference model was validated, it was scaled down from 1300 tNH_3/d to 130 tNH_3/d using fixed length to diameter ratios for the major reactors. Heat exchangers used in the reference model were scaled to 10 % of their heat exchange area in the small-scale model, and columns were scaled using fixed height to diameter ratios.

2.3. Dynamic Simulations and Disturbance Testing

The steady state reference model and small-scale model were converted to flow driven dynamic models in Aspen Dynamics®. The amine absorbers of each model were replaced with separators of equivalent CO_2 removal efficiency, due to the lack of support for rate-based absorption in Aspen Dynamics®. Additional modifications were made to heat exchangers and valves used in the model according to Aspen Plus® recommendations to improve model robustness.

The following studies were performed on the open-loop of the models in Aspen Dynamics®: (a) Haber-Bosch (HB) reactor stability analysis; (b) and full plant stability analysis. In the HB reactor stability analysis, HB reactors were studied in isolation to explore the effect of size on their stability. Each HB reactor was fed with a feed of H_2, N_2, and NH_3 at a mole fraction of 0.73, 0.23, and 0.04, respectively, at 250 °C and 20.0 MPa. The following disturbances were introduced; (a) a reactor feed temperature pulse of +20 °C and -20 °C for 1h; (b) a reactor feed flow pulse of +23.1 % and -23.1 % for 1 h; and (c) a reactor feed flow noise modelled as a sine wave with amplitude 23.1 % and a period of 30 minutes for 8 h. In the full plant stability analysis, the HB reactor stability was examined in response to a +5 % bump in natural gas flow to the ammonia process.

3. Results and Discussion

3.1. Model Validation

A summary of the model tuning and validation is presented in Table 1, in terms of reactor outlet composition of the primary reformer (PR), the high temperature shift reactor (HTS), the methanator (MTH), and the ammonia reactor (AM) against their respective reference values, marked as Ref. Specifically, the PR outlet was compared to the data of an industrial primary reformer (Tran et al., 2017), the HTS was compared to data by Fabian et al. (2020), the MTH was compared to data by Er-Rbib and Bouallou (2014), and the ammonia reactor outlet was compared with the industrial plant data provided in Appl (2011). Overall, each process component was tuned to be in excellent agreement with literature data.

Table 1: Component validation results.

	CH_4	H_2	CO	CO_2	H_2O		CH_4	H_2	N_2	NH_3	Ar
PR	3.7	45	5.7	7.6	37.6	MTH	13	25	-	-	49.9
Ref	3.8	47	5.7	8.8	34.3	Ref	12	24.8	-	-	50.5
HTS	-	34	7.1	26.9	31.7	AM	5	57	18	19	1
Ref	-	35	6.5	27.4	31.5	Ref	6	56	18	15	2

3.2. Disturbance Testing

The Haber-Bosch (HB) reactors of the reference model and small-scale model were subjected to disturbances in feed temperature and flow rate, and an excerpt of disturbance and response plots is shown in Figure 2. First, the HB reactors were subjected to a -20 °C pulse in reactor feed temperature, which resulted in limit cycle behavior in both models in agreement with the literature (Morud and Skogestad, 1998; Gullberg, 2018) shown in Figure 2(a) and Figure 2(b) for the reference model and small-scale model respectively. After the pulse, the reference model returned to steady state while the small-scale model sustained oscillations of 10 °C for over 30 simulated hours. Next, the HB reactors were subjected to a +20 °C pulse in reactor feed temperature and a -23.1 % reduction in reactor feed flow rate, where no process instabilities were observed in agreement with Gullberg (2018). Thereafter, the HB reactors were subjected to a +23.1 % pulse in reactor feed flow rate, which resulted in reaction extinction in both models, as evident by the rapid drop in reactor outlet temperature shown in Figure 2(c) and Figure 2(d) for the reference model and small-scale model, respectively. The immediate increase in flow rate to the system began to induce the limit cycle behavior shown in Figure 2(c) and Figure 2(d), however the sustained increase in flow rate resulted in a decrease in reactor feed temperature beyond limit cycle to reactor extinction. Lastly, the HB reactors were subjected to a sinusoidal disturbance in feed flow rate, which resulted in sustained oscillations of 7 °C in the reference model and reaction extinction in the small-scale model.

In testing the full plant model at different scales, a +5 % bump in natural gas flow rate resulted in a HB reactor outlet temperature decrease of 10 °C in the reference model, shown in Figure 2(e), and large oscillations in the HB reactor of the small-scale model, shown in Figure 2(f). In response to the +5 % bump in natural gas flow rate, the HB reactor outlet temperature of the small-scale model oscillated within 20-100 °C for over 20 simulated hours, with a corresponding flow rate oscillation between 100-550 kmol/h. The precipitous changes experienced by the small-scale model could plausibly result in system failure similar to those reported by Morud and Skogestad (1998).

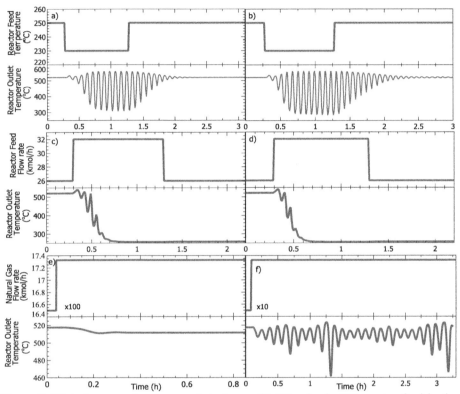

Figure 2. Disturbance and response plots for: a -20 °C pulse in HB reactor feed in the reference model (a), and small-scale model (b); a +23.1 % pulse in HB reactor flow in the reference model (c), and small-scale model (d); and a +5 % bump in natural gas flow to the reference model (e), and small-scale model showing the response in HB reactor outlet

In previous studies, it has been shown that decreasing the HB reactor feed temperature can lead to limit cycle behavior (Morud and Skogestad, 1998), in this study we show that an increase in natural gas flow rate to the production plant can also lead to such behavior, seen in Figure 2(f). Evidently, the behavior shown in Figure 2(f) is also due to a reduction in HB reactor feed temperature. As the stream of higher flow rate enters the preheater of the HB reactor, it exchanges heat with the smaller reactor outlet flow, and is not sufficiently heated to the desired operating temperature. Thereafter, the decreased inlet temperature increases the reaction rate of the forward exothermic reaction, which in turn increases the reactor bed temperature, until the reverse endothermic reaction dominates, and the reactor bed temperature is decreased. As the reactor beds cycle between the forward exothermic reaction and the reverse endothermic reaction of the Haber-Bosch process, the effects are transferred through the reactor by the intermediate quenches and preheater, creating a feedback loop of snowballing effects (Morud and Skogestad, 1998).

Ammonia synthesis reactors operate with a small margin of stability, which this study suggests decreases with system size. To improve ammonia production stability at small scale the following could be explored: (a) a reactor design with no intermediate quenches or heat integration, thus eliminating the ability for snowball effects to permeate through the system at the expense of ammonia yield and potentially economic feasibility; (b) advanced control structures such as those proposed by Gullberg (2018) or Araújo and Skogestad (2008); and (c) a chemical looping reactor (Burrows et al., 2021), to decouple ammonia synthesis and eliminate the potential of the exothermic forward reaction competing with the endothermic reverse reaction.

4. Conclusion

In this study, ammonia production stability was explored at different scales to assess the impact of stranded resource variability on small-scale ammonia production. A state-of-the-art ammonia production process was modelled, scaled down and subjected to disturbances in reactor feed temperature, flow rate and natural gas feed to the process. It was found that the reference model is more robust than the small-scale model, when subjected to the same disturbances. Interestingly, after only a 5% increase in natural gas flow rate, the small-scale model exhibited large oscillations in the ammonia reactor temperature and flow, whereas the reference model remained stable. Future distributed ammonia production work should focus on improving the stability of the ammonia synthesis reactor by: reducing the ability of large oscillations to permeate through the reactor, employing advanced controls, or decoupling the ammonia synthesis reaction using intermediates that assist with N_2 or H_2 fixations, such as those in chemical looping.

References

W. A, Allman, P. Daoutidis, 2016, Ammonia supply chains: A new framework for renewable generation with a case study for Minnesota. Comput. Chem. Eng. 38, 1395-1400.

J. Andersson, J. Lundgren, 2014, Techno-economic analysis of ammonia production via integrated biomass gasification. Appl. Ener. 130, 484-490.

M. Appl, 2011, Ammonia, 2. Prod. Pro. Ull. Enc. Ind. Chem. 2, 2019-211, Dan-Sch, Germany.

A. Araújo, S. Skogestad, 2008, Control structure design for the ammonia synthesis process, Comput. Chem. Eng. 32: 2920-2932.

P. Arora, A. Hoadley, S.M Mahajani, A. Ganesh, 2016, Small-Scale Ammonia Production from Biomass: A Techno-Enviro-Economic Perspective, Ind. Eng. Chem. Res. 55, 6422-6434.

L. Burrows, P. Gao, G.M. Bollas, 2021, Thermodynamic feasibility analysis of distributed chemical looping ammonia synthesis, Chem. Eng. J, 426, 131421.

H. Er-Rbib, C. Bouallou, 2014, Methanation Catalytic Reactor, Comp. R. Chemie. 17 (7): 701–6.

R. Gullberg, 2018, Controllability Analysis of Ammonia Synthesis Loops, Ph.D. Thesis, Norwegian University of Science and Technology, Trondheim, Norway.

J. Morud, S. Skogestad, 1998, Analysis of instability in an industrial ammonia reactor, AIChE J., 44, 888-895.

F. Rosner, A. Rao, S. Samuelsen, 2020, Water gas shift reactor modelling and new dimensionless number for thermal management/design of isothermal reactors, Appl. Ther. Eng. 173: 115033.

Aspen Technology, 2008, Aspen Plus® Ammonia Plant Model, Bedford MA, USA.

Aspen Technology, 2013, Aspen Plus® Rate Based Absorption Model, Bedford MA, USA.

A. Tran, A. Andres, H. Durand, M. Crose, P. D. Christofides, 2017, CFD Modeling of a Industrial-Scale Steam Methane Reforming Furnace, Chem. Eng. Science 171: 576–98.

Proceedings of the 14th International Symposium on Process Systems Engineering – PSE 2021+
June 19-23, 2022, Kyoto, Japan © 2022 Elsevier B.V. All rights reserved.
http://dx.doi.org/10.1016/B978-0-323-85159-6.50151-2

Simulation Analysis of Gas Feed Method for Development of Ru-Based Catalyst for Ammonia Production

Hideyuki Matsumoto[a*], Masashi Kikugawa[b], Anthony Basuni Hamzah[a],
Marie Ishikawa[c], Yoshihiro Goto[b], Shinichi Ookawara[a], Yuichi Manaka[d],
Masayasu Nishi[e], Tetsuya Nanba[d]

[a] Department of Chemical Science Engineering, Tokyo Institute of Technology, Tokyo 152-8550, JAPAN
[b] Toyota Central R&D Laboratories, Aichi 480-1192, JAPAN
[c] Toyota Motor Corporation, Aichi 471-8571, JAPAN
[d] Renewable Energy Research Center, AIST, Fukushima 963-0215, JAPAN
[e] Energy Process Research Institute, AIST, Ibaraki 305-8569, JAPAN
*Corresponding Author's E-mail: matsumoto.h.ae@m.titech.ac.jp

Abstract

In the present study, we investigate a new strategy for design of modular, energy-efficient green ammonia production system, which is equipped with a reactor system utilizing novel Ru-based catalyst and novel heat management. In order to maximize the performance of the reactor, which employs two stages consisting of Fe-based (first stage) and the new Ru-based (second stage) catalysts, we propose a split feed method for main feed gas, of which a portion of the feed gas serves as quench gas at inlet of the second stage. Through sensitivity analysis, we demonstrate that split feed method for nitrogen gas could achieve higher process efficiency than other feed methods.

Keywords: Process Synthesis; Green ammonia; Process simulation; Optimization.

1. Introduction

To realize the net-zero emission of carbon dioxide by 2050, a supply chain of green ammonia (NH_3) needs to be established. A key component of such supply chain would be modularized, decentralized, small- and medium-scale plant for production of NH_3 (10-100 ton-NH_3/day) from renewable-derived hydrogen. It is necessary to overcome some key problems, namely high specific energy consumption, harsh operating condition, and slow response towards rapidly-fluctuating operating parameters. These challenges have to be addressed with development of new catalysts, as well as novel process design tailored to realize their potentials.

Ruthenium (Ru) catalysts have been widely studied and utilized in industrial scale due to its high activity under milder operating temperature (~400 °C) and pressure (<12 MPa). In addition, Ru-based catalysts are considered to be superior to the start-up performance in comparison with conventional iron-based catalysts. On the other hand, hydrogen poisoning has been identified as major obstacle for application of Ru-based catalysts, and therefore various types of catalyst supports have been put forward in the literature. Our research group has developed new Ru/lanthanoid oxide catalysts that performed high NH_3 yield and less hydrogen poisoning under high pressure conditions.

From process system design perspective, unique optimum operating condition window of NH_3 synthesis over such type of catalysts, which includes lower H_2/N_2 ratio (1.0 – 1.5) and temperature (380 – 400 ºC) than that of conventional catalysts, warrants specific attention and eventually new strategy for the intensification of the process. This is achievable by adjusting the gas feed condition, however, relative complexity of the process itself (e.g. unreacted gas recycle and multi-bed configuration of reactors) presents challenge towards its implementation.

In the present study, we introduce and demonstrate a new strategy for design of modular, energy-efficient green NH_3 production system, which utilizes integration of reactor system equipped with novel Ru-based catalyst and internal quench gas feed, as well as novel heat management. To the authors' knowledge, there is a scarcity of publications and studies in regards of gas feed methods specifically designed for the above-mentioned Ru/lanthanoid oxide-type catalysts. Therefore, a purpose of the present contribution is to quantitatively clarify the effect of the gas feed method on the process efficiency for the overall process system using the catalyst by process simulation.

2. Derivation of reaction rate equation for developed Ru-based catalyst

Various reaction rate models based on the Langmuir-Hinshelwood mechanism have been proposed in the previous literature on NH_3 synthesis reactions using Ru-based catalysts (Aika, 2017; Y. Kobayashi et al., 2017). Most reaction rate equation models have been derived assuming that the reaction rate determining step (RDS) is the dissociative adsorption of nitrogen. In addition, various assumptions have been made regarding the adsorption of reaction intermediates on the surface of the catalyst, and it was considered difficult to deductively determine the RDS for Ru/lanthanoid oxide catalysts that we have developed. Therefore, in derivation of the reaction rate equation model for our developed catalyst, RDS is also assumed to be dissociative adsorption of nitrogen. Furthermore, all possible reaction intermediates, namely H*, N*, and nitrogen hydrates groups NH_x*, have to considered for the surface coverage balance.

Table 1 Elementary reactions and reaction rate equations

	Reaction	Rate expression	Eq.
A-1	$N_2(g) + * \leftrightarrow N_2*$	$\theta_{N2*} = k_{A,1}\theta_* P_{N2}$	(1)
A-2	$N_2* + * \leftrightarrow 2N*$	$r = k_{A,2,f}\theta_*\theta_{N2*} - k_{A,2,b}\theta_{N*}^2$	(2)
B-1	$N* + H* \leftrightarrow NH* + *$	$\theta_{NH*} = k_{B,1}'\dfrac{\theta_{N*}\theta_{H*}}{\theta_*}$	(3)
B-2	$NH* + H* \leftrightarrow NH_2* + *$	$\theta_{NH2*} = k_{B,2}'\dfrac{\theta_{NH*}\theta_{H*}}{\theta_*}$	(4)
B-3	$NH_2* + H* \leftrightarrow NH_3* + *$	$\theta_{NH3*} = k_{B,3}'\dfrac{\theta_{NH2*}\theta_{H*}}{\theta_*}$	(5)
B-4	$NH_3* \leftrightarrow NH_3(g) + *$	$\theta_* = k_{B,4}\dfrac{\theta_{NH3*}}{P_{NH3}}$	(6)
C-1	$H_2(g) + 2* \leftrightarrow 2H*$	$\theta_{H*} = \theta_*\sqrt{k_{C,1}'P_{H2}}$	(7)

Table 1 shows the assumed elementary reactions and their respective reaction rate equations in deriving the reaction rate equation model based on the Langmuir-Hinshelwood mechanism. Reactions A-*i*, B-*i* and C-*i* represent the dissociative adsorption of nitrogen, the formation of nitrogen hydrides (NH_x), and the dissociative adsorption of hydrogen, respectively. The balance of the coverage of the reaction intermediate on the catalyst surface species was assumed to be Eq. (8).

$$\theta_{H*} + \theta_{N*} + \theta_{NH*} + \theta_{NH2*} + \theta_{NH2*} + \theta_{NH3*} + \theta_{*} = 1 \tag{8}$$

The reaction rate equation based on the Langmuir-Hinshelwood mechanism, which can be derived from Eqs. (1) - (8), was shown in Eq. (9). The second to sixth terms of the denominator of the Eq. (9) represent the reaction suppression by adsorption of H*, N*, NH*, NH$_2$*, and NH$_3$*, respectively. The Arrhenius-type estimation equations for the forward reaction rate constant k_f and the adsorption constant K_j are Eq. (10) and Eq. (11), respectively.

$$r = \frac{k_f P_{N2} - \left(\dfrac{k_f}{K_{eq}}\right)\dfrac{P_{NH3}{}^2}{P_{H2}{}^3}}{\left(1 + K_{H*}P_{H2}{}^{0.5} + K_{N*}\dfrac{P_{NH3}}{P_{H2}{}^{1.5}} + K_{NH*}\dfrac{P_{NH3}}{P_{H2}{}^{1}} + K_{NH2*}\dfrac{P_{NH3}}{P_{H2}{}^{0.5}} + K_{NH3*}P_{NH3}\right)^2} \tag{9}$$

$$k_f = A_f \, exp\left(\frac{-E_{a,f}}{RT}\right) \tag{10}$$

$$K_j = A_j \, exp\left(\frac{Q_{j,ads}}{RT}\right) \tag{11}$$

By using experimental data for the catalytic activity test, the parameters in Eqs. (9) to (11) based on the isothermal plug flow reactor (PFR) model were estimated. Figure 1 shows the results of parameter estimation. The plots in Figure 1 represent the activity test data, and the solid lines (red and blue) represent the simulation data based on estimated values for the parameters. In the region for operating condition far from the equilibrium concentration (dash line in the figure), an acceptable agreement was seen between the simulation data and the activity test data. Hence, by considering not only H* and N* but also the reaction intermediate NH_x* for the balance of coverage of the reaction intermediate on the surface of the catalyst / support, a reaction rate equation with higher predictive performance could be derived.

The estimated values of parameters in the reaction rate equation model based on the Langmuir-Hinshelwood mechanism were analyzed afterwards. The value of activation energy $E_{a,f}$ in the reaction rate constant of the forward reaction (Eq. (10)) was estimated to be 21.0 kJ/mol. It was found that the $E_{a,f}$ value was slightly lower than the activation energy ($\sim$ 24-50 kJ/mol) of the Ru-based catalyst using an alkali oxide as a carrier reported in the previous literatures (Dahl et al., 2000; Siporin and Davis, 2004). It was considered that the support of lanthanoid oxide exhibited higher degree of electron donation to ruthenium, which resulted in the cleavage of nitrogen triple bonds at lower energy levels.

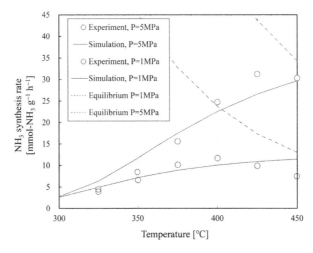

Figure 1 Comparison of experimental data and simulation data of NH_3 synthesis rate for Ru/lanthanoid oxide catalyst (Operating pressure $P = 1$ MPa, 5 MPa; $H_2/N_2 = 3.0$).

The orders of value of the adsorption equilibrium constants of the reaction intermediates calculated from the estimated values of the parameters was as follows.

$K_{NH3*} < K_{NH*} < K_{H*} < K_{NH2*} < K_{N*}$

It was considered that the adsorbed hydrogen H* was certainly an important intermediate for the balance of coverage of absorbed species, since it depended on the partial pressure of hydrogen, which was higher than partial pressure of ammonia under operating conditions.

3. Simulation analysis for application of methods for split feed of gas

Upon obtaining the kinetic rate equation of the synthesis reaction, process simulation of a small-scale NH_3 production system (250 kg-NH_3/h) operating under low pressure conditions (≤ 8 MPa) was carried out to investigate favorable operating conditions, consisting of inlet composition and flow ratio of quench gas (N_2 or H_2). Schematic diagram of the system is seen in Figure 2, which shows the dual-stage reactor configuration. In the present paper, a conventional Fe-based catalyst and the Ru/lanthanoid oxide catalyst developed in the present study were filled in the first stage (hereinafter, "Bed 1") and the second stage (hereinafter, "Bed 2") of the reactor, respectively. In addition, heat integration of the entire system was investigated. An in-situ heat removal system was adopted for both of two stages in the reactor, and a system of heat exchange of the reactor inlet gas with reactor outlet gas and recycled gas was also applied in this simulation.

The inlet temperature of the Bed 1 of the reactor was set at 673 K (400 °C). A quench flow (573 K) of N_2 or H_2 between Bed 1 and 2 was added not only to shift the Bed 2 inlet composition to favorable ratio, but also to decrease the Bed 1 outflow to favorable temperature of 673 K. Variable parameters in this process simulation include the

composition (H_2/N_2 ratio) and ratio of flow rate of quench gas to the main feed. The
system performances were evaluated by using two indices: process efficiency ($\eta_{process}$)
and specific energy consumption (SEC).

$$SEC = \frac{System\ energy\ consumption}{NH_3\ production} \tag{12}$$

$$\eta_{process} = \frac{Q_{NH_3\ combustion}}{Q_{H_2\ combustion} + energy\ consumption} \times 100 \tag{13}$$

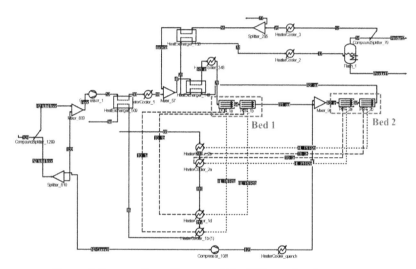

Figure 2 Process flow diagram of the NH_3 production system

Figures 3 and 4 show results of sensitivity analysis of composition of the main feed gas
and the flow ratio of quench gas to the main feed with respect to the process efficiency
and the SEC. It was seen that process operation with high H_2/N_2 ratio of ~2.75 at the
inlet of Bed 2 adjusted by H_2 (or N_2) quench with medium rate (50% of total feed of H_2
or N_2) was preferable. Interestingly, when the H_2/N_2 ratio of the main feed was constant,
change in values for the above evaluation indices with respect to the operating
conditions for quenching (gas type and feed ratio) was extremely small. Through the
process simulations, the optimum performance of the evaluated process was ~61% and
~ 7500 kJ / kg-NH_3 for process efficiency and SEC, respectively.

In addition, the ratio of each energy consumption of the reactor, separator, etc. to that of
the entire system was calculated for each case using split quench gas of hydrogen and
nitrogen. The proportion of energy consumption associated with the separation of NH_3
and the recycling of separated gas was also seen to be significant, and thus it is
considered that reduction of the energy consumption for NH_3 separation / recovery unit
will continue to be an important issue, which will be subject in further study.

4. Conclusions

A novel small-scale green ammonia synthesis process system design was proposed
herein, which employs dual-stage reactor with Fe- and newly-developed Ru/lanthanoid

oxide catalysts and split feed method. For the development of the process system model, the reaction rate equation for ammonia synthesis over the novel Ru catalyst was derived based on the activity test data collected under realistic operating pressure conditions. To optimize the system performance, we proposed a split feed method for main feed gas to utilize as quench gas at inlet of Bed 2. Through sensitivity analysis by process simulation, it was demonstrated that the split feed method for nitrogen gas could achieve higher process efficiency than other feed methods.

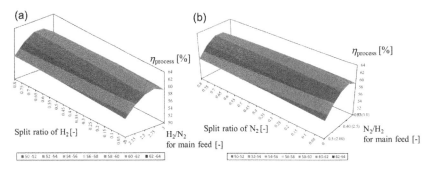

Figure 3 Sensitivity analysis of operating conditions to the process efficiency; (a) H_2 and (b) N_2 quench

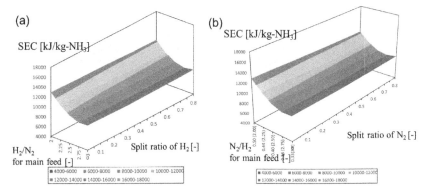

Figure 4 Sensitivity analysis of operating conditions to the SEC; (a) H_2 and (b) N_2 quench

References

K. Aika, 2017, Role of alkali promoter in ammonia synthesis over rutheniumcatalysts—Effect on reaction mechanism, Catalysis Today, **286**, 14–20.

S. Dahl et al., 2000, Surface science based microkinetic analysis of ammonia synthesis over ruthenium catalysts, Journal of Catalysis, **192**(2), 391-399.

Y. Kobayashi et al., 2017, Kinetic evidence: the rate-determining step forammonia synthesis over electride-supported Rucatalysts is no longer the nitrogen dissociation step, Catal. Sci. Technol., **7**, 47–50.

S.E. Siporin and R.J. Davis, 2004, Use of kinetic models to explore the role of base promoters on Ru/MgO ammonia synthesis catalysts, Journal of Catalysis, **225**(2), 359-368.

Proceedings of the 14th International Symposium on Process Systems Engineering – PSE 2021+
June 19-23, 2022, Kyoto, Japan © 2022 Elsevier B.V. All rights reserved.
http://dx.doi.org/10.1016/B978-0-323-85159-6.50152-4

Estimation of the effect of liquid viscosity on gas-liquid mass transfer in a bioreactor using CFD-PBM coupled model

Young Seok Bak[a] and Jong Min Lee[a*]

[a]*School of Chemical and Biological Engineering, Seoul National University, 1 Gwanak-ro, Gwanak-gu, Seoul 08826, KOREA*
jongmin@snu.ac.kr

Abstract

Stirred tanks are widely used as aerated fermenters for cell cultivation. Mass transfer inside the bioreactor is important for reactor control and design, as it directly affects productivity. Even if mixing and aeration are considered sufficient, insufficient local oxygen mass transfer may occur due to the highly inhomogeneous nature of reactor hydrodynamics. Furthermore, it is well known that the increase in viscosity greatly reduces the amount of oxygen mass transfer, which is inevitable as cell cultivation progresses. In order to analyze the effect of viscosity on mass transfer of bioreactor , this work proposes a modeling and computational framework that combines CFD (Computational Fluid Dynamics) and PBM (Population Balance Model). A 6-blade Rushton tank was selected as the target system, and the model was validated with the measurement results at the nominal water-viscosity, 1cp. Then, the change in mass transfer rate was analyzed. As the viscosity increases, the mass transfer rate gradually decreases, and the level of decrease was consistent with the empirical correlations.

Keywords: Bioreactor, Computational fluid dynamics, Population balance model, Gas-liquid mass transfer, Liquid viscosity

1. Introduction

Control and design of bioreactors aim to maximize productivity by creating an optimized environment for cell cultivation. However, due to the lack of understanding of reactor hydrodynamics, maintaining an optimal environment for bioreactors with various scales remains a challenging task.

Oxygen is one of the most important materials required by cells. However, the inhomogeneous nature of the hydrodynamics of the stirred tank bioreactor creates the regions with locally deficient oxygen supply. Traditionally, the mass transfer rate between gas and liquid has been estimated from the interfacial area and mass transfer coefficient. Since these two factors are influenced not only by the hydrodynamics of the continuous phase, the liquid, but also by the dynamics of the disperse phase, the bubble, a comprehensive simulation of both phases is required. Using the population balance model (PBM), it is possible to describe the bubble dynamics such as coalescence and breakage.

In this study, an integrated model framework consisting of both CFD and PBM is suggested to reliably predict the oxygen mass transfer rate inside the bioreactor. As a 6-blade Rushton turbine tank system was targeted, the model was validated through measurement results using the viscosity of water. Then, the change in oxygen mass transfer rate was further analyzed by increasing the viscosity tenfold.

2. Methodology

The Eulerian-Eulerian approach was employed for multiphase simulation. Only the drag force was considered as the interactive force between the gas and liquid phases. In order to reflect the drag change due to the non-spherical shape of bubbles, the Ishii-Zuber model was employed. In addition, to reflect the dense dispersion of bubbles and the bubble cavity formed after the impeller, Behzadi correlation-based drag coefficient modification was included. The final drag model is given by

$$C_{D,modified} = \begin{cases} C_{D,IZ} \left(e^{3.64\alpha_g + \alpha_g^{0.864}} \right) & 0 < \alpha_g \leq 0.6 \\ C_{D,IZ}(-62.5815\alpha_g + 51.0651) & 0.6 < \alpha_g < 0.8 \\ C_{D,IZ} & 0.8 \leq \alpha_g < 1 \end{cases} \tag{1}$$

$$C_{D,IZ} = \max \left\{ \min \left(\frac{24}{Re} (1 + 0.15Re^{0.687}), \frac{72}{Re} \right), \frac{8}{3} \frac{Eo}{Eo+4} \right\} \tag{2}$$

, where α_g is the gas volume fraction, and E is the Eotvos number. The SST $k - \omega$ model, one of the Reynolds averaging Navier-Stokes approaches, was employed for the turbulence model.

 Population balance equation (PBE) was used to simulate the bubble coalescence and breakage. In this study, a quadratic method of moments (QMOM) based approximation was employed to solve the equation. The number of ODEs in the PBM was determined by the number of tracked moments and the number of bins. For the gas-liquid systems, such as bubble columns or stirred tanks, three nodes and 6-moments equations are widely selected as an option to guarantee both accuracy and stability. The equations of PBE and QMOM are

$$\frac{\partial n(L;\mathbf{x},t)}{\partial t} + \nabla \cdot [\vec{u}n(L;\mathbf{x},t)] = \\ B_{ag}(L;\mathbf{x},t) - D_{ag}(L;\mathbf{x},t) + B_{br}(L;\mathbf{x},t) - D_{br}(L;\mathbf{x},t) \tag{3}$$

$$\frac{\partial m_k}{\partial t} + \nabla \cdot [\vec{u}m_k] = \overline{S_{m_k}} \tag{4}$$

$$m_k = \int_0^\infty n(L)L^k dL \approx \sum_{i=1}^{N=3} w_i L_i^k \tag{5}$$

$$\overline{S_{m_k}} = \frac{1}{2} \sum_{i=1}^{N=3} w_i \sum_{j=1}^{N=3} w_j h_{ij} \left[(L_i^3 + L_j^3)^{\frac{k}{3}} - L_i^k - L_j^k \right] + \sum_{i=1}^{N=3} w_i g_i (\overline{b}_i^k - L_i^k) \tag{6}$$

$n(L; \mathbf{x}, t)$ is a function of property and m represents the moments of property function. g_{ij} and h_{ij} are called kernels and have different forms depending on physical phenomena. The above equation assumes QMOM with three nodes.

Since QMOM employs approximation using moments and nodes, it is necessary to transform the source term, which reflects the physical phenomenon, into the moment space. Because the problem must be closed in the moment space, the source term has a rather complicated form. In this study, the kernels for bubble coalescence and breakage phenomena are given by

$$
\begin{aligned}
&h(L_1, L_2) \\
&= C_1(L_1 + L_2)^2 \epsilon^{\frac{1}{3}} \sqrt{L_1^{2/3} + L_2^{2/3}} \exp\left(-C_2 \frac{\mu_l \rho_l \epsilon}{\sigma^2}\left(\frac{L_1 L_2}{L_1 + L_2}\right)^4\right)
\end{aligned}
\tag{7}
$$

$$
g(L) = C_3 \epsilon^{\frac{1}{3}} \mathrm{erfc}\left(\sqrt{C_4 \frac{\sigma}{\rho_L \epsilon^{\frac{2}{3}} L^{\frac{5}{3}}} + C_5 \frac{\mu_l}{\sqrt{\rho_L \rho_G} \epsilon^{\frac{1}{3}} L^{\frac{4}{3}}}}\right)
\tag{8}
$$

$$
\beta(L, \lambda) = 180\left(\frac{L^2}{\lambda^3}\right)\left(\frac{L^3}{\lambda^3}\right)^2\left(1 - \frac{L^3}{\lambda^3}\right)^2
\tag{9}
$$

, where h is the coalescence kernel, g is the breakage kernel, and β is the daughter bubble size distribution. The kernel of Prince and Blanch with the collision efficiency of Coulalglou and Tavlarides was employed for the coalescence kernel, and the kernel of Laakkonen was employed for breakage and daughter bubble size distribution. The built-in QMOM framework in Fluent® was used, and other optional kernels and drag models were implemented via the user-defined macros in Fluent®.

The volumetric mass transfer rate was calculated as the product of the mass transfer coefficient K_L and the interfacial area a. In this study, the interfacial area was directly obtained from the CFD simulation results, and the mass transfer coefficient was estimated by the slip velocity model:

$$
a = a_{Sauter} * R
\tag{10}
$$

$$
a_{Sauter} = \sum_i \pi d_{b,i}^2 n_i \approx \frac{6a_g}{d_{32}}
\tag{11}
$$

$$
R = 1 + 0.163 E_o^{0.757}
\tag{12}
$$

$$
k_L = \frac{2}{\sqrt{\pi}}\sqrt{\frac{D_L v_b}{d_b}}
\tag{13}
$$

where a_{Sauter} is the interfacial area calculated from the Sauter mean diameter, and R is the aspect ratio of bubbles with ellipsoidal shape. D_L is the diffusivity of oxygen in water, and v_b is the slip velocity.

3. Numerical strategy

A 6-blade Rushton turbine tank with a ring sparger was selected as the target system. The geometry of Laakkonen was referenced, and the thickness of blades and baffles was set to 4mm, which is similar to that of the actual Rushton tank. The multiple reference frame (MRF) method was employed to model the impeller movement. A Green-Gauss node-based formulation was used for calculating gradients, QUICK scheme for the momentum equations, PRESTO! scheme for the pressure balance equation, and the 1st order upwind scheme was used for all other equations. The pressure outlet was used for the outlet boundary condition. A grid sensitivity study was conducted using 4 fully structured hexagonal meshes of 419k, 666k, 729k and 930k elements, and the 666k elements mesh was finally selected. The shape of grid is shown in Figure 2.

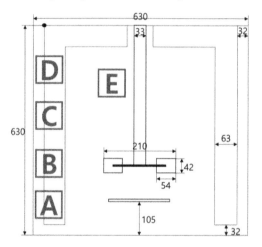

Figure 1 Schematic figure of a 6-blade Rushton tank with a ring sparger. The alphabets indicate where Laakkonen measured the diameter of bubbles. Model validation was performed through comparison with the measurement results.

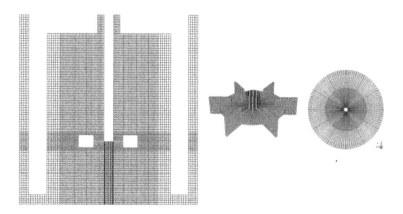

Figure 2 Structure of grid with 666k hexagonal elements. From left, front view, rotor view, and top view

4. Results and discussion

4.1. Model validation

The overall gas hold-up was 4.35%, which is in fairly good agreement with the measured value of 6%. The power number was 2.2, estimated from the turbulent dissipation rate. Although the typical power number of a Rushton tank is about 5, it is widely known that the estimation of power number from the turbulent dissipation rate leads to underestimated values. Moreover, previous studies also obtained power number ranging 1 to 2. Since the power number is used as an indicator for judging whether an appropriate level of turbulence was simulated in this work, the above power number is acceptable for this study. Figure 3 shows the contours of bubble sauter mean within the reactor.

The reactor-volume-average $K_L a$ was 0.0465, which showed good agreement with the measurement. The local bubble size results achieved an error of less than 15% with experimental measurements at all the measured points, which is an improvement over previous studies. Figure 4 shows the results of a local bubble size comparison.

4.2. Effect of liquid viscosity on oxygen mass transfer
From nominal water-viscosity, the change in oxygen mass transfer was analyzed by increasing the viscosity of liquid up to ten times. At 10 cp, it was estimated that only 28% of the oxygen transfer in nominal water was delivered. The rate of oxygen mass transfer in the reactor was found to be inversely proportional to the viscosity power of 0.653, and the R square value was 0.933. These results are consistent with the empirical correlations widely used. Figure 5 below shows the change of oxygen mass transfer with increasing viscosity.

5. Conclusions

This work showed that the CFD-PBM model can reflect the heterogeneous hydrodynamics of a 200L bioreactor including baffles, rotors, and sparger. The results of local bubble size distribution and overall gas volume fraction are consistent with the measurement results. In addition, the volume-averaged oxygen mass transfer rate was predicted to decrease by 28%, and a relationship between viscosity and oxygen mass transfer was estimated to be inversely proportional to the 0.653 power.

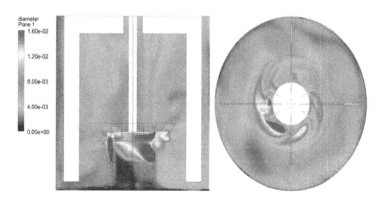

Figure 3 Contour of bubble diameter (1cp Case)

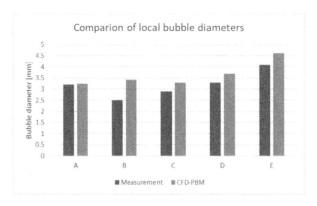

Figure 4 Comparison of local bubble diameters of 5 points

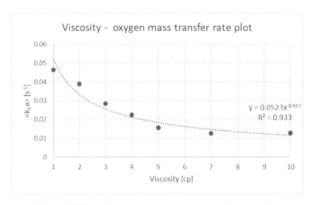

Figure 5 Viscosity and oxygen mass transfer rate plot

Acknowledgements

This paper was supported by Korea Institute for Advancement of Technology(KIAT) grant funded by the Korea Government(MOTIE) (P0008475, The Competency Development Program for Industry Specialist)

References

Y.S. Bak, and J. M. Lee, "Integration of Population Balance Model with Computational Fluid Dynamics for Estimation of Oxygen Mass Transfer Rate in Bioreactor", Mater's Thesis, https://www.dcollection.net/handler/snu/000000167087

A. Behzadi, R. Issa, and H. Rusche, "Modelling of dispersed bubble and droplet flow at high phase fractions," *Chemical Engineering Science,* vol. 59, no. 4, pp. 759-770, 2004.

J. Gimbun, C. D. Rielly, and Z. K. Nagy, "Modelling of mass transfer in gas–liquid stirred tanks agitated by Rushton turbine and CD-6 impeller: A scale-up study," *Chemical Engineering Research and Design,* vol. 87, no. 4, pp. 437-451, 2009.

M. Laakkonen, P. Moilanen, V. Alopaeus, and J. Aittamaa, "Modelling local bubble size distributions in agitated vessels," *Chemical Engineering Science,* vol. 62, no. 3, pp. 721-740, 2007.

M. J. Prince and H. W. Blanch, "Bubble coalescence and break-up in air-sparged bubble columns," *AIChE Journal,* vol. 36, no. 10, pp. 1485-1499, 1990.

Proceedings of the 14th International Symposium on Process Systems Engineering – PSE 2021+
June 19-23, 2022, Kyoto, Japan © 2022 Elsevier B.V. All rights reserved.
http://dx.doi.org/10.1016/B978-0-323-85159-6.50153-6

Knowledge-matching based computational framework for genome-scale metabolic model refinement

Kiumars Badr, Q. Peter He and Jin Wang*

Department of Chemical Engineering, Auburn University, Auburn, AL, 36849, USA
Corresponding Author's E-mail: wang@auburn.edu

Abstract

Genome-scale metabolic models (GEMs) are mathematically structured knowledge base reconstructed from annotated genome of different organisms. With the advancement of next-generation sequencing technology, many organisms have had their genomes sequenced. However, obtaining a high-quality GEM is highly time-consuming, even with the introduction of several genome-scale reconstruction tools that offer automated draft network generation and gap filling. It has been recognized that the iterative process of manual curation and refinement is the limiting step of GEM development, and how to expedite the GEM refinement is still an open question. As cellular metabolism is a complex system with very high degree of freedom and redundancy, the principles and techniques developed in process systems engineering can be adapted to expedite GEM refinement. In this work we present a knowledge-matching based computation framework for GEM refinement, and demonstrate the effectiveness of the proposed solution using the refinement of a GEM for *Clostridium tyrobutyricum* .

Keywords: Genome-scale metabolic model; manual curation; system identification; multivariate analysis; visualization.

1. Introduction

A genome-scale metabolic model (GEM) is a mathematically structured knowledge base that is reconstructed from annotated genome of an organism (King et al., 2016)). A GEM contains a list of biochemical reactions, metabolites and (annotated) genes involved in the cellular metabolism for a specific organism, as well as a set of biophysical constraints (e.g., nutrient uptake and substrate availabilities, etc.). A high-quality GEM can be used to conduct simulations to answer various questions about the capabilities of the organism, serve as a framework to integrate and interpret omics data collected through experiments, and guide the design of mutant for metabolic engineering, etc.

The GEM reconstruction process generally consists of the following steps (Thiele and Palsson, 2010): (1) a draft network is reconstructed based on the annotation of a genome and the prediction of candidate metabolic functions; (2) the draft reconstruction is refined or curated by the user in an iterative manner through an exhaustive review of each reaction, metabolite and gene in the network; (3) the reconstruction is transformed into a mathematical structure, with an objective function and a set of constraints to account for different culture conditions. With the mathematical representation, the resulting GEM can be evaluated by reproducing the experimental data. If the GEM predictions do not match the experimental data, the manual refinement process will be repeated till the quality of the GEM is satisfactory.

It has been recognized that the iterative process of manual curation and refinement is the limiting step of GEM development (Mendoza et al., 2019)). To expedite the development process, several genome-scale reconstruction tools that offer automated draft network generation and gap filling have been reported. However, a systematic assessment of seven GEM reconstruction tools (Mendoza et al., 2019)) concluded that none of the tools performed well in all of the evaluated categories, and there was a relatively large discrepancy between the automatic reconstruction and the high-quality manual curation. Therefore, it is no surprise that the currently validated high-quality GEMs collected in BiGG Models are all manually curated (King et al., 2016)).

For GEM refinement, one big challenge is to quickly identify the root cause of an erroneous model prediction. Because of the complex interconnectivity in the GEM, many times seemingly unrelated reactions located far away from the "problematic" reactions (i.e., reactions that are not carried out in the expected way) play a key role in correcting the model behavior. Directly comparing the model prediction with experimental data usually yields limited information on the "hidden" relations between the erroneous model prediction and its corresponding root cause reactions. Currently, GEM refinement relies heavily on the modeler's knowledge and capability to sort out clues from various simulation results, and is labor intensive and time consuming.

As cellular metabolism is a complex system with very high degree of freedom and redundancy, we hypothesize that the principles and techniques developed in process systems engineering can be adapted to address some of the challenges associated with GEM refinement. In this work, we first review the foundation of the proposed solution, i.e., a knowledge-matching based computational framework for GEM analysis, then we present the developed GEM refinement approach, and demonstrate the effectiveness of the proposed solution using the development of a GEM for *C. tyrobutyricum*.

2. Knowledge-matching based framework for GEM analysis

In essence, a high-quality GEM is a comprehensive knowledge base of the organism's cellular metabolism. If the key qualitative knowledge captured by a GEM could be extracted and visualized, then GEM refinement could be expedited through knowledge-matching, i.e., by comparing the extracted knowledge with the available ones. The knowledge captured by a GEM is usually embedded in numerical model predictions under various environmental perturbations (e.g., culture media and conditions) and/or genetic perturbations (e.g., mutant), which are difficult to extract and visualize.

To address this challenge, we have developed a system identification (SID) based computational framework for knowledge-matching based GEM analysis (Damiani et al., 2015). In the SID framework, three main steps are involved for GEM analysis, as shown in Figure 1a. First, a set of *in silico* experiments are designed to cover the whole transition path between two metabolic states, where each simulation represents an incremental change along the path. The experiments represent a one-dimensional perturbation to the cellular metabolism and result in a flux matrix containing a series of cellular metabolic states along the transition path; next, system identification tools (such as principal component analysis or PCA) are applied to extract the knowledge contained in the flux matrix (e.g., how the cells respond to the perturbation); finally, the extracted knowledge is visualized against the metabolic network map and compared with the existing knowledge for GEM analysis. Here we use an illustrate example (Figure 1b) to demonstrate how the SID-based GEM analysis works.

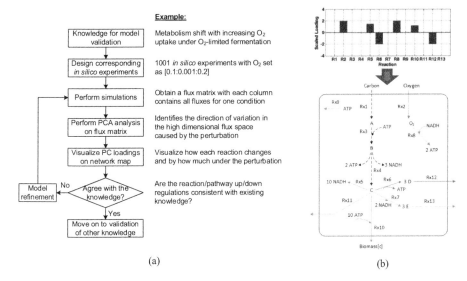

(a)

(b)

Fig. 1 (a) Illustrated flow chart of the SID-based GEM analysis; (b) an example showing the loadings (top) and their visualization on a simulated network (bottom).

As shown in the bottom part of the Figure 1b, the illustrative example is a toy metabolic network with 13 reactions, which consumes both carbon and oxygen to produce biomass and three potential by-products (C, D and E). To determine if the model correctly captures the metabolic capabilities of the network, we examine if the knowledge captured by the model on how the network respond to an increased O_2 supply under oxygen-limited condition is correct. This response is well understood and well conserved among different microbes, and we expect to see increased flux through electron transport chain due to the availability of additional O_2 (electron acceptor) and increased biomass growth. To do so, we conducted a set of *in silico* experiments, where the carbon uptake was fixed, while the upper limit of O_2 uptake was gradually increased from 0.1 to 0.2 mmol/gDCW/min. These simulations resulted in a 13×1001 flux matrix where each column contains all fluxes within the network under a given O_2 uptake flux. Next, PCA, which we have applied in a novel closed-loop subspace identification algorithm (Wang and Qin, 2006), is applied to extract the knowledge contained in the flux matrix. Due to the linear network structure and one-dimensional perturbation, one principal component (PC) is expected to capture 100% of variation in the flux matrix provided that the whole transition path is located within the same phenotype. Indeed, our result showed that one PC captured 100% of variation. The PC loading captures the knowledge of how the perturbation propagates through the network, i.e., how each reaction flux in the network is affected by the perturbation. The scaled loading is plotted in Figure 1b (top part) and visualized on the network structure in Figure 1b (bottom part). Figure 1b shows that with increasing oxygen supply, the carbon flux in the network shifts from production of by-product D toward biomass production, together with upregulated electron transport chain which converts reducing power (NADH) to produce ATP. This model response agrees with existing understanding as described before, and confirms the model quality. This example further illustrates that although rooted in numerical simulations, the knowledge-matching offered by the SID-based framework is qualitative in nature, which offers enhanced robustness against systematic error among experimental results reported in different literature.

3. SID-based GEM refinement

To identify the root cause of an erroneous model prediction, we adapt the SID-based framework to identify a few candidates which drastically narrows the search space for the potential root causes. The SID-guided GEM refinement process consists of three steps: (1) conducting a set of *in silico* experiments with forced correct model behaviors by applying additional hard constraints; (2) applying PCA to determine how each reaction is affected by the forced correct behavior; (3) identify the candidate root cause reactions – we hypothesize that the reactions affected the most by the forced model behavior are the potential root cause reactions that contribute to the erroneous model behavior. Once the candidate reactions are identified, they will be examined against existing knowledge to see if any of them is the actual root cause. Below we use the development of a GEM for *C. tyrobutyricum* as an example to illustrate how the SID-guided GEM refinement works.

C. tyrobutyricum is a novel and promising industrial chassis strain that plays an important role in carboxylic acids production from lignocellulosic substrates. Since a GEM for *C. tyrobutyricum* is currently not available, we first developed a draft GEM based on a published GEM for *C. beijerinckii*, iCM925 (Milne et al., 2011). Genome analysis revealed that *C. tyrobutyricum* does not use phosphotransbutyrylase nor butyrate kinase for butyric acid production; instead, it uses a CoA transferase to mediate the butyric acid production from butyryl-CoA by reassimilation of acetic acid (Lee et al., 2016). Therefore, the corresponding reaction pathways were deleted from or added to iCM925 to obtain the draft GEM for *C. tyrobutyricum* (iKB917).

Experimental results showed that when cultivated on glucose, *C. tyrobutyricum* excretes butyrate, acetate, hydrogen and carbon dioxide, in addition to cell growth (Lee et al., 2016). However, when the draft GEM was tested by using the experimentally reported glucose uptake rate as the only constraint to predict cell growth and product excretion, the model does not produce butyrate at all, but over-produces acetate, hydrogen and biomass, while under-produces CO_2 (Table 1). Since the draft GEM contains 939 reactions, it is not clear which reaction pathway(s) could be the causes for this erroneous modeling behavior and should be modified. To improve the GEM, we applied the SID-based GEM refinement, as shown in Figure 2.

Table 1. Comparison of measured data with predicted data by the GEM

No.	Condition	Glucose	Acetate	Butyrate	H_2	CO_2	Biomass
1	Experimental measurement	-2.594	0.717	1.895	4.75	4.34	0.052
2	Draft GEM prediction	-2.594	4.223	0	7.96	4.17	0.074
3	Refined GEM prediction	-2.594	0.823	1.834	4.81	4.45	0.053

(1) To force the correct model behavior, i.e., butyrate production, we added a hard constraint to force butyrate production flux gradually increased from 0 to 1.0 mmol/gDCW/min, to produce a flux matrix of 939×1001.

(2) PCA was applied to analyze the flux matrix, and the PC loadings of selected reactions are plotted in Fig. 2 (bottom plot). Clearly, the affected reactions were widespread across multiple pathways. However, the reactions that were affected the most are concentrated in two reaction pathways, i.e., H_2 and H_2O syntheses.

(3) Additional review of literature suggests that due to physiological constraints, the amount of H_2 and CO_2 produced by the cells are proportional to each other (Jo and

Kim, 2016). Since the GEM does not contain any regulatory mechanism, it over produces H_2. To correct this erroneous behavior, we implemented a soft constraint on the ratio of H_2/CO_2 production. Such a soft constraint could provide similar effects as regulatory mechanisms without adding hard constraints, therefore provides more flexibility for the GEM to simulate different phenotypes under different conditions.

(4) The refined GEM (with the added soft constraint) was tested again, which showed significantly improved prediction accuracy (low row of Table 1). The refined GEM not only predicts the excretion of butyrate, but also predicts the excretion of all the byproducts whose fluxes showed excellent agreement with experimental results.

This example highlights the challenge of GEM refinement and effectiveness of the SID-guided refinement. Without the guidance of the SID framework, it can take much longer to figure out what would be the root cause of the erroneous model behavior.

4. Conclusions

GEM has been recognized as a highly effective tool to elucidate the complex cellular metabolisms. It offers a foundation to integrate various omics data, and helps reveal genotype-phenotype relationships, which is fundamental to biology. Despite the recent advancement in automated GEM draft reconstruction and gap filling, manual curation and refinement of GEM remains the limiting step in GEM development. To help address this challenge, we developed a knowledge-matching based computational framework to expedite the GEM refinement. By adapting the principles and techniques in process systems engineering, the proposed SID-guided GEM refinement can quickly identify the "hidden" root cause for the erroneous modeling behavior, therefore significantly expedite the GEM refinement process. The effectiveness of the SID-guided GEM refinement framework is demonstrated through improving a draft GEM of *C. tyrobutyricum*.

References

Damiani, A.L., He, Q.P., Jeffries, T.W., Wang, J., 2015. Comprehensive evaluation of two genome-scale metabolic network models for Scheffersomyces stipitis. Biotechnology and Bioengineering 112, 1250–1262.

Jo, J.H., Kim, W., 2016. Carbon material distribution and flux analysis under varying glucose concentrations in hydrogen-producing Clostridium tyrobutyricum JM1. Journal of Biotechnology 228, 103–111.

King, Z.A., Lu, J., Dräger, A., Miller, P., Federowicz, S., Lerman, J.A., Ebrahim, A., Palsson, B.O., Lewis, N.E., 2016. BiGG Models: A platform for integrating, standardizing and sharing genome-scale models. Nucleic Acids Research 44, D515.

Lee, J., Jang, Y.-S., Han, M.-J., Kim, J.Y., Lee, S.Y., 2016. Deciphering Clostridium tyrobutyricum Metabolism Based on the Whole-Genome Sequence and Proteome Analyses. mBio 7, e00743--16.

Mendoza, S.N., Olivier, B.G., Molenaar, D., Teusink, B., 2019. A systematic assessment of current genome-scale metabolic reconstruction tools. Genome Biology 2019 20:1 20, 1–20.

Milne, C.B., Eddy, J.A., Raju, R., Ardekani, S., Kim, P.-J., Senger, R.S., Jin, Y.-S., Blaschek, H.P., Price, N.D., 2011. Metabolic network reconstruction and genome-scale model of butanol-producing strain Clostridium beijerinckii NCIMB 8052. BMC Syst Biol 5, 130.

Thiele, I., Palsson, B.Ø., 2010. A protocol for generating a high-quality genome-scale metabolic reconstruction. Nature Protocols 2010 5:1 5, 93–121.

Wang, J., Qin, S.J., 2006. Closed-loop subspace identification using the parity space. Automatica 42, 315–320.

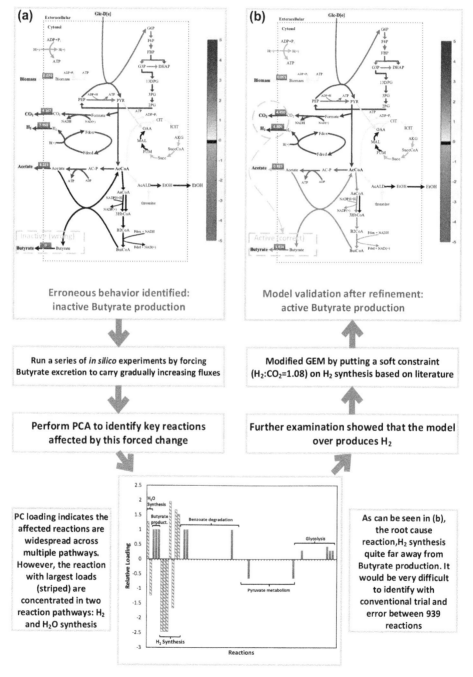

Figure 2. Demonstration of the SID based framework for GEM refinement

Proceedings of the 14th International Symposium on Process Systems Engineering – PSE 2021+
June 19-23, 2022, Kyoto, Japan © 2022 Elsevier B.V. All rights reserved.
http://dx.doi.org/10.1016/B978-0-323-85159-6.50154-8

Multi-Regional Surrogate Model Selection (MRSMS) approach for the analysis and optimal fitting of univariate responses

Srikar V Srinivas[a], and I.A.Karimi[a*]

[a]*Department of Chemical & Biomolecular Engineering, National University of Singapore, 4 Engineering Drive, 117585 Singapore*
cheiak@nus.edu.sg

Abstract

This study focuses on the development of a Multi-Regional Surrogate Model Selection (MRSMS) approach for the optimal fitting and analysis of univariate responses. Using a library of simple curve fitting and regression models, the proposed approach can be used to provide surrogate model recommendations at each section of the response based on the user specified selection of the residual error metric and its corresponding data fit range. The efficacy of the proposed approach is validated using the Henry Hub Natural Gas price dataset and its fitting performance is compared with Piecewise Linear (PL), Neural Network (NN) and Support Vector Regression (SVR) models. It was found that proposed MRSMS approach outperformed the fitting performance of the considered models.

Keywords: Surrogate Model; Optimal Data Fitting; Univariate Responses, Piecewise Linear Model

1. INTRODUCTION

The idea of employing simple and less complex surrogates (or) surrogate models in estimating a functional relationship of a complex chemical phenomenon has gained traction in the research community over the last few decades. Surrogate models, also known as meta-models (or) response surfaces, are used to accurately mimic the relationship between the inputs and outputs of a system (McBride and Sundmacher (2019)).

The selection of a surrogate model for a particular system (or) phenomenon is an extremely challenging task. Although there is no consensus or clear-cut mantra to select a particular model, the existing popular custom in surrogate-based modelling of complex phenomena is to fit one (or) more surrogate models and select the best fitting model (based on an error metric) over an entire data response.

Several studies have aimed at finding the best surrogate model for a particular dataset. While some research works were heavily reliant on the trial-and-error approach of trying one model after another on a dataset and then comparing its performance with its fellow member models (Williams and Cremaschi (2020)); other research works have focused on the development of ensemble model approaches, where the individual member models are combined to form a weighted ensemble through some optimization framework (Goel et.al (2007)). In recent times, the concept of meta-learning has gained traction, where the best surrogate model can be selected through an automated platform utilizing an exhaustive library of models, error metrics, rules, and datasets. Cozad et al. (2014) developed the ALAMO model approach to determine the optimal mix of nonlinear basis functions by iteratively solving a MILP based optimization problem. Cui et al. (2016) developed a framework for surrogate selection using a meta-learning approach. Their approach involved the characterization of the datasets into several quantitative features, which were then used as a selection guide in identifying the best modeling technique. S.Garud et al. (2018) developed the LEAPS2 model for finding the best surrogate model based on the given input-output data relationship and drew comparisons with Cui's meta-learning model. M.Ahmad and Karimi (2021) further revised the existing LEAPS2 framework through the inclusion of more surrogate models, attribute sets and weight metrics in their analysis database and drew positive comparisons of their revised framework's accuracy against the earlier LEAPS2 framework.

Based on the above literature, we have found that most of the developed approaches only provide surrogate recommendations valid over the entire sample size of a data response. The number of research works providing surrogate model recommendations at different sections of a data response have been very limited and this study focuses on the development of a multi-regional surrogate model selection (MRSMS) approach for the optimal fitting and analysis of univariate responses. The proposed approach has been applied on the Henry Hub Natural Gas price dataset and its performance has been compared with the widely used Piecewise Linear (PL), Neural Network (NN) and Support Vector Regression (SVR) models.

2. METHODOLOGY

The proposed approach has been implemented with MATLAB v2020b used as the programming language and steps of the proposed MRSMS approach are as follows:

I. Step 1: On acquiring the required data and user-specific inputs, the first segment of acquired data (W_{size}) is fitted using all the member models of the library and their in-sample fitting performances are recorded in a matrix. The list of member models and user-specific inputs can be found in Tables 1 and 2 respectively.

II. Step 2: Subsequent data points and their responses are iteratively added to the existing segment based on the step size (S_{size}) value and all the models respective in-sample performances are recorded and appended to the existing performance matrix. The number of models having a fitting performance within the range of Fit_{min} & Fit_{max} are noted at each iteration. Overfitting models (or) models having a fit greater than Fit_{max} are assigned a 'NaN' or null value at every iteration.

III. Step 3: The performances of all models are recorded at every iteration and the termination of a data segment (or) region of data is executed when none of the models are within the given user-specified range of fit for a given number of user-specified consecutive validation steps (V_{steps}).

IV. Step 4: Once the termination of a data segment is executed, the best characteristic model for this segment is determined to be the model with the best average performance (within the user-specified levels of fit) over this region. In the hypothetical case that if two models were found to have the same fitting performance over a data segment, then the best model for the segment is determined to the model with the lowest SQS score developed by M. Ahmad and Karimi (2021). Unlike the commonly used Akaike Information Criteria (AIC), which assumes that the model parameters are determined using the 'maximum likelihood estimate' theory and can sometimes favour its goodness of term (gof) over the second penalty term, the SQS metric developed to addresses these limitations, provides a proportional weightage between a model's fitting accuracy and its complexity. The formula of the SQS score is displayed in Eq.(1).

$$SQS_{model} = (1 - R^2_{model}) \cdot \left(\frac{\ln(1 + DOF_{model})}{\ln(1 + K_{segment})} \right)^{0.5} \tag{1}$$

Where, R^2_{model} represents the fit of the model, DOF_{model} represents the number of independent model parameters and $K_{segment}$ represents the sample size of the current data segment under analysis.

Step 5: The last point (or) the point where all the model performances started falling outside the regions of user-specified fit with the current segment of data indicates the termination of that segment and this final point is recorded as a breakpoint. The process is repeated from Step1 from the latest breakpoint until all the points in the response are fitted optimally.

All the member models in this approach have been implemented using the Curve Fitting and Mathematics Toolbox of MATLAB. The model parameters of these models are estimated using the least squares approximation. We would like to point out that the results of fit, segment sizes and the location of these breakpoints obtained from this approach are subject to change depending on the characteristic nature of the dataset, the type of models present in the library and the user specified inputs.

Table 1: MRSMS Member Models

Model	Model Form
2nd Degree Polynomial model	$y = ax^2 + bx + c$
Exponential model	$y = a \cdot exp(bx)$
Gaussian Model	$y = a \cdot exp(-(x - b) \cdot c^{-1})^2)$
Power Law Model	$y = ax^b$
Sinusoidal Function	$y = a \cdot \sin(bx + c)$
Hyperbolic Tangent Function	$y = a \cdot \tanh(bx)$
Root Function	$y = \sqrt[a]{x}$
Rational Function	$y = (ax + b) \cdot (cx + d)^{-1}$
Sigmoid Function	$y = \left(1 + \exp(-c1 \cdot (x - c2))\right)^{-1}$
Logarithmic Function	$y = a \cdot \log(bx + c)$

Table 2: MRSMS User-Specific Inputs

Parameter	Meaning	Default Value
Fit_{min}	Minimum threshold of desired fit	-
Fit_{max}	Maximum threshold of desired fit	-
S_{size}	Step size	1
W_{size}	Minimum size of a segment	2·(DOF of largest model in the library)
V_{steps}	Validation steps (or) number of continuous iterations to confirm change of model	6

3. CASE STUDY

The Henry Hub Natural Gas Price dataset containing the monthly prices of natural gas (in Dollars/Millions BTU) from January 1997 onwards, is obtained from the U.S Energy Information Administration (EIA) website (EIA (2021)). The default settings of S_{size} = 1, W_{size} = 8, & V_{steps}=6 is used here. The aim is to have an R^2 fit between 0.70 and 0.98 for the first 200 points of this dataset.

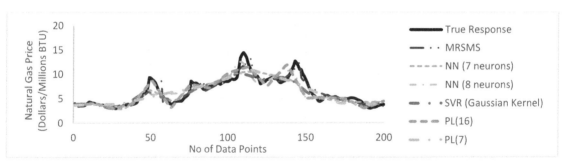

Figure 1: Comparison of the MRSMS fit with various models.

Table 3: MRSMS summary of fitting performance on Henry Hub data

Segment No	Starting Point	Ending Point	Model Form	R^2_{fit}
1	1	11	Polynomial	0.905
2	12	55	Polynomial	0.899
3	56	81	Polynomial	0.875
4	82	111	Gaussian	0.932
5	112	125	Polynomial	0.840
6	126	140	Polynomial	0.892
7	141	200	Rational	0.816

Based on Table 3, it was found that there are 7 optimal segments (or 7 optimal models) required to fit the dataset within the given user-specifications. Out of the 7 models required for fitting the curve, 2nd degree polynomial models (with different coefficients) were found to be the best models in most of the segments except for segments 4 and 7 where the Gaussian and Rational functions were found to the best models respectively.

Due to the concerns about the paper length, the results of fit using the R^2 metric are only presented. However, the MRSMS fitting performance on this dataset has been verified using other commonly used error metrics such as the Root Mean-Squared Error (RMSE), Mean-Squared Error (MSE), and Mean Absolute Error (Metric) as well.

Table 4 provides a comparison of the MRSMS fitting performance against the considered regression models. To establish a valid basis for comparison, the number of hidden neurons for NN models and the no of segments for PL models (D'Errico, J (2009)) were initially set to be equal to the number of segments obtained from the MRSMS approach. These settings were then modified to identify the respective model structures required to outperform the MRSMS fitting performance.

Table 4: Comparison of MRSMS fitting performance with other models

Approach	No of Segments	Average R^2_{fit}	Parameters	No of Parameters	RMSE
MRSMS	7	0.879	Model-Coeffs	22	0.855
PL	7	0.649	Model-Coeffs	14	1.383
PL	16	0.916	Model-Coeffs	32	0.753
NN (7)	1	0.834	Weights & biases	22	1.105
NN (8)	1	0.897	Weights & biases	25	0.869
SVR (Gaussian)	1	0.842	Support Vectors	106	1.08

From Table 4, it can be inferred that for almost the same number of parameters, the developed MRSMS approach provides a better fitting performance than the PL models (7 segments), NN model (7 neurons) and even the SVR model (with Gaussian Kernel & 106 support vectors). Although the NN (8 neurons) and PL (16 linear segments) models were found to out-perform the fitting ability of the MRSMS approach, the number of parameters involved in their data fitting are much higher than that of the MRSMS approach. Modelling a dataset with a lesser number of model parameters that achieves a similar fitting performance obtained from more complex models demonstrates a significant advantage of using the developed approach. We believe that the proposed MRSMS approach can guide researchers in understanding the different types of model behaviour present at different sections of their univariate response.

5. Conclusion

This study focuses on the development of the MRSMS approach its application for optimally fitting of the Henry Hub Natural Gas price dataset. Relying on a library of models and user-specified inputs, the developed MRSMS approach is compared with several linear and nonlinear models in terms of fitting performance, and we found that the MRSMS approach outperformed these models in optimally fitting the given univariate response for the given user specified inputs. Our future works will focus on conducting sensitivity analysis of the user-specified inputs on the overall fitting performance, validation on other univariate chemical engineering responses (generated with the help of the Aspen Hysys Software), comparison with other models such as regression trees and finally, the application of the methodology towards the accurate modelling and analysis of Multi-Input Single Output (MISO) responses.

6. Acknowledgements

This research work is supported by the NUS Research Scholarship (co-funded by SDPPVO) at the National University of Singapore (NUS). We would like to acknowledge MathWorks and AspenTech Inc. for providing the academic licenses (for software usage) to NUS. We also would like to express our acknowledgment and gratitude to all the reviewers for their detailed comments and reviews of this manuscript.

7. References

Ahmad, M., & Karimi, I. A. (2021). Revised learning based evolutionary assistive paradigm for surrogate selection (LEAPS2v2). *Computers & Chemical Engineering*, *152*, 107385. https://doi.org/10.1016/j.compchemeng.2021.107385

Cozad, A., Sahinidis, N. V., & Miller, D. C. (2014). Learning surrogate models for simulation-based optimization. *AIChE Journal*, *60*(6), 2211–2227. https://doi.org/10.1002/aic.14418

Cui, C., Hu, M., Weir, J. D., & Wu, T. (2016). A recommendation system for meta-modeling: A meta-learning based approach. *Expert Systems with Applications*, *46*, 33–44. https://doi.org/10.1016/j.eswa.2015.10.021

D'Errico, J. (2009). SLM-shape language modeling. *SLM-Shape Language Modeling.. http://www. mathworks. com/matlabcentral/fileexchange/24443-slm-shape-language-modeling: Mathworks.*

Garud, S. S., Karimi, I. A., & Kraft, M. (2018). LEAPS2: Learning based Evolutionary Assistive Paradigm for Surrogate Selection. *Computers & Chemical Engineering*, *119*, 352–370. https://doi.org/10.1016/j.compchemeng.2018.09.008

Goel, T., Haftka, R. T., Shyy, W., & Queipo, N. V. (2007). Ensemble of surrogates. *Structural and Multidisciplinary Optimization*, *33*(3), 199–216. https://doi.org/10.1007/s00158-006-0051-9

McBride, K., & Sundmacher, K. (2019). Overview of Surrogate Modeling in Chemical Process Engineering. *Chemie Ingenieur Technik*, *91*(3), 228–239. https://doi.org/10.1002/cite.201800091

US Energy Information Administration. (2021). Short-Term Energy Outlook, July 2021.

Williams, B., & Cremaschi, S. (2021). Selection of surrogate modeling techniques for surface approximation and surrogate-based optimization. *Chemical Engineering Research and Design*, *170*, 76–89. https://doi.org/10.1016/j.cherd.2021.03.028

Proceedings of the 14th International Symposium on Process Systems Engineering – PSE 2021+
June 19-23, 2022, Kyoto, Japan © 2022 Elsevier B.V. All rights reserved.
http://dx.doi.org/10.1016/B978-0-323-85159-6.50155-X

A Digital Reality Pilot Plant for Research and Learning

Deborah E CARBERRY[a*], Mark N JONES[b], Khosrow BAGHERPOUR[a], Christian BEENFELDT[c], Martin P ANDERSSON[a], Seyed Soheil MANSOURI[a*],

[a] Department of Chemical and Biochemical Engineering, Technical University of Denmark, Søltofts Plads, Building 228A, 2800 Kgs. Lyngby, DENMARK
[b] Molecular Quantum Solutions ApS, Maskinvej 5, 2860 Søborg, DENMARK
[c] Knowledge Hub Zealand, Holbækvej 141B 4400 Kalundborg, DENMARK
debca@kt.dtu.dk, seso@kt.dtu.dk

Abstract

Technological advancements increase the demand for more diverse skill sets across industry. To meet this growing demand, digitally-based education and training interventions are a common solution. For practical skills development, digital tools have the potential to increase the capacity of provisioned educational experiences by allowing more people to be trained on more skills using less physical infrastructure. Having analyzed the learning objectives for several PILOT PLANT courses delivered at the Chemical and Biochemical Engineering Department at the Technical University of Denmark (DTU-KT), eight broad competencies have been identified across undergraduate and graduate programs. These competencies, for which the learning objectives are intended, is for the effective operation of a number of unit operations. One way to map these competencies to the respective unit operations and their corresponding theoretical frameworks is via two cognitive interfaces. The first of these interfaces is concerned with cognition and learning whilst the second is concerned with User and spatial Interaction. An educational virtual reality (VR) platform is currently being developed and implemented at DTU-KT. It is designed to introduce learners to the physical structures and components that make up a unit operation, whilst demonstrating the functionality and processes for which the unit operation is intended. This paper will start out by presenting the cognitive framework that was designed and utilized for the design of digital reality learning tools at the PILOT PLANT at DTU-KT. Thereafter, it will present a design study for the recently developed 360° VR learning tool that was developed for a Citric Acid Crystallizer.

Keywords: Education; Pedagogy, Unit Operations; Experiments, Virtual Reality.

1. Introduction

In December 2020, not least because of the limitations imposed on situated learning as a result of COVID 19, a product idea was born at the Department of Chemical and Biochemical Engineering at the Technical University of Denmark (DTU-KT). This idea was to leverage eXtended Reality (XR) technologies to build learning experiences for PILOT PLANT courses. It would take another three months for the concept to take shape, by the end of which time, it was understood that the Team would endeavor to deliver walk-throughs for Unit Operation experiments. The Citric Acid Crystallizer was selected for a project to build a prototype and the Instruction Manual for the experiment was to serve as a foundation in forming a product that could be described as a deconstructed linear narrative (Note: A linear narrative is a narrative (story) with a fixed sequence of steps (events). In other words, there is only one sensible path to navigate the content. Whilst a deconstructed linear narrative breaks the narrative down into smaller steps, facilitating flexible entry and exit points.). At the same time, a technology partner was on boarded, and in April 2021, the development of a prototype commenced.

This paper will set out some of the preceding and initial design activities that informed the prototype project. It will commence by introducing the learning objectives and desired outcomes for existing course offerings at DTU.KT that served as a means to understand the purpose of the respective courses. It will then move on to demonstrate a model that was used to understand the connection between the product features and cognition (or learning), with a view to bridging the product to the learning objectives.

Finally, this paper will present a design study to explore how specific design features were formed in response to anticipated cognitive conditions, and subject to the constraints of the product architecture.

2. Existing Course Offering

At DTU.KT, several courses are on offer for operator training at both undergraduate and graduate level. The design team commenced by reviewing the learning objectives for each course and grouped them according to eight core competencies. This categorization strategy was leveraged to make it easier to think about how to design the product to serve various knowledge and skills requirements for students studying at different levels. The categories, education level, and their corresponding definitions are set out in Table 1 and Figure 1 below.

For the prototype our target user was undergraduate students. Of the four intended competencies for undergraduate students, two were deemed to be appropriate for a mixed reality tool, namely 'Familiarity' and 'Basic Operations'. Hence, the design team would seek to develop a product that would respond to the learning objectives that sought to facilitate students in demonstrating familiarity with the various pieces of equipment and instrumentation, and, to demonstrate a capacity to operate same.

Intuitively, it was felt that spatial reasoning was one of a number of theories that could assist the design team in selecting a number of teaching theories that could further guide the work. Spatial reasoning is a diffused area of research (Davis & Francis 2020). It involves, but is not limited to, a range of abstract reasoning skills that can identify, translate, transform and synthesize information about the geometry, scale, direction and motion of physical objects. More fundamentally, it exploits the physical context of our own body in relation to our environment. In the section that follows, a model will be employed to articulate how relevant learning and teaching theories can be understood in the context of mixed reality education products.

Table 1: Definitions for desired competency categories

Learning Objectives	Translating theoretical understanding to a practical situation
Safety	Knowledge of safe and responsible work practices
Planning	Independently able to plan experiments
Familiarity	Familiar with the equipment and instrumentation
Operations	Capable of operating equipment and instrumentation
Calculations	Able to carry out calculations on given or collected data
Interpreting	Able to make sense of the raw data and calculated data
Contrasting	Can anticipate the correct values for collected and calculated data. Where discrepancies occur, can identify the source(s) of error
Communication	Can communicate goals, processes and findings

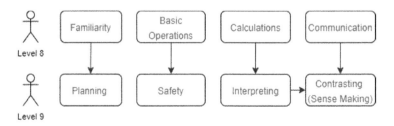

Figure 1: Summary of learning outcomes, based on level of Education

3. A Cognitive Framework for the design of digital reality learning tools

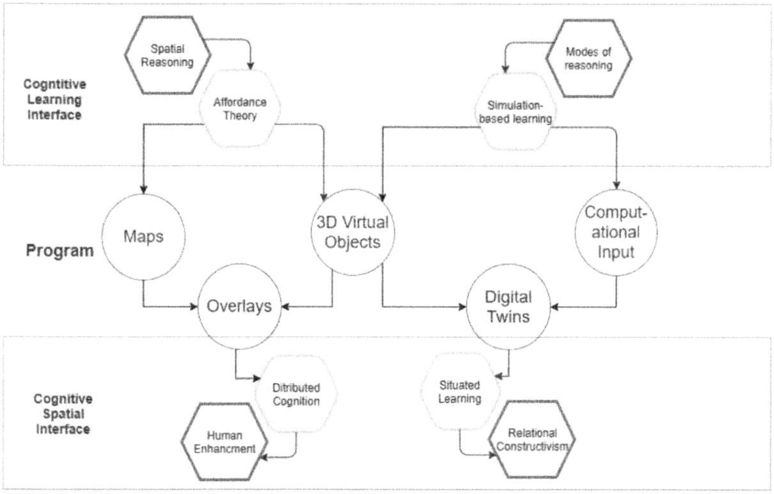

Figure 2: A Cognitive-Program Model
Note: Teaching theories can be identified as hexagons with lighter borders and softer corners than their learning theory counterparts. Affordance Theory (Gibson, 1979) Simulation-based learning (Ton De Jong & Sarti, 1994) (Nazir et al, 2012) Distributed Cognition (Hutchins, 1991) Situated Learning (Lave & Wenger, 1991)

Educational theories can be broken down into theories of learning and theories of teaching (Davis & Francis 2020), where learning theories seek to understand how learning happens and teaching theories are methods to facilitate learning. As was the case for competencies, the design team sought to develop a simple model for rapid conceptualization of pedagogical design and cognitive processes in light of their existing and proposed digital systems. Bearing in mind that this is merely a model, the purpose of which is to facilitate understanding, and, keeping in mind that it is by no means exhaustive, a Cognitive-Program Model was devised for the project and is represented in Figure 2 above.

The model consists of three layers; a cognitive mental interface layer, a program layer (or product layer), and, a cognitive spatial interface layer. The cognitive mental interface is devoted to human learning whilst the cognitive spatial interface is devoted to the relationship one has with their environment. Sitting between the two cognitive interfaces is the digital program, mediating the relationship between how one thinks and how one interacts with their surroundings.

In our Cognitive-Program Model, you can draw a vertical line through the center of the diagram to produce two discrete product groups. To the left, is a system for a mixed reality solution that leverages affordances to create a distributed cognitive system. This mixed reality system exploits human perception, with a view to reducing cognitive load, for the purpose of enabling a user to focus their attention on the task at hand. Distributed cognition, as it relates to cognitive load, can be understood by two actions. The first is the potential to transfer content from our working memories and locate it elsewhere in our environment, for example, as a list on a piece of paper. The second action is the potential to access information that is annotated in our environment such as is the case with signs and symbols that populate motorways. Combining these two actions is a powerful methodology to reduce cognitive overload. Moreover, a learning environment with these capabilities is ideal for learners who are largely unfamiliar or inexperienced with a subject or skill. On the right side of the diagram, is a system for a digital twin which leverages simulation in a situated context. In contrast, the digital twin is suitable for those with a good fundamental understanding of their subject and whom are capable of engaging in a variety of reason-based cognitive activities. This paper will not concern itself with the design of digital twins.

In the section that follows, a design study will be presented that demonstrates how some of the learning and teaching theories from our Cognitive-Program Model were applied to the design of a VR prototype at DTU in 2021.

4. Design Study: The PID

An affordance can be described as 'the quality or property of an object that defines its possible uses or makes clear how it can or should be used' (Merriam-Webster.com). A Piping and Instrumentation Diagram (PID) is a language of related symbols. The symbols in a PID do not necessarily have strong affordances. On the other hand, the components and instrumentation for a unit operation are designed to tell a user how they can be used. In nature it is more common to be exposed to a thing itself before one encounters or creates a symbol for the same thing. However, often in formal education, as is the case for learning PILOT PLANT operations at DTU, it happens in reverse.

At the 1st project meeting, the value of the PID was emphasized. As a language in Chemical Engineering, and one that most students are fluent in, it was a feature that offered significant pedagogical value in the overall design. Hence, it was decided to exploit it as a device that learners could use to comprehend the virtual renditions. An initial design was proposed, however, the choice of hardware and software for the prototype did not facilitate the design of bespoke features. On the contrary, the technical architecture had been selected for the speed of implementation, and not for flexibility. As such the design team needed to be creative.

In this design study, both the proposed and the implemented design for integrating the PID into the walkthrough for a pilot scaled experiment will be outlined. In both cases, the solution seeks to achieve the same goal, which is to use the PID as a way to navigate and make sense of pilot scaled experiments.

4.1 Original Design

Excerpts from the original design specification:

'The PID will serve as a navigation device in the experiment. For each step in the experimental process, the PID will change dynamically from step to step, illustrating which components are involved in each corresponding step.'

'A user can locate individual components of the unit operation by selecting the corresponding unit in the PID, and vice versa'.

Figure 3: Mockup of how the PID could change dynamically from step to step

Note: The vertical axis located on the right side of the screen acts as a navigation system for tracking the user's current location in the experiment. In Figure 3, steps 1.3 – 1.6 are in view. Arrows on both ends of the axis allow the user to move back and forward through the experiment/narrative. The PID can be visible or invisible (see Figure 4). When the PID is visible, only the objects in the PID that are relevant to that step will be visible (not shown here).

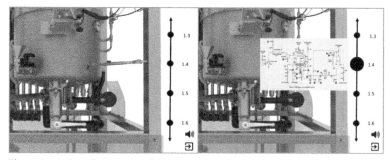

Figure 4: Mock up for how to activate the PID as a navigation tool
Note: A user can activate the PID overlay by performing an action on the corresponding step on the navigation axis. Otherwise, the PID will be invisible.

The first of the two use cases from the requirement specification is illustrated as mockups in Figure 3 and Figure 4 above. In the mockups, the PID has been scaled up to facilitate understanding, however, in a VR environment, the relative size of the PID to the unit operation would be significantly smaller.

This proposed solution responded to the requirements for the product by developing an interactive play between the PID and virtual unit operation. The feature permitted the user to project knowledge about something they already understood, i.e. the PID, onto a new knowledge domain, i.e. physical unit operations. This process is referred to as scaffolding, a theory that states that learners build new knowledge by using their existing knowledge (Wood, Ross, Bruner, 1976). And whilst attractive as a concept, time constraints dictated that an alternative solution was required, at least initially. As such, the proposed features are currently part of the product backlog for future development.

4.2 Implemented Design

The solution that was implemented for the prototype project took advantage of a 360 VR development environment called present4D. The main staple for the content delivery portion of the product was the development of a series of animated videos for each step in the experiment. It was decided that in order to capture the value of the PID for each step in the experiment, cut scenes between a PID (highlighting relevant components for that step) and animated segments (that demonstrated the required action and location of the corresponding components) could serve to bridge the two. This is illustrated in Figure 5 below.

The navigation system for the prototype was designed using an identical architecture to the proposed design, however the UX in the prototype is somewhat different. Rather than using a linear axis for example, the user selects from a menu of modules, and then, from a menu of steps.

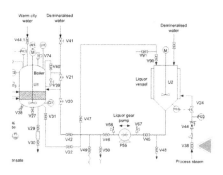 

Figure 5: Left: PID with arrow pointing to V38 (valve 38). Right: Screen shot from animation with tag attached to V38 (valve 38).

5. Conclusion

VR is a visual medium and ideal for addressing pedagogical challenges that involve visual learning such as object recognition, process demonstrations and simulations of body active experiences. There are several potential value propositions for developing digital reality tools to teach unit operations as part of chemical and biochemical engineering education, not least for remote learning. Based on our experience, it is advantageous to consider the goals and the assumptions of the same courses offered in their current format, to guarantee that the competencies sought (or part thereof) are consistent.

Technical architectures will shape the possibilities for product design, however, it is often possible to achieve the same requirements using different technologies, albeit via different design features. This does not necessarily mean that the designs for each medium will be of equal value therefore the choice of technical architecture should be informed by their suitability to address the product goals. In the case of the prototype for DTU.KT, a full scale user testing program is yet to be implemented, however, the current implemented solution has recently been made available to both Teachers and Students at the department as a working prototype. Early feedback suggests that the product is a useful tool for experiment preparation for both sets of users.

Acknowledgements

The authors would like to acknowledge the Department of Chemical and Biochemical Engineering at the Technical University of Denmark, Erasmus+: Higher Education – International Capacity Building project TESS (Application number 609925-EPP-1-2019-1-NO-EPPKA2-CBHE-JP), and Novo Nordisk Foundation through Fermentation Based Manufacturing Initiative (Grant number NNF17SA0031362), for providing financial support.

References

Davis, B., & Francis, K., 2020, "Spatial Reasoning" in Discourses on Learning in Education. https://learningdiscourses.com.

Kraus, B., 2017, Plädoyer für den Relationalen Konstruktivismus und eine Relationale Soziale Arbeit - In: Forum sozial, 1, S. 29-35 - URN: urn:nbn:de:0111-pedocs-153817 - DOI: 10.25656/01:15381

Gibson, J.J., 1979,. The Ecological Approach to Visual Perception

Hutchins, E., 1991, The social organization of distributed cognition

Ton De Jong, Sarti, L., 1994, Design and Production of Multimedia and Simulation-Based Learning Material. Dordrecht, Netherlands ; Boston, Kluwer.

Nazir, S., Totaro, R., Brambilla, S., Colombo, S., Manca, D., 2012, Virtual Reality and Augmented-Virtual Reality as Tools to Train Industrial Operators, Editor(s): Lockhart Bogle I.D, Fairweather M., Computer Aided Chemical Engineering, Elsevier, Volume 30, Pages 1397-1401, https://doi.org/10.1016/B978-0-444-59520-1.50138-X.

Lave, J., & Wenger, E. (1991). Situated learning: Legitimate peripheral participation. Cambridge University Press. https://doi.org/10.1017/CBO9780511815355

"Affordance." Merriam-Webster.com Dictionary, Merriam-Webster, https://www.merriam-webster.com/dictionary/affordance. Accessed 29 Oct. 2021.

Wood, D., Bruner, J.S. and Ross, G., 1976, THE ROLE OF TUTORING IN PROBLEM SOLVING. Journal of Child Psychology and Psychiatry, 17: 89-100 https://doi.org/10.1111/j.1469-7610.1976.tb00381.x

Proceedings of the 14th International Symposium on Process Systems Engineering – PSE 2021+
June 19-23, 2022, Kyoto, Japan © 2022 Elsevier B.V. All rights reserved.
http://dx.doi.org/10.1016/B978-0-323-85159-6.50156-1

Soft sensors development for industrial reactive distillation processes under small training datasets

Andrei Torgashov[a], Svetlana Samotylova [a], Fan Yang[b*]

[a]*Process Control Laboratory, Institute of Automation and Control Process FEB RAS, 5 Radio Str., Vladivostok, Russia*
[b]*Beijing National Research Center for Information Science and Technology and Department of Automation, Tsinghua University, Beijing 100084, China*
yangfan@mail.tsinghua.edu.cn

Abstract

Under real industrial conditions, there are usually missing values in the data. This is due to measurement errors, sensor failures, missing values in real-time databases, irregular measurement intervals, and data that are not covering the total operation range of the plant. Due to the lack of data, the soft sensor (SS) model is of poor quality. The functioning of this model is also unsatisfactory in the new operating points of the plant in the case of a small training sample. We propose the use of a calibrated rigorous (first-principles) process model with acceptable limits of parametric uncertainty to extend the training dataset, which allows us to take into account the physicochemical characteristics of the process. It is shown that the extension of the training sample based on the rigorous model makes it possible to obtain a nonlinear SS of higher accuracy.

Keywords: soft sensor; small training dataset, rigorous model; sample extension; reactive distillation.

1. Introduction

Small samples in the development of SSs lead to overfitting and poor interpretability of the models of an industrial plant when using existing approaches of multiple regression and deep learning (Zhu et al., 2018). To improve the accuracy of SSs under conditions of small samples, we propose approaches based on the generation of virtual data. The approach based on the generation of virtual samples (Virtual Sample Generation - VSG) is used to obtain a large number of new virtual data based on information obtained from small data sets in order to increase the accuracy of SSs. To reduce gaps in the training data set, an information-expanded function based on triangular membership has been developed (Chen et al., 2017). For iterative evaluation of the most appropriate training samples, an approach based on particle swarm optimization with VSG (PSOVSG) was proposed. Zhu et al. (2020) propose a novel locally linear embedding based on a virtual sample generation (LLEVSG) approach. In their proposed LLEVSG method, locally linear embedding is first used to extract features from the original data space. Next, back-propagation neural network (BPNN) and a method of random interpolation are utilized to generate effective virtual samples in the sparse region of the original data.

Within the framework of Industry 4.0, one of the important aspects should be noted, which is the use of a physically based first principles model, intended not only to model an industrial plant, but also to validate collected data for building a reliable model by monitoring the process in various operating points (Vaccari et al., 2021). Thus, the use of a physically based model for virtual sampling is an advanced approach, as it allows the taking into account of the physicochemical features of the chemical process, and it becomes possible to take into account various modes of operation of the industrial unit (Ko et al., 2021).

Hsiao et al., 2021 proposed a methodology for developing SSs that combines a calibrated, physically based model to extend the training dataset and transfer learning to develop them. In this current work, we propose the use of a calibrated rigorous process model for sample extension in case of parametric uncertainty in the phase equilibrium model, which is often seen in practice. The superiority of the proposed approach based on the sample extension compared to the traditional PSO and PSO with bootstrapping is demonstrated based on the industrial reactive distillation of methyl tert-butyl ether (MTBE) production.

2. Statement of problem and its analysis

We have considered The problem of developing an SS for estimating the output product of a reactive distillation column produced by a high-octane additive of gasoline as MTBE in a small training sample (Fig. 1). The mass fraction of MTBE (grade A) should exceed 98% in the product.

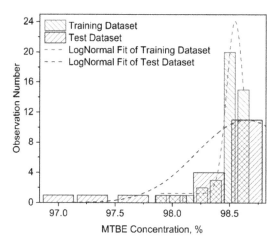

Figure 1: Histograms of the output variable distribution

To build an SS, a training sample with input variables (Table 1) was used $U=\left[u_1, \ldots, u_n\right] \in R^{42 \times 6}$ and output variable observations $Y=\left[y_1, \ldots, y_n\right] \in R^{42 \times 1}$.

To test the developed models, a test sample was used with $U=\left[u_1, \ldots, u_n\right] \in R^{18 \times 6}$ and $Y=\left[y_1, \ldots, y_n\right] \in R^{18 \times 1}$.

Basically, the "black box" model is used when building SS. The main drawback of this approach is the lack of use of available a priori knowledge about the process. To solve the problem of a small training sample and improve the accuracy of the SS, we propose the use of a rigorous analytical model for a reactive distillation (RD) process.

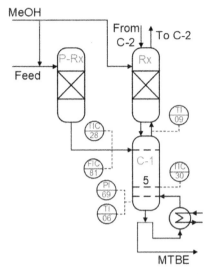

Figure 2. The MTBE synthesis flowsheet diagram

Table 1. Process variables

No	Process variable, u	Tag name	Units of meas.
1	Feed of column C-1	FIC81	m³/hr
2	Bottom pressure of column C-1	PI69	MPa
3	Bottom temperature of column C-1	TI06	°C
4	Top temperature of column C-1	TI09	°C
5	Feed temperature of column C-1	TIC28	°C
6	5th tray temperature of column C-1	TIC30	°C

However, it is also not possible to directly use the rigorous model of RD to build an SS, e.g. using the concept of a "gray box" (Ahmad et al., 2020) here, due to the high dimension of the model. A set of highly nonlinear equations can be obtained by a material balance equation (1), enthalpy balance equation (2), Murphree mass transfer efficiency equation (3), phase equilibrium equation (4), molar fraction summation equation (5) and chemical reaction rate equation (6) (Wang et al., 2020, Mendoza et al., 2013):

$$F\mathbf{x}_{Fi} - V\mathbf{y}_i - L\mathbf{x}_i + \sum_r V_{ir}R_r = 0 \qquad (i = 1,\ldots,C) \qquad (1)$$

$$F\mathbf{h}_F - V\mathbf{h}^V - L\mathbf{h}^L = 0 \qquad (2)$$

$$E^{MV}\left(\mathbf{y}_i^* - \mathbf{y}_i\right) - \left(\mathbf{y}_i - \mathbf{y}_i\right) = 0 \qquad (i = 1,\ldots,C-1) \quad (3)$$

$$\mathbf{K}_i\mathbf{x}_i - \mathbf{y}_i^* = 0 \qquad (4)$$

$$1 - \sum_{i=1}^{C}\mathbf{y}_i^* = 0, \quad 1 - \sum_{i=1}^{C}\mathbf{y}_i = 0, \quad 1 - \sum_{i=1}^{C}\mathbf{x}_i = 0 \qquad (5)$$

$$r_r = f\left(T, P, \mathbf{x}_i, \mathbf{y}_i\right) \qquad (6)$$

where F, V, and L denote the mass flow rates of the feed; "V" and "L" represent the internal liquid and vapor streams; $\mathbf{x}_{Fi}$ is the mass fraction of the component i of the feed; $\mathbf{x}_i$ and $\mathbf{y}_i$ are the mass fractions of the component i of the liquid and vapor phases; V_{ir} is stoichiometric coefficient component i of the reaction r; R is the extent of the reaction, $mol \cdot s^{-1}$; $\mathbf{h}_F$, $\mathbf{h}^V$ and $\mathbf{h}^L$ are the feed, vapor and liquid mass enthalpies; $\mathbf{y}_i^*$ is the equilibrium mass fractions of the component i of the vapor phase; E^{MV} is Murphree mass transfer efficiency; r_r is the reaction rate of the reaction r; T is the temperature, K; P is the pressure, MPa.

3. Soft sensor evaluation based on the sample extension

Therefore, we propose the use of a rigorous model of the RD plant to simulate the steady-state operating points under various conditions in order to extend the training sample. The proposed algorithm for developing the SS for estimating the quality of MTBE production in case of a small training dataset is shown in figure 2.

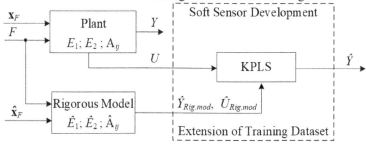

Figure 3. The scheme of algorithm for developing the SS in case of a small sample of industrial data.

Kernel partial least squares (KPLS) (Jin et al., 2014, Liu et al., 2010) are used for developing the SS to estimate the quality of MTBE. Giving the input matrix $U = [u_1, ..., u_n] \in R^{n \times m}$ and output matrix $Y = [y_1, ..., y_n] \in R^{n \times p}$ used, where n is the number of observations, and m and p represent the number of process variables and quality variables, respectively.

The rigorous model of reactive distillation was calibrated on industrial data and the following Murphree efficiencies were estimated: $\hat{E}_1 = 0.8$ (trays 1-5); $\hat{E}_2 = 0.6$ (trays 6-28). It should be noted that the calibration of the rigorous model is also influenced by the parameters of binary interaction. For the MTBE production process, the parameters of the binary interaction of isobutylene (DIB) dimers (2,4,4-trimethyl-1-pentene, and 2,4,4-trimethyl-2-pentene) are practically absent in the literature. However, DIB is often detected in the output product as an impurity component. Binary parameters for MTBE and DIB are $A_{MTBE,DIB} = -17.13$ K, $A_{DIB,MTBE} = 45.75$ K. (Sundmacher et al., 1999). For a rigorous model, the activity coefficients of the MTBE-system are calculated from the UNIQUAC-model. In this regard, the deviations of the calibrated rigorous model parameters $\Delta \hat{A}_{ij}$ of the process under study were introduced as $\Delta \hat{A}_{ij} = \left| A_{ij} - \hat{A}_{ij} \right|$. To determine the threshold values of deviations $\Delta_{\hat{A}_{ij}}^{opt.th}$, the % of reduction of R^2 (δR^2) was estimated for the range of parametric uncertainty $\Delta \hat{A}_{ij} \in [0.1, 0.4]$ relative to the base case when the model exactly corresponds to the plant, i.e. relatively to $\Delta \hat{A}_{ij} = 0$. If δR^2 exceeded 5%, then a threshold deviation value was assigned for the corresponding binary parameters under which the extension of the training dataset leading to improvement of soft sensor model accuracy (Table 2).

Table 2. R^2 and *MAE* obtained on the test sample before and after the extension of the training sample

Criterion	Extension of the training dataset (number of added observations)			
	0	10	20	30
Particle swarm optimization				
MAE	0,1626	0,1595	0,1548	0,1503
R^2	0,5514	0,6060	0,6897	0,7025
Particle swarm optimization and bootstrap				
MAE	0,1626	0,1579	0,1495	0,1489
R^2	0,5514	0,6243	0,7077	0,7139
Rigorous model				
MAE	0,1626	0,1501	0,1483	0,1408
R^2	0,5514	0,7053	0,7245	0,7316

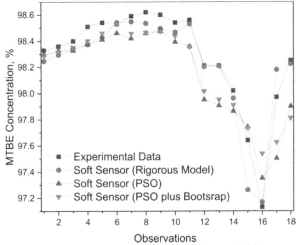

Figure 4: Comparative study of several SSs

The proposed algorithm based on the rigorous model for extending the training sample is compared with well-known approaches for building models to evaluate the quality of end products in conditions of small training samples (Fig.4)—for example, expanding the training sample using particle swarm optimization (Chen et al., 2017), as well as the joint application of particle swarm optimization with bootstrap (Fortuna et al., 2009, Zhang et al., 2021). The value of *MAE* for an SS to estimate the concentration of MTBE using the proposed approach is reduced by $((0.1626-0.1408)/0.1626)\times100 \approx 13.41\%$.

4. Conclusions

The use of a calibrated, physically based model of the process with acceptable limits of parametric uncertainty of binary parameters to extend the training sample allows us to take into account the physico-chemical characteristics of the process. The use of nonlinear methods for building soft sensors on an extended training sample allows to increase the accuracy of the developed SS.

5. Acknowledgements

The reported study was partially funded by RFBR and NSFC (project numbers 21-57-53005 and 62111530057).

References

Ahmad, I., Ayub, A., Kano, M., and Cheema, I.I., 2020, Gray-Box Soft Sensors in Process Industry: Current Practice, and Future Prospects in Era of Big Data, Processes, 8, 243

Chen, Z.S., Zhu, B., He, Y.-L., and Yu, L.A., 2017, A PSO Based Virtual Sample Generation Method for Small Sample Sets: Applications to Regression Datasets, Engineering Applications of Artificial Intelligence, 59, 236–243

Fortuna, L., Graziani, S., and Xibilia, M. G., 2009, Comparison of Soft-Sensor Design Methods for Industrial Plants Using Small Data Sets, IEEE Transactions on Instrumentation and Measurement, 58, 2444–2451

Hsiao, Y.D., Kang, J.L., and Wong, D.S.H., 2021, Development of Robust and Physically Interpretable Soft Sensor for Industrial Distillation Column Using Transfer Learning with Small Datasets, Processes, 9(4), 667

Jin H., Chen X., Yang J., Wu L., 2014, Adaptive Soft Sensor Modeling Framework Based on Just-In-Time Learning and Kernel Partial Least Squares Regression for Nonlinear Multiphase Batch Processes, Computers & Chemical Engineering, 71, 77-93

Ko, C., Lee, H., Lim, Y., and Lee, W.B., 2021, Development of Augmented Virtual Reality-Based Operator Training System for Accident Prevention in a Refinery, Korean Journal of Chemical Engineering, 38(8), 1566-1577

Liu, J., Chen, D.S., and Shen, J.F., 2010, Development of Self-Validating Soft Sensors Using Fast Moving Window Partial Least Squares, Industrial & Engineering Chemistry Research, 49(22), 11530-11546

Mendoza, D. F., Palacio, L. M., Graciano, J. E., Riascos, C. A., Vianna Jr, A. S., Le Roux, G. C., 2013, Real-Time Optimization of an Industrial-Scale Vapor Recompression Distillation Process. Model Validation and Analysis, Industrial & Engineering Chemistry Research, 52(16), 5735-5746

Sundmacher, K., Uhde, G., Hoffmann, U., 1999, Multiple Reactions in Catalytic Distillation Processes for the Production of the Fuel Oxygenates MTBE and TAME: Analysis by Rigorous Model and Experimental Validation, Chemical Engineering Science, 54, 2839-2847

Vaccari, M., Bacci di Capaci, R., Brunazzi, E., Tognotti, L., Pierno, P., Vagheggi, R., Pannocchia, G., 2021, Optimally managing chemical plant operations: An example oriented by Industry 4.0 paradigms, Industrial & Engineering Chemistry Research, 60, 7853−7867

Wang, L., Sun, X., Xia, L., Wang, J., Xiang, S., 2020, Inside–Out Method for Simulating a Reactive Distillation Process, Processes, 8(5), 604

Zhang, X.-H., Xu, Y., He, Y.-L., Zhu, Q.-X., 2021, Novel Manifold Learning Based Virtual Sample Generation for Optimizing Soft Sensor with Small Data, ISA Transactions, 109, 229-241

Zhu, J., Ge, Z., Song, Z., and Gao, F., 2018, Review and Big Data Perspectives on Robust Data Mining Approaches for Industrial Process Modeling with Outliers and Missing Data, Annual Reviews in Control, 46, 107-133

Zhu, Q.X., Zhang, X.-H., He, Y.L., 2020, Novel Virtual Sample Generation Based on Locally Linear Embedding for Optimizing the Small Sample Problem: Case of Soft Sensor Applications, Industrial & Engineering Chemistry Research, 59(40), 17977-17986

Proceedings of the 14th International Symposium on Process Systems Engineering – PSE 2021+
June 19-23, 2022, Kyoto, Japan © 2022 Elsevier B.V. All rights reserved.
http://dx.doi.org/10.1016/B978-0-323-85159-6.50157-3

Comprehensive Quantification of Model Prediction Uncertainty for Simulated Moving Bed Chromatography

Kensuke Suzuki, Tomoyuki Yajima, Yoshiaki Kawajiri[*]

Department of Materials Process Engineering, Nagoya University, Furo-cho 1, Chikusa, Aichi 464-8603, Japan
kawajiri@nagoya-u.jp

Abstract

To realize robust process design and operation of simulated moving bed (SMB) chromatography, prediction uncertainty in a model must be quantified. In this study, we quantify the prediction uncertainty as predictive distributions stemming from a model parameter uncertainty estimated from experimental data. The resulting predictive distributions provide insights into selecting experimental methods to assure reliability of the model predictions and parameters.

Keywords: Simulated Moving Bed; Uncertainty Quantification; Bayesian Inference; Predictive Distribution; Sequential Monte Carlo.

1. Introduction

Simulated moving bed (SMB) chromatography is a continuous separation process widely used for the separation of petrochemicals, enantiomers, and chiral compounds (Schmidt-Traub et al., 2012). The SMB process consists of multiple chromatographic columns connected in a semi-closed-loop structure, and a mixture is continuously separated by cyclic operation. Between each column, there are inlet valves for supplying feed and desorbent streams and outlet valves for withdrawing extract and raffinate streams. The positions of these four streams are simultaneously switched along the flow direction at a regular time interval, called step time.

A lot of research has been carried out on modeling of SMB, process design, and optimization using mathematical models. In most of these studies, the SMB model consists of a system of partial differential algebraic equations (PDAEs). In this model, there are unknown parameters that are dependent on adsorbents and components to be separated. To estimate parameters, many estimation methods have been studied; in general, these unknown model parameters are estimated from single-column batch experiments and applied to the SMB model. Research to optimize operating conditions—the four flow rates and step time—by model simulation using estimated parameters has also been extensively conducted.

To assess the SMB model in terms of reliability and robustness, uncertainty in the model prediction—product concentration, purity, recovery, and internal concentration profile—should be quantified, but there has been little research on the quantification of uncertainty of the SMB model prediction so far. Uncertainty in model prediction stems from uncertainties in model parameters, implementation of design and operation, and measurement. This prediction uncertainty can be quantified by estimating the predictive distribution. By obtaining the predictive distribution, the reliability of the model prediction can be assessed under various uncertainties, which is crucial for robust process design and optimization; however, the predictive distributions of purity and recovery, which are essential for evaluating the process performance of SMB, have not been sufficiently investigated, especially for systems with nonlinear adsorption behavior.

In this study, we rigorously estimate uncertainty in SMB model predictions derived from uncertainty in model parameters and analyze an influence of the parameter uncertainty. We consider the separation of the mixture of two components described by the Langmuir isotherm (Bentley et al., 2013). Uncertainty in model parameters is quantified as the posterior distribution via Bayesian inference from the artificial simulation data of single-column batch experiments. We employ sequential Monte Carlo (SMC), which parallelizes numerical sampling for efficient implementation of Bayesian inference (Yamamoto et al., 2021). The predictive distributions are obtained based on the estimated parameter uncertainty. The resulting predictive distributions provide insights into the reliability of parameter estimation results and model predictions, as well as the robustness of processes and operating conditions.

2. Methodology

2.1. SMB Process Model

A system of PDAEs, called the LDF model that is widely used to describe adsorption phenomena inside columns, is adopted in this study. Details of this model are given in Schmidt-Traub et al. (2012). The mass balance in the liquid phase is,

$$\varepsilon_{\mathrm{b}} \frac{\partial C_i^j(x,t)}{\partial t} + (1 - \varepsilon_{\mathrm{b}}) \frac{\partial q_i^j(x,t)}{\partial t} + u^j(t) \frac{\partial C_i^j(x,t)}{\partial x} = 0 \tag{1}$$

where $C_i^j(x,t)$ and $q_i^j(x,t)$ are concentrations in the liquid and solid phases, respectively, of component $i \in \{A, B\}$ in the $j \in \{1, 2, \dots, N_{\mathrm{col}}\}$th column at axial position x at time t; ε_{b} is the overall bed porosity; $u^j(t)$ is the superficial liquid velocity; A and B are components to be separated; and N_{col} is the number of columns in the SMB. The mass balance in the solid phase is

$$\frac{\partial q_i^j(x,t)}{\partial t} = k_i \left(q_i^{\mathrm{eq},j}(x,t) - q_i^j(x,t) \right) \tag{2}$$

where k_i is the overall mass-transfer coefficient of component i; and $q_i^{\mathrm{eq},j}(x,t)$ is the equilibrium concentration in the solid phase. This equilibrium concentration is given by the Langmuir isotherm:

$$q_i^{\mathrm{eq},j}(x,t) = \frac{H_i C_i^j(x,t)}{1 + b_A C_A^j(x,t) + b_B C_B^j(x,t)} \tag{3}$$

where H_i is Henry's constant and b_i is the affinity coefficient.

2.2. Bayesian Inference and Predictive Distribution

In this study, we estimate the predictive distribution due to uncertainty in the model parameters. Generally, an observation $y \in \mathbb{R}^M$ is modeled using a deterministic model $f(\theta)$ and an observation error as $y = f(\theta) + \varepsilon$, where θ is the model parameter and ε is the observation error. The observation error is often assumed to follow a multivariate normal distribution with mean $\mathbf{0}$ and a covariance matrix $\mathbf{\Sigma}$. Under this assumption, the probability density $p(\mathbf{y}|\boldsymbol{\theta})$ is given by

$$p(\mathbf{y}|\boldsymbol{\theta}) = (2\pi)^{-\frac{M}{2}}|\mathbf{\Sigma}|^{-\frac{1}{2}}exp\left\{-(\mathbf{y}-f(\boldsymbol{\theta}))^T\mathbf{\Sigma}^{-1}(\mathbf{y}-f(\boldsymbol{\theta}))\right\} \tag{4}$$

The parameters $\boldsymbol{\theta}$ in the model $f(\boldsymbol{\theta})$ are estimated from observed data $\mathbf{Y}^{\text{data}}$ via Bayesian inference:

$$p(\boldsymbol{\theta}|\mathbf{Y}^{\text{data}}) \propto p(\mathbf{Y}^{\text{data}}|\boldsymbol{\theta})p(\boldsymbol{\theta}) \tag{5}$$

where $p(\boldsymbol{\theta}|\mathbf{Y}^{\text{data}})$ is the posterior distribution; $p(\boldsymbol{\theta})$ is the prior distribution; and $p(\mathbf{Y}^{\text{data}}|\boldsymbol{\theta})$ is the likelihood distribution formulated as $p(\mathbf{Y}^{\text{data}}|\boldsymbol{\theta}) = \prod_{k=1}^{N_{\text{data}}} p(\mathbf{y}_i^{\text{data}}|\boldsymbol{\theta})$ when the data is given by $\mathbf{Y}^{\text{data}} = \left[\mathbf{y}_1^{\text{data}}, \mathbf{y}_2^{\text{data}}, ..., \mathbf{y}_{N_{\text{data}}}^{\text{data}}\right]^T$.

The predictive distribution $p(\mathbf{y}|\mathbf{Y}^{\text{data}})$ using the posterior distribution of the parameter, $p(\boldsymbol{\theta}|\mathbf{Y}^{\text{data}})$ obtained by Eq. (5), is given as follows:

$$p(\mathbf{y}|\mathbf{Y}^{\text{data}}) = \int p(\mathbf{y}|\boldsymbol{\theta})p(\boldsymbol{\theta}|\mathbf{Y}^{\text{data}})\,d\boldsymbol{\theta} \tag{6}$$

where $p(\mathbf{y}|\mathbf{Y}^{\text{data}})$ is usually approximated using a Monte Carlo method.

In this study, the model $f(\boldsymbol{\theta})$ is Eqs.(1)-(3), $\boldsymbol{\theta} = [H_A, H_B, k_A, k_B, b_A, b_B]^T$, and the observation is $\mathbf{y} = \left[\bar{C}_{\text{Ext},A}, \bar{C}_{\text{Ext},B}, \bar{C}_{\text{Raff},A}, \bar{C}_{\text{Raff},B}\right]^T$ where $\bar{C}_i$ is the average product concentration and subscripts Ext and Raff refer to extract and raffinate, respectively. The data $\mathbf{Y}^{data}$ are the time-series concentration data sets obtained from the artificial simulation data of single-column batch experiments as follows: $\mathbf{Y}^{\text{data}} = \left[C_1^{\text{data}}, C_2^{\text{data}}, ..., C_{N_{\text{data}}}^{\text{data}}\right]^T$ where C_k^{data} refers to the kth experimental data set as $C_k^{\text{data}} = \left\{(t_l, C(L, t_l))\right\}_{l=1}^M$; L is the length of the column; and t_l is observation time in kth experiment.

3. Experimental

3.1. SMB Model, Operating and Simulation Condition

The model parameters, as well as design and operating conditions in Bentley et al. (2013) for the separation of cyclopentanone (c5) and cyclohexanone (c6) with SMB were used in this study. The final parameter values repetitively refined in their study were employed as true values in this study. Their design conditions—the number of columns $N_{\text{col}} = 4$, column length $L = 0.25$ [m]—were adopted, and their operating conditions—flow rates and step time—were also employed. The covariance matrix $\mathbf{\Sigma}$ in Eq.(4) was assumed to be a diagonal matrix, and the diagonal element σ_{ii} was assumed to satisfy the following equation for the element y_i of $\mathbf{y}$: $1.96\sigma_{ii} = 0.03y_i$ [g/L].

3.2. Artificial Data of Single-Column Experimental

Simulation of the single-column batch experiment was conducted to obtain the artificial data. Two experimental data were generated using a mixture of c5 and c6 with 34 g/L of each component as a feed and a flow rate $Q = 3.0$ [mL/min]: (A) 40 μL injection test. (B) 20 mL injection test. For (A) and (B), the number of experimental points was $M = 1000$; the observation time was $t_M = 1200$ [s]; and Gaussian noise was added as the observation error. Bayesian inference was performed with two different data sets— Set α and Set β: Set α contains only (A) ($N_{data} = 1$) while Set β contains (A) and (B) ($N_{data} = 2$).

3.3. Implementation of sequential Monte Carlo

The posterior distribution of the model parameters was estimated using SMC with the likelihood tempering (Yamamoto et al., 2021). SMC approximately estimates the posterior distribution in Bayes' theorem (Eq.(5)), which cannot be solved analytically in general, from data using a large number of particles. The number of particles was 1,000 and the number of likelihood tempering depended on data sets, 24 for Set α and 31 for Set β. The prior distribution was set with the method shown in Yamamoto et al. (2021).

4. Results

4.1. Posterior Distribution of Model Parameters

Comparing the posterior distributions estimated using Set α and Set β, the posterior distributions estimated from Set β were found to have smaller uncertainty than that of Set α. Table 1 shows the mode values and 95% credible intervals of the posterior distributions from Set α and Set β, respectively. The 95% credible intervals for all parameters were narrower for Set β than for Set α; especially, the intervals of the equilibrium constants H_i and b_i were reduced from Set α to Set β by 86%, 89%, 99%, and 96%, for H_{c5}, H_{c6}, b_{c5}, and b_{c6}, respectively. This uncertainty reduction of the equilibrium constants is due to the addition of the breakthrough test (B) data, where the interaction between b_{c5} and b_{c6} sufficiently appears, making it easier to determine values of H_i and b_i.

Table 1. True values, modes, and 95% credible intervals of posterior distributions of model parameters estimated from Set α and Set β.

Parameter	True	Posterior distribution (Set α)	Posterior distribution (Set β)
H_{c5} [−]	2.13	$2.13^{+5.23\times10^{-3}}_{-6.55\times10^{-3}}$	$2.13^{+5.53\times10^{-4}}_{-1.07\times10^{-3}}$
H_{c6} [−]	3.82	$3.82^{+4.15\times10^{-3}}_{-4.75\times10^{-3}}$	$3.82^{+4.72\times10^{-4}}_{-5.36\times10^{-4}}$
k_{c5} [s^{-1}]	0.312	$0.312^{+1.14\times10^{-3}}_{-1.44\times10^{-3}}$	$0.312^{+1.23\times10^{-3}}_{-1.13\times10^{-3}}$
k_{c6} [s^{-1}]	1.19	$1.19^{+1.09\times10^{-2}}_{-7.26\times10^{-3}}$	$1.19^{+5.20\times10^{-3}}_{-4.22\times10^{-3}}$
b_{c5} [g/L]	1.7×10^{-2}	$1.57 \times 10^{-2}{}^{+7.03\times10^{-3}}_{-6.51\times10^{-3}}$	$1.70 \times 10^{-2}{}^{+6.88\times10^{-5}}_{-4.42\times10^{-5}}$
b_{c6} [g/L]	4.2×10^{-2}	$4.35 \times 10^{-2}{}^{+2.28\times10^{-3}}_{-1.67\times10^{-3}}$	$4.21 \times 10^{-2}{}^{+6.90\times10^{-5}}_{-1.00\times10^{-4}}$

4.2. Prediction uncertainty in internal concentration of SMB

The two parameter uncertainties estimated from Set α and Set β were propagated to the SMB model predictions. Figures 1 (a) and (b) show the simulation results at the true parameter and the uncertainty of the internal concentration profile by median and 68 %, 95 %, and 99.9 % prediction intervals (PI). These PIs were estimated by solving the SMB model with 1,000 sets of model parameters sampled from each of the posterior distributions from Set α and Set β. For each simulation, 20 cycles of continuous operation were performed to ensure that the process reached the cyclic steady state (CSS). The width of the 99.9 % PI for the internal concentration of each component is clearly narrower in (b) than in (a).

The reduction in the uncertainty on the internal concentration profiles of Set β from Set α can be explained by the data addition of the breakthrough test (B) used for parameter estimation. In the region where the two components are mixed, indicated by the arrow in Figure 1 (a), the median of PIs deviates significantly from the true value; in the same interval in Figure 1 (b), there is almost no spread in PIs. The interaction between b_{c5} and b_{c6} may appear significantly in the interval in which the two components mix at high concentrations, where the uncertainty can be reduced remarkably by including the data of the breakthrough test (B).

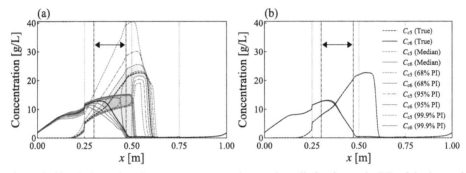

Figure 1. Simulation using the true parameter values and prediction intervals (PI) of the internal concentration profile. (a) PIs estimated from the posterior distribution from Set α. (b) PIs estimated from the posterior distribution from Set β.

4.3. Predictive Distribution of Product Purities and Recoveries

Similarly to the uncertainty of the internal concentration profile (Figure 1), the predictive distribution of product purity and recovery estimated from the posterior distribution of Set β was much less uncertain than that of Set α. Figure 2 (a1) to (a4) and (b1) to (b4) show the predictive distributions of purity $Pur_{Raff,c5}$ and $Pur_{Ext,c6}$ and recovery $Rec_{Raff,c5}$ and $Rec_{Ext,c6}$ estimated from the posterior distributions of Set α and Set β, respectively. In each graph, the abscissa is the purity or recovery, and the ordinate is the probability density, obtained from the model using the true parameters and two types of predictive distributions: one propagating only the parameter uncertainty and the other including observation error. As in Figure 1, the predictive distribution was estimated using 1,000 sets of parameters sampled from the posterior distribution. The predictive distributions for (b1) through (b4) are much sharper than those for (a1) through (a4).

By comparing the predictive distributions with and without observation error, we conclude that the influence of the parameter uncertainty estimated from Set β is sufficiently smaller than that of the observation error. For Set α, the two predictive distributions shown in Figure 2 (a1) to (a4) overlap each other, indicating that the parameter uncertainty is more dominant than the observation uncertainty. In contrast, for Set β shown in (b1) to (b4) of Figure 2, the magnitudes of the variances for the two predictive distributions differ significantly; the predictive distributions without observation error are very sharp, while those with observation error is widely distributed as nearly symmetric distributions; i.e., the observation uncertainty given as Gaussian noise is more dominant than the parameter uncertainty. This result confirms that, under the observation error assumed in this study, the influence of the parameter uncertainty estimated from Set β on the SMB model predictions is reduced sufficiently.

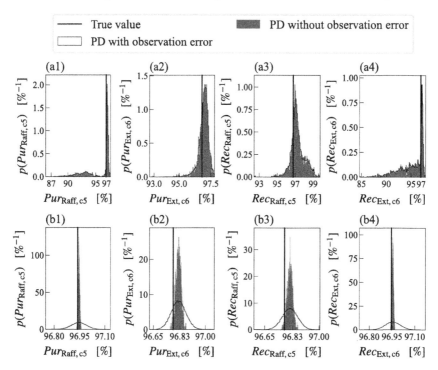

Figure 2. Predictive distributions (PD) of purity and recovery estimated from the posterior distributions of Set α—(a1), (a2), (a3), and (a4)—and of Set β—(b1), (b2), (b3), and (b4).

5. Conclusions

In this study, we quantified the prediction uncertainty in an SMB model and analyzed the influence of the parameter uncertainty on predictions from two different experiments. The resulting distributions allow us to evaluate the reliability of the model predictions and parameters and identify the necessary experiments. Estimating a predictive distribution that considers the uncertainty of the operating conditions such as flow rates and step time will be future work.

References

Bentley, J., Sloan, C., Kawajiri, Y., 2013. Simultaneous modeling and optimization of nonlinear simulated moving bed chromatography by the prediction-correction method. J. Chromatography. A 1280, 51–63.

Schmidt-Traub, H., Schulte, M., Seidel-Morgenstern, A., 2012. Preparative chromatography, 2nd ed. WILEY-VCH Verlag GmbH & Co.

Yamamoto, Y., Yajima, T., Kawajiri, Y., 2021. Uncertainty quantification for chromatography model parameters by Bayesian inference using sequential Monte Carlo method. Chem. Eng. Res. Des. 175, 223–237.

Proceedings of the 14th International Symposium on Process Systems Engineering – PSE 2021+
June 19-23, 2022, Kyoto, Japan © 2022 Elsevier B.V. All rights reserved.
http://dx.doi.org/10.1016/B978-0-323-85159-6.50158-5

A predictive model for multi-criteria selection of optimal thermochemical processing pathways in biorefineries

Mohammad Alherbawi, Ahmed AlNouss, Rajesh Govindan, Gordon McKay, Tareq Al-Ansari*

College of Science and Engineering, Hamad Bin Khalifa University, Qatar Foundation, Doha, Qatar.
*talansari@hbku.edu.qa

Abstract

The rapid growth of the global economy, combined with the growing demand for energy, environmental degradation from greenhouse gas emissions, and fluctuating fossil fuel prices, have emphasised the importance of renewable sources of energy. Biofuels produced from biomass conversion processes accounts for at least 13% of the gross global energy consumption and 70% of the world renewable energy mix. The biomass resources, including municipal, industrial and forestry waste, were proven to have a great potential for deriving various forms of energy in an affordable and reliable manner. In this regard, several thermochemical technologies have been developed to convert biomass waste into energy. However, due to the extremely heterogeneous characteristics of biomass resources, the feasibility and efficiency of these processes may greatly vary, depending on the biomass category and composition. Intensive experiments, simulations and optimisation models were developed to select the optimal processing pathway for each feedstock, which generally consume significant time and effort. To address this issue, it is desirable to seek novel and accurate mathematical representations that enable rapid performance estimation and multi-criteria selection for the optimal biomass processing pathway based on the physical properties and chemical compositions of different biomass categories, without the need for expensive experimental setup or time-consuming simulations. The objective of this study is to develop a mathematical model which links the biomass' proximate and elemental analyses to three crucial technology performance criteria; including the return on investment, energy efficiency, and carbon intensity. For this purpose, intensive simulations and sensitivity analyses were carried out using Aspen Plus to examine three main processes including gasification, pyrolysis and hydrothermal liquefaction (HTL). The comprehensive simulation data were subsequently used to develop and compare multiple meta-models for their accuracy of representation using regression algorithms. This model is believed to expedite the ongoing research on biomass thermo-processing and play a significant role towards enhancing biomass sustainability.

Keywords: Prediction model, Biomass, Gasification, Pyrolysis, Liquefaction.

1. Introduction

Biofuels, which are produced from biomass, nowadays contribute to nearly 70% of renewable mix and considered as a promising alternative fuel to reduce greenhouse gas emissions (WBA, 2019). In this context, wastes are the most abundant biomass for almost every country to be processed into valuable energy products. While thermochemical conversion pathways (i.e., gasification, pyrolysis, HTL) are now gaining more interest at the expense of the time-consuming biochemical processes like anaerobic digestion. Nevertheless, there is no single technology can efficiently accommodate all different types of wastes due to their extremely heterogeneous nature. Therefore, the selection of technologies that can handle this diversity is very important for bio-refineries. Selecting an optimal technology to process specific biomass resources have been presented earlier using different optimization techniques (Al-Ansari et al., 2020; Alherbawi et al., 2021a). However, these models are biomass-specific and do not often accommodate a wide range of biomass resources. As such there is a persistent need to provide a general model that can predict the optimal technology to process different biomass resources based on their composition and characteristics without the need to perform any intensive experiments or simulations. The assessment and the selection of the optimal waste to energy technology is a tricky process as it is closely linked with socio-economic and environmental factors, hence an appropriate solution for the above challenge has to be arrived at based on multi-criteria decision-making. For example, Yap and Nixon employed the analytic hierarchy process (AHP) model to identify the most suited waste to energy technology in the UK and India (Yap and Nixon, 2015). It was reported that gasification is the most appropriate technology for treating wastes in UK while anaerobic digestion is the best technique for India. Therefore, this study presents a prediction model for the selection of optimal thermochemical technology based on the proximate and elemental characteristics of biomass. The targeted processes are modelled using Aspen Plus, and evaluated in terms of their technical, environmental, and economic performance for a wide set of biomass compositions. The obtained data are utilized to develop a regression prediction model that correlates the different biomass compositions to the energy recovery, the return on investment and the possible greenhouse gas reduction relative to fossil resources.

2. Methodology

2.1. Processes Modelling

Advanced System for Process Engineering (Aspen Plus V.10) software is utilised for the development of the three thermochemical processes. All processes are modelled based on the assumptions of steady-state and isothermal conditions. For gasification modelling, Peng-Robinson package is selected to estimate fluid properties. In addition, biomass is initially defined as a nonconventional component referring to its proximate and elemental attributes. The nonconventional attributes are then converted into their corresponding components using a Fortran code. Steam is used as a gasifying medium with a steam to biomass ratio of 0.75, while the process is conducted at 850 °C and atmospheric pressure (AlNouss et al., 2021). The "RGibbs" reactor is used to simulate the key reactions which operates based on the minimization of the Gibbs' free energy. By the end of the process, biochar is collected using a cyclone, while the condensable volatiles are collected upon the cooling of the stream. The gasification process flowsheet is presented in Figure 1.

For pyrolysis process, biomass is initially dried then introduced into a grinder, whereby, the energy requirement for drying and grinding is adapted from (Cheng et al., 2020). The nonconventional stream is then converted into conventional components using a Fortran code based on the products distribution model of (Swagathnath et al., 2019). The process is simulated in an "RYield" reactor at 600 °C and atmospheric pressure with the supply of nitrogen gas to ensure an inert atmosphere (Alherbawi et al., 2021a). Char is then collected using a cyclone, while the volatile stream is cooled down for the collection of syngas and bio-oil. The process flowsheet of pyrolysis is presented in Figure 2.

A predictive model for multi-criteria selection of optimal thermochemical
processing pathways in biorefineries
951

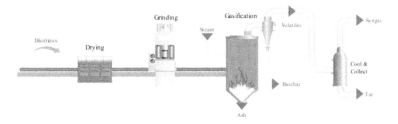

Figure 1: A simplified process flowsheet of gasification.

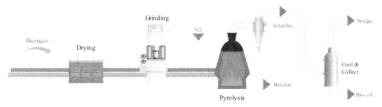

Figure 2: A simplified process flowsheet of pyrolysis.

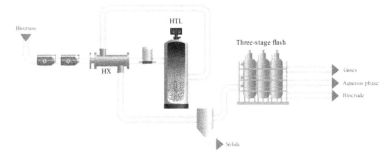

Figure 3: A simplified process flowsheet of hydrothermal liquefaction.

For HTL modelling, the non-random two-liquid (NRTL) thermodynamic package is used, while biomass is defined based on its proximate and elemental attributes. Water as added to create a slurry ensuring the organic solids do not exceed 20%. The slurry is then pumped using two consecutive high-performance pumps into the HTL reactor. The key sub-process is simulated using an "RYield" reactor, whereby, the maximum biocrude and minimum hydrochar yields are restricted based on the model developed by (Zhong and Wei, 2004) using a Fortran code. While the biocrude and hydrochar compositions are adapted from (Pedersen et al., 2017) and (Lentz et al., 2019) respectively. The syngas composition is then calculated in an "RGibbs" reactor via the minimization of the Gibbs' free energy. The process is conducted at 350 °C and 100 bar. In addition, solids are collected using a hydro-cyclone, while a three-stage flash drum is utilised to split the remaining stream into three phases: gas, biocrude and an aqueous phase. The HTL flowsheet is illustrated in Figure 3.

2.2. Technical, environmental and economic studies

Three criteria are selected to develop the prediction model for optimal processing pathway selection, including technical, environmental and economic aspects. At technical level, energy recovery is evaluated as a ratio of the generated energy to the consumed energy for each process. The generated energy is estimated based on the lower heating value of all products, while the consumed energy comprises utilities requirement and the calorific value of biomass. Whereas for the environmental study, the global warming potential (GWP) at process level (gate-to-gate approach) is evaluated. It comprises the greenhouse gases emitted to atmosphere during the process, as well as the GWP of utilities based on an emission factor of 0.58 $kgCO_2$-e/kWh (Spath and Mann, 2000). The GWP of each process is then evaluated in relation to that of charcoal (Bhattacharya et al., 2002). Nevertheless, an economic study is conducted for all processes using Aspen Process Economic Analyzer (APEA V.10). To achieve a high accuracy of capital costs evaluation, the key equipment prices are based on actual market prices, while scaled up/inflated based on the Chemical Engineering Plant's Cost Index (CEPCI) (Alherbawi et al., 2021b). The year 2019 is considered as the base year of analysis, while all processes plants are assumed to have a feed capacity of 30 t/h and a lifespan of 25 years. The return of investment (ROI) parameter is used for the comparison between the different processes and runs, which provides a ratio between net income and investment cost.

2.3. Regression Model

Regression approach is utilized to develop a prediction model that correlates the biomass characteristics and thermochemical processes performance. Six input parameters are considered in the model including moisture, ash, carbon, hydrogen, oxygen and nitrogen contents of biomass. Whereas three responses are observed including the energy recovery (%), the GHG reduction relative to charcoal (%), and the return on investment (%). Each input parameter is varied, while the remaining parameters are normalised with reference to a baseline biomass composition. The parameters are varied as follows: moisture (10-50 %), ash (6-18 %), carbon (30-70 %), hydrogen (4-12 %), oxygen (20-40) and nitrogen (1-5 %). The fixed carbon is assumed to be 50% of total carbon for all runs, while the volatile matter is found based on the difference (100% - fixed carbon – ash). In total 54 runs are conducted and evaluated. The obtained responses are then processed to develop a regression prediction model using Excel's Data Analysis tool.

2.4. Model Evaluation

The models have then been evaluated through providing three different biomass feedstocks to test the model performance against reported results from Aspen simulation.

Table 1: Biomass types for model evaluation.

Biomass	M*	FC	VM	Ash	C	H	N	O
Food waste	70.0	33.07	61.13	5.80	43.97	4.97	2.14	43.12
MWS	7.56	24.21	57.99	17.8	48.47	5.14	1.16	27.43
Waste Plastics	0.41	0.28	97.28	2.44	83.93	12.83	0	0.80

* M: moisture content on wet basis (%).

3. Results and Discussion

The developed model is evaluated by analysing the values of regression coefficients and analysis of variance (ANOVA). Besides, the extent of fit of the model equation is expressed by the determination coefficient R^2, while the model significance is evaluated through F-significance as presented in Table 2. The predicted R^2 values of (70.57 – 99.83 %) reflect a good correlation between the actual and predicted values of the responses. While the model significance is high since the lack of fit values (F-significance) are extremely low (0.01-8.5×10^{-13}). A maximum "F" value of 0.01 means that only 1% of the input data may possibly not fit into the model. The model suggested that the moisture, carbon and oxygen contents are the key influencing parameters for all responses.

Table 2: Regression models and their data fitting evaluation.

	Regression model*	F-Significance	R^2
Gasification	*Energy recovery* (%) $= 1.005 * C + 1.868 * O - 0.292 * M$	2.9×10^{-07}	97.07 %
	Emissions reduction (%) $= 4.036 - 4.456 * C - 5.217 * O - 0.639 * M$	2.5×10^{-05}	92.23 %
	Return on investment (%) $= 0.638 - 0.131 * C - 0.891 * O - 0.292 * M$	8.5×10^{-13}	99.83 %
Pyrolysis	*Energy recovery* (%) $= 1.303 - 0.316 * C - 0.476 * O - 1.060 * M$	8.2×10^{-11}	99.52 %
	Emissions reduction (%) $= 1.112 - 1.033 * O - 0.437 * M$	1.0×10^{-02}	70.57 %
	Return on investment (%) $= 0.777 - 0.307 * C - 0.974 * O - 0.453 * M$	1.5×10^{-08}	98.49 %
HTL	*Energy recovery* (%) $= -4.148 + 5.627 + 7.040 * O - 0.961 * M$	2.8×10^{-07}	97.10 %
	Emissions reduction (%) $= 2.619 - 2.006 * C - 2.887 * O + 0.248 * M$	1.6×10^{-04}	88.28 %
	Return on investment (%) $= -0.742 + 1.088 * C + 1.263 * O - 0.3 * M$	1.5×10^{-04}	88.40 %

* M: moisture content on wet basis (%), C & O: carbon and oxygen mass contents on dry basis (%).

The three responses are combined in one formula to indicate an overall efficiency for each process, considering an equal relative weight for each response. The final prediction model is presented in Eq.(1-3). The overall efficiency is a function of biomass characteristics which facilitates selecting the optimal processing pathway for each biomass, by satisfying the technical, environmental and economic aspects of the process. The highest overall efficiency amongst the three processes indicates the optimal technology for the tested biomass.

$$\textbf{\textit{Gasification overall efficiency}} \ (\%) = 1.668 - 1.057 * C - 1.413 * O - 0.408 * M \quad (1)$$

$$\textbf{\textit{Pyrolysis overall efficiency}} \ (\%) = 1.064 - 0.2076 * C - 0.828 * O - 0.65 * M \quad (2)$$

$$\textbf{\textit{HTL overall efficiency}} \ (\%) = -0.757 + 1.5698 * C + 1.8057 * O - 0.338 * M \quad (3)$$

The model is evaluated using the three biomass feedstocks in Table 1. The results as illustrated in Figure 4 demonstrate the excellence of HTL in the case of food waste that is high in moisture, fixed carbon and oxygen, gasification in the case of municipal solid waste (MSW) that is moderate in attributes, and pyrolysis in the case of waste plastic that is high in volatile matter and carbon content.

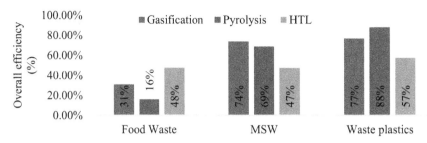

Figure 4: Results of model evaluation.

4. Conclusions

The study in hand presented a prediction model for the selection of optimal thermochemical processing pathway without the need for the costly experiments or time-consuming simulations. Whereby, the prediction model satisfies the technical, environmental and economic aspects of the selected optimal process based on the proximate and elemental attributes of different biomass resources. As such, this model is expected to contribute to the development of sustainable biomass-based energy production and expediate the ongoing research in biorefining field.

References

Al-Ansari, T., AlNouss, A., Al-Thani, N., Parthasarathy, P., ElKhalifa, S., Mckay, G., Alherbawi, M., 2020. Optimising Multi Biomass Feedstock Utilisation Considering a Multi Technology Approach, in: Pierucci, S., Manenti, F., Bozzano, G.L., Manca, D.B.T.-C.A.C.E. (Eds.), 30 European Symposium on Computer Aided Process Engineering. Elsevier, pp. 1633–1638.

Alherbawi, M., AlNouss, A., McKay, G., Al-Ansari, T., 2021a. Optimum sustainable utilisation of the whole fruit of Jatropha curcas: An energy, water and food nexus approach. Renew. Sustain. Energy Rev. 137, 110605.

Alherbawi, M., McKay, G., Mackey, H.R., Al-Ansari, T., 2021b. A novel integrated pathway for Jet Biofuel production from whole energy crops: A Jatropha curcas case study. Energy Convers. Manag. 229, 113662.

AlNouss, A., Mckay, G., Al-Ansari, T., 2021. Utilisation of Carbon Dioxide and Gasified Biomass for the Generation of Value Added Products, in: Türkay, M., Gani, R.B.T.-C.A.C.E. (Eds.), 31 European Symposium on Computer Aided Process Engineering. Elsevier, pp. 1567–1572.

Bhattacharya, S.C., Albina, D.O., Abdul Salam, P., 2002. Emission factors of wood and charcoal-fired cookstoves. Biomass and Bioenergy 23, 453–469.

Cheng, F., Luo, H., Colosi, L.M., 2020. Slow pyrolysis as a platform for negative emissions technology: An integration of machine learning models, life cycle assessment, and economic analysis. Energy Convers. Manag. 223, 113258.

Lentz, Z., Kolar, P., Classen, J., 2019. Valorization of Swine Manure into Hydrochars. Processes 7, 560.

Pedersen, T.H., Jensen, C.U., Sandström, L., Rosendahl, L.A., 2017. Full characterization of compounds obtained from fractional distillation and upgrading of a HTL biocrude. Appl. Energy 202, 408–419.

Spath, P.L., Mann, M.K., 2000. Life Cycle Assessment of a Natural Gas Combined-Cycle Power Generation System.

Swagathnath, G., Rangabhashiyam, S., Parthsarathi, K., Murugan, S., Balasubramanian, P., 2019. Modeling Biochar Yield and Syngas Production During the Pyrolysis of Agro-Residues BT - Green Buildings and Sustainable Engineering, in: Drück, H., Pillai, R.G., Tharian, M.G., Majeed, A.Z. (Eds.), . Springer Singapore, Singapore, pp. 325–336.

WBA, 2019. Global Bioenergy Statistics 2019.

Yap, H.Y., Nixon, J.D., 2015. A multi-criteria analysis of options for energy recovery from municipal solid waste in India and the UK. Waste Manag. 46, 265–277.

Zhong, C., Wei, X., 2004. A comparative experimental study on the liquefaction of wood. Energy 29, 1731–1741.

Proceedings of the 14th International Symposium on Process Systems Engineering – PSE 2021+
June 19-23, 2022, Kyoto, Japan © 2022 Elsevier B.V. All rights reserved.
http://dx.doi.org/10.1016/B978-0-323-85159-6.50159-7

Numerical Investigation of the Shear Rate Variation in Cooling Crystallization

Ken-Ichiro Sotowa[a*], Soranasataporn Pattana[a], Osamu Tonomura[a] and Sanghong Kim[b]

[a]Dept. of Chemical Engineering, Kyoto University, Nishikyo-ku, Kyoto 615-8510 Japan
[b]Dept. of Applied Physics and Chemical Engineering, Tokyo University of Agriculture and Technology, Naka-cho, Koganei, Tokyo 184-8588 Japan
sotowa@cheme.kyoto-u.ac.jp

Abstract

A recent numerical study on the mass transfer around a crystal showed that the mass transfer rate in a shear flow is greater than that in a uniform flow. In this study, we also demonstrated that this effect was greater for small crystals. This implies that under shear flow conditions, fine crystals grow faster, and a greater number of effective nuclei can be generated. In this study, the effect of shear flow on the size distribution of the product crystals was investigated. The evolution of the crystal size distribution in a batch cooling crystallizer was simulated by solving a population balance equation. Because batch crystallizers are operated under unsteady state conditions, the consequence of applying a shear in the early stage of the operation is expected to differ from that in the final stage. The numerical results obtained in this study showed that the crystal size distribution could be controlled by varying the profile of the shear rate.

Keywords: cooling crystallization, population balance equation, mass transfer, shear rate, dynamic operation

1.   Introduction

Crystallization is an important class of unit operation for purification. The quality of product crystals is largely determined by their size distribution. There are several different operations that create supersaturation, which is the driving force behind crystal deposition. One of the typical operations is cooling crystallization, in which the solution temperature is lowered such that the saturation concentration decreases below the solute concentration. In cooling crystallization, the temperature profile is the only parameter that can be manipulated to control the crystal size distribution. The impact of manipulating the temperature profile on the crystal size distribution was demonstrated using the programmed cooling method (Mullin and Nývlt, 1971).

Recently, a new type of crystallizer, which utilizes the Taylor–Couette flow, has drawn considerable attention because it allows better control over the crystal size (Nguyen et al., 2017). A Taylor–Couette crystallizer comprises two concentric cylinders with a small gap. The inner cylinder rotates and produces a uniform shear flow in the solution in the gap. A previous study claimed that this type of crystallizer could produce finer crystals with a smaller coefficient of variation (Nguyen et al., 2017). The characteristics of the Taylor–Couette apparatus have been investigated experimentally (Nguyen et al, 2010, Khuu et al, 2016), but the physics behind the improved size distribution has not been clarified.

Notably, the fluid in a stirred tank, which is used in cooling crystallization, is not uniform with respect to the mixing intensity. The turbulent intensity is high and the fluid rapidly deforms near the impeller, whereas circulating motion with the fluid around the mixing axis is dominant when the fluid element and the impeller are distant. The fluid motion in the Taylor–Couette crystallizer is different from that in the mixing tanks. The fluid is subject to a uniform and high shear rate, which differentiates the Taylor–Couette crystallizer from the stirred-tank crystallizer.

A recent numerical study on the mass transfer around a crystal showed that the mass transfer rate in shear flow is greater than that in a uniform flow (Kitagawa, 2018). The study also showed that this effect was magnified for small crystals. This implies that under shear flow conditions, the fine crystals grow faster, and a greater number of effective nuclei can be generated.

This study focused on the effect of the shear rate on the size distribution of crystals obtained from a cooling crystallizer. A simple model was developed to express the growth-enhancing effects of the shear flow. The evolution of the crystal size distribution was calculated using the population balance equation. The results showed that an increase in the shear rate reduced the average size of the crystals. The simulation study also showed that by dynamically changing the shear rate, both the average size and coefficient of variation can be controlled.

2.   Numerical model

The variation in the crystal size distribution in the cooling crystallizer was modeled using a population balance equation (Eq. 1).

$$\frac{\partial n}{\partial t} + \frac{\partial (Gn)}{\partial L} = 0 \quad n|_{L=0} = \frac{B}{G|_{L=0}}, \tag{1}$$

where n is the population density (number weighted) $[\#\cdot m^{-1}\cdot kg^{-1}]$, t is the time [s], L is the particle diameter, G is the growth rate $[m\cdot s^{-1}]$, and B is the nucleation rate $[\#\cdot s^{-1}\cdot kg^{-1}]$. The total mass balance of the solute is given by Eq. 2.

$$\frac{dC}{dt} = -3\rho_c k_v \int_0^\infty nL^2 G dL \tag{2}$$

Here, k_v and ρ_c are the volumetric shape factor [-] and crystal density $[kg\cdot m^{-3}]$, respectively. C $[kg\cdot(kg\ solvent)^{-1}]$ is the solute concentration in the bulk liquid. The solution of Eq. 2 is used to calculate the degree of supersaturation and subcooling, which are the driving forces of crystallization.

The kinetic parameters and solubility data for the numerical study were taken from a study on the cooling crystallization of potassium sulfate (Kobari et al., 2011, Kobari et al., 2012). The growth and nucleation rates are described as power functions of the degree of subcooling.

The kinetic data obtained from the literature were identified using data obtained from an experiment using a stirred tank. It is anticipated that each crystal in a stirred tank is subjected to a uniform flow of solution for most of the time. Kitagawa et al. (2018) numerically simulated mass transfer around a particle under uniform and shear flows. The results indicated that shear flow enhanced the mass transfer around the particles, in turn,

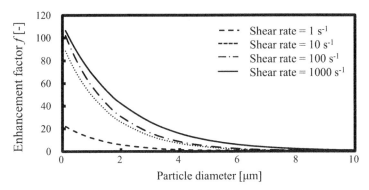

Figure 1 Enhancement factor as a function of the diameter and shear rate.

suggesting that the application of shear leads to increased nucleation and growth rates. The mass transfer data calculated by Kitagawa et al. (2018) were analyzed in this study, and the ratio of mass transfer rate under shear flow to that under uniform flow was expressed as a function of particle size and the shear rate (this ratio is referred to as the enhancement factor f [-] in the sequel).

To account for the effect of the shear rate on the crystallization, the growth rate was assumed to be greater than that obtained in a stirred tank experiment by a factor of f. This assumption holds when the rate-limiting step of crystal growth is the mass transfer of the solute from the bulk to the crystal surface. Another important assumption used in this study is that the mass transfer rate also results in an increase in the nucleation rate by a factor of f for $L=0$. In crystallization experiments, an increase in the stirring rate results in the formation of finer product crystals; thus, it is widely accepted that intensified mixing results in a higher nucleation rate. Because mixing is an act of enhancing mass transfer, this observation qualitatively justifies the assumption of the effect of shear rate on the nucleation rate.

The population balance equation (Eq. 1) was discretized using a backward difference scheme. A simulation program based on the Euler method was coded using the Python programming language. The simulation conditions were determined to reflect real crystallizer operations. No crystals existed at the beginning of cooling. The initial concentration of the solute was 0.199 kg·(kg solvent)$^{-1}$, and the initial temperature was the saturation temperature of the solution. The temperature of the solution was lowered by 20 °C at a constant rate.

3.   Results and discussion

A simulation of the cooling crystallizer was conducted for different cooling and shear rates. The resulting number-based average size decreased with increasing shear rate (Fig. 2). The model used in this study was built on the assumption that shear enhances both the nucleation and growth rate. An increased nucleation rate reduces the size of the crystals, but a greater growth rate leads to increased crystal size. The simulation results indicate that the nucleation rate has a stronger effect on the crystal size than the growth rate under the current simulation conditions.

 The effect of shear on the coefficient of variation (CV) is summarized in Fig. 3. The range of CV variation was approximately 0.28–0.38. With increasing cooling rate, CV

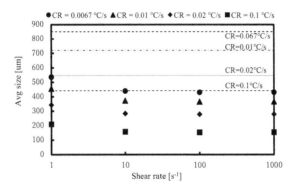

Figure 2 Effect of shear rate and cooling rate (CR) on the number-based average size. Plots show the results with shear, whereas lines indicate the average size of crystals when no shear was applied.

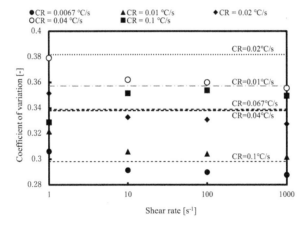

Figure 3 Effect of shear rate and cooling rate (CR) on the coefficient of variation. Plots show the results with shear, whereas lines indicate the average size of crystals when no shear was applied.

increased but reached a maximum when the cooling rate was 0.02 °C/s in the crystallizer operation without shear. The maximum CV was also recorded when the cooling rate was 0.04 °C/s in an operation with shear.

Because the cooling crystallizer is always in an unsteady state, the dynamic change in shear rate is expected to be a useful approach for controlling the crystal size distribution. Thus, we investigated the effect of stepwise changes in the shear rate on the crystal size distribution. In this simulation, the shear rate was zero at the beginning of the simulation and increased to 1000 s^{-1} at a certain time. Fig. 4 shows the variation in the number-based average size by the time of the step increase in the shear rate. The average size can be further reduced by applying a shear at the right time. When the shear started at the early stage of crystallization, the average size was insensitive to the time of the step increase. If the shear rate was changed near the end of the operation, the enhancement effect was small, and the average size approached that measured under the no shear condition. It was revealed that the maximum degree of subcooling was observed when approximately 1500 s lapsed. When shear was applied at this moment, numerous nuclei were formed, which, in turn, led to a reduction in the average size. However, when shear was applied after 1500 s, CV significantly increased, and then reached 0.7 when shear was applied at 1900 s. When the shear flow was applied too late, the nucleation process that was already ending started again, and this produced a second group of crystals.

The consequence of the step decrease in the shear rate was also examined. In this case, the shear rate was 1000 s^{-1} from the beginning of the simulation and reduced to 0 s^{-1} in a stepwise manner. The CV increased slightly and then decreased significantly as the step change time was delayed. The increase was caused by the change in shear rate, which resulted in the formation of two groups of crystals. However, as the high shear rate was applied longer, the number of crystals in the first group significantly increased because the degree of subcooling increased with time and greatly promoted the nucleation rate. At a certain point, this first group of particles, formed when the shear rate was high, will dominate over the group of crystals formed later. Consequently, the resulting crystal size distribution was nearly unimodal, and the overall CV decreased. However, if the shear flow was applied for too long, an excess number of particles would form and the average size would decrease, causing the CV to increase again.

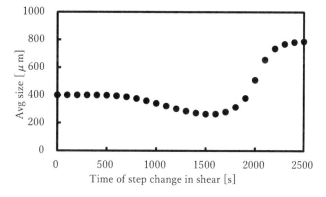

Figure 4 Time of step increase in the shear on the average size

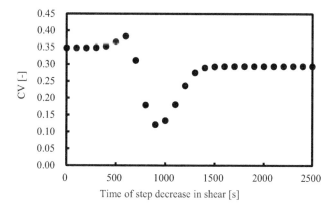

Figure 5 Time of step decrease in the shear on the average size

4. Conclusions

In this study, a model of a cooling batch crystallizer that reflects the effect of shear flow was developed. Various shear profiles were assumed, and their effects on crystal size distribution were investigated. It was demonstrated that shear flow could be utilized to reduce both the average size and coefficient of variation. It is anticipated that a further study on the optimal profile of shear rate will provide more insight into the operation of Taylor–Couette crystallizers.

Acknowledgements

This work was supported by JSPS KAKENHI (Grant Number 17H01339).

References

C.Q. Khuu, T.G. Dang, D.T. Nguyen, T.H. Le, T.T. Phan, T.T. Trinh and A.T. Nguyen, 2016, "Crystallization in Couette-Taylor crystallizer: Effect of Taylor vortices flow on the nucleation and reconstruction of L-glutamic acid in cooling crystallization," Journal of Science and Technology, **54**(5), pp. 625–631.

N. Kitagawa, K.-I. Sotowa, T. Horikawa and J.R. Alcantara-Avila, 2018, "The effect of shear flow on mass transfer rate around a crystal," The 31st International Symposium on Chemical Engineering, OF 07.

M. Kobari, N. Kubota and I. Hirasawa, 2011, "Computer simulation of metastable zone width for unseeded potassium sulfate aqueous solution," Journal of Crystal Growth, **317**(1), pp. 64–69.

M. Kobari, N. Kubota and I. Hirasawa, 2012, "Secondary nucleation-mediated effects of stirrer speed and growth rate on induction time for unseeded solution," CrystEngComm, **14**(16), pp. 5255–5261.

J.W. Mullin and J. Nývlt, 1971, "Programmed cooling of batch crystallizers," Chemical Engineering Science, **26**(3), pp. 369–377.

A.T. Nguyen, J. Kim, S. Chang and W. Kim, 2010, "Taylor vortex effect on phase transformation of guanosine 5-monophosphate in drowning-out crystallization," Industrial and Engineering Chemistry Research, **49**(10), pp. 4865–4872.

A.T. Nguyen, T. Yu and W. Kim, 2017, "Couette–Taylor crystallizer: Effective control of crystal size distribution and recovery of l-lysine in cooling crystallization," Journal of Crystal Growth, **469**, pp. 65–77.

Proceedings of the 14th International Symposium on Process Systems Engineering – PSE 2021+
June 19-23, 2022, Kyoto, Japan © 2022 Elsevier B.V. All rights reserved.
http://dx.doi.org/10.1016/B978-0-323-85159-6.50160-3

Application of machine learning model to optimization of the hydrogen liquefaction process

Seongwoong Min[a], Amjad Riaz[a], Muhammad Abdul Qyyum[b], Hansol Choe[a], Sang-gi Moon[a], Moonyong Lee[a*]

[a]*Process Systems Design & Control Laboratory, School of Chemical Engineering, Yeungnam University, Gyeongsan, 38541 Republic of Korea*
[b]*Department of Petroleum & Chemical Engineering, Sultan Qaboos University, OMAN*
mynlee@yu.ac.kr

Abstract

Process optimization is an essential step for a feasible and cost-effective process design. However, problems arise due to more decision variables within the process for a complex system. In complex processes, many design and target variables have large nonlinear relationships that make it challenging to achieve the global optima. This study attempted to overcome the complexity of hydrogen liquefaction and nonlinear optimization processes. Optimize the simulation model to measure the time taken and compare it to the estimate made by the machine learning model. The basic process was simulated in Aspen HYSYS, while the machine learning model and optimization were carried out using the particle swarm optimization algorithm in MATLAB environment. Interestingly, the model optimization results of the ANN approach showed significantly less time and improved prediction.

Keywords: hydrogen liquefaction; machine learning; optimization; surrogate

1. Introduction

Liquefaction is one of the methods for storage and transportation of hydrogen (Durbin & Malardier-Jugroot, 2013), which is considered the future energy source (International Energy Agency, 2019). The liquefaction of hydrogen occurs at a very low temperature, 20 K, making it an energy-intensive process. Therefore, it is critical to minimize energy consumption through optimization in design, such as process simulation of the hydrogen liquefaction process. However, due to the fundamental problem of many optimization variables, direct optimization of the simulation process requires a considerable amount of time and effort, even with high-performance computers. In this situation, the applicability of machine learning techniques has great potential, as foretold by Qadeer et al. (2018) in their study for offshore LNG units.

Machine learning is a field of artificial intelligence technology that implements human intelligence through computers. Learning techniques include supervised learning, unsupervised learning, and reinforcement learning. The computers trained in these methods provide predictions or judgments for their models (Batta, 2020; Lecun et al., 2015). When a model is well-learned about a relationship, it is also called a surrogate model because it can provide the same results as a specific 'real' model that actually describes the relationship.

In this study, the relationship between design variables and performance parameters of the hydrogen liquefaction process was learned through machine learning, and the optimization results and computational load of two models optimized with the same algorithm were compared. It is expected to improve the computational load of a complex hydrogen liquefaction process using a well-trained surrogate model.

2. Hydrogen liquefaction Process

In this study, a triple mixed refrigerant (TMR) cycles hydrogen liquefaction process is considered from our previous works (Riaz et al., 2021), from now on called as Base Model (BM). BM process uses different mixed refrigerants (MR) for three refrigeration cycles; Precooling MR, Cooling MR, and Liquefaction MR's refrigeration. Figure 1 shows the process flowsheet diagram, whereas Table 1 shows feed conditions and mass flow rate of gaseous hydrogen (GH2) and liquid hydrogen (LH2) (Aasadnia & Mehrpooya, 2018).

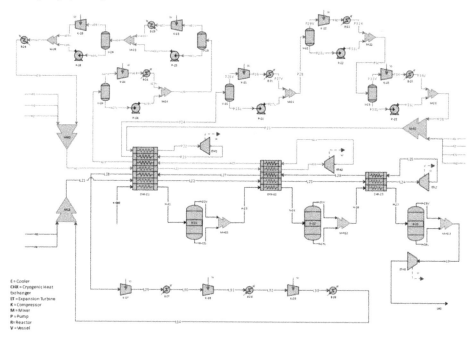

E = Cooler
CHX = Cryogenic Heat Exchanger
ET = Expansion Turbine
K = Compressor
M = Mixer
P = Pump
R = Reactor
V = Vessel

Figure 1 Process flowsheet of the BM (Riaz et al., 2021)

The hydrogen feed stream is precooled to 118 K and then sent to the ortho-para conversion (OPC) reactor. At 118 K, conversion reaches 13% and increases the share of para-hydrogen from 25 % to 35 %. At 34 K, the outlet stream flows to the next OPC reactor, increasing the para-hydrogen composition to 92.6 % with a percent conversion of 88.5 %. Similarly, the third reactor increases the molar percentage to 99.4 % by achieving 92 % conversion. As a result, a 100 % saturated liquid hydrogen (LH$_2$) is obtained as a product.

In each cycle, the hot pressurized refrigerant stream is cooled to the same temperature as the H$_2$ stream. The respective cold stream gives its pressure energy in the form of useful work in an expander. The resultant cold stream is returned through the cryogenic heat exchanger (CHX) as cooling media. These streams enter the compression section at the hot end to close the loop.

Table 1 Process conditions of the gaseous and liquid hydrogen

Parameter		GH2	LH2
Temperature, K		298	21
Pressure, bar		21	1.3
Mass Flowrate, kg/s		1	1
Molar composition, %	Ortho-	74.92	0.59
	Para-	25.08	99.41

The design parameters and assumptions for the hydrogen liquefaction process presented in Table 1 and Table 2 are kept the same as BM. The low temperature of the cooling cycle is achieved because of a relatively high content of nitrogen and hydrogen in an optimum ratio. Also, it approaches the critical temperature of H_2 (33K). In terms of hydrogen, the high flow rate of H_2 increases the power requirement. In the refrigerant stream, Helium, one of the refrigerant candidates, in the refrigerant stream decreases the power needed by slightly increasing the flow rate. The presence of a high-boiling or low-boiling part as refrigerant results in little or no waste thermodynamically. For reducing energy consumption, it needs an optimal combination of refrigerants.

Table 2 Details of the BM refrigeration cycles (refrigerant flowrates and suction/discharge pressures

Component	Precooling cycle	Cooling cycle	Liquefaction cycle
C1 [kg/s]	4.683	2.280	
C2 [kg/s]	1.438		
C3 [kg/s]	18.291		
N2 [kg/s]	2.075	23.021	
H2 [kg/s]		3.185	1.640
He [kg/s]			0.173
Suction P [bar]	3.8	2.9	4.4
Discharge P [bar]	42	59	34

3. Machine learning application result

This study analyzed the results by utilizing the possibility of imitation of machine learning-based models for complex relationships between inputs and outputs. Furthermore, the results were compared by applying the optimization to the simulated base model (BM) and the trained machine learning model (MLM).

The base model is the TMR Cycles H_2 liquefaction process simulated in Aspen HYSYS, and the MLM is trained in MATLAB with a fully connected neural network structure (Figure 2). The learning of the MLM used about 1,600 randomly generated data from the BM case study. In machine learning, data were used for training/validation/testing at a ratio of 70:15:15. The result of machine learning is shown in Figure 3. As shown in Figure 3, R is greater than 0.999, and the mean squared error, which means the performance of the MLM, is also 0.01, so it can be seen that the MLM is well learned, and the BM is described with high accuracy.

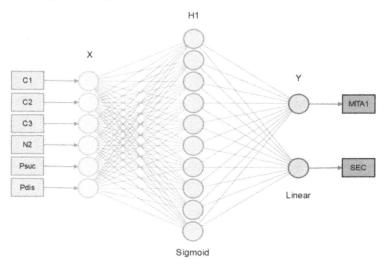

Figure 2 Artificial neural network structure of MLM

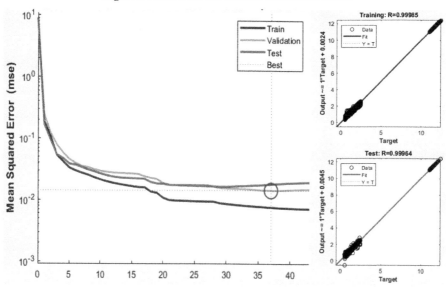

Figure 3 Training result of MLM

Both models were optimized using the Particle Swarm Optimization algorithm (PSO) (Zhou & Liao, 2013) programmed in MATLAB. The PSO algorithm is an algorithm that mathematically models the social information sharing behavior of individuals belonging to groups of ants, fish, and birds. From a probabilistic point of view, it is effective to find the global optimum. We tried to learn and optimize the MLM for all existing models. However, there were too many decision variables, so we focused on the precooling section of the hydrogen liquefaction process for preliminary research.

Therefore, there are 15 determinant variables in the base hydrogen liquefaction process. However, only six variables were considered: the precooling unit's suction and discharge pressures and the mass flow rate of the mixed refrigerant components. The optimization will proceed to minimize the specific energy consumption (SEC) of the hydrogen liquefaction process with these six variables. The constraints to be applied during optimization were kept such that the heat exchanger's minimum temperature approach (MITA) was not less than 1 °C. Table 3 shows the PSO results and elapsed time of BM and MLM.

Table 3 PSO best position and optimal parameters of BM and MLM

Input variables	BM	MLM
N2 Mass Flow [kg/s]	1.746	1.8475
C1 Mass Flow [kg/s]	5.103	5.3193
C2 Mass Flow [kg/s]	1.604	0.72
C3 Mass Flow [kg/s]	20.170	20.2719
Discharge Pressure [kPa]	4,600.456	5,459.604
Suction Pressure [kPa]	522.245	570
Optimal output parameters		
MITA [°C]	0.99943	1.041078
SEC [kWh/kgH2]	11.040	11.01352
Elapsed time [s]	43,133.30073	3.243759

In Table 3, the values of the six decision variables and the optimal parameter values are slightly different, but it can be seen that they are within an acceptable range. On the other hand, the optimization time took 10,000 times more for BM than for MLM. This is due to the fundamental difference between the mathematical calculation models of BM and MLM. BM is a fundamental process simulation model, and it is a result value derived through material and energy balance and thermodynamic calculations. Various processing units between input and output delay the calculation time even more. However, on the other hand, MLM has a very light neural network structure to have many advantages in terms of time.

4. Conclusions

This study checked the machine learning model's performance as an imitation. We analyzed how well the self-learning model imitates the existing model and how different the results are for certain tasks under the same conditions. Based on these results, for the analysis of the hydrogen value chain in various scenarios in the future hydrogen economy society, the limited system in this study can be expanded with a deeper and more advanced surrogate model. However, the system's expansion, such as the entire hydrogen liquefaction process, is accompanied by more determinants, making it difficult to collect and learn data. Therefore, it is necessary to actively utilize artificial intelligence and machine learning technology. It is essential to introduce big data processing techniques such as dimension reduction using principal components analysis.

Acknowledgment

This work was supported by the National Research Foundation of Korea (NRF) grant funded by the Korean government (MSIT) (2021R1A2C1092152); Priority Research Centers Program through the National Research Foundation of Korea (NRF) funded by the Ministry of Education (2014R1A6A1031189); "Human Resources Program in Energy Technology" of the Korea Institute of Energy Technology Evaluation and Planning (KETEP), granted financial resource from the Ministry of Trade, Industry & Energy, Republic of Korea. (*No. 20204010600100*).

References

(IEA), I. E. A. (2019). *The Future of Hydrogen*. OECD. https://doi.org/10.1787/1e0514c4-en

Aasadnia, M., & Mehrpooya, M. (2018). Conceptual design and analysis of a novel process for hydrogen liquefaction assisted by absorption precooling system. *Journal of Cleaner Production, 205*, 565–588. https://doi.org/10.1016/j.jclepro.2018.09.001

Batta, M. (2020). Machine Learning Algorithms - A Review. *International Journal of Science and Research (IJ, 9*(1), 381-undefined. https://doi.org/10.21275/ART20203995

Durbin, D. J., & Malardier-Jugroot, C. (2013). Review of hydrogen storage techniques for on board vehicle applications. *International Journal of Hydrogen Energy, 38*(34), 14595–14617. https://doi.org/10.1016/j.ijhydene.2013.07.058

Lecun, Y., Bengio, Y., & Hinton, G. (2015). Deep learning. *Nature, 521*(7553), 436–444. https://doi.org/10.1038/nature14539

Qadeer, K., Qyyum, M. A., & Lee, M. (2018). Krill-Herd-Based Investigation for Energy Saving Opportunities in Offshore Liquefied Natural Gas Processes [Research-article]. *Industrial and Engineering Chemistry Research, 57*(42), 14162–14172. https://doi.org/10.1021/acs.iecr.8b02616

Riaz, A., Qyyum, M. A., Min, S., Lee, S., & Lee, M. (2021). Performance improvement potential of harnessing LNG regasification for hydrogen liquefaction process: Energy and exergy perspectives. *Applied Energy, 301*(April), 117471. https://doi.org/10.1016/j.apenergy.2021.117471

Zhou, F., & Liao, Z. (2013). A particle swarm optimization algorithm. *Applied Mechanics and Materials, 303–306*, 1369–1372. https://doi.org/10.4028/www.scientific.net/AMM.303-306.1369

Proceedings of the 14th International Symposium on Process Systems Engineering – PSE 2021+
June 19-23, 2022, Kyoto, Japan © 2022 Elsevier B.V. All rights reserved.
http://dx.doi.org/10.1016/B978-0-323-85159-6.50161-5

Density Functional Theory on the CO_2 Absorption Process with Ionic Liquids

Diego Román-Montalvo, Myrna H. Matus*

*a*Instituto de Química Aplicada, Universidad Veracruzana, Av. Luis Castelazo Ayala S/N, Col. Industrial-Ánimas, Xalapa, Ver., 91190, Mexico
myhernandez@uv.mx

Abstract

CO_2 is a pollutant which is commonly produced through industrial processes. In this work, Computational Chemistry tools are applied to seven choline based ionic liquids (ILs), which are used as an alternative to traditional organic solvents in the CO_2 extraction. The study was performed at the PBE-D3/6-311++G** level of calculation, including the solvent effect (water in this case), thus analyzing weak interactions. It was found that these ILs form hydrogen bond networks which favors the complex formation with CO_2, therefore this allows a more efficient absorption process. In addition, the complex formation process was found to be close to the thermodynamic equilibrium, which is key in the IL recovery, with the aim to be used in several CO_2 absorption cycles.

Keywords: Ionic liquids, CO_2 absorption, computational chemistry.

1. Introduction

Production of green-house gases is a worldwide problem linked to global warming and climate change. One of the main greenhouse gases is carbon dioxide (CO_2), which is generated as a byproduct in a variety of chemical reactions, such as combustion, which are part of all kinds of industrial processes (Lamb *et al.*, 2021). Therefore, research has focused on diverse strategies to diminish CO_2 production, which otherwise would be released to the environment. In this case, certain solvents are used to absorb and capture these green-house gases; however, organic solvents, such amines, are used for this purpose thus producing other waste which also generates pollution (Mazari, 2015).

For this reason and guided by Green Chemistry principles (Anastas & Eghbali, 2010), there is an interest in employing more environmentally friendly solvents, such as ionic liquids (ILs). ILs present many interesting properties, for example, low vapor pressure, high thermal stability, low toxicity, high solvation efficiency, and wide versatility; in addition, they can be recovered once the process has been carried out, thus being reutilized for several cycles. In that way, they are considered as green solvents and they may be a good choice for replacing traditional solvents (Plechkova & Seddon, 2008; Weingärtner, 2008).

To develop efficient absorption processes, it is necessary that ILs present a very good affinity to the CO_2. In previous theoretical studies, ILs with amino-acids as anions have been used for this purpose, for example, with amino-groups (Kasahara *et al.*, 2016), 1–butyl–3–methylimidazolium (Noorani & Mehrdad, 2020), or phosphonium-groups (Shaikh *et al.*, 2020) as the corresponding cations. In this work, Computational Chemistry tools are proposed to carry out a thermochemical analysis for the CO_2 absorption with choline based and amino-acids ILs, as well as a non-covalent interactions analysis for the IL-CO_2 complexes under study. The selection of choline *versus* other cations is due to its non-toxicity, since it is considered an essential dietary amine (Rakkar & Hillier, 2007), therefore these ILs can be cataloged as green solvents (Anastas & Eghbali, 2010).

2. Methodology

In this study, the choline cation ([Ch^+]) was employed together with the organic anions: alaninate ([Ala^-]), butanoate [But^-], propanoate [$EtCO2^-$], glycinate [Gly^-], leucinate [Leu^-], lysinate [Lys^-], and salicylate [Sal^-].

Initial preoptimization of the ion structures was carried out through the PM3 semiempirical (Stewart, 1989), the lowest energy structures were calculated with the B3LYP functional (Andzelm & Wimmer, 1992; Becke, 1993; Stephens *et al.*, 1994) and the DGDZVP2 basis set (Godbout *et al.*, 1992), and again the lowest energy structures were selected to be reoptimized with the PBE functional (Perdew *et al.*, 1996), including dispersion (D3; Grimme *et al.*, 2010), and the basis set 6-311++G** (Hehre *et al.*, 1986). Once the ions of the ILs were obtained, ILs were built, employing several spacial distributions between anions and cations with the aid of the electrostatic potential surfaces of the corresponding ions.

The lowest energy structures of the ILs were thus employed to obtain the complexes with the CO_2 molecule, IL-CO_2, and the gas-phase lowest energy structures were calculated including the solvent effect of water through the COSMO implicit solvation model (Klamt & Schüürmann, 1993). Calculations for the IL formation were carried out through the program package Gaussian 09 (Frisch *et al.*, 2016); whereas the complex formation calculations and addition of the solvent effect were performed using NWChem 6.6 (Valiev *et al.*, 2009). Additionally, frequency calculations were included to ensure the minima on the potential energy surface.

The thermochemistry of the ILs and the IL-CO_2 complexes formation was obtained according to Eqs. (1, 2). For IL, the reactants were the corresponding anion and cation, and the product was the IL under study; in the case of the complexes, the reactants were the IL and the CO_2, and the product was the IL-CO_2 complex. Basis set superposition errors (BSSE) were included through the Counterpoise method (Boys & Bernardi, 1970).

$$Cation + Anion \rightarrow IL \tag{1}$$

$$IL + CO_2 \rightarrow IL - CO_2 \tag{2}$$

In addition, inter- and intramolecular interactions present in the ILs and the IL-CO_2 complexes were analyzed through the Atoms in Molecules (AIM; Bader, 1991) and Non-Covalent Interactions (NCI; Johnson *et al.*, 2010) methodologies as implemented in GPUAM (Hernández-Esparza *et al.*, 2014; Hernández-Esparza *et al.*, 2019; Cruz *et al.*, 2019).

3. Results and Discussion

3.1. Ionic liquids

Table 1 shows the thermochemistry for the formation of the choline based ILs under study. According to the results, the IL formation is a slightly exothermic process, as shown by the enthalpy; whereas the Gibbs energy presents a non-spontaneous or endergonic process, through positive values, except for the complex with leucinate as anion, which is slightly negative. Even though the formation process in not spontaneous at standard conditions, it may be achieved in the laboratory by changing the conditions of the experiment.

Table 1. Thermochemistry for the formation of the choline based ILs under study at standard conditions.

IL	ΔH [kJ/mol]	ΔS [J/mol*K]	ΔG [kJ/mol]
[Ch][Ala]	-35.80	-140.13	5.99
[Ch][But]	-38.81	-163.45	9.92
[Ch][EtCO2]	-43.25	-166.51	6.36
[Ch][Gly]	-43.12	-169.02	7.29
[Ch][Leu]	-56.94	-189.79	-0.33
[Ch][Lys]	-48.99	-199.92	10.63
[Ch][Sal]	-40.91	-189.87	15.74

An example from the AIM and NCI results is shown in Fig. 1, where [Ch][EtCO₂] presents interactions between the hydroxyl group of the choline cation and the carboxylate of the anion (pink lines); in this case, NCI results show a strong hydrogen bond through the red isosurface. In addition to the hydrogen bonds in the IL structure, van der Waals interactions (green isosurfaces) were also found, which is key to the stability.

In a similar way, intramolecular interactions between the cation and the anion are also depicted. Similar interactions are found in all the studied ILs, where O–H···O and C–H···O hydrogen bonds are formed between the cation, as hydrogen bond donor, and the anion, as hydrogen bond acceptor. A slightly different behavior is present for ILs containing [Ala⁻], [Leu⁻], and [Lys⁻], since the carboxylate group is near the amine group; in a similar way, [Sal⁻] presents an intramolecular O–H···O hydrogen bond with the carboxylate group.

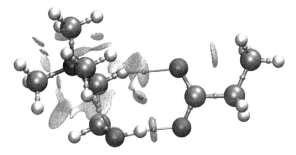

Figure 1. AIM and NCI for the [Ch][EtCO₂].

3.2. Ionic liquids and CO₂ complexes

Table 2 shows the thermochemistry for the formation of the IL-CO₂ complexes under study. The enthalpy for the formation process of the IL-CO₂ complex is less exothermic, in comparison with the formation of the sole IL. In a similar trend, the Gibbs energy is more endothermic in comparison with the IL, indicating a non-spontaneous process, which may be overcome through experiments at non-standard conditions. These values also indicate that IL-CO₂ complexes are more stable structures in comparison with the corresponding IL.

An interesting characteristic can be appreciated in the complex formation process, which in all cases is close to the thermodynamic equilibrium. This is very important, since this would allow the recovery of the IL; in this way, the ILs under study could be reused in several cycles of the absorption process.

Table 2. Thermochemistry for the formation of the IL-CO₂ complexes under study.

IL-CO₂ Complex	ΔH [kJ/mol]	ΔS [J/mol*K]	ΔG [kJ/mol]
[Ch][Ala]-CO₂	-20.10	-194.94	38.02
[Ch][But]-CO₂	-6.87	-107.64	25.25
[Ch][EtCO2]-CO₂	-8.83	-105.67	22.69
[Ch][Gly]-CO₂	-9.34	-65.65	10.26
[Ch][Leu]-CO₂	-8.92	-91.19	18.25
[Ch][Lys]-CO₂	-1.72	-104.67	29.52
[Ch][Sal]-CO₂	-4.02	-91.69	23.32

Fig. 2 shows an example related to Fig. 1, i.e., the AIM and NCI results for the [Ch][EtCO₂]-CO₂ complex. In this case, interactions between CO₂ and the ions of the IL are present; this can be observed through the NCI green isosurfaces, which show van der Waals interactions, as well as through the pink lines of the AIM results. In addition, possible hydrogen bonds were also found in the structure, especially those between the cation and the anion, where the smallest distance is 1.62 Å (see red isosurface). Similar results were found for the rest of the ILs.

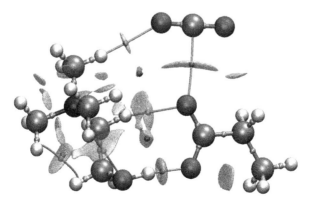

Figure 2. AIM and NCI for the [Ch][EtCO₂]-CO₂ complex.

4. Conclusions

In this work, the thermochemistry for the IL and IL-CO$_2$ complex formations were studied. Results show that hydrogen bonds between the carboxylates from the anions and cholinium cation are the main structural characteristic which provides stability to the ILs. In a similar way, IL-CO$_2$ complexes also present weak interactions between the ions and the CO$_2$, this consideration includes hydrogen bonds, where these interactions are important for the CO$_2$ absorption process.

With respect to the thermochemistry, energetics show that the IL-CO$_2$ complex formation is close to the thermodynamic equilibrium. This characteristic is very important since it is related to the possibility of the IL to be easily recovered and reused.

According to the results, all the studied ILs are good for the CO$_2$ absorption process, however, there is a slight preference for [Ch][Leu], since it presents an exergonic value for the Gibbs energy. The rest of the ILs are energetically close, therefore other considerations must be taken into account, such as cost and availability. In this way, CO$_2$ may be absorbed and further employed in other processes, such as biomass production.

Acknowledgments

MHM acknowledges Conacyt for grant CB-2016-284220. DRM acknowledges Conacyt for the scholarship No. 284220-28391-4307 through grant CB-2016-284220 and for the Master's degree No. 775129. Part of this work was carried out in the Yoltla Supercomputer at the *Laboratorio Nacional de Cómputo de Alto Desempeño* (LANCAD), Universidad Autónoma Metropolitana-Iztapalapa.

References

P. Anastas & N. Eghbali, 2010, Green Chemistry: Principles and Practice, Chem. Soc. Rev., 39, 1, 301-312.

R. F. W. Bader, 1991, A Quantum Theory of Molecular Structure and its Applications, Chem. Rev., 91, 893–928.

S. F. Boys & F. Bernardi, 1970, The Calculation of Small Molecular Interactions by the Differences of Separate Total Energies. Some Procedures with Reduced Errors, Mol. Phys., 19, 4, 553–566.

A. D. Becke, 1993, A New Mixing of Hartree–Fock and Local Density-Functional Theories, J. Chem. Phys., 98, 2, 1372–1377.

J. C. Cruz; R. Hernández-Esparza; A. Vázquez-Mayagoitia; R. Vargas; J. Garza, 2019, Implementation of the Molecular Electrostatic Potential Over Graphics Processing Units, J. Chem. Inf. Model, 59, 7, 3120–3127.

N. Godbout; D. R Salahub; J. Andzelm; E. Wimmer, 1992, Optimization of Gaussian-Type Basis Sets for Local Spin Density Functional Calculations. Part I. Boron Through Neon, Optimization Technique and Validation, Can. J. Chem., 70, 2, 560–571.

S. Grimme; J. Antony; S. Ehrlich; H. Krieg, 2010, A Consistent and Accurate Ab Initio Parametrization of Density Functional Dispersion Correction (DFT-D) for the 94 Elements H-Pu, J. Chem. Phys., 132, 15, 154104.

W. J. Hehre; L. Random; P. v. R. Schleyer; J. A. Pople, 1986, Ab Initio Molecular Orbital Theory, Wiley.

R. Hernández-Esparza; S. M. Mejía-Chica; A. D. Zapata-Escobar; A. Guevara-García; A. Martínez-Melchor; J. M. Hernández-Pérez; R. Vargas; J. Garza, 2014, Grid-based Algorithm to Search

Critical Points, in the Electron Density, Accelerated by Graphics Processing Units, J. Comput. Chem., 35, 31, 2272–2278.

R. Hernández-Esparza; A. Vázquez-Mayagoitia; L. A. Soriano-Agueda; R. Vargas; J. Garza, 2019, GPUs as Boosters to Analyze Scalar and Vector Fields in Quantum Chemistry, Int. J. Quantum Chem., 119, 2, e25671.

E. R. Johnson; S. Keinan; P. Mori-Sánchez; J. Contreras-García; A. J. Cohen; W. Yang, 2010, Revealing Noncovalent Interactions, J. Am. Chem. Soc., 132, 6498–6506.

S. Kasahara; E. Kamio; A. R. Shaikh; T. Matsuki; H. Matsuyama, 2016, Effect of the Amino-Group Densities of Functionalized Ionic Liquids on the Facilitated Transport Properties for CO_2 Separation, J. Membr. Sci., 503, 148–157.

A. Klamt; G. J. Schüürmann, 1993, COSMO: A New Approach to Dielectric Screening in Solvents with Explicit Expressions for the Screening Energy and its Gradient, J. Chem. Soc., Perkin Trans., 2, 5, 799–805.

W. F. Lamb; T. Wiedmann; J. Pongratz; R. Andrew; M. Crippa; J. G. J. Olivier; D. Wiedenhofer; G. Mattioli; A. A. Khourdajie; J. House, 2021, An Review of Trends and Drivers of Greenhouse Gas Emissions by Sector from 1990 to 2018, Environ. Res. Lett., 16, 7, 073005.

S. A. Mazari; B. S. Ali; B. M. Jan; I. M. Saeed; S. Nizamuddin, 2015, An Overview of Solvent Management and Emissions of Amine-based CO_2 Capture Technology, Int. J. Greenh. Gas Control, 34, 129-140.

N. Noorani & A. Mehrdad, 2020, CO_2 Solubility in some Amino Acid-Based Ionic Liquids: Measurement, Correlations and DFT Studies, Fluid Phase Equilibr., 517, 112591.

R. G. Parr & W. Yang, 1989, Density Functional Theory of Atoms and Molecules, Oxford University Press, 989.

J. P. Perdew; K. Burke; M. Ernzerhof, 1996, Generalized Gradient Approximation Made Simple, Phys. Rev. Lett., 77, 18, 3865.

N. V. Plechkova, & K. R. Seddon, 2008, Applications of Ionic Liquids in the Chemical Industry, Chem. Soc. Rev., 37, 1, 123–150.

M. Rakkar & K. Hillier, 2007, "Choline" in xPharm: The Comprehensive Pharmacology Reference, S. J. Enna & D. B. Bylunds, Eds., Elsevier, 1–4.

A. R. Shaikh; M. Ashraf; T. AlMayef; M. Chawla; A. Poater; L. Cavallo, 2020, Amino Acid Ionic Liquids as Potential Candidates for CO_2 Capture: Combined Density Functional Theory and Molecular Dynamics Simulations, Chem. Phys. Lett., 745, 137239.

P. J. Stephens; F. J. Devlin; C. F. N. Chabalowski; M. J. Frisch, 1994, Ab Initio Calculation of Vibrational Absorption and Circular Dichroism Spectra Using Density Functional Force Fields, J. Phys. Chem., 98, 45, 11623–11627.

J. J. Stewart, 1989, Optimization of Parameters for Semiempirical Methods I. Method, J. Comput. Chem., 10, 2, 209–220.

M. Valiev; E. J. Bylaska; N. Govind; K. Kowalski.; T. P. Straatsma; H. J. Van Dam; D. Wang; J. Nieplocha; E. Apra; T. L. Windus; W. A. De Jong, 2009, NWChem: A Comprehensive and Scalable Open-Source Solution for Large Scale Molecular Simulations, Comput. Phys. Commun., 181, 9, 1477–1489.

H. Weingärtner, 2008, Understanding Ionic Liquids at the Molecular Level: Facts, Problems, and Controversies, Angew. Chem. Int. Ed., 47, 4, 654-670.

Proceedings of the 14th International Symposium on Process Systems Engineering – PSE 2021+
June 19-23, 2022, Kyoto, Japan © 2022 Elsevier B.V. All rights reserved.
http://dx.doi.org/10.1016/B978-0-323-85159-6.50162-7

Transport of CO_2/CH_4 through PEBA membranes: experiments and mass transfer modelling

Alejandro Solis-Jácome[a], Victor M. Rivera[a], Griselda Castruita de León[b], Miguel A. Morales-Cabrera[a*]

[a]*Facultad de Ciencias Químicas, Universidad Veracruzana, Xalapa, Veracruz, C.P. 91000, México.*
[b]*Centro de Investigación en Química Aplicada, Saltillo, Coahuila, C.P. 25294, México*
migmorales@uv.mx

Abstract

This work presents a study of the CO_2 transport process in Block Polyether Amide (PEBA) membranes, based on an experimental design and mathematical modelling, considering a fickian and non-fickian diffusion models. PEBA membranes were synthesized using the plate casting method and were thermally characterized by differential scanning calorimetry and thermogravimetric analysis. Subsequently, experimental measurements of the concentration of permeated gases were carried out, using different pressure and temperature conditions for a fixed CO_2/CH_4 mixture. The permeability, selectivity, diffusivity, and solubility of CO_2 were determined. It was found that the membranes are highly selective to CO_2 over the CH_4. The experimental data of the permeated CO_2 concentration throughout the operating time, the solubility and diffusivity were employed in the mathematical models to describe the solution-diffusion phenomenon. It was found that the fickian model was only able to reproduce the behaviour of the process at the steady state conditions. In contrast, the non-fickian model achieved an appropriate description of the process.

Keywords: CO_2 separation, dense membranes, solution-diffusion mechanism, mathematical modelling.

1. Introduction

Gas separation is one of the essential processes in the field of Chemical Engineering; specifically, the separation of acid gases (CO_2, H_2S, and SO_2) presents a considerable environmental and industrial importance, such as greenhouse gases capture and natural gas cleaning (Xu et al., 2019; Dai et al., 2016). For example, CO_2 accounts for approximately 60% of the total greenhouse gas emissions (Tan et al., 2019; Wang et al., 2019).

Natural gas, when burned, has a CO_2 emission factor of 26% and 41% lower than that emitted by oil and coal, respectively. Therefore, expanding natural gas consumption will be one of the effective measures to reduce CO_2 emissions (Li et al., 2018). However, nowadays, natural gas is extracted in large quantities and often contains an excess of CO_2, which must be removed to improve its heat power, reduce the volume of gas to be transported, avoid atmospheric pollution, and reduce corrosion in pipelines.

The most common methods of CO_2 separation are cryogenic distillation, adsorption, and absorption (Li et al., 2018; Kidnay et al., 2011). Among these methods, amine absorption is the most advanced commercial technology; however, this method implies an increase of 50-90% in the energy cost of the plant (Ibrahim et al., 2018; Ji et al., 2010), as well as the corrosion of the equipment, and these are just some of the disadvantages of this technology (Ibrahim et al., 2018). A promising method to reduce the cost of CO_2 separation is the use of membranes, which, in comparison to chemical absorption, has advantages such as low cost and high energy efficiency (Ji et al., 2019; Li et al., 2016; Mahmoudi et al., 2015).

In the field of membrane technology, polymeric membranes have been widely used to capture CO_2 from different gas mixtures due to their selectivity and permeability, as well as their chemical and thermal resistance, low material costs, among others (Xu et al., 2019; Li et al., 2018; Dai et al., 2016). However, despite all the technological advances in the study of the CO_2 separation process using polymeric membranes, this is still an open field for research.

Another way to analyse the CO_2 separation process using membranes is through mathematical models and numerical simulations, validated with experimental data. However, most of the mathematical models reported in the literature for dense membranes use Fick's Law to describe the mass transport process. It may not be appropriate, since dense membranes are not a homogeneous medium and consequently predict the process far from reality. Therefore, this work proposes an analysis of the CO_2 transport in a dense membrane (PEBA) based on the determination of experimental data and a mathematical modelling that considers an effective diffusivity coefficient.

2. Methodology

Through sequential steps based on the elaboration and characterization of the membranes, properties such as permeability and selectivity of CO_2 were calculated using a gas stream consisting of methane including the variation of pressure and temperature.

The permeability of CO_2 and CH_4 was calculated through the following correlation.

$$\frac{\mathcal{P}}{L} = \frac{QN}{A(p_{in} - p)} \tag{1}$$

Where $\mathcal{P}$ is the permeability, Q is the volumetric flow rate of the permeate gas, A is the active area of the membrane, p_{in} and p are the inlet and permeate partial pressures, respectively, and N is the permeate gas concentration.

For selectivity (α), it was calculated following the next expression.

$$\alpha_{CO_2/CH_4} = \frac{\mathcal{P}_{CO_2}}{\mathcal{P}_{CH_4}} \tag{2}$$

It was also possible to determine certain parameters, such as molecular diffusion (D) and solubility (S).

$$D_{CO_2} = \frac{L^2}{6\theta} \tag{3}$$

$$S_{CO_2} = \frac{\mathcal{P}_{CO_2}}{D_{CO_2}} \tag{4}$$

D_{CO_2} was calculated from the ratio obtained from the thickness (L) of the membrane and six times the period (θ) in which the concentration of the permeated gas reaches the steady state. Then, the S_{CO_2} coefficient was calculated from the relationship of the permeability of CO_2 and its diffusion coefficient through the membrane.

3. Mathematical Model

The solution-diffusion mechanism has been considered to study mass transfer in dense membranes, with diffusion inside the polymeric matrix and solubility at the limits of the membrane. The proposed mathematical model of this work focuses on determining the behaviour of CO_2 in the membrane, based on Fick's second law of diffusion, and considering an effective diffusivity.

$$\frac{\partial C_{CO_2}}{\partial t} = D_{eff}\frac{\partial^2 C_{CO_2}}{\partial x^2} \tag{5}$$

In Eq. (5), the coefficient D_{eff} is defined as a function of the molecular diffusion of CO_2 and a parameter ϕ, $D_{eff} = D_{CO_2}\phi$. A parametric estimation employing the Levenberg-Marquardt method was used to determine the parameter ϕ.

$$\mathbb{P}_{k,i+1} = \mathbb{P}_{k,i} + (J^T J + \lambda I)^{-1}J^T(y_i - y_{m,i}^k) \tag{6}$$

Where: $\mathbb{P}$ represents the parameter to be estimated; k and i are counters; J and J^T are the Jacobian and transposed Jacobian matrix, respectively; λ, the damping factor; I, an identity matrix; y_i, the real data; and y_m, the data based on the modelling. The CO_2 concentration data measured in the lower chamber of the membrane were used as real data in this work.

4. Results

4.1. Characterization of the membrane

Dense membranes with a uniform, flexible, and homogeneous appearance were synthesized from PEBA and characterized by Differential Scanning Calorimetry (DSC) and Thermogravimetric Analysis (TGA).

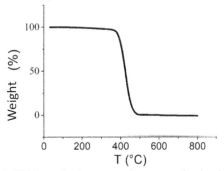

Figure 1. TGA analysis to membrane synthesized from PEBA.

The TGA was carried out to analyse the possible thermal decomposition of the PEBA membrane, as shown in Figure 1. A thermal decomposition for PEBA starts at 380 °C, where membrane degradation begins; this temperature is consistent with other studies reported in the literature (Soloukipour et al., 2017; Li et al., 2016).

4.2. Membrane permeability and selectivity

The permeabilities of CO_2 and CH_4 were calculated as a function of the pressure and the temperature (Figure 2). The CO_2 permeability values were in a range of 118.59 to 196.76 Barrer. These values are within the scope of 40 to 400 Barrer, reported in the literature (Zhang et al., 2019; Zou et al., 2006). Regarding the permeability for CH_4, the values obtained were all smaller than 1 Barrer.

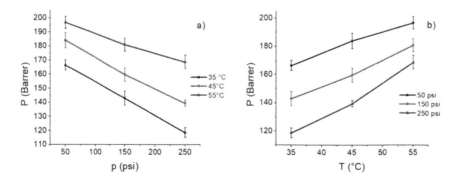

Figure 2. Effect of the pressure and the temperature on the permeability of PEBA membranes for CO_2 absorption. a) Effect of pressure. b) Effect of temperature.

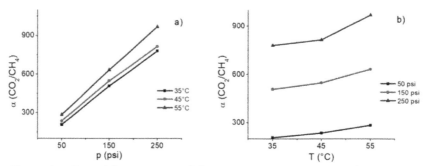

Figure 3. Effect of the pressure and the temperature on the selectivity of PEBA membranes for CO_2 absorption. a) Effect of pressure. b) Effect of temperature.

Figure 3 shows the values obtained for selectivity in a range of 207 to 970. Thus, these values are within 40 to 1200, as reported in the literature (Zhang et al., 2019; Kobayashi et al., 2019).

The calculated diffusion coefficients (D), with the effect of pressure and temperature, presented values between 2.5 to 6.5 x 10^{-6} cm^2/s. In the case of the solubility, values were found in a range of 2 to 6 cm^3 (STP) cm^{-3} cm Hg^{-1}, which are in good agreement with those reported in the literature (Kalantari et al., 2019; Hou et al., 2018).

4.3. Mathematical modelling

Prediction of the measured experimental CO_2 concentrations was carried out with both models, the classical fickian model and the non-fickian model proposed in this work. In addition, the parametric adjustment used molecular diffusivity and solubility.

Simulations were carried out with all operating conditions, as experimentally evaluated. For illustrative purposes, Figure 4 only shows the data corresponding to 35 °C and 50 psi. However, in all cases, the non-fickian model was the one with the best performance.

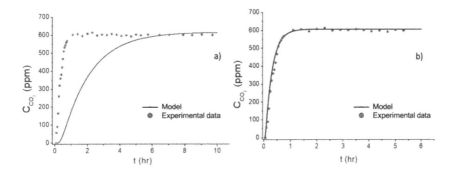

Figure 4. Dynamic behaviour of the CO_2 concentration in the membrane's lower chamber. a) Fickian model. b) Non-fickian model.

The non-fickian model required the adjustment of only one parameter, as included in the definition of the effective diffusivity coefficient ($D_{eff} = D_{CO_2}\phi$). The values of the parameter ϕ, determined by the Levenberg-Marquardt method, and the plasticization factor, reported by Minelli (2013) for several dense membranes, presented the same order of magnitude.

5. Conclusions

Experimental tests determined that the membranes under study are highly permeable and selective to CO_2, in comparison to CH_4, for all the evaluated pressures and temperatures. The permeation rate of CO_2 increased with the temperature and decreased with the pressure. The highest permeability value was 196.76 Barrer at a temperature of 55 °C and a pressure of 50 psi. In addition, pressure and temperature increments favoured the CO_2/CH_4 selectivity.

The mathematical modelling showed that, to describe the CO_2 transport process in dense membranes, a non-fickian model is required, where additional factors are included for the effective diffusion coefficient. It is important to remark that these factors must be a function of the operating conditions and the properties of the dense membranes.

References

Dai, Z., Noble, R. D., Gin, D. L., Zhang, X., & Deng, L., 2016, Combination of ionic liquids with membrane technology: A new approach for CO_2 separation. Journal of Membrane Science, 497, 1-20.

Hou, J., Li, X., Guo, R., Zhang, J., & Wang, Z., 2018, Mixed matrix membranes with fast and selective transport pathways for efficient CO_2 separation. Nanotechnology, 29(12), 125706.

Ibrahim, M. H., El-Naas, M. H., Zhang, Z., & Van der Bruggen, B., 2018, CO_2 capture using hollow fiber membranes: A review of membrane wetting. Energy & fuels, 32(2), 963-978.

Ji, Y., Zhang, M., Guan, K., Zhao, J., Liu, G., & Jin, W., 2019, High-performance CO_2 capture through polymer-based ultrathin membranes. Advanced Functional Materials, 29(33), 1900735.

Kalantari, S., Omidkhah, M., Amooghin, A. E., & Matsuura, T., 2019, Superior interfacial design in ternary mixed matrix membranes to enhance the CO_2 separation performance. Applied Materials Today, 100491.

Kidnay, A.J., Parrish, W.R., McCartney, D.G., 2011, Fundamentals of Natural Gas Processing. Taylor & Francis Group, Boca Raton.

Kobayashi, Y., Nakamitsu, Y., Zheng, Y., Takashima, Y., Yamaguchi, H., & Harada, A., 2019, Preparation of cyclodextrin-based porous polymeric membrane by bulk polymerization of ethyl acrylate in the presence of cyclodextrin. Polymer, 177, 208- 213.

Li, L., Wong-Ng, W., Huang, K., & Cook, L.P., 2018, Materials and processes for CO_2 capture, conversion, and sequestration. John Wiley & Sons.

Li, Y., Shen, J., Guan, K., Liu, G., Zhou, H., & Jin, W., 2016, PEBA/ceramic hollow fiber composite membrane for high-efficiency recovery of bio-butanol via pervaporation. Journal of Membrane Science, 510, 338-347.

Mahmoudi, A., Asghari, M., & Zargar, V., 2015, CO_2/CH_4 separation through a novel commercializable three-phase PEBA/PEG/NaX nanocomposite membrane. Journal of Industrial and Engineering Chemistry, 23, 238-242.

Minelli, M., & Sarti, G. C., 2013, Permeability and diffusivity of CO2 in glassy polymers with and without plasticization. Journal of membrane science, 435, 176-185.

Soloukipour, S., Saljoughi, E., Mousavi, S. M., & Pourafshari Chenar, M., 2017, PEBA/PVDF blend pervaporation membranes: preparation and performance. Polymers for Advanced Technologies, 28(1), 113-123.

Tan, X., Li, H., Guo, J., Gu, B., & Zeng, Y., 2019, Energy-saving and emission-reduction technology selection and CO_2 emission reduction potential of China's iron and steel industry under energy substitution policy. Journal of cleaner production, 222, 823-834.

Wang, S., Wang, J., Fang, C., & Li, S., 2019, Estimating the impacts of urban form on CO_2 emission efficiency in the Pearl River Delta, China. Cities, 85, 117-129.

Xu, B., & Lin, B., 2019, Can expanding natural gas consumption reduce China's CO_2 emissions? Energy Economics, 81, 393-407.

Zhang, J., Xin, Q., Li, X., Yun, M., Xu, R., Wang, S., & Zhang, Y., 2019, Mixed matrix membranes comprising aminosilane-functionalized graphene oxide for enhanced CO_2 separation. Journal of membrane science, 570, 343-354.

Zou, J., & Ho, W. W., 2006, CO_2-selective polymeric membranes containing amines in crosslinked poly (vinyl alcohol). Journal of Membrane Science, 286(1-2), 310-321.

Proceedings of the 14th International Symposium on Process Systems Engineering – PSE 2021+
June 19-23, 2022, Kyoto, Japan © 2022 Elsevier B.V. All rights reserved.
http://dx.doi.org/10.1016/B978-0-323-85159-6.50163-9

Mathematical modelling, simulation and optimisation of an indirect water bath heater at the Takoradi distribution station (TDS)

Richard Yentumi[a], Bogdan Dorneanu[b], Harvey Arellano-Garcia[b,*]

[a]*Engineering Department, Ghana National Gas Company, Atuabo, Ghana*
[b]*LS Prozess- und Anlagentechnik, Brandenburgische Technische Universität Cottbus-Senftenberg, Cottbus, D-03046, Germany*
arellano@b-tu.de

Abstract

In this contribution, a dynamic first principles model of an existing 3.01 MW natural gas fired water bath heater (WBH) in operation at the Takoradi Distribution Station (TDS) in Ghana is developed primarily to predict the outlet temperature of the natural gas stream being heated. The model is intended to be applied during operations to provide useful data to optimise material and energy consumption, as well as minimise CO_2 emissions. Due to the low thermal efficiencies of WBHs, even small improvements in efficiency can result in significant savings. The firetube and process coils are both modelled as one-dimensional (1D) thin-walled tubes and the entire model incorporates mass and energy conservation equations, heat transfer rate relations and rigorous thermodynamic p-V-T relations. In contrast to what commonly exists in literature, this model accurately estimates the enthalpy change of the natural gas stream being heated by accounting for its enthalpy departure correction term due to pressure, in addition to the ideal gas heat capacity relation which is a function of only temperature. The coupled ordinary differential and algebraic equations are implemented using gPROMS® ModelBuilder® V4.2.0, a commercial modelling and simulation software. Verification of the model results showed good agreement between the model predictions and actual on field measurements. With excess air at 15%, the simulation results closely approximate measured data with an absolute error of about 0.31 %. More importantly, the results show that significant savings of up to 30% per annum can be made through optimal operation of the water bath heater.

Keywords: modelling, optimisation, simulation, heater.

1. Introduction

In natural gas transportation systems, pressures must often be reduced from transmission pipeline to distribution pipeline values at regulating and metering (R&M) stations. This pressure reduction process with the accompanying temperature drops, a phenomenon known as the Joule-Thomson effect, is an isenthalpic expansion process. Consequently, if the natural gas chills to sufficiently low temperatures, owing to a huge pressure reduction across the throttling valve, for instance, some of the heavier components of the natural gas stream can condense out of the vapour phase into a liquid phase potentially forming hydrates in the presence of free water and causing corrosion problems. Hydrates can damage pipeline components or cause blockages that disrupt gas export operations. Therefore, to protect downstream consumers such as natural gas-fired turbine power plants, indirect water bath heaters (WBH) are typically provided upstream of pressure regulating packages in R&M stations to superheat the natural gas stream. Normally, the natural gas is in a superheated state if it is at a temperature of at least 28 °C above the hydrocarbon dewpoint temperature at the specified operating pressure. Figure 1 shows a simplified schematic of an indirect WBH.

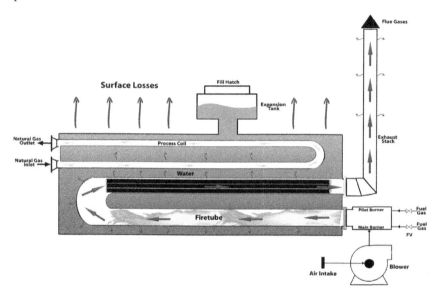

Figure 1: Indirect water bath heater at the TDS

As most process heaters, indirect WBHs are energy intensive units. However, they have relatively lower overall thermal efficiencies when compared to direct fired heaters, for instance. As a percentage of the total energy input (LHV basis), a large majority of previous research estimated that the stack losses were somewhere between 25 – 60% while the wall losses range from 0.5 to 2% of the total energy input. Stack losses were therefore, identified as a major source of energy wastage accounting for the low thermal efficiencies of indirect water bath heaters. Through a 12-month statistical data collection and analysis, Khalili et al. (2010) estimated the thermal efficiency of an indirect water bath heater to be between 41.6 and 52.0%. Similarly, Romocki et al. (2018), reported the thermal efficiency of a WBH to be around 46%. Clearly, such low thermal efficiency levels of the existing water bath heaters are incongruous with the looming transition into a low-carbon future which stipulates drastic reductions in carbon emissions and high energy efficiency. In this light, mathematical modelling and simulation can be a very powerful tool that can be used to gain deeper insight into the underlying phenomena involved in WBH design and operations and in effect, help to improve operating efficiencies. Accordingly, Azizi et al. (2014), proposed an energy integration approach by placing a heat exchanger upstream of the indirect water to extract heat energy from the flue gases released from the water bath heater, which hitherto, would have been released into the atmosphere to pre-heat the natural gas stream and thus, reduce the total energy input leading to a lower overall fuel consumption. Romocki et al. (2018), proposed the replacement of indirect WBH with an Immersion Tube Thermosyphon Heater (ITTH) as it offered a thermal efficiency of about 90% leading to a reduction in both fuel consumption and CO_2 emissions.

Interestingly, only a handful of these previous works were conducted to model and simulate the dynamic performance of these process heaters such as cold start-up operations. Moreover, one of the main weaknesses of the existing models was the estimation of enthalpy changes of the natural gas stream being heated based on the ideal gas heat capacity relation, which is a function of only temperature and does not account for enthalpy departure correction term due to pressure of the natural gas. The overall objective of this work is to achieve optimal operation of the TDS WBH by identifying optimal operating variables that minimise fuel gas use (increasing energy efficiency) for a given process heat duty while also minimising CO_2 emissions.

2. Model development

2.1. Process description

Three (3) indirect fired heaters are installed in a 3 x 50 % configuration (3 x 202.5 MMscf/D, design heating duty per heater is 3.01 MW) upstream of the pressure regulating package at the TDS. A cascaded temperature control loop is provided for controlling the temperature of the water bath. In addition, a cascaded temperature control loop is also provided for controlling the outlet temperature of the natural gas stream being heated. The water bath temperature is controlled and normally set at 60 °C (333.15 K). The design setpoint is 86 °C (359.15 K). Depending on the downstream customer requirement, the natural gas is typically heated to between 30 °C (303.15 K) and 52 °C (325.15 K); normal setpoint temperature is 40 °C (313.15 K). The complete model comprises firetube zones 1 and 2, the non-flow water bath, the process tube, and the natural gas stream. The various sub-models are then interconnected by energy flows shown in Figure 2.

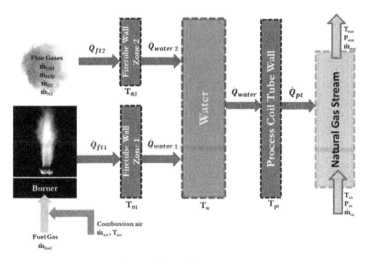

Figure 2: Model connectivity

The model considers the overall energy balance for the WBH control volume, as well as for the various sub-components, the combustion of a natural gas stream containing both nitrogen and carbon dioxide in the presence of excess air, the transfer of the heat to the first pass of the firetube through a combination of radiation and convection.

The outlet temperature of the natural gas stream, $T_{ng,2}$ is estimated from the relation:

$$q_{\dot{n},ng} \cdot d\bar{h} = \dot{Q}_{ng} \tag{1}$$

Changes in the specific molar enthalpy of the natural gas between two thermodynamic equilibrium states is estimated from the relation:

$$d\bar{h} = \bar{h}_2(T_{ng,2}, P_{ng,2}) - \bar{h}_1(T_{ng,1}, P_{ng,1}) \tag{2}$$

In general, the specific molar enthalpy at each state is calculated from the relation:

$$\bar{h}_i = \bar{h}_{ideal} + \bar{h}_{dep} \tag{3}$$

The first term on the RHS of Eqn. (3) represents the ideal gas enthalpy change for the individual components of the natural gas mixture at reference conditions of 298.15 K and 1 atm to the state temperature and at ideal gas conditions; the second term on the RHS represents the enthalpy departure (pressure correction term) involved in taking the fluid to the state pressure. The Lee-Kesler (LK) Equation of State (EOS) method (Lee and Kesler, 1975) was used to estimate this term as it is the most accurate enthalpy calculation model for gas mixtures (Changjun et al., 2011). The compressibility factor of the natural gas stream at each state is calculated using the Peng-Robinson EOS. (Peng and Robinson, 1976). Physical property data and binary interaction parameters were obtained from ASPEN® HYSYS® V11. Since the flue gas flow through the firetube is calculated to fall under forced convection, the Dittus-Boelter correlation as discussed in Incropera et al., (2007) is used for estimating the convection heat transfer coefficients in all cases. All external free convection heat transfer coefficients are estimated using the GPSA Engineering Data Book.

2.2. Optimisation model

The complete optimisation problem is posed in the form below:

Minimise:

$$f = n_{days} \cdot 24 \cdot c_{fuel} \cdot q_{\dot{m},fuel-MB} \cdot LHV_{fuel}$$

Subject to:

$$50 \frac{kg}{hr} \le q_{\dot{m},fuel-MB} \le 620 \frac{kg}{hr}$$
$$333.15\ K \le T_w$$
$$313.15\ K \le T_{ng,2}$$

The objective function is the total cost of fuel gas burned, in $ per annum. The % valve opening, and ambient air temperature are set as decision variables in the gPROMS® optimisation settings. The water bath (T_w) and the hot natural gas outlet ($T_{ng,2}$) temperatures, which are external discontinuities, are set as constraints. The fuel gas flow rate ($q_{\dot{m},fuel-MB}$) flowing through the modulating flow control valve is set as an additional constraint.

2.3. Parameter specifications

Firetube Zone 1: $D_{i,ft1}$ = 0.89534 m; $D_{o,ft1}$ = 0.9144 m; $A_{o,ft1}$ = 24.0264 m²; $A_{i,ft1}$ = 23.5256 m²; m_{ft1} = 2739.50 m²; cp_{steel} = 0.4610 kJ/kg K; k_{steel} = 0.0450 kW/m K;

Firetube Zone 2 - Single Firetube in Zone 2: $D_{i,ft2}$ = 0.06268 m; $D_{o,ft2}$ = 0.073 m; $A_{o,ft2}$ = 1.4147 m²; $A_{i,ft2}$ = 1.2147 m²; m_{ft2} = 2739.50 m²; n_{tubes} = 52;

Firetube Zone 2 – Total Number of Firetubes in Zone 2: $A_{o,ft2}$ = 73.5621 m²; m_{ft2} = 2764.00 m

2.4. Variable specifications

$\varepsilon = 1.15$; $\eta_{MB} = 0.95$; $q_{m,fuel} = $ Min (Valve_Flow, 620) kg/hr; $LHV_{ng} = 47,990.08$ kJ/kg; $\alpha_{ft1} = 0.90$; $e_f = 0.90$; $e_{ft1} = 0.50$; $T_{amb,air} = 298.15$ K; $h_{ws} = 0.120$ kW/m² K; $h_{al\text{-}air} = 0.00250$ kW/m² K; MW_ng $= 18.6529$ kg/kmol; $w = 0.0259$; $q_{std,v} = 85.23$ MMscf/D; $T_1 = 26.10$ °C ($T_{ng,1} = 299.25$ K); $P_1 = 68.00$ barg; $v_{m,1} = 0.8221$ m³/kmol; $P_2 = 67.75$ barg; $v_{m,2} = 0.2964$ m³/kmol;

The calculated Lee-Kesler pseudo-critical properties for the natural gas composition are: $T_c = -63.53$ °C and $v_c = 0.1063$ m³/kmol; $F_1 = 0.05$ and $F_2 = 0.85$.

3. Results and discussion

Per the cold start-up operating procedure of the WBH, motor operated valves (MOVs) are opened to allow for natural gas flow and heating only once the setpoint of the water bath is reached. This discontinuity in the process was captured in the model execution in gPROMS®. A summary of the cold start-up simulation results for a water bath set point temperature of 60 °C (333.15 K) and a natural gas outlet temperature setpoint of 40 °C (313.15 K) is presented in Table 1. The initial cold conditions were 27.1 °C (300.25 K) for the water bath and 26.1 °C (299.25 K) for the cold inlet natural gas stream.

Table 1: Summary of TDS WBH Cold Start-up Simulation Results for 3,050 seconds

Valve % Travel	%	47	50	-6.00%
Time Taken to Reach Water Bath Setpoint Temperature	s	2,152	2,192	-1.82%
Outlet Temperature of Natural Gas Stream	K	314.28	313.30	0.31%

The temperature profiles of the water bath and the natural gas stream for the cold start-up simulation period are illustrated by Figures 3.

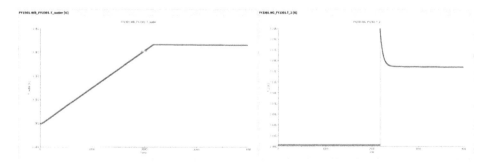

Figure 3: Temperature profiles of the water bath (left) and the natural gas (right)

The results obtained demonstrate that the TDS WBH model closely approximates the actual behaviour of the key operating variables such as water bath and outlet natural gas temperature. At the same time, the model deviates quite significantly in predicting other variables such as thermal efficiency which the manufacturer specifies as a minimum of 75%.

A model-based dynamic optimisation operation was conducted in gPROMS to determine the operating variables that minimise fuel gas purchasing cost. Considering a 24 h over 340 days operation in a year and a natural gas purchase cost of $0.004265/MJ, the results obtained indicate that the annualised purchasing cost of natural gas for the base case is $674,065 from cold start up to steady state, a total time of 2,296 seconds (38.26 minutes). The optimised case shows significant savings between 10 – 30% can be realised for a total time of 3,600 seconds (60 minutes) from cold start up to steady state.

The objective function was particularly sensitive to the % opening of the modulating flow control valve on the main burner fuel gas supply line.

4. Conclusions

The simulation and optimisation study results clearly demonstrate that the dynamic model proposed in this work is a powerful predictive tool for process improvement and to aid decision making at TDS as it closely approximates the behaviour of the actual water bath heater, FY2301A/B/C under varied operating conditions. The model, thus, affords an insight into the dynamics of the process that did not exist previously. Further work should be done to validate the model with experimental data and verify the optimisation results. Moreover, a robust process controller can be designed to accurately control and optimise the operations of the WBH.

References

E. Khalili, et al., 2010, Efficiency and heat losses of an indirect water bath heater installed in natural gas pressure reduction station; Iran, shahrekord, pp. 1-9

S. Romocki, et al., 2018, An indirect heating solution to reduce CO_2 emissions and improve efficiency of gas distribution networks, Energy Reports, Elsevier Ltd.

S. Azizi, et al., 2014, Study of preheating natural gas in gas pressure reduction stations by the flue gas of indirect water bath heaters, International Journal of Science and Engineering Investigations 3 (27)

B.I. Lee, et al., 1975, A generalized thermodynamic correlation based on three-paramter corresponding states, AIChE Journal 21 (3)

L. Changjun, et al., 2012, Application of Lee-Kessler equation of state to calculating compressibility factors of high-pressure condensate gas, 2nd International conference on advances in Energy Engineering, Energy Procedia 14, pp. 115-120

D. Peng, D.B. Robinson, 1976, A new two-constant equation of state, Ind. Eng. Chem., Fundam. 15 (1), pp. 59-64

F.P. Dewitt, et al., 2007, Introduction to heat transfer, 5th Edition, John Wiley & Sons

Gas Processors Suppliers Association (GPSA), 2012, Engineering Data Book, 13th Edition

Proceedings of the 14th International Symposium on Process Systems Engineering – PSE 2021+
June 19-23, 2022, Kyoto, Japan © 2022 Elsevier B.V. All rights reserved.
http://dx.doi.org/10.1016/B978-0-323-85159-6.50164-0

Marine SOx Scrubber: Mass transfer Analysis, Design, Simulation and Experiment

Dongyoung Lee[a*], Van D. L. Nguyen[a,1], Gwangsik Kim[a,1], Myungjin Kim[b],
Choongyong Kwag[b], Youngmok Lee[b], Sungwon Lee[b], Moonyong Lee[a*]

[a]School of chemical Engineering, Yeungnam University, Gyeongsan 712-749, South Korea
[b]Hanbal Masstech Ltd, golden root complex, Gimhae, South Korea
mynlee@ynu.ac.kr

Abstract

The International Marine Organization (IMO) established regulations on SO2 emissions in the MARPOL Annex VI, which is applied from 1st January 2020. The emissions standard was 3.5 % in weight, but now, sulphur emissions for oceangoing vessels must be equivalent to a sulphur content in fuel lower than 0.5 % in weight worldwide. Especially, in some coastal regions named "Sulphur Emission Control Areas", SECAs sulphur emissions have to be lower than 0.1 % in weight. Due to economical compliance to the environment regulation, wet flue gas desulfurization (FGD) process is preferred. In this work, experiments are performed using scrubber, which has square-based shape and fresh water with addition of sodium hydroxide as absorbent, to treat flue gas from a marine diesel engine (720 kW) that has to comply with current regulation. The experimental tests in spray column indicate that the absorption efficiency above 95 % can be achieved. The experimented performances match well with the simulated results

Keywords: Process design; Marine flue gas desulfurization(FGD); The International Marine Orgarnization(IMO)

1. Introduction

In the worldwide, trade by sea consists more than 90 % of the total trade amount. In transport activities, large ships often use cheap heavy fuel oil, resulting in sulfur oxides (SOx)exhaust, which can negatively affect human health and marine communities.(Nielsen,2014) IMO and several governments have put into use rules to control the damages from sulfur emission. In particular, a maximum limit for equal sulfur emission of less than 0.1 % in weight was established for some coastal areas termed as sulfur emission control areas (January 1, 2015). In addition, from January 1, 2020, sulfur emission for oceangoing ships worldwide must be equal to those given-off by fuel with sulfur content lower than 0.5% in weight.(Flagiello, 2019) These rules have forced ship owners to scarch for solutions to meet the needed things, not only for new ships, but more importantly for the current fleet of ships.(Strandberg, 2017)

For controlling sulfur emissions effectively, FGD is a viable option, which the wet processes consists around 87 % of those used worldwide.(Srivastava, 2017) Shipments can apply open loop with seawater, closed loop with sodium hydroxide (NaOH), or hybrid systems which be able to switch the modes.(Oikawa, 2003) Seawater's natural alkalinity and large availability make absorption ability. However, open loop system has several limitation such as it requires large amount of seawater which cause corrosion on process equipment and several countries have banned any discharge from open loop system. (Eason, 2018) Thus, the closed-loop mode using NaOH is preffered alternative. In this paper, a new square-shaped closed-loop scrubber with spray has been proposed for marine applications. By applying the square shape, the spray scrubber can reduce its volume, area and weight, which are essentially considered for installation on board. We performed design, construction, experiment, and simulation to evaluate the proposed FGD square-shaped closed-loop scrubber with spray.

2. Closed-Loop Square Scrubber With Spray

2.1. Proposed Methodology

As the first step, a literature survey on the availability of components in Aspen Plus, solubility or equilibrium data, reaction parameters, requirements, and constraints of a marine FGD was performed. Subsequently, a rigorous simulation and a sensitivity analysis were performed to evaluate the scrubber and identify the variables affecting its performance with actual feed conditions. Finally, the simulation and experimental data were compared to validate the proposed systematic methodology.

2.2. Process Description

Existing FGD systems are coastal and commercial marine scrubbers that usually consist of spray towers fed with pure seawater (open loop) or water doped with an alkaline neutralizing agent (closed loop). NaOH is commonly used as an alkaline agent(MAN,2020) to neutralize the sulfuric acid in the scrubber water. When SO2 is absorbed into solutions, the diffusion of SO2 molecules from the current gas phase core to the gas/liquid interface and the dissolution in the washing agent should be initially considered, as described by Eq. (1).(Wang,2015) The dissolution process is considered to obey Henry's law for low concentrations of SO2 in effluent gases.

$$SO_2(g) \leftrightarrow SO_2(l) \tag{1}$$

Some dissolved acid gas molecules dissociate according to reaction (2), and others directly react with hydroxide ions according to reaction (3). In turn, hydrogen sulfite reacts with the additional hydroxide ions to form sulfite, as shown in reaction (4).

$$SO_2 + H_2O \leftrightarrow HSO_3^- + H^- \tag{2}$$

$$SO_2 + OH^- \leftrightarrow HSO_3^- \tag{3}$$

$$HSO_3^- + OH^- \leftrightarrow SO_3^{2-} + H_2O \tag{4}$$

Reaction (3) is very fast while reaction (4) has a considerably higher rate constant than reaction (3). Thus, both reactions can be considered as instantaneous.(Hikita,1977) The above processes are related with the dissociation of water (Eq. 5) and NaOH (Eq. 6):

$$H_2O \leftrightarrow H^+ + OH^- \tag{5}$$

$$NaOH \leftrightarrow Na^+ + OH^- \tag{6}$$

$$H_2SO_3 + 2NaOH + 1/2O_2 \leftrightarrow Na_2SO_4 + 2H_2O \tag{7}$$

$$SO_2(g) + 2NaOH(aq) + 1/2O_2(g) \leftrightarrow 2Na^+ + SO_4^{2-} + H_2O \tag{8}$$

$$CO_2(g) \leftrightarrow CO_2(l) \tag{9}$$

$$CO_2 + H_2O \leftrightarrow HCO_3^- + H^+ \tag{10}$$

$$CO_2 + OH^- \leftrightarrow HCO_3^- \tag{11}$$

$$HCO_3^- + OH^- \leftrightarrow CO_3^{2-} + H_2O \tag{12}$$

Figure 1 shows a simplified closed-loop FGD process in which water is recirculated through the scrubber with no discharge at sea.

2.3. Design of Square Spray Column

Spray towers have traditionally been used in several applications such as low pressure drop is essential, a high degree of separation is not required, and there are solid particles and precipitating solvents.(Yeh,2003) They have advantages such as low pressure drop, lightness, simple construction and operation, and low investment, operating, and maintenance costs.(Bandyopadhyay,2012)

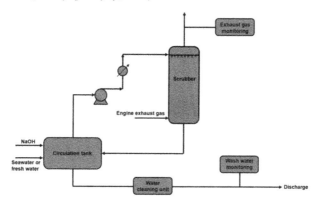

Figure 1 Schematic diagram of the closed-loop FGD process.

3. Materials And Methods

3.1. Materials

Fresh water with the addition of NaOH was used as an alkaline neutralizing agent. NaOH 5 % was purchased from Hanwha Solutions.

3.2. Diesel Engine

In the scrubber experiment, a Shinko marine diesel engine (Figure 2a) with a power of 720 kW was operated with high sulfur fuel oil containing 3.5 % in weight. Figure 2b shows the effect of the engine speed on the flow rate of flue gas. During the scrubber experiment, an engine speed of 800 rpm was fixed.

(a)   (b)

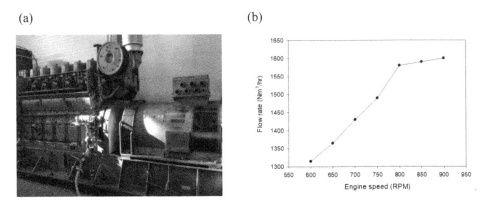

Figure 2 (a) Marine engine and (b) influence of engine speed on the flow rate of flue gas.

3.3. Spray Column

The square spray tower, with a cross section of 800×800 mm, length of 11,400 mm, and operated at 35 °C and 1 atm, was constructed after the design phase. The liquid flow rate, L, was supplied at the top by a centrifugal pump controlled by a globe valve. For spray scrubbing, a good atomizer should produce a fairly uniform spray with drop diameters sufficiently small to generate a large interfacial area of contact and sufficiently large to prevent excessive entrainment.(Bandyopadhyay,2012)

3.4. Analytical Methods

The Testo 350 exhaust gas analyzer equipped with an electrochemical sensor was used to measure SO2 based on the principle of ion selective potentiometry. The experimental SO2 removal efficiency (η_{SO_2}) was calculated as follows:

$$\eta_{SO_2} = \frac{C^o_{SO_2(g)} - C_{SO_2(g)}}{C^o_{SO_2(g)}} \tag{13}$$

where $C^o_{SO_2}(g)$ and $C_{SO_2}(g)$ are the inlet and outlet SO2 concentrations, respectively.

4. Results and Discussion

4.1. Simulation

The simulation was performed using the simulator Aspen Plus V10. The Electrolyte NRTL activity coefficient model was used for the prediction of the vapor–liquid equilibrium of these simulations. In this study, during the experiment and simulation, the pH value of the solvent was maintained at approximately 8.

Figure 3 shows the influence of the gas velocity, flue gas temperature, and liquid/gas ratio (L/G) on the removal efficiency. The results indicate that the removal efficiency reduces from approximately 97 % to 92 % when the flue gas velocity increases from 0.5 m/s to 2.5 m/s (Figure 3a). In addition, the influence of flue gas temperature within 30–90 °C is negligible (Figure 3b). Furthermore, the removal efficiency increases with increasing L/G (Figure 3c).

(a)   (b)   (c)

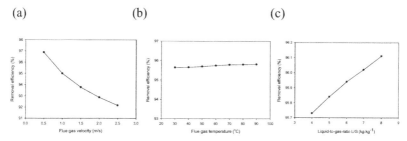

Figure 3 Influence of the (a) flue gas velocity, (b) flue gas temperature, and (c) L/G on the removal efficiency of SO2

4.2. Scrubber Operation

The flue gas from the engine was quenched in a venturi scrubber before entering a cyclone to remove particulate matter. 100 ppm SO2 was involved in feed gas. The industrial-scale scrubber unit constructed at the Hanbal Masstech company was used to scrub SO2 from the flue gas. When the column was wetted, the engine was activated to generate flue gas, which was fed into the scrubber unit. To maintain the operating temperature at 35 °C, fresh water was pumped to the air cooler system.

The analyses of the flue gas inlet and outlet were performed using the Testo 350 exhaust gas analyzer. The results showed that under the designed operating conditions, the outlet SO2 was 5 ppm, resulting in an outlet SO2(ppm)/CO2(%) ratio of 0.64. It was possible to achieve an absorption efficiency higher than 95% by using a liquid-to-gas mass ratio of approximately 4.32 kg.kg-1. The results also showed that the unit had small pressure drops (0.5 mbar).

4.3. Comparison Between Simulation And Experimental Results

The experimental outlet SO2 ppm was compared with the simulation results obtained using the Aspen Plus software, which were based on actual conditions. Excellent agreement was observed between the experimental and simulated performances. In particular, the real operation indicated an outlet SO2 of 5 ppm, which is similar to the simulated outlet SO2 of 4.3 ppm (Figure 4a).

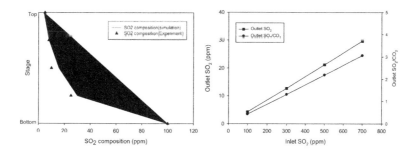

Figure 4 (a)SO2 profile in scrubber. (b)Influence of the inlet SO2 on the scrubber performance.

The results indicated that the higher the inlet SO2, the higher the outlet SO2 and the SO2(ppm)/CO2(%) ratio (Figure 4b). This implies that, in this range, the designed scrubber can comply with the IMO regulation.

5. Conclusions

A compact, light, and effective square scrubber equipped with spray was proposed for SOx removal in this study. Through the proposed systematic methodology, the design, construction, simulation, sensitivity analyses, and experiment were successfully accomplished. The results indicated a good agreement between experimental and simulation results. The proposed square scrubber system can achieve high SO2 removal efficiency with low water consumption and low pressure drop. In particular, an SO2 removal efficiency higher than 95 % was achieved using a liquid-to-gas mass ratio of approximately 4.32 kg.kg-1. Most part of mass and heat transfers occurred in the bottom section of the scrubber. In addition, the results indicated that the unit exhibited comparatively low pressure drop.

6. Acknowledgement

This work was supported by the National Research Foundation of Korea (NRF) grant funded by the Korea government(MSIT)(2021R1A2C1092152) and by Priority Research Centers Program through the National Research Foundation of Korea (NRF) funded by the Ministry of Education (2014R1A6A1031189).

References

[1] R.F.Nielsen, F.Haglind, U.Larsen, 2014, Design and modeling of an advanced marine machinery system including waste heat recovery and removal of sulphur oxides, Energy Convers, 85, 687–693.

[2] D.Flagiello, A.Parisi, A.Lancia, C.Carotenuto, A.Erto, F.Di Natale, 2019, Seawater desulphurization scrubbing in spray and packed columns for a 4.35 MW marine diesel engine, Chem. Eng. Res. Des., 148, 56-67.

[3] P.Strandberg, 2017, Marine exhaust gas scrubber, US 9,776,125 B2.

[4] R.K.Srivastava, W.Jozewicz, C.Singer, 2001, SO2 scrubbing technologies: A review, Environ. Prog, 20, 219-228.

[5] K.Oikawa, C.Yongsiri, K.Takeda, T.Harimoto, 2003, Seawater flue gas desulfurization: its technical implications and performance results, Environ. Prog, 22, 67-73.

[6] C.Eason, 2018, Announcement: Scrubber maker response to Singapore ban on open loop scrubbers, https://fathom.world/announcement-scrubber-maker-response-to-ro-singapore-ban-on-open-loop-scrubbers/

[7] MAN, 2020, Emission project guide, MAN B&W Two-stroke marine engines, https://indico.cern.ch/event/659434/attachments/1528657/2391369/MAN_BW_Two-stroke_Marine_Engines.pdf

[8] Z.Wang, Y.Peng, X.Ren, S.Gui, G.Zhang, 2015, Absorption of sulfur dioxide with sodium hydroxide solution in spray columns, Ind. Eng. Chem. Res, 54, 8670−8677.

[9] H.Hikita, S.Asai, T.Tsuji, 1977, Absorption of sulfur dioxide into aqueous sodium hydroxide and sodium sulfite solutions, AIChE J, 23 (4), 538.

[10] N.K.Yeh, G.T.Rochelle, 2003, Liquid-phase mass transfer in spray contactors, AIChE J, 49, 2363-2373.

[11] A.Bandyopadhyay, M.N.Biswas, 2012, CO2 capture in a spray column using a critical flow atomizer. Sep. Purif. Tech, 94, 104-114.

Proceedings of the 14th International Symposium on Process Systems Engineering – PSE 2021+
June 19-23, 2022, Kyoto, Japan © 2022 Elsevier B.V. All rights reserved.
http://dx.doi.org/10.1016/B978-0-323-85159-6.50165-2

Connecting the Simulation Model to the Digital Twin to help drive Sustainability

Julien de Beer[a]*, Mihaela Hahne[b]

[a]AVEVA, 5 square Felix Nadar, 94300 Vincennes, France
[b]AVEVA, 26561 Rancho Parkway South, Lake Forest, CA 92630, USA
*julien.debeer@aveva.com

Abstract

The chemicals industry is facing a highly dynamic environment. Demand is continually fluctuating, and the pressure for new sustainable processes and products is rising. New environmental regulations are always expanding and becoming less harmonized globally, and customers are demanding sustainable products that are friendly to the environment. Owner operators in all industries are maximizing the value that can be extracted from their projects and have been seeking out new and innovative ways to drive greater efficiency and productivity. Efficiency, safety and quality must be guaranteed and therefore more stringent control over compliance and regulation requirements has to be at the heart of every aspect of the design process. Profitability, safety and efficiency must be intrinsically linked.

Today, companies need to find ways to be more efficient in the execution of the engineering projects. One way is to compress engineering cycles and adapt processes and products to comply with sustainable KPIs and new demands. The Unified Engineering methodology is one option enabled by the latest technologies and tools available. For decades, engineering to design and build industrial plants has been developed through projects with a complex and highly iterative workflow, using siloed solutions. The entire process is very time consuming, and the final deliverable to the owner of the operation is a set of documents with disperse data, with no guarantee of consistency.

In order to compress engineering cycles, a data-centric approach must be used. With this approach, documents and applications are always kept up to date with the latest validated data. The data-centric approach is the first step to apply the Unified Engineering methodology, which will evolve later to the plant Digital Twin. The Unified Engineering methodology uses a single source of information that is available for all the teams involved in the project. Engineers become more efficient and work with reliable information as documents and models are updated in a controlled way as soon as any change is made. For even greater sustainability and effectiveness, the best way is to use the Unified Engineering methodology in the cloud.

Unified Engineering reduces capital project costs, risks, and delays, enabling shorter engineering cycles required to deliver new sustainable projects. By minimizing engineering errors and accelerating project execution, companies can get 50% faster FEED stage, 30% increase in engineering efficiency, and 5% reduction in TIC (Total Installed Cost).

Keywords: sustainability; simulation; design; digital twin; predictability

1. Introduction

As an industrial software provider, we support chemical companies achieve superior performance in their quest to make sustainable products, align with the circular economy and demonstrate product stewardship throughout the product life cycle. By digitally connecting assets, process, and people, our solutions empower companies to run safe and responsible operations, mitigating EHS risks, and moving toward more circular systems, while remaining profitable.

With more than 50 years of industrial software innovation, AVEVA enables 13 of top 15 chemical companies and most of the world's petrochemical crackers, with the most comprehensive portfolio that ties profitability to sustainability goals.
Research typically identifies the following Critical Sustainability Drivers:
- Demand higher transparency on a company's environmental, social & governance (ESG) performance by stakeholders
- Manage a complex environment and provide safety to employees, processes, products and local communities
- Minimize energy and utilities consumption, so as emissions
- Manage liquid effluents, waste and suppliers, seeking the circular economy
- Commitments to global and local regulations
- Portfolio management towards innovation and sustainable products

Today's technology allows suppliers to develop better solutions to those markets that are in constant change. The Digital Twin technologies, initially adopted mainly by the automotive and aerospace industries, are now promoting big changes in how chemical plants are operated and managed. This type of technology can change the decision-making process since more reliable information is available in real time.
A significant step was taken recently in terms of process simulation. Now it is possible for the engineering and operating companies to build the Digital Twin of the process plant. The Digital Twin is built on a simulation platform that will support the entire plant lifecycle, from design to operation.

2. The Digital Twin

The new generation of process simulation uses a platform approach that evolves the simulation model from the conceptual engineering to the operation optimization. It allows a new approach to be implemented so companies can transition from the conventional scenario to the use of the process simulation Digital Twin, expanding benefits to the entire plant lifecycle. The same platform is used for process simulation and process utilities (cooling water, flare, steam and others), allowing engineers to further evaluate how each system impacts the other. Heat and material balances can be re-evaluated after equipment and pipeline sizing, since that information is in the simulation from the beginning, as a result, little or no extra engineering effort is required. Once sizing is validated, the simulation is switched to dynamic mode, in which control loops are included to the simulation model to validate the process control strategy. As it is seamless to shift the simulation to dynamic mode, rather than build a completely new model using the conventional approach or converting a model that cannot be taken back to the steady state mode, dynamic studies are performed earlier in the project lifecycle. This promotes savings in equipment acquisition and in operating costs, since control logic responses are evaluated in earlier stages. Plus, when something doesn't respond as expected, simulation is taken back to steady state mode, for re-evaluation of heat and material balance and re-sizing. The ability to go back and forth between steady state and dynamic modes is critical to increase efficiency in the project lifecycle, leading to huge savings in engineering effort.

3. Unified Engineering

Companies are beginning to make progress on their digitalization journey, finding the right applications for digital transformation and seeing increasingly better returns on their investment. While the age-old market environment challenges (such as supply and demand, cost and price) haven't gone away, competitive pressures are making the digital transformation opportunity more pressing than ever. Many have already started to leverage the latest data-centric technology and work processes for their workforce to collaborate and take control of their data, reducing the risk for errors, delays and increased project cost throughout the asset lifecycle. By doing so they are in a stronger position to become more competitive, increase their margins and win new business.

As outlined by an AVEVA whitepaper (2019), Unified Engineering is a new proposition to break down the silos between FEED and Detailed Design to minimize risk and maximize return on Capital Investment.
Unified Engineering enables global multi-discipline teams to work concurrently in a common data-centric environment, controlling and managing change across the entire project. This breaks down the silos between FEED and detailed design. The simulation data created in FEED is readily available for use in detailed design and is checked and validated in real-time, increasing efficiency, minimizing risk, and maximizing return on investment on your Capital Projects.

Never have the stakes been higher for companies when it comes to making improvements to their engineering work processes to maximize ROI on Capital Projects. Productivity has not developed in decades – the average Capital Project schedule lags by 20 months and goes over budget by 80%. These are results that have been shared by Jayanth (2017) during the Rice Global E&C Forum Roundtable.
In many of today's Capital Projects, there is a disconnect between FEED and Detailed Design. In response, AVEVA are the first industrial software provider to pioneer a new solution to break down the silos between these engineering disciplines.

Unified Engineering consists of two main components, the Unified Lifecycle Simulation Platform (one model), and Integrated Engineering and Design (one database). The two are combined to form a robust process model and an engineering database that is able to synchronize through bi-directional flow of all 1D, 2D and 3D data on one platform. The bi-directional integration of a steady state and dynamic process model with an engineering database makes the process seamless and eliminates the need for MS Excel or other intermediate steps to transfer information between tools.

With the Unified Engineering model, you can have:
- Verification that the plant will operate as expected, and that controls are properly configured
- Verification that equipment and piping are properly sized
- One single version of the truth that remains up to date

Simulation Platform
One single platform instead of multiple point solutions with and interactive Process and Control Engineering

Unified Digital Engineering

Integrated Engineering & Design
A single, data-centric platform for discipline engineers to work together on, keeping all 1D, 2D and 3D engineering data in one place

- Accurate and mature design deliverables
- Efficient collaboration and automated updates
- Bi-directional data flow
- Digital Twin Data Model

The process model and the engineering database syncronizes through bi-directional flow from a single platform

Figure 1 - Unified Engineering principles

4. Process Simulation lifecycle

Process simulators are irreplaceable tools for every process engineer. Since the nineteen seventies, process simulators have found widespread adoption within operating companies in oil & gas, refining and chemical industries, as well as the engineering companies and equipment manufacturers that service these industries. The tools available in the market today have incrementally improved over the years to provide more features and functionality. However, they trace their origins to legacy architectures, operating systems and aftermarket user interfaces, which create inherent limitations:

- They cannot support the full plant lifecycle as they are limited by their single-purpose architecture such as steady state process simulation, dynamic simulation, optimization, or flow network analysis for which they were originally designed

- Extending their functionality can be performed by a very small number of software developers with chemical engineering knowledge, software programming skills, and/or knowledge of that particular specialized program

- They are often based on decades old programming code that cannot leverage the more recent technological developments within the software industry

Today's simulators typically only support a single phase of the lifecycle and are often based on thermodynamics of different simulation vendors and different calculation methods. This not only leads to lack of trust in the results but causes substantial rework by having to build a new simulation model in each new tool. And the results are hard to compare.

The technological limitations of incumbent process simulation tools forestall improvements in engineering workflows. Collaboration only occurs outside the simulation because the software cannot accommodate it. Engineering departments send analysis and optimization questions to outside specialists because they cannot easily perform advanced simulations with their in-house tools and software expertise. These complications trap engineering workflows in a waterfall project management paradigm where development is forced into a linear process. Iteration is to be avoided because legacy software makes it cumbersome, error-prone, and tedious. Willetts and Depew (2020) describe in detail the current challenges and how a Process Digital Twin will significantly help improve efficiency and drive increased sustainability.

Global competition, pricing pressure and energy alternatives are now driving the need for a new approach. The oil & gas industry has seen high volatility and the lower price level of today is seen as the "new normal". The chemicals industry has a continuous need to innovate for greater agility and lower costs.

The next generation of workers also expects a modern, scalable and easy to use solution with technology they now take for granted – high speed internet access, mobile devices, touch screens and virtual reality. New concepts like the Industrial Internet of Things (IIoT), Industry 4.0, and Artificial Intelligence have created greater opportunities with a new next generation platform that provides a "Digital Twin" of the plant through the process lifecycle that cannot be provided with today's tools.

A next generation process simulation platform means that one process model is extended throughout the entire lifecycle of the plant, from concept through to operations. This requires a process design mode, a fluid flow/rating mode and a dynamic mode, in combination with the ability to toggle back and forth between modes. Optimization may be provided to any mode.

A single, easy-to-use simulation platform will allow engineers to move seamlessly between questions of design, analysis, and optimization. Engineers will be able to assess the impact of design and specification changes quickly and with a holistic view of multiple disciplines. Intensive collaboration becomes commonplace. In this environment, organizations will be able to adopt agile engineering workflows based on smaller pieces of work with continuous integrated testing to reduce development cost while eliminating surprises at the end of the project.

5. Conclusion

Lifecycle process simulation has been a vision for process simulation providers and their customers for a long time. Today's simulators cannot leverage the rapid developments occurring in the software industry due to legacy architecture.

Looking at the industry's increasing demand for higher transparency, this can only be achieved using a data-centric Digital Twin approach. This data-centricity enables an ideal platform for new product and process development to create new models and include the management of complex environments bringing together both steady-state and dynamic simulation with constant iteration and constant solving capabilities.

The integration of the process analysis and simulation with other Engineering & Design disciplines also allows to breakdown the silos that were typically existing previously. Connecting and remotely controlling previously unconnected processes will increase sustainable operations and improve business efficiency in a sustainable environment. Over the long term the impact will drive resilience and sustainable performance through technologies.

References

Portfolio Marketing group, AVEVA, 2019, Unified Engineering: A new proposition to break down the silos between FEED and Detailed Design to minimize risk and maximize return on Capital Investment – Whitepaper

T.G. Jayanth, Expert – Capital Projects & Infrastructure, McKinsey & Co, 2017, Reinventing Construction - a route to higher productivity, McKinsey, Rice Global E&C Forum Roundtable

Ian Willetts, Vice President Process and Simulation, Cal Depew, Product Owner, AVEVA, 2020, Building a process Digital Twin for your plant with Unified Lifecycle Simulation – Whitepaper

Proceedings of the 14th International Symposium on Process Systems Engineering – PSE 2021+
June 19-23, 2022, Kyoto, Japan © 2022 Elsevier B.V. All rights reserved.
http://dx.doi.org/10.1016/B978-0-323-85159-6.50166-4

Development of predictive model for the size of gas and liquid slugs formed in millimeter scaled T-junctions

Fabian Lechtenberg[a,b], Osamu Tonomura[b,*], Satoshi Taniguchi[b], Shinji Hasebe[b]

[a]*Aachener Verfahrenstechnik, RWTH Aachen University,
Forkenbeckstraße 51, Aachen, 52074, Germany*
[b]*Department of Chemical Engineering, Kyoto University, Kyoto 615-8510, Japan*
Corresponding Author's E-mail: tonomura@cheme.kyoto-u.ac.jp

Abstract

Gas-liquid slug flow in micro/millimeter-scale channels is attractive in a broad range of applications. The sizes of slugs need to be known precisely, since the mass transfer characteristic depends on the slug length. To estimate the slug length from design and operating conditions, a number of models have been developed so far for T-junctions, but parameters of such models need to be empirically determined through many experimental trials. To reduce the experimental efforts, the physically sound model has been developed but are limited to micrometer-scale T-junctions. In this study, the applicability of the existing physically sound model is experimentally investigated in the case of millimeter-scale T-junctions. The results show that the volume added to the slug during the squeezing period is strongly affected by the condensed phase or liquid volumetric velocity. Taking this result, the combination of physical and empirical models is newly developed in this study. Our developed model will ensure the high accuracy in the design of the millimeter-scale T-junctions with gas-liquid slug flows.

Keywords: Millimeter-scale T-junctions; Gas-liquid slug flow; Slug generation mechanism; Slug size; Process modelling.

1. Introduction

Gas-liquid slug flows are attractive in a broad range of applications, such as in chemical, bio-chemical and material synthesis, drug discovery, medical diagnostics (Suryawanshi et al., 2018). The slug generation mechanism can be divided in different regimes such as squeezing, dripping and jetting, based on the capillary number (Zhu and Wang, 2016). The focus of the present research lies on T-junctions operating in the squeezing regime (cf. Fig. 1). The squeezing regime is governed by surface tension forces, making the pinch-off mechanism independent from fluid parameters like viscosity. Extensive work

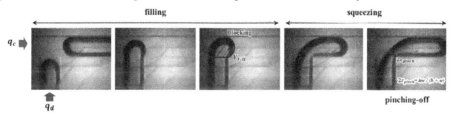

Figure 1. Slug generation mechanism in a T-junction with liquid flowrate Q_c and gas flowrate Q_d.

in this area has been done which resulted in models trying to predict the slug size from feed flows and channel geometry. In the present research, experimental validation of the proposed model by van Steijn et al (2010) is performed in millimetre scaled channels and channel geometries that have not been tested for this model. Based on the results, the shortcomings of the model are explained and tried to overcome.

2. Method

This chapter introduces the applied methods. The model by van Steijn et al. (2010) and the optical sensor and micrograph measurements is briefly explained.

2.1. Steijn's Model

The proposed model by van Steijn et al. (2010) enables the prediction of slug sizes within the squeezing regime at low capillary numbers Ca < 0.01. In this area, the slug formation mechanism is dominated by surface forces rather than viscous forces. It is a physically sound expression based on continuity, geometrical assumptions and the pinch-off mechanism. The slug formation mechanism can be divided into a filling and a squeezing part (cf. Fig. 1). The filling period ends when the bubble confines the whole main channel, leading to the accumulation of continuous phase fluid behind the bubble. This accumulating fluid squeezes the neck of the bubble during the squeezing period until it collapses. The upcoming dispersed phase then starts to fill the main channel again. This cyclic mechanism creates a segmented flow within the main channel.

In Steijn's model, it is possible to determine the filling shape of a bubble from simple geometrical calculations. During the squeezing period, the continuous phase flow is obstructed by the bubble which confines the main channel. Continuity states that the incoming continuous phase accumulates behind the bubble and a part of it bypasses the bubble as gutter flow. Herein, the ratio of gutter flowrate (Q_{gut}) to continuous phase fluid flowrate (Q_c) is assumed to be constant 0.1 (van Steijn et al., 2009).

2.2. Optical Signal Measurements

Slug sizes can be measured by using pairs of optical sensors, which need to be placed along the channel, capturing the altering light transmission due to scattering and absorption. Using the signals from two optical probes placed a certain interval, the two signals can be cross-correlated to determine the time lag and then yield instantaneous superficial velocity of slug flow and slug lengths of gas and liquid (Ide et al., 2009).

2.3. Micrograph Measurements

A method to capture the gutter flow has been developed and implemented in Python. During the experiments, the T-junction needs to be aligned with the camera's field of vision. The video's contrast should be high and capturing the whole pinch-off area for accurate performance. The procedure to acquire the gutter flow is automatized.

3. Experimental

This chapter describes the experimental setup and procedure.

3.1. Setup

The experimental setup composed of three sections can be seen in Fig. 2. The first one being the green underlined liquid feed section. The continuous liquid phase (ethanol) is supplied by a syringe pump. Additionally, the pressure in the liquid feed line is observed to determine the start of steady state operation. The second section is the yellow underlined gas feeding section. The dispersed gas phase (nitrogen) comes from a gas cylinder. The flowrate is regulated by a mass flow controller (MFC). A subsequent mass flow meter (MFM) is used to check for steady state operation. The gas then flows through a barrier channel (BC) into the T-junction. The barrier channel is used to enable steady state operation by reducing the effects of pressure swings within the channel on MFC. The third section is the blue underlined channel section. A variety of channels has been used. In all of them, the continuous liquid phase intersects with the dispersed gas phase coming from the perpendicular oriented feed channel. At this point, the segmented flow starts in the main channel. The T-junction itself is observed by a camera. Further downstream, the pair of optical sensors is placed, observing the segmented gas-liquid flow. The fluids are then led into a beaker at constant liquid level to ensure constant outlet pressure during the operation.

Five different device geometries have been used. Their dimensions are given in Table 1. The devices were fabricated both in polymethyl methacrylate (PMMA) and glass. The relative production accuracy is 5% of the stated lengths. This information was confirmed with the available microscope and a micro scale.

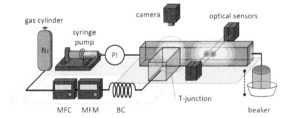

Figure 2. Schematic illustration of experimental setup.

Table 1. Millimeter-scale devices.

device	h [mm]	w [mm]	w_{in} [mm]
A-1	1.0	1.0	1.0
B-1	1.5	1.5	1.5
C-1	2.0	2.0	2.0
E-1	1.0	2.0	2.0
E-3	1.0	2.0	1.0

3.2. Procedure

For each device, the connection to the feeding lines and beaker were reconnected. The surface of the T-junction should be cleaned for optimal image quality. The temperature of the ethanol supplied to the syringe pump was adjusted to room temperature. During start-up procedure, the gas must be supplied first to prevent backflow of liquid in the gas feed line. The setpoints for the feed flowrates are inserted into the syringe pump and MFC. The pressure signal from the liquid feed line and the display from the MFM are observed to determine reach of steady state operation. Then, the sensor signals are recorded for 60s at a sampling rate of 1ms^{-1}. During this time, the video data was captured for usually 15s. After the data has been saved for one configuration, the feed rates were adjusted again.

4. Results and discussion

This chapter summarizes and discusses the main results of the conducted experiments. In the first section, the prediction accuracy of Steijn's model is evaluated. After that, the experimental validation of the gutter flow evolution is given. The following section shows how additional process information influences the prediction accuracy of Steijn's model. Based on this finding, an additional series of experiments was conducted with the goal to derive a gutter flow prediction submodel. The derivation and prediction results are described in final section.

Table 2. Prediction accuracy of Steijn's model for dimensionless gas slug volume.

(a) PMMA				(b) Glass			
Device	Max [%]	Min [%]	Mean [%]	Device	Max [%]	Min [%]	Mean [%]
A-1	-43	-12	29	A-1	-41	-7	22
B-1	-46	-21	31	B-1	-37	-2	16
E-1	31	0	8	E-1	34	3	19
E-3	-28	-5	17	E-3	24	-2	8

4.1. Steijn's Model Evaluation

The measured dimensionless gas slug volume from the experiments has been compared to the predictions by Steijn's model. Table 2 shows the boundaries and mean prediction errors. It can be seen that there is a general underestimation of the gas slug volumes. The underlying reasons are discussed in the following section.

4.2. Gutter Flow Ratio

Q_{gut} is one of influencing parameters in Steijn's model as described in section 2.1. The gutter flow during the squeezing period was captured for every conducted experiment. Q_{gut} can be determined by the Python script from the micrograph video data. Figure 3 shows a scatter plot of all gutter flow ratios over linear flow velocities for all conducted experiments. From this data it is clear that the assumption of a global constant gutter flow ratio does not hold for the scope of the performed research. It is confirmed that bigger channels inhibit higher gutter flow and flat channels E-1 and E-3 have lower gutter flows than quadratic channels. There is a slight material dependency of the gutter flow ratio. For glass devices the measured ratio was generally lower. This could be due to the corner roundness of the glass devices. The sharp corners of PMMA devices may lead to a bigger gutter area, allowing for more fluid to pass the bubble. A general trend of decreasing gutter flow ratio with increasing flow velocity can be seen. While the flat devices inhibit gutter flow ratios in the vicinity of Steijn's assumption, the other devices have considerably higher ratios. In the following, it is tested if the use of additional information about the ratio in Steijn's model improves the prediction accuracy and how the gutter flow ratio can be modeled.

4.3. Incorporated Gutter Flow

Using the additional information about the gutter flow, it is possible to calculate adjusted gas slug sizes from Steijn's model. For each experiment the information about the gutter flow ratio has been inserted into the prediction model resulting in new prediction errors. As a result, the prediction accuracy improved. Figure 4 visualizes the error distribution of PMMA and glass devices before and after the incorporation of gutter flow data. It can be seen, that in most cases the width of the error region narrows and gets shifted towards zero. The mean error of the PMMA predictions drops from 21.6% to 11.9%. For glass devices the error drops from 16.8% to 9.7%.

4.4. Gutter Flow Model Construction

From the previous experiments, it was shown that using the actual measured gutter flow ratio in the prediction model leads to improved prediction accuracy. For system design purpose, it is necessary to have a descriptive model for the gutter flow ratio. Here, a possible model derived from experimental data is constructed and evaluated.

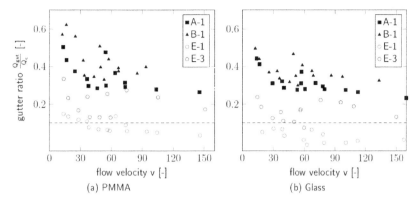

Figure 3. Gutter flow to continuous phase ratio of all conducted experiments for PMMA and glass devices. The dashed line shows Steijn's model assumption of a constant ratio of 0.1.

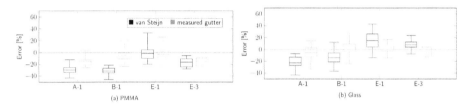

Figure 4. Prediction error of Steijn's model with conventional assumption (black) and with incorporation of gutter flow data (see Fig. 3) (orange).

The main influencing factors for the gutter flow ratio appeared to be the channel geometry, the flow velocity v and the ratio of feed flowrates Q_d/Q_c. To reduce the complexity and experimental effort, in this research the geometrical influence was not included in the model but the extrapolation ability of the model has been tested. A set of experiments has been designed to cover the variable space ranging from $v = 4$-70 mm/s and $Q_d/Q_c = 0.5$-4. In total 27 samples have been acquired. It turned out that with increasing v and Q_d/Q_c, Q_{gut}/Q_c decreases. As there is no physical description of this mechanism, it is tried to fit a function candidate to the data. Plotting the measured data points according to Eq.(1) leads to a scatter that resembles a hyperbolic dependency for both variables. For this reason the following model has been selected:

$$\frac{Q_{gut}}{Q_c} = a \cdot v^{-b} \cdot \left(\frac{Q_d}{Q_c}\right)^{-c} \tag{1}$$

The three empirical parameters a, b, c have been determined from least squares optimization. A cross-validation procedure was chosen in which four random samples have been chosen from the training set. The remaining samples were used for the parameter fitting. This procedure was repeated ten times to get an impression of the model sensitivity towards the selected training samples. The optimal parameters fall within a short range around $a = 0.9$, $b = 0.2$, $c = 0.1$ and the cross-validation shows high robustness towards training sample selection. It can be concluded that the constructed gutter flow model performs well within its training range for glass device C-1. To test the models extrapolation ability, it was used to predict Q_{gut}/Q_c for the other devices. The results can be seen in Table 3(a).

Table 3. Extrapolation ability of the constructed gutter flow model.

(a) Device	C-1	A-1	B-1	E-1	E-2	(b) Device	C-1	A-1	B-1	E-1	E-2
RMSE [-]	0.011	0.084	0.041	0.356	0.240	RMSE [-]	0.034	0.060	0.031	0.328	0.215

It is evident that the constructed model is only valid within its training region for device C-1. The closest prediction accuracy is achieved for device B-1 which has the same aspect ratios only scaled down. The accuracy for A-1 is even worse and the prediction for E-1 and E-3 barely compare to the measured data. The gutter flow ratio behaves similar for devices with same aspect ratios (A, B and C-1) as can be seen from Fig. 3. To obtain a model that can describe the gutter flow for channels with aspect ratios $h = w = 1$ and $w_{in} = w = 1$, it was tried in a next step to fit the parameters a, b and c to the whole database for these devices. In this case, the training set consisted of 57 samples and a "10-fold leave 6-out" cross validation approach was applied. The best model in this training procedure slightly differs from previous one. The newly obtained parameters are $a = 0.94$, $b = 0.23$ and $c = 0.099$. The prediction accuracy for this model can be seen in Table 3(b). Using the broader training data leads to a more uniform prediction error for the quadratic devices. The accuracy for B-1 and A-1 increased slightly on the cost of C-1 accuracy. For the flat devices E-1 and E-3 no qualitative difference can be identified.

5. Conclusions

In this research, an experimental evaluation of a model for slug size prediction in T-junctions has been performed. The channel sizes in this study were one order of magnitude bigger than those from the original study and made from PMMA and glass. The chemical system was a gas-liquid system of ethanol as continuous and nitrogen as dispersed phase. For these conditions, mean prediction error of 21.6% and 16.8% for PMMA and glass devices respectively could be achieved with Steijn's model. Methods were developed to calculate the actual slug volume from light sensor data and capturing the gutter flow volume from micrograph data. Incorporating the measured gutter flow data improved the prediction accuracy to 11.9% and 9.7%. An empirical gutter flow model was derived and trained to the acquired database. This model was found to describe channels of same aspect ratio (A-1, B-1, C-1) with a reasonable accuracy while the flat channels (E-1, E-3) cannot be described by the constructed model.

References

H. Ide, R. Kimura, M. Kawaji, 2009, Optical measurement of void fraction and bubble size distributions in a microchannel, Heat Transfer Eng. 28, 713-719.

P.L. Suryawanshi, S.P. Gumfekar, B.A. Bhanvase, S.H. Sonawane, M.S. Pimplapure. 2018, A review on microreactors: Reactor fabrication, design, and cutting-edge applications, Chemical Engineering Science, 189, 431-448.

P. Zhu, L. Wang, 2016, Passive and active droplet generation with microfluidics: a review. Lab Chip, 17, 1, 34-75.

V. van Steijn, C.R. Kleijn, M.T. Kreutzer, 2010, Predictive model for the size of bubbles and droplets created in microfluidic T-junctions. Lab Chip, 10, 19, 2513-2518.

V. van Steijn, C.R. Kleijn, M.T. Kreutzer, 2009, Flows around confined bubbles and their importance in triggering pinch-off. Phys Rev Lett, 103, 21, 214501.

Proceedings of the 14th International Symposium on Process Systems Engineering – PSE 2021+
June 19-23, 2022, Kyoto, Japan © 2022 Elsevier B.V. All rights reserved.
http://dx.doi.org/10.1016/B978-0-323-85159-6.50167-6

Enviro-economic assessment of DME synthesis using carbon capture and hydrogen from methane pyrolysis

Andrea Bernardi[a,b], Fatima Bello[a], Antonio Valente[c], David Chadwick[a], Gonzalo Guillen-Gonzalbez[c], Benoit Chachuat[a,b,*]

[a] *Sargent Centre for Process Systems Engineering, Imperial College London, UK*
[b] *Department of Chemical Engineering, Imperial College London, UK*
[c] *Department of Chemistry and Applied Bioscience, ETH Zurich, Switzerland*
Corresponding Author's E-mail: benoit.chachuat@imperial.ac.uk

Abstract

The catalytic conversion of captured CO_2 and H_2 into fuels is recognised as an interesting option to decarbonise the transport sector in the short-midterm future. DME has been identified as an ideal diesel-substitute for heavy-duty vehicles due to its high cetane number and excellent combustion properties, but to be competitive with diesel a low-cost and low-carbon H_2 production route is a key enabler. Recent developments indicate that methane pyrolysis has the potential to produce H_2 at a similar cost compared to steam methane reforming, the main H_2 production route nowadays, yet with no direct CO_2 emissions. This paper presents an enviro-economic assessment of 12 life-cycle pathways for DME production. Our results show that DME produced using H_2 from methane pyrolysis could be competitive with diesel, both economically and environmentally, but is highly dependent upon the utilisation of the carbon by-product.

Keywords: Dimethyl ether; Process simulation; Life cycle assessment; Enviro-economic assessment.

1. Introduction

Decarbonisation of the transport sector is a long-standing challenge for our modern societies and an important step towards a sustainable future. Fuels that can be produced from CO_2 hydrogenation (methanol, dimethyl ether (DME), oxymethylene ethers (OME), Fisher-Tropsch fuels) are gaining significant attention. DME, in particular, has been identified as an ideal diesel-substitute for heavy-duty vehicles (HDVs). The combustion of DME compared to diesel offers several advantages (no particulate matter or SO_x emissions, reduced NO_x and CO_2 emissions), and major truck producers such as Volvo and Mack have already developed and tested DME-fuelled trucks with positive results (Szybist *et al.* 2014). While the DME production process has been extensively studied in the literature, the economic feasibility and environmental benefits of DME over its whole life cycle are yet to be proven (Royal Society, 2019).

In a recent paper, Matzen and Demirel (2016) carried out a life cycle assessment of DME from methanol dehydration, considering CO_2 and H_2 from water electrolysis powered by wind energy as raw materials and found that DME outperforms diesel from an environmental perspective. However, a techno-economic analysis focusing on the same route showed that DME is not cost competitive in the current market conditions (Michalios *et al.* 2019). The main cost driver is H_2 production, which is 4 to 6 times more expensive when produced by renewable energy compared to methane reforming, the main H_2 production route nowadays (Al-Quatani *et al.* 2021). This is in line with the results of similar studies focusing on other alternative fuels such as methanol (Gonzales-Garay *et al.* 2019) and OME (Rodríguez-Vallejo *et al.* 2021). Recent developments indicate that methane pyrolysis, a thermal decomposition of methane into H_2 and solid carbon in a non-oxidative environment, produces H_2 with no direct CO_2 emissions and at a cost between \$0.4 and \$1.9 /kg_{H2} which compares favourably against steam methane reforming, for which the estimated cost is \$1.2 /kg_{H2} (Parkinson *et al.* 2018, 2019).

The objective of this work is to assess DME production pathways that use H_2 from methane pyrolysis and compare them with diesel, when both are used to power HDVs. A distinctive feature of our analysis is that it relies on detailed kinetic models, calibrated against experimental data to simulate the DME synthesis process and generate the foreground inventories used in both the techno-economic analysis (TEA) and life-cycle assessment (LCA). A total of 12 life-cycle pathways for DME production are compared with diesel from and economic and environmental point of view using a well-to-wheel (WTW) approach.

2. Material and methods

Figure 1 summarises the DME pathways considered in this work and the following subsections provide additional information on the modelling assumptions and approaches used to carry out the TEA and LCA.

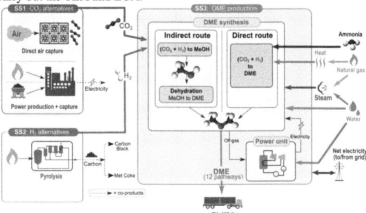

Figure 1: scope of the DME infrastructure divided in CO_2 procurement (SS1), H_2 production (SS2), DME production (SS3) and DME utilization in HDV.

2.1. Process simulation and economic analysis

Our focus is on two DME production processes: the direct synthesis where CO_2 and H_2 are converted to DME in a one-step process; and the indirect synthesis that first produces methanol that is subsequently dehydrated to form DME. Detailed process simulations relying on kinetic models calibrated against experimental data were implemented in Aspen HYSYS (version 11). The modified Peng-Robinson fluid package (PRSV) was used to simulate the methanol synthesis, while the UNIQUAC with the Redlick-Kwong activity model was used for methanol dehydration and direct DME synthesis.

Feed composition. Both DME synthesis processes are fed with a mixture of CO_2 and H_2 with a stoichiometric molar ratio of 1:3. The CO_2 is assumed to be available at 1 bar with

2.5 %$_{mol}$ of water and nitrogen, regardless the source. The H$_2$ is available at 30 bar, with 2.5 %$_{mol}$ of methane.

Indirect DME synthesis. The indirect DME plant is based on previous work by Van Dal *et al.* (2013) for methanol synthesis and by Luyben (2017) for methanol dehydration. Methanol is produced in an adiabatic reactor operating at 75 bar with a feed temperature of 210 °C, in accordance with Michalios *et al.* (2019). The unreacted gases are separated from the liquid products (methanol and water) in two consecutive flash drums then a distillation column separates the methanol from the water. A small (2 %) fraction of the unconverted feed is purged and burnt to produce electricity, while the rest is recycled back to the reactor. The electricity production unit is simulated as a syngas-fired gas turbine integrated with a steam turbine. The gas turbine cycle comprises a compressor to pressurize the air at 15 bar, a combustion chamber represented as a conversion reactor in Aspen HYSYS, and an expander. The hot flue-gas is used to produce additional electricity with a Rankine cycle. Operating variables, such as the pressure of the combustion chamber, and parameters, such as the compressors and turbines efficiencies, are taken from Narvaez *et al.* (2019). The methanol is fed at 240 °C to the DME reactor where it is dehydrated under 12 bar. The reactor is cooled to keep the internal temperature lower than 400 °C to avoid catalyst deactivation, and the outlet stream exits at 360 °C. Two distillation columns are used to separate the products. DME is extracted from the top of the first column at the 99.5 %$_{mol}$ purity, while methanol is separated from the water in the second column and recycled to the methanol reactor.

Direct DME synthesis. In the direct DME process the mixture of H$_2$ and CO$_2$ is fed to an isothermal reactor operated at 55 bar and 260 °C (Bernardi *et al.* 2020). The outlet stream contains the unreacted syngas, DME, methanol and water. It is cooled to 35 °C before entering an absorption column where a mixture of water and methanol is used as the absorbing agent. The gas stream leaving the absorption column has most of the unreacted H$_2$, CO, and CO$_2$ with traces of DME. 2 % of the unreacted syngas is used to produce electricity with the combined gas and steam turbine described before, while the rest is recycled to the reactor. DME, methanol and water exit the absorption column in the liquid stream and are fed to a distillation train. The first column separates water and methanol from the DME and gaseous impurities. Water and methanol are in part recycled to the absorption column and in part fed to a second distillation column for their separation. The top stream of the first column is fed to a third column operating under 10 bar where DME is recovered from the bottom at 99.5 %$_{mol}$ purity. A small (3 %) fraction of DME is lost from the top of this column in order to maintain a temperature above 20 °C in the condenser. A refrigeration cycle with ammonia as working fluid is used to operate this cryogenic distillation column.

Economic analysis. The capital and operating costs of the DME production plants are estimated using Aspen Economic Analyzer and considering that the plant is operating in the UK. An annual capital charge of 0.16 is used to annualize the capital cost. The CO$_2$ and H$_2$ prices are taken from Gonzales-Garay *et al.* (2019) and Parkinson *et al.* (2018) respectively. The H$_2$ price depends on the selling price of the carbon by-product, and values of $150 /ton and $500 /ton are assumed for the metallurgical coke (MC) as carbon black (CB). The diesel production cost considered here is the average price excluding VAT and duty between 2017-2021 reported in BEIS (2021).

2.2. Life-cycle analysis

Goal and scope: The functional unit (FU) for the LCA analysis is chosen as "*1 ton transported over 100 km with a heavy-duty vehicle*" (i.e.: FU = 1 tkm). The assessment of DME entails the analysis of the fuel use, as well as three background subsystems as shown in Figure 1. Subsystem SS1 involves the procurement of CO_2 and three alternatives are considered in this work: direct air capture (DAC), carbon capture from a natural gas power plant (NG), and carbon capture from a coal power plant (C). Subsystem SS2 is concerned with the H_2 production via methane pyrolysis. Two alternative uses of the carbon by-product are considered: carbon black (CB) and metallurgical coke (MC). Subsystem SS3 is the DME production step using either the direct or indirect process. Apart from DAC the other CO_2 and H_2 production pathways are multi-product and require dealing with *multi-functionality*. Following the recommendation by von der Assen *et al.* (2013) *system expansion via substitution* was adopted in this work. It is important to note that CB is a more valuable product compared to MC, but CB market demand is two orders of magnitude lower than MC and would not be enough if a large share of the HDV fleet was to be converted from diesel- to DME-fueled trucks.

Data collection and life cycle inventory: The life-cycle inventories (LCIs) for SS3 are obtained by the simulations described in Section 2.1, while the inventories for the other subsystems are gathered from the literature:
- SS1: LCIs are taken from Gonzales-Garay *et al.* (2019). The electricity produced by the power plants is assumed to substitute electricity from a conventional power plant located in UK and using the same fuel;
- SS2: The inventory data for methane pyrolysis are derived from Parkinson *et al.* (2018), and the credits for the by-products are taken from the ecoinvent database;
- Fuel use: fuel consumption and associated direct emissions are estimated for diesel and DME using the software GREET (version 1.3), considering heavy-duty trucks.

Environmental impact assessment. ReCiPe2016 is the impact assessment methodology used in this work (Huijbregts *et al.* 2017). The methodology provides midpoint indicators, which quantify the effects of resource utilization and emissions on a specific environmental category (e.g.: global warming); and endpoint indicators, which represent the three areas of protection: human health, ecosystems quality, and resources. In our analysis we converted the endpoint indicators into a common monetary basis according to the economic penalties proposed by Weidema (2015), a process known as monetization of the environmental externalities. The environmental assessment is conducted in Simapro (version 9.1.1.1), using ecoinvent 3.6 for the background process inventories.

3. Results and discussion

3.1. Midpoint environmental analysis - emissions

Figure 2a compares the GWP of DME with diesel in our WTW analysis. The labels indicate: the DME process, (indirect synthesis, iDME; direct synthesis, dDME); the use of carbon by-product (metallurgical coke, MC; carbon black. CB), and the CO_2 source (direct air capture, DAC; carbon capture from natural gas power plant, NG; and from coal power plant, C).

We can observe that all the 12 pathways lead to a reduction of the GWP_{WTW}: the pump-to-wheel (PTW) impacts are similar to those of diesel, but the well-to-pump (WTP) impacts are negative for 11 out of 12 pathways. This is the consequence of the negative GWP of the raw materials: the CO_2 from DAC is accounted for as a negative emission, while the other multifunctional processes are associated with environmental credits for the avoided by-products. These credits exceed the direct emissions from the DME production stage, except for dDME-MC-C. We can also observe that iDME slightly outperforms dDME when the same CO_2 and H_2 sources are considered. DME also outperforms diesel in terms of life-cycle PM, NO_x, and SO_2 emissions.

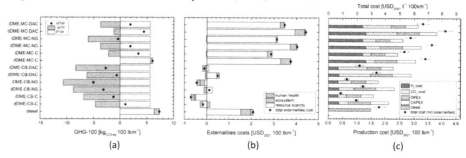

(a)　　　　　　　　　(b)　　　　　　　　　(c)

Figure 2: Enviro-economic assessment of DME- and diesel-powered HDV considering "*1 ton transported for 100 km*" as functional unit: (a) GWP; (b) externalities cost; (c) production cost. The error bars in (c) represent the minimum and maximum production costs considering a ±20% variation in the cost of the CO_2 and H_2 and historical prices for diesel in the period 2017-2021.

3.2. Endpoint analysis and total cost

Figure 2b shows the monetized values of the endpoint environmental impacts. We can observe that CB is the by-product of methane pyrolysis DME outperforms diesel, otherwise the total externalities cost of DME is higher than diesel. The damage to resources always represents the largest share. In the other two areas of protection DME is superior to diesel, except for impacts on ecosystems by dDME-MC-C and dDME-MC-DAC that are comparable to diesel. As for the GWP, iDME compares favorably against dDME also from an endpoint perspective.

Turning to economic considerations, finally, figure 2c shows the production and total cost per functional unit. We can observe that: (i) iDME outperforms dDME, and (ii) iDME is cost competitive with diesel only if the CO_2 is captured from power plants and CB is the by-product of pyrolysis. iDME outperforming dDME is the result of an easier separation between products and unreacted reagents, that leads to a lower amount of CO_2 and H_2 lost in the purge streams. CO_2 from DAC and H_2 when MC is the by-product are the most expensive alternatives, and if used together they account for approximately 60% of the total production cost. In terms of total cost (including externalities) the alternative selling CB as by-product achieves a lower total cost compared to diesel as a result of the significantly lower monetized externalities.

Conclusions

This paper has presented an enviro-economic comparative assessment of different DME production pathways using H_2 from methane pyrolysis and considering two alternatives for the solid carbon by-product. Using "1 ton transported by 100 km by HDV" as the basis of comparison, our results show that direct and indirect DME production routes using H_2 from methane pyrolysis have a similar enviro-economic performances, and that they both have the potential to be cost-effective and to present lower environmental impacts compared to diesel, provided that the carbon by-product of the methane pyrolysis is sold in the market as carbon black. If the solid carbon is sold as metallurgical coke, DME might still offer benefits at midpoint level in terms of GWP, PM, NO_x and SO_2 emissions, but at endpoint level DME has higher monetized externalities than diesel due to high damages to resources. Future work will aim to assess the robustness of our results incorporating a sensitivity analysis to account for uncertainty in the life-cycle inventories and investigate the impact of key assumptions of the LCA study. Moreover, different low-carbon H_2 production routes, such as electrocatalytic routes using renewable electricity, will be included in the comparison to assess the role of methane pyrolysis in the context of sustainable H_2 production.

Acknowledgements

This paper is based upon work supported by the Engineering and Physical Sciences Research Council (EPSRC) under Grants EP/P016650/1 and EP/V011863/1.

References

A. Al-Qahtani, B. Parkinson, K. Hellgardt, N. Shah, G. Guillen-Gosalbez, 2021. Uncovering the true cost of hydrogen production routes using life cycle monetisation. Applied Energy, 281, 115958.

BEIS, 2021. https://www.gov.uk/government/statistical-data-sets/oil-and-petroleum-products-monthly-statistics. [last accessed 5 Nov 2021]

A. Bernardi, Y. Chen, D. Chadwick, & B. Chachuat, 2020. Direct DME synthesis from syngas: a techno-economic model-based investigation. Computer Aided Chemical Engineering 48, 655-660.

A. González-Garay, M.S. Frei, A. Al-Qahtani, C. Mondelli, G. Guillén-Gosálbez J. Pérez-Ramírez, 2019. Plant-to-planet analysis of CO2-based methanol processes. Energy & Environmental Science, 12, 3425

M.A. Huijbregts, Z. Steinmann, P. Elshout, G. Stam, F. Verones, M. Vieira, & R. Van Zelm, 2017. ReCiPe2016: a harmonised life cycle impact assessment method at midpoint and endpoint level. The International Journal of Life Cycle Assessment, 22(2), 138-147.

M. Matzen, & Y. Demirel, 2016. Methanol and dimethyl ether from renewable hydrogen and carbon dioxide: Alternative fuels production and life-cycle assessment. Journal of cleaner production, 139, 1068-1077.

S. Michailos, S. McCord, V. Sick, G. Stokes, & P. Styring, 2019. Dimethyl ether synthesis via captured CO2 hydrogenation within the power to liquids concept: A techno-economic assessment. Energy Conversion and Management, 184, 262-276.

A. Narvaez, D. Chadwick, & L. Kershenbaum, 2019. Performance of small-medium scale polygeneration systems for dimethyl ether and power production. Energy, 188, 116058.

W.L. Luyben, 2017. Improving the conventional reactor/separation/recycle DME process. Computers & Chemical Engineering, 106, 17-22.

B. Parkinson, M. Tabatabaei, D. Upham, B. Ballinger, C. Greig, S. Smart, E. McFarland, 2018, Hydrogen production using methane: Techno-economics of decarbonizing fuels and chemicals. International Journal of Hydrogen Energy, 43(5), 2540-2555.

B. Parkinson, P. Balcombe, J. F. Speirs, A. Hawkes, K. Hellgardt, 2019, Levelized cost of CO2 mitigation from hydrogen production routes. Energy & environmental science, 12(1), 19-40.

D. Rodríguez-Vallejo, A. Valente, G. Guillén-Gosálbez, & B. Chachuat, 2021. Economic and life-cycle assessment of OME 3–5 as transport fuel: a comparison of production pathways. Sustainable Energy & Fuels, 5(9), 2504-2516.

The Royal Society, 2019, Sustainable synthetic carbon-based fuels for transport: policy briefing, London, UK Royal Society

J. P. Szybist, S. McLaughlin, & S. Iyer, 2014. Emissions and performance benchmarking of a prototype dimethyl ether fueled heavy-duty truck. Papers of the american chemical society, 248, 1155.

E.S. Van-Dal, & C. Bouallou, 2013. Design and simulation of a methanol production plant from CO2 hydrogenation. Journal of Cleaner Production, 57, 38-45.

N. von der Assen, J. Jung, A. Bardow, 2013, Life-cycle assessment of carbon dioxide capture and utilization: avoiding the pitfalls. Energy & Environmental Science, 6(9), 2721-2734.

B. P. Weidema, 2015, Comparing three life cycle impact assessment methods from an endpoint perspective. Journal of Industrial Ecology, 19(1), 20-26.

Proceedings of the 14th International Symposium on Process Systems Engineering – PSE 2021+
June 19-23, 2022, Kyoto, Japan © 2022 Elsevier B.V. All rights reserved.
http://dx.doi.org/10.1016/B978-0-323-85159-6.50168-8

Operational Envelopes of Cost-effective Sour Gas Desulfurization Processes

Chinmoy B. Mukta, Selen Cremaschi and Mario R. Eden[*]

Department of Chemical Engineering, Auburn University, Auburn, AL 36849, USA
edenmar@auburn.edu

Abstract

Cost-effective desulfurization of sour gas is of paramount importance not only in terms of safety, but also for the effective utilization of natural gas resources, as a significant amount of the gas content of a shale oil well is currently burned or emitted, which is detrimental for both the environment and the economy. Therefore, we need robust and cost-effective desulfurization technologies that can handle a wide range of gas flowrates and hydrogen sulfide concentrations. There has been significant progress in developing new desulfurization technologies, however determining their cost-effectiveness at different scales remains a challenge. Process modeling of these emerging desulfurization processes can help elucidate the parameters/uncertainties that impact their performance and thus help identify the best solution for a given system configuration. In this work, three natural gas desulfurization processes, i.e., oxidative sulfur removal (OSR) SourCat™ (Deng *et al.*, 2020), iron-chelate redox systems LO-CAT® (Faramawy *et al.*, 2016) , and Triazine based scavenger (Lozano & Trauffer, 2000) are simulated for natural gas feeds ranging from 1 to hundred thousand MSCFD and inlet H_2S concentrations from 500 to 2,500 ppm.

Keywords: Desulfurization; Process Simulation;

1. Introduction

Fossil fuels are still an indispensable part of modern living for human society, keeping cars running and houses heated, for example. Due to the renewed emphasis on renewables and rigorous environmental scrutiny on other dirtier fossil fuels (coal, oil), there is an increasing demand for natural gas as a cleaner energy resource. Moreover, with disinvestment happening around the energy industry, it has become imperative to utilize natural gas resources effectively. Sour gas is a natural gas resource that contains a significant fraction of hydrogen sulfide (H_2S) and carbon dioxide. The high hydrogen sulfide content severely limits the technical, economic, and environmental viability of certain natural gas resources. Hydrogen sulfide is toxic and corrodes pipelines if untreated. Sour gas from the gas well is processed by separating the H_2S to give a sweet natural gas with specifications appropriate for transport and use by customers (maximum of 4 ppm H_2S).

Natural gas produced in lesser but not insignificant quantities or at remote locations is termed as stranded gas. These natural gas resources are typically vented or flared because of high transportation and processing costs. Processing stranded sour gas resources requires the development of scalable and easily deployable gas sweetening processes.

Modularization of chemical processes is a process intensification option that provides significant economic and safety benefits because of flexibility and robustness in the transportation, deployment, and operation of a processing facility (Baldea *et al.*, 2017; Bielenberg *et al.*, 2019). Modularized desulfurization of stranded gas is highly beneficial for better utilization of natural gas and prevention of environmental emission.

In this work, three natural gas desulfurization processes, i.e., oxidative sulfur removal (OSR) SourCat[TM], iron-chelate redox systems LO-CAT®, and Triazine based scavenger (Hugo *et al*, 2000) are simulated for a natural gas feed at various scales (1 to hundred thousand MSCFD) and inlet H_2S concentrations (500 to 2,500 ppm). For each set of operating conditions, the desulfurization cost is calculated for each process. The calculated cost is depicted and analyzed through heat maps. The process with the lowest desulfurization cost is identified for each operating condition.

2. Process Simulations and Desulfurization Cost Calculations

2.1. Triazine-based scavenger process

Scavenger-based absorption is used hydrogen sulfide removal method for small sour gas cleaning. The process does not employ solvent regeneration and can be discarded to the environment as the spent liquid are readily biodegradable (Taylor *et al.*, 2019). A process flow diagram (PFD) for the triazine-based absorption process is given in Figure 1. Sour gas (10-70°C) is injected into an absorber with a 52 wt% triazine-based scavenger, and the liquid-gas mixture is separated in a tower where sweet gas is collected from the top and spent liquid scavenger from the bottom (Lozano & Trauffer, 2000). To avoid solids formation, the inlet triazine is kept at 20% excess. Finally, the gas phase is maintained with sulfur content lower than 4 ppm, and the liquid phase is the reacted Triazine which will be disposed of.

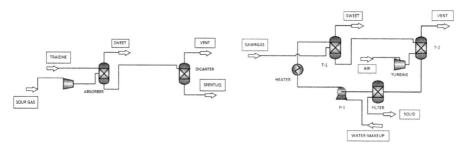

Figure 1. Triazine-based PFD　　　　　　　　　Figure 2. LOCAT® PFD

2.2. Liquid redox process

In the LO-CAT® process, H_2S is oxidized to elemental sulfur using a chelated iron sodium ferric ethylenediaminetetraacetate (EDTA FeNa) solution (Faramawy *et al.*, 2016). This process is primarily used for small scale desulfurization of natural gas. The process flow diagram of the LO-CAT® process is given in Figure 2 (Faramawy *et al.*, 2016; Speight, 2018). In the absorber vessel (T-1), H_2S from sour gas is absorbed by the EDTA solution, where ferric ions oxidize H_2S to form solid sulfur. Subsequently, in vessel T-2, ferrous ions are oxidized back to ferric ions when reacted with oxygen in air. Sweet gas with the required specification (<4 ppm H_2S) leaves the top of the absorber. The ferric ion solution is recycled back to the absorber. Fresh EDTA solution is added to the recycle loop to compensate for losses related to the wet sulfur cake. To prevent iron precipitation and accelerate H_2S absorption, NaOH or KOH is used to maintain the solution pH between 8 and 9.

2.3. Chemical oxidation (SourCat^TM) process

The SourCat^TM process is a newly patented solid catalyst-based oxidative sulfur removal (OSR) desulfurization process developed by IntraMicron, Inc., an Auburn University spin-off company (Deng *et al.*, 2020). A process flow diagram of the simulation is given in Figure 3. Sour gas and air are injected into the solid fixed-bed catalytic reactor, where H_2S is converted to solid sulfur and a small amount of SO_2 with high selectivity to elemental sulfur (over 90%). The reactor effluent is washed and cooled with water to remove solid elemental sulfur and most SO_2. The solid sulfur is collected by a filter and discarded as sulfur cake. The small amount of SO_2 produced is carried by the gas stream and separated from the sweet gas by an adsorption bed (V-2).

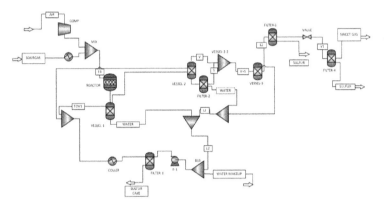

Figure 3: SourCat^TM PFD

2.4. Cost calculation

Desulfurization costs are defined as the cost of sweetening one thousand standard cubic feet (MSCF) natural gas. Aspen Plus^TM process simulations are used to calculate the raw material/utility requirements and equipment sizes for each process. Given this information, the capital expenses (CAPEX) and operating expenses (OPEX) are calculated using standard cost calculation coefficients (Turton *et al.*, 2008). Next, the desulfurization cost before and after paying back the capital investment is calculated using Equations (1) and (2), respectively. In Eq. (1), the annual interest rate, r, is assumed at 10%, and the payoff time, t, is set as 5 years. The variable capacity represents the sour gas flow rate in thousand standard cubic feet per day (MSCFD).

$$Desulfurization\ Cost\ before\ payback\ = \frac{CAPEX \times \frac{r(1+r)^t}{(1+r)^t-1} + OPEX}{Capacity} \qquad (1)$$

$$Desulfurization\ Cost\ after\ payback\ = \frac{OPEX}{Capacity} \qquad (2)$$

2.5. Modularization criteria

In this work, a simple modularization criterion is used to limit the size of principal equipment in each process to allow for easy transportation. In sizing the conventional process, each piece of equipment was scaled freely according to the process requirements. On the other hand, to identify the size of the modularized plants, we constrained the size of the equipment based on federal transportation guidelines (Morris, 2003). The sizing algorithm for the modularization is illustrated in Figure 4 (Shao *et al.*, 2020).

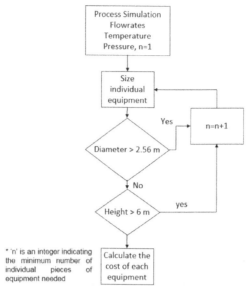

Figure 4. Method and criteria used for modularization.

3. Results & Discussion

After the cost calculations to compare three different desulfurization processes, a plot is generated comparing desulfurization cost before and after the payback of the equipment. In Figure 7 (left), the cost before payback is shown, and Figure 7 (right) shows after payback. Both plots show the cost for SourCat™ process is minimum at ten thousand MSCFD, for before and after payback time, respectively.

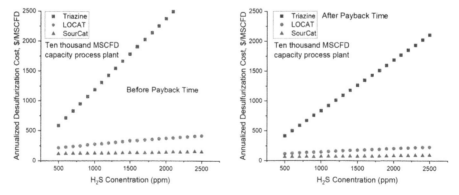

Figure 7: Desulfurization cost at 10,000 MSCFD before (left) and after (right) payback.

In Figure 8 (left), the cost before payback is shown, and Figure 8 (right) shows after payback for 100,000 MSCFD. Both plots show that the cost of the SourCat™ process is the lowest at 100,000 MSCFD, both before and after payback. LOCAT could only compete at very low H_2S concentration. The Triazine-based process cost has been excluded from the plots as it is significantly more expensive than the others at 100,000 MSCFD.

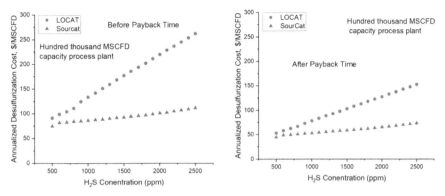

Figure 8: Desulfurization cost at 100,000 MSCFD before (left) and after (right) payback.

Based on the cost calculation results, heat maps illustrating the competing technologies for different combinations of flowrate and H_2S concentration have been developed and shown in Figure 9. Both plots indicate that at higher natural gas flowrates, SourCat™ may be the most cost-effective technology, but at very low natural gas flowrates and particularly at lower hydrogen sulfide concentrations, the Triazine-based scavenger process can be cost-effective.

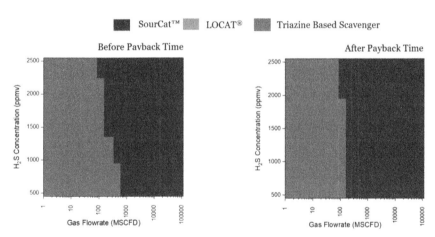

Figure 9: Desulfurization cost heat map.

Similarly, heat maps illustrating the comparison of the three technologies for the modularized case have been developed and are shown in Figure 10. It shows that at high flow rates of 100,000 MSCFD and low H_2S concentration, LOCAT can be cost-competitive, however for most cases investigated here, the best choices are Triazine for low flow rates, and SourCat™ for higher flowrates (>100 MSCFD).

4. Conclusions

In this paper, we have investigated three natural gas desulfurization technologies at a range of gas flowrates and hydrogen sulphide concentrations. Conventional designs, as well as modularized configurations, have been compared. For all combinations of gas flowrate and H_2S concentration, the technology with the lowest sulphur removal cost has been identified. The new SourCat™ process appears to be the most cost-effective and economically favorable process for flowrates above 100 MSCFD regardless of H_2S concentration, while the Triazine-based Scavenger process is more suitable for small capacity/lower flowrate systems. The LOCAT® process only shows promise at a very high flowrates and very low H_2S concentration, even in the modularized configuration. Therefore, while the Triazine-based process has potential for very small systems, the flexibility and scalability of the SourCat™ process lends itself more to process intensification and deployment at medium to larger size systems.

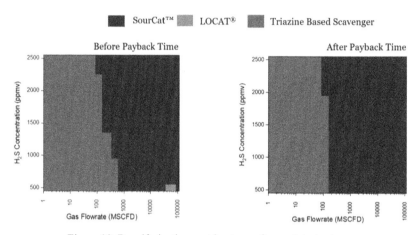

Figure 10. Desulfurization cost heat map for modularized process.

References

Baldea, M., Edgar, T. F., Stanley, B. L., & Kiss, A. A. (2017). Modular manufacturing processes: Status, challenges, and opportunities. AIChE journal, 63(10), 4262-4272.

Bielenberg, J., & Palou-Rivera, I. (2019). The RAPID Manufacturing Institute–Reenergizing US efforts in process intensification and modular chemical processing. Chemical Engineering and Processing-Process Intensification, 138, 49-54.

Deng, Y., Xu, S., Webb, K., Wright, H., Dimick, P. S., Cremaschi, S., & Eden, M. R. (2020). Sensitivity Analysis of Desulfurization Costs for Small-Scale Natural Gas Sweetening Units. In Computer Aided Chemical Engineering (Vol. 48, pp. 973-978). Elsevier.

Faramawy, S., Zaki, T., & Sakr, A. E. (2016). Natural gas origin, composition, and processing: A review. Journal of Natural Gas Science and Engineering, 34, 34-54.

Lozano, H., & Trauffer, E. A. (2000). Re-generable H_2S Scavenger. In Proceedings of the Laurance Reid Gas Conditioning Conference, pp. 47-78.

Morris, J. R. (2003). TRB Special Report: Regulation of Weights, Lengths, and Widths of Commercial Motor Vehicles. TR News, (228).

Speight, J. G. (2018). Natural gas: a basic handbook. Gulf Professional Publishing.

Taylor, G., Smith-Gonzalez, M., Wylde, J., & Oliveira, A. P. (2019, March). H2S Scavenger Development During the Oil and Gas Industry Search for an MEA Triazine Replacement in Hydrogen Sulfide Mitigation and Enhanced Monitoring Techniques Employed During Their Evaluation. In SPE International Conference on Oilfield Chemistry. OnePetro.

Turton, R., Bailie, R. C., Whiting, W. B., & Shaeiwitz, J. A. (2008). Analysis, synthesis and design of chemical processes. Pearson Education.

Shao, Y., & Zavala, V. M. (2020). Modularity measures: Concepts, computation, and applications to manufacturing systems. AIChE Journal, 66(6), e16965.

Proceedings of the 14th International Symposium on Process Systems Engineering – PSE 2021+
June 19-23, 2022, Kyoto, Japan © 2022 Elsevier B.V. All rights reserved.
http://dx.doi.org/10.1016/B978-0-323-85159-6.50169-X

Process Alternatives for the Co-Production of Hydrogen and Methanol using Fuel Switch and Energy Mix Systems

Usama Ahmed [a,b], Umer Zahid [a, c], Nabeel Ahmad [d], Nauman Ahmad [e]

[a] *Chemical Engineering Department, King Fahd University of Petroleum & Minerals, Dhahran 31261, Saudi Arabia*
[b] *Interdisciplinary Research Center for Hydrogen and Energy Storage, King Fahd University of Petroleum & Minerals, Dhahran 31261, Saudi Arabia*
[c] *Interdisciplinary Research Center for Membranes & Water Security, King Fahd University of Petroleum & Minerals, Dhahran 31261, Saudi Arabia*
[d] *Department of chemical engineering, COMSATS University Islamabad, Lahore campus 54000, Pakistan*
[e] *Minhaj Univeristy Lahore, 54000, Pakistan*
usama.ahmed@kfupm.edu.sa

Abstract

With the increase in the global energy requirements, the utilization of fossil fuels have been also increased which not only increased greenhouse gas (GHG) emissions but also caused global warming. The sharp reduction in the GHG emissions demands for utilizing the energy mix and fuel switch technologies to develop the cleaner fuels. In this study, process simulation framework has been proposed to simultaneously produce two fuels (methanol and H_2) in the co-generation process integration framework. Two process models have been developed in Aspen Plus ® V12 followed by the techno-economic assessment to analyze the process feasibility. Case 1 is considered as the base case process, where the process initiates with the coal-biomass gasification to produce the synthesis gas. The synthesis gas is then treated in the acid gas removal units to remove the CO_2 and H_2S. The synthesis gas is then fed to the methanol synthesis unit to produce methanol, whereas, the unconverted CO is treated in the water-gas shift (WGS) reactors to convert CO into the H_2 and CO_2 followed by CO_2 removal in the AGR section. Case 2 design represents the novel process for co-production of methanol and H_2, where the coal-biomass gasification technology is sequentially integrated with the methane reforming technology to maximize the heat utilization without any energy penalties. Both the models are techno-economically compared in terms of methanol and H_2 production rates, specific energy requirements, carbon conversion, CO_2 specific emissions, overall process efficiencies, fuel production costs and project feasibilities. The results showed that the case 2 design offers higher methanol and H_2 production rates with the low energy requirements. Also, the process efficiency of case 2 is 3.8% higher than the case 1 design, where, the specific energy requirements of case 2 is almost 16% less compared to the case 1 design. While performing some sensitivity studies, it has been analyzed that the case 2 process offers better process feasibility in terms of process performance and economics.

Keywords: gasification, reforming, hydrogen, methanol.

1. Introduction

The global energy demand has increased manifolds during the last few decades due to rapid industrialization and continuously relying on the conventional processes for heat and power generation. Also, the recent report issued by Global Energy Outlook (GEO, 2020) also forecasted an increase in energy demand up to 30% in the near future. To minimize the difference between energy demand and supply, conventional and economical fuels have been used for power generation, where, coal and natural gas are among the most widely used feedstock's. However, the recent increase in the fuel prices has put more pressure to use the cleaner fuels and reduce the carbon emissions. Since, the coal fee stocks are widely available and most of the infrastructure is developed based on the coal based processes, it is expected that the coal will be used in the coming decades. Therefore, an attention has been made to convert the coal into clear fuels i.e. syngas, H_2, methanol, FT chemicals, etc.

Natural gas to methanol and hydrogen (NGTMH) technology has been widely used to produce hydrogen and methanol. Steam methane reforming (SMR) is an intermediate step to convert the natural gas into syngas with the HCR of 2.0-2.5. The syngas can be further transformed into various products including H2, methanol, and FT chemicals. On the other hand, hydrogen and methanol can be produced from the coal by converting it into syngas using gasification techniques, which, can be further transformed into methanol and H_2. Coal to methanol and hydrogen (CBH) processes have received a lot of attention due to lower coal prices, however, hydrogen to carbon (HCR) from the coal-based processes lies in the range of 1:2, which is not suitable for methanol production. Therefore, water gas shift (WGS) and CO_2 removal systems are deployed to enhance the H_2 production and minimizing the CO_2 emissions. On the other hand, an integrated approach to utilize the natural gas reforming and coal gasification is the single process can be also used to enhance the overall hydrogen production. This approach utilizes the heat from the gasification unit in the natural gas reforming unit to minimize the overall energy needs while producing additional syngas. Mixing the gasifier and reformer derived syngas; the overall HCR can be increased to make it suitable for the methanol and hydrogen production. Yi et al. (2015) reported that the 2.6 ton of CO2 is emitted for each ton of methanol production while using the CTM technologies. On the other hand, SMR processes showed a potential of lower carbon emissions due the higher HCR ratio in the synthesis gas. Recently, Blumberg et al. (2019) also performed the exergy analysis and developed the alternative designs by integrating different reforming technologies to enhance the H_2 production that can improve the overall methanol production. Ahmed et al. (2021, 2021, and 2021) also integrated the syngas production processes to enhance the overall H_2 production rates that can influence the downstream methanol production.

This study utilizes coal and biomass feedstocks, which are gasified to generate the syngas. Moreover, the gasification unit is integrated with the methane-reforming unit, where, the heat from the gasification unit is utilized in the reforming unit. The key idea is to use the multiple feedstocks that can involve the biomass to reduce the overall carbon footprint, while, enhancing the syngas production. The technical and economic analysis is performed to determine the overall process efficiency, carbon emissions fuel production costs.

2. Modelling and Simulation

Aspen Plus (V12) has been used in this study to develop the simulation models for the production of methanol and hydrogen. The Peng Robinson with Boston Mathias (PR–BM) is used as the effective thermodynamic package, where, coal and biomass are defined based on proximate and ultimate analysis. Table 1 represents the process conditions and some of the main units of the overall process:

Process	Conditions
Reformer (RGibbs)	Temperature: 900°C, Pressure: 32 bar NG flow rate: 5.50kg/s, $H_2O:CH_4 = 3:1$, Ni-based catalyst
Gasification (RGibbs)	Temperature: 1350-1370°C, Pressure: 56 bar Coal Flow Rate: 62.2kg/s Biomass flow rate: 6.2kg/s
Methanol Reactor(RGibbs)	Temp/Pressure = 200°C / 5.5 MPa
Heat Exchangers (MHeatX)	$\Delta Tmin=10°C$
Water Gas Shift Rector (REquil Reactor)	Adiabatic reactors, Steam/CO: ~2.2

3. Process Description

Two process models have been developed in Aspen Plus (V12). Figure 1 shows the base case model, where, coal and biomass are used to produce syngas in the gasification unit.

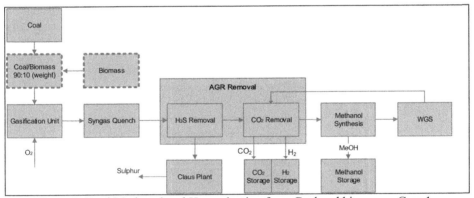

Figure 1: Dual Methanol and H_2 production from Coal and biomass – Case 1

The temperature of the syngas is then reduced in the radiant coolers to generate high-pressure steam. The syngas is then passed through the acid gas removal unit to remove the H_2S and CO_2 from the syngas. The synthesis gas is then allowed to enter in the methanol synthesis unit, in the presence of copper-based $CuO/Al_2O_3/ZnO$ catalyst, to produce the methanol. The unconverted syngas from the methanol unit is then fed to the WGS unit to convert the CO in the syngas to CO_2 and H_2. The mixture of CO_2 and H_2 is then fed to the CO_2 removal unit to capture excess of the CO_2 and to get the pure H_2, which is sent to the storage section. Figure 2 represents the case 2 process model, which uses biomass, natural gas and coal feedstocks for the production of methanol and H_2. Case 2 mainly integrates the coal/biomass gasification process with the natural gas reforming technology, where, the energy from the gasification unit is utilized in the reforming unit. The overall aim of this integration is to minimize the energy needs of the process while increase the production of syngas and H_2.

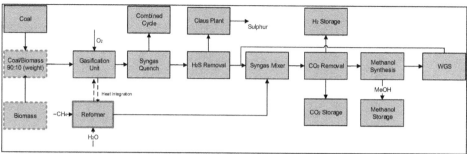

Figure 2: Production of H_2 and Methanol from Coal, Biomass and Methane in an integrated process – Case 2

4. Results and Discussion

4.1 Methanol and H_2 Production Rates and Overall Process Performance

The results from the case 1 and case 2 are compared to analyze the overall process efficiency and to evaluate the production rates of the methanol and H_2 from both cases. The results showed that the case 2 design has higher syngas production rates with the higher HCR in the syngas. The results are also compared in terms of higher heating value (HHV) of the syngas, where, the HHV of the syngas in case 1 and case 2 is calculated as 16.24MJ/kg and 18.84MJ/kg, respectively. The production rates of methanol for case 1 and case 2 have been calculated as 31.17kg/s and 45.44kg/s, respectively. Similarly, the H_2 production rates for case 1 and case 2 have been calculated as 3.1kg/s and 2.58kg/s, respectively, as shown in Figure 3.

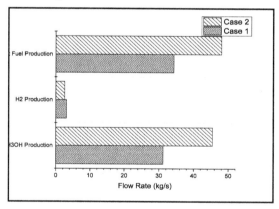

Figure 3: Methanol and Hydrogen Production Rates

The specific energy requirement is an important indicator to find out the energy required for each unit of product formed. It has been seen from the results that methanol specific energy requirement for case 1 and case 2 is 20.51kg/GJ and 26.15 kg/GJ. Also, the H_2 specific energy requirement for case 1 and case 2 is 2.04 kg/GJ and 1.48kg/GJ, respectively. It is also important to estimate the overall process performance of case 1 and case 2 for comparative analysis. The efficiency for both the cases have been calculated based on thermal energy of feedstocks and produced fuels (methanol and H_2) as represented in the equation 1.

$$\text{Process Efficiency} = \frac{\text{Methanol thermal energy [MWth]} + H_2 \text{ thermal energy [MWth]}}{\text{Feed stock thermal energy [MWth]} + \text{Energy consumed [MWth]}} \times 100\% \quad (1)$$

The results showed that the overall process efficiency of case 1 and case 2 is 65.3% and 69.9% respectively. Moreover, it has been seen from results that the specific production energy requirement for case 1 and case 2 is 44.33GJ/MT and 36.18GJ/MT of energy, respectively. Moreover, the carbon conversion efficiency for case 1 and case 2 is calculated around 30% and 40%, respectively. In terms of emissions, case 1 and case 2 generated 0.31 kg and 0.19 kg of uncaptured CO_2 for each kg of fuel (methanol and H_2) produced.

5. Economic Analysis and Project Feasibility

Economic analysis includes the estimation of the capital expenditure (CAPEX) and the operational expenditure (OPEX) to estimate the cost of the final product. The CAPEX mainly involves the cost the equipment, piping and installation, instrumentation, civil work etc. On the other hand, OPEX is calculated on the base of cost of raw material or feedstocks, utilities, catalyst replacement, maintenance, etc. The CAPEX is calculated by sizing all the equipment depending upon the operational conditions and the flow rates of the stream through each unit. The CAPEX is calculated using equation 2, where the $CEPCI_{old}$, $Capacity_{old}$ and $Cost_{old}$ values are taken from the literature for the corresponding units along and the new CEPCI of 618 for the year 2021 has been chosen to estimate the cost of new units along with new production capacities taken from the model. The value of x is taken as 0.6 (6/10th rule) for keeping the comparative analysis simple.

$$\text{Cost}_{New} = \text{Cost}_{Old} \times \left(\frac{\text{Capacity}_{New}}{\text{Capacity}_{Old}}\right)^X \times \frac{\text{CEPCI}_{New}}{\text{CEPCI}_{Old}} \quad (2)$$

The results from the economic analysis is represented in the Table 2. The results showed that CAPEX/MT required for case 1 and case 2 is 75.37 \$/MT and 66.51\$/MT, respectively. Moreover, the OPEX/MT for the case 1 and case 2 is calculated as 250.82 \$/MT and 217.02 \$/MT, respectively. The CAPEX and OPEX calculations are used to determine the total production cost (TPC) and minimum selling price (MSP). The results showed that the selling price of the methanol for case 1 and case 2 is estimated as 322.73 \$/MT and 256.93 \$/MT, respectively. Moreover, the selling price of the H_2 for case 1 and case 2 is estimated as 36.09 \$/MT and 54.96 \$/MT, respectively.

Table 2: Economic Analysis

	Units	Case 1	Case2
CAPEX	USD/MT	75.37	66.51
OPEX	USD /MT	250.82	217.02
Total (CAPEX+OPEX)	USD /MT	326.20	283.53
10% Profit Rate	USD /MT	32.62	28.35
MSP od Fuel (H_2+CH_3OH)	USD /MT	358.82	311.88
MSP of Methanol	USD /MT	322.73	256.93
MSP of H_2	USD /MT	36.09	54.96

The cash flow analysis for both the cases have been also done to analyze the project feasibility, where, the lifetime of the plant in both cases is taken as thirty three (33) years as represented in the Figure 4. The results showed that the case 2 design offers higher rate on return on the investment as compared to the case 1 design.

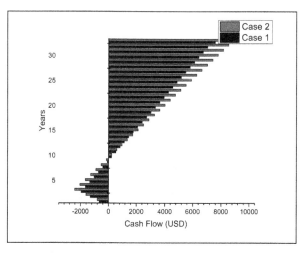

Figure 4: Cumulative Cash Flow Analysis

6. Conclusions

This study represented the technical and economic analysis of two process models for the production of hydrogen and methanol. Both the models were developed in Aspen Plus, where, the base case model used coal and biomass for the production of hydrogen and methanol. On the other hand, the alternative model used the natural gas along with the coal and biomass, where, the sequential integration between the gasification unit and reforming unit is done to minimize the energy needs. The two models were compared in terms of process efficiencies, fuel production rates and carbon conversion. The results showed that the case 2 performs better compared to the case 1 design in terms of both process performance and economics.

Acknowledgements

The authors would like to acknowledge the support provided by the Deanship of Scientific Research (DSR) at King Fahd University of Petroleum & Minerals (KFUPM) for funding this work through project No. SB201019.

References

Ahmed, U., Zahid, U., Onaizi, S. A., Abdul Jameel, A. G., Ahmad, N., Ahmad, N., & AlMohamadi, H. (2021). Co-production of hydrogen and methanol using fuel mix systems: Technical and economic assessment. Applied Sciences, 11(14), 6577.

Ahmed, U., Hussain, M. A., Bilal, M., Zeb, H., Zahid, U., Onaizi, S. A., & Jameel, A. G. A. (2021). Utilization of Low-Rank Coals for Producing Syngas to Meet the Future Energy Needs: Technical and Economic Analysis. Sustainability, 13(19), 10724.

Ahmed, U. (2021). Techno-economic analysis of dual methanol and hydrogen production using energy mix systems with CO2 capture. Energy Conversion and Management, 228, 113663.

Blumberg, T., Morosuk, T., & Tsatsaronis, G. (2019). CO2-utilization in the synthesis of methanol: Potential analysis and exergetic assessment. Energy, 175, 730-744.

Newell, R., Raimi, D., Villanueva, S., & Prest, B. (2020). Global energy outlook 2020: Energy transition or energy addition?

Yi, Q., Li, W., Feng, J., & Xie, K. (2015). Carbon cycle in advanced coal chemical engineering. Chemical Society Reviews, 44(15), 5409-5445.

Proceedings of the 14th International Symposium on Process Systems Engineering – PSE 2021+
June 19-23, 2022, Kyoto, Japan © 2022 Elsevier B.V. All rights reserved.
http://dx.doi.org/10.1016/B978-0-323-85159-6.50170-6

Documenting Models Comprehensively Using a Minimal Graphical Language

Heinz A Preisig

Department of Chemical Engineering, NTNU, N-7491 Trondheim, Norway
Heinz.Preisig@chemeng.ntnu.no

Abstract

A small graphical language provides the means to document and discuss process models in details without engaging into a programming environment. It proved to be a powerful tool to discuss model on the back of an envelope as well as for defining a graphical user interface for ontology-based modelling suite ProMo.

Keywords: Modelling ontologies, simulation, control, design, operations

1.1 Background

Mathematical models are the core of any computational engineering activity and models are used in various contexts. Traditionally modelling tools attempt to construct process models from basic building blocks. The nature of the building blocks is often not transparent to the user. The tools are constructed with expecting only basic knowledge of the basic building blocks. The actual realisation is usually left to an expert and remains mostly hidden from the process model builder. This approach works fine as long as the building blocks are matching the behaviour the user expects. If the match is not good enough, the user has no hands on learning about the detailed implementation and the expert has to be called on the scene.

Independent on the type of user, it is good practice to provide a complete documentation of the building blocks and the resulting process model. It is often essential to get the insight on what the person constructing the model assumed and how it was "seen". Modelling tools are also mostly integrated with a solver environment, which in the past often used to be visible and accessible. Today, a myriad of solvers are available and it is often desirable to move from one solver environment to an other, which brings the issue of generating code compatible into the limelight. One quickly also gets interested using models with different solvers and thus one formalised the problem of transferring models between different environments. The CAPE-OPEN project (2020) is the most outstanding in chemical engineering, while the Modelica community designed functional mock-up interfaces (FIM 2021). In both cases, one retains the actual code and resorts to wrapper technology (for example SWIG 2021). We have taken a different approach by lifting model documentation and behaviour to a higher level.

2. Foundation: Reductionism

Chemical engineering software builds on implementing basic principles of physics, chemistry and biology, enriched, when necessary, with black-box models. Latter to capture behaviours that can for one or the other reason not be captured by a mechanistic description. Either it is too complicated, which is probably the most common cause, or it is merely not sufficiently well known what is going on between the excitation and the response of the part in question.

Most simulators have a graphical input language, just because it is easier for people to generate models using a graphical interface in contrast to a textual interface. So why then a graphical language for documenting/describing models?

Graphical tools for capturing a plant's behaviour may or may not have models attached to the visual object representing them. Some systems are purely focusing on a graphical representation (example: ConceptDraw, 2021). Simulators, in contrast, do have models linked to the items shown on the screen. Examples are gProms™ (2021), Aspen™ (2021), etc., but also Matlab's Simulink to mention a product with another background.

Flowsheet simulators require experts to build the building blocks. The blocks typically describe the behaviour of a process entity, like a unit operation. The individual blocks are hand written pieces of code including all the necessary mathematical relations that describe their behaviour. Thus these facilities do include mathematical models, but the new development of constructing models based on ontologies, opens a whole new approach.

Ontology-based model construction has the flavour of the system theory's concept of minimal realisation. It aims, and succeeds, in defining based entities from which models are being constructed. The approach is based on using reductionism. Reductionism is a commonly applied technology for analysing and describing objects. It takes the object of interest and recursively subdivides it into smaller and smaller pieces until a granularity is reached that is rich enough to represent the process. We use reductionism to define the smallest domain-specific entities required to represent the considered classes of processes. The base entities are captured in an ontology, which is used to define the mathematical behaviour of the base entities. A small language serves to define the equations, and the analysing parser is combined with a template machine generating different output codes suitable for different programming environments.

Once the base entities are associated with a graphical representation, one can use them in a visual tool to construct process models on a canvas. This process we have described before {references}.

The graphical language can, though, also be used as a manual design tool. Choosing the base entities carefully, keeping in mind a minimal set of objects for the given application domain, one generates a powerful graphical language that serves a multitude of purposes: Paper and pencil model design, model documentation, and graphical input to ProMo's model composer software.

The graphical language captures frame information, thus time and space. The time scale characteristics, being constant, dynamic and event-dynamic and the space characteristics being the distribution nature: 0D for lumped systems, where the relevant intensive properties are not a function of the spatial coordinates. 1-3 D where they are a function of the named number of spatial coordinates. Defining a set of arcs depicting the interactions between the base entities, captures how they interact and what is being transported.

3. Language as paper-and-pencil tool and documentation

We shall first use the language to demonstrate the use of the graphical language as a discussion and documentation tool.

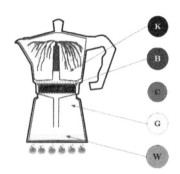

Figure 1: A typical Italian espresso maker

3.1. Example espresso maker

The traditional traditional espresso maker has a lower part, where the water is being filled in after unscrewing the upper part. In the middle is a filter section, where the coffee powder is being added. The filter section is connected to the fountain of the top section when screwing the top part onto the lower.

When heating at the bottom, the water temperature rises until it the pressure in the lower gas phase is large enough to push the hot water up the immersed pipe into the ground coffee and further up to the fountain to the top coffee reservoir. Once the water level is low and the upwards pipe is not anymore in the water, steam is passing through the pipe, the filter cake and spits out the remaining fluid through the fountain. Voila – espresso is ready for consumption.

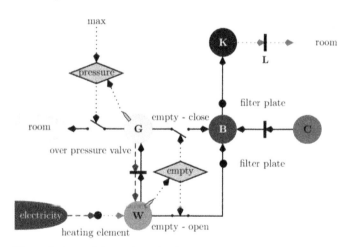

Figure 2: A possible topology for the espresso maker

The topology shows the room and the electricity source as reservoirs. The gas phase (G), the water (W), the fluid in the filter container (B), the ground coffee (C), and the product (K) are shown as lumped systems. The operation associated with having first hot water and in the end steam passing upwards is shown as a control element with two switches. This is a typical example, where the MODEL is controlled, in contrast where there is a physical controller acting on some flow. The over pressure valve is a physical element and can be seen as a controller that is built into the valve. We use circles for lumped systems, and semi-open olives for reservoirs. The arrows stand for the transfer of extensive quantity, like mass or energy in one or the other form. Phase interfaces appear as bars. For the control we introduce an observer picking information from the inside of a system and the rhomboids are control decision elements. Control signals are dotted lines. Arrows are in all cases defining a reference coordinate for the represented flow.

The direction of the arrows define a reference coordinate system for the flow. Flow in the direction of the arrow is positive, while the flow in the opposite direction is negative. The full line arrows show mass flow. Notice that the coffee being leached is only one arrow, though the water is flowing in the negative direction and the leached product into the positive direction. The dashed arrows are associated with work. The arrow from the electricity reservoir to the heating element is an electrical work flow, while the same type of arrows between the gas phase, the interface and the water stand for volumetric work, as the gas phase increases in volume while the liquid phase shrinks. The heating element is shown as and ideal converter of electrical energy into heat, latter flowing into the water. Some heat is lost through the lid into the room. The capacity effect of the construction is neglected, as no element is shown in the topology that represents the construction.

3.2 Example: A melting process

Melting of a solid in a heated device is characterised by going through three stages: (i) heat the solid (ii) melt the solid (iii) heat the liquid. The first and last stage have only one phase, while the second stage is characterised by having two phases. The model is being switched with the triggered by the formation of a first liquid phase and the completed disappearance of the solid phase.

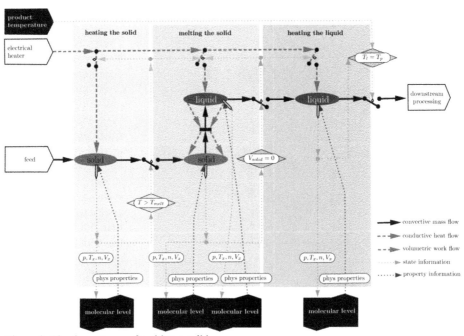

Figure 3: The three stages of melting a solid

The melting of solid topology has three control stuctures. Two are controlling the model, namely the two triggering the switching between the stages and one that is a physical controller opening the outflow tap once the desired temperature in the liquid is achieved. Notice that the model will not work if the product temperature is below the melting temperature. The ontology models the two phases as distributed systems, thus assuming that the temperature is a function of the position within the respective phase.

Notice that that the graphical elements are enriched with olives for the representation of distributed systems and connectors to other parts of the model.

3.3. Example molecular modelling

The top-level of the molecular-level model has a couple of interesting control structures.

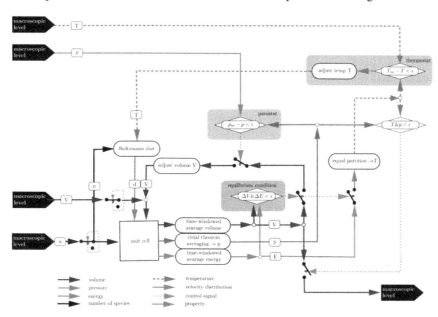

Figure 4: Molecular modelling level of properties

The overall process is iterative. The state of the molecules in the unit cell is adjusted by changing the temperature and the volume until the temperature and the pressure is close enough to the required temperature and pressure. The two involved control loops include a thermostate and a barostate, which are triggered by the check on the volume and the energy change over the iteration period. On the molecular level, we essentially only deal with information flows. We thus carefully mark the individual signals.

The graphical model contains all the information except than the specification details of the unit cell. While it is possible to provide the graphical model for the unit cell, it is not very instructive. One better resorts to a modified version in which the number of molecules is provided as well as the type of interacting forces and the associated assumptions and those forces that are neglected.

3.4. Corrosion – a moving boundary process

An interesting class of models deal with moving boundaries. As an example we show a corrosion process in which the iron bars in concrete are attacked by an active component forming a rust layer. The reaction takes place in the boundary volume on top of the iron. It is modelled as a infinite small volume. The interfaces control the species transfer. So W, A, R are not transported into the iron, for example. So on the top we show the presence of the species while on the lower row, we indicate, which species are not transferred. Thus we define semipermeable walls representing the interfaces. The circles again represent lumped systems, here iron. The bars are interfaces with the indication of what group of species is not transferred. The dot system is an infinite small capacity in which the reaction takes place.

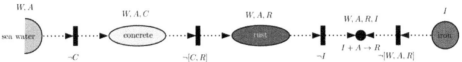

Figure 5: A corrosion process. The active component A and water W is diffusing through the concrete and the corrosion product layer (rust) to react with the substrate

1.2 Conclusions

We present a graphical method for representing process models on different scales. On the macroscopic level we have capacities on the three time scales: constant, dynamic and event-dynamic. The dynamic and the event-dynamic capacities are further detailed with the distribution information (1D-3D) and interfaces are abstracted to semi-permeable walls. An important aspect is the separation of the control of the plant, thus a physical object, and the control of the model. Latter implements some logic operations into the model, like a state limit is reached and the model changes structure like in the melting process. The result is always a directed graph showing the physical part of the process, the model control structure and the physical control structure. The directions provide the reference coordinate for each flow, which in the physical process are always extensive quantities.

Acknowledgments:

ProMo research was funded in parts by: (i) Bio4Fuels Research Council of Norway (RCN) project 257622 (ii) MARKETPLACE H2020-NMBP-25-2017 Grant Agreement No 760173 (iii) VIPCOAT Horizon2020 Grant Agreement No 952903 (iv) MODENA FP7-Framework Grant Agreement ID: 604271

References

Aspen, 2021, https://www.aspentech.com/enproducts/engineering/aspen-plus (last visited 27-10-2022)

Cape-Open, 2021, http://colan.org (last visited 27-10-2022)

ConceptDraw, 2021, https://www.conceptdraw.com/ (last visited 27-10-2022)

Elve, A. T. & Preisig, H. A., 2018, A framework for multi-network modelling, *Computer Aided Chemical Engineering, 44*, 2215ff

Functional Mock-up Interfaces, http://fmi-standard.org (last visited 27-10-2022)

gproms, 2021, https://www.psenterprise/.com/products/gproms (last visited 27-10-2022)

Preisig, H. A., 2021, Ontology-Based Process Modelling-with Examples of Physical Topologies *Processes, 9*

Preisig, H. A., 2020, ProMo -- A Multi-disciplinary Process Modelling Suite, *Computer-Aided Chemical Engineering,* 571-576

MatLab / Simulink, 2021, https://www.mathworks.com/products/simulink.html (last visitied 27-10-2022)

SWIG, 2021, http://www.swig.org (last visited 27-10-2022)

Proceedings of the 14th International Symposium on Process Systems Engineering – PSE 2021+
June 19-23, 2022, Kyoto, Japan © 2022 Elsevier B.V. All rights reserved.
http://dx.doi.org/10.1016/B978-0-323-85159-6.50171-8

Simulation and CO_2 emission analysis for co-processing of bio-oil and vacuum gas oil

Jingyu Zhang, Shuai Zhang, Le Wu[*], Yuqi Wang, Lan Zheng

School of Chemical Engineering, Northwest University, Xi'an 710069, China
lewu@nwu.edu.cn

Abstract

To reduce the CO_2 emission of a refinery and lower the production cost of bio-fuels, the co-processing of vacuum gas oil (VGO) and bio-oil has been proposed to add the renewable carbon into the co-processing products. However, the accurate CO_2 emission of the co-processing scheme is still unclear. In this work, a simulation of the whole co-processing scheme is built in Aspen Plus according to the date from actual industrial operations and reports. Based on the simulation results, the total CO_2 emission consisting of the direct emission from fuel combustions and indirect emission from utility consumptions is calculated to give a fully understand of co-pressing scheme. This work not only provides a whole simulation model, but also gives a basic understanding of the CO_2 emission and optimization for the co-processing scheme.

Keywords: Co-processing; Bio-oil; Vacuum gas oil; Aspen; CO_2 emission

1. Introduction

Environmental problems such as fossil energy shortage and global warming are becoming more and more serious. To ensure socially sustainable development, it is imperative to develop renewable fuels with low CO_2 emission. As the only carbon-containing renewable energy, biomass can be converted into gas, liquid and solid products, and bio-fuels derived from biomass can partially replace fossil fuels. Furthermore, as bio-fuels can effectively solve the shortage of resource and environmental pollution, bio-fuels development has gradually attracted attention.

The prices of bio-gasoline and bio-diesel are generally higher than those of petroleum-derived gasoline and diesel, because the biomass is more expensive than crude oil and bio-refinery needs a great deal of capital investment (Nuno, C et al, 2019). In addition, bio-diesel and bio-gasoline contain only partial fractions of diesel and gasoline and need further blending processes. Therefore, how to reduce the production costs of bio-fuels satisfying national fuel standards has become a research hotspot (Vasalos I A et al, 2016; Kan T et al, 2016).

Generally, there are three advantages in co-processing of bio-oil and vacuum gas oil in an existing refinery. Firstly, the utilization of the existing refinery infrastructure can greatly reduce the investment cost of bio-refineries. Secondly, the transportation cost from bio-fuel blending can be saved by using existing blending processes. Finally, the refinery mature fuel distribution system can be effectively used for the distribution of co-processing products. Thus, co-processing of bi-oil and vacuum gas oil is one of the effective ways to reduce bio-fuel production cost (Wu L et al, 2019).

According to the previous studies, co- processing of bio-oil and vacuum gas oil in an FCC to produce diesel and gasoline containing a certain amount of bio-carbon showed a highly technical feasibility. As fast pyrolysis and catalytic pyrolysis both can be used to produce bio-oil, they are both investigated for bio-oil co-processing with VGO. For the co- processing of fast pyrolysis oil and VGO, Pinho et al. (2017) co-fed fast pyrolysis and VGO directly in FCC. In order to reduce coke yield, the bio-oil co-processing ratio should less than 20%. Huynh et al. (2016) studied 20% hydrodeoxygenation (HDO) bio-oil and 80% VGO in FCC and found similar yields of gasoline and diesel were obtained compared with the yields of pure VGO cracking. Due to the high oxygen content and low enthalpy value, fast pyrolysis bio-oil needs further hydrogenation before co-pressing with VGO to ensure the yields of co-processing gasoline and catalytic diesel.

Due to high enthalpy value as well as low oxygen and water content, catalytic pyrolysis bio-oil can be directly co-processed with VGO. Wang et al. (2018) drew a conclusion that the diesel and gasoline yield would not be affected when co-processing 10% catalytic pyrolysis oil and 90% VGO. According to ^{14}C analysis, there are more than 7% renewable carbon in gasoline products. Lindfors et al. (2015) analyzed the differences in the co-processing of fast pyrolysis oil, HDO oil and catalytic pyrolysis oil with VGO in the FCC. The results showed that if the adding proportion of bio-oil exceeded 20%, the coke yield increased. The liquid fuel yield of fast pyrolysis oil was the lowest while the yields of HDO oil and catalytic pyrolysis oil were similar to the yields of pure VGO cracking (Sauvanaud L et al, 2018).

The key advantage of co- processing technology is to reduce environmental pollution by introducing renewable energy into fossil fuel refineries, and the technical and economic analysis of bio-oil co-processing with VGO in FCC by Wu et al. (2019) shows that the price of gasoline produced by co- processing was only $2.63/gallon. Thus, the further promotion and application of co-processing technology has attracted great attention. However, the CO_2 emission during co-processing are still not clear, especially in the context of "carbon peak and carbon neutralization".

In this paper, the co- processing of 10% bio-oil and 90% VGO in an FCC is taken as an example. The co-processing process of fast pyrolysis, catalytic pyrolysis and pure VGO was simulated and sensitivity analyzed by using Aspen Plus, and the CO_2 emission were analyzed and compared.

2. Process description

As it is shown in Figure 1, the co-processing process can be divided into two parts, the bio-oil production process and the co-processing of VGO and bio-oil in the existing infrastructure of the refinery. Considering that both fast and catalytic bio-oil can co-processing with VGO in FCC. In this paper, we simulate the fast pyrolysis bio-oil and VGO co-processing scenario (fast pyrolysis scenario), catalytic pyrolysis bio-oil and VGO co-processing scenario (catalytic pyrolysis scenario), and pure VGO cracking scenario (pure VGO scenario) to further compare and analyze the CO_2 emission of different biomass sources and pure VGO cracking, the specific flow is shown in Figure 1.

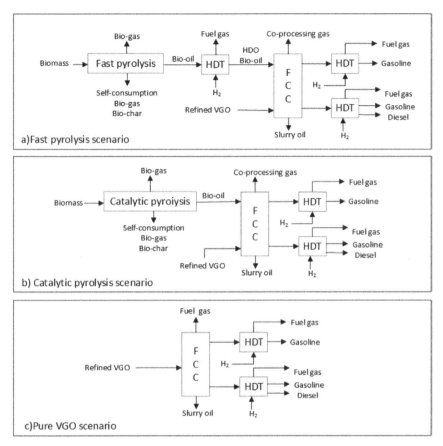

Figure 1 Diagram of co-processing of bio-oil and VGO. a) Fast pyrolysis, b) Catalytic pyrolysis, c) Pure VGO

2.1. Bio-oil production

In the fast pyrolysis scenario, the biomass raw material enters the grinder before entering the dryer to allow for a more efficient removal of additional water. Then mixture of dry biomass and hot sand enters the pyrolysis reactor to obtain bio-gas, bio-oil and biomass carbon. The reaction effluent is separated in a cyclone to obtain sand and bio-char from the bottom and bio-gas and bio-oil from the top. Bio-oil is separated with the bio-gas in a separator; the sand and bio-char are reentered into the pyrolysis reactor to reuse the sand. The biomass raw material and the recycle sand are heated by the combustion the bio-char and partial bio-gas. Due to the high content of oxygen, water and low enthalpy values, fast pyrolysis oil requires further hydrogenation treatment (HDT) to remove excess oxygen and water. Fast pyrolysis oil is pressurized by the pump and mixed with high pressure hydrogen into a hydrodeoxygenation (HDO) reactor. Then several separators are used to obtain reaction wastewater, fuel gas and HDO oil.

In the catalytic pyrolysis scenario, the catalytic pyrolysis process is similar to the fast pyrolysis process, and the catalyst regenerator is involved besides the above equipment. Since the high enthalpy values of the catalytic pyrolysis oil can be directly co-processed with the VGO, the bio-oil hydrogenation device is not included in this scenario.

Since the pure VGO scenario feeds only VGO, the scenario does not contain the bio-oil preparation process.

2.2. Bio-oil co-processing with VGO

According to Figure 1, HDO bio-oil or catalytic pyrolysis oil are co-fed with VGO into FCC reactor where the reaction effluent was separated into fuel gas, FCC gasoline, FCC diesel and slurry oil. Separated diesel and gasoline are refined in the corresponded HDT process to remove sulfur, nitrogen, and oxygen impurities from gasoline and diesel.

3. Aspen Simulation

Massachusetts Institute of Technology developed Aspen software for process simulation in the late 1970s. The software has been widely used in the chemical field, not only can conduct production device design, steady-state simulation optimization, but also can establish a process simulation system, so that the process can get more intuitive prediction results before operation. Effectively reduce casualty accidents caused by design errors. The software also establishes model simulation processes, sensitivity analysis, and physical properties and regression analysis.

3.1. Component provision and material method
The density of VGO is 0.85 to 0.9 g/cm³, distillation range is 350 to 540 °C; the density of bio-oil density is 1.1~1.2 g/cm³, distillation range is 140 to 350 °C. N_2, H_2O, CO_2, NO_2 and CH_4, C_2H_6, C_3H_8 are conventional fractions and type Conventional. The data in the oil virtual component is from the reference (Cruz P L et al, 2017). GRAYSON was selected as the physical property method.

3.2. Process module analysis
Firstly, select the Heater to pretreat the mixed oil; then, mixer module is selected to mix VGO and HDO oil, separation was performed according to the group shunt rate; select Plug and Yield reactor to simulate the co-processing process of the bio-oil and VGO; sep module shall be adopted and used to separate productions.

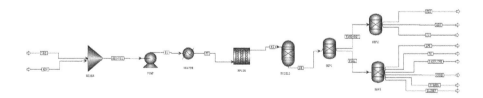

Figure 2 The process of the simulation by Aspen

3.3. Simulation results
The total CO_2 emission in co-processing process is 2.94×10^6 t·y⁻¹ and the total CO_2 emission is 3.27×10^6 t·y⁻¹ in pure vacuum gas oil. The amount of CO_2 emission from co-processing process was 10.36% less than in the case of pure vacuum gas oil. The result is similar to recent studies, which indicates that the simulation result is accurate.

4. Results and discussion

4.1. CO₂ emission

The total CO_2 emission consisting of the direct emission from fuel combustions and indirect emission from utility.

The CO_2 emission from fuels are calculated as formula (1).

$$E_{CO_{2,1}} = \frac{M_{CO_2}}{A_C} P\omega_C \tag{1}$$

where $E_{CO_{2,1}}$ is the CO_2 emission from raw material or product combustion, in t / a; M_{CO_2} and A_C is the molar mass of CO_2 and C, respectively, in g/mol; P is the raw material consumption or product generation, in t/a; ω_C is the carbon quality fraction in the raw material or product, in %.

CO_2 indirect emission from utility consumption are calculated as formula (2).

$$E_{CO_{2,2}} = u^{H_2} f_{CO_2}^{H_2} + u^{Stream} f_{CO_2}^{Stream} + u^{Water} f_{CO_2}^{Water} + u^{Elec} f_{CO_2}^{Elec} \tag{2}$$

where u^{Stream} and u^{Water} is consumption of steam and recycle water, in t/a; u^{H_2} is consumption of hydrogen, in m³/a; u^{Elec} is consumption of electricity, in kW/a; $f_{CO_2}^{Stream}$ and $f_{CO_2}^{Water}$ is CO_2 emission coefficient of steam and recycle water respectively, in t-CO₂/t; $f_{CO_2}^{Water}$ is CO_2 emission coefficient of hydrogen, in t-CO₂/m³; $f_{CO_2}^{Elec}$ is CO_2 emission coefficient of electricity, in t-CO₂/kW.

4.2. Results

By calculation, we obtained the results in Table 1.

Table 1 CO₂ emission

CO₂ emission t/y	Fast pyrolysis	Catalytic pyrolysis	Pure VGO
Utility	2.98×10^5	2.93×10^5	1.76×10^5
Product combustion	2.71×10^6	2.74×10^6	3.20×10^6
Total	3.01×10^6	3.03×10^6	3.38×10^6

The results in Table 2 show that the CO_2 emission of both co-processing methods, fast and catalytic pyrolysis, are less than in the case of pure vacuum gas oil. Therefore, the use of co-processing technology can effectively reduce the amount of CO_2. As an environmental protection technology, co-processing technology has great research prospects.

5. Conclusion

Using the co-processing process of 10% bio-oil and 90% vacuum gas oil in FCC, the co-processing process and the CO_2 emission were analysed. The results show that the total CO_2 emission at co-processing process was 2.94×10^6 t·y⁻¹ and the total CO_2 emission was 3.27×10^6 t·y⁻¹ for pure vacuum gas oil. To sum up, compared with the pure vacuum gas oil technology, co-processing technology is an environment-friendly technology which can reduce carbon emissions to some extent. Therefore, when producing gasoline and diesel fuel which contain biomass, we should not only pay attention to the carbon emissions of the product, but also the CO_2 emissions generated in the process. While reducing the carbon emissions of the product, we should reduce the CO_2 emissions in the product production process.

References

Cruz P L, Montero E, Dufour J, 2017, Modelling of co-processing of HDO-oil with VGO in a FCC unit, Fuel, 196, 362-370.

Huynh T M, Armbruster U, Atia H, et al, 2016, Upgrading of bio-oil and subsequent co-processing under FCC conditions for fuel production. Reaction Chemistry & Engineering, 1, 239-251.

Kan T, Strezov V, Evans T J, 2016, Lignocellulosic biomass pyrolysis: A review of product properties and effects of pyrolysis parameter. Renewable & Sustainable Energy Reviews, 57, 28, 1126-1140.

Lindfors C, Paasikallio V, Kuoppala E, et al, 2015, Co-processing of Dry Bio-oil, Catalytic Pyrolysis Oil, and Hydrotreated Bio-oil in a Micro Activity Test Unit, Energy & Fuels, 29, 6, 3707-3714.

Nuno, C., Cruz, et al. 2019, Critical review of key variables affecting potential recycling applications of ash produced at large-scale biomass combustion plants, Resources Conservation & Recycling, 150, 104427.

Pinho A, Almeida M D, Mendes F L, et al, 2017, Fast pyrolysis oil from pinewood chips co-processing with vacuum gas oil in an FCC unit for second generation fuel production, Fuel, 188, 10, 462-473.

Sauvanaud L, Mathieu Y, Corma A, et al. 2018, Co-processing of lignocellulosic biocrude with petroleum gas oils, Applied Catalysis A: General, 551, 9, 139-145.

Vasalos I A, Lappas A, Kopalidou E P, et al, 2016, Biomass catalytic pyrolysis: process design and economic analysis, Wiley Interdisciplinary Reviews: Energy and Environment, 5, 3, 370-383.

Wang C, Venderbosch R, Fang Y, 2018, Co-processing of crude and hydrotreated pyrolysis liquids and VGO in a pilot scale FCC riser setup, Fuel Processing Technology, 181, 9, 157-165.

Wu L, Wang Y, Zheng L, et al, 2019, Design and optimization of bio-oil co-processing with vacuum gas oil in a refinery, Energy Conversion and Management, 195, 5, 620-629.

Wu L, Wang Y, Zheng L, et al, 2019, Techno-economic analysis of bio-oil co-processing with vacuum gas oil to transportation fuels in an existing fluid catalytic cracker, Energy Conversion & Management, 197.

Proceedings of the 14th International Symposium on Process Systems Engineering – PSE 2021+
June 19-23, 2022, Kyoto, Japan © 2022 Elsevier B.V. All rights reserved.
http://dx.doi.org/10.1016/B978-0-323-85159-6.50172-X

Dynamic Simulation and Optimization of a Subcritical Coal-Fired Power Plant During Load-Ramping Operations

Jinliang Ma[ac*], Miguel A. Zamarripa[ac], John C. Eslick[ac], Quang M. Le[d], Debangsu Bhattacharyya[d], Lorenz T. Biegler[e], Stephen E. Zitney[b], Anthony P. Burgard[a], David C. Miller[a]

[a]National Energy Technology Laboratory, Pittsburgh, PA, 15236, USA
[b]National Energy Technology Laboratory, Morgantown, WV, 26507, USA
[c]NETL Support Contractor, Pittsburgh, PA, 15236, USA
[d]Dept. of Chem. Engineering, West Virginia University, Morgantown, WV, 26506, USA
[e]Dept. of Chem. Engineering, Carnegie Mellon University, Pittsburgh, PA, 15213, USA
jinliang.ma@netl.doe.gov

Abstract

With increasing penetration of renewable energy sources, traditional power plants are required to operate more flexibly with higher ramp rates than originally planned for by design. A dynamic model for a subcritical coal-fired power plant was developed in the open-source, equation-oriented IDAES (Institute for the Design of Advanced Energy Systems) modeling framework. PID-based regulatory controllers and a supervisory-level coordinated control system (CCS) were also implemented. The plant-wide dynamic model and controls were used to investigate and optimize flexible operations. Plant-wide dynamic simulations were performed under load-ramping cycles from full load to 50 % load and back to full load at different ramp rates. In addition, dynamic optimizations were performed at ramp rates of 5 % full load per minute. The objective of the dynamic optimization was to maintain a stable main steam temperature (MST) at the boiler exit while maximizing plant efficiency during ramping. Dynamic simulation results show large excursions in MST, which are detrimental to equipment health. The CCS implementation leads to a drop in MST during the ramp down and an overshoot during the ramp up when attemperator water spray capacity is limited. Through dynamic optimization, the maximum MST deviation is reduced from 12 K, at a 5 %/min ramp rate from full load to 70 % load, to within 2 K by changing three manipulated variable profiles: the furnace stoichiometric ratio, the water spray valve opening, and the setpoint for sliding-pressure operation. This improves the average plant efficiency slightly, while the reduced MST excursion benefits the health of the steam turbine.

Keywords: Power Generation; Dynamic Simulation; Optimization; Flexible Operation.

1. Introduction

Due to the intermittency of renewable energy, conventional fossil-fueled power plants originally designed to operate at full load are increasingly load following. To conduct quantitative assessments of flexible operations, predictive nonlinear first-principles models are highly desired to capture equipment dynamics for off-design conditions. Moreover, distributed-parameter equipment models should be developed to resolve temperature and pressure distributions so that health-related performance variables such as thermomechanical stresses can be calculated. The major contributions of this work are the development of an open-source, first-principles plant-wide dynamic model and its application to large-scale dynamic optimization for maximizing plant efficiency, while minimizing equipment degradation during transient load-ramping operation.

Dynamic models of coal-fueled power plants have previously been reported in the literature. Oko and Wang (2014) developed a gPROMS dynamic model for a 500 MW subcritical power plant and validated it at full load and three off-design conditions. However, the study did not consider optimization and equipment health under flexible operations. Chen et al. (2017) developed a 605 MW subcritical plant model in Modelica/Dymola and performed dynamic simulations with step changes in fuel flow rate. In an extended work, Chen and Bollas (2018) performed dynamic optimization to maximize the integral of plant efficiency over a predetermined time horizon of 24 hours based on a defined load profile proportional to a typical daily market demand. However, the ramp rate is very small and time step size is large (hours). Therefore, the dynamic model does not capture the effects of rapid (minutes) load ramping typical of a plant dispatch event. For a supercritical plant, Sarda et al. (2018) developed an Aspen Plus Dynamics model and compared three control configurations for load decreases from 100 % to 40 % at a ramp rate of 3 % maximum continuous rating per minute; however, no dynamic optimization was reported.

The work reported here is focused on dynamic simulation and optimization during load ramping. A generic (non-plant specific) 300 MW net subcritical coal-fired power plant is developed and used to simulate flexible operations at different ramp rates using a coordinated control system. To improve plant performance, dynamic optimization is conducted based on predefined load ramping profiles at 5 % full-load power output per minute. The optimization objectives are to limit deviation of MST from its setpoint to avoid high thermal shock to the superheaters and steam turbine while keeping plant efficiency as high as possible during ramping. The power plant dynamic flowsheet model is described in Section 2, followed by dynamic simulation and optimization results in Sections 3 and 4, respectively. Conclusions are drawn in Section 5.

2. Dynamic model description

Figure 1 shows the process flow diagram of the 300 MW subcritical power plant (boiler subsystem and steam cycle) developed using the open-source IDAES modeling framework (Lee et al., 2021). IDAES offers an extensive library of power plant models (see https://github.com/IDAES/idaes-pse) and associated documentation at https://idaes-pse.readthedocs.io/en/stable/technical_specs/model_libraries/index.html. Details of the first-principles unit operation models and their validation using operating data from an existing subcritical power plant are reported by Eslick et al. (2021). The dynamic models implement mass and energy balance equations with temporal or accumulation terms to account for fluid inventories in boiler waterwall and heat exchanger tubes and in large vessels including the boiler drum, deaerator, feedwater heaters (FWHs), and condenser hotwell. Since metal components such as tubes and vessel walls have high density and high heat capacity, their thermal holdups are also considered. Distributed-parameter models are used for convective heat exchangers and the boiler drum and waterwalls. Performance equations include first-principles relationships for heat transfer and pressure change. Due to its complexity, the boiler fire-side model is a surrogate model based on a rigorous 1D/3D hybrid model developed previously (Ma et al., 2016).

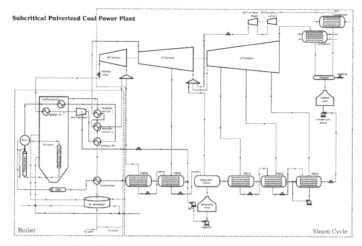

Figure 1. Process flow diagram of a 300 MW coal-fired subcritical power plant

Unit models with relatively small time constants, including the boiler fire-side, turbine stages, pumps, and valves, are treated as steady-state models in the dynamic flowsheet. Regulatory proportional-integral (PI) controllers are applied to control the water levels of the FWHs, condenser hotwell, and deaerator tank. The drum level is controlled by a three-element controller involving two cascading PI controllers. The MST is controlled by the attemperator through a proportional only controller by default. The power demand is met by a CCS with a turbine master controlling the power output by adjusting the steam flow through the throttle valve before the high-pressure (HP) turbine and a boiler master controlling the fuel and air flow rates to bring the main steam pressure to a desired sliding pressure, coordinated with the turbine master.

3. Dynamic simulations

Three dynamic simulations were performed for cycling from 100 % load to 50 % and back to 100 % using ramp rates of 5 %, 3 %, and 1 % of full load power output per minute, respectively. The simulations are based on the default settings of the control system with desired sliding pressure defined as a linear function of the load demand. Figure 2 shows the dynamic simulation results for the three load ramping cases. Figure 2(a) shows the predicted MST profiles (solid lines) along with the defined load demand profiles as inputs (dashed lines). Figure 2(b) shows the stoichiometric ratio (SR) and the attemperator control valve open fraction profiles calculated by the control system.

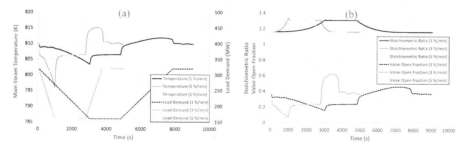

Figure 2. Dynamic simulation results of three load cycling cases: (a) Load demand and main steam temperature (MST), (b) SR and valve opening fraction

We observe that the MST drops below the setpoint of 810 K when ramping down. This occurs because the coal flow rate is reduced and is lower than the steady-state values due to release of stored energy in the system. The drop in MST cannot be corrected immediately by the attemperator. The 5 % ramping case has its maximum MST drop greater than 21 K during ramp down and the highest MST increase is greater than 8 K during ramp up. The deviation of the MST from its setpoint has detrimental effects on the health of superheaters and steam turbine. MST deviation can be partially mitigated by attemperator control, but it usually cannot eliminate the deviation, especially when ramping down at high rates and when the valve opening reaches its 5 % minimum set by the model. In the default controller setting, the furnace SR is set to be a polynomial function of coal flow rate with a higher SR used at a lower coal flow rate, such that MST maintains its setpoint of 810 K at steady-state. The large MST drop when ramping down is due to the release of stored energy in the system (mainly in drum and waterwalls), which reduces required coal flow rate below the corresponding steady-state value. To correct this, the SR can be increased beyond its required steady state value. This leads to higher air flow rate, slightly higher coal flow rate, and reduced flame temperatures inside the furnace, thus providing reduced heat absorption by the waterwalls, increased flue gas flow rate, and increased heat absorption by the superheaters. From Figure 2 we observe that higher ramping rates lead to higher MST deviations from the setpoint, since the effect of stored energy is stronger.

4. Dynamic optimization

While dynamic simulation provides insight into the impact of load ramping on system performance—especially MST deviation—dynamic optimization has the potential to reduce MST deviation. The 5 % ramp rate was chosen for dynamic optimization, since its impact is strongest among the three control cases considered here. To reduce CPU time for dynamic optimization, up and down ramps are modelled separately, and the load range was confined between 70-100 %. Only ramp down cases are reported here. Case A is without dynamic optimization, i.e., based on default controller settings. Case B has attemperator spray valve opening and furnace SR as decision variables for the optimization. Case C extends Case B with an additional decision variable, sliding-pressure deviation from the default value calculated as a linear function of load.

The objectives of the dynamic optimization are to minimize the MST deviation during the transient ramp while minimizing the coal flow rate or maximizing the plant efficiency. The objective function for the multi-objective optimization is defined as:

$$f_{obj} = 0.001 \sum_{i=0}^{N} \left(T_{steam,i} - T_{steam,setpoint} \right)^2 + \sum_{i=0}^{N} \frac{\dot{m}_{coal,i}}{\dot{m}_{coal,full\_load}} \qquad (1)$$

where $T_{steam,i}$ is MST at time point i and $T_{steam,setpoint}$ is the setpoint (810 K). $\dot{m}_{coal,i}$ and $\dot{m}_{coal,full\_load}$ are coal flow rate at time point i and at the initial steady-state full load, respectively. A weighting factor of 0.001 is adopted for the temperature deviation term. Ranges for the manipulated variables are between 1.15 and 1.3 for furnace SR, 5 % and 95 % for spray valve opening, and ±0.5 MPa for the sliding pressure adjustment.

The dynamic optimization cases were modelled on the IDAES platform leading to nonlinear programs with over 60,000 variables and were solved with IPOPT. The simulation problem (Case A) required 7 CPU minutes, while Cases B and C required the equivalent of up to 170 simulations. The dynamic optimization results are provided in Figure 3. Figure 3(a) shows the coal flow rates required to meet load demand.

Compared to Case A, the average coal flow rates during the 8-minute period are
reduced by 0.03 % for Case B and 0.29 % for Case C. Figure 3(b) shows the MST
profiles. The MST drops as low as 12 K below the setpoint of 810 K near the end of the
ramp in Case A. In contrast, the maximum MST deviation is reduced to about 1.5 K in
Case B and to only 1 K in Case C. Figure 3(c) shows the profiles of the spray valve
open fraction for the three cases. The valve is closed quickly to the minimum open
fraction of 0.05 at the beginning of the ramp (before 100 s) in the two optimized cases
(Cases B and C) to offset the MST drop. Figure 3(d) shows the furnace SR profiles. A
higher SR is used for the two optimized cases, which is the main reason for preventing
the MST from dropping too low, as discussed in Section 3. Figure 3(e) shows the main
steam pressure profiles. Note that the profiles of Cases A and B follow the trend of load
demand since the sliding pressure setpoint is proportional to load demand. In Case C,
the main steam pressure is optimized to go even lower to improve plant efficiency.
Figure 3(f) shows the steam temperature at the HP turbine inlet (after throttle valve).
The temperature drop at the HP turbine inlet is also reduced for the two optimized cases,
mitigating the negative impact on turbine health during load ramping.

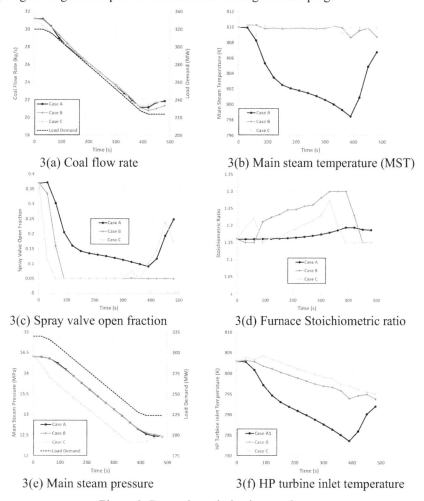

3(a) Coal flow rate   3(b) Main steam temperature (MST)

3(c) Spray valve open fraction   3(d) Furnace Stoichiometric ratio

3(e) Main steam pressure   3(f) HP turbine inlet temperature

Figure 3. Dynamic optimization results

4. Conclusions

An equation-oriented, plant-wide dynamic model of a subcritical coal-fired power plant was developed using the open-source IDAES model library and applied to perform dynamic simulations and optimization using state-of-the-art solvers. The nonlinear first-principles dynamic unit operation models, including distributed-parameter models, along with the coordinated control system, provide the ability to predict the excursion of performance variables such as the main steam temperature during fast load ramping. Through dynamic optimization of three manipulated variable profiles, main steam temperature deviation can be dramatically reduced while plant efficiency can be kept unchanged or slightly improved, thus mitigating the negative effect on equipment health.

Acknowledgement & Disclaimer: We graciously acknowledge support by the U.S. Department of Energy, Office of Fossil Energy and Carbon Management, Simulation-Based Engineering Program. This was prepared as an account of work sponsored by an agency of the United States Government. Neither the United States Government nor any agency thereof, nor any of their employees, nor the support contractor, nor any of their employees, makes any warranty, express or implied, or assumes any legal liability or responsibility for the accuracy, completeness, or usefulness of any information, apparatus, product, or process disclosed, or represents that its use would not infringe privately owned rights. Reference herein to any specific commercial product, process, or service by trade name, trademark, manufacturer, or otherwise does not necessarily constitute or imply its endorsement, recommendation, or favoring by the United States Government or any agency thereof. The views and opinions of authors expressed herein do not necessarily state or reflect those of the United States Government or any agency thereof.

References

C. Chen, Bollas, G. M., 2018, Dynamic optimization of a subcritical steam power plant under time-varying power load, Processes, 6(8), 114, https://doi.org/10.3390/pr6080114.

C. Chen, Z. Zhou, G. M. Bollas, 2017, Dynamic modeling, simulation and optimization of a subcritical steam power plant. Part I: Plant model and regulatory control. Energy Conversion and Management, 145(9), 324-334, https://doi.org/10.1016/j.enconman.2017.04.078

J.C. Eslick, M. Wang, J. Ma, M.A. Zamarripa, D. Bhattacharyya, S.E. Zitney, A.P. Burgard, D.C. Miller, 2021, Predictive Modeling of an Existing Subcritical Pulverized-Coal Power Plant for Optimization: Data Reconciliation, Parameter Estimation, and Validation, submitted for publication.

A. Lee, J.H. Ghouse, J.C. Eslick, C.D. Laird, J.D. Siirola, M.A. Zamarripa, D. Gunter, J.H. Shinn, A.W. Dowling, D. Bhattacharyya, L.T. Biegler, A.P. Burgard, D.C. Miller, 2021, The IDAES Process Modeling Framework and Model Library –Flexibility for Process Simulation and Optimization, Journal of Advanced Manufacturing and Processing, 3 (3).

J. Ma, J.P. Eason, A.W. Dowling, L.T. Biegler, D.C. Miller, 2016, Development of a first-principles hybrid boiler model for oxy-combustion power generation system, International Journal of Greenhouse Gas Control, 46, 136–157.

E. Oko, M. Wang, 2014, Dynamic modelling, validation and analysis of coal-fired subcritical power plant, Fuel, 135(1), 292-300.

P. Sarda, E. Hedrick, K. Reynolds, D. Bhattacharyya, S.E. Zitney, B. Omell, 2018, Development of a dynamic model and control system for load-following studies of supercritical pulverized coal power plants, Processes, 6(11), 226, https://doi.org/10.3390/pr6110226.

Proceedings of the 14th International Symposium on Process Systems Engineering – PSE 2021+
June 19-23, 2022, Kyoto, Japan © 2022 Elsevier B.V. All rights reserved.
http://dx.doi.org/10.1016/B978-0-323-85159-6.50173-1

Solvent Screening Methodology considering Techno-Economic and Environmental Sustainability criteria for Algae Lipid Extraction

Santiago Zapata-Boada[a*], Maria Gonzalez-Miquel[b], Megan Jobson[a], and Rosa Cuellar-Franca[a]

[a] *Department of Chemical Engineering, The University of Manchester, Manchester, M13 9PL, United Kingdom*
[b] *Department of Chemical and Environmental Engineering, Universidad Politécnica de Madrid, Madrid, 28006, Spain*
santiago.zapataboada@manchester.ac.uk

Abstract

Solvent extraction plays a crucial role in biorefinery processes, such as the extraction of lipids from algae biomass to produce biodiesel. Volatile organic solvents, such as hexane, are typically used to extract algae lipids, but this involves high energy consumption for solvent recovery and negative environmental impacts due to its hazardous, volatile, and flammable nature. This study proposes a systematic methodology combining molecular simulation techniques, data classification methods, and process simulation to screen solvents for lipid extraction from wet algae biomass. The novelty relies on the integration of techno-economic, environmental and safety criteria, such that all three sustainability dimensions are considered in solvent selection. First, thermodynamic equilibrium data of solvent-lipid systems are predicted with the COSMO-RS method. Then, a clustering method (K-means algorithm) is used to identify and select the solvents with the highest partition coefficient and selectivity towards lipids. After this, the selected solvents are further screened considering their physicochemical properties (solubility in water, density, viscosity, boiling point) and health, safety, and environmental performance. Finally, the lipid extraction process with the shortlisted solvents is simulated in Aspen Plus to obtain techno-economic and environmental sustainability performance indicators. Out of 88 initial solvent candidates, limonene and ethyl tert-butyl ether are identified as promising alternatives to the benchmark solvent (hexane), as they are non-hazardous and have higher selectivity towards lipids. However, their use involves higher energy requirements, operating costs, and greenhouse gas emissions in the lipid extraction process. This methodology can be applied to other extraction processes to find sustainable alternatives for the conventional solvents and identify trade-offs from a techno-economic and environmental perspective at the early stages of process design.

Keywords: COSMO-RS, process simulation, biobased solvents.

1. Introduction

Solvent screening methods are used to identify promising solvents depending on application-specific technical performance; health, safety, and environmental (HSE) criteria; and process-specific economic considerations (Clarke et al., 2018). Solvent technical performance (extraction efficiency and selectivity) can be evaluated with experimental equilibrium data or molecular simulation methods, such as COSMO-RS

(Eckert and Klamt, 2002). The capability of the COSMO-RS method to predict partition ratios as a key parameter for solvent selection has been successfully validated in previous studies (López-Porfiri et al., 2020). HSE criteria of solvents can be found in solvent selection guides, such as CHEM21 (Prat et al., 2016), which give a preliminary ranking of solvent "greenness" based on their physical properties and hazard statements. Process-specific considerations can be captured with process simulation, which is used to calculate performance indicators for measuring energy consumption, economic viability and environmental sustainability and for exploring design improvements (Sheldon, 2018).

Key applications of solvent extraction include the downstream processing of biorefinery applications, which are challenging due to the broad range of impurities, heat-sensitive components, and high dilution of the feed streams, and can account for 15-80% of the total costs (Ghosh, 2007). The extraction of lipids from algae biomass to produce biodiesel is an important biorefinery application (Chen et al., 2018). Conventional processes for lipid extraction use volatile organic solvents derived from fossil resources, such as hexane, but its toxicity and high volatility make it environmentally unfavourable (Clarke et al., 2018). Alternative solvents, such as terpenes, have been identified in experimental screening studies (Dejoye Tanzi et al., 2012) and proposed as ideal alternatives to hexane due to their higher extraction efficiency and selectivity. However, the impact of these alternative solvents on the economic viability and environmental sustainability at a process level has not been considered. This study presents a novel approach that combines molecular and process simulation techniques to integrate techno-economic, environmental and safety indicators to screen solvents for algae lipid extraction. The following section describes the methodology, followed by the results and the conclusions.

2. Methodology

The proposed methodology for solvent screening is illustrated in Figure 1. It consists of five steps: liquid-liquid equilibrium (LLE) data calculation using COSMO-RS method, LLE data analysis and classification, evaluation of physicochemical properties of solvents, evaluation of HSE performance of solvents, and process simulation.

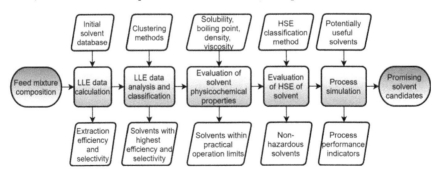

Figure 1. Methodology proposed to evaluate solvents at the process development stage

2.1. Liquid-liquid equilibrium data calculation

The feed (wet algae biomass) is a dilute aqueous stream with a water content of 80% wt., lipid content of 6% wt., and protein and carbohydrates content of 14% wt. It is assumed that the lipids are represented by the molecule triolein, which is one of the most common triglycerides found in algae lipids (Yao et al., 2015). Glutamine, a polar molecule found in algae biomass, is assumed to represent other components. The extraction conditions are set to 25°C and 101.325 kPa, which are typical values for algae lipid extraction. An initial solvent database (Sels et al., 2020) is used to propose a 'long list' of candidate solvents. Then, solute (triolein and glutamine) activity coefficients at infinite dilution in the aqueous and organic phases are calculated using the COSMOthermX software, which implements the COSMO-RS method (Eckert and Klamt, 2002).

The extraction efficiency is expressed as the partition coefficient of the solute between the aqueous and organic phases (K_i). At low solute concentrations (dilute systems), the partition coefficient can be predicted by modelling the solute activity coefficient at infinite dilution ($\gamma^{a,\infty}$) according to Eq.(1), where x is the mole fraction of the solute i, s corresponds to the solvent phase and w to the aqueous phase. The selectivity of the solvent between components i and j ($\beta_{i,j}$) is defined as the ratio of the partition coefficients of i (triolein) and j (glutamine).

$$K_i = \frac{x_i^s}{x_i^w} = \frac{\gamma_i^w}{\gamma_i^s} \approx \frac{\gamma_i^{w,\infty}}{\gamma_i^{s,\infty}} \tag{1}$$

2.2. LLE data analysis and classification

A clustering method, namely the k-means method (Bock, 2007), is used to classify the solvents according to the partition coefficient of triolein in the aqueous and organic phases and the selectivity of solvents to triolein. The number of clusters (seven) is selected based on an analysis of the cluster inertia (sum of squared distances of samples to the nearest cluster center), aiming for a small inertia value, which is a sign of good and meaningful clustering. The solvents belonging to the cluster with the highest partition coefficients and selectivity to triolein are selected for further evaluation.

2.3. Evaluation of physicochemical properties of solvents

Further screening of the selected solvents resulting from the previous step is conducted based on practical considerations: (a) avoiding loss of solvent to the raffinate phase; (b) avoiding thermal degradation of the solute; (c) ease of recovery; (d) ease of handling. The following limits are defined for the physicochemical properties of solvents: solubility in water < 1% wt. (to form a two-phase system and minimize solvent loss to the aqueous phase); boiling point < 200 °C (to prevent thermal degradation of triolein), density < 1.5 kg/L, and viscosity < 2 mPa.s (ease of handling and storage). Solvents that do not meet these criteria are discarded.

2.4. Evaluation of health, safety, and environmental performance of solvents

The HSE performance of the selected solvents from the previous step is evaluated using the CHEM21 methodology (Prat et al., 2016), which considers health, safety, and environmental scores, and indicates whether a solvent is 'hazardous', 'problematic' or 'recommended'. Hazardous solvents are discarded, as their substitution during process development is a priority of this work. Finally, a shortlist of potentially useful solvents for the application is obtained.

2.5. Process simulation

A conceptual process design is proposed for continuous extraction of lipids from 20 t h-1 of wet algae biomass, using the shortlisted solvents from the previous step. Aspen Plus V8.8 is used to simulate the process (see Figure 2). The NRTL activity coefficient model is used to simulate phase equilibrium for the lipids-solvent-water system, and missing interaction parameters are estimated using the UNIFAC method. Solvents' performance is compared by assuming that a counter-current extraction column with five stages is needed to extract lipids from algae biomass (Stephenson et al., 2010). The solvent-to-dry feed mass ratio is assumed to be 5 to 1 (Davis et al., 2014).

Mass and energy flows obtained from the process simulation are used to calculate technical, economic, and environmental performance indicators of the extraction process. Two technical performance indicators are proposed: lipid recovery (LR), the ratio of extracted lipids to the total lipids in the feed; and solvent intensity (SI), the ratio of the mass of solvent entering the extractor to the extracted lipids. One economic performance indicator is proposed: total annualized cost (TAC), including capital and operating costs. These are calculated using Aspen Process Economic Analyzer. Two environmental indicators are used: energy intensity (EI), the ratio of the energy input to the process (heat used in the stripping column for solvent recovery) to the mass flowrate of extracted lipids; and global warming potential (GWP), estimated from the greenhouse gas emissions resulting from the combustion of fuel (natural gas) used to supply the energy to the process.

3. Results

Out of 88 initial solvent candidates, 37 solvents are identified in the cluster that exhibits the highest partition coefficients and selectivity to triolein. These solvents are selected for further evaluation. All these solvents are non-polar and include hydrocarbons derived from fossil resources (e.g., heptane); bio-based hydrocarbons (e.g., limonene); ethers (e.g., ethyl tert-butyl ether); and esters (e.g., methyl laurate). After evaluating the selected solvents' physicochemical properties and HSE performance, 26 solvents are discarded due to their solubility in water > 1% wt. (e.g., tetrahydrofuran), boiling point > 200 °C (e.g., methyl laurate), density > 1.5 kg/L (e.g., carbon tetrachloride), and hazardous nature (e.g., chloroform). As a result, only 11 solvents are shortlisted for further investigation via process simulation. Table 1 presents process performance indicators of the shortlisted solvents, calculated from the simulation results. The indicators consider the impact per unit of product (kg lipid).

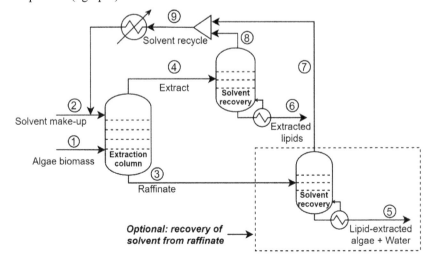

Figure 2. Process flow diagram of the lipid extraction process

Table 1. Process performance indicators of the screened solvents

Solvent	LR (%)	SI (kg solvent/ kg lipid)	TAC (USD/kg lipid)	EI (MJ/kg lipid)	GWP (kg CO$_2$ eq./kg lipid)
Hexane*	99.9	0.09	2.10	9.48	0.49
Cyclohexane	99.8	0.09	2.13	10.13	0.52
Methylcyclohexane	99.7	0.09	2.15	10.46	0.54
Heptane	99.9	0.09	2.17	10.73	0.55
Ethyl cyclopentane	99.7	0.09	2.14	10.71	0.55
Toluene	98.1	0.10	2.14	11.60	0.60
O-xylene	99.2	0.09	2.22	12.98	0.67
Limonene	100	0.08	2.67	13.26	0.68
Cymene	99.9	0.08	2.80	12.73	0.66
Pinene	96.6	0.09	2.54	14.98	0.77
ETBE	91.6	0.18	2.29	9.74	0.50
Dibutyl ether	96.0	0.10	2.57	12.65	0.65

LR: Lipid recovery; SI: Solvent intensity; TAC: Total annualized costs; EI: Energy intensity; GWP: Global warming potential. *Hexane is evaluated for benchmarking purposes

LR is over 98% for all the fossil-based hydrocarbons (cyclohexane, methylcyclohexane, heptane, ethyl cyclopentane, toluene, o-xylene), as they all have a high partition coefficient and high selectivity towards triolein. SI of all conventional solvents is comparable due to the similar losses of solvent in the extract and raffinate phases. Cyclohexane presents the lowest TAC, EI, and GWP among the fossil-based hydrocarbons due to the low reboiler duty required for evaporation. For example, TAC of cyclohexane is comparable to TAC of hexane (1.5% higher). On the other hand, TAC, EI, and GWP of o-xylene are the highest for all fossil-based hydrocarbons due to its high boiling point and enthalpy of vaporization.

LR of terpenes (limonene, cymene and pinene) are over 96%. As Table 1 shows, limonene has the highest LR among the solvents due to its high partition coefficient and selectivity to triolein. Also, terpenes perform better than hexane in terms of SI due to their lower volatility and evaporation losses. For example, SI of limonene is 9% lower. However, terpenes have higher TAC, EI, and GWP than hexane: for pinene, TAC, EI, and GWP are 21%, 58%, and 57% higher. LR of ethers (ETBE and dibutyl ether) are lower than LR of terpenes and fossil-based hydrocarbons, which can be attributed to the more polar nature of ethers. SI of ETBE is nearly double that of hexane due to the higher losses of ETBE in the lipid-extracted algae. However, ETBE is the only alternative solvent that performs similarly to hexane in terms of EI and GWP (within 3% of those of hexane).

Overall, limonene and ETBE are identified as promising alternative solvents to hexane. Both are non-conventional solvents that can be obtained from biomass-based resources. Limonene performs well in terms of LR and SI. ETBE has the lowest EI and GWP of all solvents other than hexane. Even though there is not a clear 'winner' that outperforms hexane in every dimension, as evidenced by the trade-offs in the process performance indicators, the proposed methodology provides a clear indication of the strengths and weaknesses of the solvent candidates, providing a shortlist of potentially attractive solvents for a more detailed evaluation.

4. Conclusions

This work proposes a systematic approach combining molecular simulation techniques, data classification methods, and process simulation to comprehensively screen solvents. The integration of techno-economic, environmental and safety criteria ensure that all three sustainability dimensions are considered in solvent selection by using this novel methodology. This methodology is demonstrated for the extraction of lipids from wet algae biomass to find alternative solvents to the benchmark solvent (hexane), whose use involves negative environmental impacts due to its hazardous, volatile, and flammable nature. A comprehensive database including 88 alternative solvents is used as a starting point, and after evaluation of techno-economic, safety, and environmental performance, limonene and ethyl tert-butyl ether are identified as promising alternatives to hexane. These solvents are non-hazardous, can be obtained from biomass-based resources, and show competitive performance indicators. Overall, the proposed methodology is helpful to identify a shortlist of potentially attractive solvents for a more detailed evaluation, providing a clear indication of the strengths and weaknesses of the solvent candidates. The methodology developed herein can be applied to other solvent extraction processes to promote the development and design of sustainable chemical processes using alternative solvents.

References

Bock, H.-H. 2007. Clustering Methods: A History of k-Means Algorithms. Berlin, Heidelberg: Springer Berlin Heidelberg.

Chen, J., Li, J., Dong, W., Zhang, X., Tyagi, R. D., Drogui, P. & Surampalli, R. Y. 2018. The potential of microalgae in biodiesel production. *Renewable and Sustainable Energy Reviews,* 90, 336-346.

Clarke, C. J., Tu, W.-C., Levers, O., Bröhl, A. & Hallett, J. P. 2018. Green and Sustainable Solvents in Chemical Processes. *Chemical Reviews,* 118, 747-800.

Davis, R., Kinchin, C., Markham, J., Tan, E., Laurens, L., Sexton, D., Knorr, D., Schoen, P. & Lukas, J. 2014. Process Design and Economics for the Conversion of Algal Biomass to Biofuels: Algal Biomass Fractionation to Lipid- and Carbohydrate-Derived Fuel Products. National Renewable Energy Lab. (NREL), Golden, CO (United States).

Dejoye Tanzi, C., Abert Vian, M., Ginies, C., Elmaataoui, M. & Chemat, F. 2012. Terpenes as green solvents for extraction of oil from microalgae. *Molecules,* 17, 8196-8205.

Eckert, F. & Klamt, A. 2002. Fast solvent screening via quantum chemistry: COSMO-RS approach. *AIChE Journal,* 48, 369-385.

Ghosh, R. 2007. *Principles of bioseparations engineering,* Singapore, World Scientific.

López-Porfiri, P., Gorgojo, P. & Gonzalez-Miquel, M. 2020. Green Solvent Selection Guide for Biobased Organic Acid Recovery. *ACS Sustainable Chemistry & Engineering,* 8, 8958-8969.

Prat, D., Wells, A., Hayler, J., Sneddon, H., McElroy, C. R., Abou-Shehada, S. & Dunn, P. J. 2016. CHEM21 selection guide of classical- and less classical-solvents. *Green Chemistry,* 18, 288-296.

Sels, H., De Smet, H. & Geuens, J. 2020. SUSSOL—Using Artificial Intelligence for Greener Solvent Selection and Substitution. *Molecules,* 25, 3037.

Sheldon, R. A. 2018. Metrics of Green Chemistry and Sustainability: Past, Present, and Future. *ACS Sustainable Chemistry & Engineering,* 6, 32-48.

Stephenson, A. L., Kazamia, E., Dennis, J. S., Howe, C. J., Scott, S. A. & Smith, A. G. 2010. Life-Cycle Assessment of Potential Algal Biodiesel Production in the United Kingdom: A Comparison of Raceways and Air-Lift Tubular Bioreactors. *Energy & Fuels,* 24, 4062-4077.

Yao, L., Gerde, J. A., Lee, S.-L., Wang, T. & Harrata, K. A. 2015. Microalgae Lipid Characterization. *Journal of Agricultural and Food Chemistry,* 63, 1773-1787.

Proceedings of the 14th International Symposium on Process Systems Engineering – PSE 2021+
June 19-23, 2022, Kyoto, Japan © 2022 Elsevier B.V. All rights reserved.
http://dx.doi.org/10.1016/B978-0-323-85159-6.50174-3

Modelling and simulation of the production of n-butyl lactate in a reactive distillation column at pilot plant scale

García, César [a], Yusti, Daniela [a], Velandia, Jessica [a,b], Ochoa, Silvia [c] and Gil, Iván D. [a]*

*a*Grupo de Procesos Químicos y Bioquímicos, Departamento de Ingeniería Química y Ambiental, Universidad Nacional de Colombia Sede Bogotá, Cra 30 # 45-03, Ed. 453, Of. 318, Bogotá – Colombia.
*b*Investigación y Desarrollo, Sucroal S.A., Recta Cali Palmira Km 18 desvío a Candelaria - Colombia.
*c*SIDCOP Grupo de investigación, Universidad de Antioquia, Colombia
*idgilc@unal.edu.co, +57 1 3165000 ext: 14100

Abstract

Petrochemical-based solvents are one of the main sources of volatile organic compounds (VOCs) in the atmosphere, which are reported to be carcinogenic under certain conditions. Different alternatives are being studied in order to reduce this problem. Special interest has been placed in lactate esters obtained from long chain alcohols like propyl, n-butyl and amyl alcohols because they are considered as green solvents due to their toxicological and environmental characteristics. These allow their use in many applications, especially as chemical feedstock, dairy-related flavouring, and drugs administration. Although most of the reported methods for lactate esters production include intensification technologies such as reactive distillation. There are not enough reports related to the evaluation of lactate esters production in a reactive distillation column at pilot plant scale, for obtaining a high productivity and a good quality control of the end-product specifications. In this work, a principles-based model, including NRTL-Raoult thermodynamic model and a pseudo-homogeneous kinetic model, was developed for a reactive distillation column at pilot plant scale located at Universidad Nacional de Colombia. The system was simulated in Matlab/Simulink R2020b considering the column design. The obtained results were validated with simulations in Aspen Plus V11, with a composition of butyl lactate >97% mole fraction.

Keywords: 1-Butyl lactate, Reactive distillation column, Phenomenological based model, Pilot plant scale, Optimization.

1. Introduction

According to the Environmental Protection Agency (EPA), Volatile Organic Compounds (VOCs) have proved to have a negative impact on people's health (EPA, 2021). In this area, chemical solvents constitute around 80% of compounds used in many important chemical processes. A percentage of 0.7% of VOC emissions come from this type of industries, while 21% of these compounds come from the general uses of these solvents (Häckl & Kunz, 2018).

New solvents called "green solvents" are compounds with potential to replace VOCs. These solvents have advantages over conventional VOCs, such as low toxicity, biodegradability, and renewability (Li et al., 2016). The global market for green solvents was valued at $ 5.4 billion in 2015, in products such as bio-alcohols, bio-glycols, and lactate esters, among others (Grand View Research, 2016).

Nowadays, there is a growing interest in lactate esters and their uses in cosmetic, food and pharmaceutical applications. The conventional process to produce lactic acid esters involves multiple reactions and purification stages. Butyl lactate has great interest due to its wide range of industrial applications. Kumar & Mahajani (2007) studied the esterification kinetic between lactic acid and 1-butanol in the presence of cation exchange resins as a catalyst and assessed the applicability of reactive distillation for this process. Peña-Tejedor et al. (2005) and Garcia et al. (2021) studied the equilibrium of the butyl lactate – 1-butanol binary system at 1, 5 and 101.325 kPa. Velandia et al. (2021) studied the thermodynamic model of the esterification system for butyl lactate production, the reactive and nonreactive residue curves maps, and carried out a conceptual design for reactive distillation.

Due to the limited information available for this system, this work evaluates the feasibility of producing butyl lactate in a pilot-scale reactive distillation column. A phenomenological-based model was developed and implemented in Matlab/Simulink 2020b. This model was validated with experimental data acquired by Kumar & Mahajani (2007) and compared with Aspen Plus V11 simulation.

2. Process Modelling

2.1 Model description

The reactive distillation column at pilot plant scale has a reactive core, a structured packaging module with the Amberlyst 70 exchange resin and other modules containing Nutter Ring No. 07 packaging. Is recirculated the organic phase formed in the decanter. The water produced is removed in the aqueous phase.

Figure 1(a) is a representation of the reactive distillation column at the pilot plant located in the Laboratory of Chemical Engineering at Universidad Nacional de Colombia. The bottom flow rate was fixed at 2.02 kg/h to obtain the higher conversion, while hydraulic restrictions are fulfilled. The lactic acid flow rate was fixed at 4.042 kg/h with a mass fraction of 0.30 of lactic acid and inlet temperature of 353.15 K. The butanol flow rate was fixed at 1.656 kg/h with a mass fraction of 0.99 for butanol and inlet temperature of 363.15 K. Figure 1(b) is a representation of the column for modelling purposes, where stage 1 is the decanter, stage 2 is the condenser and stage 14 is the reboiler.

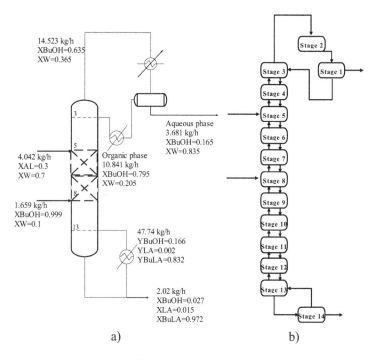

Figure 1. Continuous reactive distillation column: a) at pilot plant scale to produce butyl lactate. b) Distributed Reactive distillation column.

Figure 2 shows a representation of the equilibrium stage model for a general reactive stage. The stages for rectifying, reactive and stripping zones are determined based on the evaluated case (Figure 1 a).

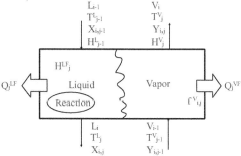

Figure 2. Equilibrium stage model

In this case, the reactive distillation column is represented by an equilibrium model kinetically controlled, which considers that there is no resistance to internal and external diffusive transport over the catalyst and that there is no resistance to transport over the fluid phases. For this reason, the phase equilibrium is achieved homogeneously.

2.2 Model assumptions

For modelling the liquid phase, NRTL model is used and the vapor phase is assumed ideal, as well as a pseudo-homogeneous kinetic model. In the decanter, NRTL model is used for predicting the liquid-liquid equilibrium and the k-value method is used to determine compositions in extracted and refined flows. The presence of oligomers is neglected as well as the kinetic and potential energy. The reboiler and condenser are modelled as trays and the equilibrium controlled by kinetics is considered. Physical properties are constant and there is no heat loss from the column. The column pressure drop is neglected, and the reaction takes place in liquid phase.

2.3 Balance Equations

In this section, the generalized mass and energy balances for reactive and non-reactive stages (Eq. 1 to 3) are presented, based on the equilibrium stage model (Figure 2). For the three additional stages (decanter, condenser and reboiler), the set of mass and energy balances are assumed as equilibrium stages.

Total Material balance:

$$\frac{dz_i}{dt} = L_{i-1} + V_{i+1} - L_i - V_i + F_i \tag{1}$$

Molar balance per component:

$$\frac{dx_{i,n}}{dt} = \frac{\left(x_{i-1,n}L_{i-1} + y_{i+1,n}V_{i+1} - x_{i,n}L_i - y_{i,n}V_i + (x_{F,n})_i q_{F,i}F_i + R_{n,i} - x_{i,n}\frac{dz_i}{dt}\right)}{Z_i} \tag{2}$$

Energy balance:

$$\frac{dT_i}{dt} = \frac{h_{i-1}L_{i-1} + H_{i+1}V_{i+1} - h_iL_i - H_iV_i + h_{F,i}q_{F,i}F_i + Q_{r,i} - h_i\frac{dz_i}{dt}}{Z_i * C_{pmix,i}} \tag{3}$$

Where Fi represents the feed flowrate (Lactic acid +Butanol), $R_{n,i}$ is the reaction rate, $X_{F,i}$ is the molar fraction of each compound (Lactic /butanol) in the feed and $Q_{r,i}$ the heat of reaction.

3. Model simulation

The column design specifications of the reactive distillation column at pilot plant scale located at Universidad Nacional de Colombia - Bogota are presented in Table 1.

Table 1. Reactive Distillation Column - Internal specifications (Sánchez et al., 2020).

Parameter	Value
Diameter [m]	0.0762
Number of reactive stages (5-8)	4
Number of non-reactive stages (1-4, 9-14)	10
Stripping zone length per stage [m]	1.1
Rectifying zone length per stage [m]	1
Catalyst (Katapak SP-11 of Sulzer)	Amberlyst 70
Operating pressure [kPa]	74.66

The thermodynamic information is presented by Garcia et al. (2021) and the NRTL binary parameters and kinetic model parameters are presented by Velandia et al. (2021). The model evaluation for the system of lactic acid (LA), butanol (BuOH), butyl lactate (BuLac) and water (W) was performed using Matlab/Simulink R2020b. The model was compared against Aspen Plus V11.

Figure 3 a) shows the composition profiles along the column. Results obtained with the developed Matlab/Simulink R2020b model are compared against Aspen Plus V11 simulator. In both cases, the results are in agreement and present the same tendency. With the presented operation conditions, BuLac with a purity of 97% can be obtained, while the BuOH is maintained in excess along the column. Figure 3 b) shows the temperature profile, where the model simulated in Matlab/Simulink shows good agreement with the results obtained in Aspen Plus.

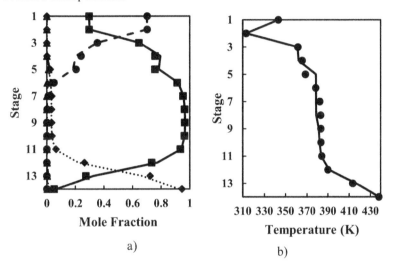

Figure 3. a) Mole fraction profiles: Aspen Plus V11 (●) W, (■) ButOH, (▲) LA, (♦) BuLac and Matlab/Simulink R2020b (---) W, (-) ButOH, (-·-) LA, (···) BuLac. b) Temperature profile: Aspen Plus V11 (●) and Matlab/Simulink R2020b (-).

4. Conclusions

Butyl lactate can be obtained in the reactive distillation column at pilot plant scale of Universidad Nacional de Colombia. In both simulations, the obtained feeding flow rates are in accordance with the technical specifications, which means that these are the nominal values of operation. The obtained BuLac, with a purity higher than 97%, follows product specifications for commercial purposes. It is important to compare these simulations against experimental information and this will be performed in a future work.

Reference

EPA, U. (2021). United States Environmental Protection Agency, Volatile Organic Compounds' Impact on Indoor Air Quality. https://www.epa.gov/indoor-air-quality-iaq/volatile-organic-compounds-impact-indoor-air-quality

Garcia, C., Velandia, J., Céspedes, M., Rodríguez, G., & Gil, I. D. (2021). Isobaric Vapor−Liquid Equilibrium for the Binary Mixture of 1-Butanol + Butyl L-Lactate at 1 and 5 kPa. Journal of Chemical and Engineering Data, 1–6.

Grand View Research. (2016). Green & Bio-based Solvents Market Size, Share & Trends Analysis Report By Product. (Lactate Esters, Methyl Soyate), By Application (Paints & Coatings, Adhesives).

Häckl, K., & Kunz, W. (2018). Some aspects of green solvents. Comptes Rendus Chimie, 21(6), 572–580.

Kumar, R., & Mahajani, S. M. (2007). Esterification of lactic acid with n-butanol by reactive distillation. Industrial and Engineering Chemistry Research, 46(21), 6873–6882.

Li, Z., Smith, K. H., & Stevens, G. W. (2016). The use of environmentally sustainable bio-derived solvents in solvent extraction applications - A review. Chinese Journal of Chemical Engineering, 24(2).

Peña-Tejedor, S., Murga, R., Sanz, M. T., & Beltrán, S. (2005). Vapor-liquid equilibria and excess volumes of the binary systems ethanol + ethyl lactate, isopropanol + isopropyl lactate and n-butanol + n-butyl lactate at 101.325 kPa. Fluid Phase Equilibria.

Sánchez, C. A., Gil, I. D., & Rodríguez, G. (2020). Fluid phase equilibria for the isoamyl acetate production by reactive distillation. Fluid Phase Equilibria, 2–30.

Velandia, J. J., García, C. A., Céspedes, M. A., Rodríguez, G., & Gil, I. D. (2021). Reactive and non-reactive residue curve maps analysis to produce Butyl Lactate by catalytic distillation. Chemical Engineering and Processing - Process Intensification, 168.

Proceedings of the 14th International Symposium on Process Systems Engineering – PSE 2021+
June 19-23, 2022, Kyoto, Japan © 2022 Elsevier B.V. All rights reserved.
http://dx.doi.org/10.1016/B978-0-323-85159-6.50175-5

Optimal Design of Offshore Wind Power Farm Considering Wind Uncertainty

Sunwoo Kim[a], Seongwhan Kang[b], Jay H. Lee[a,*]

[a]*Department of Chemical and Biomolecular Engineering, Korea Advanced Institute of Science and Technology (KAIST), 291, Daehak-ro, Yuseong-gu, Daejeon, 34141, Republic of Korea*
[b]*R&D Campus Daejeon, LG Energy Solution (LGES), 188, Munji-ro, Yuseong-gu, Daejeon, 34122, Republic of Korea*
jayhlee@kaist.ac.kr

Abstract

This study presents an optimization-based framework for the design of offshore wind power farms (OWFs). First, the main characteristics of the OWF facilities are decided including the size and type of the turbines and the capacity of the inter-array cables. Second, a feasible location for installing the facility is identified by considering various geographical characteristics such as average wind speed and water depth, with the aid of a geographic information system (GIS). Finally, we construct a mixed-integer fractional programming (MIFP) optimization model to decide on the exact locations of the wind turbines and the offshore substations as well as the routes of the inter-array cables, by minimizing the unit cost which is the total installation cost divided by total power generated. A case study is conducted based on the 6th regional energy plan of Jeju island, South Korea, which plans to construct two 100 MW and one 125 MW OWFs. The optimized unit cost of the OWFs turns out to be 2.3 MM\$/MW, which is at par with existing OWFs. Furthermore, we introduce a stochastic programming model to consider various potential wind scenarios directly in the design. The robust design obtained via stochastic programming approach showed an improved average unit cost by ~5% compared to the nominal design which assumed a specific scenario of wind speed and direction.

Keywords: Offshore Wind Power Farm (OWF), Geographical Information System (GIS), Stochastic Programming

1. Introduction

Offshore wind power farms (OWFs) are becoming popular, with GW-scale projects appearing in many parts of the world, owing to its high potential in terms of scale and efficiency. The OWF market is expected to grow significantly, i.e., from 23 GW in 2018 to 228 GW in 2030 which is about a ten-fold increase. However, the high install and operating cost of OWF is still a barrier to more widespread adoption. Since the overall cost of OWF is greatly affected by its geographical characteristics (e.g., wind speed, water depth) as well as its design (e.g., spatial arrangement of the turbines, routes of the inter-array cables), the location selection and design must be carried out carefully, both for economic feasibility evaluation and actual installation. Also, the intermittency of wind speed depending on season and weather must be precisely considered for the optimal design of OWF.

There have been relatively few studies that addressed the design of OWFs using GIS under considering wind uncertainty. Recently, a mixed-integer linear programming (MILP) optimization model that decides routes of the inter-array cables and locations of the substations was suggested and applied to the Navitus Bay Windpark in the U.K by Pillai et al. (2015). However, the locations of the wind turbines, which affect the installation cost and power generation greatly, were not considered in this study. Spyridonidou et al. (2020) suggested a design framework of OWFs which uses GIS where the case study is performed in Greece and, sixteen candidate areas for constructing OWF were selected considering geographical criteria. However, the task of determining the optimal layout of the OWF was not addressed in this study. Also, Banzo et al. (2011) suggested a stochastic optimization model to decide on the location of the substation and the cross-sections of cable connection considering wind uncertainty and applied the model to a case set in Hrons Rev OWF in Denmark. However, this study did not address the micro-siting problem of locating the turbines at the site.

To overcome the limitations of previous research, this paper suggests a stochastic programming based design framework of OWF using GIS and considering the wind variability/uncertainty. We screen for candidate locations of OWF utilizing GIS. Then an optimization model is formulated for each candidate location where the main decision variables are locations of the turbines and the offshore substations, and routes of the inter-array cable and the objective are to minimize the average unit cost over possible scenarios of the wind speed/direction.

This paper is organized as follows. The design framework for OWF is explained in section 2. Then the detailed formulation of the optimization is presented in section 3. The results of the case study involving the design of OWFs in Jeju Island, Korea are presented in section 4. Some conclusions are given in section 5.

2. Problem definition

Our research aims to develop an optimization based framework for designing OWFs while considering relevant geographical information and wind uncertainty. The consideration of geographical characteristics is important as they significantly affect the bottom-line economics of OWFs. Previously, Kang et al. (2020) presented a three-stage framework for designing a biorefinery, which consists of the steps of facility design, GIS analyses, and optimization model development. Firstly, key characteristics of the facility such as the sizes of the main processing units and main yield parameters are specified. Then, important geographical information such as the land use and climates are considered to select candidate locations. Finally, the specified facility and geographical information are used to construct a mathematical optimization problem that carries out specific designs for economic evaluations.

In our research, the above three-stage framework is adapted for the design of OWFs. In the first step, we select 5 MW wind turbines found in the reference by NREL. The power curve of the turbine and the installation costs of the various items of the facility are specified. In the second step, candidate locations for installing the facilities are identified with the aid of GIS analyses. Key geographical information such as water depth, wind speed, and distance data are collected to be used as input data for the optimization model. Also, we quantify the wake effect, the reduction in the wind speed as the wind passes through other turbines at each candidate location. Lastly, the objective function of the optimization model is defined. In our case, the unit cost, which is the total installation cost divided by the total power generation ($/kWh), is to be minimized. Finally, the optimization was solved to obtain the optimal OWF design under 200 wind scenarios generated from the stochastic model. To analyze the economics, another 200 wind scenarios were generated to compare the average unit costs among the different designs.

3. Problem formulation

The power curve of the wind turbine is approximated as a piecewise linear function of wind speed as in Eq.(1) where a is the slope, b is the y-intercept, $WS_{i,a}$ is the wind speed and $P_{i,a}$ is the power generated at location i under scenario a. The installation costs of the turbine and the substation are estimated using Eq.(2) and Eq.(3), respectively, which were proposed by Gonzalez et al. (2017), where P^{total} is the total installed power capacity of the OWF (MW), N is the number of turbines installed in the OWF, WD is the water depth, P_i is the capacity of each turbine (MW), and A, B, C, D are constants. The capacity and installation cost of the inter-array cables are summarized in Table 1.

$$P_{i,a} = a \times WS_{i,a} + b \tag{1}$$

$$C^{turbine}(k\$) = A \times \frac{(p^{total})^{0.87}}{N} + (B \times WD^2 - C \times WD + D) \times P_i \tag{2}$$

$$C^{sub}(k\$) = 3040.8 + 106.4 \times P^{total} \tag{3}$$

Table 1. Installation cost and capacity of electric cables

Cable type	Capacity (Maximum number of turbines)	Capital cost ($/meter)
Inter-array cable	5	135
	7	250
	9	370
Export cable (Offshore)	25	885
Export cable (Onshore)	-	762

Secondly, the distance data of the wind turbines are obtained from GIS analysis and reduced wind speed by wake effect is calculated by Eq.(4), where $dc_{i,j,a}$ represents how much the wind speed of turbine at location i get reduced due to the adjacent turbine j and X_i is the binary variable representing whether the turbine is installed or not.

$$WS_{i,a}^d = WS_{i,a} \times X_i - \sum_j dc_{i,j,a} \times X_j \tag{4}$$

For stochastic optimization, wind speed scenarios are generated as following procedures. First, at each observatory near the candidate location, the deviation in the annual average wind speed compared to the average value of the data for the 12 years was calculated as a percentage value. Second, the calculated value of deviation is discretized into 10 steps based on the maximum and minimum value of the wind speed deviation. Then, the number of deviation data corresponding to each deviation step is counted to get the possibility distribution $Step_a$, Finally, the wind speed of scenario a is generated by randomly selecting one of the deviation steps from $Step_a$ and random variable $\xi_{i,a}$ is used to fill the gap of possible wind speed range between each step randomly as presented in Eq.(5).

$$WS_{i,a} = \overline{WS_i} * (1 + Step_a + \xi_{i,a}) \tag{5}$$

Finally, a MIFP optimization problem is constructed to decide the locations of the substation, wind turbines, and the routes of the inter-array cables. The objective is to minimize the unit cost which represents described in Eq.(6), where $C^{facility}$ is the installation cost of each facility type and $P_{i,a}$ is the power generated by the turbine on location i under scenario a. Unit cost represents how much power is generated from the initial investment capital.

$$\min \frac{C^{total}}{P^{total}} = \frac{C^{turbine} + C^{sub} + C^{cable}}{\sum_{i,t} P_{i,t}} \tag{6}$$

The major constraints of our problem are the power flow balance and those arising from the spatial limitation. Energy flow $F_{i,j}$ is defined as the number of turbines connected through the inter-array cable. Notice that the offshore substation has only inflow energy, and the turbines have one more inflow of energy than outflows, which is expressed as Eq.(7). For each location, at most one facility can be constructed, which is expressed as Eq.(8), where $S_i^{100\,MW}$ and $S_i^{125\,MW}$ are the binary variables representing whether or not a substation of the particular scale is installed.

$$\sum_{i,j \neq i} F_{i,j} - F_{j,i} = X_i - 20 \times S_i^{100\,MW} - 25 \times S_i^{125\,MW} \tag{7}$$

$$X_i + S_i^{100\,MW} + S_i^{125\,MW} \leq 1 \tag{8}$$

4. Case study

According to the 6th regional energy plan of Jeju Island, two 100 MW and one 125 MW OWFs are being planned for construction. We use the three-stage framework to design the OWFs in Jeju Island according to this plan. In our case study, the main decision variables are the locations of the substation and wind turbines, and the routes of the inter-array cables. The main assumptions are summarized as below:

- The wind speed is represented by its annual average value.

- There is no transmission loss through an electric cable.

- Seven times the blade diameter is the minimum allowed distance between turbines, (882 m)

- Length of the onshore export cable is 20% longer than the Euclidean distance

To consider wind uncertainty, 200 scenarios of wind speed are generated and used to design the optimal OWF (multi-scenario design) and compared with the design where only the average wind speed is used (nominal-scenario design). Another 200 scenarios of wind speed are generated for economic analyses of each OWF design.

In Figure 1, the difference between the multi-scenario design and the nominal scenario design is illustrated. Although the average value of wind speed is the same, as the specifics of the wind speed differ for each scenario, the average amount of power generated is different. This is because the power curve shows varying slopes for different wind speed ranges. The different OWF layouts lead to different economic results. In all zones, the multi-scenario design showed improvements over the nominal scenario design. The detailed economic results are presented in Table 2, where the multi-scenario design shows ~5% lower average unit cost compared to the nominal scenario design, and the percentage of the scenarios showing improvements is about 92%. In all zones, the use of 100 MW units resulted in a lower unit cost. Since the number of candidate locations is ~40, 100 MW units presented more options than 125 MW units which required only 21 installations. The comparison of the unit cost is given in Figure 2. As a result, we can conclude constructing 100 MW OWF in zone 1 and zone 2, and constructing 125 MW in zone 3 is the best solution for meeting the plan.

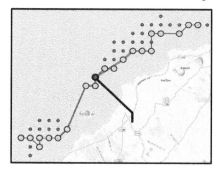 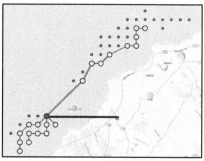

Figure 1. Optimized layout of the OWF in zone 1 (a) nominal scenario design (b) multi-scenario design

Table 2. Detailed economic comparison between the nominal scenario design and the multi-scenario design

Capacity	Zone	Scenario type	Average C^{total} (MM$)	Average P^{total} (GWh)	Average C^{total}/P^{total} ($/MWh)	Percentage of improved scenarios (%)
100MW	1	Nominal	223.1	230.4	968.4	7.5
		Multiple	231.4	242.4	954.5	92.5
	2	Nominal	228.2	245.8	928.4	7.5
		Multiple	231.6	257.3	900.0	92.5
	3	Nominal	223.6	289.7	771.8	8.5
		Multiple	205.3	281.4	729.6	91.5
125MW	1	Nominal	288.0	290.4	991.7	7.5
		Multiple	283.5	303.6	933.8	92.5
	2	Nominal	283.7	294.8	962.5	7.5
		Multiple	294.3	315.7	932.1	92.5
	3	Nominal	286.0	360.8	792.7	8.5
		Multiple	261.1	351.2	743.6	91.5

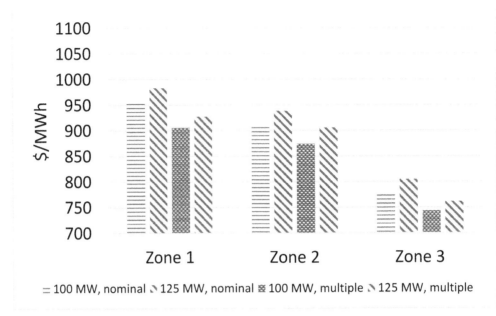

Figure 2. Comparison of the unit cost between the nominal scenario OWF and the multi-scenario OWF

5. Conclusions

In this paper, we adapt the three-stage framework originally developed for biorefinery design to the design of optimal OWFs considering wind uncertainty. Candidate locations are selected by using GIS and important geographical data from GIS are used in the optimization model. MIFP is constructed to design OWFs according to the 6th regional energy plan in Jeju Island as a case study. The economics of two different designs, a nominal scenario design and a multi-scenario design using stochastic programming were analyzed. In all candidate zones, the multi-scenario design showed improved economics with the average unit cost lower by ~5%, and improvements were shown for about 92% of the scenarios tried. For future research, the operation of designed OWFs will be addressed where various dispatch and storage decisions are made to manage energy supply and demand while addressing the intermittency and uncertainty of wind speed.

References

S. Kang et al. Three-stage design of high-resolution microalgae-based biofuel supply chain using geographic information system. *Applied Energy* 265 (2020): 114773.

M. Blanco et al., The economics of wind energy. *Renewable and sustainable energy reviews* 13.6-7 (2009): 1372-1382.Reviews, 13, Science Direct, Amsterdam, Netherlands 2009, 1372-1382.

A. Pillai et al., Offshore wind farm electrical cable layout optimization. *Engineering Optimization.* 2015;47:1689-708.

S. Spyridonidou et al., Strategic Planning of Offshore Wind Farms in Greece. *Sustainability.* 2020;12.

M. Banzo et al.,. Stochastic optimization model for electric power system planning of offshore wind farms. *IEEE Transactions on Power Systems* Aug. 2011; 26(3): 1338–1348.

Proceedings of the 14th International Symposium on Process Systems Engineering – PSE 2021+
June 19–23, 2022, Kyoto, Japan ©2022 Elsevier B. V. All rights reserved.
http://dx.doi.org/10.1016/B978-0-323-85159-6.50176-7

Economic and environmental impact of fouling in produced water re-injection

Otavio Fonseca Ivo[a]*, Lars Struen Imsland[a]

[a] *Department of Engineering Cybernetics, Norwegian University of Science and Technology, O. S. Bragstads plass 2, 7034 Trondheim, Norway*

fonseca.i.otavio@ntnu.no

Abstract

Produced water re-injection (PWRI) is an enhanced oil recovery technique which aims to increase the recovery factor of a reservoir while reducing produced water (PW) discharges to the ocean. Re-injection of PW is challenging as fouling in pipelines can lead to inefficient operation of the PWRI facility. In this work, we perform sensitivity analysis at a PWRI facility. As inputs, we have selected the riser roughness coefficient and processed PW flowrate. Furthermore, we consider two different re-injection strategies and assess the impact of varying those inputs over key economic and environmental performance indicators. Results show the negative effect that fouling has over several performance indicators. Furthermore, they suggest that one should constantly re-evaluate the fouling level at the pipelines of a PWRI facility before performing decision-making for production optimization.

Keywords: Sensitivity analysis, Waterflooding, Produced water re-injection, Production optimization, Fouling

1. Introduction

Produced water (PW) is by far the largest waste stream in the offshore oil and gas industry (Neff *et al.*, 2011). PW can be defined as formation water and/or water that has previously being injected into the formation. Due to its nature, PW is a complex mixture that contains dispersed oil, dissolved organic compounds, solid particles, and bacteria (Nasiri *et al.*, 2017). Moreover, it is considered a continuous source of contaminants to the continental shelf ecosystems (Beyer *et al.*, 2020). To increase operational environmental safety level, it is advised that operators follow the best practices for management of PW. These guidelines are grounded in four pillars: avoid, prevent, reduce, and treat (Miljødirektoratet, 2015).

To reduce marine pollution, several Norwegian operators started using waterflooding as a primary PW management solution (Steinar *et al.*, 2016). Waterflooding is an enhanced oil recovery (EOR) technique in which water is injected at a reservoir formation to displace residual oil towards production wells, increasing oil recovery factors (Bautista and Dahi Teleghani, 2017). However, continuous re-injection of PW can lead to fouling of scale-prone or tar-like (*i.e.* "schmoo") substances in the produced water re-injection (PWRI) facility (Bader, 2007), leading to inefficient operation (Rossini *et al.*, 2020). Inspired by operational issues encountered at a real offshore PWRI facility, we investigate the economic and environmental impact of fouling in waterflooding operation.

2. Motivating example

The studied PWRI facility is represented in Figure 1. During normal operation, PW enters the system through the separation vessel. From the vessel, PW can be sent to either the ocean discharge and/or the pumping station (PS). In the PS, there are recycle systems located downstream of each pump to prevent inadequate pumping operation. When PW enters the pumping system, it is split between two fixed-speed pumps (FSPs). Downstream of the FSPs, the non-recycled PW is mixed and is boosted by the variable-speed pump (VSP). Downstream of the VSP, throttling valves regulate the passage of PW for re-injection in the re-injection templates (RITs) α and β. The connections between the PS and the RITs are performed by risers. Each RIT has choke valves which regulate the shared re-injection ratio between each re-injection well.

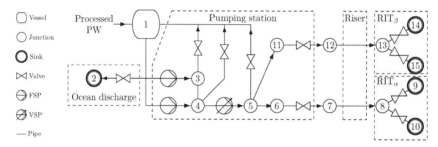

Figure 1: Produced water re-injection facility.

The PWRI model considered in this work is based on Ivo and Imsland (2021). It is desired to maximize the revenue (R) obtained during operation of the PWRI facility, which is given by:

$$
\begin{aligned}
R = \$_{oil} \left(\lambda_\alpha \sum_{i=9}^{10} d_i + \lambda_\beta \sum_{i=14}^{15} d_i \right) \\
- (\$_{fuel} + \$_{CO_2} E_d) \left(W^s_{(1,2)} + W^s_{(1,3)} + W^s_{(4,5)} \right),
\end{aligned}
\tag{1}
$$

with constants $\$_{oil}$ as the market oil price; $\$_{fuel}$ as the fuel price; $\$_{CO_2}$ as the carbon tax; λ_α and λ_β as respectively the re-injection effectiveness of RIT_α and RIT_β; and E_d as the fuel energy content. Furthermore, $W^s_{(1,2)}$, $W^s_{(1,3)}$ and $W^s_{(4,5)}$ are the pumping shaft-power; and d_i is the PW demand at node i.

In addition, we consider key environmental performance indicators which are divided into two segments. The first is related to PW management, in which re-injection rate accounts for percentage of PW re-injected; and waste-to-value accounts for the conversion of re-injected PW to oil produced. These performance indicators are represented below:

$$
RR = \left(\sum_{i=9}^{10} d_i + \sum_{i=14}^{15} d_i \right) / |d_1|
\tag{2a}
$$

$$WtV = \left(\lambda_\alpha \sum_{i=9}^{10} d_i + \lambda_\beta \sum_{i=14}^{15} d_i \right) / |d_1| \tag{2b}$$

where RR is the re-injection rate; and WtV is the waste-to-value conversion. The second environmental segment is related to CO_2 emissions, in which the total emission of CO_2 accounts for total emission; the CO_2 production intensity considers the emission rate relative to oil production; and CO_2 re-injection intensity contemplate the emission rate relative to PW re-injection. These CO_2 emission indicators are shown below:

$$T_{CO_2} = E_f \, E_d \left(W^s_{(1,2)} + W^s_{(1,3)} + W_{(4,5)} \right) \tag{3a}$$

$$I_{oil} = T_{CO_2} / \left(\lambda_\alpha \sum_{i=9}^{10} d_i + \lambda_\beta \sum_{i=14}^{15} d_i \right) \tag{3b}$$

$$I_{PW} = T_{CO_2} / \left(\sum_{i=9}^{10} d_i + \sum_{i=14}^{15} d_i \right) \tag{3c}$$

where T_{CO_2} is the total CO_2 emission; I_{oil} is the CO_2 production intensity; I_{PW} is the CO_2 re-injection intensity; and E_f is the CO_2 emission factor.

To perform sensitivity analysis in the PWRI facility, a parametric optimization problem was formulated. The problem is represented by the following nonlinear program (NLP):

$$\min_{\boldsymbol{\theta}} \quad \Phi\left(\boldsymbol{\theta}, \mathbf{p}\right), \tag{4a}$$

$$s.t. \quad \mathbf{g}\left(\boldsymbol{\theta}, \mathbf{p}\right) = 0, \tag{4b}$$

$$\mathbf{h}\left(\boldsymbol{\theta}, \mathbf{p}\right) \leq 0, \tag{4c}$$

where $\Phi : \mathbb{R}^{n_\theta} \times \mathbb{R}^{n_p} \to \mathbb{R}$ is the objective function; $\mathbf{g} : \mathbb{R}^{n_\theta} \times \mathbb{R}^{n_p} \to \mathbb{R}^{n_g}$ is the vector of equality constraints; and $\mathbf{h} : \mathbb{R}^{n_\theta} \times \mathbb{R}^{n_p} \to \mathbb{R}^{n_h}$ is the vector of inequality constraints. Moreover, $\boldsymbol{\theta} \in \mathbb{R}^{n_\theta}$ is the vector of decision variables; and $\mathbf{p} \in \mathbb{R}^{n_p}$ is the vector of parameters. The compact form shown in Eq.(4) enables one to perform sensitivity analysis to study how optimal decision variables $\boldsymbol{\theta}^*(\mathbf{p})$ and optimal objective function $\Phi^*(\mathbf{p})$ behaves due to changes performed in parameters.

For the considered application, the sensitivity analysis was done by varying the PW entering the PWRI facility with $d_1 \in [-480, -1818]$ m³/h. Moreover, we vary the roughness coefficient in the Hazen-Williams equation of riser$_{(7,8)}$ to represent an increase in flow resistance due to fouling, $C_{(7,8)} \in [140, 80]$. Notice that lower values of $C_{(7,8)}$ translates into more friction. The interval of interest for these parameters were based in operational data gathered from an offshore producer. Due to that, we analyze two strategies: the exclusive re-injection strategy (ERI), and the shared re-injection strategy (SRI). In ERI, re-injection should be performed exclusively at RIT$_\alpha$, while in SRI re-injection can be performed at both RITs.

3. Results and Discussion

3.1. Operational Behavior

Understanding the operational behavior of the PWRI facility is crucial for assessing the system performance. We showcase in Figure 2a the VSP operation; and in Figures 2b and 2c the PW re-injected at the RITs. Each curve is associated with a roughness coefficient value and a strategy.

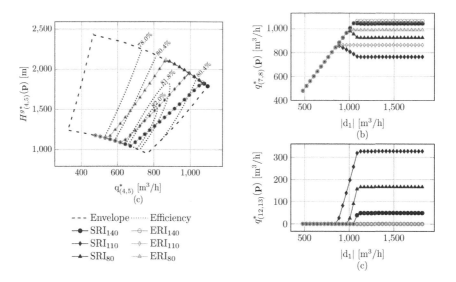

Figure 2: Overview of the PWRI facility operation for different roughness coefficients of the Hazen-William equation, in which: (a) Head gain of the VSP with operational envelope and efficiency islands; (b) re-injection flowrate of PW to the RIT_α; and (c) re-injection flowrate of PW to the RIT_β.

The operational point of a VSP is given by the intersection of the system resistance and pumping curves (Gülich, 2008). For the lowest value of $|d_1|$, 480 m^3/h, the operation point of the VSP is at the minimum rotation and $q^*_{(4,5)}$ is also at 480 m^3/h. Once $|d_1|$ increases, valves$_{(6,7),(8,9),(8,10)}$ widen their opening to re-inject more PW at RIT_α. This dislocates the system resistance curve to the right until these valves reach their maximum opening. At this point, the resistance curve in the ERI strategy cannot be further dislocated to the right. As for the SRI strategy, valves$_{(11,12),(13,14),(13,15)}$ can be opened to decrease the system resistance. However, due to the low effectiveness of RIT_β, it is instead optimal to re-injection more PW to RIT_α by increasing the VSP rotation. This tendency last for both strategies, until the VSP reaches its maximum operational rotation. For the ERI strategy an increase in re-injection cannot be achieved as the system lacks degrees of freedom, which represents a process bottleneck. For the SRI strategy, the valves associated with RIT_β start to open until $q^*_{(4,5)}$ reaches the VSP envelope limit. This point represents a process bottleneck for the SRI strategy as the VSP reaches its operational limits.

3.2. Economic and environmental performance

The economic and environmental performance of each strategy with distinct roughness coefficient are shown in Figure 3. Overall, fouling has impacted negatively most of the considered indicators for both strategies at some interval of $|d_1|$. The only exception is the re-injection ratio of the SRI strategy, as shown by the overlapping curves $\text{SRI}_{140,110,80}$ in Figure 3b.

While the VSP operates at minimum rotation, it is not observed any significant impact of fouling in the studied indicators. Nevertheless, when the VSP operates strictly inside its operational envelope, it is seen that fouling impacts negatively the total CO_2 emission in Figure 3d, CO_2 production intensity in Figure 3e, and CO_2 re-injection intensity in Figure 3f. This behavior is seen as fouling increases hydraulic losses in the riser$_{(7,8)}$, requiring additional usage of fuel to re-injection the same quantity of PW in RIT_α, which increase CO_2 emissions.

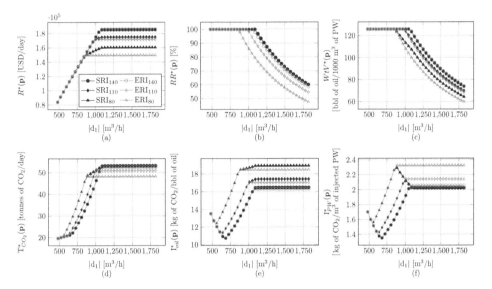

Figure 3: Economic and environmental performance for distinct strategies with different roughness coefficients of the Hazen-William equation. (a) Total revenue; (b) re-injection ratio; (c) waste-to-value; (d) total CO_2 emission; (e) CO_2 production intensity; and (f) CO_2 re-injection intensity.

As the VSP operates at maximum rotation, it is possible to see that fouling has worsened mostly indicators for the ERI strategy, except for total CO_2 emission in Figure 3d, which improves as less PW is re-injected at RIT_α. For the SRI strategy, fouling causes worsening of several indicators, except for re-injection ratio in Figure 3b, total CO_2 emission in Figure 3d, and CO_2 re-injection intensity in Figure 3f, in which differences due to fouling cannot be observed.

4. Conclusion

In this work, we have shown that fouling in PW re-injection can impact significantly the economic and environmental performance of a PWRI facility. Furthermore, it was shown that a RIT with lower effectiveness has the potential to mitigate several issues caused by fouling if included in a decision-making framework. However, it is important to notice that scaling can also occur at other risers during operation. Thus, monitoring of scaling and revaluation of decisions should be regularly performed for improving short and long term decision-making over waterflooding operation.

5. Acknowledgement

This research is a part of BRU21 – NTNU Research and Innovation Program on Digital and Automation Solutions for the Oil and Gas Industry (www.ntnu.edu/bru21) and supported by OKEA ASA. In addition, we would like to acknowledge license partners Neptune Energy Norge AS, and Petoro AS for allowing the usage of field data. The authors would like to thank employees at OKEA Per Magne Bjellvåg, Alf Sebastian Lackner, and Raymond Hellerud for their valuable input.

References

J. Beyer, A. Goksøyr, D.Ø. Hjermann, and J. Klungsøyr, 2020, Environmental effects of offshore produced water discharges: A review focused on the Norwegian continental shelf, Marine environmental research.

J. Neff, K. Lee, and E. DeBlois, 2011, Produced Water: Overview of Composition, Fates, and Effects, Produced Water: Environmental Risks and Advances in Mitigation Technologies, New York, NY, USA.

J.F. Bautista, and A. Dahi Taleghani, 2017, The state of the art and challenges in geomechanical modeling of injector wells: a review paper, Journal of Energy Resources Technology, 139, 1.

J.F. Gülich, 2008, Centrifugal pumps, Berlin, Germany.

Miljødirektoratet, 2015, Utredning av beste tilgjengelige teknikker (BAT) for rensing av produsert vann som slippes ut fra petroleumsvirksomheten til havs, Norway.

M.S.H. Bader, 2007, Seawater versus produced water in oil-fields water injection operations, Desalination, 208, 1-3, 159-168.

M. Nasiri, I. Jafari, and B. Parniankhoy, 2017, Oil and gas produced water management: a review of treatment technologies, challenges, and opportunities, Chemical engineering communications, 204, 8, 990-1005.

N. Steinar, G. Eimund, and D. Egil, 2016, Produced Water Management Under the Norwegian "Zero Harmful Discharge Regime" – Benefits With the Risk Based Approach, Society of Petroleum Engineers - SPE International Conference and Exhibition on Health, Safety, Security, Environment, and Social Responsibility, 1-9.

O.F. Ivo, L.S. Imsland, 2021, Analysis of Optimal Control Strategies for Efficient Operation of a Produced Water Reinjection Facility for Mature Fields, IFAC-PapersOnLine, 54, 3, 115-121

S. Rossini, G. Roppoli, P. Mariotti, S. Renna, M. Manotti, A. Viareggio, and L. Biassoni, 2020, Produced water quality impact on injection performance: Predicting injectivity decline for waterflood design, International Petroleum Technology Conference.

Proceedings of the 14th International Symposium on Process Systems Engineering – PSE 2021+
June 19-23, 2022, Kyoto, Japan © 2022 Elsevier B.V. All rights reserved.
http://dx.doi.org/10.1016/B978-0-323-85159-6.50177-9

Mathematical Modelling of Reactive Inks for Additive Manufacturing of Charged Membranes

Xinhong Liu[a], Riju De[b], Alexander Pérez[c], John R. Hoffman[a], William A. Phillip[a], Alexander W. Dowling[a*]

[a]*Department of Chemical and Biomolecular Engineering, University of Notre Dame, Notre Dame, IN 46556, USA*
[b]*Department of Chemical Engineering Goa, BITS Pilani, Goa 403726, India*
[c]*Department of Mechanical Engineering, University of Puerto Rico-Mayagüez, Mayagüez, PR 00681, USA*
adowling@nd.edu

Abstract

Patterned charged membranes with engendered useful characteristics can offer selective transport of electrolytes. Chemical patterning across the membrane surface via a physical inkjet deposition process requires precise control of the reactive-ink formulation, which enables the introduction of charged functionality to the membrane. This study develops a new dynamic mathematical model for the primary step of the batch reactive-ink formulation considering an ink mixture of copper sulphate and ascorbic acid. Nonlinear least squares parameter estimation is performed to infer three kinetic model parameters by analysing data from nine dynamic experiments simultaneously. Global sensitivity and Fisher information matrix (FIM) analyses reveal only one kinetic parameter is identifiable from time-series pH measurements. The fitted model can capture the overall nonlinear dynamics of the batch reaction and works best for initial Cu^{2+} concentrations between 30 and 50 mM. Time-series Cu^{2+} or Cu^+ concentration measurements are recommended in future experiments to elucidate the kinetics of reactive-ink formulation.

Keywords: Sensitivity analysis, Parameter estimation, Additive manufacturing, Fisher information matrix, Nanostructured membrane, Data science

1. Introduction

A critical need for more selective membranes has emerged as their applications in modern separations and sensing processes continue to expand. To this end, membranes with chemically patterned surfaces such as charge-patterned mosaics and Janus membranes are an emerging approach for accessing higher selectivity (Qu et al., 2017). The state-of-the-art fabrication process of such membranes involves printing reactive inks on the nanostructured substrates, where the charged functionality is induced through the copper-catalysed azide-alkyne cycloaddition (CuAAC) reaction mechanism. Hoffman et al. (2019) demonstrated that this approach requires precise control of the reactive-ink formulation to ensure the membrane manufacturing process remains in the transport-limited regime. The reactive-ink formulation comprises of a sequence of reactions occurring between reactants, i.e., copper sulphate ($CuSO_4$), ascorbic acid (DH_2), and an alkyne, to facilitate the formation of the dinuclear-copper alkyne complex (DNCAC). The concentration of the DNCAC is essential for the CuAAC reaction to proceed and therefore should be optimized to achieve a smooth chemical patterning while ensuring a controlled charged functionalization rate of the membrane at the same time (Worrell et al., 2013).

Focusing on the primary step which involves the reaction between $CuSO_4$ and DH_2, there are only a few models available in the literature that explains the mechanism of the DH_2-$CuSO_4$ reaction (Shtamm et al., 1979; Xu and Jordan, 1990). However, these models are limited to either the final Cu^{2+} reduction or the Cu^+/hydronium ions (H^+) formation. None have discussed a comprehensive and detailed rate law-based model that captures all the species involved in the reaction to the best of our knowledge.

In this paper, we develop a first-principles-based kinetic model for reactive ink formulation. Considering the anaerobic reaction scheme for the ascorbic acid dissociation as reported in the literature, rate constants that are unavailable in the literature are posed as model parameters and related to known equilibrium constants from Shtamm et al. (1979). Parameter estimation is performed to identify kinetic rate constants from time-series pH data. Local and global sensitivity analyses are performed to determine which model parameters are identifiable and design future experiments.

2. Dynamic mathematical model for reactive-ink formulation

The simplest reactive-ink solution is an aqueous mixture of ascorbic acid and copper sulphate. The reaction scheme involves a sequential dissociation of ascorbic acid via two reversible reactions in equilibrium as given by Eqs. (I), (II) and a final forward reaction as in Eq. (III), which describes the conversion of Cu^{2+} to Cu^+. Shtamm et al. (1979) proposed the following reaction scheme for the reduction of Cu^{2+} to Cu^+:

$$DH_2 \underset{k_{b1}}{\overset{k_{f1}}{\Longleftrightarrow}} DH^- + H^+ \tag{I}$$

$$Cu^{2+} + DH^- \underset{k_{b2}}{\overset{k_{f2}}{\Longleftrightarrow}} CuDH^+ \tag{II}$$

$$Cu^{2+} + CuDH^+ \overset{k_{i1}}{\longrightarrow} 2Cu^+ + D + H^+ \tag{III}$$

The equilibrium constants for reaction (I) and reaction (II) reported by Shtamm et al. (1979) are $K_{e1} = {k_{f1}}/{k_{b1}} = 5 \times 10^{-5}$ M and $K_{e2} = {k_{f2}}/{k_{b2}} = 200$ M^{-1}, respectively. Here, k_{f1} and k_{f2} denote the forward rate constant, whereas k_{b1} and k_{b2} symbolize the backward rate constants for reactions I and II, respectively. The rate constant for the final reaction (III) reported by Shtamm et al. (1979) is $k_{i1} = 6000$ mol^{-1}·L·min^{-1}. We consider a fully dynamic kinetic model for reactions (I) to (III) with five differential variables and five ordinary differential equations:

$$\frac{d[DH_2]}{dt} = -k_{b1}K_{e1}[DH_2] + k_{b1}[DH^-][H^+] \tag{1}$$

$$\frac{d[DH^-]}{dt} = k_{b1}K_{e1}[DH_2] - k_{b1}[DH^-][H^+] - k_{b2}K_{e2}[DH^-][Cu^{2+}] \\ + k_{b2}[CuDH^+] \tag{2}$$

$$\frac{d[H^+]}{dt} = k_{b1}K_{e1}[DH_2] - k_{b1}[DH^-][H^+] + k_{i1}[CuDH^+][Cu^{2+}] \tag{3}$$

$$\frac{d[Cu^{2+}]}{dt} = -k_{b2}K_{e2}[DH^-][Cu^{2+}] + k_{b2}[CuDH^+] \\ - k_{i1}[CuDH^+][Cu^{2+}] \tag{4}$$

$$\frac{d[CuDH^+]}{dt} = k_{b2}K_{e2}[DH^-][Cu^{2+}] - k_{b2}[CuDH^+] \\ - k_{i1}[CuDH^+][Cu^{2+}] \tag{5}$$

Here, $[DH_2]$, $[DH^-]$, $[H^+]$, $[Cu^{2+}]$, and $[CuDH^+]$ denote the concentrations of ascorbic acid, anion, hydrogen ion, cupric ion, and the complex, respectively, in unit of M. The model includes three unknown kinetic parameters, k_{b1} [mol⁻¹·L·min⁻¹], k_{b2} [min⁻¹] and k_{i1} [mol⁻¹·L·min⁻¹], that characterize the reaction progress.

3. Materials and methods

3.1. Materials

Initially, 200 mM ascorbic acid (DH₂) and copper sulphate (CuSO₄) solutions were prepared separately in 5 mL sample vials. Subsequently, the solutions were mixed to form 10 mL solutions. The pH of the mixtures was measured at every 1 min time interval for 5 min. The procedure was repeated in triplicate with CuSO₄ solutions at 200, 150, 100, 66.7, 50.0, 40.0, 33.3, 28.6, 25.0 mM for a total of (3 x 9 =) 27 experiments.

3.2. Parameter estimation with multi-start

To estimate the three unknown kinetic model parameters, $\theta = \{k_{b1}, k_{b2}, k_{i1}\}$, we solve the least-square nonlinear regression problem, shown in Eq. (6), which minimizes the square of the difference between the model predicted and the experimentally measured concentration of H⁺ ions (residuals) for the 9 experimental conditions.

$$\hat{\theta} = \arg\min_{\theta} \sum_{i=1}^{n_{exp}} \sum_{j=1}^{n_{tri}} \left([H^+]_{pred,i,j} - [H^+]_{exp,i,j}\right)^2 \tag{6}$$

Eq. (6) is solved numerically using scipy.optimize in Python with a customized multi-start strategy to help find the (near) global optima.

3.3. Local and global sensitivity analysis

The Fisher information matrix (FIM), which is defined as the inverse of the parameter covariance matrix, is computed at the best fit parameter values $\hat{\theta}$ based on local sensitivities of the model predictions to each parameter. The eigendecomposition of the FIM reveals which parameters are identifiable (Rothenberg and Thomas, 1971).

Similarly, a global sensitivity analysis is conducted via grid search by evaluating the objective function over a wide range of model parameters: $k_{b1} = [400, 900]$ mol⁻¹·L·min⁻¹, $k_{b2} = [1E-05, 1]$ min⁻¹ and $k_{i1} = [1, 6000]$ mol⁻¹·L·min⁻¹.

4. Results and discussion

4.1. Parameter estimation with multi-start

Table 1 shows the parameters estimated from regressing time-series pH measurements from the 27 experiments simultaneously. When each dataset (experimental condition) is regressed independently, parameters k_{b1} varies from 260 to 1,100,00 $mol^{-1} \cdot L \cdot min^{-1}$ and k_{i1} varies from 12 to 6,000 $mol^{-1} \cdot L \cdot min^{-1}$. These non-unique parameters motivate both simultaneous regression (Table 1) as well as formal identifiability analysis.

Table 1. Parameter estimation and local sensitivity from analysing 9 experiments simultaneously.

Estimated parameters			Residuals squared	Eigenvalues of FIM	Eigenvectors of FIM		
k_{b1}	k_{b2}	k_{i1}			k_{b1}	k_{b2}	k_{i1}
$(mol^{-1} \cdot L \cdot min^{-1})$	(min^{-1})	$(mol^{-1} \cdot L \cdot min^{-1})$	(M^2)				
				2.18E-12	-1.00	1.55E-09	4.40E-04
17601.30	0.0074	105.69	68.62	2.74E-06	-4.40E-04	8.35E-07	-1.00
				2.84E+06	-1.92E-09	-1.00	-8.35E-07

4.2. Local and global sensitivity analysis

The eigenvalues and eigenvectors of the Fisher information matrix (FIM) are also reported in Table 1. Two eigenvalues are near zero, 2.18E-12 and 2.74E-06, which implies the FIM is near singular and model is partial non-identifiable. The corresponding eigenvectors are predominantly in the direction of k_{b1} and k_{i1}, respectively, which indicate these parameters cannot be reliably estimated from these data. Conversely, the eigenvector of the largest eigenvalue, 2.84E+06, is in the direction of k_{b2}. This difference of more than 12 orders of magnitude in eigenvalues implies only k_{b2} is identifiable based on the pH measurements from 9 experimental conditions considered in triplicate.

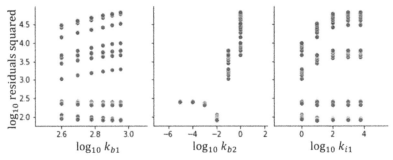

Fig. 1. Global sensitivity of the log_{10}-transformed sum of residuals squared for three model parameters.

Fig. 1 shows the results from a global sensitivity analysis which confirm that k_{b2} is the most sensitive model parameter. Parameters k_{b1}, k_{b2} and k_{i1} are varied with a grid search, and the log_{10}-transformed sum of residuals squared for the 27 experiments are computed. The plots with respect to k_{b1} and k_{i1} show the sum of residuals squared is only slightly impacted by the value of k_{b1} and k_{i1}. In other words, for a constant value of k_{b1} or k_{i1}, the sum of residuals squared changes by two orders of magnitude when varying the other two parameters. In a contrast, varying k_{b2} causes one to four orders of magnitude changing in the sum of residuals squared. Moreover, the sum of residuals squared is minimized around $k_{b2} = 10^{-2}$ min^{-1}. For $k_{b2} \leq 10^{-2}$ min^{-1}, varying k_{b1} or k_{i1} has almost no impact on the sum of residuals squared, but the model becomes sensitive to k_{b1} and k_{i1} when $k_{b2} \geq 10^{-2}$ min^{-1}. A possible physical explanation for this result is that reaction (II) is rate limiting when $k_{b2} \leq 10^{-2}$ min^{-1}, hence the model predictions are not sensitive to the other reaction kinetic constants (provided they are sufficiently large to not be rate limiting).

4.3. Partial parameter estimation

The local and global sensitivity analyses above both show only k_{b2} can be reliably estimated from the available timeseries pH measurements from the 27 experiments. Since k_{b1} characterize the rate for the ascorbic acid dissociation, it only affects the beginning of Cu$^+$ formation and has little influence on the subsequent reaction progress. Therefore, we select $k_{b1} = 600$ mol^{-1}·L·min^{-1} for reasonable H$^+$ profiles and $k_{i1} = 6000$ mol^{-1}·L·min^{-1} based on literature (Shtamm et al., 1979).

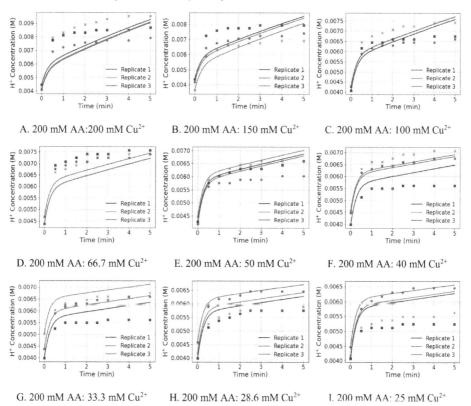

Fig. 2. Comparison for model predictions and experimental pH measurements for the 27 experiments (9 initial concentrations A-I repeated in triplicate).

Fig. 2 shows the results from partial parameter estimation with k_{b1} and k_{i1} fixed. The best fit value for k_{b2} is 0.0082 ± 0.0002 min^{-1}. As seen in Fig. 2, the continuous H$^+$ concentrations predicted from the fitted model match the overall the reaction progress as measured by the timeseries pH data. Experiments with initial Cu^{2+} concentrations between

28.6 and 50 mM (Fig. 2E-H) are best predicted with their relative sum of residuals squared less than 4%. However, for the experiments conducted with higher $[Cu^{2+}]_0$, the model overestimates the H^+ concentration after 5 minutes (Fig. 2A-D). Also, the relative sum of residuals squared increases monotonically from 7 % to 44 % as $[Cu^{2+}]_0$ increases from 66.7 to 200 mM, respectively. Similarly, for $[Cu^{2+}]_0 = 25.0$ mM, the model overestimates the H^+ concentration and the relative sum of residuals squared equals 11%. Together, these results suggest that copper complexes, which are not modeled, are important.

5. Conclusions

We developed a mathematical model for the Cu-DH$_2$ reaction system. Local and global sensitivity analysis reveals that only reaction rate parameter, k_{b2}, can be identified from timeseries pH measurements. Partial parameter estimation is performed to estimate k_{b2}, which is, to our knowledge, one of the first reported values for k_{b2} in literature.

While the fitted model captures the overall nonlinear dynamics of the batch reaction, several extensions should be considered as future work. We hypothesize measuring timeseries Cu^{2+} or Cu^+ concentrations will enable some of the remaining model parameters to be identified. Likewise, adding intermediate chemical species such as complexes to the model may improve the quality of fit. Ultimately, a predicted dynamic model, such as the one presented in this paper, may be used to optimize the ink formulations for additive manufacturing of chemically patterned membranes.

Acknowledgments

We gratefully acknowledge support from the United States National Science Foundation (NSF) awards CMMI-1932206 and CBET-1941596. A.P. and J.R.H. thank Notre Dame for support from the NDnano Undergraduate Research Fellowship and the Patrick and Jana Eilers Graduate Student Fellowship for Energy Related Research, respectively.

References

J.R. Hoffman, A.D. Mikes, F. Gao and W.A. Phillip, 2019, Controlled postassembly functionalization of mesoporous copolymer membranes informed by fourier transform infrared spectroscopy, ACS Appl. Polym. Mater, 1, 8, 2120-2130, 10.1021/acsapm.9b00419

S. Qu, Y. Shi, S. Benavides, A. Hunter, H. Gao and W.A. Phillip, 2017, Copolymer nanofilters with charge-patterned domains for enhanced electrolyte transport, Chem. Mater, 29, 2, 762-772, 10.1021/acs.chemmater.6b04660

T.J. Rothenberg, J. Thomas, 1971, Identification in parametric models. Econometrica, 39, 577–592, 10.2307/1913267

E.V. Shtamm, A.P. Purmal and Y.I. Skurlatov, 1979, Mechanism of catalytic ascorbic acid oxidation system Cu2+-ascorbic acid-O2, Int. J. Chem. Kinet, 11, 5, 461-494, 10.1002/kin.550110503

B.T. Worrell, J.A. Malik and V.V. Fokin, 2013, Direct evidence of a dinuclear copper intermediate in Cu(I)-catalyzed azide-alkyne cycloadditions, Science, 340, 6131, 457-460, 10.1126/science.1229506

J. Xu and R.B. Jordan, 1990, Kinetics and mechanism of the reaction of aqueous copper(II) with ascorbic acid, Inorg. Chem, 29, 16, 2933-2936, 10.1021/ic00341a015

Proceedings of the 14th International Symposium on Process Systems Engineering – PSE 2021+
June 19-23, 2022, Kyoto, Japan © 2022 Elsevier B.V. All rights reserved.
http://dx.doi.org/10.1016/B978-0-323-85159-6.50178-0

Economic Analysis of a Hydrogen Liquefaction Process Based on Techno-Economic and Energy Optimization

Heechang Son[a], Bjørn Austbø[b], Truls Gundersen[b], Jihyun Hwang[c, *], Youngsub Lim[a, d] *

[a]Department of Naval Architecture and Ocean Engineering, Seoul National University, Seoul, 08826, Republic of Korea
[b]Department of Energy and Process Engineering, Norwegian University of Science and Technology (NTNU), NO-7491, Trondheim, Norway
[c]Scool of energy technology, Korea Institute of Energy Technology, Naju, 58217, Republic of Korea
[d]Research Institute of Marine Systems Engineering, Seoul National University, Seoul 08826, Republic of Korea
jihyun.hwang@kentech.ac.kr
s98thesb@snu.ac.kr

Abstract

Efforts to be eco-friendly are becoming essential, and hydrogen is attracting attention as an eco-friendly fuel. As the hydrogen demand increases, the interest in liquid hydrogen is increasing because it is safer and more efficient for large-scale hydrogen transport and storage than compressed gaseous hydrogen. Since hydrogen must be cooled to about −253 °C to be liquefied, this represents a high proportion of the cost in a hydrogen liquefaction plant. Reducing the unit price of hydrogen is the key to achieve a hydrogen economy, and it is also important to reduce the cost of the hydrogen liquefaction process for price competitiveness of liquid hydrogen. The purpose of this study, therefore, is to perform an economic analysis of a hydrogen liquefaction process based on both techno-economic and energy-based optimization. The objective functions for techno-economic optimization and energy optimization are total annualized cost and total power consumption, respectively. The results show that the influence of operating expenditure is greater than that of capital expenditures, and the cost of the compressors is dominant in the capital expenditures. These results provide technical background data that can be used to improve the economic viability of the hydrogen liquefaction process as an important element in the hydrogen economy.

Keywords: Hydrogen liquefaction process; Techno-economic optimization; Energy optimization; Economic analysis.

1. Introduction

Eco-friendly efforts to solve the climate crisis are becoming an essential factor, leading to an era of great energy transition. Accordingly, hydrogen is in the spotlight as a promising fuel in the future because of its advantages: 1) abundant amount, 2) higher gravimetric energy density than conventional fossil fuels, and 3) eco-friendly fuel with no carbon emission (Yin and Ju, 2020).

The hydrogen value chain can be divided into three areas (production, storage/transportation, and utilization), and various research and development efforts are underway to lower the unit price of hydrogen in each area. In the hydrogen storage/transportation stage, three methods are being discussed as promising means to replace the conventional compressed hydrogen gas in order to increase the storage and transportation efficiency; i.e. Liquid organic hydrogen carrier (LOHC), Ammonia (NH_3) and Liquid hydrogen (LH_2). LOHC is a method of storing hydrogen in a liquid compound, and methylcyclohexane (MCH) is often considered as a candidate for this. Similarly, NH_3 synthesis is widely considered as a method for storing and transporting hydrogen. In LH_2, the hydrogen is stored and transported in liquid form, similar to the method of liquefied natural gas (LNG).

Since LH_2 has the high volumetric energy density compared to the gaseous hydrogen and the high gravimetric energy density compared to the LOHC and NH_3, it is expected to be the most suitable hydrogen storage method in large-capacity scenarios. However, liquefying hydrogen is technically challenging.

First, hydrogen is liquefied at −253 °C, and therefore a harsher cryogenic environment than LNG is required. Accordingly, a hydrogen liquefaction process requires about 30 times higher energy consumption compared to a natural gas liquefaction process (e.g. typical specific energy consumption (SEC) of natural gas liquefaction is about 0.3 kWh/kg LNG, while a typical SEC of hydrogen liquefaction is about 10 kWh/kg LH_2). In addition, hydrogen molecules occur in two different spin isomers, orthohydrogen (ortho-H_2) and parahydrogen (para-H_2). Normal hydrogen (normal-H_2) that can be observed at room temperature is composed of 75 % ortho-H_2 and 25 % para-H_2. As hydrogen is cooled from room temperature, the ratio of spin isomers forming equilibrium hydrogen (equilibrium-H_2) changes. As the temperature is reduced, ortho-H_2 is converted into para-H_2, which is an exothermic process. Since the natural ortho-/para-H_2 conversion (OPC) process occurs relatively slowly, liquefied non-equilibrium-H_2 can be vaporized by the heat of conversion unless the OPC processes are rapidly achieved through catalytic reactions while cooling hydrogen. This is because the heat of conversion (about 1063 J/mol) is higher than the heat of vaporization of liquid hydrogen (about 954 J/mol) (Zhuzhgov et al., 2018). Therefore, in an actual hydrogen liquefaction plant, a catalyst-filled heat exchanger is used to achieve a catalytic reaction for rapid OPC, such that the conversion heat can be removed in the cooling process.

Currently, much effort is made to lower the unit price of hydrogen to achieve a hydrogen economy, and thereby it is important to reduce the cost of the hydrogen liquefaction process as much as possible in order to have price competitiveness for liquid hydrogen. This study, therefore, aims to present technical background data for an economical hydrogen liquefaction process design through economic analysis based on techno-economic and energy optimization.

2. Process description

The Claude cycle presented by Berstad et al. (2021) is selected as a base model for a hydrogen liquefaction process in this study. Figure 1 shows the process flow diagram of the hydrogen liquefaction process in consideration. First, hydrogen feed gas is introduced in the precooling cycle at a rate of 125 ton/day at 20 bar and 298.15 K. The hydrogen feed gas is cooled to 114 K by passing PC-HX in the precooling cycle and then enter the main cryogenic cycle. Here, it is assumed that any impurities are removed through an adsorber before entering the main cryogenic cycle. A mixed refrigerant (MR) is used for the precooling cycle. The MR is composed of nitrogen (N_2), methane (C_1), ethane (C_2), propane (C_3), n-butane (n-C_4), and i-pentane (i-C_5). The MR is compressed to about 35 bar by two compression stages with intercoolers. It is assumed that the adiabatic efficiencies of each compressor and the pump in the precooling cycle are 85 % and 75 %, respectively. The high-pressure MR is pre-cooled to 114 K by passing PC-HX and then expanded to low pressure by a Joule-Thomson (J-T) valve bringing the stream to a lower temperature. The resulting low-temperature MR stream passes through PC-HX, cooling the hydrogen, and returns to the compression system.

After passing through an ortho-/para-H_2 conversion unit, the hydrogen gas is cooled from 117.9 K to 106 K in MC-HX2. The resulting hydrogen stream undergoes OPC through another conversion unit. In the simulation, equivalent heat exchangers using conversion reactor units are applied to simulate catalyst-filled heat exchangers for the OPCs as shown in Figure 1. The hydrogen is cooled to 22 K through HX3-HX8 with the OPCs and then expanded to 1.5 bar by a J-T valve. The final LH_2 conditions are 1.5 bar, 21.7 K, and 97 % para-LH_2 concentration. In the main cryogenic cycle, the normal-H_2 refrigerant is compressed to about 30 bar by four compression stages with intercooling in between. It is assumed that the adiabatic efficiency of C-3 and C-4 and the adiabatic efficiency of C-5 and C-6 are 82 % and 85 %, respectively. Side streams from the resulting refrigerant are drawn and expanded to intermediate pressures by expanders. The isentropic efficiency of each expander is assumed to be 85 %. The main refrigerant stream from MC-HX5 is depressurized by a liquid expander and a J-T valve. The resulting refrigerant stream at about 21 K passes through all heat exchangers and is returned to the compression system to provide the cooling duty. The side streams are mixed with the returning main refrigerant stream at intermediate pressure. The process parameters applied in the simulation are shown in Table 1.

Process modeling was done using Aspen HYSYS® V10.0. A modified Benedict-Webb-Rubin equation of state (MBWR) and the Peng-Robinson equation of state (PR) were applied to the main cryogenic cycle and precooling cycle, respectively.

3. Process optimization

For energy optimization, the net power consumption was used as the objective function, as shown in Eq.(1). The net power consumption can be calculated by subtracting the power produced in all j expander stages from the power consumed in all i compressor stages.

For techno-economic optimization, the cost estimation methodology presented by Turton et al. (2008) was used to calculate equipment cost, module cost and capital expenditures (*CAPEX*) of the hydrogen liquefaction process. Table 2 shows the equipment types considered here and their corresponding cost parameters. In this study, different types of heat exchangers for the precooling cycle and the main cryogenic cycle were selected in consideration of the type of refrigerant used. The cost of the catalyst used was assumed to be equal to 15 % of the cost of the heat exchanger without catalyst, and this assumption was used to calculate the cost of equivalent heat exchangers to which the OPCs are applied. The calculated *CAPEX* can be converted to an estimated annual *CAPEX* as shown in Eq.(2). Here, it was assumed that the interest rate (i) and the lifetime of the plant (L) are 10 % and 20 years, respectively. In addition, operating expenditures (*OPEX*) were estimated considering the total power consumption and the electricity cost (c_{elec} = 0.06 USD/kWh) as shown in Eq.(3). Consequently, the total annualized cost (*TAC*) of the hydrogen liquefaction process can be calculated by summing annual *CAPEX* and *OPEX*. This was used as the objective function for the techno-economic optimization, as shown in Eq.(4).

$$\min \sum \dot{W}_{total} = \left(\sum_i \dot{W}_i - \sum_j \dot{W}_j \right) \tag{1}$$

$$\text{Annual } CAPEX = CAPEX \cdot \frac{(i * (1 + i)^L)}{(1 + i)^L - 1} \tag{2}$$

$$OPEX = c_{elec} \sum \dot{W}_{total} \tag{3}$$

$$\min TAC = \text{Annual } CAPEX + OPEX \tag{4}$$

Here, a genetic algorithm (GA) was used for the optimization, and the process optimization was performed by connecting the GA loaded from MATLAB R2021a with Aspen HYSYS®. Optimization variables include the discharge pressure of each compressor and the expansion pressure of each expander, as well as the MR flow rate and normal-H_2 flow rate that are the flow rates of refrigerants.

Table 1. Process parameters used in the simulations

Parameter	Value	Unit
Hydrogen feed pressure	20	bar
Hydrogen feed temperature	298.15	K
Hydrogen feed mass flow	125	t/d
Inlet fraction of para-H_2	25	mol %
Liquid hydrogen pressure	1.5	bar
Liquid hydrogen temperature	21.6	K
Outlet fraction of para-H_2	≥ 95	mol %
Adiabatic efficiency of compressors	82–85	%
Isentropic efficiency of expanders	85	%
Minimum temperature approach of heat exchangers	0.5	K
Intercooler temperature	298.15	K

Table 2. Types and cost parameters for each equipment in the hydrogen liquefaction process

Equipment	Type	Cost parameters		
		K_1	K_2	K_3
Main cryogenic heat exchanger	Flat plate	4.6656	-0.1557	0.1547
Precooling heat exchanger	Spiral tube	3.9912	0.0668	0.243
Compressor	Centrifugal	2.2897	1.3604	-0.1027
Expander	Axial gas turbines	2.7051	1.4398	-0.1776

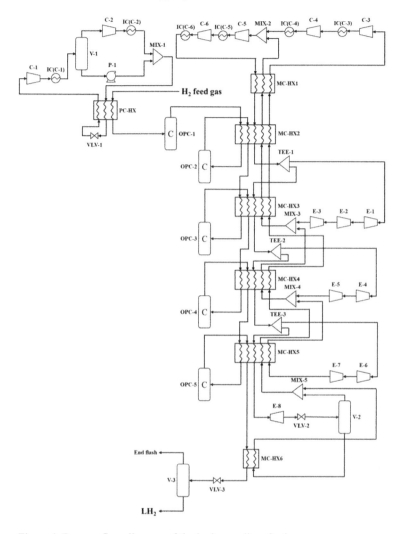

Figure 1. Process flow diagram of the hydrogen liquefaction process

4. Results

The economic analyses of the energy and techno-economic optimization results as well as the base model are shown in Figure 2. Since the hydrogen liquefaction process consumes a lot of energy, the influence of *OPEX* in *TAC* is greater than that of *CAPEX*, and therefore the compressor cost is dominant in the *CAPEX*. However, in the case of energy optimization, the *TAC* is larger compared to the base model and techno-economic optimization because the heat exchanger capacity is excessively increased.

As a result, for the hydrogen liquefaction process, it is advantageous in terms of *TAC* to increase process efficiency and save *OPEX*, but care must be taken not to excessively increase the capacity of the heat exchangers during energy optimization.

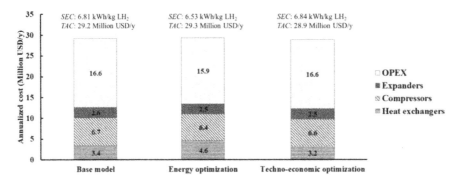

Figure 2. Economic analyses for base model, and energy and techno-economic optimization

5. Discussion

In this study, values for the overall heat transfer coefficient (U values) were assumed when estimating the heat exchanger cost in the techno-economic optimization; i.e. U value for the main cryogenic heat exchanger was set to 3000 W/m²·°C, while the U value for the precooling heat exchanger was set to 5000 W/m²·°C. Since these values are taken from natural gas liquefaction process data, future studies are required to apply more appropriate U values for the hydrogen liquefaction process. In addition, since the liquid expander (E-8) cost-wise was treated in the same way as the gas expanders, this also needs to be improved in future studies.

6. Conclusions

An economic analysis of a hydrogen liquefaction process was performed based on techno-economic and energy optimization. The total annualized costs were calculated by applying the cost estimation methodology selected for the techno-economic optimization. In conclusion, the influence of *OPEX* on the hydrogen liquefaction process cost is high, and thereby it is important to increase the process efficiency. In addition, if energy optimization is used for the hydrogen liquefaction process design, it should be noted that the heat exchanger capacity can be excessively increased leading to an increase in *TAC*.

References

D. Berstad, G. Skaugen, and Ø. Wilhelmsen, 2021, Dissecting the exergy balance of a hydrogen liquefier: Analysis of a scaled-up claude hydrogen liquefier with mixed refrigerant pre-cooling, International Journal of Hydrogen Energy, 46, 8014–8029.

R. Turton, R. C. Bailie, W. B. Whiting, and J. A. Shaeiwitz, 2008, Cost Equations and Curves for the CAPCOST Program in Analysis, synthesis and design of chemical processes, 3rd ed., London, UK: Pearson Education, 923–954.

L. Yin and Y. Ju, 2020, Process optimization and analysis of a novel hydrogen liquefaction cycle, International Journal of Refrigeration, 110, 219–230.

A. V. Zhuzhgov, O. P. Krivoruchko, L. A. Isupova, O. N. Mart'yanov, and V. N. Parmon, 2018, Low-Temperature Conversion of *ortho*-Hydrogen into Liquid *para*-Hydrogen: Process and Catalysts. Review, Catalysis in Industry, 10, 1, 9–19.

Proceedings of the 14th International Symposium on Process Systems Engineering – PSE 2021+
June 19-23, 2022, Kyoto, Japan © 2022 Elsevier B.V. All rights reserved.
http://dx.doi.org/10.1016/B978-0-323-85159-6.50179-2

How Digital Twins are Propelling Metals Industry to Next Generation Decision-Making: A Practitioner's View

Yale Zhang[a*], Mitren Sukhram[a] and Ian Cameron[a]

[a] Hatch Ltd., 2800 Speakman Drive, Mississauga, Ontario Canada L5K 2R7
* yale.zhang@hatch.com

Abstract

The digital twin is a technology to digitally transform asset lifecycle in the metals industry, from improving project delivery to empowering operational intelligence toward next-generation decision-making. In this paper, Hatch's digital twin framework is presented and demonstrated using a real-world blast furnace twin example, followed by development practice and lessons learned from our practice experience.

Keywords: Digital Twin, Analytics, Decision-making, Mining and Metals, Blast Furnace

1. Introduction

The metals industry is concerned with the processing of bulk ore resources into various basic materials, such as steel, aluminum, copper, etc. It is an asset-centric industry, where key assets are heavily invested and have their own lifecycle. With the growing maturity of the Industrial Internet of Things (IIoT), Machine Learning and Artificial Intelligence (ML/AI) technologies, the digital twin becomes a powerful tool to transform the industrial asset lifecycle from process design, construction to operation. It drives the metals industry toward better decision-making to improve project delivery, yield and resource efficiency, as well as plant operation and maintenance.

At Hatch, the digital twin is often considered under a bigger picture of industrial asset lifecycle and enterprise value chain. As shown in Figure 1, it first contextualizes the asset information during the process design, engineering, and construction phase. Such information like asset structure, Piping and Instrumentation Diagrams (P&IDs), design basis, equipment information, etc. are all connected to static and dynamic process models as well as discrete event simulation models to optimize project design, Capex/Opex, and schedule. The dynamic process models (with possible expansion to include thermo- and fluid dynamics) are further integrated with a control system emulator to build digital twins for operator training and accelerate the process commissioning phase. Once processes are in operation, the above models together with data-driven, ML/AI algorithms are used to develop digital twins to support operational intelligence, for example, "process twins" for anomaly detection, scenario analysis, and operational guidance; "asset twins" for predictive maintenance, and risk management; and "connected twins" considering integrated mass flow, energy flow, cash flow, and carbon flow for end-to-end value chain simulation and optimization.

This paper focuses on the digital twins of operating assets. It starts with a review of three selected digital twin frameworks and then presents a commercial digital twin use case for ironmaking blast furnaces. Hatch's digital twin development approach and lessons learned are also shared from an industrial practitioner's perspective.

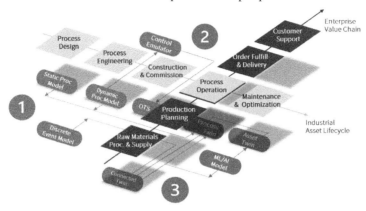

Figure 1. Digital twins across industrial asset lifecycle and enterprise value chain

2. Understand Digital Twin Technology

The digital twin concept has been around for many years, and it is always evolving with the latest development of Industry 4.0 technologies. Many different digital twin definitions and frameworks have been presented recently by technology vendors and industrial practitioners. Three representative digital twin frameworks are selected and discussed in this section. Each of them has its own foci, but they share some common components, which are crucial to digital twin design and development.

Deloitte is one of the early practitioners in applying digital twin technology to help their manufacturing clients create new values. In its definition, the digital twin framework is a near real-time comprehensive integration between the physical and digital worlds (Mussomeli, *et al.*, 2020). Such integration relies on four key components: sensors and actuators from the physical side, and data and analytics from the digital side. Sensors are distributed throughout the industry processes, continuously generating real-time data to represent the current situation of physical assets. The data are ingested into a digital twin platform and consumed by analytical algorithms and models to produce actionable insights. The insights can be implemented by actuators to apply direct changes to physical processes in an automatic or semi-automatic way. DNV is an independent assurance and risk management organization, who proposed a unique framework by decomposing a digital twin into multiple manageable functional elements (DNV-GL, 2020). Each element contains five key components: (1) data streams, (2) asset information model, (3) computation models, (4) dashboard and quality indicator, and (5) need and key decision. These components normally serve one specific purpose (i.e., use case) but may also be shared across multiple elements. In DNV's view, the digital twin is a collection of functional elements, which work together holistically to provide decision support over the entire life cycle of a physical asset. Hatch 3I's digital twin framework is presented in Figure 2 (Zhang, *et al.* 2021), which consists of Integration, Intelligence, and Interaction.

Integration is to establish a dynamic visualization environment, where all sources of engineering, production, maintenance, environment, health, and safety data together with high-fidelity 2D/3D asset models are combined to create a "Single Source of Truth". It presents on-demand, contextualized information and ensures data transparency and availability for all designated users through a secured cloud infrastructure.

Intelligence is the key differentiator between the previous generation of BI dashboards and a digital twin. The latter provides a fully and meaningfully connected analytical platform to effectively combine first-principle models, big data, and ML/AI technology to generate actionable insights and make intelligent decisions related to the physical twin's safety, reliability, efficiency, and profitability.

Interaction focuses on value connectivity. A digital twin adds value to business by creating innovative and more meaningful points of interaction between humans and machines through rich visualization and services, for example, augmented operator training, remote expert support, and collaborative decision-making.

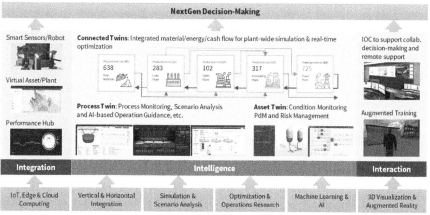

Figure 2. Hatch 3I's Framework of Digital Twin

Some common components of digital twin are evident based on the above frameworks and should be considered for every digital twin implementation. They are: (1) **Data** is a fundamental component of digital twins. Effective decision-making requires insights based on true and contextualized data from multiple sources. It becomes critically important that a well-designed data platform is utilized by digital twins for data connection, ingestion, manipulation, and storage. (2) **Model** is the core of digital twins. The models based on first principles, ML/AI algorithms, simulation, and/or optimization technology are used in different digital twin use cases to generate insights and make decisions for specific purposes. (3) **Visualization** is the aspect that describes the user interface of a digital twin. It represents actionable insights through various technologies, from widely used business intelligence dashboards, 3D visualization, to the latest virtual and augmented reality.

3. An Industrial Example: Blast Furnace Digital Twin

Several digital twins have been successfully implemented at Hatch clients' sites by a joint digital and process engineering team following Hatch 3I's framework, for example, blast furnace digital twins for the steel industry, autoclave digital twins for the refractory gold industry, and others. In this section, one use case of blast furnace digital twin is presented as an example to demonstrate digital twin's value through timely decision-making.

Casting is an important part of blast furnace stable operation. It is a critical task for cast-house floor operators to control hearth liquid heights and avoid large liquid accumulation. The presence of excessive liquids can exert back-pressure on the tuyere raceways in the furnace, distort the gas flow, and create an overall negative impact on furnace operations, such as slow burden movement, hanging and slipping, elevated heat load on the bosh and lower stack leading to increased coke consumption and carbon emissions. Many blast furnace operators follow casting rules that are enacted from experience but in most cases, there are no real-time measurements of hearth liquid heights to validate the rules.

As part of the blast furnace digital twin, a casting guidance use case was developed for a better understanding of the accumulation and drainage of iron and slag. It integrated real-time furnace operational data (e.g., hot metal smelting rate, hot blast pressure, slag and blow time, etc.) with the first-principle model developed by Cameron, *et al.* (2020) to establish a true representation of blast furnace hearth and provides an operational intelligence tool with the following three key functions.

Real-time monitoring and prediction of hearth liquid heights to improve process safety and stability. As illustrated in Figure 3, this function provides a 3D visualization of the blast furnace hearth together with real-time casting information, hot metal/slag heights, and their predictions. High liquid height alerts, operational recommendations, and non-adherence to casting Standard Operating Procedures (SOPs) will be sent to operators directly either through an on-screen notification center or mobile text messages.

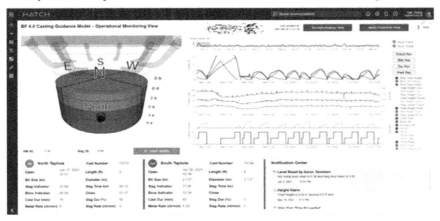

Figure 3. Example of blast furnace digital twin

Scenario analysis of future cast operations to provide operational guidance towards optimal production. With this function, process engineers and/or cast-house planners can develop a custom response to the current material heights by adjusting some operational levers such as taphole sequence, cast start time, drill bit size, hot metal production rate, etc. Through various scenario analyses based on the current operating conditions, they can experiment with the ideal response to a challenging hearth condition, for example, high slag heights.

Model parameter auto-tuning based on real-time data to minimize plant-model mismatch. This function is performed at the end of each cast to automatically update key process model parameters such as taphole roughness and wear rate to make the digital twin a true representation of its physical twin through consistent self-learning. Our study showed that the auto-tuning function contributed to a 17% improvement in model prediction accuracy.

The casting guidance use case has been rolled out to the client's Blast Furnace Command Center since late 2020, which provided a data-centric decision tool to furnace/shift coordinators and also enabled Hatch experts to provide remote technical support. Some tangible benefits have been observed, including more consistent hot metal and slag heights inside the blast furnace, a 45% decrease of non-casting time along with a notable reduction in furnace hearth temperature and energy consumption.

4. Development Approach and Lessons Learned

It has been a very challenging but rewarding journey over the past three years to establish digital twin as one of the service offerings at Hatch Digital. We have made some great successes to deploy digital twins across a plant site but also failed by mistakes. This session discusses some lessons learned as a way of sharing our experience from a practitioner's perspective.

Focusing on value delivery is the only way to meaningfully apply a digital twin. At the beginning of digital twin development, it is critically important to identify digital twin values specific to users and differentiate them from other technologies such as Business Intelligence (BI) dashboard or simulation applications. The values need to be tangible and measurable to justify potential investments. We have experienced a predictive maintenance use case, in which the initial costs of developing a failure prediction model are difficult to justify due to the low probability of the failure occurrence.

Digital twins are always evolving so as the development approaches – be agile. It should be completely fine to start with a Minimum Viable Product (MVP) just to address one or two key features, and then add new ones gradually based on users' feedback. Taking the casting guidance as an example, along the six-month development process, we added new features almost every month, from 3D unity model for enhanced visualization, real-time notification via mobile text messages, to model tuning and auto-tuning functions. Today we are developing a new AI technology to characterize the changes of taphole based on image analysis to further improve the model accuracy.

Accelerate your time-to-value by adopting a low-code digital twin platform. Developing a digital twin requires the connection of real-time data, orchestration of process models, and customization of user interfaces to support data visualization and user interactions. We found that some low-code digital twin platforms (such as XMPro, etc.) have developed great built-in data connection and visualization features, allowing us to concentrate more on intelligence and insight development and help our clients realize benefits sooner and faster, which is key to the success of digital twin projects.

Make your digital twin a trustworthy tool to operators. The most common failure in digital twin implementation is that users stopped using it for decision support after the initial commissioning stage because the digital twin can no longer represent its physical processes. This can be caused by several different reasons related to, for example, data quality, model/algorithm robustness, and/or digital system stability. To prevent this situation from happening, certain quality assurance measures need to be incorporated into digital twin design. Some of them may include real-time validation of input operational data, continuous monitoring of model health, built-in model self-learning capabilities to adapt to possible process changes over t.me, and/or a consistent and meaningful way to interpret and present digital twin results to avoid any ambiguity and misunderstanding from users' point of view.

Last but not least, *your commercial model is either a roadblock or a lubricant to the success of digital twin projects*. Although this is not a technical issue, we often found that in many cases, a promising digital twin project may quickly lose the support either from the developer- or client-side as the commercial model is not sustainable. In other words, the costs of creating and running a digital twin are not met by the values created. We have to respect that there is no one commercial model that can fit all. A flexible commercial model with a focus on long-term benefits will help solve the issue.

Keep these lessons learned in mind, we have established a proven, agile development approach to transforming a conceptual idea into a real-world digital twin solution, which consists of the following five steps:

(1) focusing our attention on understanding a wide range of user needs, and grouping them into multiple categories such as functional requirements, data requirements, user experience requirements, or security requirements, etc.

(2) conducting persona workshops to identify goals, key users, and pain points for each use case, and prioritizing them based on their potential benefit and implementation cost.

(3) proposing a solution with high-priority use cases, and using an interactive mockup as a communication tool to visualize different ideas and solicit stakeholders' feedback.

(4) commissioning an MVP through plant trials, targeting a quick delivery with added values, and continuously improving it during the following development.

(5) comparing with the original requirements to ensure all needs are fully satisfied by MVP or its further improved versions. It is worth mentioning that this step often serves as a new round of innovation process that may lead to further design improvements.

5. Conclusion

Our view on digital twins, development practice as well as lessons learned from the past project experience are shared from an industrial practitioner's perspective in this paper. We believe, with strong support from Industry 4.0 technologies, the digital twin will continue to be a powerful technology tool to solve different plant operation, maintenance, and value chain optimization challenges, and provide a good starting point of the digital journey of driving toward next-generation decision-making for the metals industry.

References

A. Mussomeli, A. Paarot, B. Umbenhauer and L. Warshaw, "Digital twins: Bridging the physical and digital," Deloitte, 15 January 2020.

DNV-GL, "DNVGL-RP-A204: Qualification and Assurance of Digital Twins," DNV, 2020.

Y. Zhang, M. Sukhram, I. Cameron, and A. Rozo, "Industrial Perspective of Digital Twin Development and Applications for Iron and Steel Processes," *Iron and Steel Technology,* no. 3, pp. 34-43, 2021

I. Cameron, M. Sukhram, K. Lefebvre, and W. Davenport, *Blast Furnace Ironmaking Analysis, Control, and Optimization.* Mississauga: Elsevier. 2020

Proceedings of the 14th International Symposium on Process Systems Engineering – PSE 2021+
June 19-23, 2022, Kyoto, Japan © 2022 Elsevier B.V. All rights reserved.
http://dx.doi.org/10.1016/B978-0-323-85159-6.50180-9

The study on feasibility of HFO refrigerants in BOG re-liquefaction process

Taejong YU[a], Donghoi KIM[b], Truls GUNDERSEN[c*], Youngsub LIM[a,d*]

[a]*Department of Naval Architecture and Ocean Engineering, Seoul National University,
1 Gwanak-ro,
Gwanak-gu, Seoul, 08826, Republic of Korea*
[b]*SINTEF Energy Research, Sem Sælands vei 11, NO-7465 Trondheim, Norway.*
[c]*Department of Energy and Process Engineering, Norwegian University of Science and
Technology
(NTNU), Kolbjørn Hejes Vei 1B, NO-7491, Trondheim, Norway*
[d]*Research Institute of Marine Systems Engineering, Seoul National University, 1
Gwanak-ro,
Gwanak-gu, Seoul, 08826, Republic of Korea*

Abstract

As regulation of ship emission established, using liquefied natural gas (LNG) as ship fuel is one of the method to reduce ship emission. For LNG carrier, boil-off gas (BOG) generated from the storage tank can be used as fuel and it is economical to adopt BOG re-liquefaction system on the vessel. In this study, we investigate the feasibility of hydro-fluoroolefins (HFO) refrigerants in the BOG re-liquefaction system. We simulate BOG re-liquefaction system and optimize it to minimize energy consumption. Then, the global warming potential(GWP) generation during lifecycle of the ship is estimated. As the results, HFO refrigerants has similar performance in BOG re-liquefaction system in terms of energy consumption compared to hydrocarbon refrigerants. In case using HFO refrigerants, the specific power consumption (SPC) of re-liquefaction process is 0.479 kWh/kg and in case using hydrocarbon refrigerants it is 0.471 kWh/kg. However, although HFO refrigerants has lower GWP than hydrocarbons, the total GWP generation is larger than when using hydrocarbons due to GWP generation caused by CO_2 emission.

Keywords: BOG re-liquefaction process, hydro-fluoroolefin refrigerants, optimization, the global warming potential.

1. Introduction

For long distance, it is economical to transport liquid form of natural gas (NG) by LNG carriers. However, LNG is stored in the storage cargo tank at -160 °C under ambient pressure (Lim et al, 2013), so part of LNG is vaporized to boil-off gas (BOG) by heat ingress into the tank. For LNG carrier, it is economical to use BOG as fuel and re-liquefy the remaining BOG to recover it to the tank. There are two types of gas propulsion engines mounted on ships: a high-pressure gas propulsion engine (ME-GI) developed by MAN B&W and a low-pressure gas propulsion engine (X-DF) developed by WIN-GD. In the initial gas propulsion engine market, the market share of high-pressure gas propulsion engines was high, but as emission regulations for nitrogen oxides (NOx) and sulfur oxides (SOx) were tightened (IMO, 1999, 2016, 2017), interest in low-pressure gas propulsion engines is increasing (IGU, 2019). For low pressure gas propulsion engine, it is advantageous in terms of energy consumption to liquefy and recover BOG using an external refrigerant cycle due to its low operating pressure.

Meanwhile, hydro-fluoroolefins (HFO) are consider as suitable alternative to conventional refrigerants established through the Montreal Protocol and other such treaties in heating, ventilation and air-conditioning (HAVC) and automobile industries. The conventional refrigerants in HAVC and automobile industries include hydrofluorocarbons (HFCs), chlorofluorocarbons (CFCs) and hydrochlorofluorocarbons (HCFCs) which have high global warming potential (GWP) or ozone depletion potential(ODP). The HFOs have double bonds in its molecular structure, so the rate of decomposition in the air is high. Thus they have little environmental impact, resulting in low GWP and ODP.

Currently, there is little research on the re-liquefaction of BOG using HFO refrigerants, so it is worth studying their feasibility in the BOG re-liquefaction system. In this study, BOG re-liquefaction process using HFO refrigerants is modeled and optimized to minimize the energy consumption. Then, GWP generation during lifecycle is estimated and compared to case of using conventional hydrocarbon refrigerants.

2. Process design

2.1 Design basis
The LNG and BOG composition is assumed as shown in Table 1. ASPEN HYSYS V10 is used as a software for process simulation, and this study uses the Peng–Robinson equation of state, which is suitable for simulating LNG, a light hydrocarbon, up to high pressure and cryogenic conditions.

Table 1. LNG (Aspelund et al, 2010) and BOG composition.

Type	Unit	Value
LNG composition		
Nitrogen	mol%	0.37
Methane	mol%	95.89
Ethane	mol%	2.96
Propane	mol%	0.72
Butane	mol%	0.06
BOG composition		
Nitrogen	mol%	0.48
Methane	mol%	99.49
Ethane	mol%	0.03

The amount of BOG generated from the tank can be estimated the Equation (1).

$$BOG_{tank} = V \cdot L_v \cdot \rho \cdot V_\gamma \tag{1}$$

where BOG_{tank} is the rate of BOG generated from the storage tank, V is the volume of the storage tank, L_v is the liquid level, ρ is the average density of the LNG, and V_γ is the evaporation rate of the storage tank. Assuming that the tank volume is 170,000 m³, the liquid level is 95%, the average density is 437.9 kg/m³, and the evaporation rate is 0.1%/day, the amount of BOG generated per hour could be estimated to be about 2938 kg/h.

To determine the BOG consumption rate for the main propulsion engine and auxiliary power generation engine, the following Equation (2) could be used.

$$BOG_{fuel} = \frac{P_e \cdot SFOC \cdot l}{LHV} \tag{2}$$

where BOG_{fuel} is the fuel consumption in kg/hr, P_e is the engine power in kW, SFOC is the specific fuel oil consumption in kJ/kWh, LHV is the lower heating value of BOG in kJ/kg based on the BOG composition, and l is the engine load in %. Table 2 shows the corresponding values of each engine are assumed.

Table 2. Engine specification (Wartsila, 2019) (WinGD, 2018).

Type	Unit	Main Engine	Aux. Engine
Manufacturer		WinGD	Wartsila
Model		X62DF	16V34DF
Power	kW	11,925 x 2	8,000
SFOC	kJ/kWh	7,132	7,679
Load	%	40	50
LHV of BOG	kJ/kg	42,900	
Fuel consumption	kg/h	1,586	716

By subtracting the fuel consumption obtained from through the above calculation from the BOG generation, the amount of BOG supplied to the BOG re-liquefaction system can be estimated as 639 kg/h.

In this study, the basic process configuration set as the single mixed refrigerant (SMR) cycle. Figure 1 shows the BOG re-liquefaction process.

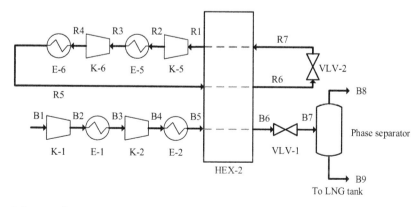

Figure 1. Process flow diagram of BOG re-liquefaction system.

2.2 Optimization

One of main purpose of this study is to investigate the cooling efficiency of HFO refrigerants. To do this, the specific power consumption (SPC), one of the key indicator of energy consumption in liquefaction process, is optimized. The SPC can be estimated as following Equation (3).

$$SPC = \frac{\sum \dot{W}}{\dot{m}_{LNG}} \tag{3}$$

where $\sum \dot{W}$ is the total power consumption of the liquefaction system, and $\dot{m}_{LNG}$ is the the total mass flow of LNG generated at the rear end of the phase separator. After selecting SPC as the objective function for comparative analysis, the optimum point to minimize SPC is found in each process. The process variables are the pressure ratio of the compressors (K-1 to K-4), expansion pressure at the rear end of the valve (R7), cooling temperature (R6), and the composition and mass flow rate of the mixed refrigerant. The constraint set the minimum temperature difference of the heat exchanger to 3 °C to prevent oversizing of heat exchanger and the vapour fraction of compression inlet stream to 1 to prevent malfunction of compressors.

2.3 Environmental assessment

In this study, total GWP generation during the lifecycle of an LNG carrier is estimated by two parts: (1) GWP caused by the disposal of refrigerants ($GWP_{disposal}$) after life cycle of the ship and (2) GWP caused by CO2 emission for power generation (GWP_{CO2}). The lifecycle of an LNG carrier is assumed to be 20 years. The $GWP_{disposal}$ is the GWP generation from a disposal of refrigerants after lifecycle of the ship. Equation (4) shows GWP value due to the disposal of the refrigerants.

$$GWP_{disposal} = GWP \cdot V_{re-liq} \cdot \rho_{mr} \cdot f_{disposal} \tag{4}$$

where $GWP_{disposal}$ is the GWP generation due to the disposal of refrigerants, GWP is the value of the global warming potential of the mixed refrigerants, V_{re-liq} is the inventory of the re-liquefaction system, and $f_{disposal}$ is the percent of refrigerant disposed and assumed 30% for medium and large commercial refrigeration (U.S. EPA, 2014). To estimate the inventory of the refrigeration in the system (V_{re-liq}), Equation (5) can be used.

$$V_{re-liq} = V_{HEX} \cdot \rho_{mr} \cdot f \tag{5}$$

where V_{HEX} is the volume of the heat exchanger and estimated by using ASPEM EDR V10 as the heat exchanger simulation program. ρ_{mr} is the density of the mixed refrigerant. f is the factor to estimate total amount of refrigerant from inventory of the heat exchanger and is assumed to be 2.38.

The GWP_{CO2} is the GWP generation due to CO2 emission for power supply to the re-liquefaction system in per year, and it can be estimated by Equation (6) (Trozzi, 2010).

$$GWP_{CO2} = P_e \cdot EF \tag{6}$$

where P_e is the power consumed in the re-liquefaction process and EF is the carbon emission factor of the fuel. It refers to the amount of CO2 generated to produce a unit of energy depending on the type of fuel and is assumed as 61.0 for LNG fuel (Australia.

Department of Industry, Science, Energy and Resources, 2017). Availability of the re-liquefaction process is assumed to be 50% per year.

3. Results and discussion

In this section, cases are classified according to the combination of refrigerants. Case 1 uses the mixture of conventional hydrocarbons. It consists nitrogen (N2), methane (C1), ethane (C2), propane (C3), and normal butane (nC4). In case 2, C3 and nC4 are replaced with HFO refrigerants: HFO 1234yf, HFO 1234ze, HFO 1233zd. Table 3 shows the results of the SPC optimization.

Table 3. Results of SPC optimization.

Parameter		Unit	Case3		Case3	
Composition		mol%	N2	11.1	N2	15.9
		mol%	C1	28.2	C1	26.3
		mol%	C2	29.5	C2	29.8
		mol%	C3	0.0	HFO 1234yf	12.2
		mol%	nC4	31.2	HFO 1234ze	2.4
					HFO 1234zd	13.4
MR flow rate		kg/h	4074		4886	
BOG feed pressure		bar	90.33		95.02	
MR compression pressure	inlet	bar	3.7		4.3	
	outlet	bar	22.8		41.8	
BOG temperature after HEX			-156.8		-156.9	
Total power consumption		kW	268.0		272.6	
SPC		kWh/kg	0.471		0.479	

In Case 1, the total flow of the MR is 4074 kg/h. The BOG is compressed to 90.33 bar and then flow into the heat exchanger and cooled to -156.8 °C and expanded in the valve. The total power consumption is 268.0 kWh, and SPC is 0.471 kWh/kg. In Case 2, the total flow rate of the MR is 4886 kg/h, and after BOG is compressed 95.02 bar, it is cooled down to -156.9 °C. The MR requires compression 41.8 bar, the total power consumption is 272.6 kWh, and SPC is 0.479 kWh/kg. As shown in the results, the total power consumptions of each case similar. There is only 1.7% difference when replacing C3 and nC4 with HFO refrigerants. After the optimization of energy consumption, GWP generation is estimated. Table 4 shows the results of GWP estimation.

Table 4. GWP generation during the lifecycle.

Case	$GWP_{disposal}$	GWP_{CO2}	Total GWP (during life cycle)
Case1	2,973	217,207	4,347,121
Case2	1,762	220,936	4,420,473

Case 2 has the lower $GWP_{disposal}$ compared to Case 1 due to lows GWP values of HFO refrigerants. If an HFO refrigerants are used, GWP generated by disposal of refrigerants after the lifecycle can be reduced by 40% compared to the hydrocarbon mixture. Although $GWP_{disposal}$ of Case 2 is lower than that of Case 1, the total GWP generation during lifecycle is much larger due to GWP_{CO2} proportional to energy consumption. This means that the use of low GWP materials for refrigerants may not contribute to reduce the GWP generation, keeping low SPC is more effective to decrease the annual GWP.

4. Conclusion

In this study, we investigate the feasibility of HFO refrigerants in the BOG re-liquefaction system. We modelled BOG re-liquefaction system and optimized it to minimize the specific power consumption of the process. Then, we estimated GWP generation during the lifecycle of the ship. As the results, when HFO refrigerants replaces hydrocarbon refrigerants, there is no large difference in energy consumption. The conventional hydrocarbon mixture has the SPC of 0.471 kg/kWh and the mixture of HFO refrigerants and hydrocarbon has 0.479 kWh/kg. However, this small difference effects on GWP generation. Although HFO refrigerants generate lower GWP when disposed, it has larger GWP value totally due to GWP generation caused by CO2 emission. When using HFO refrigerants, $GWP_{disposal}$ is 1762 and when using hydrocarbons, it is 2973. GWP_{CO2} is 217,207 and 220,936 in each case. Consequently, total GWP generation is 4,437,121 in case of HFO refrigerants and 4,420,473 in case of hydrocarbon refrigerants. This means that energy consumption has a greater influence on GWP production than GWP of refrigerant.

References

Aspelund. A, Gundersen. T, Myklebust. J, Nowak. M, Tomasgard. A, An optimization-simulation model for a simple LNG process, Comput. Chem. Eng, 34, 1606–1617.

Austraila. Department of Industry, Science, Energy and Resources, 2017, National greenhouse accounts factors.

EPA, 2014, Direct Fugitive Emissions from Refrigeration, Air conditioning, Fire Supression, and Industrial Gases, Environmental Protection Agency, US.

IGU, 2019, World LNG Report 2019, Internatinal Gas Union.

IMO, 1999, International Convention for the Prevention of Pollution from Ships MARPOL 73/78: The Regulations for the Prevention of Air

Pollution from Ships (AnnexVI), Internatinal maritme organization, London, UK, 1999.

IMO, 2016, Marine Environment Protection Committee (MEPC), 70th Session, Internatinal maritme organization, London, UK.

IMO, 2017, Prevention of Air Pollution from Ships, Internatinal maritme organization, London, UK.

Lim. W, Choi. K, Moon.I, 2013, Current Status and Perspectives of Liquefied Natural Gas (LNG) Plant Design, Ind. Eng. Chem. Res, 52, 3065-3388.

Trozzi. C, 2010, Emission Estimate Methodology for Maritime Navigation, T. Consulting, Editor.

Wartsila, 2019, Wärtsilä 34DF Brochure; Wartsila, Helsinki, Finland.

WinGD, 2018, Low-Pressure X-DF Engines FAQ, WinGD, Winterthur, Switzerland.

Proceedings of the 14th International Symposium on Process Systems Engineering – PSE 2021+
June 19-23, 2022, Kyoto, Japan © 2022 Elsevier B.V. All rights reserved.
http://dx.doi.org/10.1016/B978-0-323-85159-6.50181-0

Crude Oil Blending Process Optimization with Precise Consideration of Fraction Properties

ZHENG Wanpeng[a], GAO Xiaoyong [a*], KUI Guofeng[a], ZUO Xin[a], ZHU Guiyao[a], XIE Yi[b]

[a] *Department of Automation, College of information Science and Engineering, China University of Petroleum, Beijing 102249, CHINA*
[b]*Beijing pipeline company of national pipeline network group, Beijing 100101, CHINA*
x.gao@cup.edu.cn

Abstract

Crude oil blending process is an integral part of the petroleum supply chain, including multiple industrial processes such as crude oil distribution, transportation, storage and blending in the production process of refinery enterprises. The optimization of crude oil blending process scheduling has high academic and industrial application value, and its related research work is currently a hot topic of academic interest. However, there are still urgent problems to be solved in the current research work. Crude oil blending process not only needs to consider a variety of delivery and distribution of crude oil, but also considers the constraint conditions that the blended product meets the production demand. Therefore, based on the continuous-time representation, a crude oil blending optimization model that precisely considers the properties of the fraction is proposed in this paper. Firstly, the important achievements in the research field of crude oil blending process optimization are briefly introduced, and the development trend and defects of the current research work are summarized. Subsequently, the MINLP model is described in detail. The model especially considers the properties demand and supply demand of mixed products in the secondary process. Finally, we verified the effectiveness of the proposed model in solving the actual blending formula optimization problem. The simulation results of a real case of a fuel refinery show that a product formulation is used to optimize the crude oil blending process, which can effectively improve the overall yield of petroleum fractions while meeting the demands of the secondary processing device.

Keywords: Optimization; Model; Simulation.

1. Introduction

Due to the variety of crude oils purchased by most refineries, properties of the material exist significantly different, while the refinery requires homogeneous and stable materials to ensure the quality and yield of the subsequent secondary processing process. Therefore, the refinery mixes crude oil according to different blending formulations in proportion during the crude oil blending process, to make the material properties meet the demand of the secondary processing device. In the 1980s, to adapt to the competitive global market, oil refining enterprises began to focus on the adjustment and optimization of industrial structure and production process. Crude oil blending can improve the quality grade of oil products, and then achieve higher economic benefits for refining enterprises. Therefore, the research on crude oil blending optimization has gradually become the focus of related fields.

In recent years, many achievements have been made in the research of crude oil blending optimization. The in-house center discretization method is proposed to deal with the long-horizon tank blending scheduling problem (Beach et al., 2020). The Lagrangean decomposition algorithm is used to solve the integration of crude oil scheduling and refinery planning (Yang et al., 2020). The operation optimization of crude oil blending and intermediate oil processing is solved to achieve the collaborative optimization of materials processing and product deployment (Li et al., 2020). With desalination as a separate task, the crude oil refinery operation of feeding a single desalination tank to multiple crude oil distillation units is studied (Bayu et al., 2020). The crude oil selection scheduling optimization is solved by two-stage stochastic programming (Li et al., 2021). Zhao et al. (2017) proposed a modelling method based on priority slots for crude oil scheduling with inconsistent component concentrations. Castillo et al. (2017) proposed a global optimization algorithm to solve a continuous-time MINLP blending scheduling model. The algorithm uses piecewise McCormick relaxation and normalized multiparametric disaggregation to calculate the global optimal estimate. Menezes et al. (2017) proposed a quantitative analysis method to optimize crude oil blending in oil refining enterprises to narrow the decision-making gap between crude oil procurement and production scheduling operations. Menezes et al. (2019) integrate scheduling operation details and time steps into different types of PSE solutions to get solutions to industrial problems faster. Franzoi et al. (2018) realized the effective optimization of complex process systems by means of parameter feedback after data coordination calculation. Franzoi et al. (2019) studied the factors affecting scheduling production performance and proposed a detailed design of a hybrid scheduling and processing unit considering flexibility, responsiveness, and management capabilities.

The optimization of the crude oil blending process generally has two main points that need to be paid attention to: one is a typical scheduling problem, such as stock limitation and device processing capacity, and the other is the properties of the blended products. During the operation of the refinery, the blended product is separated by the atmospheric and vacuum distillation unit, and then become the material for the secondary processing device. Material properties that do not meet the demand of the processing devices will bring serious problems, affect the production of the factory. For example, for catalytic reforming device, when producing BTX, the required material is petroleum fraction between 60-145°C intervals. When producing high-octane gasoline, the required material is petroleum fraction between 80-200°C intervals. In addition, the catalytic reforming device has different limits on the sulfur content, nitrogen content, heavy metal content and molecular structure of the materials when producing different pro-ducts. Therefore, according to the demands of secondary processing devices, it is valuable to consider the properties of petroleum fractions precisely, but the current research work is too simple to consider the properties of petroleum fractions.

In this paper, we precisely consider the demand for secondary processing devices on the properties of materials. Inspired by Mendez's work in the field of gasoline blending optimization, based on continuous-time representation method, a crude oil blending optimization model is proposed considering the yield of blending products, sulfur content, nitrogen content, molecular structure and other properties, and minimizes the gap between the blended product and the desired product as the objective function (Mendez et al., 2006). According to an actual case, we obtained the results through program simulation, and verified that the model can be applied to different types of refining enterprises, provide reliable blending formula, and ensure that the properties of blending products can meet the demands of the secondary processing device.

2. Model description

In the production process of refining enterprises, different secondary processing devices always have different demands on the properties of petroleum fractions obtained by constant vacuum distillation of blended products. For example, catalytic cracking mainly uses heavy distillates and residuals as processing materials, while hydrocracking mainly uses VGO, CGO and residuals as processing materials. There are great differences in the properties of these petroleum fractions. In the atmospheric and vacuum distillation process, the main influencing factor that determines the distribution of petroleum distillates is to

adjust the yield of crude oil in each fraction interval. In addition, high sulfur content will cause catalyst pollution and inactivation, affect the quality of petroleum products and cause device corrosion, high nitrogen content can cause catalyst poisoning and affect the stability of petroleum products, heavy metal content (Ni+V) will cause catalyst deactivation and bed blockage, the difference in molecular structure will affect the production process and the selection of catalysts. Therefore, according to the processing demands of the secondary processing device, the model not only needs to consider the yield of the blended crude oil in each fraction, but also needs to consider whether the sulfur content, nitrogen content, heavy metal content and molecular structure in the blended crude oil meet the demand of the device.

Before presenting the proposed mathematical models, the nomenclature in the model formula is explained as follows:

Indices

e – secondary processing device
i – crude oil component
p – CDU device processed product
t – time slot

Sets

I – set of the crude oil component
P – set of CDU device processed product
T_d – set of time slots postulated for the sub-interval ending at due date d

Parameters

d – due dates of product demand
h – time horizon
w – fraction temperature
$cor_{p,t}$ – correction factor of product p in time slot t
$cp_{i,p}^{max}$, $cp_{i,p}^{min}$ – maximum/minimum concentration of component i in product p
$D_{p,d}$ – demand of product p
$D_{p_l,d}$, $D_{p_c,d}$, $D_{p_h,d}$ – demand of light/middle/heavy fraction of product p at the end
$d_{p,d}$ – demand of product p to be satisfied at due date d
f_i – constant delivery rate of component i
fr_p^{max} , fr_p^{min} – maximum/minimum flowrate of product p in time slot t
$gra_{p,t}$ – specific gravity of product p in time slot t
in_p, in_i – initial inventory of product p/component i
met_p^{max} , N_p^{max} , S_p^{max} –maximum heavy metal/nitrogen/sulfur content specified by device e
met_i , N_i , S_i – heavy metal/nitrogen/sulfur content of component i
$mst_{p,e}^{max}$, $mst_{p,e}^{min}$ – maximum/minimum molecular structure (hydrocarbon or gum composition) ratio specified by device e

mst_i – molecular structure ratio of component i

n_t – maximum number of blenders that can be working in parallel in time slot t

V_p^{max}, V_p^{min} – maximum/minimum storage capacity of product p

V_i^{max}, V_i^{min} – maximum/minimum storage capacity of component i

$vin_{p,w}$ – ideal yield of product p at temperature w

TEP_{p_l}, TEP_{p_c}, TEP_{p_h} – the initial boiling point of the light/middle/heavy fraction of product p

$TIBP_p$ – the final boiling point of product p

$TIBP_{p_l}$, $TIBP_{p_c}$, $TIBP_{p_h}$ – the final boiling point of the light/middle/heavy fraction of product p

$tbp_{p,w}^{max}$, $tbp_{p,w}^{min}$ – maximum/minimum yield of product p at temperature w

$tbp_{i,w}$ – yield of component i at temperature w

$tbploss_i$ – yield loss of component i

ρ_i – density of component i

Variables

Ap,t – binary variable denoting that product p is blended in time slot t

e_t – ending time of time slot t

$F_{i,p,t}^I$ – the amount of component i being transferred to product p in time slot t

$F_{p,t}^P$ – the amount of product p being blended in time slot t

s_t – starting time of time slot t

$V_{p,t}^P$ – the amount of product p stored at the end of time slot t

$V_{i,t}^I$, $V_{i,t}^{I'}$ – the amount of component i stored at the end/beginning of time slot t

$TBP_{p,w,t}$ – yield value of product p at time t, temperature w

$TBP_{p,i}$ – yield value of product p

TEP_p – the initial boiling point of product p

The MINLP model we proposed partitions the entire time horizon into a predefined number of sub-intervals, the length of each sub-interval will depend on the product due dates. In addition, the proposed model has the following features: 1)Divide the scheduling horizon into multiple sub-intervals, and set a set of time slots with unknown time and location for each sub-interval; 2) Assuming that the flow of components and product is constant throughout the scheduling horizon; 3) Final product properties are based on a volumetric average and a correction factor computed through the proposed iterative process; 4) A particular product demand can be satisfied by one or more periods. The constraints and variables of the model are described as follows:

2.1. Composition and material balance constraint

To ensure that the product p is mixed with the crude oil component i of a limited type, the component equation constraint is as shown in constraint (1); to meet product quality demands and crude oil supply constraints, upper and lower limits can be imposed on the component concentration of product p, as shown in Constraint (2); to ensure the material balance of product p, the constraint of material balance equation can be applied, as shown in constraints (3); to ensure the material balance of component i, the constraint of material balance equation can be applied, as shown in constraints (4) and (5).

$$\sum_i F_{i,p,t}^I = F_{p,t}^P, \forall p,t \qquad (1)$$

$$cp_{i,p}^{min} F_{p,t}^P \le F_{i,p,t}^I \le cp_{i,p}^{max} F_{p,t}^P, \forall i,p,t \qquad (2)$$

$$V_{p,t}^P = in_p + F_{p,t}^P - d_{p,d}, \forall p,t \qquad (3)$$

$$V_{i,t}^I = in_i + f_i e_t - F_{i,p,t}^I, \forall i,t \qquad (4)$$

$$V_{i,t}^{I'} = in_i + f_i s_t - F_{i,p,t}^I, \forall i,t \qquad (5)$$

2.2. Device and inventory constraint

To meet the operating limits of the device, the upper and lower limit is imposed on the volume flow of product p, as shown in constraint (6); to meet the inventory limit, the upper and lower limit constraints are imposed on the quantity of product p and component i, as shown in constraint (7), (8) and (9); to ensure the balance of the productivity of the CDU device, equation constraints are proposed as shown in (10) and (11).

$$fr_p^{min}(e_t - s_t) - fr_p^{min} h(1 - Ap,t)$$
$$\le F_{p,t}^P \le fr_p^{max}(e_t - s_t), \forall p,t \qquad (6)$$

$$V_p^{min} < V_{p,t}^P < V_p^{max}, \forall p,t \qquad (7)$$

$$V_i^{min} < V_{i,t}^I < V_i^{max}, \forall i,t \qquad (8)$$

$$V_i^{min} < V_{i,t}^{I'} < V_i^{max}, \forall i,t \qquad (9)$$

$$\sum_p TBP_{p,i} + tbploss_i = 1 \qquad (10)$$

$$TBP_{p,i} = \sum_{w=TIBP_p}^{TEP_p} tbp_{p,w} \qquad (11)$$

2.3. Supply constraint

To meet the total supply-demand of subsequent secondary processing process, a lower limit constraint can be imposed on the quantity of product p, as shown in Constraint (12); in addition, the supply constraints of light fraction, middle fraction and heavy fraction processed by CDU device are shown in constraints (13), (14) and (15); the demands for different fractions must be less than or equal to the total demand, as shown in constraint (16).

$$ini_p + \sum_{t<d} F_{p,t}^P \ge D_{p,d} \qquad (12)$$

$$\sum_{t<d} \sum_{w=TIBPp_l}^{TEPp_l} tbp_{p,w} F_{p,t}^P \ge D_{p_l,d} \qquad (13)$$

$$\sum_{t<d} \sum_{w=TIBPp_c}^{TEPp_c} tbp_{p,w} F_{p,t}^P \ge D_{p_c,d} \qquad (14)$$

$$\sum_{t<d} \sum_{w=TIBP_{p_h}}^{TEP_{p_h}} tbp_{p,w} F_{p,t}^P \geq D_{p_h,d} \quad (15)$$

$$D_{p,d} \geq D_{p_h,d} + D_{p_c,d} + D_{p_l,d} \quad (16)$$

2.4. Yield and property constraint

To meet the processing demands, the upper and lower limits can be imposed on the product yield, as shown in constraint (17); to meet the demand of secondary processing device for the properties of materials, the upper limits on sulfur content, nitrogen content, and heavy metal content (Ni+V) can be imposed, as shown in constraint (18), (19) and (20).

$$tbp_{p,w}^{\min} F_{p,t}^P \leq \sum_i tbp_{i,w} F_{i,p,t}^I$$
$$\leq tbp_{p,w}^{\max} F_{p,t}^P, \quad \forall i,p,t \quad (17)$$

$$\sum_i S_i F_{i,p,t}^I \leq S_{p,e}^{\max} F_{p,t}^P, \forall i,p,t \quad (18)$$

$$\sum_i N_i F_{i,p,t}^I \leq N_{p,e}^{\max} F_{p,t}^P, \forall i,p,t \quad (19)$$

$$\sum_i met_i F_{i,p,t}^I \leq met_{p,e}^{\max} F_{p,t}^P, \forall i,p,t \quad (20)$$

In particular, the distribution of sulfur, nitrogen and heavy metal elements is similar: with the increase of boiling point, their content will increase, mainly concentrated in residual oil. Therefore, sulfur content, nitrogen content and heavy metal content in different fractions can be estimated roughly according to the material balance equation and analytical test results.

2.5. Set of molecular structure constraints

To meet the production needs and device limitations of the secondary processing process, the upper and lower limits can be imposed on the molecular structure of the product, as shown in constraints (21) and (22).

$$mst_{p,e}^{\min} F_{p,t}^P \leq \sum_i mst_i F_{i,p,t}^I + cor_{p,t} F_{i,p,t}^I$$
$$\leq mst_{p,e}^{\max} F_{p,t}^P, \quad \forall i,p,t \quad (21)$$

$$\sum_i mst_i F_{i,p,t}^I + cor_{p,t} F_{i,p,t}^I = \frac{\sum_i mst_i \rho_i F_{i,p,t}^I}{gra_{p,t}}, \forall i,p,t \quad (22)$$

In particular, for light fraction, middle fraction and heavy fraction, the molecular structure constraints are different. For light fraction, the main molecular structure constraints include the ratio of alkanes, cycloalkanes and aromatic hydrocarbons; for middle fraction, the constraints include the ratio of alkanes, cycloalkanes, aromatic hydrocarbons and alkenes; for heavy fraction, the constraints include the ratio of saturated hydrocarbons, aromatic hydrocarbons and gums. Since the crude oil distillation process is purely physical, the molecular structure of the product depends on the concentration of the crude oil in the blending process. For the secondary processing process, molecular structure constraints are necessary, which can effectively guarantee the stable operation of processing devices and improve efficiency and profitability.

The molecular structure constraint was first proposed in the relevant research on crude oil blending optimization. Although the current constraint still needs to be compensated and corrected, the modified result can still ensure that the product properties of fractions can meet the needs of secondary processing devices, which is of great significance.

2.6. Set of time slot timing constraints

To allow more flexible solutions and avoid overlapping time slots, correct order and sequence between postulated time slots must be established through the next set of constraints. Time slot duration constraint is shown in constraint (23); time slot sequencing constraint is shown in constraint (24); sub-interval bounds constraint is shown in constraint (25) and (26); time slot assignment constraint is shown in constraint (27).

$$e_t - s_t \leq h \sum_p A_{p,t}, \forall t \quad (23)$$

$$e_t \leq s_{(t+1)}, \forall t \quad (24)$$

$$s_t \geq d-1, \forall t \quad (25)$$

$$e_t \leq d, \forall t \quad (26)$$

$$\sum_p A_{p,(t+1)} \leq n_t \sum_p A_{p,t}, \forall (t,t+1) \in T_d \quad (27)$$

2.7. Objective function

While satisfying all the above constraints, the objective function of the optimization model is to minimize the gap between the blended crude oil yield of each fraction and the expected ideal crude oil yield, as shown in equation (28).

$$\min \sum_w \left| \frac{(tbp_{p,w} - vin_{p,w})}{vin_{p,w}} \right| \quad (28)$$

In particular, the expected ideal yield $vin_{p,w}$ is the product optimal value obtained under a certain operating mode assuming that the refinery has sufficient reserves for each type of crude oil, and the inventory capacity and processing capacity of the device can meet the demands. But in reality, due to inventory, devices and other factors, the yield of ideal products is impossible to achieve.

3. Simulation case

In order to verify the effectiveness and stability of the model in solving practical problems, we use a set of real fuel-based refinery devices data for simulation, the initial product is *p*. The production materials of the fuel-based refinery device come from the petroleum distillate separated from the CDU device: the material of catalytic reforming unit is naphtha and gasoline distillate in the range of 80-200℃; the material of catalytic cracking unit is heavy distillate and residual distillate in the range of 450-530 ℃ ; the material of hydrocracking unit is CGO distillate and VGO distillate in the range of 200-450℃; the delayed coking unit the vacuum residuum fraction above 530℃. The simulation device set includes ten storage tanks, three blending tanks, one crude oil distillation unit, one catalytic reforming unit, one catalytic cracking unit, one hydrocracking unit, one delayed coking unit. The simulation components and product data set include ten crude oil components and two products. An illustrative view of the set of simulation devices is shown in Figure 1.

The yield of each component and product is divided into 23 interval ranges according to actual production needs. In the simulation process, we consider two real production situations, the first situation is that the process plan is mainly used to produce gasoline, and the by-product is liquefied petroleum gas, petroleum coke, etc., the petroleum fraction product is $p1$ at this time. The second situation is the process plan mainly produces diesel, with by-products such as gasoline, petroleum coke, etc., and the petroleum distillate product currently is $p2$.

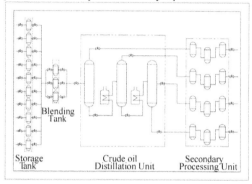

Fig.1. The illustrative view of the fuel-based refinery device

According to the optimization model proposed above, the two production situations can be expressed as minimizing the yield gap between the actual product and the ideal product in the objective function on the premise of satisfying the constraint (1-25). In order to better illustrate the results, we selected three optimization models proposed by research work related to the optimization of crude oil blending process between 2018 and 2021, and simulated and solved the above case. It should be noted that for the selected model, usually, only a few types of crude oil participate in the blending process. Therefore, increasing the types of crude oil participating in the blending process will have a huge negative impact on the solution results. In order to ensure the validity of the solution results, we performed relaxation and disaggregation on some constraints of the selection model. The solution results are compared with the model proposed in this paper. Table.1. details the product yield in a specific distillation interval according to the solution results.

Table.1. Product yield in specific distillation interval

Product name	p	p^*	$p(m)$	$p(m1)$	$p(m2)$	$p(m3)$
The first situation: mainly produce gasoline						
80-100°C interval	2.97	4.95	4.41	4.12	3.62	4.00
100-130°C interval	4.65	6.25	5.85	5.56	5.18	5.47
130-160°C interval	4.73	6.00	5.76	5.42	5.16	5.51
160-180°C interval	3.55	3.84	3.78	3.72	3.64	3.66
180-200°C interval	2.97	3.09	3.09	3.04	3.01	3.04
80-200°C interval	18.87	24.13	22.89	21.86	20.60	21.68

The second situation: mainly produce diesel						
350-365°C interval	2.70	2.53	2.60	2.60	2.52	2.68
365-395°C interval	4.35	4.65	4.46	4.52	4.46	4.47
395-425°C interval	4.94	5.28	5.17	5.03	5.09	4.98
425-460°C interval	4.28	4.89	4.72	4.43	4.57	4.38
460-475°C interval	2.43	2.65	2.58	2.46	2.47	2.49
475-500°C interval	3.49	3.62	3.62	3.59	3.54	3.57
350-500°C interval	22.19	23.61	23.14	22.61	22.65	22.57

(p - Initial blended product; p^* - Blended product with ideal yield; $p(m)$ - Blended product optimized by the model proposed in this paper; $p(m1)$, $p(m2)$, $p(m3)$ - Blended products were optimized by the models proposed in the other three papers)

Solved by the simulation program, the gap of gasoline fraction yield between $p(m)$ and p^* is 0.23, and the yield of the fraction used to produce gasoline is increased by 4.02% compared to the original product p; the gap of diesel fraction yield between $p(m)$ and p^* is 0.62, and the yield of the fraction used to produce diesel is increased by 0.95% compared to the yield of the original product p. Compared to the model proposed in this paper, the blended products obtained by the other three optimization models have a larger gap with the ideal product, and the target fractional yield is less improved than the initial product: the gap of gasoline fraction yield between $p(m1)$, $p(m2)$, $p(m3)$ and p^* is 2.27, 3.52, 2.45, and the yield of the fraction used to produce gasoline is increased by 2.99%, 1.73%, 2.82% compared to the original product p; the gap of diesel fraction yield between $p(m1)$, $p(m2)$, $p(m3)$ and p^* is 1.00, 0.94, 1.04, and the yield of the fraction used to produce diesel is increased by 0.42%, 0.46%, 0.38% compared to the yield of the original product p. The comparison between the $p(m1)$, $p(m2)$, $p(m3)$ and $p(m)$ is shown in Figure 2 and Figure 3.

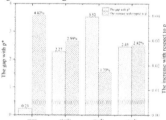

Figure.2. Simulation result comparison of the first situation

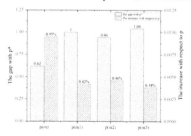

Figure.3. Simulation result comparison of the second situation

According to the comparison of simulation results, the optimization model proposed by us can effectively reduce the yield gap between the blended product and the expected ideal product, and ensure that the properties of the blended product are stable. And in different cases, our model improved the yield of the blended product in the ideal fraction, effectively optimized the product distribution of the blended product after being processed by the CDU unit, and then met the material requirements of the subsequent secondary processing unit. Combined with the previous simulation results, we verified the effectiveness of the proposed model in solving the actual blending formula optimization problem, and can reduce the fluctuation of distillate properties, improve the yield of distillate required by the secondary processing unit, greatly improve the production efficiency of oil refining enterprises, and ensure the stable operation of production and processing.

4. Conclusions

This paper first briefly summarizes the main research results and progress in the field of crude oil blending optimization in recent years. Subsequently, this paper considers the constraints of typical scheduling issues such as material balance, device constraints, and inventory constraints in the crude oil blending process. On this basis, it also considers the product yield, sulfur content, nitrogen content, heavy metal content and molecular structure constraints. These constraints are closely related to the secondary processing process. A MINLP model based on continuous-time representation is described in detail through constraints and variables. Finally, through simulation, this paper verifies that the model has certain advantages in maximizing the yield of the target fractionation interval. It can provide refiners with more accurate blending plans, optimize blended crude oil formulas, and meet the demands of subsequent secondary processing devices. However, current research work also has shortcomings. The model we proposed does not consider the economic benefits of the entire blending process, which leads to the higher cost of the crude oil blending formula. In the next stage, we will consider the multi-objective optimization of the economic benefits and properties of the crude oil blending process.

Acknowledgements

This research was supported by the National Natural Science Foundation of China (No. 22178383, 21706282), and the Research Foundation of China University of Petroleum (Beijing) (No. 2462020BJRC004, 2462020YXZZ023).

Reference

B.Beach, R.Hildebrand, K.Ellis, B.Lebreton.
An Approximate Method for the Optimization of Long-Horizon Tank Blending and Scheduling Operations.
Computers & Chemical Engineering (2020)
DOI: 10.1016/j.compchemeng.2020.106839

H.Yang, D.E.Bernal, R.E.Franzoi, F.G.Engineer, K.Kwon, S.Lee, I.E.Grossmann.
Integration of Crude-oil Scheduling and Refinery Planning by Lagrangean Decomposition.
Computers & Chemical Engineering(2020)
DOI: 10.1016/j.compchemeng.2020.106812

M.Li.
Refinery Operations Optimization Integrated Production Process and Gasoline Blending.
Journal of Physics: Conference Series(2020)
DOI: 10.1088/1742-6596/1626/1/012111

F.Bayu, M.A.Shaik, M.Ramteke.
Scheduling of Crude oil Refinery Operation with Desalting as a Separate Task.
Asia-Pacific Journal of Chemical Engineering (2020)
DOI: 10.1002/apj.2539

F.Li, F.Qian, W.Du, M.Yang, J.Long, V.Mahalec.
Refinery Production Planning Optimization under Crude oil Quality Uncertainty.
Computers & Chemical Engineering(2021)
DOI: 10.1016/j.compchemeng.2021.107361

Y.Zhao, N.Wu, Z.Li.
A Novel Solution Approach to Scheduling of Crude-oil Operations Based on An Improved Continuous-time Formulation.
2017 IEEE 14th International Conference on Networking, Sensing and Control. May 16-18, 2017, Calabria, Italy.
DOI: 10.1109/ICNSC.2017.8000140

P.A.C.Castillo, P.M.Castro, V.Mahalec.
Global Optimization of Nonlinear Blend-scheduling Problems.
Engineering(2017)
DOI: 10.1016/J.ENG.2017.02.005

B.C.Menezes, I.E.Grossmann, J.D.Kelly..
Enterprise-wide Optimization for Operations of Crude-oil Refineries: Closing the Orocurement and Scheduling Gap.
Computer Aided Chemical Engineering(2017)
DOI: 10.1016/B978-0-444-63965-3.50210-5

B.C.Menezes, J.D.Kelly.
High-quality Blend Scheduling Solution for Sizing, Selecting, Sequencing, Slotting and Spotting in the Processing Industries.
Computer Aided Chemical Engineering(2019)
DOI: 10.1016/B978-0-12-818634-3.50303-9

R.E.Franzoi, B.C.Menezes, J.D.Kelly, J.W.Gut.
Effective Scheduling of Complex Process-shops Using Online Parameter Feedback in Crude-oil Refineries.
Computer Aided Chemical Engineering(2018)
DOI: 10.1016/B978-0-444-64241-7.50208-1

R.E.Franzoi, B.C.Menezes, J.D.Kelly, J.W.Gut.
Design for Online Process and Blend Scheduling Optimization.
Computer Aided Chemical Engineering(2019)
DOI: 10.1016/B978-0-12-818597-1.50030-8

C.A.Mendez, I.E.Grossmann, I.Harjunkoski, P.Kabore.
A Simultaneous Optimization Approach for Off-line Blending and Scheduling of Oil-refinery Operations.
Computers & Chemical Engineering (2006)
DOI: 10.1016/j.compchemeng.2005.11.004.

Proceedings of the 14ᵗʰ International Symposium on Process Systems Engineering – PSE 2021+
June 19-23, 2022, Kyoto, Japan © 2022 Elsevier B.V. All rights reserved.
http://dx.doi.org/10.1016/B978-0-323-85159-6.50182-2

Novel Design of Optimum Heat Exchanger Networks for Textile Dyeing Process to Maximize Wastewater Heat Recovery Efficiency

Yurim Kim[a§], Jonghun Lim[a,b§], Hyungtae Cho[a], Juwon Lee[a,b], Il Moon[b], Junghwan Kim[a*]

[a]Green Materials and Process R&D Group, Korea Institute of Industrial Technology, 55, Jonga-ro, Jung-gu, Ulsan 44413, Republic of Korea
[b]Department of Chemical and Biomolecular Engineering, Yonsei University, 50, Yonsei-ro, Seodaemun-gu, Seoul 03722, Republic of Korea
[§]Yurim Kim and Jonghun Lim contributed equally to this work as first authors.
kjh31@kitech.re.kr

Abstract

The current dyeing process uses steam to heat the fresh water used for reactive dyeing. After the dyeing process, the wastewater is forcibly cooled and discharged for biological treatment. A large amount of energy is consumed for heating the fresh water and cooling the wastewater owing to the absence of a heat recovery process. This study suggests a novel design of optimum heat exchanger networks for textile dyeing process to maximize wastewater heat recovery efficiency. First, a process model was developed by integrating a heat exchanger with a heat pump. The model was designed to recover high-temperature and low-temperature wastewater through a heat exchanger and a heat pump, respectively. Second, the heat exchanger network of the developed process model was retrofitted based on pinch analysis to reduce operating costs. From the simulation results, the hot and cold utility consumption of the proposed model was quantitatively analyzed. Finally, a techno-economic analysis (TEA) was conducted to confirm the appropriateness of the proposed process model. The total annualized cost (TAC), based on the equivalent annual cost and the total product cost, was determined for both the current and potential future economies. As a result, the TAC was reduced by 43.2 %, and the economic efficiency of the proposed energy-saving measures demonstrates a payback period (PBP) of up to 0.65 y.

Keywords: Textile dyeing process; Wastewater heat recovery; Modeling, Analysis, and Simulation; Heat integration; Techno-economic analysis.

1. Introduction

The exhaust dyeing method is commonly used in the textile dyeing process for increased productivity. Here, a reactive dye is dissolved in a solution containing cellulose fibers, and is fixed to the surface of the fiber. The advantage of this method is that a large amount of fibers can be dyed over a short period. However, the fresh water must be heated for reactive dyeing, and the wastewater must be forcibly cooled for biological treatment after the dyeing process, resulting in high operating costs. To reduce the high operating costs, active research has been undertaken recently to recover the heat from the large amount of wastewater discharged and reuse it in the dyeing process. This is because the discharged wastewater has a significant amount of heat that can be recycled, so if it is used to preheat fresh water, operating costs for heating fresh water and cooling wastewater can be reduced. Rakib et al. (2017) reduced the operating costs of 47,100 $/y by installing a counter-flow heat exchanger to utilize the wastewater heat during the dyeing process. They confirmed the feasibility of installing a heat exchanger through a short payback period (PBP) of approximately 11 months. Pulat et al. (2009) reduced the total annualized cost (TAC) by 423,837 $/y by designing a system that recovered the heat of the collected wastewater. They confirmed the validity of the wastewater heat recovery (WWHR) system through a PBP of approximately four months.

Despite the contributions of conventional WWHR systems to increase energy efficiency, several challenges remain. First, because the textile industry discharges wastewater at different temperatures over time, the energy efficiency of the WWHR system varies depending on how the wastewater heat is recovered. However, few studies have considered the various method of recovering heat from wastewater. Second, the conventionally developed WWHR system is not optimally configured, so the energy recovery efficiency cannot be maximized. Thus, heat recovery from wastewater in different ways and maximizing the energy recovery efficiency by optimally configuring a WWHR system is crucial.

To address these challenges, we propose a novel design of optimum heat exchanger networks for textile dyeing process to maximize WWHR efficiency. First, to improve the energy efficiency of the WWHR system, a process model was designed to recover high-temperature wastewater through a heat exchanger and low-temperature wastewater through a heat pump. Second, to maximize the energy efficiency of the wastewater, the heat exchanger network of the developed process model was modified through pinch analysis. Finally, techno-economic analysis (TEA) was conducted to confirm the appropriateness of the proposed process.

The novelty of this study is as follows. First, the WWHR system integrated a heat pump with a heat exchanger is proposed for the first time to improve heat recovery efficiency. Second, since the developed WWHR system was modified by pinch analysis to maximize heat recovery efficiency, this study can contribute to economic and environmental improvement in the textile dyeing industry.

2. Process description

Currently, the textile industry is largely classified into the pre-treatment, dyeing, and after-treatment processes to improve the quality of the final dyed products. First, in the pre-treatment process composed of bleaching, washing, and acidification, bleaching agents are used to remove impurities in the fibers that interfere with dyeing and to make the fibers white. Second, in the dyeing process, the fibers whose impurities have been removed are dyed. Finally, in the after-treatment process, consisting of cold rinsing, washing, hot rinsing, and finishing, reactive dyes and residues in the dyed fabric are removed. Table 1 shows the operation time, discharged wastewater temperature, and flow rate during each stage of the textile industry.

Table 1. The operation time, temperature and flow rate during each stage of the discharged wastewater

	Process	Process time [min]	Temperature [°C]	Mass flow rate [kg/h]
1	Bleaching	30	96	2,900
2	Washing	20	96	4,350
3	Acidification	10	50	8,700

4	Dyeing	60	96	1,450
5	Cold rinsing	10	30	8,700
6	Washing	20	90	4,350
7	Hot rinsing	10	70	8,700
8	Finishing	20	40	4,350

The dyeing process was performed in several steps. First, the fresh water was heated from 18 °C to 60 °C before the dyeing process, and then with reactive dyes, additives, and fabrics, it was heated to 96 °C to operate the dyeing process. Finally, because the wastewater discharged at each stage contains chemicals such as reactive dyes, discharging without additional treatment can have a fatal impact on the environment. Therefore, to treat the dyeing wastewater discharged from each stage, it was cooled to 40 °C.

3. Methodology

3.1. Development of the process model

In this study, Aspen Plus V 11.0 was used to model a process model of the WWHR system. In the process model, the Peng-Robinson equation was used as the thermodynamic model to consider the equilibrium among the various mixed substances in dyeing wastewater.

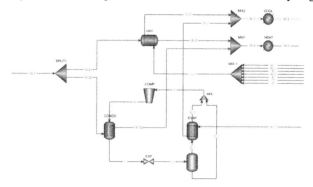

Figure 1. Process model of the WWHR system

Figure 1 presents the process model of the WWHR system. To recover the heat from the wastewater discharged at different temperatures and flow rates over time efficiently, a heat pump was used when the temperature of the wastewater was below 30 °C. Above this temperature, the heat was recovered through a heat exchanger (Kemp, 2007). Finally, to satisfy the target temperature of wastewater and fresh water, they were passed through a cooler and a heater, respectively.

3.2. Model modification by pinch analysis

The process model of the WWHR system was modified by pinch analysis to increase its energy efficiency. This method is used to modify the configuration of the heat exchanger network (HEN) to increase the efficiency of the heat recovery process. The more the energy recovery from the heat exchange between the streams, the lower the energy consumption, thus lowering the operating costs. However, the capital cost of the heat recovery process increases with increasing the heat exchange area to exchange more heat; thus, there is a trade-off relationship between the capital cost and the operating cost. Therefore, it is crucial to apply the supertargeting method that derives the targets of designing a cost-optimal heat recovery process with improved energy efficiency to pinch analysis.

In this study, first, after deriving the cost-optimal pinch point through supertargeting, the energy target, heat transfer area target, the number of units target, and cost targets for the process modification were obtained. Then, the process was modified according to the targets by re-sequencing and re-piping existing heat exchangers, installing a new heat exchanger, and adding a stream split.

3.3. Techno-economic analysis

In this section, the TEA was conducted to confirm the feasibility of the proposed WWHR system through pinch analysis. The TAC and PBP of the proposed WWHR system were calculated by considering both the capital cost and the operating costs. The equations for the TAC and PBP are as follows (Eqs. 1-3) (Lim et al., 2021):

$$TAC = AF \times CC + OC \tag{1}$$

$$AF = \frac{\left(\frac{ROR}{100}\right) \times \left(1 + \frac{ROR}{100}\right)^{PL}}{\left(1 + \frac{ROR}{100}\right)^{PL} - 1} \tag{2}$$

$$PBP = \frac{CC}{OC - OC_0} \tag{3}$$

where CC and OC represent the capital cost and operating cost of WWHR system, respectively. AF, ROR, and PL represent the annualization factor, rate of return, and plant life, respectively. This study assumed a ROR of 10 % and a PL of 5 years. OC_0 represents the operating cost of the conventional dyeing process in the textile industry without a WWHR system.

4. Results and discussion

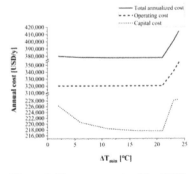

Figure 2. The cost targets of the HEN according to ΔT_{min}

Table 2. Model modification targets at cost-optimal ΔT_{min}

Targets	Units	Value
Heat exchanger area	m^2	25.9
The number of units	-	4
Hot utility	kJ/h	3,916,942
Cold utility	kJ/h	-
Capital cost	$/y	217,569
Operating cost	$/y	320,285
TAC	$/y	377,679

Figure 2 shows the cost targets of the HEN of the WWHR system process model according to ΔT_{min}. First, the operating cost when ΔT_{min} of the HEN falls below 21.46 °C does not change by the threshold problem requiring only hot utilities because the heat exchange between the streams is sufficient. However, if ΔT_{min} is higher than 21.46 °C, the operating cost increases because both hot and cold utilities are required. Therefore, when ΔT_{min} falls below 21.46 °C, the operating cost does not change, but it increases when ΔT_{min} is higher than 21.46 °C. Second, the capital cost of the HEN increases as ΔT_{min} decreases. If ΔT_{min} becomes higher than 21.46 °C, the capital cost of the HEN also increases because both the heater and the cooler are required. Therefore, the cost-optimal ΔT_{min} of the HEN of the proposed process model was 21.46 °C. Table 2 lists the model modification targets at the cost-optimal ΔT_{min}.

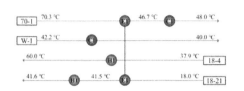

Figure 3. Grid diagram – HEN of the WWHR system before modification

Figure 4. Grid diagram – HEN of the WWHR system after modification

Figure 3 shows the grid diagram – HEN of the WWHR system before modification, and Fig. 4 shows the grid diagram – HEN of the WWHR system after modification according to Table 2.

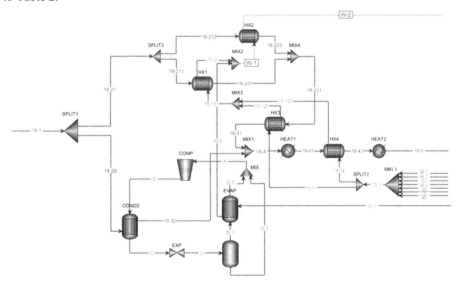

Figure 5. Modified process model of the WWHR system

Table 3. The specification of the modified process model of the WWHR system

	Units	Value
Heat exchanger area of HEN	m^2	27.3
The number of units of HEN	-	6
Hot utility of HEN	kJ/h	3,916,942

Cold utility of HEN	kJ/h	-
Total capital cost	$	217,569
Total operating cost	$/y	320,285
TAC	$/y	377,679

Figure 5 shows the modified process model of the WWHR system, and Table 3 shows the specifications of the HEN modification results. As a result, the TAC of the suggested WWHR system was $ 377,679, which reduced the TAC by 43.2 % compared to the conventional textile industry. Also, the PBP of the proposed WWHR system was 0.65 y, confirming the feasibility in applying the WWHR system to the textile industry.

5. Conclusions

In this study, we propose a novel design of an optimum WWHR system in the textile industry to maximize energy efficiency. This study makes two major contributions to the literature. First, this work is the first attempt to integrate a heat exchanger with a heat pump to effectively recover wastewater heat. Second, a pinch approach is suggested to maximize the energy efficiency of the WWHR system. Through this novel 2-step approach, the optimum WWHR system reduced the TAC by 43.2 % compared to the conventional textile industry without the WWHR system, and the PBP was 0.65 y confirming the validity of the proposed system. This study provides a guideline for future WWHR system designs.

Acknowledgements

This work was supported by the Korean Institute of Industrial Technology within the framework of the following projects: "Development of Global Optimization System for Energy Process [grant number EM-21-0022, IR-21-0029, IZ-21-0052]" and "Development of complex parameter smart analysis modules for color customering [grant number EH-21-0008]"

References

M.I. Rakib, R. Saidur, E.N. Mohamad, A.M. Afifi, Waste-heat utilization – The sustainable technologies to minimize energy consumption in Bangladesh textile sector, J. Clean. Prod. 142 (2017) 1867–1876. https://doi.org/10.1016/j.jclepro.2016.11.098.

E. Pulat, A.B. Etemoglu, M. Can, Waste-heat recovery potential in Turkish textile industry: Case study for city of Bursa, Renew. Sustain. Energy Rev. 13 (2009) 663–672. https://doi.org/10.1016/j.rser.2007.10.002.

I.C. Kemp, 3 - Data extraction and energy targeting, in: I.C. Kemp (Ed.), Pinch Anal. Process Integr. (Second Ed., Second Edi, Butterworth-Heinemann, Oxford, 2007: pp. 41–98. https://doi.org/https://doi.org/10.1016/B978-075068260-2.50008-0.

Lim, J., Jeong, S., Kim, J., Deep neural network-based optimal selection and blending ratio of waste seashells as an alternative to high-grade limestone depletion for SOX capture and utilization, Chem. Eng. J. 133244 (2021). https://doi.org/10.1016/j.cej.2021.133244

Proceedings of the 14th International Symposium on Process Systems Engineering – PSE 2021+
June 19-23, 2022, Kyoto, Japan © 2022 Elsevier B.V. All rights reserved.
http://dx.doi.org/10.1016/B978-0-323-85159-6.50183-4

Study on the Kinetic Parameters of Crystallization Process Modelled by Partial Differential Equations

Jiali Ai[a], Jindong Dai[a], Jianmin Liu[a], Chi Zhai[b*] and Wei Sun[a*]

[a]College of Chemical Engineering, Beijing University of Chemical Technology, North Third Ring Road 15, Chaoyang District, Beijing and 100029,China
[b] Kunming University of Science and Technology, 727 South Jingming Road, Chenggong District, Kunming and 650500, China
zhaichi@kmust.edu.cn, sunwei@mail.buct.edu.cn

Abstract

The physical properties of the crystal are affected by the crystal morphology, and the morphology will be affected by the crystallization environment. To obtain the expected physical properties, it is necessary to study the relationship between crystal growth conditions and crystal morphology. As snowflake is rich in crystal morphology, it is very suitable for studying this relationship. Crystal growth kinetics can be used to explore the mechanism of how the crystal growth conditions influence on crystal morphology. However, due to the impact of growth conditions in both time and space coordinates, it is difficult to identify the kinetic parameters of the crystallization process. In this work, the dynamic equation of snowflake growth was established through data regression, and the relationship between snowflake morphology and snowflake growth conditions was studied. In general, cellular automata (CA) is used to simulate the growth process of snowflakes, and the data of whether different positions are in crystallization state and the change of water vapor density with time are extracted, so as to avoid the interference of complex growth conditions on the growth data. Then, data are regressed from the perspective of the reaction-diffusion system, and the crystallization kinetics in the form of partial differential equation (PDE) related to time and space is obtained. This equation is solved by finite difference method to simulate the complex snowflake morphology under different conditions, to analyse the influence of different reaction rate and diffusion rate on the crystal morphology. This work provides a new way to study how crystal morphology is impacted by process parameters, which could be a reference for the planning of crystallization experiments to obtain the specified crystal morphology.

Keywords: Crystal morphology; Reaction-diffusion system; Crystal growth kinetics; Finite difference method.

1. Introduction

Crystallization is an important unit operation in the chemical industry. Different growth conditions during the crystallization process, such as solvent, temperature, supersaturation, etc., will impact the crystal morphology, which is an important factor to determine the physical properties of crystals, including melting point, solubility and dissolution rate (Variankaval et al., 2008). These changes not only affect subsequent process operations, but also cause differences in crystal quality. Therefore, how to prepare crystals with specific morphology is becoming more and more important in academia and industry (Yang and Han, 2016).

Crystal growth kinetics can be employed to predict the crystal morphology by its growth conditions, so it is very helpful for exploring methods to control the morphology of crystals. However, it is difficult to find a suitable growth kinetics equation to describe it. With the development of computer technology and data-based methods, it provides a new way to find the kinetic equation for crystal growth, bypassing the complicated mechanism. Nonlinear dynamic partial differential equation function identification (PDE-FIND) is such a method proposed by Samuel H. Rudy in 2017. It finds the governing partial differential equation(s) of a given system by sparse regression of time series measurements in spatial domain and has been successfully applied to reaction-diffusion systems. From the perspective of systems engineering, the crystallization process can be regarded as a generalized reaction-diffusion system, as the process of solute attaching to the surface of the growing crystal and changing phase is considered as a reaction, and the process of solute moving randomly to the surface of crystal is treated as diffusion. Both are important factors affecting the crystal morphology (Wang et al., 2013). Therefore, this method can be used to explore the crystallization kinetic equation.

Snowflakes are ice crystals that grow from water vapor. They form a large number of exquisite, symmetrical, and complex patterns in atmosphere, with rich crystal morphologies (Libbrecht, 2017). At the same time, it is almost only affected by the density of water vapor in the atmosphere. Therefore, snowflake is a good research object for exploring crystallization conditions and crystal morphology. In order to obtain the crystallization kinetic equation, it is necessary to obtain the dynamic information of solid-liquid two phases, especially the accurate measurement of water vapor density data. However, there are several difficulties in obtaining the accurate real-time data because of the error of the crystal growth in the experiment, and the challenges of identifying the crystallinity, concentration and density in the solution from the actual images. With the fast development of computer technology, crystallization process can be simulated with appropriate computational tools. Therefore, it is possible to study and fit the kinetic equation based on simulated crystallization data. In our previous work, the snowflake growth process was simulated by cellular automata (CA) (Liu et al., 2020).

In this work, the relationship between crystal growth conditions and crystal morphology, especially the effects of diffusion coefficient and reaction coefficient on crystal morphology, is discussed by establishing a kinetic equation, which is obtained from the process data of snowflake growth. The paper is organized as follows: in the Section 2, how to obtain water vapor density data through simulated images is introduced, including a CA method for simulating an ideal snowflake formation system. Then, PDE-FIND algorithm is used to find the dynamic equation of this process, which is put into the Section 3. In the Section 4, the kinetic equation is divided into two parts: diffusion and reaction, and the effects of each part on snowflake morphology are discussed respectively. The last part is a summary of the full work.

2. Data for snowflake formation process: CA simulation

For the snowflake formation process, its morphology is closely related to the water vapor density. If the water vapor density during the formation of snowflakes is recorded as an image, a series of real images of crystal growth process can be used as data for studying crystal crystallization kinetics. However, it is still hard to experimentally obtain such images in time series with the required quality for model establishment according to literatures. Here, images of snowflake growth under ideal conditions simulated by CA were chosen as the substitute for the real picture of snowflake growth.

First of all, in order to establish the model, the ideal system is framed by selecting fewer variables and parameters for research. The system is assumed with a constant temperature and unaffected by impurities. Without considering the influence of stirring and the external environment of the crystallizer on the crystallization process and crystal dissolution, the ideal process of crystallization of water vapor into snowflakes is simulated. According to the conservation of mass and classical diffusion theory, the rules of CA are established. The model mainly consists of two variables, water vapor density α and three-dimensional increment β. References for specific simulation methods is available in the work of Liu (2020) et al. . Here, the model parameters $\alpha = 0.4$ and $\beta = 0$ are selected, and the result is shown in Fig.1.

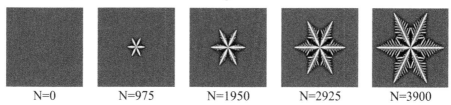

| N=0 | N=975 | N=1950 | N=2925 | N=3900 |

Fig.1. Simulated time series of snowflake growth by CA, where water vapor density $\alpha = 0.4$ and three-dimensional increment $\beta = 0$. N represents different simulation time steps.

Matlab is used to encode and integrate the data. By identifying the grey value of each point in the simulated image, the water vapor density and crystallization state are obtained. Therefore, an image can be converted into a two-dimensional data matrix, in which each element of the matrix corresponds to one pixel, and a large three-dimensional array is obtained from a series of images with equal time intervals. In order to show the snowflake growth mechanism better and remove the influence of the background on PDE recognition, only the 80×80 pixel area in the centre of images are identified, and the images here are 100 images with 10 time step interval.

3. The dynamic equation of snowflake formation based on data: the establishment of partial differential equations

In order to obtain the dynamical equations of the snowflake reaction-diffusion system, the PDE-FIND algorithm proposed by Rudy et al. is applied to obtain the partial differential equations of time and space. For this algorithm program, the data at each position in the time series are collected and numerically differentiated, and then the data are combined into a large matrix, and PDE candidates are also combined. Specific calculation methods and mathematical details are in Rudy 's work. The data in the three-dimensional array obtained in the second part are imported into the PDE-FIND algorithm program and got the PDEs as follows.

$$\frac{dn}{dt} = a_1 n^3 + b_1 n^2 + c_1 n + d_1 + (a_2 n^3 + b_2 n^2 + c_2 n + d_2)(\frac{\partial n}{\partial x} + \frac{\partial n}{\partial y}) +$$
$$(a_3 n^3 + b_3 n^2 + c_3 n + d_3)(\frac{\partial^2 n}{\partial x^2} + \frac{\partial^2 n}{\partial y^2}) + (a_4 n^3 + b_4 n^2 + c_4 n + d_4)(\frac{\partial^2 n}{\partial x \partial y}) \tag{1}$$

$a_1 = 1.3 \times 10^{-3}$ $a_2 = -9.2 \times 10^{-2}$ $a_3 = 8.4 \times 10^{-2}$ $a_4 = 3.7 \times 10^{-2}$

$b_1 = 1.5 \times 10^{-3}$ $b_2 = 2.0 \times 10^{-2}$ $b_3 = -2.0 \times 10^{-2}$ $b_4 = -1.2 \times 10^{-2}$

$$c_1 = -1.5 \times 10^{-3} \quad c_2 = 7.3 \times 10^{-2} \quad c_3 = -7.6 \times 10^{-2} \quad c_4 = -2.5 \times 10^{-2}$$

$$d_1 = 0 \quad d_2 = 5.6 \times 10^{-6} \quad d_3 = -2.8 \times 10^{-6} \quad d_4 = -4.2 \times 10^{-6}$$

The finite difference (FD) method is used to discretize and approximate the partial differential term. For the Laplace operator, a five-point difference scheme is adopted, and forward difference method is adopted for the rest. The specific difference format is shown in the Eq.(2-5). The time interval θ is 0.01, and the space interval h is 0.5. The simulation results are shown in Fig.2.

$$\frac{dn}{dt} = \frac{n(i,j)^{t+1} - n(i,j)^t}{\theta} \tag{2}$$

$$\frac{\partial n}{\partial x} + \frac{\partial n}{\partial y} = \frac{(n(i-1,j)^t - n(i+1,j)^t + n(i,j-1)^t - n(i,j+1)^t)}{2h} \tag{3}$$

$$\frac{\partial^2 n}{\partial x^2} + \frac{\partial^2 n}{\partial y^2} = \frac{1}{h^2}(n(i-1,j)^t + n(i+1,j)^t + n(i,j-1)^t + n(i,j+1)^t - 4n(i,j)^t) \tag{4}$$

$$\frac{\partial^2 n}{\partial x \partial y} = \frac{1}{h^2}(n(i-1,j-1)^t + n(i+1,j+1)^t + n(i+1,j-1)^t + n(i-1,j+1)^t - 4n(i,j)^t) \tag{5}$$

| a | b1: N=100 | b2: N=200 | b3: N=300 | b4: N=500 |

Fig.2. Simulated time series of snowflake growth by FD, where water vapor density $\alpha = 0.4$ and three-dimensional increment $\beta = 0$. N represents different simulation time steps. a: compare the pictures in Figure 1 and Figure 2 when the time step is 3900. b: Simulation results at different time steps.

It can be seen that the simulation result in Fig.2(b) is similar to those of CA method in Fig.1. Therefore, the equation is considered to be the kinetic equation of snowflake crystal growth when the water vapor density is 0.4.

4. The influence of process parameters on snowflakes morphology: from the perspective of the reaction-diffusion system

From a mathematical point of view, the reaction-diffusion system can be described by the following equation:

$$\frac{dx}{dt} = \nabla^2 x + F(x) \tag{6}$$

According to Eq.(6), the position-independent part in Eq.(1) is regarded as the reaction term denoted by $g(n)$, and the position-related part is regarded as the diffusion term denoted by $f(n)$. Then $f(n)$ and $g(n)$ are as Eq.(7) and Eq.(8), respectively.

$$f(n) = (a_2n^3 + b_1n^2 + c_1n + d_1)(\frac{\partial n}{\partial x} + \frac{\partial n}{\partial y}) + (a_3n^3 + b_1n^2 + c_1n +$$

$$d_1)(\frac{\partial^2 n}{\partial x^2} + \frac{\partial^2 n}{\partial y^2}) + (a_4n^3 + b_1n^2 + c_1n + d_1)(\frac{\partial^2 n}{\partial x\partial y})$$

$$(7)$$

$$g(n) = a_1n^3 + b_1n^2 + c_1n + d_1 \tag{8}$$

4.1. The influence of reaction parameters on the morphology of snowflakes

The reaction related terms were multiplied by 0.9 and 1.1 respectively, and simulated by the finite difference method to study the effect of the change of the reaction coefficient on the morphology of the snowflake. The simulation results are shown in Fig.3 and Fig.4.

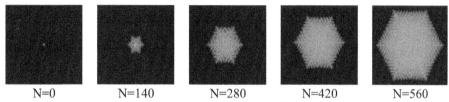

| N=0 | N=140 | N=280 | N=420 | N=560 |

Fig 3. Simulated time series of snowflake growth by FD, where g(n) × 0.9 and f(n) not changed.

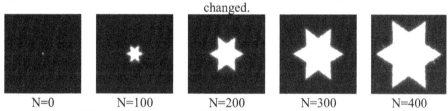

| N=0 | N=100 | N=200 | N=300 | N=400 |

Fig 4. Simulated time series of snowflake growth by FD, where g(n) × 1.1 and f(n) not changed.

It can be seen that with the increase of reaction rate, snowflakes tend to form very dense hexagons, while when the reaction rate decreases, snowflakes tend to form hexagons with obvious branching.

4.2. The influence of diffusion parameters on the morphology of snowflakes

The diffusion related terms were multiplied by 0.99 and 1.01 respectively, and simulated by the finite difference method to study the effect of the change of the deffusion coefficient on the morphology of the snowflake. The simulation results are shown in Fig.5 and Fig.6.

| N=0 | N=130 | N=260 | N=390 | N=520 |

Fig 5. Simulated time series of snowflake growth by FD, where f(n) × 0.99 and g(n) not changed. N represents different simulation time steps.

It can be seen that as the increase of diffusion rate, snowflakes tend to form hexagons with obvious branches, while when the diffusion rate decreases, snowflakes tend to form tight branches of hexagons.

N=0   N=120   N=240   N=360   N=480

Fig 6. Simulated time series of snowflake growth by FD, where f(n) × 1.01 and g(n) not changed. N represents different simulation time steps.

5. Conclusions

In this paper, the reaction-diffusion equation of snowflake formation is established by using the method of data regression, and the effects of different reaction rates and diffusion rates on the morphology of snowflakes are studied. The ideal state of the snowflake growth images simulated by CA is used as a substitute for the real image to obtain the time series data in the spatial domain. Meanwhile, by adjusting the diffusion and reaction coefficients in the kinetic equation, different snowflake morphologies are formed. With the increase of the reaction rate, snowflakes tend to form very compact hexagons, and on the contrary, dendrites become sparser. When the diffusion rate is high, snowflakes are more likely to form with distinct branches and buds, and conversely, the branches are denser. In other words, if a crystal product with a sparse network structure is a better choice, some methods could be used to achieve this, such as changing the medium to gel to increase the diffusion rate; If a crystal product with a dense block structure is a better choice, some methods could be used to realize this, such as increasing the degree of supersaturation and lowering the crystallization temperature to increasing the reaction rate. By studying the formation of different crystal morphologies in the crystallization system under the adjustment of diffusion and reaction rate, it is hoped to provide reference for the reasonable synthesis and structural design of materials.

Acknowledgements: The National Natural Science Foundation of China (Grant No. 21878012).

References

K. G. Libbrecht, 2017, Physical Dynamics of Ice Crystal Growth, Annual Reviews, 47, 271-295.

J. Liu, J. Dai, C. Han, J. Zhang, J. Ai, C. Zhai, X. Liu, W. Sun, 2020, Simulation of the Crystallization Process based on Cellular Automata--- Snowflake Formation from Pure Water System, 30th European Symposium on Computer Aided Process Engineering.

S. H. Rudy, S. L. Brunton, J. L. Proctor, J. N. Kutz, 2017, Data-driven discovery of partial differential equations, Science Advances, 3, 4, e1602614.

N. Variankaval, A. S. Cote, M. F. Doherty, 2008, From form to function: Crystallization of active pharmaceutical ingredients, AIChE Journal, 54, 7, 1682-1688.

H. Wang, Y. Han, J. Li, 2013, Dominant Role of Compromise between Diffusion and Reaction in the Formation of Snow-Shaped Vaterite, Crystal Growth & Design, 13, 5, 1820-1825.

T. Yang, Y. Han, 2016, Quantitatively Relating Diffusion and Reaction for Shaping Particles, Crystal Growth & Design, 16, 5, 2850-2859.

Proceedings of the 14th International Symposium on Process Systems Engineering – PSE 2021+
June 19-23, 2022, Kyoto, Japan © 2022 Elsevier B.V. All rights reserved.
http://dx.doi.org/10.1016/B978-0-323-85159-6.50184-6

Graphical user interface for development of dynamics model of fermentation process applying long short-term memory networks

Felipe M. M. Sousa[a], Rodolpho R. Fonseca[b], Flávio V. Silva[a*]

[a]School of Chemical Engineering, University of Campinas, Albert Einstein Avenue 500, Campinas, 13083-852, Brazil
[b]Chemical Engineering Department, Federal University of Sergipe, Marechal Rondon Avenue, São Cristóvão, 49100-000, Brazil
flaviovs@unicamp.br

Abstract

Fermentation is a complex process highly influenced by many variables whose effects usually are not accounted for in mathematical models, hindering their accuracy. As an alternative to surpass this issue, empirical models, especially deep learning algorithms, can extract abstract hidden information from real data, enhancing the model accuracy. We present a freeware graphical user interface that enables any user to develop a long short-term memory (LSTM) network to model the dynamics of a fermentation process based on macro variables usually monitored in industrial plants. The algorithm is coded in Python, ensuring platform independence, easy installation, and flexibility to include new variables if required. It also allows the use of the model as a software sensor, assisting in the decision-making of changes. The results are provided in graphics that can be saved as high-definition images or in spreadsheets.

Keywords: Fermentation, Long Short-Term Memory, Graphical User Interface.

1. Introduction

Fermentation is a biotechnological process widely employed in the pharmaceutical, food, and energy industries. Although fermentation and its phenomenological models have been extensively studied over the years, the continuous operation is highly susceptible to the effects of several unaccounted variables, making the phenomenological models less accurate due to simplifications. In this regard, empirical modeling based on deep learning algorithms represents a viable alternative to phenomenological modeling and permits the introduction of the effects of important operational factors. These deep learning models can be obtained from information commonly monitored through the supervisory control system and saved in highly dense databases, making the generated models more relatable to the real system.

Among the deep learning algorithms, Long Short-Term Memory (LSTM) networks represent a powerful tool for developing dynamic models, due to the introduction of recurrent patterns of the predictions through the network. Moreover, LSTM networks are less amenable to problems often observed during the optimization phase in comparison to other recurrent networks, guaranteeing a more reliable model. These networks were successfully applied for generating models in many fields such as the stock market (Althelaya, El-Alfy and Mohammed, 2018; Ghosh, Neufeld and Sahoo, 2021), rainfall-runoff (Yin *et al.*, 2021), prediction and reconstruction of ocean wave heights (Jörges, Berkenbrink and Stumpe, 2021), COVID-19 transmission (Ibrahim *et al.*, 2021; Luo *et al.*, 2021) and fermentation process (Sousa, Fonseca and Silva, 2021), indicating their high applicability and accuracy in complex-forecasting processes. Although widely studied, this technique does not seem to be made available for larger audiences, especially in chemical and biochemical plants.

This work aimed at developing an intuitive graphical user interface (GUI) for users unfamiliar with deep learning techniques that permits the generation of LSTM models for the prediction of volume, cell content, and substrate and ethanol concentrations (referred to as endogenous variables from now on) in a fermentation process based on the user's available database concerning flowrate, cell content and substrate concentration (exogenous variables) in the inlet flow.

2. Program overview and technical description

The developed GUI focus on 1) facilitating the acquisition of transient models for the fermentation process employing LSTM networks, 2) applying the real data obtained from the process, 3) providing qualitative and quantitative performance analysis of the models, and 4) applying the model as a software sensor.

The software was developed using Python, an interpreted language, ensuring a free tool with easy installation and platform independence. The program is distributed as a source code, permitting the addition and change of the model variables if necessary. As an interpreted language, the changes can be written and tested in small section and does not require compilation.

The LSTM models are developed using Tensorflow and Keras, specialized and free libraries for deep learning applications. Besides these, a few other libraries are utilized during the complete run of the GUI and must be installed on the computer. A description of all required libraries is available in a READ.ME file that accompanies the source code.

3. The Graphic User Interface (GUI)

The main window of the program (Figure 1) is divided into two sections. At the top left corner, an entry bar requires the specification of the number of timesteps used in an already saved model employed that will be utilized as a software sensor. This information is needed before the selection of any other option concerning the software sensor application. A button bar to invoke the different program routines is placed right below the entry bar. These routines include data acquisition, model training, performance assessment, saved model upload, and software sensor prediction.

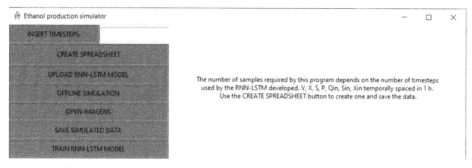

Figure 1 – The main window of the program.

The hyper-parameters for the development of a new LSTM model can be set in a pop-up window, as illustrated in Figure 2. This GUI permits to choose the number of timesteps for the new model, neurons in the output layer of each LSTM gate, weights for the L1 and L2 regularizations, dropout rate, initial weight distribution, percentage of training and test split, the maximum number of epochs for training, batch size, percentage of the training dataset saved for using in early-stopping algorithm and its maximum number of successive errors to cease the training.

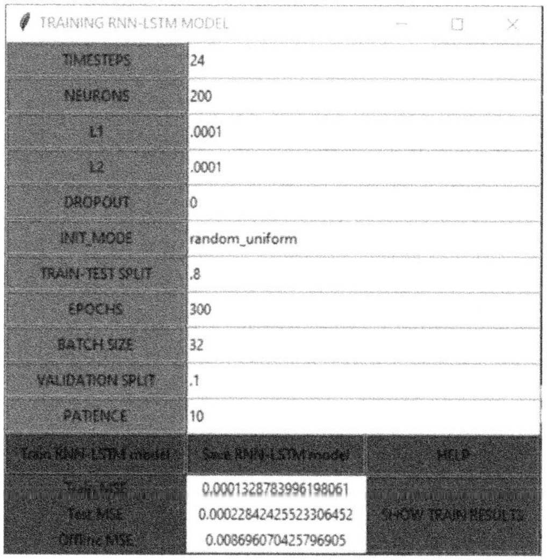

Figure 2 – Pop-up window for setting the network's hyper-parameters during the training stage.

The database for training must be provided in an Excel® spreadsheet and can have any number of vectors. Due to the transient nature model, the division between training and test datasets is sequential, as presented in the spreadsheet. The data is kept unshuffled during the training and test stages.

The program provides a help window (Figure 3) that briefly explains the function of each hyper-parameter aforementioned and their valid inputs. It also illustrates the structure that must be followed in the spreadsheet containing the complete database.

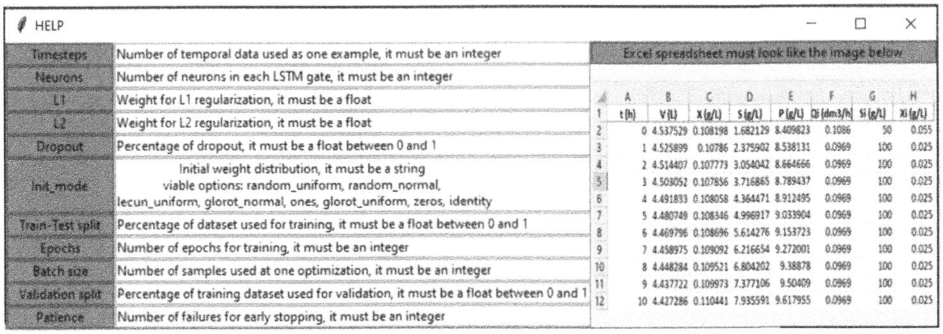

HELP		— □ ×
Timesteps	Number of temporal data used as one example, it must be an integer	
Neurons	Number of neurons in each LSTM gate, it must be an integer	
L1	Weight for L1 regularization, it must be a float	
L2	Weight for L2 regularization, it must be a float	
Dropout	Percentage of dropout, it must be a float between 0 and 1	
Init_mode	Initial weight distribution, it must be a string / viable options: random_uniform, random_normal, / lecun_uniform, glorot_normal, ones, glorot_uniform, zeros, identity	
Train-Test split	Percentage of dataset used for training, it must be a float between 0 and 1	
Epochs	Number of epochs for training, it must be an integer	
Batch size	Number of samples used at one optimization, it must be an integer	
Validation split	Percentage of training dataset used for validation, it must be a float between 0 and 1	
Patience	Number of failures for early stopping, it must be an integer	

Figure 3 – Help menu for selection of the LSTM model's hyper-parameters.

The use of the GUI for software sensor applications demands an initial state that must be provided in a pop-up window (Figure 4). This window is accessed through the 'create spreadsheet' button available in the main menu (Figure 1). The number of rows is determined by the timestep value defined in the entry bar of the main window, and this information can be quickly acquired from an Excel® spreadsheet. The GUI also requires uploading files in the formats .json and .h5 specifying the LSTM structure and weight values. It must be mentioned that the GUI keeps the last values for the exogenous variables throughout the length of the prediction.

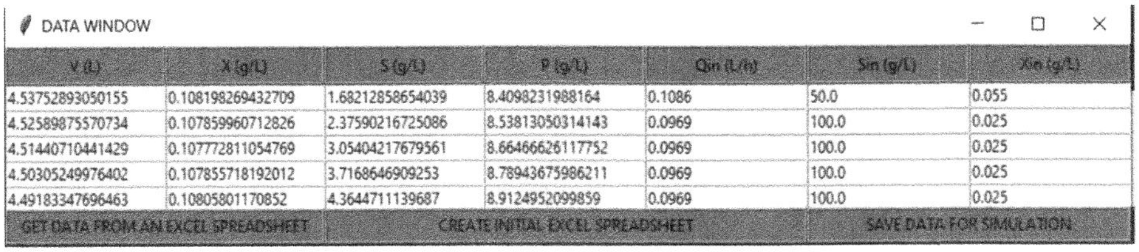

V (L)	X (g/L)	S (g/L)	P (g/L)	Qin (L/h)	Sin (g/L)	Xin (g/L)
4.53752893050155	0.108198269432709	1.68212858654039	8.4098231988164	0.1086	50.0	0.055
4.52589875570734	0.107859960712826	2.37590216725086	8.53813050314143	0.0969	100.0	0.025
4.51440710441429	0.107772811054769	3.05404217679561	8.66466626117752	0.0969	100.0	0.025
4.50305249976402	0.107855718192012	3.7168646909253	8.78943675986211	0.0969	100.0	0.025
4.49183347696463	0.10805801170852	4.3644711139687	8.9124952099859	0.0969	100.0	0.025
GET DATA FROM AN EXCEL SPREADSHEET		CREATE INITIAL EXCEL SPREADSHEET		SAVE DATA FOR SIMULATION		

Figure 4 – Definition of the initial state for software sensor application.

4. Network performance and results visualization

The results from the training stage can be visualized in the window shown in Figure 5 and accessed through the 'show train results' button (Figure 2). The window generates comparative graphics showing the performance of the model for all four predicted variables using the training and test databases and the cost function using the training and validation sets. The test database can also be used and compared in the software sensor application. All graphics can be saved in PNG format and 600 dpi. The window also allows the user to zoom in and change specific graph settings.

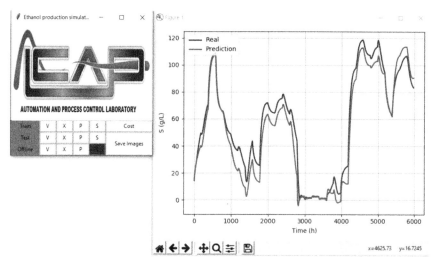

Figure 5 – Results window for training stage and generalization analysis.

Figure 6 illustrates the results window for the software sensor application. This window, accessed through the 'offline simulation' button (Figure 1), shows the predicted results for the endogenous variables using a previously saved model and new data acquired. The results can be viewed, zoomed and saved as PNG images or in an Excel® spreadsheet.

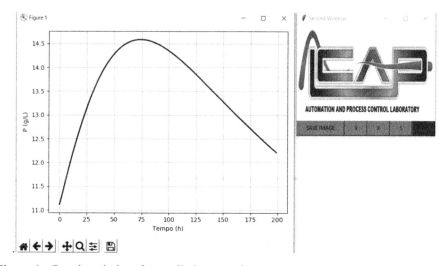

Figure 6 – Results window for prediction as software sensor.

5. Availability

The GUI described is available free of charge to all users and can be used in any operating system to run Python code. The program can be obtained at https://github.com/msousaeq/etGUI.

6. Conclusions

In this work, we developed an easily used Graphical User Interface employing Python code for obtaining the dynamics model of fermentation processes using long short-term memory networks.

The GUI allows the user to train a new model based on their database, defining the major hyperparameters of the model. Its performance is quickly assessed quantitative and qualitatively, saving the generated model for future uses. The rendered graphics for the qualitative analysis of all output variables and the cost function throughout the optimization stage can be saved, zoomed in, and changed.

The GUI also permits the use of the LSTM model as a software sensor for longer predictions, assisting in the decision-making of changes in operating conditions of the fermentation process from an initial state. The results obtained in this application can be graphically analyzed and saved in a spreadsheet for posterior uses.

Acknowledgments

The authors appreciate the financial support provided by the National Council for Scientific and Technological Development– CNPq (Grant number: 131783/2019-0).

References

Althelaya, K. A., El-Alfy, E.-S. M. and Mohammed, S. (2018) 'Stock Market Forecast Using Multivariate Analysis with Bidirectional and Stacked (LSTM, GRU)', in *2018 21st Saudi Computer Society National Computer Conference (NCC)*. IEEE, pp. 1–7. doi: 10.1109/NCG.2018.8593076.

Ghosh, P., Neufeld, A. and Sahoo, J. K. (2021) 'Forecasting directional movements of stock prices for intraday trading using LSTM and random forests', *Finance Research Letters*, p. 102280. doi: 10.1016/j.frl.2021.102280.

Ibrahim, M. R. *et al.* (2021) 'Variational-LSTM autoencoder to forecast the spread of coronavirus across the globe', *PLOS ONE*. Edited by C. Rozenblat, 16(1), p. e0246120. doi: 10.1371/journal.pone.0246120.

Jörges, C., Berkenbrink, C. and Stumpe, B. (2021) 'Prediction and reconstruction of ocean wave heights based on bathymetric data using LSTM neural networks', *Ocean Engineering*, 232, p. 109046. doi: 10.1016/j.oceaneng.2021.109046.

Luo, J. *et al.* (2021) 'Time series prediction of COVID-19 transmission in America using LSTM and XGBoost algorithms', *Results in Physics*, 27, p. 104462. doi: 10.1016/j.rinp.2021.104462.

Sousa, F. M. M., Fonseca, R. R. and da Silva, F. V. (2021) 'Empirical modeling of ethanol production dynamics using long short-term memory recurrent neural networks', *Bioresource Technology Reports*, 15, p. 100724. doi: 10.1016/j.biteb.2021.100724.

Yin, H. *et al.* (2021) 'Rainfall-runoff modeling using LSTM-based multi-state-vector sequence-to-sequence model', *Journal of Hydrology*, 598, p. 126378. doi: 10.1016/j.jhydrol.2021.126378.

Proceedings of the 14th International Symposium on Process Systems Engineering – PSE 2021+
June 19-23, 2022, Kyoto, Japan © 2022 Elsevier B.V. All rights reserved.
http://dx.doi.org/10.1016/B978-0-323-85159-6.50185-8

The biorefinery concept for the industrial valorization of pineapple leaves co-producing ethanol, citric acid, and xanthan gum: a techno-economic analysis

Juan Murcia[a,b*], Rolando Barrera[a], Alba Ardila[b], and Edwin Zondervan[c]

[a]Department of Chemical Engineering, University of Antioquia, 67-53108, Medellin 050010, Colombia
[b]Faculty of Basic Social and Human Sciences, Jaime Isaza Cadavid Colombian Polytechnic, 48-7151, Medellin 4932, Colombia
[c] Faculty of Science and Technology, University of Twente, Drienerlolaan 5, Enschede 7522, The Netherlands
fernando.murcia@udea.edu.co

Abstract

Processing pineapple field residues (PR), a significant waste from the pineapple industry, into multiple value-added products based on the biorefinery concept can reduce waste disposal and contribute to sustainable development goals. Although PR has been used to produce several added-value products, the production of ethanol, citric acid, and xanthan gum, with its economic feasibility at an industrial scale, has not been investigated so far. The present study evaluates the viability of a biorefinery process of PR by performing a comparative techno-economic analysis of three processing scenarios: (1) a whole biorefinery process that fully utilizes PR biomass and produces ethanol, citric acid, and xanthan gum (E+CA+XG) (2) a process that produces CA and XG, and (3) a process that produces only E. A plant capacity of 4 metric tons/hour was considered in the analysis to mimic an intensive pineapple plantation size. Each processing scenario was modeled using SuperPro Designer, and the economic performance was evaluated based on the internal rate of return (IRR), net present value (NPV), and payback period. Among the three scenarios, the whole biorefinery process (CA+XG+E) showed the highest techno-economic performance with the net present value (NPV), internal rate of return (IRR), and payback period of 122.3 million US-$, 34.8%, and 3.5 years, respectively, due to the diverse revenues and minimized waste disposal cost. On the other hand, the E plant showed the lowest economic performance with a negative NPV.

Keywords: Pineapple biorefinery; Modeling; Simulation; Techno-economic analysis.

1. Introduction

Globally nearly 76 million tons of pineapple field residues (PR) are generated every year and end as waste (Satyanarayana et al., 2007). Therefore, the vast number of PR calls for cost-effective and environmentally friendly management options, such as transforming them into multiple value-added products based on the concept of biorefinery (Elbersen, and Hengsdijk, 2019; Russland et al., 2017; Zhang et al., 2011). A growing body of research evidence that PR is full of valuable molecules such as cellulose, hemicellulose, and soluble mono-sugars (glucose and xylose), amino acids, vitamins, and minerals, which are a potential feedstock for microbial conversion to produce fuels (i. e., alcohol) and value-added products (i.e., organic acids and hydrocolloids). Although PR has been used to produce single-cell protein, ethanol, energy (Chen et al., 2020), and substrates of fiber, among other end-products under the broad concept of biorefinery (Roda and Lambri, 2019; Banerjee et al., 2019), the production of ethanol, citric acid, and xanthan gum, with its economic feasibility at an industrial scale have not been investigated.

A biorefinery concept that integrates processes and technologies to produce multiple value-added products from pineapple stubble have the potential to manage this residual biomass due to the following advantages: 1) synergistic effects among processes for the reduced energy consumption and labor demands; 2) minimal waste generation because the waste discarded by one process could be the input for another process; 3) diverse revenues due to the generation of multiple products (Jin et al.,2018b). The techno-economic assessment of biorefinery concepts has been used to evaluate the bioprocess viability of lignocellulosic biomass conversion into several products such as ethanol, xylitol, furfural, and others (Giuliano et al., 2018, Giuliano et al., 2014).

The present study aims to evaluate the economics of a biorefinery process of PR by performing a comparative techno-economic analysis of three processing scenarios: (1) a whole biorefinery process that fully utilizes PR biomass and produces ethanol, citric acid, and xanthan gum (E + CA + XG), (2) a process that produces citric acid and xanthan gum (CA + XG), and (3) a process that produces only ethanol (E). Each processing scenario was modeled in detail using SuperPro Designer. The economic performance was evaluated based on the internal rate of return (IRR), net present value (NPV), and payback period. Results from this study will provide information to the pineapple industry to help direct their residual biomass management.

2. Biorefinery process description

Approximately 250 metric tons of fresh pineapple plant residues (wet basis, mainly leaves) are removed every two years per hectare (Elbersen and Hengsdijk, 2019). Therefore, the first step is collecting pineapple leaves from different plantations and transporting them to the processing plant. After receiving, pineapple leaves are transferred by a conveyor to a crusher, where the juice is extracted. After the extraction, two streams of juice (192.5 tons) and fibrous material (45 tons) were obtained (Chen et al., 2020). Although pineapple leaves bagasse, the solid fraction obtained from the juice extraction, can be further processed into its main components or sent directly to a thermal valorization route, these options were beyond the scope of this study.

The composition of pineapple stubble used in the simulations and reactor data assumed from the literature on citric acid, xanthan gum, and ethanol fermentation are presented in Table 1. A plant capacity of 4 metric tons/hour was considered in the analysis to mimic an intensive pineapple plantation size. The plant has an operation period of 330 days (11 months) per year and 24 h per day, corresponding to a processing capacity of 31,680 metric tons (equivalent to 35,000 tons) of pineapple field residues per year.

The process simulation of the biorefinery was carried out by implementing a process flowsheet in SuperPro Designer v12. Figure 1 reports the general simplified biorefinery

The biorefinery concept for the industrial valorization of pineapple leaves
co-producing ethanol, citric acid, and xanthan gum: a technoeconomic
analysis
1113

Block Flow Diagram (BFD), including possible process pathways. Each block corresponds to a SuperPro Designer flowsheet containing a specific process section of the plant.

The designed biorefinery process generates three significant products: ethanol, citric acid, and xanthan gum. The process block diagram, flow diagram, and critical parameters applied in the process are shown in Figures 1 and 2 and Table 1. The biorefinery process can fully utilize pineapple leaves to produce multiple products for maximal revenue. However, the large number of unit operations involved in producing various products increases the capital and operating costs, which may negatively affect economic performance. Therefore, the biorefinery process was compared with another two processes where only citric acid and xanthan gum were produced from pineapple leaves to understand economic competitiveness better. Thus, three processing scenarios were considered in this study (1) a whole biorefinery process that fully utilizes PR biomass and produces ethanol, citric acid, and xanthan gum (E + CA + XG), (2) a process that produces citric acid and xanthan gum (CA + XG), and (3) a process that produces only ethanol (E).

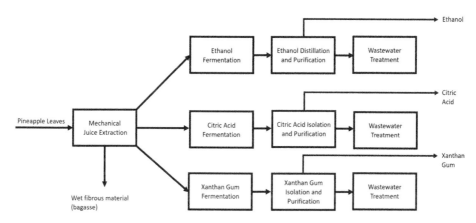

Figure 1 General Flowsheet of the multi-product pineapple biorefinery

2.1 Ethanol Production Steps

Glucose and xylose in the pineapple leaves juice to produce bioethanol with the *Zymomonas mobilis* bacteria, appropriate microorganisms for pentose and hexose fermentation. The fermentation process is carried out at 32°C for 48h in a bioreactor inoculated with 2% Z. mobilis (Aden and Foust, 2009). Following centrifugation of the fermentation medium, the produced bioethanol is distilled in a two-stage process using conventional distillation columns.

2.2 Xanthan Gum Production Steps

The fermentation process is carried out at the conditions of 0.01 vvm oxygen for 48 h and a temperature of 32 °C by inoculating the bioreactor with 2% *Xanthomonas campestris*. In downstream processing, the bacterial cells are inactivated by pasteurization and removed from the system in the solid phase by centrifugation. In the liquid phase, XG is obtained in solid form by precipitation with ethanol and separated by centrifugation. The solid XG is dried with a drum dryer, ground, and packaged. Finally, the liquid phase is distilled to recover and recycle the ethanol (Saydam et al., 2020).

2.3 Citric Acid Production Steps

The microorganism used to carry out the aerobic transformation of glucose and xylose into citric acid is *Aspergillus niger*. The fermentation is carried out under the following parameters: aeration rate of 1.25 vvm, stirring speed of 250 rpm, pH of 4.0, and a temperature of 30° C. When the fermentation is completed, the citric acid present in the fermentation product liquor is separated by two reaction-filtration stages, first with sulfuric acid and later with calcium hydroxide, to be purified in a crystallization stage. Finally, the separated citric acid crystals are dehydrated in a rotary dryer, obtaining the final product (granulated citric acid) with ~99% purity (Heinzle et al., 2006).

Table 1. Pineapple stubble data, conversion data of process simulations

Major components in the pineapple leaves, juice, and fibrous material	Whole leaf	Juice	Wet fibrous material
%Total solid (TS)	13.8	6.2	51.6
Cellulose (%TS)	22.6	---	36.8
Hemicellulose (%TS)	26.1	---	28.1
Lignin (%TS)	7.3	---	5.1
Glucose (g/L)	---	10.6	---
Xylose (g/L)	---	16.4	---
Crude Protein (%TS)	6.9	14	5.7
Crude Fat(%TS)	3.0	3.5	4.0
Ash (%TS)	6.1	10	1.7
Potassium (%TS)	2.6	3.8	0.6
Total carbohydrates (%TS)	---	72.5	---

Reactor's data	Conversion (%)	residence time (h)
Xylose to ethanol	70	18
Glucose to ethanol	93	18
Xylose to citric acid	80	160
Glucose to citric acid	85	160
Xylose to xanthan gum	55	80
Glucose to xanthan gum	60	80

3. Economic Analysis

Economic analysis of the several cases was performed by estimating capital and operating costs. The purchased equipment, together with equipment installation, instrumentation and controls, processing piping, electrical systems, buildings, yard improvements, and service facilities, makes up the total plant direct cost. The total fixed capital investment consists of whole plant direct and complete plant indirect costs. With working capital and land, the fixed capital investment makes up the total capital investment (Peters et al., 2003).

Capital costs were estimated by power-law correlations based on unit capacity. In addition, data relevant to biorefinery sections were taken from the literature. Finally, the factorial method was applied to obtain the total investment cost. Raw materials mainly give operating costs. Therefore, a 40 US$/ton purchase cost for pineapple stubble was assumed.

Moreover, the prices of microorganisms, chemicals, and water required for pretreatment were also accounted for. In addition, the costs of salaries, maintenance, and insurance were assessed by the factorial method. The summary of the parameters used to carry out each process's technoeconomic assessment is presented in Table 2.

The biorefinery concept for the industrial valorization of pineapple leaves   1115
co-producing ethanol, citric acid, and xanthan gum: a technoeconomic
analysis

Revenues consist of products sales (ethanol, citric acid, and xanthan gum). Linear depreciation was assumed. A discounted cash flow analysis was carried out to obtain ethanol's Payback Selling Price (PSP) provided the price of the other possible by-products. The PSP was calculated as the value that makes the Present Net Value equal to zero after 20 years of plant life.

Table 2. Parameters for the techno-economic assessments

Economic data	
Plant life (y)	20
Ethanol Price (USD/L)	1
Citric Acid Price (USD/kg)	2
Xanthan gum Price (USD/kg)	9
Biomass Price (USD/ton)	40
Discount Rate (%)	7
Electricity cost (USD/MWhe)	100

4. Results

Based on the results of total capital costs, total operating costs, and revenues, the economic performances of the three plants were evaluated using NPV, IRR, and payback period as the indicators. Although the E + CA + XG plant had the highest total capital cost, it provided multiple products to generate revenue. From Table 3, we can see that the IRR for the E + CA + XG plant was 34.8%, with an NPV of 122.3 million US-$ and a payback period of 3.5 years. Although the biorefinery process of PR is new to the industry at the current stage, the products (ethanol, citric acid, and xanthan gum) from the process already have an established market. The positive NPV, the 34.8% of IRR, and the payback period of 3.5 years obtained from the techno-economic analysis suggested an economically feasible investment for this biorefinery process. Compared with the E + CA + XG plant, the CA + XG plant had lower revenue with the NPV, IRR, and payback period of 54.3 million US-$, 23.5%, and 4.3 years, respectively. The E plant produced ethanol as the sole product and had the worst economic performance among the three plants, showing a negative NPV of −15.6 million US-$, the lowest IRR of −2.1%, and the most extended payback period of 18.0 years, which was considered as economically unfavorable.

Table 3 Economic indicators (NPV, IRR, and payback period)

Item	E+CA+XG	CA+XG	E
NPV (million US-$)	122.3	54.3	-15.6
IRR (%)	34.8	23.5	-2.1
Payback period (year)	3.5	4.3	18

5. Conclusions

A techno-economic analysis was carried out on a biorefinery processing pineapple leaves to obtain ethanol, citric acid, and xanthan gum. The techno-economic model of pineapple stubble biorefinery process was developed with three scenarios: a single-product scenario (ethanol, E), a dual-product scenario (Citric Acid and Xanthan Gum, CA + XG), and an integrated biorefinery scenario (Ethanol, Citric Acid, and Xanthan Gum, E + CA + XG). Among the three scenarios, the E + CA + XG scenario showed the best economic performance with the NPV, IRR, and payback period of 122.3million US-$, 34.8%, and 3.5 years, respectively, which was considered economically viable. Overall, this study demonstrated that the biorefinery of GP to produce multiple products is technically and financially feasible at a commercial scale. However, we are aware that this result might be significantly affected by the plant capacity, products price, and juice sugars content and deserves a sensitivity analysis, which will be addressed in future works.

References

A. Aden, & T. Foust, 2009, Techno-economic analysis of the dilute sulfuric acid and enzymatic hydrolysis process for the conversion of corn stover to ethanol. Cellulose, 16(4), 535-545.

S. Banerjee, A. Patti, V. Ranganathan, & Arora, 2019, A. Hemicellulose based biorefinery from pineapple peel waste: Xylan extraction and its conversion into xylooligosaccharides. Food and Bioproducts Processing, 117, 38-50.

A. Chen, Y. Guan, J. Bustamante, M. Uribe, L. Uribe-Lorío, M. Roos, & Y. Liu, 2020, production of renewable fuel and value-added bioproducts using pineapple leaves in Costa Rica. Biomass and Bioenergy, 141, 105675.

H. Elbersen, & H. Hengsdijk, 2019, Costa Rica pineapple field residue valorisation. In 27th European Biomass Conference and Exhibition, EUBCE 2019.

A. Giuliano, M. Poletto, & D. Barletta, 2015. Process design of a multi-product lignocellulosic biorefinery. In Computer Aided Chemical Engineering (Vol. 37, pp. 1313-1318). Elsevier.

A. Giuliano, D. Barletta, I. De Bari, & M. Poletto, 2018. Techno-economic assessment of a lignocellulosic biorefinery co-producing ethanol and xylitol or furfural. In Computer Aided Chemical Engineering (Vol. 43, pp. 585-590). Elsevier.

E. Heinzle, A. Biwer, & C. Cooney. 2006. Citric Acid-Alternative Process using Starch. Development of Sustainable Bioprocesses: Modeling and Assessment, 125-160.

Q. Jin, S. O'Keefe, A. Stewart, A. Neilson, Y. Kim, & H. Huang, 2021, Techno-economic analysis of a grape pomace biorefinery: Production of seed oil, polyphenols, and biochar. Food and Bioproducts Processing, 127, 139-151.

M. Peters, K. Timmerhaus & R. West. 2003. Plant design and economics for chemical engineers (Vol. 4). New York: McGraw-Hill.

A. Roda, & M. Lambri, 2019, Food uses of pineapple waste and by-products: a review. International Journal of Food Science & Technology, 54(4), 1009-1017 (2019).

N. Ruslan, N. Aris, N. Othman, A. Saili, M. Muhamad, & N. Aziz, 2017. A preliminary study on sustainable management of pineapple waste: the perspective of smallholders. Int J Acad Res Bus Soc Sci, 7(6):1-7.

K. Satyanarayana, J. Guimarães, & F. Wypych, 2007. Studies on lignocellulosic fibers of Brazil. Part I: Source, production, morphology, properties, and applications. Compos Part A Appl Sci Manuf, 38(7):1694-1709 (2007).

D. Saydam, A. Koulouris, & A. Dalgıç. 2020. Process simulation of integrated xanthan gum and sorbitol bioproduction: economic and sensitivity analysis with Taguchi approach. Process Integration and Optimization for Sustainability, 4(3), 279-295.

H. Zhang, D. Hu, J. Chen, X. Ye, S. Wang, J. Hao, & Z. An, 2011. Particle size distribution and polycyclic aromatic hydrocarbons emissions from agricultural crop residue burning. Environ Sci Technol, 45(13):5477-82.

Proceedings of the 14th International Symposium on Process Systems Engineering – PSE 2021+
June 19-23, 2022, Kyoto, Japan © 2022 Elsevier B.V. All rights reserved.
http://dx.doi.org/10.1016/B978-0-323-85159-6.50186-X

First Principles Based Development of Hybrid Models of Distillation Towers

Carlos Rodriguez[a], Prashant Mhaskar[a], Vladimir Mahalec[a]*

[a] Department of Chemical Engineering, McMaster University, Hamilton, ON, L8S 4L7, Canada
mahalec@mcmaster.ca

Abstract

In this work, we developed a simultaneous hybrid model with a novel error correction model for distillation columns that can be used in process monitoring, scheduling, and optimization. The proposed hybrid model consists of two parts a simplified first principles model (SFPM) and an error correction term. The SFPM is specific for distillation columns and consists of mass, energy, and equilibrium equations for all the trays of the column. For the error correction term, we used a traditional residual model that predicts the differences between the flow outputs of the SPFM and plant flow outputs, and we introduced a novel multiplicative correction model (MCM). The MCM corrects the output mass fractions predictions of the SFPM using a multiplicative factor. The advantage of using the MCM is that the predictions of the hybrid model are physically meaningful and more accurate than the residuals model when inputs are extrapolated beyond the training region. The proposed hybrid multiplicative model has a mean relative percentage error of less than 2% compared to rigorous simulations for interpolation and extrapolation inputs.

Keywords: Hybrid modeling; Distillation column; Process optimization; Process monitoring; Error correction models

1. Background

Optimal operation of refining and petrochemical plants requires that distillation towers meet product quality targets while minimizing energy consumption, which requires that accurate models of distillation towers be included in the plant-wide optimization models. Over the last decade, there has been a growing realization that rigorous plant models used in real-time optimization (RTO) lead to large-scale and challenging to maintain models. In addition, due to the model complexity, it is not possible to model an entire refinery via rigorous models and optimize such a model. In addition, if the distillation tower efficiency changes over time, the parameters of the rigorous models need to be adjusted by an expert. All of this indicates a need for simpler and yet accurate distillation models that can be used for inferential monitoring of plant operation and optimization.

Early work on approximate models of distillation towers employed partial least squares (PLS) models to predict product compositions from tray temperatures (Mejdel et al., 1991). Kano et al. (2000) introduced a dynamic PLS model which employed tray temperatures and manipulated variables. Even though these approaches lead to reasonable predictions in the region where training data is available, they do not extrapolate well if the tower moves to a region of increasingly nonlinear behavior.

Hybrid models of distillation tower employ first-principles mass and energy balances and approximate models of separation (Mahalec and Sanchez, 2012). In this work, we developed a simultaneous hybrid model for distillation columns consisting of a simplified first principles model and an error correction model. The hybrid model can be used for process monitoring or optimization applications. We introduce a multiplicative correction term to demonstrate that it performs better than the traditionally used additive error correction term.

2. Case study

A butane splitter was selected as the study case for this work. A butane splitter is a standard unit in natural gas processing plants. It is the last distillation column of a separation train of natural gas liquid streams. The function of the butane splitter is to separate a binary mixture of isobutane iC4 and normal butane nC4. The relative volatility between these two components is close to one. Thereby, a distillation column with a high number of trays is required to achieve a successful separation.

Aspen plus steady-state simulations were used as a substitute for actual plant data. Due to the distillation column's components and pressure, the Peng-Robinson was selected as the property package in the simulations. The tower specifications are presented in Table 1 based on the work of (Aljuhani, 2016). The feed pressure, flow rate, and temperature were kept constant in the simulation, whereas the composition of the feed and product purities are varied in the simulation. Two datasets were created for the same butane splitter an interpolation and an extrapolation dataset, the difference being the feed mass fraction of iC4. The interpolation range of the feed mass fraction of iC4 is 0.20-0.35, whereas the extrapolation values of the feed mass fraction of iC4 are 0.15 and 0.4.

3. Modeling approach

Traditionally, series hybrid models have been used for modeling chemical units. We present a simultaneous hybrid model that combines the series approach (i.e., estimation of parameters of the model) with the parallel approach (i.e., correction model), as shown in Figure 1. The reason for combining both approaches is to obtain a hybrid model that is easy to train, update and compute while leveraging the knowledge and structure of fundamental equations and that can be updated for different tower conditions. The model's outputs are the mass fraction and mass flow for each of the components in the distillation tower.

Table 1 Butane splitter specifications

Tower conditions		Tower design		Operation range	
Feed pressure	12.1 bar	Number of trays	101	Feed $x_{F,iC4}$	0.15-0.40
Pressure drop	1 bar	Feed tray	50	Distillate $x_{D,iC4}$	0.96-0.99
Temperature	44 °C	Murphree efficiency	100 %	Bottoms $x_{B,nC4}$	0.96-0.99

3.1. Simplified first principles model

Distillation rigorous models consist of mass, equilibrium, summation, and heat (MESH equations). However, one of the main challenges of solving these equations is the non-linearity of the equilibrium equations (Biegler et al., 1997). Therefore, we introduce parameters estimated using data-driven models to reduce the complexity of the MESH equations while keeping the structure of mass, energy, and equilibrium equations. The SFPM can be applied to all distillation columns with the following characteristics: one feed, no sides streams, total condenser, and partial reboiler. The SFPM consists of two different matrices of linear equations. In the first matrix, the overall mass balances equations Eq.(1) and energy equations Eq.(2) for each of the trays alongside the reflux ratio $RR = L_1/D$ and the specific reboiler duty $q_{reb} = Q_{reb}/F$ are used to find the total liquid and vapor flow in each of the distillation column trays. Where L_i denotes the total liquid flow in tray i numbered from top to bottom, V_i total vapor flow, H_i the liquid enthalpy, and the h_i vapor enthalpy. The temperature T of each tray is estimated using a data-driven model. It is assumed that it is possible to linearly approximate the enthalpies around one base operation as shown in and Eq.(3) and Eq.(4). Where the $^\circ$ denotes standard operation and C_p is the heat capacity.

$$F_i + V_{i+1} + L_{i-1} - L_i - V_i = 0 \tag{1}$$

$$\boldsymbol{F_i H_i + V_{i+1} h_{i+1} + L_{i-1} H_{i-1} - L_i H_i - V_i h_i = 0} \tag{2}$$

$$H_i = H_i^\circ + Cp_{i,liq}^\circ (T_i - T_i^\circ) \tag{3}$$

$$h_i = h_i^\circ + Cp_{i,vap}^\circ (T_i - T_i^\circ) \tag{4}$$

The second matrix consists of the equilibrium equations, the mass balances for each component, the reflux ratio for each of the components, and the summation equations (e.g., the sum of the flow of each of the components in the liquid has to be equal to the total liquid flow). This matrix is used to solve the mass flows of each of the components. The equilibrium equations are presented in Eq.(5) where the j subindex is the number of components and β is the equilibrium factor predicted with the empirical model. The mass balance equation for each of the components is presented in equation Eq.(6).

$$V_{i,j} = \frac{V_i}{L_i} \beta_{i,j} L_{i,j} \tag{5}$$

$$F_{i,j} + V_{i+1,j} + L_{i-1,j} = L_{i,j} + V_{i,j} \tag{6}$$

3.2. Error correction models

Parallel hybrid models have been used in the literature to correct the predictions of FPM. In this work, in addition to modeling the residuals (i.e., the difference between the actual flows for each of the components and the predictions of the SFPM), we present a multiplicative correction model.

The problem with using traditional residual models is that they don't have restrictions on feasible predictions. Therefore, it is possible in certain instances to obtain negative flows for some of the components that are in a lower proportion in the distillation column. For that reason, we introduced the multiplicative correction model (MCM). The objective of MCM is to predict the ratio between the actual mass fraction and the prediction mass fraction of the SFPM of each of the components.

Hybrid multiplicative model

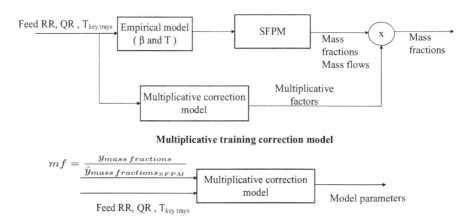

Figure 1 Hybrid multiplicative model structure for predicting and for training the multiplicative correction model

3.3. Training data-driven models

The temperature and equilibrium factor for each of the trays are estimated with empirical models. Neural networks (NN) and partial least squares (PLS) were used to predict those parameters. Although NN models are nonlinear mappings that can approximate any continuous function, they have several drawbacks, including the large amount of data to train them, local minima, and the overfitting problem. Therefore, linear models are often preferred as empirical models. The empirical models were trained using two different sets of inputs. The first set of inputs consists of the operating variables (reflux ratio and reboiler duty). The second set of inputs extends the first set with the addition of temperature measurements. The included temperatures are the temperatures next to the reboiler and condenser and the temperatures of the key trays. The key trays were determined using sensitivity analysis (Aljuhani, 2016). The models were trained using 80% of the interpolation dataset. The number of components for the PLS and the architecture of the NN was determined using the testing dataset, which is 10% of the interpolation dataset. The validation interpolation dataset determines the performance of the different hybrid models. The extrapolation performance of the models was evaluated using the extrapolation dataset. The metrics used to assess the models are the coefficient of determination R2, root mean squared error RMSE, mean relative percentage error MeanRE%, and the maximum relative percentage error MaxRE%.

4. Results and discussion

The first step of the hybrid model is the prediction of the parameters. The models for the parameters were trained using the set of inputs with temperatures and without temperatures of the key trays. The R2 of the prediction of the equilibrium factors evaluated using the validation dataset of the PLS models without the temperatures is 0.765 and 0.75 for the predictions of the temperatures. The R2 of the NN models without the temperatures of the key trays is 0.988 for the temperature and 0.984 for the equilibrium factors. The inclusion of the temperatures of the key trays in the inputs, increases the R2 of PLS models to 0.993 and 0.992 for the equilibrium factors and temperatures, respectively. Therefore, it is possible to estimate the temperature and equilibrium factors of the trays only using linear models instead of nonlinear models. For that reason, PLS models were selected for the prediction of the parameters of the SFPM.

Table 2 Summary results predictions using different surrogate models for the mass fraction of nC4 in the distillate

	Interpolation Validation			Extrapolation		
	SFPM	Hybrid additive	Hybrid multiplicative	SFPM	Hybrid additive	Hybrid multiplicative
R2	0.998	0.9997	0.9996	0.988	0.9861	0.9984
RMSE	4.677e-4	1.915e-4	2.018e-4	1.095e-3	1.174e-3	3.956e-4
MeanRE%	1.69	0.694	0.694	3.5	4.91	1.41
MaxRE%	7.27	2.35	3.30	12.46	28.79	4.52

Table 3 Summary results predictions using different surrogate models for the mass fraction of iC4 in the bottoms

	Interpolation Validation			Extrapolation		
	SFPM	Hybrid additive	Hybrid multiplicative	SFPM	Hybrid additive	Hybrid multiplicative
R2	0.9962	0.9999	0.9987	0.9922	0.9996	0.9978
RMSE	6.132e-4	9.107e-5	3.558e-4	8.84e-4	2.08e-4	4.743e-4
MeanRE%	2.02	0.243	0.915	2.46	0.76	1.25
MaxRE%	5.36	0.84	2.37	11.74	5.26	9.16

A PLS model was developed for the additive correction model (i.e., correction of the mass flow of each of the components) and the multiplicative correction model. A summary of the results for the prediction of the mass fraction of the products of the butane splitter is presented in table 2 and table 3. For inputs within the training region (interpolation), both hybrid models perform better than only using the SFPM. However, when using the model outside of the training region, the predictions of the hybrid additive model are worse than the SFPM predictions for the nC4 in the distillate. In contrast, the hybrid multiplicative model corrects the predictions of the SFPM even for extrapolation inputs. Another advantage of hybrid multiplicative is that the predictions of concentrations can never become negative after the correction. The observed versus predicted plots for both components are shown in figure 2. We can observe from this figure that the differences between observed and predicted values are low for the validation interpolation inputs and the extrapolation inputs.

5. Conclusions

A novel simultaneous hybrid model for distillation columns is presented in this work. The hybrid model consists of a SFPM based on mass, approximate energy, and approximate equilibrium equations, and an error correction term. Separation factor and temperature profiles at the new operating state (which are predicted by using empirical models) are used in SFPM to predict product composition. The prediction of the SFPM is improved by using a multiplicative correction model. The presented hybrid model predicts product compositions with MeanRE% of less than 2% relative to the rigorous tower model, and it extrapolates well beyond its training region.

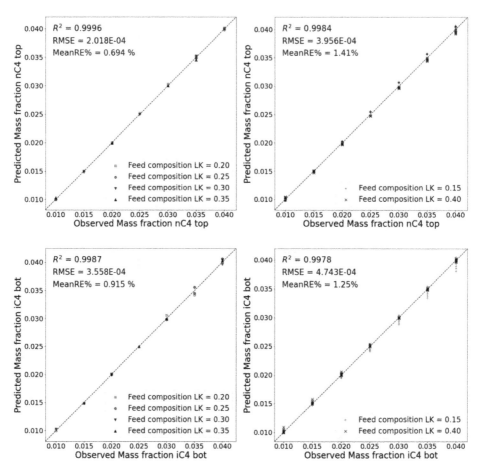

Figure 2 Observed versus predicted plots for the product composition of the distillates and bottoms. The results on the left represent the results of the validation dataset. The results on the right represent the results of the extrapolation dataset.

6. References

Aljuhani, F., 2016. Hybrid Model for Monitoring and Optimization of Distillation Columns ; McMaster University, M.A.Sc. Thesis

Biegler, L.T., Grossmann, I.E. and Westerberg, A.W., 1997. Systematic methods for chemical process design.

Kano, M., Miyazaki, K., Hasebe, S. and Hashimoto, I., 2000 Inferential control system of distillation compositions using dynamic partial least squares regression. J. Proc. Control, 10, 157-166

Mahalec, V. and Sanchez, Y., 2012. Inferential monitoring and optimization of crude separation units via hybrid models. Computers & chemical engineering, 45, pp.15-26.

Mejdell, T. and Skogestad, S. 1991 Estimation of distillation compositions from multiple temperature measurements using partial-least-squares regression. I&ECR, 30, pp. 2543-2555

Proceedings of the 14th International Symposium on Process Systems Engineering – PSE 2021+
June 19-23, 2022, Kyoto, Japan © 2022 Elsevier B.V. All rights reserved.
http://dx.doi.org/10.1016/B978-0-323-85159-6.50187-1

Model-Based Development of Fuel Cell Stack and System Controllers

Shigeki Hasegawa[a][*][,b], Yusuke Miyamoto[b], Sanghong Kim[c], Yoshihiro Ikogi[b], Miho Kageyama[a], and Motoaki Kawase[a]

[a] *Department of Chemical Engineering, Kyoto University, Kyoto 615-8510, JAPAN*
[b] *Commercial ZEV Product Development Div., Toyota Motor Corporation, Aichi 471-8571, JAPAN*
[c] *Department of Applied Physics and Chemical Engineering, Tokyo University of Agriculture and Technology, Tokyo 184-8588, JAPAN*
s.hasegawa@cheme.kyoto-u.ac.jp

Abstract

Fuel cell (FC) system controllers for stack, air, H_2, and cooling systems are developed, and integrated with the system hardware models. These controllers allow flexible changes of system hardware specifications and operating conditions under a closed-loop simulation. The virtual FC-system hardware and controller design and system performance evaluation were demonstrated and confirmed to be beneficial for the actual product system development process.

Keywords: Fuel cell system; Model-based development; Physical modeling; Controller design

1. Introduction

The role of the FC-system controller is to ensure the optimal conditions in the FC stack by manipulating the system component considering the hardware limitations to achieve the maximum system performance such as the system efficiency and acceleration response. In many FC-system manufacturers, the controller design activities can be conducted only after the prototypes of system testbeds are manufactured. Since it takes a long lead-time as well as a great expense for the preparation of the system testbeds, the integrated FC-system simulator for the virtual controller development and evaluation has been strongly demanded. Though studies on control system are of such great importance, the fuel cell itself has been more intensively investigated (Weber et al., 2014), and much less research has been done on the FC stack, the FC system including the system components of air, H_2, and cooling systems, and the FC-system controllers. The authors have developed the integrated FC-system simulator with the physical models of the FC stack (Hasegawa et al., 2021a) and the system components of air, H_2, and cooling systems (Hasegawa et al., 2021b). This simulator can estimate the dynamic behavior of the entire FC system of 2nd-generation MIRAI, the latest commercial fuel cell electric vehicle (FCEV) shown in Fig. 1 (Takahashi et al., 2021), with the acceptable accuracy and allowable calculation time. The simulator can be utilized for the wide range of application system development of passenger vehicles, commercial vehicles of buses and tracks, railways, marine vessels, aviation, and stationary power generator purposes, though it consists of only hardware models of the FC stack and the FC-system components and the controllers are not included.

In this study, the entire FC-system controller with a streamlined configuration was developed, where the setpoints of the FC-system net power, the FC-stack state variables, and the actuation values of the FC-system components can be determined independently and it is remarkably easy to modify, replace, add, and remove the controller specifications. These controllers were integrated with the FC-system hardware model described above to obtain the closed-loop FC-system simulator. The simulator reduces the lead-time of the entire FC-system and controller development and the expenses for the prototypes of different applications systems. The effect of the coolant radiator size on the FC-system performance, the dynamic setpoint tracking performance of the FC-system net power and the FC-system net efficiency, were investigated by using the developed closed-loop simulator.

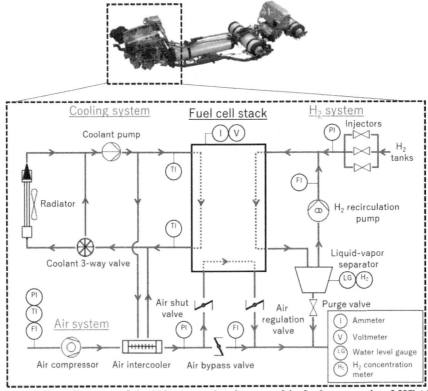

Fig. 1. Flow diagram of the FC system implemented in 2nd-generation MIRAI

In the FC-system applications, a setpoint of net power is given to the controller, and the setpoint tracking performance and high system net efficiency are the primary requirements.
The FC-system net power is defined by Eq. (1),

$$P_{FC}^{net} = P_{FC}^{gross} - (P_{ACP} + P_{HP} + P_{WP} + P_{others}) \tag{1}$$

where P_{FC}^{net} is the FC-system net power [W], P_{FC}^{gross} is the FC-stack gross power, P_{ACP}, P_{HP}, P_{WP} are the consumed power by the air compressor, hydrogen pump, and water pump [W], and P_{others} is the consumed power by the other system components such as a DC–DC convertor [W]. The FC-system net efficiency is defined as Eq. (2)

$$\eta_{\text{FC}}^{\text{net}} = \frac{P_{\text{FC}}^{\text{net}}}{P_{\text{FC}}^{\text{gross}} + \dot{q}_{\text{FC}}} \tag{2}$$

where $\eta_{\text{FC}}^{\text{net}}$ is the FC-system net efficiency [-], and $\dot{q}_{\text{FC}}$ is the heat generation rate from the FC stack [W]. $P_{\text{FC}}^{\text{gross}}$ and $\dot{q}_{\text{FC}}$ are expressed by Eqs. (3) and (4),

$$P_{\text{FC}}^{\text{gross}} = I_{\text{FC}} V_{\text{FC}} \tag{3}$$

$$\dot{q}_{\text{FC}} = I_{\text{FC}} \left(V_{\text{FC}}^{\text{OC}} - V_{\text{FC}} \right) \tag{4}$$

where I_{FC}, V_{FC}, and $V_{\text{FC}}^{\text{OC}}$ are the FC-stack current [A], voltage [V], and open-circuit voltage [V]. They can be measured by the current and voltage sensors shown in Fig. 1.

2. FC-system controller and closed-loop simulation of the entire FC system

The configuration of the closed-loop FC-system simulator which consists of the FC-system controllers developed in this study and the FC-system hardware model is shown in Fig. 2. In this simulator, setpoint of the FC-system net power, the ambient temperature, and atmospheric pressure are inputs to the electric power controller. The calculated FC-system net power is output as well as the other calculated values in the FC system, the FC-stack polarization states such as current, voltage, and resistance, the distributions of state variables across the system such as pressure, flowrate, temperature, and gas composition, and the actuation values of the FC-system component such as pump speed and valve opening.

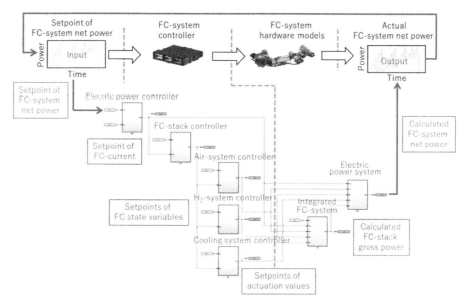

Fig. 2. Flow diagram of the closed-loop simulation of the entire FC system

The controllers in Fig. 2 consist of the electric power controller, the FC-stack controller, and the actuator controllers for the system components in air, H_2, and cooling systems. The electric power controller determines the setpoint of FC-current to minimize the error between the setpoint and calculated values of system net power. The FC-stack controller consists of air, H_2, and cooling state controllers. Each state controller determines the setpoints of the state variables such as pressure, flowrate, temperature, and gas composition at the inlet and outlet of the FC stack based on the FC-stack current and coolant outlet temperature measured by the sensors depicted with I and TI in Fig. 1 and pre-calibrated functions. The actuator controllers of air, H_2, and coolant determine the setpoints of actuation values such as the pump speed and valve opening to minimize the error between the setpoint of the state variables from the FC-stack controller and the actual value of state variables measured by the sensors shown in Fig. 1. Such a simple and streamlined controller configuration enables independent investigations of the optimal stack operating conditions and hardware specifications.

Fig. 3 is the algorithm of the electric power controller included in the Simulink flow diagram. Firstly, the setpoint of the FC-system net power is mediated with the upper limit, lower limit, minimum, and the gradient limitations determined by the system hardware limitations. Then the control error of the FC-system net power is compensated by determining the setpoint of the FC-stack current by a simple PI-control method including the supplemental functions of integral anti-windup and integral reset methods for the stable operation.

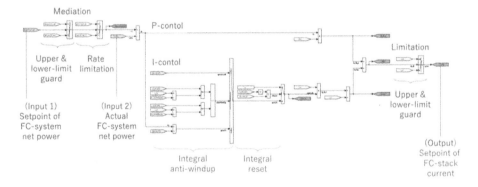

Fig. 3. Flow diagram of the electric power controller

Fig. 4 is the air pressure determination algorithm included in the Simulink flow diagram. The setpoints of the FC-stack current and temperature were given to the pre-determined functions, which were built based on experimental data to achieve the maximum FC-system net efficiency considering the electric power consumption and loss of air compressor. Then, the setpoint of air pressure is calculated. Pre-determined functions are used also for the determination of the setpoints of the other state variables. In the air, H_2, and cooling system controllers, the setpoints of the state variables outputted from the FC-stack controller are converted to the actuation values such as pump speed and valve opening by the same PI-control based algorithm in the electric power system controller shown in Fig. 3. By virtue of the closed loop simulator shown in Fig. 2, the pre-determined functions and the PI-controller parameters could be optimized and determined without manufacturing the integrated FC-system hardware. This reduces the considerable effort and expense for the hardware preparation.

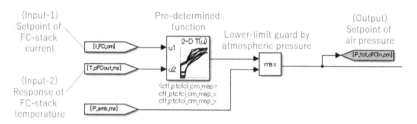

Fig. 4. Simulink flow diagram of air pressure setpoint determination in the FC-stack controller

3. Simulation results and discussion

Fig. 5 shows the results of the closed loop simulation shown in Fig. 2 to confirm the setpoint tracking performance of the FC-system net power when the vehicle speed is kept constant at 160 km/h and the coolant radiator size is varied. It was confirmed that the FC-system net power could trace the setpoint within an acceptable deviation less than 1 % in the case of the base-size radiator as shown in Fig. 5 (a). Fig. 5 (b) shows the 3 % deviation of the FC-system net power from the setpoint occurs during 660 – 670 s when the coolant radiator size is 70 % of the base size. In this period, the average coolant temperature is raised to 105 ℃ as shown in Fig. 5 (c), where IV performance of the FC stack deteriorated due to the severe dry condition as shown in Fig. 5 (d). From these results, it was suggested that the limitation of the radiator size reduction is around 85 % in the given operating condition.

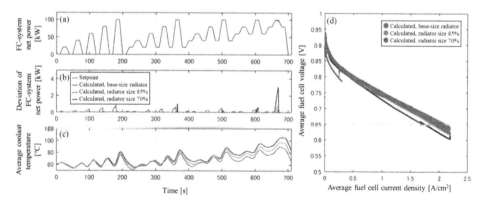

Fig. 5. Closed loop simulation results of the sensitivity of the coolant radiator size on (a) the setpoint and calculated value of the FC-system net power, (b) the deviation between the setpoint and calculated value of FC-net power, (c) the average coolant temperature, and (d) the FC-stack IV performance

Fig. 6 shows closed-loop simulation results of the FC-system efficiency described in Eqs. (1) and (2). The FC-system net efficiency was confirmed to be around 40–70 % in 20–90 kW with every radiator size, which was sufficiently high compared with conventional internal combustion engine systems.

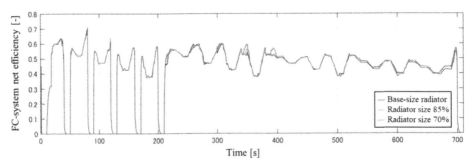

Fig. 6. Closed loop simulation outputs of the FC-system net efficiency

It was shown by the examples in Figs. 5 and 6 that the closed-loop simulation of the entire FC system in this study enabled the detailed system hardware and control investigation before manufacturing the costly FC-system testbed and test vehicles. On the other hand, control parameters, such as the gains in PI-control in Fig. 3 and the pre-determined function of target state variables in Fig. 4, were calibrated by the time-consuming trial-and-error and the maximum FC-system net efficiency cannot be ensured theoretically. The more efficient and sophisticated controller parameter determination process should be implemented by introducing the state-of-art optimization technologies such as model predictive control (MPC).

Conclusions

The controllers for the entire FC system were developed. These controllers were integrated with the FC-system hardware models to serve a closed-loop simulation. It enabled the design of the hardware and controllers in the entire FC system without manufacturing the costly system prototypes. The control parameters were calibrated on the developed simulator until the prospective controller performance was confirmed. The sensitivity of coolant radiator size on the setpoint tracking performance of the FC-system net power and the FC-system net efficiency were investigated with the calibrated controller as the demonstration of the model-based FC-system development.

Acknowledgement

This work was supported by the FC-Platform Program: Development of design-for-purpose numerical simulators for attaining long life and high performance project (FY 2020–2022) conducted by the New Energy and Industrial Technology Development Organization (NEDO), Japan.

References

A. Z. Weber et al., 2014, *Journal of The Electrochemical Society*, **161** (12) F1254-F1299

S. Hasegawa, M. Kimata, Y. Ikogi, M. Kageyama, S. Kim, and M. Kawase, 2021a, *ECS Transactions*, 104 (8) 3-26

S. Hasegawa, S. Matsumoto, Y. Ikogi, T. Takahashi, S. Kim, M. Kageyama, and M. Kawase, 2021b, *The 14th International Symposium on Process Systems Engineering* (*PSE 2021+*)

T. Takahashi and Y. Kakeno, 2021, *EVTeC 2021 Proceedings*, No. B1.1.

Proceedings of the 14th International Symposium on Process Systems Engineering – PSE 2021+
June 19-23, 2022, Kyoto, Japan © 2022 Elsevier B.V. All rights reserved.
http://dx.doi.org/10.1016/B978-0-323-85159-6.50188-3

A Nested Schur Decomposition Approach for Multiperiod Process Optimization

Noriyuki Yoshio[a], Lorenz T. Biegler[b*]

[a]*Kureha Corporation, 16, Ochiai, Nishiki-Machi,Iwaki, Fukushima 974-8686, Japan*
[b]*Carnegie Mellon University, 5000 Forbes Ave, Pittsburgh, PA 15213, USA*
biegler@cmu.edu

Abstract

This work develops an algorithm for solving multiperiod optimization (MPO) problem using a nested Schur decomposition (NSD) approach. The NSD approach decomposes MPO using a Schur complement and allows us to solve the decomposed nonlinear programming (NLP) problem in parallel. The NSD partitions the MPO into a two-level problem with individual NLPs at the lower level. The problem-level decomposition facilitates the flexible selection of the lower-level solver.

In this paper, the NSD approach is demonstrated with different process models for MPO in parallel computation. The solutions are also compared with the direct approach, which solves the entire MPO problem simultaneously. The demonstration shows IPOPT could be more efficient than CONOPT when the problem is well-conditioned. Moreover, it is noted that the NSD outperforms the direct approach when the size of the process model is large with CONOPT as the lower-level solver. From those results, we observe that NSD is well-suited to solve large MPO problems for chemical processes in an efficient, flexible, and robust manner.

Keywords: Optimization; Multiperiod; Applications.

1. Introduction

MPO problems are an important class of optimization problems that often consider design and operating plans for predicted demands over a given time horizon. For chemical processes, rigorous process models are highly integrated with multiple unit models and thermodynamic property models, which lead to a large system of nonlinear equations. MPO problems of such process models could be significantly larger and more complex than a single process model. The chemical industry highly demands strategies to extend a single process model to MPO in a robust, flexible, and efficient way over their process development.

To solve such a large-scale nonlinear problem in efficient and tractable ways, several decomposition approaches have been developed in the past. Those approaches can be classified into internal and external decompositions. The former internal decomposition approaches for an interior-point algorithm have been developed. The overview of the developments and the applicable problem structures can be seen in (Kang et al., 2015). The approach utilizes block-angular or general block-bordered structure in the solution of the augmented system for decomposition at the linear algebra level. Hence, the internal decomposition approach can fully utilize the advantage of interior-point methods in solving large-scale nonlinear problems. The methods, however, face difficulties when there are degeneracies in the problem constraints. In such case, we often rely on active set methods such as CONOPT (Drud, 1985), which handles dependent constraints efficiently as part of the active set selection.

On the other hand, external decomposition approaches decompose the problem at the problem formulation level. The external approach could be more flexible and easier in the implementation than the internal one because the approach is less intrusive. For example, Benders decomposition and the alternating direction method of multipliers (ADMM) are one of the external decompositions. These methods utilize only the first order information of the decomposed problems. Thus, the methods are inefficient due to the lack of the exact Hessian information from the lower problem, which is fully utilized in the internal decomposition approach.

To address this problem, we develop the nested Schur decomposition (NSD) approach and demonstrate it with MPO problems for chemical processes. The approach applies an external decomposition so that we can flexibly utilize interior-point or active set solvers for the lower-level problem. On the other hand, as a Schur decomposition approach it has the same KKT structure and fast convergence properties which allows us to use the Hessian information of the lower-level problem as the internal Schur decomposition approach. Moreover, it retains the computational advantage of the parallelization in the external decomposition framework.

2. Problem statement

We consider the general MPO problem of the form

$$
\begin{aligned}
\min \quad & \bar{f}_0(x) + \sum_{i=1}^{N} \bar{f}_i(x, z_i) \\
\text{s.t.} \quad & h_0(x) = 0 \\
& h_i(z_i, d_i) = 0 \\
& g_i(z_i, d_i) + s_i = 0, \quad s_i \geq 0 \\
& z^L \leq z_i \leq z^U, \quad i = 1, \dots, N \\
& x^L \leq x \leq x^U
\end{aligned}
\tag{1}
$$

where N is the number of periods, $x \in \mathbb{R}^{n_x}$ is the vector of global variables and $z_i \in \mathbb{R}^{n_{z,i}}$ are the decision variables in each period i. Some of the global variables are exposed to process constraints h_i and g_i of each period via $d_i \in \mathbb{R}^{n_{d,i}}$. The coupling (or complicating) variables d_i are also included in the global variable vector x. s_i are the slack variables for the inequality constraints g_i. The global constraints h_0 could be linking, common, and demand constraints, and the linking constraints use the information of adjacent periods to describe inventory updates. The common constraints enforce the same value for all periods such as design parameters. The demand constraints reflect the limitation of the sales for the demand with given demands or demand forecast models.

For the problem level decomposition, we reformulate Problem (1) as a two-level optimization problem by disaggregating the complicating variable d_i and introducing artificial variables δ_i and dummy constraints. The upper level problem is written as:

$$\min \quad \Phi_0(x) \equiv f_0(x) + \sum_{i=1}^{N} f_i\big(z_i(x), \delta_i(x)\big) + \sum_{i=1}^{N} \beta q_i(x)^T e$$

$$\text{s.t.} \quad h_0(x) = 0$$
$$h_i(z_i, d_i) = 0 \tag{2}$$
$$x^L \le x \le x^U$$

where $z_i(x)$, $\delta_i(x)$ and $q_i(x)$ are solutions from each lower-level problem $i = 1, \dots, N$:

$$\min \quad \Phi_i(x) \equiv f_i\big(z_i(x), \delta_i(x)\big) + \beta q_i(x)^T e$$

$$\text{s.t.} \quad h_i(z_i, d_i) = 0$$
$$g_i(z_i, d_i) + s_i = q_{g,i}, \ \ s_i \ge 0 \tag{3}$$
$$z^L \le z_i \le z^U, \ \ i = 1, \dots, N$$
$$h_{d,i} = \delta_i - G_i x - C_{d,i}\big(q_{+,i} - q_{-,i}\big) = 0, \ \ q_i = \big[q_{+,i}^T, q_{-,i}^T, q_{g,i}^T\big]^T \ge 0$$

where $G_i \in \mathbb{R}^{n_{d,i} \times n_x}$ is a mapping matrix to assign the global variables x onto each period and $C_{d,i} \in \mathbb{R}^{n_{d,i} \times n_{d,i}}$ is a scaling matrix whose diagonal elements have scaling factors for δ_i. $q_{+,i} \in \mathbb{R}^{n_{d,i}}$ and $q_{-,i} \in \mathbb{R}^{n_{d,i}}$ represent positive and negative violation values for the relaxation of the dummy constraints. $q_{g,i} \in \mathbb{R}^{n_{g,i}}$ is also positive violation value for the relaxation of the inequality constraints. The values are penalized in the objective along with the penalty constant β and $e^T = [1, 1, \dots, 1]$. The purpose of the relaxation is to avoid an infeasible solution of the process model in each period. Furthermore, the original objective $\bar{f}$ is also modified to f so that the problem is separated into two parts.

3. Solution strategy

In order to collect the lower-level problems' information Φ_i into the upper-level problem, inequality constraints in the lower-level problems are replaced by barrier terms and the lower-level problems are assumed to be solved with interior point strategies. By considering the KKT conditions for each barrier problem of lower-level problem, the assembled Newton step is written as:

$$
\begin{bmatrix}
K_1 & & & & E_1 & & & & \\
 & K_2 & & & & E_2 & & & \\
 & & \ddots & & & & \ddots & & \\
 & & & K_N & & & & E_N & \\
E_1^T & & & & & & & & -G_1 \\
 & E_2^T & & & & & & & -G_2 \\
 & & \ddots & & & & & & \vdots \\
 & & & E_N^T & & & & & -G_N \\
 & & & & -G_1^T & -G_2^T & \cdots & -G_N^T & 0
\end{bmatrix}
\begin{bmatrix}
\Delta y_1 \\ \Delta y_2 \\ \vdots \\ \Delta y_N \\ \Delta \gamma_1 \\ \Delta \gamma_2 \\ \vdots \\ \Delta \gamma_N \\ \Delta x
\end{bmatrix}
= -
\begin{bmatrix}
0 \\ 0 \\ \vdots \\ 0 \\ 0 \\ 0 \\ \vdots \\ 0 \\ m
\end{bmatrix}
\tag{4}
$$

where $\gamma_i \in \mathbb{R}^{n_{d,i}}$ is the dual of the dummy constraints and the other primal and dual variables are represented $y_i \in \mathbb{R}^{n_y}$. $E_i = \nabla_{y_i} h_{d,i} \in \mathbb{R}^{n_{d,i} \times n_y}$. $K_i \in \mathbb{R}^{n_y \times n_y}$ is the KKT matrix where E_i is excluded. Furthermore, the right-hand side is set to zero except for m because we can solve problem (3) for each period individually. m is the gradient information with respect to x and is written as $m = -\sum_{i=1}^{N} G_i^T \gamma_i$. By pivoting the block matrices in (4) we obtain:

$$
\begin{bmatrix}
K_1 & & & & E_1 & & & & \\
& K_2 & & & & E_2 & & & \\
& & \ddots & & & & \ddots & & \\
& & & K_N & & & & E_N & \\
\hline
-P_1 & & & & & & & & -G_1 \\
& -P_2 & & & & & & & -G_2 \\
& & \ddots & & & & & & \vdots \\
& & & -P_N & & & & & -G_N \\
\hline
-G_1^T & -G_2^T & \cdots & -G_N^T & & & & & M
\end{bmatrix}
\begin{bmatrix}
\Delta y_1 \\
\Delta y_2 \\
\vdots \\
\Delta y_N \\
\hline
\Delta \gamma_1 \\
\Delta \gamma_2 \\
\vdots \\
\Delta \gamma_N \\
\hline
\Delta x
\end{bmatrix}
= -
\begin{bmatrix}
0 \\
0 \\
\vdots \\
0 \\
\hline
0 \\
0 \\
\vdots \\
0 \\
\hline
m
\end{bmatrix}
\tag{5}
$$

where $M = \sum_{i=1}^{N} G_i^T P_i^{-1} G_i$, $P_i = E^T K_i^{-1} E$. Note that $P_i^{-1} G_i$ can be generated directly by solving the following equation.

$$
\begin{bmatrix} K_i & E_i \\ E_i^T & 0 \end{bmatrix} \begin{bmatrix} X_1 \\ X_2 \end{bmatrix} = \begin{bmatrix} 0 \\ -G_i \end{bmatrix}
\tag{6}
$$

where $X_2 = P_i^{-1} G_i$ and $M = \sum_{i=1}^{N} G_i^T X_2$. M and m are the Hessian and gradient of the objective for the part of the lower-level problem. Thus, the augmented Hessian of the objective in the upper-level problem is $\nabla^2 \Phi_0(x) = \nabla^2 f_0(x) + M$. The gradient of the objective is $\nabla \Phi_0(x) = \nabla f(x) + m$.

When the lower-level problems' information augments the upper problem's objective, the upper-level problem becomes just a constrained nonlinear optimization problem. The upper problem can be solved with Newton-type solvers, an interior-point solver such as IPOPT, or a trust region solver such as *trust-constr* from Scipy by providing the augmented Hessian and gradient information. For the lower problem, each period is solved individually, as seen from the zero residuals on the right-hand side of Eq. (4). Although the approach is derived based on the interior point strategy with the barrier approach, any NLP solver such as IPOPT or CONOPT can be used, as long as the lower problem successfully converges and the KKT information can be retrieved. This is because the barrier parameter is equivalent to a Hessian projection upon convergence of the lower-level problem.

4. Implementation

As mentioned in Section 3, we can use any solver as long as the upper problem solver is a globally convergent Newton-type solver for constrained optimization. Here, we present the implementation scheme with *cyipopt* (Aides et al., 2021) as the solver of the upper problem, which is a python wrapper for IPOPT. The lower problems (3) are formulated in *Pyomo* (Hart et al., 2017), and solved with CONOPT or IPOPT. Then, the primal, dual values and the bound multipliers are extracted. The solution is utilized for the initial values of the next inner problem to use a warm start. After that, the part of the Hessian of the Lagrangian and the Jacobian of the constraints in the KKT system is evaluated with *Pynumero* (Laird et al., 2019). The Hessian of the bounded variables in the barrier term is separately evaluated in Python with the extracted primal and multiplier values. The evaluation method follows the procedure of IPOPT (Wächter and Biegler, 2006).

5. Case study

In this section, we demonstrate the NSD approach with MPO problems for Williams-Otto (WO) process and benzene chlorination (BC) process. The upper level of the MPO problem consists of the inventory update and demand constraint which are set over the entire period. The lower level of the MPO problem consists of the process models for each time period to evaluate the production rate. The detailed problem formulation can be seen in (Yoshio and Biegler, 2021). Here, we focus on the computational performance. Different problem sizes are used from $N = 3$ to $N = 14$ periods and the problem size increases with N, as shown in Table 1 for the cases of both WO and BC processes. The WO process model is relatively small model. On the other hand, the BC process is considerably large model. In the performance test, the parallelized NSD approach uses N processes for solving each period in parallel. The computational time is compared with the direct solution that solves the entire MPO problem simultaneously without decomposition. For the lower-level solver, CONOPT is used for both the WO and BC processes, and IPOPT is used for the WO process. For comparison a direct solution of problem (1) is obtained with CONOPT.

The computational comparison can be seen in Figure 1. For the WO process, Figure 1(a) compares the computational time for the direct approach and NSD with both IPOPT and CONOPT as lower-level solvers. As seen in the figure, the direct approach is approximately 10-20 times faster than the NSD approaches. This is because the problem size of the WO process model is relatively small and the overhead of the NSD dominates any savings gained from the parallel solution of the lower-level problems. On the other hand, for parallel NSD, IPOPT outperforms CONOPT on the lower problems. This result indicates IPOPT for the lower problem solver could be more efficient than CONOPT for this well-conditioned problem. For the BC process, Figure 1(b) compares the computational time for the direct approach and NSD with CONOPT as a lower-level solver. The computational result shows that the computational time proportionally increases in the direct approach as N increases. For the parallel NSD approach, the wall clock time remains constant as the number of periods N increases. We note that parallel NSD outperforms the direct approach when N > 8.

Table 1 The number of variables in MPO problems

N	3	4	5	6	7	8	9	10	11	12	13	14
WO	149	198	247	296	345	394	443	492	541	590	639	688
BC ($\times 10^4$)	2.8	3.7	4.6	5.5	6.5	7.4	8.3	9.2	10	11	12	13

6. Conclusions

We have developed and demonstrated an NSD algorithm for solving large-scale nonlinear optimization problems, especially MPO problems. The NSD facilitates the parallelization of the decomposed problem within the algorithm by utilizing the structure of the KKT system. The approach was applied to MPO problems of the WO process and BC process. The studies show the capability of flexible solver choice for the inner problem. NSD is a reliable option to parallelize large-scale nonlinear problems because the flexible solver choice enables us to utilize robust active set solvers efficiently for degenerate problems.

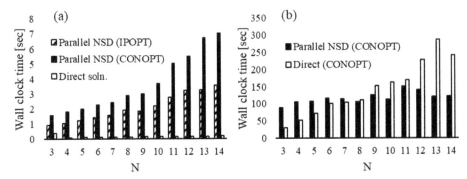

Figure 1 The comparison in the computational time for MPO of (a) WO process and (b) BC process.

Furthermore, the NSD approach has the computational advantage of the parallelization when the lower-level problem is large. This flexible, robust, and efficient approach could provide a number of benefits for current practical process development. In the future, NSD will be considered for a number of large-scale nonconvex NLP applications, including multiset and multi-effect parameter estimation problems, stochastic programming problems for process optimization under uncertainty, decomposition of integrated site-wide optimization problems with complex subsystems, and decomposition for optimization of spatially distributed energy networks.

References

A. Aides, A. Andreasen, M. Kümmerer, A. Toscano, W. Brendel, J.K. Moore, B. Bocklund, H. Wang, A. Pommel, A. De, S. Brockie, Y. Schälte, 2021. A Cython wrapper to the IPOPT optimization package. Technical Report. Accessed on Feb 6. https://pypi.org/project/ipopt/

A. Drud, 1985. Conopt: a grg code for large sparse dynamic nonlinear optimization problems. Math Program 31 (2), 153–191

W.E. Hart, C.D. Laird, J.-P. Watson, D.L. Woodruff, G.A. Hackebeil, B.L. Nicholson, J.D. Siirola, 2017. Pyomo–optimization modeling in python, vol. 67, 2nd Springer Science & Business Media . Hart, W.E. , Watson, J.-P. , Woodruff, D.L. , 2011. Pyomo: modeling and solving mathematical programs in python. Mathematical Programming Computation 3 (3), 219–260

J. Kang, N. Chiang, C.D. Laird, V.M. Zavala, 2015. Nonlinear programming strategies on high-performance computers. In: 2015 54th IEEE conference on decision and control (CDC). IEEE, pp. 4612–4620

C.D. Laird, B.L. Nicholson, J.S. Rodriguez, 2019. Parallel Numerical Algorithms for Structured Problems with PyNumero and Pyomo. Technical Report. Sandia National Lab.(SNL-NM), Albuquerque, NM (United States)

A. Wächter, L.T. Biegler, 2006. On the implementation of an interior-point filter line-search algorithm for large-scale nonlinear programming. Math Program 106 (1), 25–57

N. Yoshio, and L. T. Biegler. "A Nested Schur Decomposition Approach for Multiperiod Optimization of Chemical Processes." Computers & Chemical Engineering (2021): 107509

Proceedings of the 14th International Symposium on Process Systems Engineering – PSE 2021+
June 19-23, 2022, Kyoto, Japan © 2022 Elsevier B.V. All rights reserved.
http://dx.doi.org/10.1016/B978-0-323-85159-6.50189-5

Design and Optimisation of Boil-off Gas Recycling Strategy in Liquefied Natural Gas Production

Ahmed AlNouss, Saad A. Al-Sobhi[*]

Department of Chemical Engineering, College of Engineering, Qatar University. Doha, Qatar
saad.al-sobhi@qu.edu.qa

Abstract

The process of liquefying natural gas is associated with many design and optimisation challenges. The formation of so-called boil-off gas (BOG) due to the difference in the bubble point of LNG and the surrounding ambient temperature around storage tanks, is one of the most challenging issues. Industries around the world are investigating the recovery of BOG to enhance the economy of design and reduce environmental impacts due to flaring. The BOG composition forms a crucial aspect of the recovery process where the nitrogen and methane content can affect the location of recovery in addition to the economy and mechanism of the recovery process. This study addresses the design and optimisation of the BOG recycling flowsheet configuration in the LNG production process. Multiple sensitivity analyses are considered to study the effect of changing temperature and mass flow of recycled BOG, in addition to the temperature and pressure of LNG feed. The observed parameters include final methane content, nitrogen content, mass flow and temperature of LNG product and fuel gas along with the Wobbe Index of LNG product. The BOG utilisation strategy focuses on recycling BOG prior the liquefaction unit with three different nitrogen rejection unit (NRU) configurations, namely, the double distillation columns, single distillation column and flash drum. To show the significance of the proposed recycling strategy, an illustrative case study is analysed and evaluated for recycling 52,000 metric tonnes of BOG annually while optimising the design conditions of the BOG and LNG streams. The results indicate the huge effect of BOG to natural gas blending ratio on the purity of the LNG product. Hence, the increase in BOG mass flow rate demonstrates to increase the methane content on the produced LNG and reduce the nitrogen content for the flash drum and double columns configurations. This highlights the potential of BOG recovery on enhancing the performance of the LNG process despite the need for an additional economic and environmental investigation.

Keywords: LNG, BOG, Flare management, Simulation, Optimisation, NRU.

1. Introduction

The global consumption of natural gas (NG) continuous to rise with the growing forecasted demand on energy and the increase in economic growth and world population. The low environmental impacts of NG relative to other fossil fuels place it as the favourable energy alternative. The liquefaction of NG in the well-known Liquefied Natural Gas (LNG) process dominates the energy market despite the intensive energy requirement. The LNG process is essential to ensure easier transportation and shipping of liquefied NG worldwide. The process comprise treatment of sour field NG to remove the presence of CO_2, H_2S and water, separation and liquefaction of sweet NG from the associated heavier hydrocarbons, extraction of left-over nitrogen and helium components, and finally the storage, loading and transportation of LNG product. The volume of the LNG product constitute 1/600 of its gas-form volume. The common employed liquefaction technology in LNG process is C3-MR consisting of propane and mixed refrigerant cryogenic cooling loops. The A-PX technology has emerged as an improvement from C3-MR. LNG process is associated with a number of challenges; one of which is the formation of boil-off gas (BOG) during LNG storage loading and shipping operations. The large difference between LNG storage conditions (-160 °C) and ambient surrounding (~25°C) in addition to sudden pressure changes and unloading operation act as driving force for the heat transfer despite advanced insulation mechanism and the partial evaporation of stored LNG producing BOG. Therefore, BOG consist mainly of methane (93wt%) and nitrogen (7wt%) and accounts for 1-3 vol% of LNG product. Venting and flaring of BOG is the common mitigation in global industries that is associated with environmental and economic concerns (Al-Sobhi et al., 2021).

Scholars have approached the aspects of BOG management from various perspectives including minimisation, recycling and quantification. For example, Kurle et al. (2015) explored different BOG recycling strategies in C3-MR process to establish optimum temperature for BOG minimisation and recycle. An optimal temperature of -166 °C found to reduce the total cost associated with the minimisation and recovery of BOG. Similarly Bao et al. (2019) compared three BOG management strategies from power output perspective while examining the effect of electricity cost, interest factor, and BOG content on the net present value (NPV). The results demonstrated an increasing trend for NPV with BOG content and a decreasing trend with interest rate. Shin et al. (2007) studied from a safety-driven objective the optimisation of BOG compression system to verify adequacy through a mixed-integer linear model. The results revealed an energy recovery potential of 11.5% from the current operating compressors.

Despite the high literature studies on BOG management, there is still a necessity to establish the optimum pathway of BOG recovery and utilisation within A-PX LNG process. This study explore the optimisation of key design parameters involved in the recovery and utilisation of BOG within different recycling configurations in the LNG production process. The liquefaction flowsheet model with recycled BOG stream is established to study the effect of changing temperature, pressure and mass flow of recycled BOG, in addition to the temperature and pressure of LNG feed on the final methane content, nitrogen content, mass flow and temperature of LNG product and fuel gas along with the Wobbe Index of LNG product. Traditional LNG plants practice the flare of BOG streams due to the intensive energy associated with liquefaction and recycling. However, flaring is not a sustainable mitigation due to the high associated NO_X and CO_2 emissions and the global burden to apply stringent environmental regulations. Hence, this study aims to establish an optimum pathway for the recovery of BOG.

2. Methodology

The overall methodology to design and optimise the BOG recycling strategy in LNG production line consist of 1) estimation of BOG rate of formation, 2) Simulation of LNG/BOG recycling scenarios, 3) execution of key sensitivity analyses, 4) formulation of optimisation problem, and 5) conclusion of optimal parameters. The BOG utilisation strategy focuses on recycling BOG prior the liquefaction section with three different nitrogen rejection unit (NRU) configurations, namely, the double distillation columns, single distillation column and flash drum. The base models have been emphasised in an earlier work (Al-Sobhi et al., 2021) with the detailed description of process models and economic and environmental benefits of BOG recycling. This study forms an extension to optimise the BOG utilisation with the variation of key design parameters. To show the significance of the proposed recycling strategy, an illustrative case study representing the state of Qatar LNG plants is analysed and evaluated for various design alternatives of recycling 52,000 metric tonnes of BOG annually while optimising the conditions of the BOG and LNG streams. BOG is assumed to be generated from five 300,000 m^3 storage tanks at a vaporisation rate of 0.5vol% per day. Aspen HYSYS is utilised to construct the integrated LNG-BOG flowsheets of different schemes. Qatar is currently producing approximately 77 million metric tonnes per annum (MMTPA) with planned future expansion up to 110 MMTPA in 2025 placing Qatar as the largest global LNG producer and exporter (Qatargas, 2019). Multiple sensitivity analyses are considered to study the effect of changing temperature and mass flow of recycled BOG, in addition to temperature and pressure of LNG feed. The observed parameters the final methane content, nitrogen content, mass flow and temperature of LNG product and fuel gas along Wobbe Index (WI) of LNG product. WI is used to correlate the high heating value (HHV) of a gas mixture to the square root of the gas specific gravity; density of mixture relative to air, as expressed in Eq. (1). It is utilised in this study as a representative of the significance of BOG recycling in enhancing energy content.

$$WI = \frac{HHV}{\sqrt{\frac{\rho}{\rho_{air}}}} \tag{1}$$

Aspen HYSYS is used to assess the variations in each operating parameter. Results of the sensitivity analyses are used to construct regression models relating WI of LNG product and methane content of fuel gas to changes in each operating parameter. The functions of the WI and methane content of LNG product for each operating parameter are employed where the weighted average of these functions is calculated to characterise the objective functions of the proposed optimisation model. The singular objective function of WI and methane content of LNG product, expressed in Eqs. (1 and 2), is then maximised to produce the optimal decision variables for each objective. Later, optimal solutions for the simultaneous computing objectives of WI and methane content of LNG product are achieved using Matlab Genetic Algorithm tool and a Pareto front is generated for each recycling configurations.

Variables:

$\dot{T}_{fuel\ gas}$: Fuel gas final temperature (°C)

$\dot{T}_{LNG}$: LNG final temperature (°C)

$\dot{m}_{fuel\ gas}$: Fuel gas production rate (t/h)

$\dot{m}_{LNG}$: LNG production rate (t/h)

$\dot{m}_{Nitrogen,fuel\ gas}$: Nitrogen content in fuel gas (t/h)

$\dot{m}_{Nitrogen,LNG}$: Nitrogen content in LNG (t/h)

$\dot{m}_{Methane,fuel\ gas}$: Methane content in fuel gas (t/h)

$\dot{m}_{Methane,LNG}$: Methane content in LNG (t/h)

WI: Wobbe Index (WI) of LNG product (MJ/Nm^3)

Decision variables:

$\dot{T}_{BOG}$: BOG inlet temperature (°C)

$\dot{T}_{LNG}$: LNG feed temperature (°C)

$\dot{m}_{BOG}$: BOG inlet rate (t/h)

$\dot{P}_{BOG}$: BOG inlet pressure (bar)

$\dot{P}_{LNG}$: LNG feed pressure (bar)

Objective function:

    Maximise: *WI*   (2)

    Maximise: $\dot{m}_{Methane,LNG}$ (3)

Constraints: *As illustrated in Table 1*

Table 1. Optimisation problem raw data

Parameter	Flow (t/h)	Variation (t/h)	T (°C)	Variation (°C)	P (bar)	Variation (bar)
NG Feed	890.4	-	-84	-100:-200	41	1:20
BOG Feed	5.94	0.5:20	-162	-100:-200	1	1:20

3. Results

The output of sensitivity analyses and singular optimisation of WI and methane content of LNG product demonstrated a variation in the resulted key decision variables. Table 1 illustrates the complete set of decision variables of the two optimisation problems for the different configurations.

Table 2. Singular optimisation results

Parameter	$\dot{T}_{BOG}$(°C)	$\dot{T}_{LNG}$(°C)	$\dot{m}_{BOG}$(t/h)	$\dot{P}_{BOG}$(bar)	$\dot{P}_{LNG}$(bar)	Objective function
Objective			Flash drum configuration			
WI	-100	-100	20	20	20	80.28
CH₄ content	-200	-200	20	2	3	884 (t/h)
Objective			Single column configuration			
WI	-165	-199	20	1	20	53.00
CH₄ content	-102	-166	0.5	19	2	578 (t/h)
Objective			Double columns configuration			
WI	-200	-167	0.5	20	2	52.61
CH₄ content	-168	-166	20	2	20	705 (t/h)

The flash drum configuration demonstrated the highest in terms of WI and CH₄ content results followed by double columns configuration and lastly single column configuration. The optimal parameters for the flash drum configurations demonstrate the requirement to feed the NG and recycled BOG at the highest temperature, pressure and flowrate of the range, -100 °C, 20 and 20, respectively, to achieve the highest value of WI and a flowrate of BOG at 0.5 t/h. Vase versa, the highest CH₄ content is achieved at the lowest temperature and pressure of the range, -200 °C, 2 and 3, respectively and the highest flowrate of BOG at 20 t/h. This represents the importance to maintain the recycle process at high pressure and low temperature to ensure achieving highest content of methane in the LNG product with highest WI. Whereas, the optimal parameters for the single column configurations demonstrate the requirement to feed the NG and recycled BOG at the temperature, pressure and flowrate of -165 °C, -199 °C, 20 and 1, respectively, to achieve the highest WI. Vase versa, the highest CH₄ content for the single column configurations is achieved at the temperature and pressure of -102 °C, -166, 19 and 2, respectively and a flowrate of BOG at 0.5 t/h. The results indicate the possibility to feed the BOG at atmospheric pressure condition with -165 °C to achieve the carryover of nitrogen content in the fuel gas while increasing these conditions will ensure the maximum methane content in the LNG product. The last configuration of double columns demonstrate the requirement to feed the NG and recycled BOG at the temperature, pressure and flowrate of -200 °C, -167 °C, 20 and 0.5, respectively, to achieve the highest WI. Vase versa, the highest CH_4 content for the double columns configurations is achieved at the temperature and pressure of -168 °C, -166, 2 and 20, respectively and a flowrate of BOG at 20 t/h. The main reason behind these results is the fact that both columns of the configuration are operated at atmospheric pressure. Hence, feeding the BOG at cold temperatures and low pressure ensures to separate most of the methane out to the LNG stream. Opposite of that ensures to have the highest WI.

Utilising the formulation to solve the two computing objectives simultaneous results on the trade-off between WI and methane content of LNG product. The optimal solutions for each recycling configurations, generated using Matlab Genetic Algorithm tool, are presented as Pareto fronts in Figures (1-3). The three figures demonstrate the trade-off between WI and methane content of LNG product where the increase in one leads to the decrease of other. These solutions represent the possible operating points of the integrated LNG-BOG system to achieve BOG recycling while maintain the process design specs.

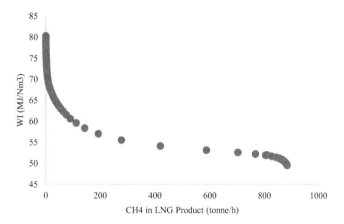

Figure 1: Pareto curve of WI and methane content objectives for flash drum configuration.

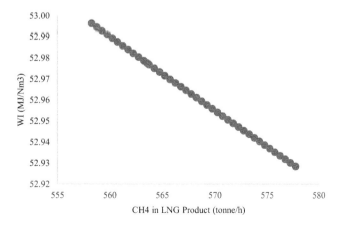

Figure 2: Pareto curve of WI and methane content objectives for single column configuration.

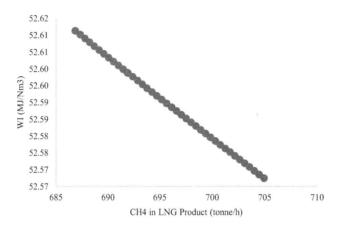

Figure 3: Pareto curve of WI and methane content objectives for double columns configuration.

4. Conclusions

The liquefaction of NG in the well-known Liquefied Natural Gas (LNG) process dominates the energy market despite the intensive energy requirement. LNG process is associated with a number of challenges; one of which is the formation of boil-off gas (BOG) during LNG storage loading and shipping operations. This study explore the optimisation of key design parameters involved in the recovery and utilisation of BOG within different recycling configurations in the LNG production process. The flowsheet models are established to study the effect of changing temperature, pressure and mass flow of recycled BOG, in addition to the temperature and pressure of LNG feed on the final methane content, nitrogen content, mass flow and temperature of LNG product and fuel gas along with the WI of LNG product. The Pareto fronts generated from the multi objective optimization demonstrate the trade-off between WI and methane content of LNG product where the increase in one leads to the decrease of other. These solutions represent the possible operating points of the integrated LNG-BOG system to achieve BOG recycling while maintain the process design specs

References

S.A. Al-Sobhi, A. AlNouss, M. Shamlooh, K. Al-Nuaimi, A. AlMulla, and M. Khraisheh, 2021, Sustainable boil-off gas utilization in liquefied natural gas production: Economic and environmental benefits, Journal of Cleaner Production, 296, 126563.
J. Bao, T. Yuan, L. Zhang, N. Zhang, and X. Zhang, 2019, Comparative study of three boil-off gas treatment schemes: From an economic perspective, Energy Conversion and Management, 201, 112185.
Y.M. Kurle, S. Wang, and Q. Xu, 2015, Simulation study on boil-off gas minimization and recovery strategies at LNG exporting terminals, Applied Energy, 156, 628-41.
Qatargas, 2019, North Field Expansion project,
M.W. Shin, D. Shin, S.H. Choi, E.S. Yoon, and C. Han, 2007, Optimization of the Operation of Boil-Off Gas Compressors at a Liquified Natural Gas Gasification Plant, Industrial & Engineering Chemistry Research, 46, 20, 6540-45.

Proceedings of the 14th International Symposium on Process Systems Engineering – PSE 2021+
June 19–23, 2022, Kyoto, Japan ©2022 Elsevier B. V. All rights reserved.
http://dx.doi.org/10.1016/B978-0-323-85159-6.50190-1

An Implicit Function Formulation for Nonlinear Programming with Index-1 Differential Algebraic Equation Systems

Robert B. Parker[a], Bethany L. Nicholson[b], John D. Siirola[b], Carl D. Laird[a], Lorenz T. Biegler[a]*

[a]*Carnegie Mellon University, 5000 Forbes Ave, Pittsburgh, PA 15213, United States*
[b]*Sandia National Laboratories, P.O. Box 5800, Albuquerque, NM 87123, United States*

biegler@cmu.edu

Abstract

A reduced space formulation for optimization of index-1 differential algebraic equation systems (DAEs) is described and implemented using PyNumero. The formulation defines implicit functions from algebraic equations and uses them to remove algebraic variables and equations from the optimization problem. The formulation is used to solve dynamic optimization problems with the Ipopt solver. In challenging case studies involving the simulation and optimization of a chemical looping combustion reactor, the reduced space formulation is more robust, solving 115 out of 125 problem instances in the first case and 52 out of 72 instances in the second case. The full space simultaneous formulation solves 50 and 24 problem instances, respectively. The results indicate the potential of this formulation to be more reliable than the full space formulation for challenging nonlinear DAE optimization problems.

Keywords: Dynamic, Optimization, Software

1. Introduction

Differential algebraic equation systems (DAEs) are an expressive class of equations for chemical and process systems engineers. They are capable of representing processes that evolve over continuous time and/or space domains and involve nonlinear physical and chemical phenomena. Complicated interactions among differential states are often described by large numbers of nonlinear algebraic equations that represent the thermodynamics, chemical reactions, and transport phenomena of the system. Due to their number and complexity, the ability to simulate or optimize a large-scale DAE relies on the ability to converge these algebraic equations without excessive problem-specific initialization.

Two common approaches for optimization of DAE systems are the sequential approach described by Goh & Teo (1988) and the simultaneous approach described by Cuthrell & Biegler (1987). Hybrid approaches have been proposed, including the quasi-sequential approach of Hong et al. (2006), which eliminates all equality constraints from the optimization algorithm but retains inequality constraints that may involve state variables. We propose a hybrid approach for DAEs that are index-1 in which only the algebraic variables and equations are eliminated from the nonlinear optimization problem using implicit functions. Our approach is simultaneous in the sense that the continuous domain is discretized and that all discretization points are considered simultaneously by the optimizer, but has the characteristic of sequential approaches that square problems are solved by an embedded solver within each iteration of the optimization solve. This is a reduced-space formulation as only the differential, input, and derivative variables are seen by the optimization algorithm. The implicit function subproblems admit exact first and second derivatives in terms of these variables and are thus compatible with second-order optimization algorithms. Our approach is conceptually similar to that of Bongartz & Mitsos (2017), where external functions are used to solve global flowsheet optimization problems in a reduced space. Rather than implementing a fully implicit function, however, they use a sequential modular function evaluation for which they compute convex relaxations.

2. Background and Implementation

A discretized DAE has the form given by Equation (1). Here F describes the differential equations, G describes the algebraic equations, d describes the discretization equations, and x_0 are the initial conditions. The equations are in terms of differential variables x, algebraic variables y, input variables u, and derivatives $\dot{x}$ with respect to a continuous domain. We consider the discretized DAE, in which variables are expressed at discrete points that evolve from point t^- to t, within the continuous domain. With the exception of initial conditions and discretization equations at the first point in the domain, these variables and equations are repeated at every point along the domain. Functions F, G, and d are vector valued and assumed to be twice continuously differentiable in all arguments.

$$\dot{x}(t) = F(x(t), y(t), u), \ G(x(t), y(t), u) = 0, \ d(x(t), x(t^-), \dot{x}) = 0, \ x(0) = x_0 \qquad (1)$$

We say that a DAE is index-1 if the Jacobian of algebraic equations with respect to algebraic variables, $\nabla_y G$, is nonsingular for all values of differential, algebraic, and input variables. In this case, by the implicit function theorem, there exists a function G_y which maps the vector (x, u) to y such that $0 = G(x, y, u)$ is satisfied.

A simultaneous nonlinear programming (NLP) formulation for the optimization of a DAE model has the form given by Equation (2). We refer to this as the full space formulation. Here, the DAE is fully discretized and equations are repeated at every point in time. We omit the time indexing for brevity.

$$\min_{(\dot{x}, x, y, u) \in \mathcal{W}} \varphi(x, u), \ \text{s.t.} \ \dot{x} - F(x, y, u) = 0, \ G(x, y, u) = 0, \ d(x, \dot{x}) = 0, \ x(0) = x_0$$

$$(2)$$

where $\mathcal{W}$ indicates the bounds for the optimization variables. A dynamic optimization problem of this form can be constructed in an algebraic modeling language such as Pyomo (Bynum et al. (2021)) if the constraints and objective are explicit functions of the variables. The optimization problem may then be solved with a generic nonlinear programming solver. In contrast, our reduced space formulation takes advantage of the index-1 property to eliminate algebraic variables and equations from the NLP. That is, $G(x, y, u) = 0$ and the index-1 property imply that $y = G_y(x, u)$, where G_y is an implicit function. The formulation is given by Equation (3).

$$\min_{(\dot{x}, x, u) \in \mathcal{W}} \varphi(x, u), \quad \text{s.t.} \ \dot{x} - F(x, G_y(x, u), u) = 0, \quad d(x, \dot{x}) = 0, \quad x(0) = x_0 \qquad (3)$$

An optimization problem of this form cannot be constructed directly in an algebraic modeling environment because G_y is an implicit function. This formulation can still be solved by a nonlinear programming algorithm, however, if G_y may be evaluated and admits sufficient derivative information. We implement an interface that evaluates such an implicit function and computes first and second derivatives via the implicit function theorem. The interface makes use of the PyNumero extension to the Pyomo algebraic modeling environment (Rodriguez et al. (2021)), and considers NLPs of the form shown by Equation (4), in which f describes the residual equations, which are exposed to the NLP solver and g describes the external equations, which are removed as an implicit function.

$$\min_{(a,b)} \varphi(a) \text{ s.t. } f(a,b) = 0, \ g(a,b) = 0, \ a \geq 0 \tag{4}$$

Assuming the Jacobian of external equations with respect to external variables, $\nabla_b g$, is nonsingular, the external equations may be removed from the NLP and used to solve for b as a function of a. The system seen by the NLP solver is given by Equation (5).

$$\min_a \varphi(a) \text{ s.t. } \bar{f}(a) = f(a, b(a)) = 0, \ a \geq 0 \tag{5}$$

To solve this NLP with a second-order optimization algorithm, the Hessian of the Lagrangian of Equation (5), $\nabla_{aa}^2 \mathcal{L}$, and the Jacobian of $\bar{f}$, $\nabla_a \bar{f}$, are necessary. These derivatives are given by Equation (6).

$$
\begin{aligned}
\nabla_a \bar{f} = & \ \nabla_a f + \nabla_a b \nabla_b f \\
\nabla_{aa}^2 \mathcal{L} = & \ \nabla_{aa}^2 \varphi + A^{-1} Z + \sum_i \nabla_{aa}^2 f_i \lambda_{f_i} + \sum_j \nabla_{aa}^2 g_j \lambda_{g_j} \\
& + \left(\sum_i \nabla_{ab}^2 f_i \lambda_{f_i} + \sum_j \nabla_{ab}^2 g_j \lambda_{g_j} \right) \nabla_a b^T \\
& + \nabla_a b \left(\sum_i \nabla_{ba}^2 f_i \lambda_{f_i} + \sum_j \nabla_{ba}^2 g_j \lambda_{g_j} \right) \\
& + \nabla_a b \left(\sum_i \nabla_{bb}^2 f_i \lambda_{f_i} + \sum_j \nabla_{bb}^2 g_j \lambda_{g_j} \right) \nabla_a b^T
\end{aligned}
\tag{6}
$$

Output coordinates of vector function f are indexed by i and coordinates of g are indexed by j. For the barrier term $A^{-1} Z$, $A = \text{diag}(a)$, $Z = \text{diag}(z)$, and z and λ_f are the bound and equality multipliers, respectively, in (5). Jacobian $\nabla_a b$ and vector λ_g are given by $\nabla_a b = -\nabla_a g \nabla_b g^{-1}$ and $\lambda_g = -\nabla_b g^{-1} \nabla_b f \lambda_f$. The derivatives in (6) are derived via the implicit function theorem and the chain rule using an approach similar to that of Heinkenschloss (2008). All Jacobian and Hessian matrices are calculated by PyNumero's interface to the Ampl Solver Library (ASL) (Gay (1997)). The matrices $\nabla_a \bar{f}$ and $\nabla_{aa}^2 \mathcal{L}$ are sent to CyIpopt via the PyNumero interface, allowing us to solve NLPs in the form of Equation (3) with the Ipopt algorithm.

With an implicit function interface for systems in the form of Equation (4), the application to DAE systems in the form of Equation (1) is straightforward. Residual constraints are differential and discretization equations, external constraints are algebraic equations, external variables are algebraic variables y, and the optimization problem is solved in the space of differential variables, x, their time derivatives $\dot{x}$, and DAE inputs u. A separate implicit function is used to describe the differential and algebraic equations at each point in the discretized domain.

3. Case Studies

3.1. Chemical Looping Combustion Simulation

A chemical looping combustion (CLC) reactor is a gas-solid hydrocarbon reactor in which fuel and air reactions occur in separate chambers, with a metal-oxide oxygen carrier loop-

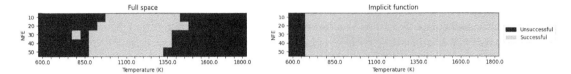

Figure 1: Convergence status of the simulation problem for each combination of NFE and gas inlet temperature for the full space and implicit function formulations.

ing between the two. Here we present results for simulation of the fuel reactor involving methane and iron oxide operating at steady state in a counter-current moving bed configuration. The reduction reaction is $CH_4 + 12Fe_2O_3 \rightarrow 2H_2O + CO_2 + 8Fe_3O_4$. The model equations form a DAE in which the continuous domain is distance along the length of the reactor. Differential variables are flow rates and pressure, and algebraic variables are thermodynamic, hydrodynamic, and kinetic properties. In the current simulation case study, the model has no inputs; inlet conditions are fixed. Further details are given by Ostace et al. (2018) and Okoli et al. (2020).

To compare robustness and solve times of the full and reduced space formulations, we perform a parameter sweep, varying the number of finite elements (NFE) in the spatial discretization and the gas phase inlet temperature. To initialize each simulation or optimization, we initialize differential variables to their inlet values, deactivate discretization equations, and solve the square problem at each discretization point individually. In addition, we apply the following scaling factors: 100 for material flows, 1e3 for gas enthalpy flow, and 1e5 for solid enthalpy flow. Figure 1 shows the convergence status of each combination of parameters for the full space and implicit function formulations. An unsuccessful simulation may be due to timeout, iteration limit, function evaluation error, or convergence to an infeasible point. Among problem instances that converge in both formulations, full space solves in less than 0.1 s, while implicit function solves take an average of 30 s. The data indicate that while the implicit function formulation takes more time for the solver to converge, it can also solve significantly more instances of the simulation problem than the full space formulation. Of the 125 problem instances, the implicit function formulation can solve 115, while the full space formulation can solve only 50, with the same initialization. While additional problem-specific tuning on initialization and scaling may improve convergence for some instances, the implicit function formulation has the advantage of fewer variables to initialize and scale.

3.2. Chemical Looping Combustion Optimization

We now present results for optimization of operating conditions of the chemical looping combustion reactor. The model is the same as in Section 3.1., but now inlet conditions are degrees of freedom and outlet conditions participate in an objective function penalizing their deviation from target conditions. The target outlet conditions are taken from the moving bed process described in Table 5 of Okoli et al. (2020).

Because inlet gas temperature is no longer a fixed parameter, we now vary the gas temperature used for model initialization, as well as the number of finite elements, in a parameter sweep. Four different NFEs and 18 temperatures are used for 72 total problem instances.

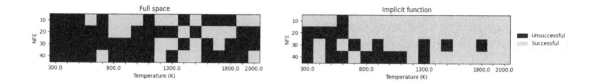

Figure 2: Convergence status of the optimization problem for each combination of NFE and initialization gas inlet temperature for both formulations

Figure 2 shows the convergence status for all combinations of parameters. Among problem instances for which both formulations converge, the average full space solve is much faster than the implicit function solve. A breakdown of solve times for the instance with 30 finite elements, initialized to 1200 K, is shown in Table 1. In this instance, the implicit function formulation takes 203 s and converges in 47 Ipopt iterations, while the full space formulation takes 1.3 s and converges in 95 Ipopt iterations. The "Interface" category refers to time spent in function and derivative evaluations, and is broken down more finely for the implicit function formulation. These calculations take 92 % of the time in this formulation, are performed independently at each point in the discretized domain, and may be done in parallel. In this instance, up to 30 processors can be utilized, in which case the entire implicit function solve would be performed in only 22 s with perfect speedup.

Table 1: Percentage of solve time spent in each activity for full and reduced space formulations of the CLC optimization problem with 30 finite elements initialized to 1200 K

Formulation	I/O	Ipopt	Interface	Function	Jacobian	Hessian	other
Full	25 %	50 %	21 %	–	–	–	4 %
Implicit	7 %	< 1 %	–	86 %	4 %	2 %	1 %

The data again indicate that although the reduced space formulation takes longer to converge than the full space formulation, there are many instances for which only the reduced space formulation converges. Out of 72 problem instances, the reduced space formulation can solve 52, and the full space formulation can solve only 24 with the same initialization. We hypothesize that the improved robustness of the reduced space formulation is because the reduced space and external Jacobians, $\nabla_a \bar{f}$ and $\nabla_a b$ in (6), are less likely to be poorly conditioned at points where the algebraic equations have been converged than at arbitrary infeasible points where the algebraic equations may have large residuals. While the implicit function formulation is slower than the full space formulation, we note that much more can be done to accelerate the implicit function formulation. The implicit function and derivative evaluations for each point in the discretized domain can be performed in parallel, implicit function computations can be performed entirely in compiled code by operating on a PyNumero `PyomoNLP` object rather than directly in Pyomo, and sparsity in the derivative matrices can be exploited. We defer these improvements to future work.

4. Conclusions

We have implemented an implicit function formulation for the simulation and optimization of index-1 DAE systems via nonlinear programming. In the application of our formulation to the simulation and optimization of a chemical looping combustion reactor, our formulation solves over twice as many problem instances as the full space formulation, illustrating its potential to be much more robust. When it converges, however, the full space formulation is significantly faster than our current implementation.

Future extensions to this work include improving the computational performance, alternative formulations removing only a subset of the algebraic equations from the optimization problem, and applying implicit functions with exact first and second derivatives to other types of decomposable optimization problems. A comparison with a fully sequential dynamic optimization formulation with exact first and second derivatives, performed with our current Ipopt/PyNumero computational framework, will also be valuable.

Disclaimer

This work was supported through the Simulation-Based Engineering, Crosscutting Research Program within the U.S. Department of Energy's Office of Fossil Energy. This report was prepared as an account of work sponsored by an agency of the United States Government. Neither the United States Government nor any agency thereof, nor any of their employees, makes any warranty, express or implied, or assumes any legal liability or responsibility for the accuracy, completeness, or usefulness of any information, apparatus, product, or process disclosed, or represents that its use would not infringe privately owned rights. Reference herein to any specific commercial product, process, or service by trade name, trademark, manufacturer, or otherwise does not necessarily constitute or imply its endorsement, recommendation, or favoring by the United States Government or any agency thereof. The views and opinions of authors expressed herein do not necessarily state or reflect those of the United States Government or any agency thereof. Sandia National Laboratories is a multimission laboratory managed and operated by National Technology and Engineering Solutions of Sandia LLC, a wholly owned subsidiary of Honeywell International Inc. for the U.S. Department of Energy's National Nuclear Security Administration under contract DE-NA0003525.

References

Bongartz, D. & Mitsos, A. (2017), 'Deterministic Global Optimization of Process Flowsheets in a Reduced Space Using McCormick Relaxations', *J. Glob. Opt.* **69**, 761–796.

Bynum, M. L., Hackebeil, G. A., Hart, W. E., Laird, C. D., Nicholson, B. L., Siirola, J. D., Watson, J.-P. & Woodruff, D. L. (2021), *Pyomo–Optimization Modeling in Python*, Vol. 67, third edn, Springer Science & Business Media.

Cuthrell, J. E. & Biegler, L. T. (1987), 'On the Optimization of Differential-Algebraic Process Systems', *AIChE J.* **33**(8), 1257–1270.

Gay, D. M. (1997), Hooking Your Solver to AMPL, Technical report, Bell Laboratories.

Goh, C. & Teo, K. (1988), 'Control Parametrization: A Unified Approach to Optimal Control Problems with General Constraints', *Automatica* **24**(1), 3–18.

Heinkenschloss, M. (2008), Numerical Solution of Implicitly Constrained Optimization Problems, Technical report, Rice University.

Hong, W., Wang, S., Li, P., Wozny, G. & Biegler, L. T. (2006), 'A Quasi-Sequential Approach to Large-Scale Dynamic Optimization Problems', *AIChE J.* **52**(1), 255–268.

Okoli, C. O., Ostace, A., Nadgouda, S., Lee, A., Tong, A., Burgard, A. P., Bhattacharyya, D. & Miller, D. C. (2020), 'A Framework for the Optimization of Chemical Looping Combustion Processes', *Powder Technology* pp. 149–162.

Ostace, A., Lee, A., Okoli, C. O., Burgard, A. P., Miller, D. C. & Bhattacharyya, D. (2018), Mathematical Modeling of a Moving-Bed Reactor for Chemical Looping Combustion of Methane, *in* 'Proc. 13th International Symposium on Process Systems Engineering (PSE 2018)', Computer-Aided Chemical Engineering, Elsevier, pp. 325–330.

Rodriguez, J., Parker, R., Laird, C., Nicholson, B., Siirola, J. & Bynum, M. (2021), 'Scalable Parallel Nonlinear Optimization with PyNumero and Parapint'. Preprint at http://www.optimization-online.org/DB_HTML/2021/09/8596.html.

Proceedings of the 14th International Symposium on Process Systems Engineering – PSE 2021+
June 19-23, 2022, Kyoto, Japan © 2022 Elsevier B.V. All rights reserved.
http://dx.doi.org/10.1016/B978-0-323-85159-6.50191-3

Multi-objective optimization of NH_3 and CO_2 separation with ionic liquid process

Yuanmeng Duan[a,b], Guoxiong Zhan[b], Fei Chang[b], Sensen Shi[b], Jens Abildskov[a], Jakob Kjøbsted Huusom[a,*], and Xiangping Zhang[b,*]

[a] Department of Chemical and Biochemical Engineering, Technical University of Denmark, Lyngby 2800, Denmark
[b] Institute of Process Engineering, Chinese Academy of Sciences, Beijing 100190, China
jkh@kt.dtu.dk
xpzhang@ipe.ac.cn

Abstract

Melamine production produces tail gas with a significant amount of both NH_3 and CO_2. Benefiting from the development of green solvents, using ionic liquids instead of traditional solvents as water for NH_3 and CO_2 separation has attracted wide attention. Multi-objective optimization (MOO) is employed to optimize the ionic liquid-based process in this work. In order to decrease the energy consumption in the ionic liquid-based separation process, a MOO research was carried out using Aspen Plus and Matlab software in this work.

In this work, one ionic liquid-based process was simulated and optimized by the nondominated sorting genetic algorithm II (NSGA-II) algorithm. The minimum total separation cost (TSC) and total process CO_2 emission (TPCOE) were set as two objective functions. With the constraints and several operational parameters optimized, the Pareto front displays a set of nondominated, optimal design parameters that satisfy the specification of the NH_3 concentration standard in outlet gas.

The results show that the effect of desorption pressure and the ratio of lean solvent to total solvent are critical for both TSC and TPCOE. After the MOO, the TSC of the ionic liquid process can be decreased by 5%, and TPCOE is reduced by 12% compared with the base case. The optimization results support the optimal design and operation of the NH_3 and CO_2 separation process with ionic liquids considering environmental and economic objectives.

Keywords: Ionic liquid; Process Design; Multi-objective optimization.

1. Introduction

Melamine is an important industrial raw material that can be prepared by condensation polymerization of melamine resin, widely used in tableware, heat insulation materials, coatings, adhesives, etc. However, for the treatment of melamine tail gas containing NH_3 and CO_2, the reaction of these two gases leads to ammonium bicarbonate crystals that cause operational difficulties. Water scrubbing and some co-productions technologies such as urea co-production, ammonia bicarbonate co-production are the primary gas treatment method employed in the industry. However, they have disadvantages such as high energy and water consumption, equipment corrosion, secondary pollution, and difficulty reaching standard discharge. Ionic liquids is a new green material and medium for the industry's gas separation and purification process. Ionic liquids have the advantage of low vapor pressure, being structurally designable, good stability. Therefore, it is interesting to use its advantage to develop new technology. Based on the functional IL [Bim][NTf₂], it can achieve the target of high absorption capacity, good selectivity of NH_3 and CO_2, no water discharge, low energy consumption, and high purity of recovery gas.

A posteriori techniques using multi-objective approach are mostly population-based stochastic optimization techniques (C.A. Coello Coello, 2007). These include NSGA-II (elitist non-dominated sorting GA), SPEA2 (strength Pareto evolutionary algorithm-2), MOEA (multi-objective evolutionary algorithm), and MOPSO (multi-objective PSO) (K. Deb, 2001). Each iteration ranks the solutions based on objective values to obtain many Pareto-optimal solutions at the end of the given stopping criterion (usually, the maximum number of iterations), all in one run of the optimizer/program. A simplified flow chart of NSGA-II is presented in Figure 1(Rangaiah et al, 2015). In the process of optimization, non-repetitive and dominant solutions and frontier sets are found in the iteration operation to retain the optimal results.

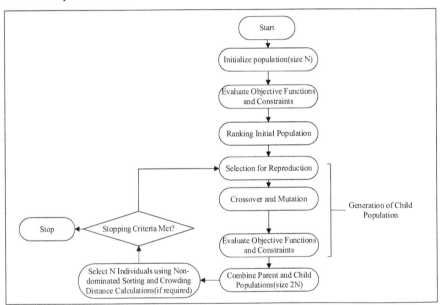

Figure 1. A flowchart of NSGA-II for MOO.

To lower the energy consumption and analyze relationships of operational parameters with TSC and TPCOE of the ionic liquid process, MOO research was carried out in the separation of NH_3 and CO_2 with the ionic liquid process using Aspen Plus and Matlab software in this work. Because of the internal relationship with different operating parameters in the ionic liquid process, the optimization may go into the local optimization solution instead of the global optimization solution. In applying chemical engineering, most practical problems usually seek to satisfy this under multiple design goals—the MOO problem of the best design scheme for these objectives. On the one hand, MOO can give full play to the role of decision-making participants, and on the other hand, it is more in accordance with reality(C.A. Coello Coello, 2007). Researchers usually integrate mathematical software and process simulation software to solve the optimization problem of multiple objective functions.

Recently, many researchers have used MOO techniques for the analysis of chemical processes. Li et al. (2021) used a MOO strategy to integrate the design and control of ionic liquid-based extractive distillation processes. The Pareto front shows the optimization results, which are based on trade-offs between controllability and economics. Zhan et al. (2021) investigated the ammonia-containing gas separation and ammonia recovery with ionic liquids. MOO was employed to finish the optimization and the result showed that using functional ionic liquids could greatly decrease purification cost and energy consumption.

However, there is limited research on MOO for the separation of NH_3 and CO_2 by the ionic liquid process. In this work, the MOO of the ionic liquid-based NH_3 and CO_2 separation process was made, using the nondominated sorting Genetic algorithm II(NSGA-II).

2. Methods

2.1 Process flow chart of NH_3/CO_2 separation with ionic liquids
The base case has been previously established and the flow chart of the NH_3/CO_2 separation process with ionic liquids is shown in Figure 2(Duan et al, 2021). The melamine tail gas contains 7.6 % nitrogen (N_2), 0.4 % water (H_2O), 55 % ammonia (NH_3) and 37 % carbon dioxide (CO_2) in mole fractions. The conceptual process consists of two sections, which are the NH_3 absorption section and absorbent desorption section. The tail gas flows to the bottom of the absorber and meets the ionic liquid in counter current flow and then NH_3 is released due to increased pressure and decreased temperature in Flash 1 and Flash 2. After tail gas separation, the NH_3 concentration below 6000 ppm (mole fraction) in the purified gas. The NH_3 product purity is set over 0.996 mass fraction.

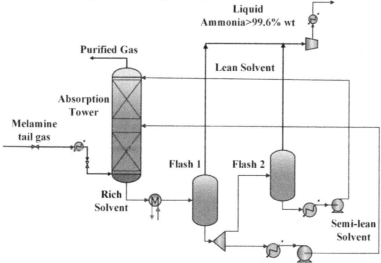

Figure 2. The flow chart of NH_3/CO_2 separation process with ionic liquids (Duan et al, 2022).

2.2 MOO of NH_3/CO_2 separation with ionic liquids
In order to investigate the internal relationship among different parameters and TSC of the ionic liquid-based process, MOO was carried out. In this work, the NSGA-II is employed in the MOO of the NH_3 and CO_2 separation process. MOGA can be employed to solve MOO to avoid falling into a local optimal solution when sequential iteration was

used in the iterative process. As a bridge between Aspen Plus and Matlab, ActiveX is used in the MOO process. Six design parameters are simultaneously optimized, including pressure of absorption, ratio of lean solvent to total solvent, total usage of solvent, temperature of Flash1, pressure of Flash1 and 2 (P, R_{LT}, F, T, P_{F1}, P_{F2}), the value range of each parameter is shown in Table 1. In this study, the tray number of absorption is not used as a decision variable, it is fixed at 8.

Table 1. Range of parameters of NH_3/CO_2 separation with ionic liquid.

Operation parameters	P (kPa)	R_{LT}	F (t/h)	T (K)	P_{F1} (kPa)	P_{F2} (kPa)
Lower bound	101	0.2	10	363.15	10	1
Higher bound	405	0.8	100	383.15	50	10

In process optimization, objective functions consist of the minimization of TSC(Total Separation Cost) and TPCOE(Total process emission of CO_2), the constraints are that $y_{NH3, purified} \leq 6000$ ppm, $x_{NH3, wt} \geq 0.996$, TSC ≥ 0, TPCOE ≥ 0, the ratio of gas and liquid 1 (GL1) ≤ 1000, the ratio of gas and liquid 1(GL2) ≤ 500. The MOO procedure of ionic liquid-based process is shown in Figure 2. The selection type is binary tournament selection. The crossover probability is 0.8. The variation method is Gaussian variation, and the variation probability is 0.1, the population size is set as 100, and the number of generations is set as 15.

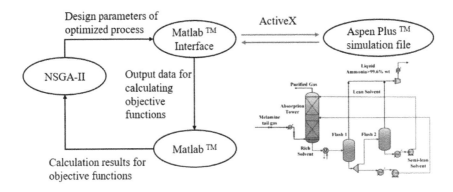

Figure 3. The MOO procedure of ionic liquid-based process.

3. Results and discussion

Based on the sensitivity analysis of the ionic liquid-based process, the MOO is conducted to obtain the solution for this chemical process, which can realize the two optimal objective functions: TSC and TPCOE. Figure 4(a) shows the relationship between TSC and TPCOE. The Pareto optimal solution of the NH_3 and CO_2 separation process indicates that TSC rises with the increasing of TPCOE. In the separation process, low TSC means low energy consumption, which leads to lower TPCOE.

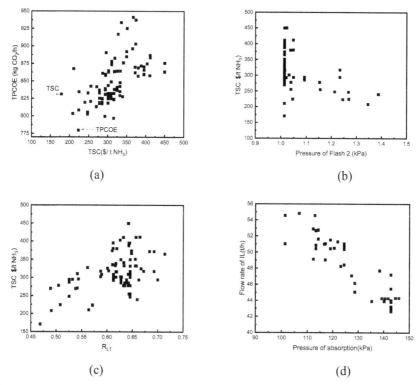

Figure 4. The MOO results. (a) The Pareto optimal result of NH₃ and CO₂ separation of TSC and TPCOE. (b) Effects of key variable ratio of lean solvent to total solvent (R_{LT}). (c) Effects of key variable pressure of Flash 2(P_{F2}). (d) Relationship between Pressure of absorption (P) and Flow rate of ionic liquids (F).

Figure 4(b) and (c) show the effects of crucial input variables (P_{F2}, R_{LT}) on TSC. From Figure 4(b), the pressure change of Flash 2 will lead to the diversification of objective function TSC. From Figure 4(c), TSC change with R_{LT} because higher R_{LT} means more lean solvent will flow into the Flash 2 and give more burden to Flash 2 with lower pressure.

For effect among the input parameters, Figure 4(d) shows the relationship between absorption pressure and flow rate of ionic liquids. With the increase of pressure, more NH₃ will be absorbed by ionic liquids, then less ionic liquids will be used in this process. Although increasing flow rate of ionic liquid can gain the solvent cost, it is observed that the operation can reduce the absorption pressure. These two parameters have a balance with each other about the effect on TSC.

Because there are two objective functions, we select the designs in the Pareto optimal solution named case 1 and 2 with the lowest TSC and TPCOE. Table 1 offers TSC and TPCOE of all configurations of the ionic liquid process. As the calculation, case 1 shows the lowest TSC as 170.87 $/t NH₃ which decreased by 5% of the base case, and case 2 has the lowest TPCOE decreased by 12% as 779.85 kg/h of the base case. In summary, the optimized results could give more detail information of ionic liquid-based NH₃/CO₂ separation process, which provides a perspective for separation technology for the future.

Table 2. Optimization results of NH_3/CO_2 separation with ionic liquid.

Operation parameters	Case 1	Case 2	Unit
Theoretical stage of absorption	8	8	-
Feed stage position of semi-lean	4	4	-
Total ionic liquid flow rate	47.09	43.90	$t \cdot h^{-1}$
Absorption pressure	128	142	kPa
Pressure of Flash 1	10	10	kPa
Temperature of Flash 1	366.10	363.98	K
Pressure of Flash 2	1	2	kPa
Temperature of Flash 2	366.10	363.98	K
R_{LT}	0.47	0.57	-
TSC	170.87	222.91	$\$ \cdot t^{-1} NH_3$
TPCOE	831.29	779.85	$kg \cdot h^{-1}$

4. Conclusion

In this work, MOO was carried to separate NH_3 and CO_2 using the ionic liquid. The result showed that desorption pressure and the ratio of lean solvent to total solvent affects TSC. In addition, the pressure of absorption and flow rate of ionic liquid have conflict and balance with each other. After optimization, the TSC and TPCOE decreased 5% and 12% compared with the base cases, respectively. The optimization results provide information for optimal design and operation of NH_3 and CO_2 separation processes with ionic liquids considering environmental and economic objectives. In next step work, the different algorithm will be employed to compare the effect to the identification of critical parameters.

References

C.A. Coello Coello, G.B. Lamont, D.A. Van Veldhuizen. Multi-objective Optimization and Multi-criteria Decision Making, Evolutionary Algorithms for Solving Multi-Objective Problems (2nd ed.), Springer, Berlin, Heidelberg (2007), 220-221.

K. Deb. Multi-objective Optimisation in Manufacturing Supply Chain Systems Design, Multi-Objective Optimization Using Evolutionary Algorithm. John Wiley & Sons, Chichester, UK (2001), 53-54.

GP. Rangaiah, S. Sharma, B. Krishna Sreepathi,2015, Multi-objective optimization for the design and operation of energy efficient chemical processes and power generation, Current Opinion in Chemical Engineering, 10, 49-62.

J. Li, L. Li, R. Li, Z.Yang, Z. Ma, L. Sun, N. Zhang, 2021, Investigation of multi-objective optimization for integrating design and control of ionic liquid-based extractive distillation, Chemical Engineering Research and Design, 170, 134-146.

G. Zhan, F. Cao, L. Bai, F. Chang, B. Zhou, Y. Duan, S. Zeng, H. Dong, Z. Li, X. Zhang. 2021, Process simulaiton and optimization of aoomnia-containing gas separation and ammonia recovery with ionic liquids, ACS Sustainable Chem. Eng, 9, 312-325.

Y. Duan, G. Zhan, F. Chang, S, Shi, S. Zeng, H. Dong, J. Abildskov, J. Huusom, X. Zhang. 2022,process simulation and evaluation for NH_3/CO_2 separation in melamine tal gas with ionic liquids, Separation & Purification technology, submitted.

Proceedings of the 14th International Symposium on Process Systems Engineering – PSE 2021+
June 19-23, 2022, Kyoto, Japan © 2022 Elsevier B.V. All rights reserved.
http://dx.doi.org/10.1016/B978-0-323-85159-6.50192-5

Primal-dual Feedback-optimizing Control with Direct Constraint Control

Risvan Dirza, Dinesh Krishnamoorthy, and Sigurd Skogestad[*]

Dept. of Chemical Engineering, Norwegian Univ. of Science & Technology (NTNU), NO-7491 Trondheim, Norway
[*]*sigurd.skogestad@ntnu.no*

Abstract

This work proposes a strategy to track steady-state changes in active constraints and minimize dynamic constraint violations in order to achieve system-wide optimal operation using simple feedback control structures and logic blocks. The strategy is based on the recently proposed primal-dual feedback-optimizing control scheme that optimally handles steady-state changes in active constraints. However, the constraints are controlled in a slow time scale by updating the dual variables (Lagrange multipliers). To reduce dynamic constraint violations, we propose a "fix-up" to the primal-dual scheme with direct control of hard constraints. We show that the improved method can reduce profit loss in the long run by allowing for smaller back-off from hard constraints. The application is to coordinated control of gas-lifted oil wells.

Keywords: Distributed feedback-optimizing control, Oil/gas, Production optimization.

1. Introduction

The optimal process operation involves making decisions in real-time to meet production goals. This is typically done in the context of real-time optimization (RTO) using mathematical concepts, process models, and real-time measurements. In the 80s, there was an increasing interest in replacing model-based numerical solvers with a simple feedback loop, named feedback-optimizing control. The idea is to translate the economic objective into a process control objective by finding a function of the controlled variables (CVs), and when it is held constant, it leads to the optimal adjustment of the manipulated variables (MVs). These MVs drives the process to optimal operating condition (Morari et al., 1980). Twenty years later, Skogestad (2000) suggested replacing the term "optimal adjustments" with "acceptable adjustments" (in terms of the loss). This idea is known as self-optimizing control (SOC). In SOC, *"when the optimum lies at some constraints, we use active constraint control where the available MVs tightly control the constrained variables"*. When the optimum may be unconstrained, the self-optimizing CVs are measured variables or combinations of them. We need a good model to determine (offline) an accurate self-optimizing CV, and it can be time-consuming if we have a complex and large-scale system. Not considering noise, the ideal self-optimizing CV is the gradient of the cost function w.r.t. the control input, that when we keep at a constant setpoint of zero, it satisfies the necessary conditions of optimality (Halvorsen et al., 2003). In constrained cases, the process reaches ideal optimal operating conditions when the gradient of the Lagrange function w.r.t. to control input is kept at a constant setpoint of zero. If the objective function is additively separable, we can decompose the problem and let each local system controls its local gradients of the Lagrange function w.r.t. local control input. *In this framework, we need a central coordinator to update the shadow price of shared constraints and broadcast it to every subsystem (Wenzel et al., 2016).*

2. Recent Works and Problem Statement

Consider the following steady-state optimization problem of N different subsystems.

$$\min_{\mathbf{u}} J(\mathbf{u}, \mathbf{d}) = \sum_{i=1}^{N} J_i(\mathbf{u}_i, \mathbf{d}_i) \tag{1a}$$

$$s.t. \ \ \mathbf{g}_s(\mathbf{u}, \mathbf{d}) \le \mathbf{0} \tag{1b}$$

where $\mathbf{u}_i \in \mathbb{R}^{n_{\mathbf{u}_i}}$ denotes the MVs for subsystem i, $n_{\mathbf{u}_i}$ is the number of MVs in subsystem i, and $\mathbf{u} = [\mathbf{u}_1 \ \ \cdots \ \ \mathbf{u}_N]^T$, $\mathbf{d}_i \in \mathbb{R}^{n_{\mathbf{d}_i}}$ denotes the disturbances in subsystem i, $n_{\mathbf{d}_i}$ is the number of disturbances in subsystem i, and $\mathbf{d} = [\mathbf{d}_1 \ \ \cdots \ \ \mathbf{d}_N]^T$, $J_i: \mathbb{R}^{n_{\mathbf{u}_i}} \times \mathbb{R}^{n_{\mathbf{d}_i}} \to \mathbb{R}$ is a function that denotes the local objective of subsystem i, $\mathbf{g}_s: \mathbb{R}^{n_{\mathbf{u}}} \times \mathbb{R}^{n_{\mathbf{d}}} \to \mathbb{R}^{n_{\mathbf{g}_s}}$ is a function that denotes the inequality (shared) constraints. $n_{\mathbf{g}_s}$ is the number of constraints. The Lagrangian function of problem (1) is $\mathcal{L}(\mathbf{u}, \mathbf{d}, \lambda_{g,s}) = \sum_{i=1}^{N} J_i(\mathbf{u}_i, \mathbf{d}_i) + \lambda_{g,s}^T \mathbf{g}_s(\mathbf{u}, \mathbf{d})$, where $\lambda_{g,s} \in \mathbb{R}^{n_{\mathbf{g}_s}}$ is the shadow price of the (shared) resource constraints. The goal of problem (1) is to determine optimal MVs to achieve system-wide steady-state optimal operation. Our motivation is to solve problem (1) using a feedback control structure that handles changing active constraints.

One possible approach is the reduced gradient approach or region-based control (Jäschke and Skogestad, 2012). *This method is easy to implement for a simple case with a few regions, and the result usually converges faster than the decomposed one for a large-scale problem. However, this method can be problematic for a complex and large case* as the number of the region is equal to $2^{n_{\mathbf{g}_s}}$. Another attractive framework is distributed feedback-based real-time optimization, which is also known as primal-dual feedback-optimizing control (Dirza et al., 2021; Krishnamoorthy, 2021). This method can avoid solving numerical optimization problems online by having real-time iteration of dual/Lagrange decomposition (e.g., Wenzel et al. (2016)). Consequently, it has a central coordinator acting as a "slow" central constraint controller. This structure makes primal-dual flexible in the presence of changing active constraints. The problem with this method is that the constraint is controlled only on the slow time scale through the manipulation of the shadow prices, which is only indirectly through the unconstrained optimization layer that affects the (physical) MVs. This causes the shadow prices (broadcasted to the actual plant) to be suboptimal during the transient. This condition may lead to dynamic violation during the transient, and later lead to an infeasible operation. This violation is unacceptable when we have a hard constraint. Thus, it is necessary to introduce a "back-off" from that constraint. *Note that this back-off will also apply at a steady-state condition, and it may then result in a considerable economic penalty, which can lead to profit loss. This work addresses this violation issue and aims to minimize the profit loss.*

3. Proposed Control Structure

Mathematically, the profit loss scale is linear with the back-off parameter. One can express this as $Loss = -\lambda_{g,s}^T \zeta_{bo}$, where ζ_{bo} is the back-off parameter, which means that by reducing the back-off parameter, one can reduce the profit loss in the long run.

Therefore, *this paper proposes an additional structure to control a hard constraint tightly in the primal-dual framework to minimize the back-off parameter.*

Because the primal-dual approach only has a central constraint controller that control the constraints on a slow time scale, we introduce direct constraint control as a "fix-up" to reduce dynamic constraint violation. The direct constraint control is based on pairing the constraint with a particular MV using a selector. This tightly controls any active (shared-) hard constraints on a fast time scale. This structure automatically switches back to the unconstrained mode when none of those existing constraints turns active. *We introduce this proposed control structure as primal-dual feedback-optimizing control with direct constraint control.* The implementation is discussed in detail in Section 4 (see Fig. 2(b)).

Selectors, which are well-known tools in the industries, are used for active constraint switching (Krishnamoorthy and Skogestad, 2020). The switching determines the assigned value to the specified MV. When using selectors, only one of some control actions is the actual input to the plant at any given time. For the ones that are not selected, the feedback loop is "broken". Consequently, the integral term is possibly building up. Thus, it is essential to implement anti-windup using a back-calculation scheme.

4. Implementation in Subsea Oil Production Network

We consider a subsea gas-lifted oil well production system, consisting of N clusters, that lift oil from the different reservoirs, completed with a fixed shared gas-lift compressor with limited available power. The production system model is like the one used in Dirza et al. (2021) and an additional model to calculate power consumption of the compressor as a linear function: $Pow_{gl} = \theta \sum_{i=1}^{N} \sum_{j=1}^{N_i} w_{gl,i,j}$, where θ is a function of a fixed ratio of outlet and inlet pressure of the compressor. Further, N_i is the total number of wells in cluster i, and $w_{gl,i,j}$ is the gas-lift rate injected to well j in cluster i.

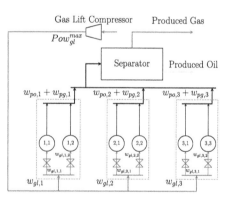

Figure 1: Field illustration

The objective function is to maximize the oil production income while minimizing the cost of the gas lift. The optimization problem is as follows.

$$\min_{\mathbf{w}_{gl}} \sum_{i=1}^{N} \left(-p_{o,i} \sum_{j=1}^{N_i} w_{po,i,j} + p_{gl,i} \sum_{j=1}^{N_i} w_{gl,i,j} \right) \tag{2a}$$

$$s.t. \quad \mathbf{f}(\mathbf{x}, \mathbf{w}_{gl}, \mathbf{d}) = \mathbf{0} \tag{2b}$$

$$\mathbf{g}(\mathbf{x}, \mathbf{w}_{gl}, \mathbf{d}) \leq \mathbf{0} \tag{2c}$$

$$\mathbf{g}_s(\mathbf{x}, \mathbf{w}_{gl}, \mathbf{d}) = Pow_{gl} - Pow_{gl}^{max} \leq 0 \tag{2d}$$

where $p_{o,i}$, $p_{gl,i}$, and $w_{po,i,j}$ are the price of produced oil, the cost of gas-lift, and the produced oil rate of well j in cluster i, respectively. Pow_{gl} is the total power consumed by the fixed compressor to inject the total gas-lift rate i, and Pow_{gl}^{max} is the maximum available power, which can also be a function of back-off parameter, ζ_{bo}. Further, $\mathbf{x} \in$

$\mathbb{R}^{n_x}$, and $\mathbf{d} \in \mathbb{R}^{n_d}$ are the vectors of states, and disturbance (i.e., gas-oil-ratio) for the entire system. $\mathbf{w}_{gl} \in \mathbb{R}^{n_{w_{gl}}}$ is the vector of inputs for the entire system, which can be seen as a vector of gas-lift rate from each well, $\mathbf{w}_{gl} = [w_{gl,1,1} \quad \cdots \quad w_{gl,N,N_N}]^T$.

Constraint (2b) and (2c) represent model and physical constraints, respectively. We assume that one locally manages constraint (2c) to maintain the focus of the discussion. The objective function (2a) is additively separable. Moreover, Eq. (2d) is a linear and hard constraint. Thus, we can decompose the problem into N subproblems. This case study considers $N = 3$ subsea clusters, where each cluster has two production wells (see Fig. 1) and has different oil prices to indicate the type of oil produced by each reservoir is different.

As primal-dual can converge to optimal steady-state conditions (Dirza et al., 2021; Krishnamoorthy, 2021), *this simulation compares primal-dual (as shown in Fig. 2(a)) with the proposed control structures (as shown in Fig. 2(b))*. Note that **y** indicates the real-time measurements set. The grey boxes represent the

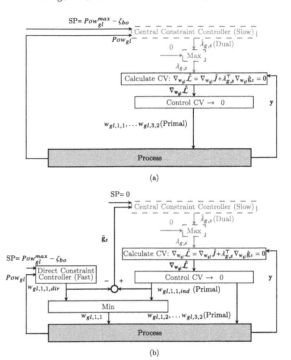

Figure 2: (a) Primal-dual control structure; (b) Proposed control structure which combines primal-dual optimization with direct constraint control.

physical system. The white boxes with solid blue lines represent a faster timescale computation block, and the white boxes with dashed red lines represent the slower ones.

Table 1: Controlled Variables, Setpoints, and Manipulated Variables

Well	CV	CV^{SP}	Calculated MV	Physical MV
1,1 (indirect)	$CV_{1,1,ind} = \nabla_{w_{gl,1,1}} \mathcal{L}_{1,1}$	0	$w_{gl,1,1,ind}$	$w_{gl,1,1}$
1,1 (direct)	$CV_{1,1,dir} = Pow_{gl}$	Pow_{gl}^{max}	$w_{gl,1,1,dir}$	$w_{gl,1,1}$
i,j^*	$CV_{i,j,ind} = \nabla_{w_{gl,i,j}} \mathcal{L}_{i,j}$	0	$w_{gl,i,j,ind}$	$w_{gl,i,j}$

*: For the remaining well j in cluster i

In the proposed control structure, we assume that well 1 of cluster 1 is technically more feasible to control hard constrained variables tightly. We have the original constraint $\mathbf{g}_s \le 0$, and by using step response, we obtain that $\frac{d\mathbf{g}_s}{dw_{gl,11}} > 0$. This means that a small value of $w_{gl,1,1}$ is good in terms of satisfying the constraint and a min selector is needed,

$w_{gl,1,1} = min(w_{gl,1,1,dir}, w_{gl,1,1,ind})$, where $w_{gl,1,1,dir}$ is the MV computed by the direct constraint controller, and $w_{gl,1,1,ind}$ is the primal MV by the optimization block. Note that we, at the optimal steady-state, must have $w_{gl,1,1,dir} \geq w_{gl,1,1,ind}$ or equivalently $\tilde{\mathbf{g}}_s = w_{gl,1,1,ind} - w_{gl,1,1,dir} \leq \mathbf{0}$. This is the constraint controlled in the proposed new structure. Table 1 shows the CVs, Setpoints, and the MVs in this case study, where $\nabla_{w_{gl,i,j}}\mathcal{L}_{i,j} = \nabla_{w_{gl,i,j}}J + \lambda_{g,s}^T\nabla_{w_{gl,i,j}}\mathbf{g}_s$. Additionally, we use the same method as Dirza et al. (2021) to estimate steady-state cost and constraint gradient, labelled by $\nabla_{w_{gl,i,j}}\hat{J}$ and $\nabla_{w_{gl,i,j}}\hat{\mathbf{g}}_s$, respectively.

The key idea is that we adjust the shadow price $\lambda_{g,s}$ so that on the long run the value of the MV computed by the direct constraint control (when it is active) is equal to the optimal primal value computed by the layer above (see Fig. 2(b)). To determine the applied $\lambda_{g,s}$, one can use a PI controller as a central constraint controller equipped with a max selector that gives 0 when the constraint is no longer active. The anti-windup is necessary to avoid $\lambda_{g,s}$ keeps changing in this case. Thus, this selector selects either 0 or the calculated shadow price $\hat{\lambda}_{g,s}$. Further, that shadow price $\hat{\lambda}_{g,s}$ at iteration k is as follows.

$$\hat{\lambda}_{g,s} = \lambda_{g,s}^k + K_p\tilde{\mathbf{g}}_s^k + \sum_{\tau=k-1}^{k}\left(K_I\tilde{\mathbf{g}}_s^\tau + K_{aw}\left(\lambda_{g,s} - \hat{\lambda}_{g,s}\right)^\tau\right) \tag{3}$$

where K_p, K_I, and K_{aw} are proportional, integral, and anti-wind-up gain, respectively.

PI controllers are tuned using the SIMC tuning method introduced by Skogestad (2003). The local controllers and the direct constraint controller have a sampling time of 1 sec. The central constraint controller updates the shadow price every 2.5 min because it may take more time to gather information from every cluster.

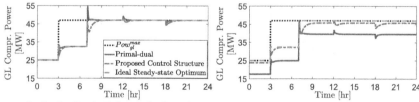

Figure 3: Left: Both Primal-dual and Proposed structure reach optimal steady-state conditions, but the constraint violation is much smaller for the proposed structure. Right: After implementing back-off from the power constraint.

Fig. 3 (left subplot) shows the simulation results when we consider $\zeta_{bo} = 0$. At time t = 3 hrs, the available power increases, and the shared constraint becomes inactive. Consequently, the gas-lift injection rates respond accordingly to achieve the optimal total available gas-lift allocation. Both primal-dual and proposed structure result in no dynamic violation at this time. At time t = 7 hrs, GOR dramatically decreases in all wells and causes extreme responses by the associated PI controllers. As a result, primal-dual significantly violates the constraint during the transient. We obtain a different result when applying the proposed control structure where Fig. 3 shows no dynamic constraint violation. At time t = 12 hrs, the GOR in most wells decreases, and the constraint is still active. The primal-dual has significant constraint violation during the transient for some time. As a comparison, the proposed structure responds accordingly and can reduce the magnitude and duration of that violation. At time t = 18 hrs, the GOR in most wells increases, and the constraint is still active. Both methods have no dynamic violation at this time. In general, the proposed structure can reduce those dynamic violations (in constrained cases) because (conceptually) direct constraint control selects the calculated direct constraint control input instead of the indirect one, which is calculated based on suboptimal shadow price during the transient.

In terms of dynamic violation magnitude, primal-dual and proposed structure can reach 7.4955 MW and 1.0329 MW, respectively. *When the maximum available power is a hard constraint, the proposed structure outperforms primal-dual as it can reduce more 'required' back-off, ζ_{bo} or even eliminate it (see Fig.3).* Fig. 4 shows the profit obtained

by both methods in this simulation. The result indicates that the proposed one can reduce profit loss as much as 22,207.00 price unit *(0.18 %)* in 24 hours when one implements a back-off strategy for the same case and duration.

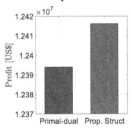

5. Conclusions

This work shows that the *proposed structure* with direct constraint control and primal-dual decomposition for optimization, is able to provide both tight constraint control on a fast timescale and optimal operation on a slow timescale. This strategy *offers* the possibility to reduce the back-off from constraints, which can give a large economic benefit.

Figure 4: Profit $(-J)$ obtained by primal-dual and proposed structure in 24 hrs.

6. Acknowledgment

The authors gratefully acknowledge the financial support from SUBPRO, financed by the Research Council of Norway, major industry partners, and NTNU.

References

R. Dirza, S. Skogestad, D. Krishnamoorthy, 2021. Optimal resource allocation using distributed feedback-based real-time optimization. IFAC-PapersOnLine 54 (3), 706–711, 16th IFAC Symposium on Advanced Control of Chemical Processes ADCHEM 2021.

I. J. Halvorsen, S. Skogestad, J. C. Morud, V. Alstad, 2003. Optimal selection of controlled variables. Industrial & Engineering Chemistry Research 42 (14), 3273–3284.

J. Jäschke, S. Skogestad, 2012. Optimal controlled variables for polynomial systems. Journal of Process Control 22 (1), 167–179.

D. Krishnamoorthy, 2021. A distributed feedback-based online process optimization framework for optimal resource sharing. Journal of Process Control (97), 72-83.

D. Krishnamoorthy, S. Skogestad, 2020. Systematic design of active constraint switching using selectors. Computers & Chemical Engineering 143, 107106.

M. Morari, Y. Arkun, G. Stephanopoulos, 1980. Studies in the synthesis of control structures for chemical processes: Part i: Formulation of the problem. process decomposition and the classification of the control tasks analysis of the optimizing control structures. AIChE Journal 26, 220 – 232.

S. Skogestad, 2000. Plantwide control: the search for the self-optimizing control structure. Journal of process control 10, 487 – 507.

S. Skogestad, 2003. Simple analytic rules for model reduction and pid controller tuning. Journal of Process Control 13, 291–309.

S.Wenzel, R. Paulen, G. Stojanovski, S. Kramer, B. Beisheim, S. Engell, 2016. Optimal resource allocation inindustrial complexes by distributed optimization and dynamic pricing. Automatisierungtechnik 64(6), 428–442.

Proceedings of the 14th International Symposium on Process Systems Engineering – PSE 2021+
June 19-23, 2022, Kyoto, Japan © 2022 Elsevier B.V. All rights reserved.
http://dx.doi.org/10.1016/B978-0-323-85159-6.50193-7

Data-driven coordination of expensive black-boxes

Damien van de Berg[a], Panagiotis Petsagkourakis[b], Nilay Shah[a], Ehecatl Antonio del Rio-Chanona[a,*]

[a]*Sargent Centre for Process Systems Engineering, Roderic Hill Building
South Kensington Campus. London, SW7 2AZ, United Kingdom*
[b] *Sargent Centre for Process Systems Engineering (CPSE), Department of Chemical Engineering, University College London, Torrington Place, London, WC1E 7JE, United Kingdom*
a.del-rio-chanona@imperial.ac.uk

Abstract

Coordinating decision-making capacities using optimization is a key factor in the success of chemical companies. However, this coordination is often inhibited by expensive, legally-constrained, or proprietary subproblem models. We propose two variations on how model-based (surrogate) derivative-free optimization (DFO) methods can be used to coordinate subproblems with few connecting variables. When these surrogates are convex quadratic, they can be efficiently exploited using semidefinite programming techniques. We compare the performance of these two variations with a distributed optimization solver (ADMM), a model-based, and a direct DFO solver (Py-BOBYQA and DIRECT-L). This comparison is done on four variations of an economic-environmental feedstock blending optimization case study. While ADMM seems to display faster initial convergence, explorative DFO optimization solvers seem promising in escaping local minimizers, especially in lower dimensions.

Keywords: Expensive black-box; Surrogate optimization; Derivative-free optimization

1. Introduction

Model-based optimization of operations is key for chemical enterprises to remain competitive in an environment of increasingly complex economical, sustainability, and safety considerations. In enterprise-wide optimization, previously disconnected chemical engineering optimization models are integrated into a single model, wherein subproblems are coupled via few complicating variables and constraints. When the complicating, also called shared or global, variables are sparse compared to the number of local, or private, subproblem variables, these applications lend themselves well to distributed optimization and decomposition techniques (Tang and Daoutidis, 2019). Examples include the planning of supply chains or the operation of interconnected processing units where regional agents decide on the shared material streams that minimize a local, private cost.

Distributed optimization is a powerful tool that allows for the solution of large-scale nonlinear problems with significant computational savings using only limited information exchange. Augmented Lagrangian methods, such as the Alternating Direction Method of Multipliers (ADMM), have garnered special attention (Boyd et al., 2010). These methods iterate between a coordination step and the parallel solution of local subproblems. While these methods have proven convergence properties on convex problems, they lose convergence guarantees on nonconvex problems. Despite this, they can often be applied in practice (Rodriguez et al., 2021).

As such, Houska et al. (2016) have proposed an Augmented Lagrangian based algorithm for distributed nonconvex optimization (ALADIN) algorithm and conditions for convergence to local minimizers on nonconvex problems. ALADIN iterates between the parallel optimization of subproblems and a sequential quadratic programming (SQP) step for the coordination. This has been applied to nonconvex model predictive control and optimal power flow (Engelmann et al., 2020), as well as sensor localization problems (Houska et al., 2016).

Both algorithms display drawbacks that impede practical applicability: ADMM, as a subgradient method, requires many iterations to converge. ALADIN requires cheap gradient expressions and an approximation of the Hessian of the subproblems for the SQP step. Derivative information might not be available if the optimal solution of the subproblems requires 'expensive black-box' evaluations. This is the case in many process systems engineering (PSE) applications when the subproblems sample the output of proprietary simulation queries, or if expressions for the local objectives and constraints are not available for security, privacy, organizational, or other reasons: multiple business entities having to coordinate on the design of a supply chain while respecting local constraints and privacy; or in multi-objective optimization, where each objective is given by a different black-box simulation or optimization model.

Black boxes are often optimized using derivative-free optimization (DFO). DFO algorithms do not require gradient information and can be broadly classified into two classes (Larson et al., 2019): direct methods which approach the optimum by handling function evaluations directly; and model-based methods which rely on the intermediate construction of surrogates. In a coordination problem, we can then use DFO to find the shared variables that minimize the sum of local subproblem objectives. The key distinction between this DFO-based coordination and distributed optimization algorithms (like ADMM) lies in how the shared variables are updated in the coordination step.

In this work, we consider the coordination of black-box subproblems using no model information except for input-output data. We propose 1) the use of DFO algorithms for the coordination step instead of distributed optimization, and 2) two purely 'data-driven' DFO strategies that rely on quadratic surrogates used within a trust region framework.. These methods are compared with ADMM, as well as a model-based, and direct DFO algorithm on all four combinations (lower- and higher-dimensional, convex and nonconvex) of a coordination problem consisting of an an economic blending and an environmental impact simulation subproblem.

2. Methodology

We are interested in solving problems of the following generic form:

$$\min_{z \in Z, x \in X} \sum_i f_i(x_i, z) \tag{1}$$

where $z \in R^{n_z}$ is the vector of global, shared, variables within the feasibility set Z, and $x \in R^{n_x}$ is the vector of local, private variables within the feasibility set X. This can be reformulated as the following min-min problem:

$$\min_{\mathbf{z}\in Z} \min_{\mathbf{x}\in X} \sum_i f_i(\mathbf{x}_i,\ \mathbf{z}) \tag{2}$$

After fixing $\mathbf{z}$, the problem becomes block separable, which makes the problem amenable to primal decomposition and distributed optimization. In fact, Eq. (2) is equivalent to the following constrained (bi-level) optimization problem:

$$\min_{\mathbf{z}\in Z} F(\mathbf{z}) \quad \text{subject to: } F(\mathbf{z}) = \min_{\mathbf{x}\in X} \sum_i f_i(\mathbf{x}_i,\ \mathbf{z}) \tag{3}$$

Decomposition techniques rely on iteratively updating $\mathbf{x}$ and $\mathbf{z}$ with the other set of variables fixed (Gauss-Seidel sweeps) (Palomar and Chiang, 2006). In the Alternating Direction Method of Multipliers (ADMM) – a distributed optimization technique - local copies of $\mathbf{z}$ are introduced $\mathbf{y}_i$. These are then penalized in the objective of (2) as added Lagrangian and Augmented Lagrangian terms. This problem can then be solved iteratively in its consensus form:

$$\mathbf{x}_i^{k+1} = \operatorname*{argmin}_{\mathbf{x}_i\in X_i,\ \mathbf{y}_i\in Z} f_i(\mathbf{x}_i,\ \mathbf{y}_i) + \frac{\rho}{2}\left\|\mathbf{x}_i - \mathbf{z}^k + \mathbf{u}_i^k\right\|_2^2 \tag{4a}$$

$$\mathbf{u}_i^{k+1} = \mathbf{u}_i^k + \mathbf{x}_i^{k+1} - \mathbf{z}^{k+1} \tag{4a}$$

where $\mathbf{z}^{k+1}$ is the average of $\mathbf{x}_i^{k+1}$, and $\mathbf{u}_i^k \in R^{n_z}$ are the scaled dual variables of iteration k and subproblem i. This method is used as a base case to compare our proposed algorithms to. What we suggest is the use of derivative-free optimization (DFO) to solve for $\mathbf{z}$ that minimizes the objective $F(\mathbf{z})$ in Eq. (3) where the latter is extended with an Augmented Lagrangian term to ensure convergence of the subproblem: when there is no feasible $\mathbf{x}_i$ for the proposed $\mathbf{z}$, the solution converges to the nearest feasible $\mathbf{x}_i$ and the associated deviation from $\mathbf{z}$ is penalized in the $\frac{\rho}{2}\|\mathbf{x}_i - \mathbf{z}\|_2^2$ term:

$$F_i(\mathbf{z}) = \min_{\mathbf{x}\in X} f_i(\mathbf{x}_i,\ \mathbf{z}) + \frac{\rho}{2}\|\mathbf{x}_i - \mathbf{z}\|_2^2 \tag{5}$$

For this work, we choose Py-BOBYQA and DIRECT-L as promising model-based and direct DFO solvers respectively. The interested reader is referred to van de Berg et al. (2021) where we have described these solvers and benchmarked them on a handful of chemical engineering applications. We have also introduced CUATRO as a trust region-based convex quadratic surrogate DFO algorithm. There are two different ways that surrogate models (such as CUATRO) could be used for the derivative-free optimization of problem (3). In both ways, a set of shared variables is broadcast to the subproblems, where the associated local objective functions (Eq. (5)) are evaluated in private. All evaluations within the trust region are then used to fit a quadratic surrogate to the evaluations. The difference lies in whether one single surrogate is fitted over the sum of the subproblem evaluations as in Eq. (6a), or whether each subproblem fits its own surrogate Eq. (6b), whose sum is then coordinated in the objective. The approach used in Eq. (6a) is similar to (Li et al., 2021), and could be loosely referred to as a `Data-driven ADMM', while the other version, with one surrogate per subproblem, resembles a `Data-driven ALADIN'.

$$\min_{\mathbf{z} \in Z} \hat{F}(\mathbf{z}) \quad \text{subject to: } \hat{F}(\mathbf{z}) = \mathbf{z}^T A \mathbf{z} + \mathbf{b}^T \mathbf{z} + c \approx \sum_i F_i(\mathbf{z}) \tag{6a}$$

$$\min_{\mathbf{z} \in Z} \sum_i^N \hat{F_i}(\mathbf{z}) \quad \text{subject to: } \hat{F_i}(\mathbf{z}) = \mathbf{z}^T A_i \mathbf{z} + \mathbf{b}_i^T \mathbf{z} + c_i \approx F_i(\mathbf{z}) \tag{6b}$$

These surrogates are then optimized within a trust region, and the best iterate and trust region radius are updated as in van de Berg et al. (2021) for the CUATRO algorithm. When A, $\mathbf{b}$, and c are fitted to be convex, semidefinite programming can be leveraged for the training and exploitation of the surrogates. This way, the algorithm overhead remains tractable compared to the expensive subproblem evaluations.

Our synthetic case study is inspired by an industrial problem where the composition of chemical feedstock needs to be optimized based on cost and environmental impact. The decision variables represent feedstock composition. The solution also needs to satisfy product performance constraints. The practitioners however only have access to the two separate problems as the output of expensive, proprietary black-boxes, preventing the two models from being integrated and exploited using conventional mixed-integer solvers. We present here a simplified case study involving 10 or 28 decision feedstocks as the shared variables $\mathbf{z}$. The economic optimization problem takes the following form:

$$\min_{\mathbf{y} \in \{0,1\}^{n_x}; \, \mathbf{z}, \mathbf{x} \in R^{n_x}} \Sigma_i (x_i Cost_i + \rho \, (x_i - z_i)^2) \tag{7a}$$

$$s.t. \quad x_i \le y_i, \quad \Sigma_i y_i \le N_{integer}, \quad \Sigma_i x_i = 1, \quad L_i \le \Sigma_i x_i A_i \le U_i \tag{7b) - (7e}$$

where the objective function (Eq. (7a)) constitutes of linear cost terms and an Augmented Lagrangian term to ensure convergence of the subproblem for all proposed $\mathbf{z}$. Eq. (7e) includes lower and upper bounds on blending quality; Eq. (7d) ensures that the total composition adds up to one; Eq. (7b) and (7c) ensure that only $N_{integer}$ variables are non-zero if there is a cap on the number of feeds in the mix. The latter constraints can be relaxed to make the problem convex. The environmental impact subproblem involves a simulation whose output is the result of linear and square terms in the composition variables with the optional addition of bilinear terms to introduce nonconvexity. The two objective evaluations are then scalarized into a single objective using a scalarization factor for the environmental impact output. We take ρ to be $1 \cdot 10^6$ and start from an initial guess where all components weigh the same, 0.0357 and 0.1 respectively.

The next section compares the convergence of the two versions of DFO solvers CUATRO, Py-BOBYQA, and DIRECT-L with ADMM in its consensus form. Each comparison is made on all four combinations of lower- and higher-dimensional as well as convex and nonconvex versions of the coordination problem.

3. Results and Discussion

Figure 1 shows the convergence of the best function evaluation with respect to the number of function evaluations of all methods on the four variations of the coordination problem. ADMM stands out as the method that makes the most progress in the least number of evaluations. Within ten evaluations, ADMM manages to approach a solution that is feasible (to an acceptable numerical tolerance) and near-optimal in all four cases. The next-best performing method, Py-BOBYQA, takes around 50 evaluations to get as close in the convex lower-dimensional case, and around 200 in the higher-dimensional nonconvex case. Otherwise, the final convergence of Py-BOBYQA is close to that of ADMM in the lower-dimensional case. It is slightly worse in the higher-dimensional convex, and slightly better in the higher-dimensional nonconvex case. It is expected that these methods perform better in the first evaluations as they are exploitative without explicit exploration.

In the lower-dimensional convex case, DIRECT-L and CUATRO with subproblem surrogates converge to the same optimum as ADMM and Py-BOBYQA, but require more evaluations. In the two higher-dimensional cases, DIRECT-L converges to a slightly worse optimum than ADMM and Py-BOBYQA in significantly more evaluations. For most cases, CUATRO constructing subproblem surrogates performs better than its single 'coordinated surrogate' counterpart. However, the lower-dimensional nonconvex case stands out, as both DIRECT-L and CUATRO employing a single coordinated surrogate perform best, converging to a better optimum than both Py-BOBYQA and ADMM.

This observation attempts to answer the central question of this work. Generally. while subgradient methods (ADMM) are slow to converge in terms of iterations, in higher dimensions, subgradient information still leads to quicker convergence than using data on its own. However, the lower-dimensional nonconvex case study suggests that derivative-free optimization solvers could shine for nonconvex applications with very few decision variables, where exploration is encouraged, and additional evaluations required to escape local minimizers. While the discussion of the relative performance of DFO algorithms is in line with that of van de Berg et al. (2021), we are not aware of any previous literature that directly compares DFO and distributed optimization coordination approaches. Additionally, since CUATRO has the capacity to explicitly handle black-box

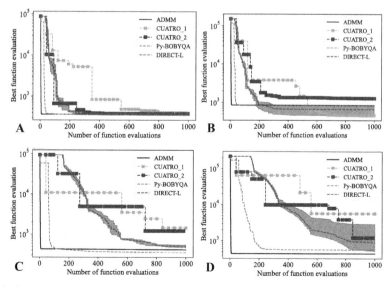

Figure 1. Convergence plots: Best function evaluation versus number of evaluations on the 10-d convex (A), 10-d nonconvex (B), 28-d convex (C), and 28-d nonconvex (D) case study using CUATRO_1 with a single coordinated surrogate (cyan dotted lines with X markers), CUATRO_2 with local subproblem surrogates over each subproblem (dark blue dotted lines with squares), ADMM (solid black line), Py-BOBYQA (dotted orange line), and DIRECT-L (dotted red line with shaded min-max range over 10 runs)

constraints, CUATRO could become useful for the navigation of more complex private constraints, e.g. when the subproblems can only access binary constraint information – is this set of global variables feasible or not? Finally, CUATRO, as a regression- rather than interpolation-model (such as Py-BOBYQA), could lead to better convergence when the subproblems involve stochasticity.

4. Conclusion

We have proposed alternatives to using distributed optimization in the case where subproblems need to be coordinated using input-output data as the only accessible information from the subproblem. It is possible to use DFO solvers that converge to the same optimum as the distributed optimization solver ADMM. However, only under specific conditions is the use of DFO solvers encouraged over that of ADMM, namely when the subproblems are highly nonconvex and connected by few shared variables. As for the DFO solvers, Py-BOBYQA displays the quickest and most reliable convergence, but as an exploitative method also regularly gets stuck in the same local minima as ADMM. DIRECT-L usually displays slow but still consistent convergence, escaping many local minima due to its partition-based nature. Finally, CUATRO should not be dismissed as a potential solver for more complex coordination problems involving stochasticity, and black-box constraints.

Acknowledgements

D.v.d.B. gratefully acknowledges financial support from the Bansal bursary. D.v.d.B. would also like to thank all BASF S.E. collaborators, especially his co-supervisors Dr. Debora Morgenstern and Dr. Inga-Lena Darkow, scientific exchange coordinator Dr. Christian Holtze, and Dr. Sangbum Lee for their invaluable support in conceptualizing this work.

References

S. Boyd, N. Parikh, E. Chu, B. Peleato, J. Eckstein, 2010, Distributed Optimization and Statistical Learning via the Alternating Direction Method of Multipliers. Trends R Mach. Learn. 3, 1–122

A. Engelmann, Y. Jiang, B. Houska, T. Faulwasser, 2020, Decomposition of Nonconvex Optimization via Bi-Level Distributed ALADIN. IEEE Trans. Control Netw. Syst. 7, 1848–1858

B. Houska, J. Frasch, M. Diehl, 2016, An augmented Lagrangian based algorithm for distributed nonconvex optimization. SIAM J. Optim.

J. Larson, M. Menickelly, S. Wild, 2019, Derivative-free optimization methods. Acta Numerica, 28, 287-404

Z. Li, Z. Dong, Z. Liang, Z. Ding, 2021, Surrogate-based distributed optimisation for expensive black-box functions. Automatica 125, 109407

D. P. Palomar, M. Chiang, 2006, A tutorial on decomposition methods for network utility maximization, IEEE Journal on Selected Areas in Communications, 24, 8, 1439-1451

J. S. Rodriguez, B. Nicholson, C. Laird, V. M. Zavala, 2018, Benchmarking ADMM in nonconvex NLPs. *Comput. Chem. Eng.* 119, 315–325

W. Tang, P. Daoutidis, 2019, Distributed control and optimization of process system networks: A review and perspective. Chinese J. Chem. Eng. 27, 1461–1473

D. van de Berg, T. Savage, P. Petsagkourakis, D. Zhang, N. Shah, E.A. del Rio-Chanona, 2021, Data-driven optimization for process systems engineering applications, Chemical Engineering Science, 117135

Proceedings of the 14th International Symposium on Process Systems Engineering – PSE 2021+
June 19-23, 2022, Kyoto, Japan © 2022 Elsevier B.V. All rights reserved.
http://dx.doi.org/10.1016/B978-0-323-85159-6.50194-9

Data-Driven Adaptive Robust Unit Commitment Assisted by Machine Learning Techniques

Ning Zhao[a*], Fengqi You[a]

[a]*Cornell University, Ithaca, New York, 14853, USA*
nz225@cornell.edu

Abstract

In this paper, we propose a novel robust unit commitment (UC) framework with data-driven disjunctive uncertainty sets for volatile wind power outputs, assisted by machine learning techniques. To flexibly identify the uncertainty space for wind power forecast error data with disjunctive structures, the uncertainty data are grouped using K-means and density-based spatial clustering of applications with noise. The disjunctive uncertainty sets are constructed accordingly as the union of multiple basic uncertainty sets, including conventional uncertainty sets, and data-driven uncertainty sets using Dirichlet process mixture model, principal component analysis coupled with kernel density estimation, and support vector clustering. The problem is formulated into a two-stage robust UC model with data-driven disjunctive uncertainty sets and with a multi-level optimization structure. To facilitate the solution process, a decomposition-based optimization algorithm is developed. The effectiveness of the proposed framework is illustrated using a case study based on the IEEE 39-bus system.

Keywords: Unit commitment, robust optimization, machine learning, disjunction.

1. Introduction

The United States is planning to use wind energy to provide 20% electricity in 2030 and 35% in 2050. Considering the intermittent nature of wind power (Ning and You, 2022), including the forecast uncertainties in the unit commitment (UC) decision-making process can help ensure power systems reliability and reduce the economic costs (Padhy, 2004). Robust UC has gained attention in recent years, owing to its robustness, flexible conservatism control, computational efficiency (Qiu et al., 2020), and effective utilization of large-scale uncertainty data (Ning and You, 2019). The robust UC problem is generally formulated into a two-stage adaptive robust optimization (ARO) model. The first stage determines the on-off decisions, and the second stage provides power output and dispatch decisions according to the worst case (Bertsimas et al., 2013). Note that the wind power forecast errors can have complex and disjunctive data structures, and studies found that it could be more appropriate to depict such uncertainty using more general distributions, such as the Gaussian mixture model (Wang et al., 2017). The finding indicates that the traditional "one-set-fits-all" approach for constructing a single uncertainty set based on all uncertainty data may not flexibly and accurately capture the uncertainty space. From a machine learning perspective, clustering has been a useful tool in detecting the disjunctive structure of a data set. To the best of our knowledge, there is no existing literature on robust optimization-based UC that systematically and effectively captures the uncertainty space based on uncertainty data with disjunctive structures by integrating clustering techniques with the ARO models. To fill the knowledge gap, this study aims to propose a novel two-stage adaptive robust UC framework that has the potential of leading to better optimization solutions by incorporating data-driven disjunctive uncertainty sets to deal with the uncertain wind power forecast error data, which are independent and identically distributed (Bludszuweit et al., 2008) and have disjunctive structures. A tailored decomposition-based optimization algorithm is developed to iteratively solve the resulting robust UC problems. To illustrate the effectiveness of the proposed framework, an application on the IEEE 39-bus system is presented.

2. Data-driven robust unit commitment with disjunctive uncertainty sets

A two-stage ARO framework with data-driven disjunctive uncertainty sets is proposed in this work for UC with uncertain wind power forecast errors, as shown in Figure 1. First, the optimal number of uncertainty data clusters is determined using the Calinski-Harabasz index. Next, the uncertainty data are clustered according to the optimal number of clusters using machine learning techniques. After integrating the uncertainty data with the clustering results, the data-driven disjunctive uncertainty sets are then constructed. Subsequently, the ARO problem is formulated by incorporating the data-driven disjunctive uncertainty sets. Lastly, the proposed ARO problem is solved iteratively using a tailored decomposition-based optimization algorithm.

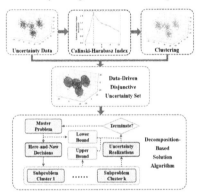

Figure 1. Flowchart of the proposed ARO framework with disjunctive uncertainty sets.

The objective function is minimizing the total UC cost under uncertainty. Note that the optimization model has a two-stage structure. Specifically, the "here-and-now" decisions for the first stage represent the commitments of generators that are determined 24 hours ahead, including online status, start-up status, and shutdown status of generators. The "wait-and-see" decisions determined after the uncertainty is realized in the second stage depict the economic dispatch process, including the power output of generators, power dispatch of a wind farm, and slack variables for balance constraints. The constraints of the robust UC model include the logic relations of generators, the minimum uptime and downtime of generators, the minimum and maximum power outputs of a generator, the ramping rates, the energy balance of the system, the capacities of transmission lines, the maximum outputs from wind farms that equal to the summation of forecasted wind power generation and the uncertain forecast errors, the initial commitment status and power outputs of generators, and the feasible region of decision variables. The maximum output constraint for wind farms holds for all potential realizations of the uncertainty, which guarantees the robustness of solutions.

A novel approach for developing data-driven disjunctive uncertainty sets is developed in this study. The conventional robust optimization adopts the "one-set-fits-all" approach that constructs a single uncertainty set to depict the uncertainty space. In contrast, the disjunctive uncertainty sets consist of multiple basic uncertainty sets (Ning and You, 2018), and the uncertainty space is represented by the union of these uncertainty sets, as shown in Eq.(1). L is the set of uncertainty data clusters.

$$\mathbf{U} = \bigcup_l \mathbf{U}_l \tag{1}$$

To determine the optimal number of clusters, the Calinski-Harabasz index is calculated, which finds the optimal number of clusters by pursuing a balance between the compactness of a data group and the distribution of all data groups. Specifically, the uncertainty data are first grouped using K-means for a range of k, and the one with the highest Calinski-Harabasz index represents the optimal number of clusters. For data clustering, two machine learning techniques, namely K-means and density-based spatial clustering of applications with noise (DBSCAN), are used to group the uncertainty data according to the optimal number of clusters. K-means is an unsupervised, non-deterministic, iterative, and centroid-based clustering algorithm, while DBSCAN is a density-based clustering algorithm.

Based on the resulting uncertainty data clusters, five types of basic uncertainty set can be constructed, including the traditional box and budget uncertainty sets, and three types of data-driven uncertainty sets using a variational inference algorithm for the Dirichlet process mixture model (DPMM) (Ning and You, 2017), principal component analysis (PCA) coupled with kernel density estimation (KDE) (Ning and You, 2018), and support vector clustering (SVC) (Shang and You, 2017, 2019). These data-driven uncertainty sets are widely adopted in the robust optimization community because of their remarkable performances in capturing the uncertainty space (Ning and You, 2019).

The two-stage robust UC with the proposed disjunctive uncertainty sets have an objective function with a multi-level structure, semi-infinite constraints, and non-convex uncertainty sets. Therefore, to facilitate the solution process, a decomposition-based optimization algorithm is developed and applied. Specifically, a master problem and a set of subproblems are iteratively solved in the decomposition-based optimization algorithm. The master problem optimizes the UC decisions under multiple optimality cuts that correspond to a partial enumeration of the extreme points of the basic uncertainty sets and provides a lower bound to the original robust UC problem. Subsequently, we fix the values of first-stage decision variables following the optimal solutions of the master problem and develop a set of subproblems to investigate economic dispatch under the worst case. Note that each basic uncertainty set U_l corresponds to an individual subproblem. To reformulate the subproblem into a single-level maximization problem that can be solved directly by off-the-shelf solvers, the classical Karush-Kuhn-Tucker (KKT) conditions and the big-M method are used. The solutions of subproblems provide upper bounds of the original problem. A set of additional optimality cuts is then generated based on the uncertainty realization in the worst case and is updated in the master problem for the next iteration. Eventually, the algorithm terminates when the relative optimality gap is below the tolerance level ξ. Furthermore, to improve the computational efficiency, the master problem and subproblem are constructed only once during the solution process, and a part of the variables and constraints are updated in the following iterations.

3. Case study based on IEEE 39-bus systems

To illustrate the effectiveness of the proposed framework with disjunctive uncertainty sets, a case study based on the IEEE 39-bus system is investigated. The system includes 39 buses, 10 generators, 46 lines, and 3 wind farms. 800 uncertainty data samples are generated from a Gaussian mixture model. The two-stage robust UC problem is coded using Pyomo in Python on a PC with an Intel i7-8700 @ 3.20 GHz CPU and 32GB RAM, running on a 64-bit Windows 10 Enterprise operating system. The reformulated master problems and subproblems are solved using Gurobi 9.1.

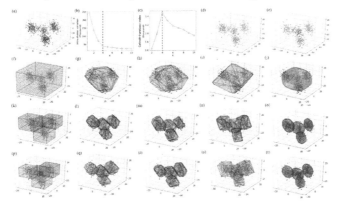

Figure 2. Uncertainty data, determination of optimal group number, clustering results, and uncertainty sets for application on IEEE 39-bus system. (a) Uncertainty data samples. (b) Elbow method. (c) Calinski-Harabasz index. (d) K-means results. (e) DBSCAN results. (f) Conventional box. (g) Conventional budget. (h) Conventional DPMM. (i) Conventional PCA & KDE. (j) Conventional SVC. (k) K-means + box. (l) K-means + budget. (m) K-means + DPMM. (n) K-means + PCA & KDE. (o) K-means + SVC. (p) DBSCAN + box. (q) DBSCAN + budget. (r) DBSCAN + DPMM. (s) DBSCAN + PCA & KDE. (t) DBSCAN + SVC.

Figure 2 presents the uncertainty data, the data clustering results, and the uncertainty sets. Wind forecast error data are shown in Figure 2(a). According to the elbow method and the Calinski-Harabasz index method in Figure 2(b)-(c), the optimal number of data groups is 4. Next, K-means and DBSCAN are applied individually to group the data into 4 data groups in Figure 2(d)-(e). Conventional and disjunctive uncertainty sets are shown in Figure 2(f)-(t). All types of data-driven uncertainty sets have the same level of conservativeness, which can be chosen by the decision makers to balance risk and robustness. The level of conservativeness is set to be 90%, represented by the same data coverage level of 90% across all types of data-driven uncertainty sets. The UC problem is solved using the proposed decomposition-based optimization algorithm. The solution time for the conventional uncertainty sets without clustering ranges from 46 to 182 seconds, and the problems with the proposed disjunctive uncertainty sets take 60-85 seconds to solve. Compared to the conventional approach that updates the entire models during the iterative solution process, the proposed algorithm can significantly improve the computational efficiency by reducing the solution time by around 70%. The optimal objective values, namely the minimum UC costs, are listed in Table 1. Higher values correspond to more conservative solutions. For comparison, the minimum cost for the deterministic case with no uncertainties is $426,443. To investigate the effectiveness of the proposed approach, we apply the price of robustness (PoR) to measure the level of additional cost for the robust optimization cases compared to the deterministic case. The proposed approach reduces PoR by 28-38%, 7.6%, 23%-29%, 27%-31%, and 21%-22% for the problems with box, budget, DPMM, PCA coupled with KDE, and SVC uncertainty sets, respectively, compared to the conventional approach. Also, the problems with disjunctive uncertainty sets constructed using DBSCAN tend to have lower optimal costs than the problems with K-means-based disjunctive uncertainty sets, showing that DBSCAN may handle the outliers of the uncertainty data more efficiently.

Table 1. Optimal objective values under uncertainty sets with different approaches.

minimum cost ($)	Box	Budget	DPMM	PCA & KDE	SVC
No Clustering	461,020	441,155	445,741	455,089	444,191
K-Means	451,178	440,041	441,277	447,271	440,508
DBSCAN	447,712	440,041	440,092	446,121	440,217

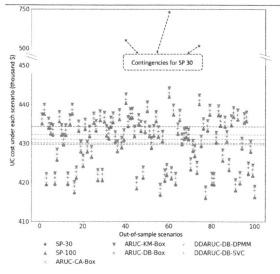

Figure 3. Simulation results under the optimal solutions from ARO and SP approaches.

To benchmark the performance of the proposed approach, we simulate the UC costs under the optimal solutions from both the ARO models and the conventional two-stage stochastic UC models. We obtain the optimal stochastic UC solutions through 30 and 100 random scenarios, denoted as SP-30 and SP-100 solutions, respectively. The stochastic UC problems tend to be more computationally demanding, as obtaining SP-30 and SP-100 solutions take 342 CPUs and 1,194 CPUs, which are more than three times longer than the solution time using the proposed framework with disjunctive uncertainty sets. Figure 3 presents the simulated UC costs following ARO and SP solutions throughout 100 randomly generated out-of-sample scenarios, where the horizontal lines indicate the average out-of-sample costs. The SP-30 solution cannot handle the systems contingencies effectively, as shown by two scenarios with UC costs over $500,000. As for the proposed approach, the solution corresponding to the K-means-based disjunctive box uncertainty sets shows a noticeably lower average UC cost than the solution using the conventional box uncertainty set. The differences of average simulated UC costs between the SP-100 solution and the robust UC solutions using the proposed data-driven disjunctive uncertainty sets are below 0.001%, while the solution time of SP-100 is 13 times longer than the proposed approach.

4. Conclusions

This paper proposed a novel robust UC framework with data-driven disjunctive uncertainty sets for the wind power forecast errors with disjunctive structures. The uncertainty data were grouped using K-means and DBSCAN, and the proposed disjunctive uncertainty sets were constructed accordingly as the union of multiple basic uncertainty sets, including conventional uncertainty sets and data-driven uncertainty sets using DPMM, PCA coupled with KDE, and SVC. The resulting problem was formulated as a two-stage robust UC model with disjunctive uncertainty sets. To facilitate the solution process, a tailored decomposition-based optimization algorithm was developed. A case study based on the IEEE 39-bus system was performed. The results presented that the price of robustness reduced by 8-48% with the proposed framework, compared to the traditional "one-set-fits-all" approach.

References

D. Bertsimas, E. Litvinov, X. A. Sun, et al., 2013, Adaptive Robust Optimization for the Security Constrained Unit Commitment Problem. IEEE Transactions on Power Systems, 28, 1, 52-63.

H. Bludszuweit, J. A. Dominguez-Navarro, A. Llombart, 2008, Statistical Analysis of Wind Power Forecast Error. IEEE Transactions on Power Systems, 23, 3, 983-991.

C. Ning, F. You, 2017, Data-driven adaptive nested robust optimization: General modeling framework and efficient computational algorithm for decision making under uncertainty. AIChE Journal, 63, 9, 3790-3817.

C. Ning, F. You, 2017, A data-driven multistage adaptive robust optimization framework for planning and scheduling under uncertainty. AIChE Journal, 63, 4343-4369.

C. Ning, F. You, 2018, Data-driven decision making under uncertainty integrating robust optimization with principal component analysis and kernel smoothing methods. Computers & Chemical Engineering, 112, 190-210.s

C. Ning, F. You, 2018, Data-driven stochastic robust optimization: General computational framework and algorithm leveraging machine learning for optimization under uncertainty in the big data era. Computers & Chemical Engineering, 111, 115-133.

C. Ning, F. You, 2019, Optimization under uncertainty in the era of big data and deep learning: When machine learning meets mathematical programming. Computers & Chemical Engineering, 125, 434-448.

C. Ning, F. You, 2019, Data-Driven Adaptive Robust Unit Commitment Under Wind Power Uncertainty: A Bayesian Nonparametric Approach. IEEE Transactions on Power Systems, 34, 2409-2418.

C. Ning, F. You, 2022, Deep Learning Based Distributionally Robust Joint Chance Constrained Economic Dispatch Under Wind Power Uncertainty. IEEE Transactions on Power Systems, 37, 191-203.

N.P. Padhy, 2004, Unit commitment-a bibliographical survey. IEEE Transactions on Power Systems, 19, 1196-1205.

H. Qiu, F. You, 2020, Decentralized-distributed robust electric power scheduling for multi-microgrid systems. Applied Energy, 269, 115146.

C. Shang, X. Huang, F. You, 2017, Data-driven robust optimization based on kernel learning. Computers & Chemical Engineering, 106, 464-479.

C. Shang, F. You, 2019, A data-driven robust optimization approach to scenario-based stochastic model predictive control. Journal of Process Control, 75, 24-39.

Y. Wang, Q. Hu, D. Meng, P. Zhu, 2017, Deterministic and probabilistic wind power forecasting using a variational Bayesian-based adaptive robust multi-kernel regression model. Applied Energy, 208, 1097-1112.

Proceedings of the 14th International Symposium on Process Systems Engineering – PSE 2021+
June 19-23, 2022, Kyoto, Japan © 2022 Elsevier B.V. All rights reserved.
http://dx.doi.org/10.1016/B978-0-323-85159-6.50195-0

Heat integration for superstructure models: A MILP formulation for easy implementation and fast computing

Philipp Kenkel [a,b*], Timo Wassermann [a,b], Edwin Zondervan [c]

[a] *Advanced Energy Systems Institute, University of Bremen, 28359 Bremen, Germany*
[b] *artec Sustainability Research Center, University of Bremen, 28359 Bremen, Germany*
[c] *SPT-PSE, University of Twente, 7522NB Enschede, Netherlands*
kenkel@uni-bremen.de

Abstract

This work presents a mixed-integer linear programming (MILP) heat integration model tailored to superstructure optimization. It includes energy targeting based on a transshipment model combined with linearized heat exchanger capital costs. A variable number of heat utilities at different temperature levels can be implemented. In addition, the model facilitates the utilization of high temperature heat pumps to benefit from low exergy waste heat. The heat integration model is part of the **O**pen s**U**perstruc**T**ure mo**D**eling and **O**ptimizati**O**n f**R**amework (OUTDOOR) and thus can be accessed easily using its intuitive excel-based interface. A model evaluation of the MILP shows low cost deviations of 1–14 % compared to more complex models, with fast solution times. Additionally, a practical superstructure case study is presented, where internal heat recovery reduces the external heat consumption of a power-to-methanol process by 40 %, thus underlining the relevance for adequate consideration.

Keywords: Superstructure optimization, Heat integration, MILP, Open-source

1. Introduction

Heat integration and the optimization of heat exchanger networks (HEN) is an important domain in chemical engineering and process synthesis. It includes three major steps: 1) minimization of external utility demand, 2) minimization of heat exchanger (HEX) area and 3) minimization of the HEX matches (Yee and Grossmann, 1990). Different approaches, from simple pinch analysis to complete simultaneous optimization of all three tasks exist, the latter resulting in complex MINLP's (**M**ixed-**I**nteger **N**on-**L**inear **P**rogramming models). Renowned MINLP approaches were developed by Yee and Grossmann as well as by Ciric and Floudas (Ciric and Floudas, 1991; Yee and Grossmann, 1990). However, the integration of MINLP's in tools for preliminary process design, like superstructure models, tends to increase their complexity. A superstructure model is a simplified representation of many possible flowsheets that is used for process synthesis (Kenkel et al., 2021a). Solving MINLP superstructures is generally much slower if not even impossible for large models. Thus, heat integration is often omitted, which can lead to suboptimal solutions if flowsheets include considerable heat integration potential. This work presents a novel MILP heat integration model tailored to superstructure models. It is implemented in the **O**pen s**U**perstruc**T**ure mo**D**eling and **O**ptimizati**O**n f**R**amework (OUTDOOR) and provides fast solution times, easy code implementation and data input together with reasonable accuracy (Kenkel et al., 2021b).

2. Methodology

2.1. Energy targeting model

The heat integration model is part of OUTDOOR's MILP superstructure model for process synthesis which is described in detail by Kenkel et al. (Kenkel et al., 2021a). OUTDOOR can be used to derive optimal flowsheets based on interaction of different unit-operations using mass and energy balances as well as cost and emission functions (Kenkel et al., 2021b, 2021a). The underlying energy targeting model is based on a transshipment model and depicted in Figure 1. Prior to optimization, the inlet and outlet temperatures of unit-operations, external heating and cooling utilities as well as heat pump (HP) inlet and outlet temperatures are defined. Those temperatures form a temperature grid. To account for a minimum temperature difference of $\Delta T_{min} = 10$ K within the temperature grid, the inlet and outlet temperatures of the hot/cold units are reduced/increased by 5 K. The required heating and cooling demands of the individual unit-operations are defined by the calculated (case specific) mass flow rates (in t/h) and a predefined specific energy demand (in MWh/t$_{input}$). These are partitioned into the different temperature intervals on the temperature grid. Heat can be exchanged in the different temperature intervals. Residual heat at high temperatures can be cascaded down to lower intervals. If a heat deficit persists, it has to be satisfied by external heat. Residual heat in the lowest temperature interval is cooled down by the cooling water utility. For every heat interval that exchanges heat, a virtual HEX is calculated, which is used for the cost calculation of the virtual HEN. The HP can raise low temperature heat to higher temperature intervals based on predefined HP inlet and outlet temperature and coefficient of performance (COP).

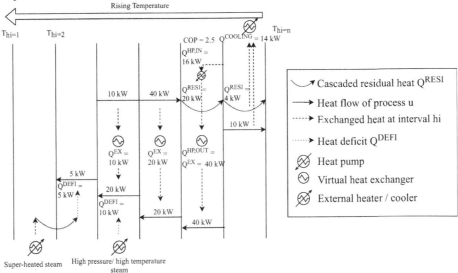

Figure 1: Representation of OUTDOOR's energy targeting model.

2.2. Heat integration costs

The heat integration costs are calculated on an annual basis using the total external utility demand and capital costs for a virtual HEX depicting the HEN. Additional costs are added for the HP if it is utilized. Heating costs are calculated based on derived heat deficits in the different temperature intervals; cooling costs are derived from the residual heat in the lowest temperature interval. Annual capital costs of virtual HEX are determined by a linear cost function presented in Eqs. (1) – (3). Here, Q_{hi}^{EX} depicts the exchanged heat flow in temperature interval hi, M_{hi} represents a large Big-M parameter and Y_{hi} a binary variable that defines if heat is exchanged in temperature interval hi. m and b are linear coefficients which are derived from several pre-simulated, sized and costed HEX using Aspen Plus. Their default values are $m = 13.459$ k€ MW^{-1} yr^{-1} and $b = 3.3893$ k€ yr^{-1}. The costs of the HP are derived from its electricity demand, which depends on the defined COP and utilized heat, plus the capital costs, which result from a linear correlation with the heat output.

$$C\_HEX_{hi} \leq m \cdot Q_{hi}^{EX} + b + M_{hi} \cdot (1 - Y_{hi}) \tag{1}$$

$$C\_HEX_{hi} \geq m \cdot Q_{hi}^{EX} + b - M_{hi} \cdot (1 - Y_{hi}) \tag{2}$$

$$C\_HEX_{hi} \leq M_{hi} \cdot Y_{hi} \tag{3}$$

3. Model evaluation

Two performance tests are performed for the MILP using well-known cases provided by Linnhoff et al. and Floudas and Grossmann (Floudas et al., 1986; Linnhoff et al., 1982).

3.1. Performance test cases

The first performance test is a simple HEN optimization given by Linnhoff et al. including two hot/cold streams together with external utilities. (Linnhoff et al., 1982). It was tested by Linnhoff et al., by usage of the MAGNETS software and the rigorous MINLP by Yee and Grossmann. (Floudas et al., 1986; Linnhoff et al., 1982; Yee and Grossmann, 1990). The second test is more complex, considering five hot streams and one cold stream. This case is an example from the MAGNETS user manual also tested by Yee and Grossmann as well as Ciric and Floudas, among others (Ciric and Floudas, 1991; Floudas et al., 1986; Yee and Grossmann, 1990). Initial data for the tests is given in Table 1 and 2.

Table 1: Initial data for performance test 1 taken from Linnhoff et al. (Linnhoff et al., 1982)

Stream name	T_{IN} (°C)	T_{OUT} (°C)	F_{cp} (kW K^{-1})	Costs ($ kW^{-1} yr^{-1})
H$_1$	169.85	59.85	30	–
H$_2$	149.85	29.85	15	–
C$_1$	19.85	134.15	20	–
C$_2$	79.85	139.85	40	–
Steam	176.85	176.85	–	80
Cooling water	19.85	39.85	–	20

Table 2: Initial data for performance test 2 taken from MAGNETS user manual (Floudas et al., 1986)

Stream name	T_{IN} (°C)	T_{OUT} (°C)	F_{cp} (kW K^{-1})	Costs ($ kW^{-1} yr^{-1})
H$_1$	226.85	46.85	6	–
H$_2$	206.85	106.85	4	–
H$_3$	186.85	86.85	6	–
H$_4$	106.85	86.85	20	–
H$_5$	106.85	46.85	12	–
C$_1$	16.85	386.85	18	–
Steam	426.85	426.85	–	140
Cooling water	26.85	46.85	–	10

3.2. Results

The implementation of the stream data in OUTDOOR only takes ca. 5 minutes due to its ready-made excel-templates. To enable a fair cost comparison, the virtual HEX capital costs are first adjusted to the according reference year by applying the chemical engineering cost plant index (CECPI) and further transformed from € to $.

The total run time of the OUTDOOR program for performance test 1 is 1.33 s of which 0.33 s are solver time by Gurobi. The calculated total annual HEN costs are 102,123 $ which is about 14 % higher than the results from Linnhoff et al., the MAGNETS solution and one case of Yee's and Grossmann's MINLP (Yee and Grossmann, 1990) (ref. Figure 2). Annual external utility costs are equal to Linnhoff's and the MAGNETS solution, whilst annual capital costs are about 20–25 % higher (Yee and Grossmann, 1990).

Total run time of the OUTDOOR program for performance test 2 is 1.96 s of which 0.72 s are solver time by Gurobi. For this case the annual HEN costs are 569,651 $ which is only about 1 % smaller than the reported solutions in literature (Ciric and Floudas, 1991; Yee and Grossmann, 1990). The total heat exchange of 3040 kW is in the range of solutions recorded by Yee (2984 kW) and Ciric (3068 kW) and depicts the energy target for a minimum approach temperature of $\Delta T_{min} = 10$ K (Ciric and Floudas, 1991; Yee and Grossmann, 1990). The two examples show that the computing time of the proposed approach is very fast, while the energy targeting along with the HEN costs provide acceptable accuracy. It is further expected, that the total cost deviation would be lower in a real process synthesis case, where HEN costs only make a minor share of the overall costs.

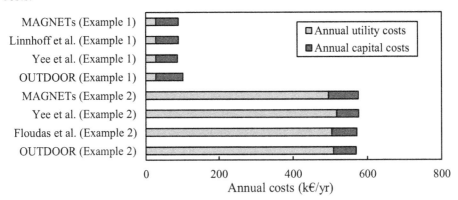

Figure 2: Cost results from performance tests.

4. Applied case study

To demonstrate the capability of the MILP to a real-world problem a case study is developed. The selected case study describes a power-to-methanol (PtM) process which was introduced in Kenkel et al. (Kenkel et al., 2021a).

4.1. Power-to-Methanol application

The superstructure optimization aims to synthesize the flowsheet of a methanol production by direct hydrogenation of CO_2. As depicted in Figure 3, different water electrolysis technologies are considered for H_2 production: Low- and high-pressure alkaline and proton exchange membrane electrolysis as well solid oxide electrolysis. Available CO_2 sources are ambient air and flue gases from an oil refinery or oxyfuel fired cement factory. Methanol synthesis is included as a tripartite process (reaction, purge separation, purification) based on data from Wassermann et al. (Wassermann et al., 2020). The purge stream is combusted to produce either steam or electricity, which can be used internally or sold. For a detailed description of the superstructure, as well as bi-criteria flowsheet optimization we refer to Kenkel et al. (Kenkel et al., 2021a). In total 18 unit-operations are implemented in the superstructure. 10 units are potentially exothermic and 3 processes are potentially endothermic. The complete superstructure model consists of 30,145 constraints, 23,709 variables of which 5,437 are binary. It was solved on a MacBook Pro with a 2 GHz-Dual Core Intel Core i5 processor and 8 GB RAM.

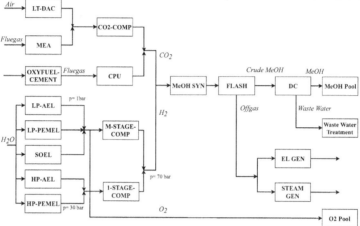

Figure 3: Simplified PtM superstructure adopted from Kenkel et al. (Kenkel et al., 2021a)

4.2. Flowsheet synthesis and heat integration results

An economic optimization of the PtM superstructure takes about 9 s on the defined computer system utilizing Gurobi (Kenkel et al., 2021a). The proposed flowsheet captures CO_2 from a refinery by absorption and provides H_2 by low pressure alkaline electrolysis with subsequent multi-stage compression. The purge stream as well as waste heat from methanol synthesis and H_2 compression is utilized for heat integration. The net production costs of the methanol are 892 € t^{-1}, where the utility supply (external heat, cooling water and HEN) makes up only 3 % of the total costs. The emerging excess heat is employed in the desorption process of the CO_2 capture, which requires heat at temperatures of about 120°C. Waste heat from methanol synthesis and H_2 compression provide ca. 28 % of the required heat, while purge stream combustion supplies further 12 %, leading to a total utility reduction of ca. 40 %. Only slightly lower shares were calculated in a detailed process analysis by Wassermann et al. (Wassermann et al., 2020).

4.3. Model limitations

The model evaluation and the applied case study show that the MILP heat integration model presents a possibility for easy implementation and fast calculation in superstructure models. Nonetheless, this formulation also comes with certain drawbacks. The main disadvantage is that only a virtual HEN is calculated, which gives good indication on the total costs, but neglects practical stream matching. A second drawback originates from the pre-calculated virtual HEX capital costs function. It is based on average gas/liquid/phase changing exchangers. If a superstructure with low pressure gas-gas HEX above all is considered the required exchange area will probably be higher, which leads to underestimation of HEN costs.

5. Conclusion

This work presents a MILP model for heat integration in superstructure models, which is part of the automated **O**pen s**U**perstruc**T**ure mo**D**eling and **O**ptimizati**O**n f**R**amework (OUTDOOR). Model evaluation determines fast solution times, intuitive data input and acceptable accuracy of total HEN costs. A practical study on a PtM case with 30,145 constraints and 23,709 variables, which is solved in 9 s, emphasizes the benefits of OUTDOORs heat integration model. The results indicate that 40 % of required heat can be supplied by heat recovery, hence highlighting the relevance of heat integration in superstructure optimization. Model limitations, concerning simplified capital costs calculation and virtual HEN construction are outweighed by benefits of considering heat recovery with first indication of additional HEN costs. This is especially true for superstructure optimization, where many different flowsheets are investigated as part of preliminary design and HEN costs only make up small shares of total costs. Additionally, heat integration adds value to process synthesis by minimizing the environmental burden from external utilities, which is particularly relevant for the design of sustainable processes. Therefore, this work can provide the basis for selecting specific process alternatives for detailed process simulation and analysis.

6. Funding

Funding of this research by the German Federal Ministry for Economic Affairs and Energy within the KEROSyN100 project (funding code 03EIV051A) is gratefully acknowledged.

References

Ciric, A.R., Floudas, C.A., 1991. Heat exchanger network synthesis without decomposition. Comput. Chem. Eng. 15, 385–396. https://doi.org/10.1016/0098-1354(91)87017-4

Floudas, C., Ciric, A., Grossmann, I., 1986. Automatic synthesis of optimum heat exchanger network configurations. AIChE J. 32, 276--290.

Kenkel, P., Wassermann, T., Rose, C., Zondervan, E., 2021a. A generic superstructure modeling and optimization framework on the example of bi-criteria Power-to-Methanol process design. Comput. Chem. Eng. 150, 107327. https://doi.org/10.1016/j.compchemeng.2021.107327

Kenkel, P., Wassermann, T., Rose, C., Zondervan, E., 2021b. OUTDOOR–An open-source superstructure construction and optimization tool, in: Computer Aided Chemical Engineering. pp. 413–418.

Linnhoff, B., Townsend, D.W., Boland, D., Hewitt, G.F., Guy, A.R., Marsland, R., 1982. A user guide on process integration for the efficient use of energy, Revised 1s. ed. IChemE, Rugby, UK.

Wassermann, T., Schnuelle, C., Kenkel, P., Zondervan, E., 2020. Power-to-Methanol at Refineries as a Precursor to Green Jet Fuel Production: a Simulation and Assessment Study, in: Computer Aided Chemical Engineering. Elsevier B.V., pp. 1453–1458. https://doi.org/10.1016/B978-0-12-823377-1.50243-3

Yee, T.F., Grossmann, I.E., 1990. Simultaneous optimization models for heat integration-II. Heat exchanger network synthesis. Comput. Chem. Eng. 14, 1165–1184. https://doi.org/10.1016/0098-1354(90)85010-8

Proceedings of the 14th International Symposium on Process Systems Engineering – PSE 2021+
June 19-23, 2022, Kyoto, Japan © 2022 Elsevier B.V. All rights reserved.
http://dx.doi.org/10.1016/B978-0-323-85159-6.50196-2

A Software Framework for Optimal Multiperiod Carbon-Constrained Energy Planning

Purusothmn Nair S Bhasker Nair[a], Dominic C. Y. Foo[a*], Raymond R. Tan[b], Michael Short[c]

[a]*Centre of Excellence for Green Technologies/Department of Chemical and Environmental Engineering, University of Nottingham Malaysia, Broga Road, 43500 Semenyih, Selangor, Malaysia*
[b]*Chemical Engineering Department/Centre for Engineering and Sustainable Development Research, De La Salle University, 2401 Taft Avenue, Manila, Philippines*
[c]*Department of Chemical and Process Engineering, University of Surrey, Guildford, Surrey GU2 7XH, United Kingdom*
dominic.foo@nottingham.edu.my

Abstract

The delay in action to mitigate climate change has resulted in a greater dependence on carbon dioxide removal (CDR) to achieve net-zero carbon targets by 2050. This work reports a newly developed optimal decarbonisation software framework that is based on a superstructure targeting approach to energy planning. The novel mathematical optimisation tool, which is formulated as a mixed-integer linear program (MILP), determines the optimum deployment of renewable energy sources, negative emission technologies (NETs), and CO_2 capture and storage (CCS) for long-term regional energy planning, subject to budget and emissions constraints. The software can be used by policymakers to determine long-term energy decarbonisation strategy including when to decommission which plants, what technologies to employ when, and which fuels could be replaced by lower-carbon alternatives. The application of the software framework is demonstrated with a case study containing seven power plants. In this multiperiod work, CCS deployment is favoured for coal-based power plants due to their high CO_2 intensity, while energy-producing NETs is deployed for all periods.

Keywords: Multiperiod Energy Planning; Negative Emission Technologies; Process Integration; Policymaking; Decarbonisation Software

1. Introduction

In 2015, 196 countries adopted the Paris Agreement, which aimed to limit global warming below 2 °C and preferably 1.5 °C above pre-industrial levels. Given the delay of major mitigation actions, there is an increasing urgency for countries to cut their emissions by 45 % by year 2030 from 2010 baseline levels (United Nations, 2021). The long-term target should be to achieve net-zero CO_2 emissions by 2050. At the current trajectory, achieving net-zero emissions would require the deployment of CDR, typically achieved via NETs. Examples of CDR methods are bioenergy with CCS and direct air capture. The former is categorised as energy-producing NETs (EP-NETs), while the latter is categorised as energy-consuming NETs (EC-NETs).

In the seminal work of carbon emissions pinch analysis (CEPA), Tan and Foo (2007) proposed the use of a graphical targeting tool to determine the minimum renewable energy sources in satisfying the emission limit in a geographical region. This graphical CEPA approach was later extended for the incorporation of CCS in energy planning (Tan et al., 2009). Lee et al. (2009) developed the automated targeting model (ATM) to complement the limitation of CEPA, which was then extended by Ooi et al. (2013) for targeting CCS retrofit during energy planning. Most recently, the deployment of NETs during energy planning was proposed using both graphical (Nair et al., 2020) and algebraic targeting approaches (Nair et al., 2021). In the past, several software had been developed to aid in energy planning, covering both technical and economic approaches. The novelty of this decision-making software framework lies in the possibility of allowing potential retrofit of various CCS technologies at point sources of CO_2, and deployment of NETs, via a multiperiod planning formulation. The framework is built on mathematical programming models, where optimal energy planning scenarios may be generated. The interpretable results can act as guides for policymakers on the optimal decarbonisation strategies to be employed at a national level.

2. Problem Statement

For period $k \in K$, the demand and CO_2 emission limits of the energy planning system are specified as D_k and L_k respectively. Power plant $i \in I$ with a lower bound energy output $F_{i,LB}$, upper bound energy output $F_{i,UB}$, CO_2 intensity CS_i and cost CT_i make up the energy planning system for period k. The removal of the CO_2 emissions in period k is aided with the deployment of CCS technology $n \in N$, EP-NETs technology $p \in P$ and EC-NETs technology $q \in Q$. In this work, the superstructural mathematical formulation is optimised to synthesise an optimal decarbonisation plan.

3. Mathematical Optimisation Formulation

For period k, the summation of the energy output from power plants $i \in I$ must be equivalent to the demand of a specified geographical region (D_k), as shown in Eq.(1). Also, the energy output from power plant i in period k ($FS_{i,k}$) should be in the range of lower ($F_{i,LB}$) and upper bound of energy output ($F_{i,UB}$).

$$\sum_i FS_{i,k} = D_k \qquad \forall k \tag{1}$$

Next, the carbon intensity of power plant i with CCS technology n in period k ($CR_{i,n}$) is determined from Eq.(2) (Ooi et al., 2013).

$$CR_{i,n} = \frac{CS_i \times (1 - RR_n)}{1 - X_n} \qquad \forall i \, \forall n \tag{2}$$

where RR_n and X_n is the removal ratio and parasitic power loss of CCS technology n.

The net energy output from power plant i with CCS technology n in period k ($FNR_{i,k,n}$) is calculated from Eq.(3). Note that the reduced energy output from power plant i is due to the parasitic power losses during CCS. Also, $FNR_{i,k,n}$ should not exceed its upper bound of energy output in period k, as shown in Eq.(4).

$$FR_{i,k,n} \times (1 - X_n) = FNR_{i,k,n} \qquad \forall i \, \forall k \, \forall n \tag{3}$$

$$FR_{i,k,n} \leq F_{i,UB} \times B_{i,k,n} \qquad \forall i \; \forall k \; \forall n \tag{4}$$

where $FR_{i,k,n}$ is the extent of CCS retrofit technology n on power plant i in period k while $B_{i,n}$ is a binary variable for selection of power plant i with CCS technology n in period k.

The summation of the extent of CCS retrofit of power plant i with all CCS technologies in period k ($FR_{i,k}$) is calculated from Eq.(5). Also, the total extent of CCS retrofit of power plant i should not exceed the energy output from power plant i in period k, as shown in Eq.(6).

$$\sum_n FR_{i,k,n} = FR_{i,k} \qquad \forall i \; \forall k \tag{5}$$

$$FR_{i,k} \leq FS_{i,k} \qquad \forall i \; \forall k \tag{6}$$

For a given period k, The summation of the net energy output by power plant i without CCS retrofit ($FNS_{i,k}$) and the extent of CCS retrofit of power plant i with CCS technology n ($FR_{i,k,n}$) should equate to the energy output from power plant i; shown in Eq.(7).

$$FNS_{i,k} + \sum_n FR_{i,k,n} = FS_{i,k} \qquad \forall i \; \forall k \tag{7}$$

For a given period k, the summation of the energy output from all energy sources e.g., compensatory energy (FC_k), EP-NETs ($FEP_{k,p}$) etc. must fulfil the total demand of the energy system; the latter includes the total power requirement (D_k) and that required by EC-NETs ($FEC_{k,q}$) etc. as demonstrated in Eq.(8). Equally, the total CO_2 load contribution from all energy sources is equivalent to the total CO_2 emissions at the end of energy planning for period k (TE_k), shown in Eq.(9).

$$\sum_i \sum_n \left(FNS_{i,k} + FNR_{i,k,n}\right) + FC_k + \sum_p FEP_{k,p} = \sum_q FEC_{k,q} + D_k \; \forall k \tag{8}$$

$$\sum_i \sum_n \left(FNS_{i,k} CS_i + \left(FNR_{i,k,n} CR_{i,n}\right)\right) + FC_k \, CIC_k$$
$$+ \sum_p FEP_{k,p} \, CIEP_k + \sum_q FEC_{k,q} \, CIEC_k = TE_k \qquad \forall k \tag{9}$$

where CIC_k, $CIEP_k$ and $CIEC_k$ represent the carbon intensities of compensatory energy, EP-NETs technology p and EC-NETs technology q in period k respectively.

Meanwhile, the total energy costs at the end of energy planning in period k (TC_k) are calculated from Eq.(10).

$$\sum_i \sum_n \left(FNS_{i,k} CT_{i,k} + \left(FNR_{i,k,n} CTR_{i,k,n}\right) + \left(CFX_{i,k,n} B_{i,k,n}\right)\right) + FC_k \, CTC_k$$
$$+ \sum_p FEP_{k,p} \, CTEP_k + \sum_q FEC_{k,q} \, CTEC_k = TC_k \qquad \forall k \tag{10}$$

where $CTR_{i,k,n}$ and $CT_{i,k}$ represent the cost of energy output by power plant i with and without CCS technology n in period k respectively, while CTC_k, $CTEP_k$ and $CTEC_k$ represent the cost of compensatory energy, EP-NETs technology p, and EC-NETs technology q in period k respectively. Meanwhile, $CFX_{i,k,n}$ represents the fixed cost of power plant i with CCS technology n in period k.

The extent of CCS retrofit on power plant i at a later period is at least equal to that in its previous period, as shown in Eq.(11). This ensures that a decision taken to CCS retrofit power plant i in period k would not be reversed in the subsequent periods.

$$(FR_i)_{k+1} \geq (FR_i)_k \qquad k = 1,2,\dots,n-1 \tag{11}$$

The constraints regarding the total CO_2 emissions and total energy costs in period k are presented in Eq.(12) and Eq.(13).

$$TE_k = L_k \qquad \forall k \tag{12}$$

$$TC_k \leq BD_k \qquad \forall k \tag{13}$$

where BD_k is the budget allocation in period k.

The mathematical formulation may be optimised according to either Eq.(14) or Eq.(15). For Eq.(14), the total energy cost is minimised subject to constraints in Eq.(1) to Eq.(12). In other words, the minimisation of the total energy costs would ensure that the CO_2 emission limit in a geographical region in period k is satisfied. Meanwhile, for Eq.(15), the total CO_2 emissions are minimised subject to the constraints in Eq.(1) to Eq.(11) and Eq.(13). In other words, the minimisation of the total CO_2 emissions is conducted subject to the budgetary constraint for period k. Therefore, the CO_2 emission limit in a geographical for period k may or may not be satisfied.

$$min\, TC_k \qquad \forall k \tag{14}$$

$$min\, TE_k \qquad \forall k \tag{15}$$

The resulting mathematical formulation is a mixed-integer linear programming (MILP) model. The model is implemented in Pyomo, with an easy-to-use input spreadsheet to formulate one's problems. A user guide is available, including installation instructions for the Octeract solver, and the code is available at https://github.com/mchlshort/DECO2.

4. Case Study

The application of the optimal decarbonisation software framework is demonstrated with a hypothetical case study. Seven power plants with various energy sources generate electricity to satisfy the demand of a geographical region. The data relating to these power plants were approximately based on the data in the work by Tan et al. (2009). The energy planning is conducted across three periods, each with a specified demand, emission limit and budget allocation. The CO_2 load reduction is achievable with the potential deployment of three types of EP-NETs and EC-NETs, alongside two choices of CCS technologies. Also, there is a choice of incorporating additional renewable energy (compensatory energy) for satisfying the CO_2 emission limit. The superstructure optimisation of the MILP model provides an overview regarding the optimal deployment of CCS, EP-NETs, EC-NETs, and compensatory energy for each period. Table 1, Table 2, and Table 3 present the data related to the power plants, NETs, and energy planning respectively, which was approximated based on the work by Tan et al. (2009).

Table 1: Power plant data

Power Plant	1	2 - 4	5	6 - 8
Fuel	Renewable	Natural gas	Oil	Coal
$F_{i,LB}$ / TWh y^{-1}	10	0	0	0
$F_{i,UB}$ / TWh y^{-1}	40	40	10	20
CS_i / Mt (TWh)$^{-1}$	0	0.5	0.8	1.0
$CT_{i,k}$ / mil USD y^{-1}	38	25	49	12
$CTR_{i,k,1}$ / mil USD y^{-1}	0	34	68	20
$CTR_{i,k,2}$ / / mil USD y^{-1}	0	29	59	16

Table 2: NETs data

Period k	$CIEP_k$ / Mt (TWh)$^{-1}$	$CIEC_k$ / Mt (TWh)$^{-1}$	$CTEP_k$ / mil USD y^{-1}	$CTEC_k$ / mil USD y^{-1}
1	-0.8	-0.6	43	49
2	-0.6	-0.4	40	37
3	-0.4	-0.2	37	24

Table 3: Energy planning data

Period k	D_k / TWh y^{-1}	L_k / Mt y^{-1}	BD_k / mil USD y^{-1}	CIC_k / Mt (TWh)$^{-1}$	CTC_k / mil USD y^{-1}
1	60	15	1,500	0	38
2	75	8	2,000	0	38
3	90	3	2,500	0	38

In addition to the power plant data in Table 1, the value of $CFX_{i,k,n}$ is assumed as 200 mil USD y^{-1}. The case study was solved for both objective functions i.e., minimum budget (Eq.(14)) and minimum emissions (Eq.(15)). For the minimum budget objective (Eq.(14)), the total costs for periods 1, 2 and 3 were determined as 1,790, 2,463 and 3,116 mil USD y^{-1} respectively, while emission limits for all periods are satisfied. Note that CCS technology 1 was solely deployed for the coal-based power plants for all periods. In other words, the optimisation model favoured the costlier CCS technology 1 due to its highest removal ratio (0.85) and lower parasitic power loss (0.15). All three periods involved the deployment of EP-NETs, specifically technology 2 in periods 1 and 2, and technology 1 in period 3. The energy requirement of EC-NETs made it less favourable for its deployment in any period. Due to the decreased CO_2 emission limit, the deployment of EP-NETs increased from 5.59 TWh y^{-1} in period 1 to 9 TWh y^{-1} in period

3. As for the minimum emissions objective (Eq.(15)), the optimisation is conducted subject to the budget constraints for each period. The total CO_2 emissions in periods 1, 2 and 3 are 27.1, 29.8 and 29.6 Mt y^{-1} respectively. Note that the total CO_2 emissions for all periods are higher than their limits, due to insufficient budget for the deployment of CCS and/or NETs. For this case, EP-NETs technology 1 was deployed, while CCS technology 1 was deployed for coal-based power plants in all periods.

5. Conclusions

The optimal decarbonisation software framework developed in this work is based on mathematical optimisation models for energy planning. The decision-making software framework is expected to aid policymakers in drafting suitable decarbonisation plans for a national/sectoral level. The MILP optimisation model provides rigorous solutions for optimal deployment of EP-NETs, EC-NETs, CCS and compensatory energy for the satisfaction of the CO_2 in each period. The case study results demonstrated that CCS technology 1 was favoured due to its highest removal ratio and lower parasitic power loss despite it being more expensive than technology 2. On the other hand, EC-NETs was less preferable due to its energy-consuming characteristic. Therefore, it is evident that this software framework could play a role in the achievement of the net-zero carbon target by 2050. Regardless, uncertainties that often arises with energy planning data and forecasts should be considered in future work for more realistic energy planning scenarios and projections.

References

Lee, S.C., Ng, D.K.S., Foo, D.C.Y., Tan, R.R., 2009. Extended pinch targeting techniques for carbon-constrained energy sector planning. Appl. Energy 86, 60–67. https://doi.org/10.1016/j.apenergy.2008.04.002

Nair, P.N.S.B., Tan, R.R., Foo, D.C.Y., 2021. A Generic Algebraic Targeting Approach for Integration of Renewable Energy Sources, CO2 Capture and Storage and Negative Emission Technologies in Carbon-Constrained Energy Planning. Energy 235, 121280. https://doi.org/10.1016/j.energy.2021.121280

Nair, P.N.S.B., Tan, R.R., Foo, D.C.Y., 2020. Extended Graphical Approach for the Deployment of Negative Emission Technologies. Ind. Eng. Chem. Res. 59, 18977–18990. https://doi.org/10.1021/acs.iecr.0c03817

Ooi, R.E.H., Foo, D.C.Y., Tan, R.R., Ng, D.K.S., Smith, R., 2013. Carbon constrained energy planning (CCEP) for sustainable power generation sector with automated targeting model. Ind. Eng. Chem. Res. 52, 9889–9896. https://doi.org/10.1021/ie4005018

Tan, R.R., Foo, D.C.Y., 2007. Pinch analysis approach to carbon-constrained energy sector planning. Energy 32, 1422–1429. https://doi.org/10.1016/j.energy.2006.09.018

Tan, R.R., Ng, D.K.S., Foo, D.C.Y., 2009. Pinch analysis approach to carbon-constrained planning for sustainable power generation. J. Clean. Prod. 17, 940–944. https://doi.org/10.1016/j.jclepro.2009.02.007

United Nations, 2021. Goal 13 : Take Urgent Action to Combat Climate Change and its Impacts [WWW Document]. Dep. Econ. Soc. Aff. URL https://sdgs.un.org/goals/goal13 (accessed 9.1.21).

Proceedings of the 14th International Symposium on Process Systems Engineering – PSE 2021+
June 19-23, 2022, Kyoto, Japan © 2022 Elsevier B.V. All rights reserved.
http://dx.doi.org/10.1016/B978-0-323-85159-6.50197-4

Superstructure optimisation in various carbon capture and utilisation supply chains

Ikhlas Ghiat, Ahmed AlNouss, Tareq Al-Ansari

College of Science and Engineering, Hamad Bin Khalifa University, Qatar Foundation, Doha, Qatar.
talansari@hbku.edu.qa

Abstract

Carbon capture and utilisation (CCU) appeared as an attractive complementary scenario to carbon capture and storage for CO_2 sequestration and climate change mitigation. CCU covers various routes that use CO_2 as a feedstock for the generation of value-added commodities, which are classified under four main categories: chemical conversion, mineral carbonation, enhanced oil recovery and biological conversion. CCU networks encompass a variety of material, process, and technology options at every node of the supply chain. This forms a superstructure network of multiple CO_2 sources, carbon capture and separation methods, transportation links, and CO_2 utilisation routes (sinks). The purpose of this work is to investigate the economic performance of different CCU pathways and to determine the most optimal CCU integrative configuration. A mixed linear integer programing (MILP) model is developed that aims at optimising the CCU supply chain. A case study for the State of Qatar is presented in this work to illustrate the application of this optimisation framework, with the use of real data for existing CO_2 sources and sinks, and transportation networks along with potential CO_2 sinks. Findings indicate that for high CO_2 concentration and gas flowrates such as the ones studied in the case study, adsorption provides the most economical option for carbon capture. Moreover, the chemical conversion to GTL route presented the best economic performance amongst the other CO_2 utilisation pathways despite the low readiness level. However, biological conversion in agricultural greenhouses could be a more environmentally viable utilisation route with the potential of a carbon-neutral network.

Keywords: Carbon capture and utilisation, CO_2 sequestration, optimisation, MILP.

1. Introduction

Economic and population growth are considered as one of the main drivers of the continued increase of greenhouse gas emissions (GHG) in the atmosphere which lead to further warming and irreversible changes in the climate system (IPCC, 2007). Global greenhouse gas emissions from anthropogenic activities have significantly increased with emissions from fossil-fuel burning activities representing a large share. Carbon dioxide is considered as a major contributor of GHG emissions from burning fossil-fuels. The share of CO_2 emissions from the energy sector accounts for more than 80% of the total CO_2 emissions (Ghiat et al., 2021a). With the COVID19 pandemic and the associated decline in oil and coal demands, CO_2 emissions have declined by 5.8% in 2020 which represents the largest ever decline. Despite the pandemic, annual CO_2 emissions in the atmosphere originating from the energy sector are still at their peak with amounts as high as 31.5 Gt, representing a concentration of around 412.5 ppm during 2020 (IEA, 2021). The undeniable evidence of the anthropogenic influence on the climate is perceived in the growing vulnerability of the natural and human systems. This suggests that it is a collective action problem that requires collaborative adaptation and mitigation measures between the different stakeholders and agents in the energy, water, and food (EWF) sectors. Co and tri-benefits can be exploited, and trade-offs can be avoided by having aligned objectives that tackle climate change challenges and deliver holistic sustainable solutions to all EWF sub-systems (IPCC, 2014). The intergovernmental panel on climate change (IPCC) recommends, as one of the Representative Concentration Pathways (RCP2.6), stabilizing the surface temperature increase below 2°C to limit CO_2-eq emissions to 450 ppm in the atmosphere by 2100 (IPCC, 2014). Carbon capture and storage or utilisation (CCUS) is considered as one of the most important CO_2 cutting schemes that can help achieve these global warming targets. CCU alone can reach a CO_2 sequestration potential of 878 Mt/year by 2060 in the case where CO_2 storage is limited. Moreover, CO_2 utilisation can also sequester CO_2 in different time-scale periods depending on the utilisation of the final product. CO_2 source-sink matching in CCU networks is a crucial and complex work that requires careful analysis and optimisation of the CCU supply chain (Ghiat and Al-Ansari, 2021b). The complexities of CCU supply chains lay in the multi-scale components of the network each having different options and being assessed separately, which renders the economic feasibility of the hybrid network. For example, the CO_2 source node can entail different CO_2 sources with different gas flowrates, CO_2 compositions and moisture contents (Hasan et al., 2015). Thus, there is a need to optimally design CCU supply chains using an inclusive and multi-scale approach that will ensure the best economic and environmental performance.

Several studies attempted to tackle the supply chain related complexities of CCU networks to reduce the associated costs and environmental impact and achieve decarbonised pathways. Kalyanarengan Ravi et al. (2017) proposed an economic optimisation model to minimise the overall costs related to a carbon capture and storage (CCS) network and implemented it for a nationwide CO_2 reduction scenario. Hasan et al. (2015) developed a multi-scale framework for the economic optimisation of CCU pathways encompassing enhanced oil recovery (EOR) and storage in both saline formation and unmineable cobalt as CO_2 sink opportunities. Similarly, Zhang et al. (2020) proposed an optimisation-based framework for assessing CCUS pathways that include more utilisation routes other than just EOR and proved its application on a network with 15 utilisation candidates. Both CCUS studies concluded that the CO_2 storage option was more economically optimal solution as compared to CO_2 utilisation, although this latter could offer a better environmental performance with a carbon-neutral cycle (Hasan et al., 2015; Zhang et al., 2020). While many studies tackled the economic optimisation of multi-scale CCUS networks, only few considered CO_2 utilisation in chemical conversion such as methanol, GTL, and urea production (Al-Yaeeshi et al., 2020). Moreover, the biological conversion of CO_2 has been neglected as a possible utilisation route within CCUS supply chains. In this work, we introduce three different CO_2 utilisation routes; 1) enhanced oil recovery (EOR), 2) chemical conversion, and 3) biological conversion; and study their integration within a multi-scale CCU network encompassing different CO_2 sources, different carbon capture (CC) technologies and CO_2 transportation. A mixed linear integer programming (MILP) model is developed to maximise the overall profit of the integrated CCU network and identify best economic pathway.

2. System description

In this study, a CCU optimisation model is developed that can encompass different CO_2 large-scale industrial sources, different carbon capture technologies and materials, CO_2 compression and transportation via pipeline, and varying CO_2 utilisation options as shown in Figure 1. The aim is to optimise the overall profit of the integrated CCU network and determine the optimal source to sink integration. The CO_2 source node can be perceived as a group of CO_2 suppliers to the network which entails different capacity restrictions and exhaust gas characteristics. Each CO_2 source can be linked to a carbon separation method and material. The integration of the CO_2 source and carbon capture nodes is implemented with the assumption of both nodes being in the same location. Moreover, each CO_2 source can only be coupled with one carbon capture technology. CO_2 transportation from source to sink is only considered via pipeline. The choice of pipeline transportation is mainly motivated by its economic feasibility over other means. In addition, CO_2 sources can deliver to as many sinks with no restrictions apart from the availability of CO_2. Three CO_2 utilisation routes are proposed in this work; 1) enhanced oil recovery (EOR), 2) chemical conversion to methanol, GTL, and urea, and 3) biological conversion in agricultural greenhouses. The proposed optimisation model is implemented for a case study in the state of Qatar comprising of three existing large scale industrial CO_2 sources (Qatargas, QAFAC and QAFCO), three different carbon capture technologies (chemical absorption with MEA or PZ, adsorption PSA with AHT or MVY and membrane separation with FSC PVAm or PEO1 or PEO2), CO_2 transportation via pipeline, and three chemical conversion routes including EOR in an existing oil well, chemical conversion to methanol, GTL and urea in existing process plants within QAFAC, QSGTL, Oryx and QAFCO, and chemical conversion in an existing agricultural greenhouse that uses CO_2 enrichment. Different scenarios are studied; scenario 1 is the baseline scenario with no added constraints, scenario 2 considers the optimisation without the CO_2 chemical conversion options given their low readiness level, scenario 3 constraints the optimisation problem to supply greenhouses with CO_2 to meet at least 21% of Qatar's self-sufficiency in vegetable production, and scenario 4 couples the constraints of both scenario 2 and 3.

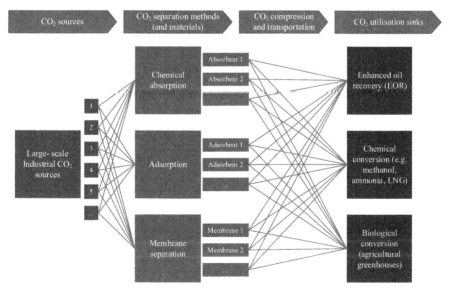

Figure 1: Carbon capture and utilisation network.

3. CCU optimisation model

A mixed integer linear programming (MILP) model is developed for the CCU supply chain network that aims at maximising the profit of the integrated system which is defined as the difference between the total annual cost and total revenue as shown in Eqs.(1&2).

$$Max \ \sum_{i,j,k}(TR - TC)F \tag{1}$$

$$= \left[\sum_k TR_k - \sum_{i,j} DC_i + ICC_{i,j} + OCC_{i,j} + \sum_{j,k} TTC_{j,k} + \sum_k UC_k\right]F \tag{2}$$

Subject to:

$$\sum_j F_{i,j} \leq 1 \tag{3}$$

The subscripts i,j,k correspond to the CO_2 sources, carbon capture technologies and CO_2 sinks respectively. TR and TC are the total annual revenues and costs respectively and F is the CO_2 flowrate. The total costs include the cost of flue gas dehydration (DC_i), carbon capture ($ICC_{i,j}$ and $OCC_{i,j}$), compression and transportation ($TTC_{j,k}$), and CO_2 utilisation (UC_k). TR_k and UC_k are taken from process-based studies conducted by Ogden et al. (2014) for EOR, Al-Yaeeshi et al. (2020) and AlNouss et al. (2021) for chemical conversion, and Ghiat et al. (2021a) for biological conversion. The presented constraint ensures that each CO_2 source is coupled with only one carbon capture technology.

- Cost of dehydration

Chemical absorption can handle saturated streams; however, adsorption and membrane separation techniques require less than 0.1% of water content. The cost of dehydration to reduce the water content to less than 0.1% is taken as 10.2$/t of CO_2 using tri-ethylene glycol (TEG) absorption (Hasan et al., 2015).

- Cost of CO_2 capture and compression

$ICC_{i,j}$ and $OCC_{i,j}$ are the investment and operational costs of carbon capture respectively depending on the carbon capture technology and material used. These costs also include the cost of CO_2 compression to a supercritical state, approximately 15 MPa. α, β, γ, α', β', γ' are parameters of each carbon capture technology and material based on the optimised economic model presented by Hasan et al. (2015).

$$ICC_{i,j} = \alpha_j + (\beta_j x_{co2_i}^{n_j} + \gamma_j)F^m \tag{4}$$

$$OCC_{i,j} = \alpha_j' + (\beta_j' x_{co2_i}^{n_j'} + \gamma_j')F^{m'} \tag{5}$$

- Cost of CO_2 transportation

The investment and operational costs of transportation via pipeline are estimated by the levelised cost in Eq.(6). This cost is estimated based on an inlet CO_2 pressure of 15 MPa and outlet CO_2 pressure of 10 MPa (Ogden, 2004).

$$TTC_{j,k}(\$/y) = (CRF + OM)CP_{base}\left(\frac{Q}{Q_{base}}\right)^{0.48} L_{j,k}\left(\frac{L_{j,k}}{L_{base}}\right)^{0.24} \tag{6}$$

where CRF is the capital recovery factor taken as 15% and OM is the fractional operational and management costs per investment cost and is taken as 4%. CP_{base} is the pipeline base capital cost taken as 700 $/m. Q is the CO_2 flowrate and Q_{base} is the CO_2 base flowrate taken as 16,000 ton/day. $L_{j,k}$ is the length of the pipeline (m) from the carbon capture technology j to the sink k, and L_{base} is the base length of the pipeline taken as 100 km (Ogden, 2004).

4. Results

The results of the optimization problem concerning the maximum profit from competing CO_2 capture and utilisation pathways revealed different results based on the applied constraints. The first scenario where no constraints on the CO_2 utilisation are applied, the results demonstrate a complete domination of GTL as the CO_2 sink and adsorption with PSA-AHT as the carbon capture technology and material with a high economic profit of $38,067. However, when constraints of technology readiness level are applied, results shift to a complete domination of EOR as the CO_2 sink and adsorption with membrane POE2 as the carbon capture technology and material with a much lower objective function estimated at $553. This reflects the importance in the technology investment to increase the readiness level of the chemical conversion as a potential sink for emitted CO_2. Further, with the application of the 21% self-sufficiency constraint in agriculture, the results of the third scenario indicate the utilisation of adsorption with PSA-MYV as the carbon capture technology and material to feed the greenhouse with the required CO_2 to achieve the self-sufficiency objective as illustrated in Figure 2a. In addition to the greenhouse, GTL is presented as the major CO_2 sink as presented in Figure 2a, achieving an overall profit of $29,083. The fourth scenario demonstrates a shift towards EOR with the elimination of GTL due to the readiness level constraint while achieving the self-sufficiency objective and with $435 profit through feeding the greenhouse with 71% of the CO_2 emitted from QAFAC source and captured using adsorption PSA MYV technology as illustrated in Figure 2b. Findings have also indicated that for high CO_2 concentration and gas flowrates such as the ones presented in the case study, adsorption provides the most economical option for carbon capture (Figure 3).

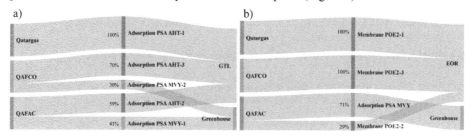

Figure 2: Optimal CO_2 source-sink allocation for a) scenario 3 and b) scenario 4.

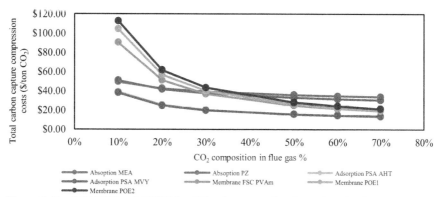

Figure 3: Total CAPEX and OPEX for CC and compression for each technology and material with a gas flow rate of 1000 mol/s.

5. Conclusions

While the principal goal of carbon capture and utilisation technologies is to mitigate CO_2 emissions, it is also important to develop CCU networks that can run on economically feasible supply chains. Hence, this study proposes a multi-scale optimisation model for CCU routes encompassing enhanced oil recovery, chemical conversion, and biological conversion as possible utilisation pathways. The aim of the model is to maximise the overall profits of the integrated CCU supply chain and determine the best optimal CCU integration. The model demonstrates its practicability as it involves different CO_2 sources, different carbon capture technologies and materials, CO_2 transportation via pipeline and finally different possible utilisation sinks. This model can be applied to specific CCU supply chains as it is the case in this study. The results of the optimisation model applied to the case study in Qatar reveal the economic feasibility of carbon capture using adsorption for the selected high CO_2 concentration and high gas flowrate sources coupled with chemical conversion for GTL production. The model can also be tailored to investigate different scenarios which can aid in the decision-making process for the deployment of CCU technologies. Finally, it is important that decision-makers help facilitate the deployment of CCU technologies by building the necessary infrastructure for CO_2 transportation and storage and by creating CO_2 source-sink clusters and networks that will use the same shared infrastructure and benefit from a circular economy.

References

A . AlNouss, G. Mckay, T. Al-Ansari, 2021, Utilisation of Carbon Dioxide and Gasified Biomass for the Generation of Value Added Products, Computer Aided Chemical Engineering, 50, 1567-1572.

A. A. Al-Yaeeshi, R. Govindan, T. Al-Ansari, 2020, Techno-economic-based dynamic network design for optimum large-scale carbon dioxide utilisation in process industries, Journal of Cleaner Production, 275, 122974. https://doi.org/10.1016/j.jclepro.2020.122974

IEA (2021), Global Energy Review 2021, IEA, Paris https://www.iea.org/reports/global energy review-2021

IPCC, 2007, Climate Change 2007: Impacts, Adaptation and Vulnerability. Contribution of Working Group II to the Fourth Assessment Report of the Intergovernmental Panel on Climate Change.

IPCC, 2014, Climate Change 2014: Synthesis Report. Contribution of Working Groups I, II and III to the Fifth Assessment Report of the Intergovernmental Panel on Climate Change.

I. Ghiat, F. Mahmood, R. Govindan, T. Al-Ansari, 2021a, CO2 utilisation in agricultural greenhouses: A novel 'plant to plant' approach driven by bioenergy with carbon capture systems within the energy, water and food Nexus, Energy Conversion and Management, 228, 113668.

I. Ghiat, T. Al-Ansari, 2021b, A review of carbon capture and utilisation as a CO2 abatement opportunity within the EWF nexus, Journal of CO2 Utililisation, 45, 101432.

J.M. Ogden, 2004, Conceptual Design of Optimized Fossil Energy Systems with Capture and Sequestration of Carbon Dioxide, UC Davis: Institute of Transportation Studies.

M.M.F. Hasan, E.L. First, F. Boukouvala, C.A. Floudas, 2015, A multi-scale framework for CO2 capture, utilization, and sequestration: CCUS and CCU, Computers and Chemical Engineering, 81, 2–21. https://doi.org/10.1016/j.compchemeng.2015.04.034

R.N. Kalyanarengan, M. Van Sint Annaland, J.C. Fransoo, J. Grievink, E. Zondervan, 2017, Development and implementation of supply chain optimization framework for CO2 capture and storage in the Netherlands, Computers and Chemical Engineering, 102, 40–51.

S. Zhang, Y. Zhuang, L. Liu, L. Zhang, J. Du, 2020, Optimization-based approach for CO2 utilization in carbon capture, utilization and storage supply chain, Computer and Chemical Engineering, 139, 106885. https://doi.org/10.1016/j.compchemeng.2020.106885

Proceedings of the 14th International Symposium on Process Systems Engineering – PSE 2021+
June 19-23, 2022, Kyoto, Japan © 2022 Elsevier B.V. All rights reserved.
http://dx.doi.org/10.1016/B978-0-323-85159-6.50198-6

Efficient Scenario Generation for Stochastic Programs with Extreme Events

David Young[a], Mark Carpenter[b], and Selen Cremaschi[a*]

aDepartment of Chemical Engineering, Auburn University, Auburn, AL 36849, USA
bDepartment of Mathematics and Statistics, Auburn University, Auburn, AL 36849, USA
selen-cremaschi@auburn.edu

Abstract

Stochastic programming (SP), a popular approach for solving optimization problems under uncertainty, is commonly used to tackle chemical engineering problems, e.g., in production planning or process synthesis. Scenarios, which represent uncertain outcomes, significantly impact the SP solution. This study evaluates seven methods to generate scenarios for a two-stage stochastic program where the decision-maker only sees benefits within the rare-event space of the uncertainty. The methods belong to one of three main categories: Monte Carlo sampling, space-filling sampling, and clustering. We assess the methods using (1) the difference between the optimum objective values and (2) the distance between the decision variable values of the optimum SP solution and the best-known solution for the problem. The results revealed that the SP solutions obtained using the scenarios generated by the clustering-based approaches were close to the best-known solutions and did not change significantly as the number of scenarios increased. The SP solution for the scenarios generated by Latin Hypercube sampling was the closest to the best-known solution for the maximum number of scenarios.

Keywords: Stochastic Programming; Rare-event Sampling; Scenario Generation.

1. Introduction

Stochastic programming (SP) is a common approach to solve optimization problems under uncertainty. Such problems arise when the decision-maker incorporates aspects of a problem that are not fully known or cannot be controlled, e.g., the weather, demand, or estimated process parameters. This uncertain information is modeled as a random distribution based on previous data or expert opinion. Generally, the SP models estimate the distribution using a discrete set of outcomes, or scenarios, generated by sampling from the distribution. Naturally, the better a set of scenarios depicts the underlying distribution, the more accurate the SP solution becomes. However, as the number of the scenarios grows, so does the problem size, resulting in computationally intractable models. An efficient scenario generation (SG) approach would balance the model size and the accuracy of the distribution estimation (Park et al., 2019; Shapiro et al., 2014).

In many stochastic programs, the most likely scenarios are enough to estimate the distribution for a high-quality solution. There are, however, some problems, such as those in safety and reliability engineering (e.g., Moskowitz et al. 2018), supply chain resilience (e.g., Ehrenstein et al. 2019), and health services, in which the least likely events have the most impact on the optimal decisions. These events occur in the tail-end(s) of the distributions. In general, a large number of scenarios would need to be generated to ensure their presence in the SP scenario set. How to properly represent the events associated with the tails of the distributions in the SP scenario set while maintaining a computationally tractable model is an open challenge.

Two recent studies assess different methods for SP scenario generation. The aim of Park et al. (2019) was to find the best scenario reduction method assuming the full scenario set was known. They concluded that a reduced scenario set generated by a distance-based method yields the closest solution to the optimum. Generating the full scenario set may be infeasible due to the sheer number of possible uncertainty realizations for some problems. Li et al. (2020) performed a comprehensive review of SG methods that have been used in energy systems SP problems. They outlined the characteristics of the methods and assessed them based on the solution stability. However, they have not considered the ability of the SG methods to capture rare events.

This paper evaluates seven SG methods (Section 3) for SP problems where the least likely events significantly impact the optimal decisions, and generating the full scenario set is infeasible. We carry out the evaluation using a healthcare-related problem (Section 2) by comparing the solutions identified by the SP models with scenarios generated using the SG methods to the best-known solution of the problem (Section 4).

2. Optimization Model – Screening Plan for Colorectal Cancer

The problem is to identify the ages at which screening for colorectal cancer (CRC) should occur to maximize the expected gain in Quality-Adjusted Life-Years (QALY). It is modeled as a two-stage stochastic program with fixed recourse. The general model form is given in Eqns. 1-4. The uncertain vector, ω_s, describes the lifetime of individual s through various health states to track the progression of CRC (Fig. 1). The first stage decision variables, x, are the age(s) at which screening with a colonoscopy takes place. The second stage variables, y_s, represent the modified lifetime of individual s based on the outcome of the recommended screening.

The objective function, Eqn. 1, calculates the expected change in QALY given the implementation of screening over every scenario, considering the loss of years due to the implementation of the screening and the gain in life due to early detection or prevention of the disease. Eqn. 2 places restrictions on the screening decisions, i.e., the maximum number of screens in a lifetime, ordering of the screenings, and only one screening test per year. Eqn. 3 implement the fixed recourse (clinical) actions following the implementation of the screening decisions, x. They modify an individual's lifetime.

$$max\ EQALY \approx max \sum_{s \in S} g_2(x, y_s, \omega_s) \tag{1}$$

$$s.t.\ A_1 x + b_1 \leq 0 \tag{2}$$

$$A_2 x + B y_s + C \omega_s + b_2 \leq 0 \qquad\qquad \forall s \in S \tag{3}$$

$$x \in \mathbf{X} = \mathbb{R}^n, y_s \in \mathbf{Y} = \mathbb{R}^m \qquad\qquad \forall s \in S \tag{4}$$

A defining feature of the problem is the impact of uncertainty on the solution. Only a small percentage of the population, 4-4.5 % (American Cancer Society, 2020), develops CRC within their lifetime, meaning that screening for CRC is a burden for most of the population. When only considering the most likely scenarios, the solution to this problem is to do nothing, as the detriments of screening outweighing the benefits. Many studies have shown that the implementation of screening for CRC is overall a benefit for society (e.g., Knudsen et al., 2016). Therefore, to properly represent the expected benefit of screening, it is essential to portray the lower probability scenarios accurately.

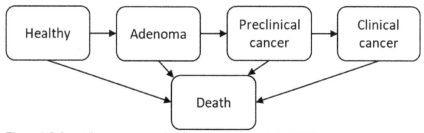

Figure 1 Colorectal cancer progression flow chart (Loeve et al., 1999)

3. Scenario Generation Methods and Their Application to the Model

The problem uncertainty space was constructed using data from a microsimulation model (Young et al., 2021; Young and Cremaschi, 2018) that simulates the progression of CRC within a population. We used the model to simulate 400 replications of a population of 1,000,000 males and recorded the values of a cancer progression random vector for each person. The vector includes the age of the first adenoma, time from the first adenoma to the first case of preclinical cancer, time from the first preclinical cancer to the first clinical cancer, and cancer survival time. This data was used to construct an empirical distribution, where each outcome of the random vector was considered a potential realization. Another empirical distribution was constructed using the US lifetables (Arias, 2002) to represent the age of death from sources other than CRC.

The SG methods fall under three main categories: Monte Carlo, space-filling, and clustering. The Monte Carlo and the space-filling methods utilized the empirical distributions to generate the scenarios. The clustering approaches used the raw data (the vectors) from the microsimulation to construct the scenarios.

3.1. Monte Carlo Methods

We consider the Crude or naïve Monte Carlo (CMC) approach and importance sampling. In the CMC approach, the scenarios are generated by directly sampling from the uncertain distributions. Importance sampling is a variance reduction technique. The random samples are generated from an auxiliary distribution, known as the importance distribution (ID), and reweighted using the likelihood ratio to tie the sample probability back to the original distribution. The construction of the ID is a challenge, as the theoretical optimal distribution requires accurate knowledge of the expectation of the distribution. We construct the ID following the work of Papavasiliou and Oren (2013) by first generating a large number of samples from the distribution and then estimating the ID using the expectation over the samples. We then resample from the estimated ID to generate the scenarios. We name this approach M-N-IS, where M refers to the initial large sample size, N to the number of samples from the ID, and IS to importance sampling.

3.2. Space-filling Methods

In space-filling methods, a quasi-Monte Carlo approach, samples are generated to avoid over-grouping or sparsity. This study considers Sobol sampling, Halton sampling, and Latin hypercube sampling (LHS). Sobol and Halton sampling techniques utilize Sobol (Sobol, 1967) and Halton sequences (Halton, 1960), low-discrepancy sequences, where discrepancy measures the uniformity of a set of samples. Latin hypercube sampling generates N samples by subdividing each distribution of a d-dimensional hypercube into N bins of equal probability and ensures that no two samples are in the same bin on any axis of the hypercube (McKay et al., 1979).

3.3. Clustering Based SG Methods

Clustering is an unsupervised machine learning approach that groups data into subsets, or clusters, of points with similar characteristics. Clustering can be used as a SG method by grouping a large dataset sampled from the uncertain distribution and generating representative samples, or "cluster centers," for each cluster. The representative samples are then used as the scenarios for the SP problem(B. Li et al., 2020). We employed k-means and x-means algorithms for determining the cluster centers. The k-means algorithm separates the data set into k (an input to the algorithm) different clusters based on the distance between the mean vectors of the data (Yadav and Sharma, 2013). We used the elbow method with the sum of the squared distance from the nearest cluster center as the metric to determine k (Yuan and Yang, 2019). As an extension of k-means, the x-means algorithm also determines the number of clusters, k, using the Bayesian Information Criterion.

4. Results and Discussion

Each sampling method was used to generate 128, 512, and 1024 scenarios, except for the k-means and x-means algorithms, where the algorithms automatically determine the number of scenarios. The scenario cases are powers of two due to Sobol sequence convergence properties. The maximum number of scenarios, 1024, was set to keep the SP solution time below 24 hours. We also studied the impact of the sample size, 100,000, 1,000,000, and 2,000,000, for M-N-IS, k-means, and x-means SG methods.

The SP solutions obtained using scenarios generated by different SG methods are assessed using the best solution located when a derivative-free optimization (DFO) framework was used with the CRC microsimulation (Young et al., 2021; Young and Cremaschi, 2018) for a maximum budget of 1,500 evaluations. The performance metrics are the absolute percent difference in the objective function values and the Euclidian distance between the SP and the best solution.

For each SG method, a summary of the resulting absolute percent difference is plotted in Fig. 2, and the Euclidian distance in Fig. 3. In general, as the number of scenarios increases, the percent difference decreases for each method, except for the Sobol and Halton methods. The SP solution obtained using 128 scenarios generated by the Sobol sampling has the lowest percent difference (Fig. 2) but the greatest distance when compared to the best solution (Fig. 3). The largest reduction in percent difference with the increase in the number of scenarios is observed for LHS. The SP solution obtained using 1024 LHS generated scenarios has the second-best object function value with a 28.8% difference. There are no significant improvements in the SP objective function value with increases in the number of scenarios generated using either the CMC approach or the two clustering approaches. The SP solutions obtained using the CMC-generated scenarios had worse percent difference values than most methods (Fig. 2).

Similar to the percent difference measure, as the number of scenarios increases, the distance from the optimum decreases (Fig. 3), except for the clustering algorithms, where the distance stays relatively constant. At 1024 scenarios, there are small differences in the distances to the best solution amongst different methods, with CMC, Sobol, and Halton sampling methods yielding slightly larger Euclidian distances. The SP solutions obtained using the scenarios generated by LHS are the closest to the best solution both at the minimum and the maximum number of scenarios. When the distances of the SP solutions obtained using CMC approach are compared to the rest, similar trends to the percent difference are observed (Figs. 2 and 3). At 1024 scenarios, the SP solutions obtained using the CMC-generated scenarios are close to the solutions obtained using other methods with at most an 11 % difference in distance.

The number of samples used by the clustering algorithms changes the number of scenarios, i.e., the number of clusters identified (Figs. 2 and 3). While the number of scenarios identified by the k-means algorithm does not change significantly, the number reaches the upper bound for the x-means algorithm for one and two million samples. This observation suggests that the scenarios identified by the x-means algorithm could be improved if a larger scenario size were allowed. For the M-N-IS method, with more samples to construct the ID, both percent difference and distance from optimal metrics are improved as the number of scenarios increase (Figs. 2 and 3). Both percent difference and distance from optimal solution improve as the samples increase for 1024 scenarios, but the inverse is observed for 124 scenarios. Using more samples to construct the ID yields a better estimate. Conversely, introducing more samples into the ID creates more possible realizations of uncertainty, requiring a greater number of sub-samples, scenarios, to better represent the ID.

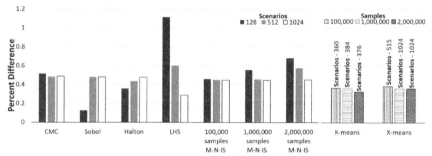

Figure 2 Summary of the absolute percent difference in the objective function values of the SP solutions obtained using scenarios generated by different SG methods and the best solution

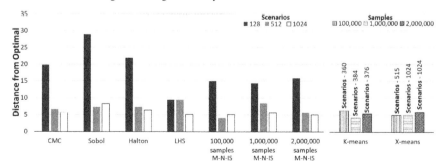

Figure 3 Summary of the Euclidian distance between the SP solutions obtained using scenarios generated by different SG methods and the best solution

5. Conclusions and Future Directions

This paper evaluated seven scenario generation methods for identifying the optimal solution and the objective value for a two-stage stochastic program where rare events significantly impact the objective. Scenarios generated by the Latin Hypercube sampling yielded the closest solution to the optimum at the largest scenario sizes. The clustering algorithms yielded solutions that were consistently close to the optimum. Future work will consider different clustering algorithms.

References

American Cancer Society, 2020. Colorectal Cancer Facts & Figures [WWW Document]. URL https://www.cancer.org/research/cancer-facts-statistics/colorectal-cancer-facts-figures.html (accessed 5.27.21).

Arias, E., 2002. United States life tables, 2000. Natl. Vital Stat. Reports 51, 1–63.

Ehrenstein, M., Wang, C.-H., Guillén-Gosálbez, G., 2019. Strategic planning of supply chains considering extreme events: Novel heuristic and application to the petrochemical industry. Comput. Chem. Eng. 125, 306–323.

Halton, J.H., 1960. On the efficiency of certain quasi-random sequences of points in evaluating multi-dimensional integrals. Numer. Math. 2, 84–90.

Knudsen, A.B., Zauber, A.G., Rutter, C.M., Naber, S.K., Doria-Rose, V.P., Pabiniak, C., Johanson, C., Fischer, S.E., Lansdorp-Vogelaar, I., Kuntz, K.M., 2016. Estimation of Benefits, Burden, and Harms of Colorectal Cancer Screening Strategies: Modeling Study for the US Preventive Services Task Force. JAMA 315, 2595–2609.

Li, B., Sedzro, K., Fang, X., Hodge, B.M., Zhang, J., 2020. A clustering-based scenario generation framework for power market simulation with wind integration. J. Renew. Sustain. Energy 12.

Li, J., Zhou, J., Chen, B., 2020. Review of wind power scenario generation methods for optimal operation of renewable energy systems. Appl. Energy 280, 115992.

Loeve, F., Boer, R., Van Oortmarssen, G.J., Van Ballegooijen, M., Habbema, J.D.F., 1999. The MISCAN-COLON Simulation Model for the Evaluation of Colorectal Cancer Screening. Comput. Biomed. Res. 32, 13–33.

McKay, M.D., Beckman, R.J., Conover, W.J., 1979. Comparison of Three Methods for Selecting Values of Input Variables in the Analysis of Output from a Computer Code. Technometrics 21, 239–245.

Moskowitz, I.H., Seider, W.D., Patel, A.J., Arbogast, J.E., Oktem, U.G., 2018. Understanding rare safety and reliability events using transition path sampling. Comput. Chem. Eng. 108, 74–88.

Papavasiliou, A., Oren, S.S., 2013. Multiarea stochastic unit commitment for high wind penetration in a transmission constrained network. Oper. Res. 61, 578–592.

Park, S., Xu, Q., Hobbs, B.F., 2019. Comparing scenario reduction methods for stochastic transmission planning. IET Gener. Transm. Distrib. 13, 1005–1013.

Shapiro, A., Dentcheva, D., Ruszczyński, A., 2014. Lectures on Stochastic Programming: Modeling and Theory, Second Edition. Lect. Stoch. Program. Model. Theory, Second Ed.

Sobol', I.M., 1967. On the distribution of points in a cube and the approximate evaluation of integrals. USSR Comput. Math. Math. Phys. 7, 86–112.

Yadav, J., Sharma, M., 2013. A Review of K-mean Algorithm. Int. J. Eng. trends Technol. 4, 2972–2976.

Young, D., Cremaschi, S., 2018. A Simulation-based Optimization Approach to Develop Personalized Colorectal Cancer Screening Strategies, in: Computer Aided Chemical Engineering. Elsevier, pp. 2125–2130.

Young, D., Haney, W., Cremaschi, S., 2021. Derivative-free optimization of combinatorial problems – A case study in colorectal cancer screening. Comput. Chem. Eng. 145, 107193.

Yuan, C., Yang, H., 2019. Research on K-value selection method of K-means clustering algorithm. J 2, 226–235.

Proceedings of the 14th International Symposium on Process Systems Engineering – PSE 2021+
June 19-23, 2022, Kyoto, Japan © 2022 Elsevier B.V. All rights reserved.
http://dx.doi.org/10.1016/B978-0-323-85159-6.50199-8

A Sustainable Framework for Optimal and Flexible Design Under Uncertainty in Separation Processes: Exergy, Energy, Economic, and Environmental Aspects

Jaime D. Ponce-Rocha[a,c], Martín Picón-Núñez[a], Andreia Santos[b], Ana Carvalho[b], Fernando I. Gómez-Castro[a], Ricardo Morales-Rodriguez[a*].

[a]*Departamento de Ingeniería química, Univeridad de Guanajuato, Guanajuato, 36050, México.*
[b]*Centro de Estudos do IST, Universidad de Lisboa, Lisboa, 1049-001, Portugal.*
[c]*Dirección de Ingeniería y Construcción de Plantas, CIATEQ A. C., Querétaro, Querétaro, 76150, México.*
ricardo.morales@ugto.mx

Abstract

The global situation forces to design processes based on sustainable metrics and capable to respond to constant changes in the world. Particularly, the field of chemical processes requires an intensive energetic demand. These requirements force the scientist to develop systematic frameworks focused on mathematical formulations and computer-aided tools. The aim of this work is to develop and implement a systematic framework for multi-objective optimization under uncertainty based on four steps, first step: a mathematical formulation is defined, second step: the uncertainty identification and sampling are implemented, third step: a computational platform is generated based on commercial computer-aided tools (aspen plus & matlab) interconnected using a COM interface, fourth step: making decision criteria and data analysis. The results showed that the framework and employed criteria (The 80 % of cumulative distribution function value) for making decision are adequate for sustainable process design under uncertainty scenarios.

Keywords: Sustainable process design, 4E analysis, MOGA, Optimization under uncertainty.

1. Introduction

Currently, the design of chemical processes demands precise guidelines related with sustainable development targets. Nevertheless, these goals have not been properly and completely associated with rigorous mathematical models, forcing the scientists to reach metrics and making-decision reliable criteria for sustainable targets (Al *et al*, 2020). The chemical processes and mainly bioprocesses are characterized for having, variable yields and unexpected behaviours due to inherent and external effects, which are directly associated with uncertainty sources; therefore, a process that is optimal under a nominal condition may be suboptimal, or infeasible, once the process conditions change. Thus, to ensure the capability to maintain feasible process operation over a range of uncertainty factors, it is necessary to introduce a flexibility approach in process design, employing mathematical formulations focused on representing these phenomena to obtain reliable and feasible designs (Adams *et al*, 2018). To tackle the concerns mentioned above, disciplines as process systems engineering promote the problem solution through systematic frameworks, based on optimal process design, integrating a collaborative and adaptable synergy between computer-aided tools (*v. g.* Chemical process simulators, programming environments) and mathematical strategies (*v. g.* multi-objective optimization, uncertainty optimization) (Avraamidou *et al*, 2019). Therefore, based on the state of the art, the objective of this work is developed and implement a systematic framework for multi-objective optimization under uncertainty (MOOUU), through a mathematical formulation using a platform based on commercial computer-aided tools, as well as the evaluation of statistical indicators as making-decision criteria for process design under uncertainty.

2. Case study

Nowadays, the use of conventional distillation continues like the principal separation and purification technique, which process large amounts of chemical products, but it is still a high energy consumption stage in the chemical industry. The preliminary structural and operational design of tray distillation columns aims to obtain their optimal specifications to meet product specifications (Gozálvez-Zafrilla *et al*, 2021). The production of Acetone-Butanol-Ethanol (ABE) using fermentation consortiums continues being an attractive pathway, for obtaining diverse intermediate chemical compounds to synthesize biofuels, bioplastics, etc. But the low and variable production, high diluted products, and the intensive energy requirements is still a challenge to tackle at industrial level. Thereby, the ABE separation and purification scheme (SPS) represents an interesting challenge, and it is employed as a case study to implement and evaluate the performance of the proposed sustainable framework for optimal and flexible design under uncertainty based on the analysis of exergy, energy, economic and environmental aspects (4E).

3. Framework description

The sustainable framework for optimal and flexible design under uncertainty in separation processes based on the 4E aspects is illustrated in the Figure 1. The framework employs the principles of stochastic programming using wait-and-see strategy, and simulation-optimization approach. The systematic steps of the framework can be summarized as follows: 1) Process simulation: rigorous thermodynamic description, process design, and state of the art update. 2) Stochastic modelling: mathematical strategies and formulation, uncertainty identification. 3) Optimizer: generation of a computational platform and algorithm selection to solve the problem, mathematical model integration. 4) Optimal design: Data analysis using graphical representations and statistical metrics as making-decision criteria for process design under uncertainty.

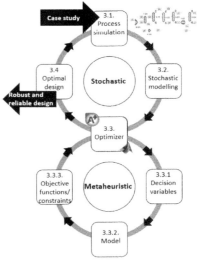

Figure 1. Visual representation of the sustainable framework.

3.1. Process simulation

Aspen plus was employed for the design of the separation process considering heuristic rules, which consists in hybrid arrangement, composed by a liquid-liquid column (C-101), followed by four conventional distillation columns (D-101, D-102, D-103, and D-104) focused on the recovery and purification of the extracting agent, acetone, ethanol, and butanol, respectively. The thermodynamic model NRTL and the equation of state Hayden-O'Connell were selected to describe the phase equilibrium (Ponce-Rocha *et al*, 2021). This work does not used surrogate models, the generated simulation was used directly in the optimization section to calculate the objective functions values.

3.2. Stochastic modelling: mathematical formulation

The MOOUU was formulated as follow [Eq. (1)]:

$$\underset{\underline{x}}{\text{Min}}\ \underline{Z} = \left[Z_k(\underline{x}, \underline{\theta}^*) \right], \text{s.t.}\ \ h(\underline{x}, \underline{\theta}^*) = 0; \ g(\underline{x}, \underline{\theta}^*) \leq 0; \ \underline{x} \in X, \underline{\theta}^* \in \Theta^* \tag{1}$$

Where $\underline{Z}$, describes the vector of k objective functions under uncertainty (Exergy, energy, economy, and environment), $\underline{x}$ represents the vector of n-dimensional states linked with structural and operational conditions (FA: extracting agent mass flow, NS: number of stages, FS: feed stage, RR: reflux ratio, DF: distillate flow, or BF: bottom flow), $\underline{\theta}^*$ is the vector of s-dimensional uncertainties present in the selected variables. **h** & **g** represent the vectors of equality and inequality constraints associated with operational and structural limitations.

3.2.1 Uncertainty representation & sampling

Latin hypercube sampling method was used for the generation of seventy-five random scenarios, all variations in the composition vectors for the feed stream (100) were generated simultaneously obtaining the following sample space: acetone (A) 2,275±112 kg/h, butanol (B) 5,931±276 kg/h, ethanol (E) 1,592±135 kg/h, water (W) 10,479±498 kg/h, and carbon dioxide (CO_2) 82±5 kg/h. The boundaries of the sampling in each flow value were obtained and adapted from previous experimental results (Valdez-Vazquez *et al.*, 2015).

3.2.2 4E aspects: Exergy, energy, economic, and environmental analysis

The 4E analysis was reported as a tool to analyse and optimize processes, which allowed improving indicators of life cycle impact assessment (LCIA) (Ponce-Rocha *et al*, 2021). 4E analysis was integrated as a tool and each component was added in the objective function employing the following mathematical equations.

3.3. Exergy

The exergy losses are a thermodynamic metric to detect the inefficient energy use in any process due to system irreversibility. The exergy losses balance was used on the process design considering heating and cooling processes (*Q*), separation (*Sep*) and concentration changes (*Conc*), over all process streams and equipment [Eq. (2)].

$$\sigma T_0 = \Delta \dot{E}x_{In} - \Delta \dot{E}x_{Out}$$

$$\sigma T_0 = \sum_{j=1}^{n} \sum_{i=1}^{m} [\Delta \dot{E}x_{Q,j} + \Delta \dot{E}x_{Sep,i} + \Delta \dot{E}x_{Conc,i}]\ [kW] \tag{2}$$

3.4. *Energy*

The ratio between total heat requirements and the total amount of purified products (ER) is a common metric to evaluate the performance of the process separation, mainly in fuel recovery [Eq. (3)].

$$ER = Energy\ requeriments\ [MJ]/Products\ [kg] \qquad (3)$$

3.5. *Economy*

Total annual cost (TAC) is a typical economic indicator that allows to relate the capital cost, payback period (set at five years), and annualized cost of utilities, as described in Eq. (4).

$$TAC = Capital\ cost/Payback\ period + Utilities \qquad (4)$$

3.6. *Environment*

The E-factor (E_{factor}) was used to evaluate the environmental impact, due to includes the waste and products ratio [Eq. (5)].

$$E_{factor} = Waste\ [kg]/Products\ [kg] \qquad (5)$$

3.7. *Optimizer: Multi-Objective Genetic Algorithm*

To solve each optimization scenario, the matlab suite: gamultiob (a variant of NSGA-II) was used in the multi-objective optimization. Each optimization considered 50 generations, 200 individuals, and a crossover fraction of 0.8 and an adaptative feasible mutation function. In addition, each design specification vector generated in the multi-objective genetic algorithm is evaluated into a defined simulation scheme, to validate the thermodynamic feasibility and estimate the values of the objective functions through a computational interface. The mass purity (P) and mass recovery (R) constraints are specified for Eq. (6) & (7).

$$[P_{HEP}, P_A, P_B, P_E] \geq [0.999, 0.950, 0.995, 0.900] \qquad (6)$$
$$[R_{HEP}, R_A, R_B, R_E] \geq [0.999, 0.995, 0.000, 0.992] \qquad (7)$$

3.8. *Optimal design under uncertainty: Making decision criteria*

The results obtained by each scenario generate a distribution of optimal designs, therefore the use of statistical indicators was employed as a tool for the selection and making decisions to obtain a single design derived from MOOUU for each evaluated scenario. In this sense, three criteria were evaluated: mean, mode and a value of 80 % for cumulative distribution function (CDF), due to provides the basis for a probabilistic interpretation of the results.

4. Results

Each optimal design specification for each scenario under uncertainty was evaluated in the process configuration, the optimal results were represented using histograms plots, and a cumulative distribution function (see Figure 2 a and b, respectively). The statistical metrics were remarked in CDF plot, identified as follow: mean (blue dots), mode (red dots), and 80 % of CDF (green dots). The structural designs of the process are reported in Table 1, where previous results without considering uncertainties are also illustrated (nominal design) (Ponce-Rocha *et al*, 2021).

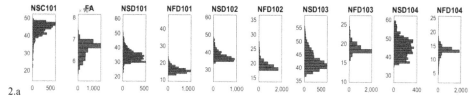

2.a

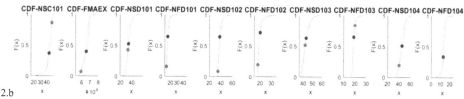

2.b

Figure 2. a) Histogram plots for structural specifications; b) Cumulative distribution function for structural specifications, mean (blue dot), mode (red dot), and 80 % of CDF (green dot).

Table 1. Comparative structural designs for each design and operating variables.

Variable	N_S C_{101}	F_A kg/h	N_S D_{101}	N_F D_{101}	N_S D_{102}	N_F D_{102}	N_S D_{103}	N_F D_{103}	N_S D_{104}	N_F D_{104}
Nominal	41	64,332	33	18	38	21	41	18	41	7
Mean	47	59,272	33	14	35	18	44	20	40	13
Mode	43	65,451	34	16	38	20	45	19	45	13
80 % CDF	47	68,080	37	17	40	20	46	20	49	14

To identify the most robust and reliable specifications of each process configuration, the obtained designs reported in Table 1 were evaluated using three flowrate vectors of the samples: minimum (Min), average (Avg), and maximum (Max) values. The results of the objective functions are reported in Table 2. These results show that the use of nominal and mean designs did not satisfy the requirements when the maximum flowrate vector is employed, in contrast to the designs using the mode and 80 % CDF value, which are robust enough to be able to fulfil the separation and purification requirements for the most extreme uncertain conditions.

Table 2. Evaluation of feed flow to SPS specifications, and objective functions values.

Design parameter	Flow	TAC (USD/year)	Exergy (MW)	Energy (MJ/kg)	E_{factor}
Nominal	Min	7.88	1.91	12.36	0.24
	Avg	8.05	1.93	11.83	0.25
	Max	-	-	-	-
Mean	Min	**7.63**	**1.85**	12.01	0.24
	Avg	7.80	1.87	11.51	0.25
	Max	-	-	-	-

Design parameter	Flow	TAC (USD/year)	Exergy (MW)	Energy (MJ/kg)	E~factor~
Mode	Min	7.94	1.92	12.44	0.24
	Avg	8.12	1.95	11.91	0.25
	Max	8.42	2.03	**11.68**	**0.24**
80 % CDF	Min	8.11	1.95	12.65	0.24
	Avg	8.29	1.98	12.08	0.25
	Max	8.59	2.06	11.84	0.24

5. Conclusion

The proposed systematic framework allowed to identify that the use of statistical indicators as mode and 80 % CDF value, guarantee the convergence of each evaluated flow vector. Both indicators could be employed as metric to making-decision criteria to design separation process under uncertainty, however, the use of 80 % CDF is considered as a better criterion, due to using probabilistic fundamentals instead of a major value frequency in a set of data values, where the propagated uncertainty is presented. Additionally, it is necessary to evaluate each feed flow vector generated on the 80 % CDF design with the aim to validate the flexibility of the selected design specifications versus the specified feed flow variation.

Acknowledgments

Jaime D. Ponce-Rocha acknowledges the National Council of Science and Technology (CONACyT) for the scholarship received to develop this project (731399). Dr. Morales-Rodriguez acknowledges the partial financial support by the Mexican Bioenergy Innovation Centre, Bioalcohols Cluster (249564) and the Universidad de Guanajuato for the development of this project.

References

T. A. Adams, T. Thatho, M. C. Le Feuvre, & C. L. E. Swartz, 2018, The Optimal Design of a Distillation System for the Flexible Polygeneration of Dimethyl Ether and Methanol Under Uncertainty, Frontiers in Energy Research, 6, 41, 1-19.

S. Avraamidou, S. G. Baratsas, Y. Tian, & E. N. Pistikopoulos, 2019, Circular Economy - a challenge and an opportunity for Process Systems Engineering, Computers & Chemical Engineering, 133, 2, 1-48.

J. M. Gozálvez-Zafrilla, J. C. Gracía-Díaz, & A. Santafé-Moros, 2021, Uncertainty quantification and global sensitivity analysis of continuous distillation considering the interaction of parameter uncertainty with feed variability, Chemical Engineering Science, 235, 116509.

J. D Ponce-Rocha, M. Picón-Núñez, A. Carvalho, A. Santos, F. I. Gómez-Castro, & R. Morales, 2021, A design and optimization framework for (bio-) chemical process based on exergo-economic and environmental aspects, Computer Aided Chemical Engineering, 50, 1897-1902.

I. Valdez-Velazquez, M. Pérez-Rangel, A. Tapia, G. Boitrón, C. Molina, G Hérnandez, & L. Amaya-Delgado, 2015, Hydrogen and butanol production from native wheat straw by synthetic microbial consortia integrated by species of Enterococcus and Clostridium, Fuel, 159, 214–222.

Proceedings of the 14th International Symposium on Process Systems Engineering – PSE 2021+
June 19-23, 2022, Kyoto, Japan © 2022 Elsevier B.V. All rights reserved.
http://dx.doi.org/10.1016/B978-0-323-85159-6.50200-1

Application of nonlinear surrogate models on optimization of carbon capture and utilization network

Wonsuk Chung and Jay H. Lee[*]

aDepartment of Chemical and Biomolecular Engineering, Korea Advanced Institute of Science and Technology, 291 Daehak-ro, Yuseong-gu, Daejeon 34141, REPUBLIC OF KOREA
jayhlee@kaist.ac.kr

Abstract

Carbon capture and utilization (CCU) can solve recent global climate change, allowing large-scale mitigation of carbon emission. Estimation of cost and carbon reduction for CCU systems is an essential step as most of them are energy-intensive and costly, hindering further adaptation. Nonlinear surrogate models can help identification of sustainability for each CCU pathway without rigorous simulations. The surrogate model as a simple equation allows being incorporated into multiscale decision-making. This work applies nonlinear surrogate models on decision making of CCU through the construction of a CCU superstructure systemization of the best CCU pathway selection problem as mathematical programming. The surrogate models that predict the capture energy and cost from the flue gas condition and CO_2 removal rate are incorporated into the network. A case study as a small CCU superstructure is performed to test ability and complexity of the CCU superstructure optimization problem as mixed-integer-nonlinear-programming (MINLP).
Keywords: Carbon capture and utilization; Superstructure; Network optimization; Surrogate model; Mined-integer nonlinear programming.

1. Introduction

Carbon capture and utilization (CCU) is a promising option for global climate change by capturing a large amount of CO_2 from plantwide flue gases and utilizes it to useful products. CCU attracts industries for its potential economic benefits in addition to reduction of carbon emission. A number of researches have been studied in carbon capture as well as carbon utilization in both technology level and process level to reduce the energy consumption and cost (Boot-Handford et al, 2014; Cuellar-Franca and Azapagic, 2015). Despite the efforts, many CCU pathways from flue gas to capture, conversion, and product are not sustainable in terms of economics and carbon reduction. The major concern in industries is on which technologies should they invest in to achieve best expected carbon reduction and profit.

A systemic approach that analyzes multiple CCU technologies as mathematical programming is extensively studied to solve the concern. CCU superstructure where the CCU pathway is identified and evaluated is constructed so that mathematical solver can optimize the superstructure and find out the best CCU pathway (Kim et al, 2013; Bertran et al, 2017; Roh et al, 2019). Those works formulated superstructure optimization problems as mixed-integer linear programming (MILP) and a pathway is represented as a set of binary integers.

The MILP approach has a limitation on flexibility in process level. The CCU processes are simulated before superstructure construction and the key performance indicators of the processes such as CO_2 capture rate and capture energy are treated as constant parameters. As a chemical process, a CCU process is nonlinear and the performance indicators change not linearly as the process input changes. To reflect this nonlinearity, the superstructure optimization problem must be formulated in mixed-integer nonlinear programming (MINLP), the most difficult type of problem. As far as our knowledge, there is little attempt to solve the problem in MINLP. Hasan et al (2015) incorporated nonlinear cost models of CO_2 capture processes on a CCU supply chain network and solved them as MILP with piecewise linearization. As direct incorporation of full process models in the systemic framework is not realistic, it is essential to apply the nonlinear cost models or surrogate models instead, and it is worthy to investigate the problem complexity of the superstructure optimization problem as MINLP.

In this work, a CCU superstructure is formulated with known surrogate models for capture processes from literature. Then the MINLP problem is formulated and solved to identify the feasible pathways. Several industrial sectors with a different number of CO_2 sources are selected and optimized in several scenarios to test the complexity of the optimization problem.

2. Optimization problem formulation

A superstructure model is defined as a network model and the embedded process interval model. The network model formulates the topology of the superstructure as a graph, treating the CO_2 source, processing interval, and products as nodes and their connections as directed arcs. The processing interval model is a set of equations where the key performances of the CCU processes are captured as interval parameters and the process cost can be calculated from the interval flowrates. The decision variable for the superstructure optimization problem is binary variable z which represents the selection of the nodes and their connections. Inside N, the user can set constraints on z using binary parameters y to prevent the selection of undesired connections as Eq (1, 2)

$$z_v \leq y_v \quad \forall v \in \mathbb{v} \tag{1}$$

$$z_a \leq y_a \quad \forall a \in \mathbb{v} \times \mathbb{v} \tag{2}$$

where $\mathbb{v}$ is the set that contains the feeds, intervals, and products, v is the node, and a is the arc. The feed-feed connection and product-product connection are prevented by y (e.g. $y_{f,f_2} = 0 \ \forall f, f_2 \in \mathbb{f}$, where $\mathbb{f}$ is the set of feeds). The logical constraints that $z = 1$ if and only if the flow is larger than zero is described by the big M method as Eq (3 and 4).

$$F_v \leq z_v M \quad \forall v \in \mathbb{v} \cup \mathbb{v} \times \mathbb{v} \tag{3}$$

$$z_v \leq F_v M \quad \forall v \in \mathbb{v} \cup \mathbb{v} \times \mathbb{v} \tag{4}$$

where F_v is the corresponded flow to z_v.

The interval models consist of raw material mixing, reaction, and separation steps (e.g. Bertran et al, 2017). The previous MILP approach only allows linear equations for all three steps with constant parameters. Instead, nonlinear surrogate models can be incorporated.

Appropriate labeling on each arc can handle the assignment of outlets after separation (Quaglia et al, 2012). The connections are labeled so that an outlet can only be assigned to one of the connections with the same label. These allocations are modeled by Eq (5 and 6)

$$\sum_{v_2 \in \mathbb{v}} z_{v,v_2} y_{v,v_2,n} \leq z_v \quad \forall v \in \mathbb{v}, n \in \mathbb{m} \tag{5}$$

$$\sum_{v_2 \in \mathbb{v}} y_{v,v_2,n} \leq z_v \quad \forall v \in \mathbb{v}, n \in \mathbb{m} \tag{6}$$

where $\mathbb{m}$ is the set of labels for arc and the labeling is determined by binary parameter $y_{v,v_2,n}$. For example, in Figure 1, Interval A has two outlets after separation. The first outlet is labeled as 1 and the second outlet is labeled as 2. The interval is connected with four intervals B to E, where the first outlet can only flow through connection A-B or A-C. Likewise, the second outlet can only flow through connections A-D and A-E.

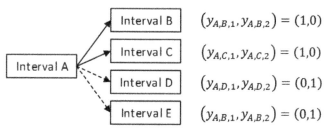

Figure 1. Labeling of arcs in the superstructure. The connections between A-B and A-C are labeled 1 (solid line) and the connections between A-D and A-E are labeled 2 (dashed line).

The objective function is to maximize the gross profit (GP) with nonnegative CO_2 reduction (E^{Red})

$$\max_z GP(z,F) \text{ s.t. } E^{\text{Red}}(z,F) > 0, I(F,\lambda) = 0 \text{ and } N(z,F,y) \geq 0 \tag{7}$$

with process interval model (I) being equality constraints with the interval parameters (λ) and network model (N) being inequality constraints so that GP and E^{Red} can be calculated from the interval flowrates (F).

The multiple pathways can be identified using integer cuts (Kim et al, 2013). The optimization problem finds an optimal pathway in the superstructure. The next optimal pathway is identified by adding additional logical constraints as Eq (8)

$$\sum_v y_{p,v} z_v \leq \sum_v y_{p,v} - 1 \quad \forall p \in \mathbb{p} \tag{8}$$

where $y_{p,v}$ is a binary parameter as the previous selection result of interval v for pathway p in pathway set $\mathbb{p}$, and z_v is a binary variable as a selection of interval v for the newly optimal pathway. After the optimization, the newly identified pathway is stored by expanding ℙ. This integer cut can be repeated until no feasible pathway is identified.

3. Case study

A case study is performed for the refinery (Figure 2). The superstructure has four flue gases with different flowrates and CO_2 mole fractions from 0.04~0.5% mol. (furnace off-gas, utility plant off-gas, fluidized catalytic cracker (FCC) off-gas, and hydrogen processing unit (HPU) off-gas, Table 1). Three capture processes are considered: monoethanol (MEA) based amine scrubbing, piperazine (PZ) based amine scrubbing, and membrane separation. Three utilization intervals are considered: combined reforming (CR) process that produces syngas (H_2:CO=2) from CO_2 CH_4, and H_2O, CO_2 hydrogenation (CH) process that produces methanol from CO_2 and H_2, and methanol synthesis (MeOHsyn) process from syngas from CR. One dummy interval (Dummy) is added that collects waste gas from intervals. Three products are considered: it is assumed that CO_2 can be directly sold with $100/ton, methanol with $293/ton, and waste gas with zero price. The superstructure has eight compounds (CO_2, N_2, O_2, H_2O, H_2, CO, MeOH, and CH_4) and three compounds (H_2, CH_4, H_2O) are treated as raw materials in utilization intervals.

Table 1. Summarization of flue gases in the case study.

	Mass flowrate (ton/sec)	Mass fraction			
		CO_2	N_2	O_2	H_2O
Furnace off-gases	0.160	12.3%	73.5%	7.8%	6.3%
Utility plant off-gas	0.237	6.2%	74.4%	13.6%	5.7%
FCC off-gas	0.035	28.2%	69.1%	2.1%	0.6%
HPU off-gas	0.035	61.1%	38.9%	0.0%	0.0%

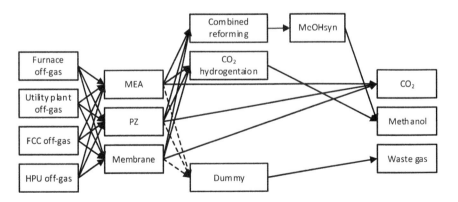

Figure 2. A CCU superstructure with four flue gases, three capture processes, three conversion processes, and two products with dummy interval and waste gas. The solid line and the dashed line indicate labeling of arc as 1 and 2, respectively.

Chung et al (2020) suggests model formula as Eq (9) and Eq (10)

$$U_{k,\text{steam}} = \alpha\big(\ln x_{CO2} + \beta \ln(1 - r_{k,\text{CAP}})\big) + f_{k,\text{steam},0}, k \in \{\text{MEA}, \text{PZ}\} \tag{9}$$

$$\ln EPC_k = \alpha\big(\ln x_{CO2} + \beta \ln(1 - r_{\text{MEA,CAP}}) - 1/r_{k,\text{CAP}}\big) + \gamma \ln F_{CO2,k} + f_{k,EPC,0}, k \in \{\text{MEA}, \text{PZ}\} \tag{10}$$

for steam consumption ($U_{k,\text{steam}}$) and equipment purchase cost (EPC_k) from inlet CO_2 mole fraction (x_{CO2}), flowrate of captured CO_2 ($F_{CO2,k}$), and CO_2 capture rate ($r_{k,\text{CAP}}$) with model parameters ($\alpha, \beta, \gamma, f_0$). The model is valid for $0.03 \leq x_{CO2} \leq 0.5$. Hasan et al (2015) suggests model formula as Eq (11)

$$IC_k \text{ or } OC_k = \alpha + (\beta x_{CO2}^n + \gamma)F_{in}^m \tag{11}$$

for operating cost and capital cost from inlet CO_2 mole fraction (x_{CO2}) and feed gas flowrate ($F_{in,k}$) with model parameters ($\alpha, \beta, \gamma, m, n$). The model is valid for $0.01 \leq x_{CO2} \leq 0.7$. The interval data for utilization processes are assumed to be constant, referred from Roh et al (2019). The case study is formulated as MINLP in Pyomo and solved by BARON (Kilinc and Sahinidis, 2018) using AMD Ryzen 9 5950X.

4. Results and discussion

There are 30 feasible pathways in the superstructure. The pathways from HPU to PZ and MEA are infeasible as the CO_2 mole fraction of HPU exceeds 0.5. A test is performed to test whether the framework can identify all the feasible pathways. Without the constraint for nonnegative CO_2 reduction, all the 30 pathways are identified within 346.262 seconds. Then, with the nonnegative CO_2 reduction constraint, the six sustainable pathways are identified (Table 2). Pathway No. 7 is at the nonnegative CO_2 reduction constraint with small production rate of methanol and a small annual profit (\$ 6.0M/yr). This pathway is originally the most profitable but non-CO_2-reducing, and the capture rate is adjusted so that the constraint is satisfied. A dummy pathway is identified (pathway No. 8) with a non-integer solution of z. This is due to the integer relaxation algorithm of BARON.

Table 2. The identified sustainable CCU pathways in the case study in order of identification by the solver. Furn means furnace off-gas. Pathway No. 7 and 8 are dummy pathways.

No.	Feed	Capture	Conversion-product	Profit (M\$/yr)	CO_2 reduction (MtCO$_2$/yr)	Computational time (sec)
1	HPU	Membrane	CR-MeOH	785.5	3.361	15.663
2	FCC	PZ	CR-MeOH	391.1	1.078	1.419
3	FCC	MEA	CR-MeOH	389.2	1.058	16.457
4	FCC	Membrane	CR-MeOH	355.2	0.994	1.160
5	HPU	Membrane	CH-MeOH	162.8	0.019	1.346
6	HPU	Membrane	CO_2	45.0	0.671	1.817
7	Furn	PZ	CR-MeOH	6.0	0.000	30.383
8*	FCC	MEA	CR-MeOH	-4.0	0.000	18.229
		No more feasible pathway is identified				17.165

Despite superstructure with small size (210 integer variables, 2710 continuous variables, and 2094 constraints), it takes several minutes to identify all the pathways in the case study. If more CO_2 sources, capture intervals, utilization technologies, and products are added, the size of the superstructure can be very large and the computational time may take hours or days. MILP approach takes only minutes to solve such a large superstructure (>100,000 variables) (Bertran et al, 2017). Other algorithms instead of solving MINLP directly (e.g. piecewise linearization) will reduce the computational time.

5. Conclusions

An optimization problem of a CCU system for the purpose of identifying sustainable pathways is formulated in MINLP. The nonlinear surrogate models for capture processes allow more accurate identifications. A case study is performed with four flue gases, three capture processes, and three utilization options to test the complexity of the problem. The results suggest that the MINLP approach can successfully identify the pathways; however, the computational times can be issues for large CCU superstructure.

References

M. Boot-Handford et al, 2014, Carbon Capture and storage update, *Energy and Environmental Science* 7, 130-189.

R. Cuellar-Franca and A. Azapagic, 2015, Carbon capture, storage and utilisation technologies: A critical analysis and comparison of their life cycle enrironmental impacts, *Journal of CO₂ Utilization* 9, 82-102.

J. Kim, M. Sen, and C. Maravelias, 2013, An optimization-based assessment framework for biomass-to-fuel conversion strategies, *Energy and Environmental Scienc*, 6, 1093-1104.

M. Bertran, R. Frauzem, A. Sanchez-Arcilla, L. Zhang, J. Woodley, and R. Gani, 2017, A generic methodology for processing route synthesis and design based on superstructure optimization. *Computers and Chemical Engineering* 106, 892-910.

K. Roh, A. Al-Hunaidy, H. Imran, and J. H. Lee, 2019, Optimization-based identification of CO₂ capture and utilization processing paths for life cycle greenhouse gas reduction and economic benefits, *AIChE Journal* e16580.

F. Hasan, E. First, F. Boukouvala, and C. Floudas, 2015, A multi-scale framework for CO₂ capture, utilization, and sequestration: CCUS and CCU, *Computers and Chemical Engineering* 81, 2-21.

A. Quaglia, B. Sarup, G. Sin, and R. Gani, 2012, Integrated business and engineering framework for synthesis and design of enterprise-wide processing networks, *Computers and Chemical Engineering* 38, 213-223.

W. Chung and Lee J. H., 2020, Input-output Surrogate Models for Efficient Economic Evaluation of Amine Scrubbing CO₂ Capture Processes, *Industrial and Engineering Chemistry Research* 59, 1895-18964.

M. Kilinc and N. Sahinidis, 2018, Exploiting integrality in the global optimization of mixed-teger nonlinear programming problems in BARON, *Optimization Methods and Software*, 33, 540-562

Proceedings of the 14th International Symposium on Process Systems Engineering – PSE 2021+
June 19-23, 2022, Kyoto, Japan © 2022 Elsevier B.V. All rights reserved.
http://dx.doi.org/10.1016/B978-0-323-85159-6.50201-3

Systematic process energy optimization via multi-level heat integration: A case study on low-temperature reforming for methanol synthesis

Alexander Guzman-Urbina[a] *, Haruka Tanaka[a], Hajime Ohno[a], Yasuhiro Fukushima[a]

aDepartment of Chemical Engineering, Graduate School of Engineering, Tohoku University, 6-6-07 Aramaki-Aza Aoba, Sendai, Japan
guzman.urbina.alexander.a6@tohoku.ac.jp

Abstract

The development of new technologies for chemical process systems is essential to achieve the sustainable development goals. To ensure the path forward is viable, technology development includes a rigorous evaluation stage that contrasts the benefits of the proposed technology with existing or alternative systems. Energy efficiency and the extent of heat integration are key indicators that directly influence the evaluation and implementation of process system technologies. Methodologies such as the pinch analysis together with mathematical optimization have been extensively applied to determine the degree of heat integration potentially achievable by chemical processes. The aim of these methodologies is to find optimal heat exchange networks (HENs) within a plant or process by minimizing the use of external utilities for heating or cooling. However, since the mathematical formulation of the conventional optimization procedure excludes factors considered important in decision-making processes (operability of complex HEN, plant configurations, safety, etc.), process evaluations fail to fully reflect the consequences of technologies that alter the process conditions. In order to close this gap, an alternative methodology for process energy optimization is proposed in this study which ranks near-optimal HENs solutions, and also considers external factors for decision-making. The methodology proposed consists of heat integration over multiple levels (e.g., sub-process level, plant level) using two major methods of mathematical optimization: the Stage-Wise Superstructure (SWS) and the Integer-Cuts Constraint (ICC). Results from the application of the proposed methodology to a case study of a methanol production process show the possibility of reducing the external utilities consumption by more than 55% compared to the non-integration scenario.

Keywords: Heat Exchange Network, Energy Optimization, Heat Integration, Superstructure, Methanol Synthesis.

1. Introduction

Making a comprehensive evaluation of the impacts of a new technology over the whole process is one of the key factors in the success of technologies for chemical systems in real-life applications. Among the most important aspects to consider when evaluating these systems are the investment cost of the technology, operation costs, environmental impacts, safety, and energy efficiency. Heating requirements, cooling requirements, and heat exchange networks are determinants for all aspects of the evaluation, especially when assessing the sustainability of a new process technology.

Heat exchanger networks have the role of transferring energy among high-temperature streams that require cooling (hot process streams) and low-temperature streams that require heating (cold process streams) to reduce the consumption of external utilities for heating or cooling. Improving energy efficiency through effective heat utilization in process systems is known as "heat integration". The variations in the extent of heat integration influence significantly the evaluation of new technologies because utility reduction leads to reductions in cost and/or environmental impact. Methodologies like the "pinch analysis" serve as a target-based design tool for revealing the minimal utility consumption (MUC) potentially achieved. Actual process systems are rarely developed considering the MUC from initial stages. Moreover, conventional optimization procedures exclude factors considered important in the decision-making processes (operability of complex HEN, plant configurations, safety, etc.). Besides, given the complexity of actual process systems, HENs determination is commonly limited to the interaction among streams within a level of sub-processes and does not extend to the whole plant. While process evaluations based on designs without any HENs may deliver some insight, such evaluations typically fail to fully reflect the consequences of process technologies that alter process conditions. Therefore, this study introduces a scheme that systematically presents multiple near-optimal HENs solutions for interaction among multiple levels (at the sub-process level and plant level).

The framework proposed by this study consists of three major steps: segmentation of the process plant in functional sub-processes, an independent heat integration at the sub-process level, and a global heat integration at the plant level. The heat integration objective at both levels is to find a rank of combinations among process streams that minimize operational costs in terms of utility consumption. For that purpose, this study employs a novel methodology that consists of a combination of two major methods of mathematical optimization. One method commonly used for HEN synthesis, known as the Stage-Wise Superstructure (SWS) (Yee & Grossmann, 1990), considers heat exchange over multiple stages, and another method used to rank the synthesized HENs, proposed by Maronese S. et al. (2015), is called the Integer-Cuts Constraint (ICC). Heat integration is performed as a bottom-up hierarchical sequence, from the sub-process level to the plant level. Here, one of the near-optimal solutions is selected for each sub-process according to a certain design criterion (safety, heat exchanger size, network configuration, etc.), and then taken for further integration at the plant level.

2. Background on heat integration and optimization

2.1 Pinch analysis

The pinch analysis is a method developed to reveal the minimal utility consumptions potentially achieved (Linnhoff & Hindmarsh, 1983). It reveals the utility consumptions when heat exchange in a process system is performed to the maximum. In this method, the heat loads of all existing streams over any given temperature range are added together in what is referred to as a "composite curve". When performing heat exchange, some temperature difference is required as a driving force. The minimum value of the temperature difference, the minimum approach temperature (ΔT_{min}), is often set empirically based on the industrial field or the combination of streams (Tatsumi & Matsuda, 2002). The maximum amount of heat exchange between process streams can be known graphically by superposing the hot composite curve and the cold composite curve separated by ΔT_{min}. However, the pinch analysis provides only the maximum value of the heat exchangeable in the processing system and the minimum value of the utility amounts achieved. The pinch analysis does not determine how hot and cold streams should be paired or to what extent heat should be exchanged. Thus, it is necessary to implement optimization methods that explicitly synthesize the heat exchanger networks based on operational and investment cost criteria.

2.2 Mathematical optimization

The mathematical optimization methods employed for HEN design usually adopt the concept of superstructure optimization (Fig. 1). Superstructure is defined as a structure that contains all possible structures as its substructures. By performing optimization, a structure containing some substructures which has the best objective function value can be obtained. By using superstructure in heat exchanger network synthesis, it is possible to know the combination of streams to exchange the heat and the amount of each heat load explicitly. There are basically two approaches to the heat exchanger network synthesis using mathematical optimizations (Escobar, M. & Trierweiler, 2013). One is to perform optimization multiple times (Papoulias & Grossmann, 1983; Floudas et al. 1986), and the other is to perform all optimizations at once (Ciric et al., 1991; Yee & Grossmann,

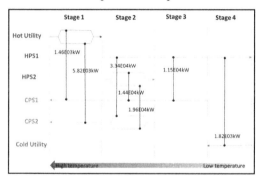

Figure 1. HEN Superstructure (4 Stages)

1990). In the former approach, the utility consumptions are first determined by minimizing the utility cost. Next, the heat exchange area is determined using the objective function of minimizing the investment cost or the sum of heat exchanger area. In the latter approach, however, the quantity of utilities, the combination of streams to be heat-exchanged, each heat load, and each heat exchanger area are determined by a single optimization. In this case, the objective function is to minimize the total annual cost of the plant.

By employing mathematical optimization, only a single optimal solution can be obtained. However, whether the solution obtained can be implemented, or even to determine if it is actually optimal, remains unknown. This is because the introduction of heat exchanger networks is often subject to factors externalized from the mathematical formulation of the design problem, such as operability, plant configuration, and safety. These factors need to be considered when deciding on whether to introduce the heat exchanger network obtained by optimization.

3. Method for process energy optimization via multi-level heat integration

The purpose of the present study was to develop a tool that systematically presents multiple heat exchanger networks for a process system. Among the methods reported which show multiple solutions in mathematical optimization, none are applied to synthesize multiple HENs. Therefore, we developed a model to synthesize multiple HENs with the intention of providing decision-makers with multiple options (near-optimal solutions) to choose from when selecting a heat exchanger. Also, in the event that there are common characteristics in the near-optimal solutions, the common characteristics highlight what should be achieved with priority when implementing the heat exchanger network. The procedure of this study is illustrated schematically in Fig. 2:

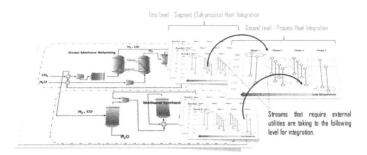

Figure 2. Optimization procedure via multi-level heat integration

The method proposed employs mathematical optimization for multiple heat exchanger networks. We adopted a method proposed by Yee & Grossmann (1990) that considers heat exchange over multiple stages. This method is called the "Stage-Wise Superstructure" (SWS). A conceptual diagram of the SWS over four stages is shown in Fig. 1. This diagram presents a structure with two hot process streams (HPs), two cold process streams (CPs), one hot utility (HU), and one cold utility (CU). The solution of this SWS is a combination of heat exchangers that minimizes the total costs and satisfies the thermodynamical constraints of heat transfer. The objective function is the minimization of the total annual cost related to heat exchange (C_{total}). The first and second terms in Eq. (1) are the operation costs, which represent the cold utility costs and hot utility costs, respectively. The third and fourth terms are the investment and operational costs.

$$
\min C_{\text{total}} = \left(\sum_{i\in HP}\sum_{j\in CU}\sum_{k\in K} C_{U,j}\cdot q_{i,j,k} + \sum_{i\in HU}\sum_{j\in CP}\sum_{k\in K} C_{U,i}\cdot q_{i,j,k} \right)
$$
$$
+ F_A\left(\sum_{i\in H}\sum_{j\in C}\sum_{k\in K} C_{F,ij}\cdot y_{i,j,k} + \sum_{i\in H}\sum_{j\in C}\sum_{k\in K} C_{A,ij}\cdot a_{i,j,k} \right) \tag{1}
$$

Where $C_{A,ij}$ represents the area cost coefficient for heat exchangers, $C_{F,ij}$ is the fixed cost for heat exchangers, and C_U is the annual cost per unit of utility, respectively. F_A is the annualization factor for investment, $a_{i,j,k}$, $q_{i,j,k}$, and $y_{i,j,k}$ represent the variables for area, heat load, and exchanger existence respectively. The subscript I, j, and k indicates the hot streams, the cold streams, and number of stages, respectively.

3.1 Optimization using the Integer-Cut Constraint method

The Integer-Cut Constraint (ICC) is a suitable method for obtaining multiple solutions in optimization problems of system synthesis (Maronese et al. 2015). For this study, the ICC method was adopted to perform system synthesis of the energy system with rank order. In the ICC method, after obtaining the optimal solution, a constraint is added to the original problem, then it prohibits the identical combination of variables as the already obtained solution (Eq. 2).

$$
\sum_{i\in H}\sum_{j\in C}(2y_{i,j,k}^n - 1)y_{i,j,k} \leq \left(\sum_{i\in H}\sum_{j\in C} y_{i,j,k}^n \right) - 1 \quad \forall\, n = 1,\dots N \tag{2}
$$

Where $y_{i,j,k}^n$ is the value of $y_{i,j,k}$ of the n-th solution, N is the number of obtained solutions, i represents the heat transfer operation, y_s is binary variable representing the existence of the unit for heat transfer ($y_s = 1$: exist, $y_s = 0$: not exist), and k is the number of optimizations. After this procedure, the HEN optimization is performed again to obtain the next best solution, which has a different combination of units from the previous solutions. In summary, the overall procedure proposed by this study consists of three major steps: an initial segmentation of the process plant in functional sub-processes, an independent heat integration at the sub-process level applying the combination of SWS-ICC, and, a global heat integration at the plant level. The heat integration is then performed as a bottom-up hierarchical sequence, from the sub-process level to the plant level. Here, one of the near-optimal solutions is selected for each sub-process according to design criteria and then taken for further integration at the plant level.

4. Implementation for Methanol Synthesis

To demonstrate the potential relevance of the scheme developed, the method was applied to the task of assisting in the development of a large-scale methanol production plant (50 kt/day) that employs a sub-process of low-temperature methane reforming. The plant was segmented primarily into six major subprocesses: a looping system, hydrogen production, syngas compression, methanol synthesis, combustion and steam generation, and methanol purification. Table 1 provides a sample of the input data for the looping system. Here, the minimum approach temperature (ΔT_{min}) was 5 K and the number of stages was set to four. The cost parameters were the area cost coefficient for heat exchangers ($C_{A,i,j}$) and fixed cost for heat exchangers ($C_{F,i,j}$), set at 350 \$/m^2 and \$10000, respectively.

Table 1. Sample of input data for the looping system

Stream	Type	Supply Temp. [K]	Target Temp. [K]	Flowrate [kW/K]	h [kW /(m^{2}K)]
CH₄F- CH₄I	Cold	298.15	573.15	99.80	0.8
Water-Steam	Cold	417.15	573.15	377.68	0.8
FR1-FR2	Hot	571.75	427.15	324.11	0.8
SR1-SR2	Hot	572.85	465.55	317.21	0.8

4.1 Results and Discussion

Figures 3a and 3b show a summary of the results obtained for the methanol case. As shown in Fig. 3a, the amount of total utility consumption achieves a reduction of 55% compared to the case when heat integration was not performed. In addition, although the empirical integration achieves a significant reduction of utilities consumption in comparison to a non-integration case, further reduction is viable by applying superstructure modeling. Fig. 3b presents a ranking of solutions for the heat integration of the looping system in terms of the transition of the objective function value. For this sub-process, the total annual cost of the first rank was 3.287 M\$/year, and that of the 10th rank was 3.298 M\$/year. In the optimal solution. In the optimization using SWS, it is possible to explicitly provide the configuration of the heat exchanger network and the values of each variable. It is possible to determine whether the solution can be actually implemented considering the factors externalized from the mathematical formulation.

5. Conclusions

In this study, a tool that presents multiple heat exchanger networks systematically was developed. By combining a method to obtain multiple solutions with different combinations of binary variables with rank order (ICC method) and a method to obtain the range of variables keeping the objective function value within a specified range and modifying them, heat exchanger networks were systematically synthesized for multiple system levels. Using this model, even if the single optimal heat exchanger network determined by optimization cannot be implemented due to factors not included in the mathematical formulation of the design problem, a heat exchanger network can be selected from a range of choices reflecting the intentions of the decision makers. Additionally, the common characteristics of the higher ranked solutions will help in the decision-making process by highlighting what should be achieved with priority in the actual implementation of heat exchanger networks.

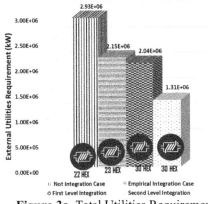
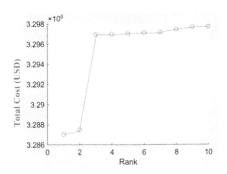

Figure 3a. Total Utilities Requirement   **Figure 3b**. Ranking for Looping sys.

Acknowledgements

This work was supported by The Japan Science and Technology Agency (JST) [Grant: JPMJMI17E4], and New Energy and Industrial Technology Development Org. of Japan NEDO.

References

Chen, Y., Eslick, J.C., Grossmann, I.E. and Miller, D.C., 2015. Simultaneous process optimization and heat integration based on rigorous simulations. Comput. Chem. Eng., 81, pp.180-199.

Ciric, A. R. & Floudas, C. A. Heat exchanger network synthesis without decomposition. Comput. Chem. Eng. 15, 385–396 (1991).

Escobar, M. & Trierweiler, J. O, 2013. Optimal heat exchanger network synthesis: A case study comparison. Appl. Therm. Eng. 51, 801–826 (2013).

Floudas, C. A., Ciric, A. R. & Grossmann, I. E. Automatic synthesis of optimum heat exchanger network configurations. AIChE J. 32, 276–290 (1986).

Linnhoff, B., Hindmarsh, E., 1983. The pinch design method. Chem. Eng. Sci. 38, 745–763.

Maronese, S., Ensinas, A. V., Mian, A., Lazzaretto, A. & Maréchal, F., 2015. Optimum Biorefinery Pathways Selection Using ICC. Ind. Eng. Chem. Res. 54, 7038–7046.

Papoulias, S. A. & Grossmann, I. E. A structural optimization approach in process synthesis—II: Heat recovery networks. Comput. Chem. Eng. 7, 707–721 (1983).

Tatsumi H., Matsuda K., 2002. Pinch Technology Energy Conservation Analysis Method and Practice. Energy Conservation Center.

Yee, T.F. and Grossmann, I.E., 1990. Simultaneous optimization models for heat integration—II. Heat exchanger network synthesis. Comput. Chem. Eng., 14(10), pp.1165-1184.

Proceedings of the 14th International Symposium on Process Systems Engineering – PSE 2021+
June 19-23, 2022, Kyoto, Japan © 2022 Elsevier B.V. All rights reserved.
http://dx.doi.org/10.1016/B978-0-323-85159-6.50202-5

Bayesian Optimization for Automobile Catalyst Development

Sanha Lim, Hwangho Lee, Shinyoung Bae, Jun Seop Shin, Do Heui Kim and Jong Min Lee*

School of Chemical and Biological Engineering, Institute of Chemical Processes, Seoul National University, 1 Gwanak-ro, Gwanak-gu, Seoul 08826, Republic of Korea
jongmin@snu.ac.kr

Abstract

In this study, we propose an efficient computational methodology for developing Selective catalytic reduction (SCR) with high NOx conversion and resistance to hydrothermal aging, using Bayesian optimization (BO). In order to focus on the catalytic performance at low temperature, Cu-Fe bimetallic catalyst supported by SSZ-13 (Si/Al = 12) is targeted. An initial surrogate model is constructed by referring experimental data from previously published papers. The next sampling points are determined from the Bayesian optimization algorithm. NOx conversion is observed under fresh condition and hydrothermally aged condition after manufacturing a catalyst sample consisting of suggested metal compositions. We also consider the catalytic activity after hydrothermal aging in the air of 900 °C containing 10 % water for 16 hours. In this way, the optimal composition for bimetallic SCR catalyst is discovered, maximizing NOx conversion and hydrothermal resistance in only a few steps of experimentation. The proposed SCR catalyst can reduce 95.86 % of nitrogen oxides at 250 °C. After hydrothermal aging, it can eliminate 88.83 % of nitrogen oxides at the same temperature.

Keywords: Bayesian optimization (BO); Selective catalytic reduction (SCR); Activity; Hydrothermal aging

1. Introduction

Diesel engines typically show higher fuel efficiency than gasoline engines, but they emit more air pollutants, such as nitrogen oxides (NOx). The emission standards for nitrogen oxides become stringent recently to decrease air pollutants emitted from automobile exhaust gas. Euro 6 regulations have already been implemented since 2014 and more strict restriction, Euro 7, is to be introduced in the near future. Selective catalytic reduction (SCR) with urea injector is a standard after-treatment system which reduces the nitrogen oxides in the exhaust gas emitted from the diesel engines. The performance of the SCR catalyst is excellent at high temperature, removing more than 90 % of nitrogen oxides in the exhaust gas. However, catalytic activity in low temperature range is a major challenge in the automobile aftertreatment catalyst field. Low NOx conversion at low temperature causes air pollution when the exhaust gas is not hot enough, for example, during cold start and on travelling short distances (Shan and Song, 2015). Furthermore, for the actual diesel engine exhaust system, the SCR catalyst suffers from the deactivation caused by hydrothermal aging due to H_2O content with high temperature exhaust gas. Therefore, achieving hydrothermal stability is also crucial for commercial SCR catalyst.

For commercial SCR for diesel vehicle, urea solution is usually applied to generate ammonia. The hot exhaust gas stream from diesel engine evaporates water droplet and thermally decomposes urea to ammonia.

$$(NH_2)_2CO \longrightarrow NH_3 + HNCO \tag{1}$$

$$HNCO + H_2O \longrightarrow NH_3 + CO_2 \tag{2}$$

The generated ammonia is adsorbed on the active sites of the catalyst to remove nitrogen oxides from the exhaust gas. The SCR reactions are usually described in three types of reactions: the standard, fast, and slow SCR reactions. (Pant and Schmieg, 2011)

$$4NH_3 + 4NO + O_2 \longrightarrow 4N_2 + 6H_2O \tag{3}$$

$$2NH_3 + NO + NO_2 \longrightarrow 2N_2 + 3H_2O \tag{4}$$

$$4NH_3 + 3NO_2 \longrightarrow 3.5N_2 + 6H_2O \tag{5}$$

Nitrogen monoxide is oxidized to nitrogen dioxide at high temperature (above 250°C). Since the extent of NO oxidation to NO_2 under low temperature is small, NO_2 concentration at the SCR inlet gas can be negligible (Olsson et al., 2008).

Many SCR catalysts have been explored to improve NOx removal efficiency. It is reported that SCR catalysts containing transitional metal, particularly Cu and Fe, show good activity at low temperature (Li et al, 2011). However, in the case of catalytic system with bimetallic components, finding the optimal composition with both excellent activity and hydrothermal stability is too inefficient and time-consuming to be proceeded only experimentally.

In this study, we propose an efficient computational methodology for developing SCR catalyst with high NOx conversion and resistance to hydrothermal aging, using Bayesian optimization (BO).

2. Methodology

2.1. Experimental condition

In this study, we focus on Cu-Fe bimetallic catalyst for SCR. In terms of catalytic structure for SCR, various types of zeolite structures have been studied: Beta, ZSM-5, and SSZ-13. Among them, Kwak et al. (2010) have reported that SSZ-13 demonstrates superior activity in comparison with beta and ZSM-5. Therefore, we prepare Cu-Fe SCR catalyst supported by SSZ-13 (Si/Al = 12) to maximize NOx conversion at low temperature.

The catalytic performance is measured using lab-scale reactor system. The feed gas contained 500 ppm NO, 500 ppm NH$_3$, 10 % O$_2$, 5 % H$_2$O, and balance N$_2$. The total gas flow rate is 200ml/min, and the gas hourly space velocity (GHSV) is 200,000/h. Most importantly, the temperature of the feed gas is maintained at 250 °C. The resistant ability to hydrothermal aging is also measured after exposure to 900 °C gas containing 10% water for 16 hours.

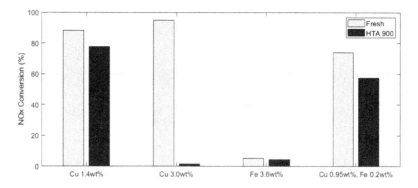

Figure 1. Experimental results for nitrogen oxides conversion of Cu/Fe SCR. Gray bar for fresh condition and black bar for hydrothermally aged (HTA) condition.

The experimental results of initial samples for Bayesian optimization are shown in Figure 1. As the copper content of SCR catalyst increases, the number of active sites on the surface of the catalyst also increases, which leads to higher NOx conversion. However, high metal content reduces catalytic stability simultaneously, making SCR catalyst susceptible to catalytic deactivation by the high temperature and water in the exhaust gas. Thus, it is required to optimize performance of the catalyst with respect to the content of active sites. The effect of two metals coexisting is also difficult to grasp intuitively. The performance of a catalyst with a specific metal content is not known until experimentally observed. A large number of trials and errors are required to develop SCR catalyst with high activity and hydrothermal resistance.

2.2. Bayesian optimization

Bayesian optimization is a useful algorithm to optimize a black-box function. It is usually employed to optimize hyperparameters of neural network. This method balances exploitation and exploration utilizing information obtained from a series of experiments (Snoek et al., 2012). Table 1 shows Bayesian optimization procedure, described by Brochu et al. (2010). $u(x)$ means the acquisition function, $f(x)$ stands for the function to be maximized, and $\mathcal{D}_{1:t}$ is the observed dataset from iteration 1 to t.

Table 1. Bayesian optimization procedure adopted from Brochu et al. (2010)

Algorithm 1 Bayesian optimization

1: for $t = 1, 2, \ldots$ do

2: Find x_n that maximizes the acquisition function over the GP (Gaussian process):

$x_t = argmax_x u(x|\mathcal{D}_{1:t-1})$.

3: Sample the objective function: $y_t = f(x_t) + \varepsilon_t$.

4: Augment the data $\mathcal{D}_{1:t} = \{\mathcal{D}_{1:t-1}, (x_t, y_t)\}$ and update the GP.

5: end for

As the acquisition function, the expected improvement (EI) is chosen, which is the widely used one. The improvement I at the point x can be expressed as follows (Jones et al., 1998):

$$I(x) = \max(f_{min} - Y, 0) \tag{6}$$

where f_{min} is the current best function value and Y is the random variable $\sim \mathcal{N}(\hat{y}, s^2)$ that corresponds to the function value at x. Since Y follows a Gaussian distribution, by taking the expected valued, we can obtain the expected improvement, $u_{EI}(x)$.

$$u_{EI}(x) \equiv E(I(x)) = \mathrm{E}[\max(f_{min} - Y, 0)] \tag{7}$$

$$u_{EI}(x) = (f_{min} - \hat{y})\Phi\left(\frac{f_{min} - \hat{y}}{s}\right) + s\phi(\frac{f_{min} - \hat{y}}{s}) \tag{8}$$

where $\phi(\cdot)$ and $\Phi(\cdot)$ are the standard normal density function and distribution function, respectively.

In this research, the optimization variable x is weight percent of copper and iron (Cu wt% and Fe wt%). The objective of the suggested algorithm is to maximize the catalytic activity in fresh condition and hydrothermally aged condition. For minimization problem, the objective function can be expressed as follows:

$$f(Cu, Fe) = -(\mathrm{DeNOx}_{Fresh} + \mathrm{DeNOx}_{HTA}) \tag{9}$$

where DeNOx stands for NOx conversion efficiency,

$$\mathrm{DeNOx} = \frac{\mathrm{NOx}_{inlet} - \mathrm{NOx}_{outlet}}{\mathrm{NOx}_{inlet}} * 100 \tag{10}$$

3. Results

We conduct Bayesian optimization for the optimal metal composition that shows the best NOx conversion at low temperature (250 °C) and resistance to hydrothermal aging. Initial dataset for the surrogate model is based on the experimental data from previously published papers (Shishkin et al., 2014, Yin et al, 2016, Wang et al., 2019). As shown in Figure 2, Bayesian optimization algorithm proposes the next experimental point that maximizes the acquisition function, u_{EI}. The Cu/Fe-SSZ-13 catalyst with the suggested metal composition is evaluated for its catalytic performance though the experimental process mentioned in section 2.1. The objective function is calculated from NOx concentration of outlet gas flow. The surrogate model of BO is updated with the newly added data. These processes are repeated until the stopping criterion is met.

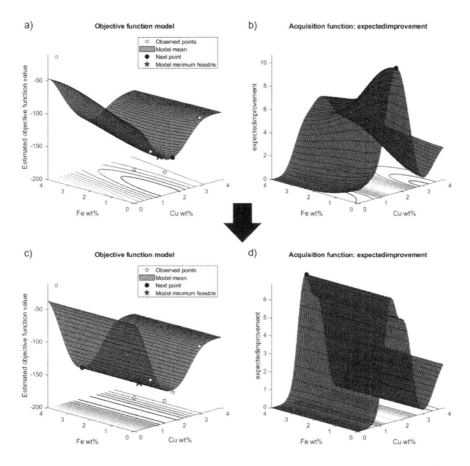

Figure 2. Bayesian optimization procedure for Cu-Fe SCR. a) objective function model of 5th step, b) acquisition function of 5th step, c) objective function of 6th step, d) Acquisition function of 6th step

After only seven steps of experiments, we found a high-performance catalyst for SCR. The optimal catalyst proposed by Bayesian optimization consists of 2.0 wt% Cu and 2.0 wt% Fe. As a result of a total of five experiments, the NOx conversions under fresh condition are 94.75 %, 94.54 %, 93.52 %, 93.71 % and 93.80 %, respectively. After hydrothermal aging of this Cu-Fe catalyst at 900 °C for 16 hours, the catalyst removes 87.75 %, 89.92 %, 89.75 %, 88.92 % and 87.81 % of nitrogen oxides. These results show as good catalytic performance as the SSZ-13 zeolite SCR catalyst presented in the recent paper. By using Bayesian optimization algorithm, automobile catalyst with high-performance can be found efficiently. The methodology suggested in this research can reduce time and cost of catalyst development.

4. Conclusions

In this work, we show that Bayesian optimization can efficiently support the experimental design to discover the optimal catalytic composition for the aftertreatment system of diesel vehicle. The target catalyst is Cu-Fe bimetallic catalyst for selective catalytic reduction (SCR), supported by SSZ-13 zeolite structure. The bimetallic catalyst proposed by Bayesian optimization has high performance to reduce nitrogen oxide, showing 95.86 % conversion. The catalyst also has resistance to the hydrothermal aging. After 16 hours of exposure to 900 °C of air containing 10 % water, the catalyst converts 88.83 % of NOx to N2. The optimal catalyst is discovered in only seven experiments. The suggested method reduces time and cost of catalyst development. We expect that our methodology can be applied to other automobile catalyst system, such as three-way catalytic converter for gasoline vehicle.

Acknowledgements

This research was supported by the National Research Foundation of Korea (NRF) grant funded by the Korean Government (MSIT) [NRF-2016R1A5A1009592]

References

W. Shan and H. Song, 2015, Catalysts for the selective catalytic reduction of NO x with NH 3 at low temperature, Catalysis Science & Technology, 5(9), 4280-4288.

A. Pant and S.J. Schmieg, 2011, Kinetic Model of NOx SCR Using Urea on Commercial Cu−Zeolite Catalyst, Industrial & Engineering Chemistry Research, 50(9), 5490-5498.

L. Olsson, H. Sjövall, and R.J., Blint, 2008, A kinetic model for ammonia selective catalytic reduction over Cu-ZSM-5, Applied Catalysis B: Environmental, 81(3-4), 203-217.

J. Li, H. Chang, L. Ma, J. Hao and R. T. Yang, 2011, Low-temperature selective catalytic reduction of NOx with NH3 over metal oxide and zeolite catalysts—A review, Catalysis today, 175(1), 147-156.

J.H. Kwak, R.G. Tonkyn, D.H. Kim, J. Szanyi and C.H. Peden, 2010, Excellent activity and selectivity of Cu-SSZ-13 in the selective catalytic reduction of NOx with NH3, Journal of Catalysis, 275(2), 187-190.

J. Snoek, H. Larochelle and R.P. Adams, 2012, Practical bayesian optimization of machine learning algorithms, Advances in neural information processing systems, 25.

E. Brochu, V.M. Cora and N. De Freitas, 2010, A tutorial on Bayesian optimization of expensive cost functions, with application to active user modeling and hierarchical reinforcement learning, arXiv preprint arXiv: 1012.2599.

D.R. Jones, M. Schonlau and W.J., Welch, 1998, Efficient global optimization of expensive black-box functions, Journal of Global optimization, 13(4), 455-492.

A. Shishjin, H. Kannisto, P.A., Carlsson, H. Härelind and M. Skoglundh, 2014, Synthesis and functionalization of SSZ-13 as an NH 3-SCR catalyst, Catalysis Science & Technology, 4(11), 3917-3926.

C. Yin, P. Cheng, X. Li and R.T. Yang, 2016, Selective catalytic reduction of nitric oxide with ammonia over high-activity Fe/SSZ-13 and Fe/one-pot-synthesized Cu-SSZ-13 catalysts, Catalysis Science & Technology, 6(20), 7561-7568.

A. Wang, Y. Wang, E.D. Walter, N.M. Washton, Y. Guo, G. Lu, C.H.F. Peden and F. Gao, 2019, NH3-SCR on Cu, Fe and Cu+ Fe exchanged beta and SSZ-13 catalysts: Hydrothermal aging and propylene poisoning effects, Catalysis Today, 320, 91-99.

Proceedings of the 14th International Symposium on Process Systems Engineering – PSE 2021+
June 19–23, 2022, Kyoto, Japan ©2022 Elsevier B. V. All rights reserved.
http://dx.doi.org/10.1016/B978-0-323-85159-6.50203-7

Capacity Planning for Sustainable Process Systems with Uncertain Endogenous Technology Learning

Tushar Rathi, Qi Zhang*

Department of Chemical Engineering and Materials Science, University of Minnesota, Minneapolis, MN 55455, USA

qizh@umn.edu

Abstract

The development and deployment of renewable technologies are key to achieving decarbonization. Optimal capacity expansion requires complex decision making that accounts for future cost reduction with increased deployment, which is also termed technology learning. Having a perfect foresight over the technology cost reduction, however, is highly unlikely. This has motivated us to develop a capacity planning model that incorporates such uncertainty. To this end, we apply a multistage stochastic programming approach with endogenous uncertainty, which results in a mixed-integer linear programming (MILP) formulation. The proposed model is applied to a case study on power capacity expansion planning, highlighting the differences in expansion decisions for low- and high-learning scenarios, which indicates the importance of stochastic optimization.

Keywords: stochastic optimization, endogenous uncertainty, technology learning

1. Introduction

Over the past few decades, the unfavorable shift in global climatic conditions has driven us to focus on renewable technology development to lower carbon emissions. The increasing energy demand has further aggravated the need for alternatives to traditional fossil energy sources. However, in addition to developing new technologies, making them economical as fast as possible remains a challenging task. In general, the cost of a technology is a function of several interrelated factors, including pricing and the number of competitors, government regulations and policies, the scale of production, and demand. The reduction in the cost of a new technology due to these factors is often termed technology learning.

Of all the stated, the scale of production constitutes a major driving force for cost reduction in new technologies. The reduction in cost as a function of installed capacity is often expressed using learning curves. Learning curves have often been used as a tool to estimate the time for a new technology to become cost-competitive. For example, Rubin et al. (2007) utilize learning curves for cost projection of power plants equipped with carbon capture and storage technology.

A less considered aspect is utilizing learning curves to make optimal capacity expansion decisions for driving down the cost of a plant or a technology in the least possible time. Most of the literature on optimization concerning learning curves assumes that they can be constructed deterministically. For example, Heuberger et al. (2017) present a power capacity expansion formulation assuming fixed learning curves for various power generation and storage technologies. However, the lack of reliable historical data, the dependence of learning on the decisions made in real time, and the influence of other external factors make it very difficult to predict the learning curves. Therefore, decisions obtained based on deterministic learning curves may be severely sub-optimal.

To increase the practical relevance of capacity expansion models, our work incorporates uncertainty in technology learning curves. Uncertainty in learning rates has been accounted for, if at all, using methods such as sensitivity analysis and Monte Carlo simulation (Kim et al., 2012). Even though such methods provide valuable insights, their inability to account for non-anticipativity constraints demands a more rigorous optimization framework. For this reason, we explore the feasibility of stochastic programming in incorporating uncertain learning curves for multiperiod capacity expansion problems.

Uncertainty is generally classified as either exogenous or endogenous. The uncertainty not affected by decisions is termed exogenous, whereas decision-dependent uncertainty is termed endogenous. Endogenous uncertainty is further classified as type-1 and type-2. Type-1 uncertainty arises when decisions alter the probability distribution of the uncertain parameters (Peeta et al., 2010), whereas type-2 uncertainty affects the timing of the realization of the uncertain parameters (Goel and Grossmann, 2006). In a capacity expansion problem with an uncertain learning curve, the uncertainty in expansion cost resolves only when the capacity is actually increased; thus, the uncertainty here classifies as type-2 endogenous. In this work, we develop a multistage stochastic programming model for capacity planning with uncertain endogenous technology learning and apply it to a power expansion case study.

2. Stochastic programming model

To capture the interconnectivity of technologies, model their simultaneous availability to satisfy product demand, and optimize their selection for capacity expansion and operations, we consider a general process network comprising process and resource nodes as illustrated in Figure 1. Processes and resources are denoted by square and circular nodes, respectively. The arcs in the network denote the directed flow of resources. Process nodes can represent chemical and manufacturing processes or, generally, technologies. Resource $j \in \mathcal{J}$ from a process $k \in \mathcal{K}$ can either serve as an input resource to process $k' \in \mathcal{K}\backslash\{k\}$, be discharged from the process network, or be purchased from outside the network.

The goal is to determine optimal capacity expansion decisions during the planning horizon $\mathcal{T}$, and devise optimal operational decisions in each scheduling horizon $\mathcal{H}_t$ based on each process's installed capacity, demand of resources, and all the involved costs. Uncertainty in technology learning curves is accommodated by considering different possible scenarios (combination of learning curves for multiple uncertain technologies).

2.1. Capacity expansion constraints

Based on the process network in Figure 1, we define binary variable x_{kits} that equals 1 if process k undergoes capacity expansion to (at least) the permissible point $i \in \mathcal{I}_k$ in time period $t \in \mathcal{T}$ of scenario $s \in \mathcal{S}$. We further define the variables C_{kts} and Δ_{kts} such that they represent the cumulative installed capacity and additional capacity installed of

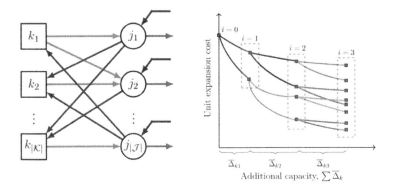

Figure 1: A general process network and an illustrative uncertain learning curve. Each discrete expansion point i acts as a source of uncertainty. In this case, we have two, four, and eight possible unit expansion costs at $i = 1, 2,$ and, 3 respectively.

a process k in time period t of scenario s, respectively. Then, the following constraints control the timing and extent of capacity expansion for each technology:

$$C_{k0s} = \overline{C}_{k0} \qquad\qquad \forall k \in \mathcal{K}, \forall s \in \mathcal{S} \quad \text{(1a)}$$

$$C_{kts} = C_{k,t-1,s} + \Delta_{kts} \qquad\qquad \forall k \in \mathcal{K}, t \in \mathcal{T}, \forall s \in \mathcal{S} \quad \text{(1b)}$$

$$\Delta_{kts} = \sum_{i \in \mathcal{I}_k} x_{kit}\overline{\Delta}_{ki} \qquad\qquad \forall k \in \mathcal{K}, t \in \mathcal{T}, \forall s \in \mathcal{S} \quad \text{(1c)}$$

$$\Delta_{kts} \le b_{kt} \qquad\qquad \forall k \in \mathcal{K}, t \in \mathcal{T}, \forall s \in \mathcal{S} \quad \text{(1d)}$$

$$x_{kits} \le \sum_{\tau=1}^{t} x_{k,i-1,\tau s} \qquad\qquad \forall k \in \mathcal{K}, i \in \mathcal{I}_k \backslash \{1\}, t \in \mathcal{T}, \forall s \in \mathcal{S} \quad \text{(1e)}$$

$$\sum_{\tau=1}^{t} x_{ki\tau s} \le 1 \qquad\qquad \forall k \in \mathcal{K}, i \in \mathcal{I}_k, t \in \mathcal{T}, \forall s \in \mathcal{S} \quad \text{(1f)}$$

$$g(Q_{hts}, C_{kts}) \le 0 \qquad\qquad \forall k \in \mathcal{K}, h \in \mathcal{H}_t, t \in \mathcal{T}, \forall s \in \mathcal{S} \quad \text{(1g)}$$

$$x_{kits} \in \{0, 1\} \qquad\qquad \forall k \in \mathcal{K}, i \in \mathcal{I}_k, t \in \mathcal{T}, \forall s \in \mathcal{S} \quad \text{(1h)}$$

$$C_{kts}, \Delta_{kts} \ge 0 \qquad\qquad \forall k \in \mathcal{K}, t \in \mathcal{T}, \forall s \in \mathcal{S} \quad \text{(1i)}$$

$$Q_{hts} \in \mathbb{R}^{|\mathcal{J}||\mathcal{K}|} \times \mathbb{Z}^{|\mathcal{K}|} \qquad\qquad \forall t \in \mathcal{T}, h \in \mathcal{H}_t, \forall s \in \mathcal{S} \quad \text{(1j)}$$

where $\overline{C}_{k0}$ denotes the initial installed capacity of process k. The incremental capacity for process k from point $i - 1$ to i is denoted by $\overline{\Delta}_{ki}$. Constraints (1a)-(1c) together represent the capacity balance. Constraints (1d) limit the capacity expansion of a process k by the available budget b_{kt} in time period t. Constraints (1e) ensure that we move in the positive direction on the learning curve in a sequential fashion, i.e., we can only install additional capacity corresponding to point i if we have already installed the additional capacity corresponding to point $i - 1$. Constraints (1f) imply that investment at any point $i \in \mathcal{I}_k$ cannot be made more than once in any time period. Constraints (1g) are a condensed representation of all the operational constraints, including production scheduling, inventory management, scheduling startup/shutdown of units, limiting emissions and storage, to name a few. Operational decision variables Q_{hts} can be both continuous and discrete and are constrained by the installed capacities of the processes in the network.

2.2. Non-anticipativity constraints

Non-anticipativity constraints (NACs) ensure the equality of decisions for all pairs of indistinguishable scenarios at any point in time during the planning horizon. Mathematically, NACs are represented as follows:

$$x_{ki1s} = x_{ki1,s+1} \quad \forall k \in \mathcal{K}, i \in \mathcal{I}_k, s \in \mathcal{S}, s < |\mathcal{S}| \tag{2a}$$

$$\begin{bmatrix} Z_t^{s,s'} \\ x_{ki,t+1,s} = x_{ki,t+1,s'} \quad \forall k \in \mathcal{K}, i \in \mathcal{I}_k \end{bmatrix} \vee \begin{bmatrix} \neg Z_t^{s,s'} \end{bmatrix} \quad \forall (s,s') \in \mathcal{P}', t \in \mathcal{T} \backslash \{T\} \tag{2b}$$

$$Z_t^{s,s'} \iff \bigwedge_{(r,i) \in \mathcal{D}(s,s')} \left[\bigwedge_{\tau=1}^{t} (\neg x_{ri\tau s}) \right] \quad \forall (s,s') \in \mathcal{P}', t \in \mathcal{T} \backslash \{T\} \tag{2c}$$

$$Z_t^{s,s'} \in \{\texttt{true}, \texttt{false}\} \quad \forall (s,s') \in \mathcal{P}', t \in \mathcal{T} \backslash \{T\} \tag{2d}$$

where $\mathcal{D}(s,s')$ is the set containing sources of endogenous uncertainty (expansion points in our case) that distinguish scenario s from s'. The Boolean variable $Z_{s,s'}^{t}$ is true if uncertainty has not been realized in any of the uncertain parameters that belong to the set $\mathcal{D}(s,s')$. Further, $\mathcal{P}'$ denotes the minimum or reduced set of scenario pairs that is sufficient to express all the NACs. The details on the disjunction and logic-based formulation of NACs for endogenous uncertainty problems can be found in Goel and Grossmann (2006). Also, we refer the reader to Hooshmand and MirHassani (2016) for redundant NAC removal strategies in case of endogenous uncertainty and an arbitrary scenario set.

2.3. Objective function

The objective is to minimize the expected net cost over the entire planning horizon; thus, the overall stochastic optimization problem can be summarized as follows:

$$\min \quad \sum_{s \in \mathcal{S}} p_s \sum_{t \in \mathcal{T}} \alpha_t \left[\sum_{k \in \mathcal{K}} \sum_{i \in \mathcal{I}_k} \left(\int_{\Phi_{k,i-1}}^{\Phi_{ki}} f_{ks}(\Phi_k) \mathrm{d}\Phi_k \right) x_{kits} + \right.$$

$$\left. \sum_{h \in \mathcal{H}_t} \sum_{k \in \mathcal{K}} \sum_{j \in \mathcal{J}} u_{jkhts}(Q_{hts}, C_{kts}) \right]$$

s.t. Eqs. (1a) - (1j), (2a) - (2d)

where p_s denotes the probability of scenario s and α_t denotes the discount factor for time period t. The learning curve for process k is encoded in the model as $f_k(\Phi_k)$ and $\Phi_{ki} := \sum_{i'=1}^{i} \overline{\Delta}_{ki}$. Note that we make no assumptions on the form of the learning curve since the integral term (expansion cost on increasing capacity from point $i-1$ to i) is a parameter that can be pre-calculated. The cost function u captures all operating costs including the cost of specific modes of operation, utilizing storage, purchasing and discharging resources, tax on emissions, etc.

3.   Industrial case study

The proposed framework is applied to a capacity expansion case study for a network of power generation technologies. Specifically, we consider seven technologies and categorize them into one of the following three categories – conventional (no cost reduction), deterministic (known learning curve), and uncertain technology (uncertain learning curve). Nuclear, coal, combined cycle gas turbine (CCGT), and open cycle gas turbine (OCGT) are considered conventional, onshore wind and solar are assumed to be deterministic, and offshore wind is assumed to have an uncertain learning curve. The model and data for this case study are partially adapted from Heuberger et al. (2017). The planning problem was modeled using JuMP v0.21.10 in Julia v1.6.3 and was solved using Gurobi v9.1.2. The model was solved to optimality (0.01% tolerance) in 3,150 s.

The planning horizon spans eight 5-year time periods from 2015 to 2055. The capacity expansion decisions are made at the start of each of these time periods. Figure 2 illustrates the eight possible learning curves for offshore wind technology and the eventual scenario tree based on the expansion decisions made. The scenario tree indicates that the offshore wind capacity increases by 2.5 GW at $t = 1$; however, as expected, we do not see any further expansion for the low-learning case (high-cost scenarios). On the contrary, for the high-learning case (low-cost scenarios), at $t = 2$, the capacity further expands by 5.8 GW, resulting in four scenario tree nodes. Thus, stochastic programming adapts its decisions to the future expansion cost, generating practically viable solutions in the process.

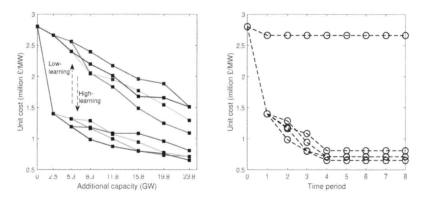

Figure 2: The possible learning curves considered for offshore wind are illustrated on the left. Scenario tree (right) reveals expansion decisions for offshore wind.

Next, Figure 3 illustrates the distribution of capacity for all technologies throughout the planning horizon. Clearly, in comparison to the high-learning scenario, the low-learning scenario does not favor offshore wind expansion. This reduced capacity expansion in offshore wind is compensated by expansions of conventional technologies such as nuclear and OCGT. Note that the expansions are governed not only by the expansion cost but also by the expansion budget, lifetime of each technology, and the time-varying power generation capacity. The proposed stochastic programming model effectively integrates the above factors with the uncertain cost to generate the optimal capacity distribution.

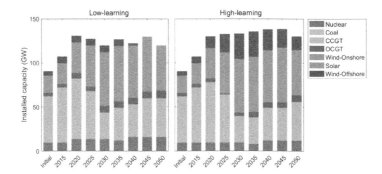

Figure 3: Capacity distribution of power generation technologies under low- and high-learning scenarios.

4.   Conclusions

In this work, we proposed a rigorous optimization framework for a general process network that can be utilized to model energy systems containing both renewable and non-renewable technologies. We utilize stochastic programming to account for the long-neglected aspect of uncertainty in technology learning curves. The case study on power capacity expansion showcases the adaptability of stochastic programming in providing decisions optimal to individual scenarios. The difference in decisions also indicates that any solution obtained through a deterministic model, which essentially is a single scenario case, would often be sub-optimal for any perturbation in the assumed deterministic learning curves.

References

V. Goel and I. E. Grossmann, 2006. A class of stochastic programs with decision dependent uncertainty. *Mathematical programming*, 108(2):355–394.

C. F. Heuberger, E. S. Rubin, I. Staffell, N. Shah, and N. Mac Dowell, 2017. Power capacity expansion planning considering endogenous technology cost learning. *Applied Energy*, 204:831–845.

F. Hooshmand and S. MirHassani, 2016. Efficient constraint reduction in multistage stochastic programming problems with endogenous uncertainty. *Optimization Methods and Software*, 31(2):359–376.

S. Kim, J. Koo, C. J. Lee, and E. S. Yoon, 2012. Optimization of Korean energy planning for sustainability considering uncertainties in learning rates and external factors. *Energy*, 44(1):126–134.

S. Peeta, F. S. Salman, D. Gunnec, and K. Viswanath, 2010. Pre-disaster investment decisions for strengthening a highway network. *Computers & Operations Research*, 37(10):1708–1719.

E. S. Rubin, S. Yeh, M. Antes, M. Berkenpas, and J. Davison, 2007. Use of experience curves to estimate the future cost of power plants with CO_2 capture. *International Journal of Greenhouse Gas Control*, 1(2):188–197.

Proceedings of the 14th International Symposium on Process Systems Engineering – PSE 2021+
June 19–23, 2022, Kyoto, Japan ©2022 Elsevier B. V. All rights reserved.
http://dx.doi.org/10.1016/B978-0-323-85159-6.50204-9

Development of a bi-objective optimisation framework for mixed-integer nonlinear programming problems and application to molecular design

Ye Seol Lee[a], George Jackson[a], Amparo Galindo[a], Claire S. Adjiman[a*]

[a]*Department of Chemical Engineering, Sargent Centre for Process Systems Engineering, Institute for Molecular Science and Engineering, Imperial College London, South Kensington Campus, London SW7 2AZ, United Kingdom*

*c.adjiman@imperial.ac.uk

Abstract

We present a novel algorithm (SDNBI) to tackle the numerical challenges associated with the solution of bi-objective mixed-integer nonlinear programming problems (BO-MINLPs), with a focus on the exploration of nonconvex regions of the Pareto front. The performance of the algorithm as measured by the accuracy of the resulting approximation of the Pareto front in the disconnected and nonconvex domain of Pareto points is assessed relative to two multi-objective optimisation (MOO) approaches: the sandwich algorithm (SD) and the modified normal boundary intersection (mNBI) method. The features of these MOO algorithms are evaluated using two published benchmark models and a molecular design problem. Initial results indicate that the new algorithm presented outperforms both the SD and the mNBI method in convex, nonconvex-continuous, combinatorial problems, both in terms of computational cost and of the overall quality of the Pareto-optimal set.

Keywords: Multi-objective optimisation, Mixed-integer nonlinear programming, Computer-aided molecular design

1. Introduction

Multi-objective optimisation (MOO) techniques have been applied to problems across a wide range of engineering fields to identify trade-offs between conflicting decision criteria that cannot easily be placed on the same quantitative footing. Some of the most widely used approaches to solving MOO problems are based on scalarisation methods and include the weighted sum method (Marler and Arora, 2004), the normal boundary intersection (NBI) method (Das and Dennis, 1998) and the sandwich (SD) algorithm (Rennen et al., 2011). However, these methods suffer from limitations that prevent them from being used to reliably producing optimal solutions along the nonconvex or discrete regions of a Pareto front. As a result, the performance of these methods during the solution of many practical problems is limited when nonconvexities are arise due to the presence of discrete decision variables and/or nonlinear model equations.

In this work, we present a robust bi-objective optimisation approach, SDNBI algorithm that combines features of the SD and NBI methods in order to overcome difficulties in converging to the true Pareto front and maintaining a well-distributed set of solutions. The main improvements introduced are the identification of regions where no further optimal solution exists, i.e., disconnected parts of the Pareto front, and the exploration of nonconvex parts of the Pareto front. The proposed approach is evaluated using two published benchmark problems with different levels of complexity in terms of problem size and numerical difficulty. The performance of the algorithm is compared with that of the SD method and of the mNBI algorithm, a modified version of the NBI method (Shukla, 2007). The comparison is based on the accuracy of the approximation of Pareto fronts generated.

The efficiency of the proposed algorithm is further investigated through a computer-aided molecular and process design (CAMPD) problem. This provides an opportunity to examine the applicability and reliability of the proposed algorithm in a mixed-integer nonlinear setting.

2.   Background and motivation

The generic mathematical formulation of the MOO problem is defined as:

$$\begin{aligned}
\min \quad & (f_1(\boldsymbol{x}), \ldots, f_m(\boldsymbol{x}))^\top \\
\text{subject to} \quad & \boldsymbol{x} \in X := \{\boldsymbol{x} \in \mathbb{R}^{n_1} \times \mathbb{N}^{n_2} \mid \boldsymbol{g}(\boldsymbol{x}) \leq \boldsymbol{0}, \boldsymbol{h}(\boldsymbol{x}) = \boldsymbol{0}\},
\end{aligned} \quad \text{(MOP)}$$

where objective functions $f_j : \mathbb{R}^n \to \mathbb{R}$, $j = 1, 2, ..., m$, $\boldsymbol{x}$ is an n-dimensional vector consisting of n_1 continuous variables and n_2 discrete variables ($K = n_1 + n_2$), $X \neq \emptyset$ is an nonempty feasible set, $\boldsymbol{g}(\boldsymbol{x})$ is a p-dimensional vector of inequality constraints and $\boldsymbol{h}(\boldsymbol{x})$ is a q-dimensional vector of equality constraints, $q \leq K$. In this paper, we are specifically interested in bi-objective problems, i.e., $m = 2$.

2.1.   The Sandwich Algorithm

The sandwich (SD) algorithm proposed by Rennen et al. (2011) provides an efficient way to approximate a convex Pareto front based on the successive solution of weighted-sum sub-problems in which the multiple objective functions are scalarised into a single objective function through a weight vector, $\boldsymbol{w}$, as follows:

$$\min_{\boldsymbol{x} \in X} \quad \boldsymbol{w}^\top \boldsymbol{f}(\boldsymbol{x}) = \sum_{i=1}^{m} w_i f_i(\boldsymbol{x}). \quad \text{(WSP}w\text{)}$$

Within the algorithm, the Pareto front is approximated by recursively improving inner and outer approximations, with the Pareto surface "sandwiched" between them. The inner approximation, which provides an upper bound of the Pareto front in the objective space, is constructed by generating a convex hull from the current set of the Pareto points, while the outer approximation, which supports the Pareto front, is improved at each iteration by adding a hyperplane tangential to any new Pareto point $\boldsymbol{z}$ identified. At each iteration, the parameters of the next sub-problem to be solved, i.e., the weight coefficients $\boldsymbol{w}$ are chosen based on the normal vector of facets derived from the inner approximation.

2.2.   The Normal Boundary Intersection Method

The NBI method was proposed by Das and Dennis (1998) to generate uniformly-spread nondominated solutions of a general nonlinear MOO problem. In the NBI method, the individual minima $\boldsymbol{Z}^{Ai}$, $i = 1, \ldots, m$, of the objective functions are found as a first step. The convex hull of individual minima (CHIM) is then generated as a set of all convex combinations of those extreme points. The CHIM can be expressed as $\boldsymbol{f}^{id} + \{\boldsymbol{\Phi}\boldsymbol{\beta} : \boldsymbol{\beta} \in \mathbb{R}_+^m, \sum_{j=1}^{m} \beta_j = 1\}$, where $\boldsymbol{f}^{id}$ is a so-called ideal point, $\boldsymbol{\Phi} \in \mathbb{R}^{m \times m}$ is a matrix with i^{th} column $\boldsymbol{z}^{Ai} - \boldsymbol{f}^{id}$. Next, the NBI sub-problem is solved for the set of reference points $\boldsymbol{\Phi}\boldsymbol{\beta}$ uniformly distributed over the CHIM, searching for the maximum distance t^* along the normal vector $\bar{\mathbf{n}}$ to the CHIM at each reference point. Here, we make use of a modified NBI subproblem suggested by Shukla (2007) to prevent convergence to a dominated boundary point of the set of feasible objective functions. The formulation of the mNBI sub-problem is as follows:

$$\begin{aligned}
\max_{\boldsymbol{x} \in X, t} \quad & t \\
\text{s.t.} \quad & \boldsymbol{\Phi}\boldsymbol{\beta} + t\bar{\boldsymbol{n}} \geq \boldsymbol{f}(\boldsymbol{x}) - \boldsymbol{f}^{id} \\
& t \in \mathbb{R}, \; \bar{\boldsymbol{n}} \in \mathbb{R}^m
\end{aligned} \quad \text{(mNBI}\beta\text{)}$$

where $\bar{\boldsymbol{n}}$ is the outer normal direction at some point on the CHIM pointing toward $\boldsymbol{f}^{id}$. Note we assume the problem is such that a constraint qualification holds.

3. Proposed Algorithm

We present a novel adaptive MOO approach, the SDNBI algorithm, for the solution of bi-objective problems. It is an improvement on the sandwich algorithm in that it is applicable to nonconvex problems, in particular to those with a disconnected Pareto front and feasible region. A new feature is the use of the mNBI sub-problem such that the mNBI parameters $(\beta, \bar{n})$ are systematically determined by the SD algorithm, in an adaptive fashion. The main aspects of the proposed methodology are explained in this section.

3.1. Inner and outer approximation

In the original SD algorithm, the outer approximation is improved at each iteration k by solving problem (WSPw) whereby a hyperplane $H(w^k, b^k)$ tangential to the Pareto front at z^k (where $b^k = z^k w^k$) is added. The inner approximation is obtained by polyhedral approximation of a current set of Pareto points Z_E. The polyhedral approximation is defined as the set of all convex combinations of points in Z_E in the space of feasible objective function values (the "objective space") and is denoted as convhull(Z_E). This approach requires a convexity assumption on the Pareto front. In the nonconvex case, the hyperplane $H(\bar{n}^k, b^k)$ generated as a solution of problem (mNBIβ) may not be tangential to z^k, leading to an erroneous lower bound. To overcome this, the generation of the inner and outer approximations is modified such that: 1) the tangential hyperplane with a normal vector w is identified as a solution of problem (mNBIβ) using a relationship arising from the Karush-Kuhn-Tucker (KKT) optimality conditions of sub-problem; and 2) a systematic decomposition of the objective space is introduced, such that the supporting hyperplanes can be used to approximate the Pareto front within each subregion.

Given an efficient solution x^*, obtained by solving an mNBI subproblem and at which $t = t^*$, there exist μ^* and ν^* such that the KKT optimality conditions for optimisation problem (mNBIβ) are satisfied and therefore:

$$\nabla_x \mathcal{L} = \mu^{*\top} \nabla_x f(x^*) + \nu^{*\top} \nabla_x \hat{h}(x^*) = 0 \tag{1}$$

$$\nabla_t \mathcal{L} = -1 + \mu^{*\top} \bar{n} = 0 \tag{2}$$

where $\mathcal{L}(x, t, \mu, \nu) = -t + \mu^\top \left(f(x) - f^{id} - \Phi\beta - t\bar{n} \right) + \nu^\top \hat{h}(x)$, $\mu \in \mathbb{R}^m$ represents the vector of the Lagrange multipliers corresponding to the augmented objective constraints $f(x) - f^{id} - \Phi\beta - t\bar{n} \leq 0$, and $\nu \in \mathbb{R}^s$ is the vector of Lagrange multipliers for the s active constraints in the set $\{g(x) \leq 0, h(x) = 0\}$, represented by the vector $\hat{h}(x) \in \mathbb{R}^s$, $q \leq s \leq p + q$.

From equation (2), it can be deduced that at least one of the augmented objective constraints must be active. This can be shown by contradiction. Let us assume that all constraints of the augmented objective constraints are inactive, i.e., $f(x) - f^{id} - \Phi\beta - t\bar{n} < 0$ and $\mu^* = 0$. Then, equation (2) is reduced to $\nabla_t \mathcal{L} = -1 \neq 0$, which is the violation of the KKT necessary conditions. Therefore, if we solve problem (mNBIβ) for any choice of parameters $(\bar{n}, \beta)$, there exists a corresponding normal vector $w \geq 0$, where the inequality is understood component-wise, that defines a tangent to the Pareto front at the nondominated solution, z, and is given by:

$$w = \frac{1}{\sum_{i=1}^m \mu_i^*} \mu^*, \ \sum_{i=1}^m w_i = 1. \tag{3}$$

3.2. Decomposition of the search space

The principle behind the decomposition strategy is to divide the objective space into sub-regions whenever there exist Pareto points that are non-interior points of the intersection of supporting hyperplanes and their half-spaces. At the initial step of the SDNBI algorithm, it is assumed that the Pareto front is convex in the objective search space C^l. The search space is then investigated whenever a new Pareto point is obtained to determine whether the assumption holds or the current space needs to be decomposed, so that valid approximations of the Pareto front can be provided, i.e., to sandwich the Pareto front. This can be done based on the rule derived from the supporting hyperplane theorem (Luenberger, 1997):

Suppose convex set C is a polyhedron defined by a finite number of half-spaces and hyperplanes $C = \{z \mid \boldsymbol{w^k}^\top \boldsymbol{z} \geq \boldsymbol{w^k}^\top \boldsymbol{z^k}, \ k = 1, \ldots, K\}$. If each point $\boldsymbol{z^k}$ is supported by the hyperplane $H(\boldsymbol{w^k}, b^k)$ where $b^k = \boldsymbol{w^k} \boldsymbol{z^k}$, then every point $\boldsymbol{z} \in C$ must satisfy $(\boldsymbol{w^k})^\top \boldsymbol{z} \geq b^k$ for all k.

If there is a Pareto point $\boldsymbol{z} \in C^l$ that violate the condition above, then the current search space C^l is decomposed into two sub-spaces C^l and C^{l+1}. The convexity or concavity of each decomposed space is postulated based on the sign of the inequalities – for example, if all Pareto points in C^{l+1} satisfy $(\boldsymbol{w^k})^\top \boldsymbol{z} \geq \boldsymbol{w^k} \boldsymbol{z^k}$, then the Pareto front in the region C^{l+1} is assumed to be convex, whereas the Pareto front in C^{l+1} is assumed to be concave if $(\boldsymbol{w^k})^\top \boldsymbol{z} \leq \boldsymbol{w^k} \boldsymbol{z^k}$.

3.3. Modification of the mNBI sub-problem

Although the use of the mNBI method makes it possible to avoid the unnecessary investigation of some boundary points that are dominated by others, the mNBI method may not be efficient when a Pareto front consists of many disconnected regions. This is because it becomes difficult to identify the next search direction where as-yet unknown nondominated points exist in the absence of a clear criterion. To address this, the following sub-problem (mNBI$\bar{n}$), which is a modification of the original mNBI sub-problem, is introduced to fathom regions where no Pareto optimal solutions exist:

$$\max_{x \in \boldsymbol{X}, t} t$$
$$\text{s.t. } \boldsymbol{\Phi\beta} + t\bar{\boldsymbol{n}} \geq \boldsymbol{f}(\boldsymbol{x}) - \boldsymbol{f^{id}} \quad \text{(mNBI}\bar{n}\text{)}$$
$$f_1(\boldsymbol{x}) \geq z_1^{k1} + \epsilon_z \text{ or } f_1(\boldsymbol{x}) \leq z_1^{k1} - \epsilon_z$$

where $\boldsymbol{z^{k1}}, \boldsymbol{z^{k2}} \in \boldsymbol{Z_E}$ are nondominated points obtained at previous iterations and the inequality $z_1^{k1} < z_1^{k2}$ holds. Given a Pareto front, whenever the solution of sub-problem (mNBIβ) for a current facet generates a previously identified solution $\boldsymbol{z^{k1}}$ or $\boldsymbol{z^{k2}}$, the facet is further explored by solving (mNBI$\bar{n}$), thereby excluding the empty part of the subspace from the search space. Note that only one constraint between $f_1(\boldsymbol{x}) \geq z_1^{k1} + \epsilon_z$ and $f_1(\boldsymbol{x}) \leq z_1^{k1} - \epsilon_z$ is imposed in (mNBI$\bar{n}$) and the choice of the constraints depends on the solution of the problem (mNBIβ) i.e., whether it converges to $\boldsymbol{z^{k1}}$ or $\boldsymbol{z^{k2}}$, respectively. If the solution of (mNBI$\bar{n}$) converges to a point that was obtained at a previous iteration, the entire facet is discarded from the search space in subsequent iterations.

4. Performance of the SDNBI algorithm

To assess the performance of our proposed algorithm, we apply it to two well-known benchmark problems, SCH2 and ZDT5 (Natarajan, 2003), and compare solution statistics with those of the SD algorithm and mNBI method. In addition, the applicability of our SDNBI to a CAMPD problem is examined for the simultaneous design of optimal working fluids and organic rankine cycle processes (Lee et al., 2020; Bowskill et al., 2020) (CS1). For a detailed description of the formulation of the test problems, the reader is referred to Natarajan (2003) and to Bowskill et al. (2020) and case study 2 (Table 1) therein.

Five criteria are chosen as quality measures for the comparison of the Pareto points produced by each algorithm: (1) the number of unique non-dominated solutions (N_{unq}); (2)

the distribution metric (DM), which captures the extent of the spread over the Pareto front approximation and the extent of the front Pareto front covered by the nondominated points; (3) the hypervolume (HV), which is the volume of the m-dimensional region in the objective space enclosed by the obtained non-dominated solutions and a reference point; (4) the average CPU time to generate a nondominated point ($t_{CPU,a}$); and (5) the total CPU time to generate all solutions ($t_{CPU,t}$).

The MOO algorithms used here are implemented in Matlab 2018a, using common sub-functions. For problems SCH2 and ZDT5, each scalarised sub-problem is solved through GAMS interfaced with the DICOPT solver, while the CAMPD problem is implemented in C++ interfaced with gPROMS ModelBuilder 7.0.7. To increase the likelihood of identifying globally optimal Pareto points, a multi-start approach is adopted for the solution of the sub-problems. The multiple starting points are generated by a Sobol' sequence (Sobol' et al., 2011) to achieve well-distributed coverage in the space of design variables x. For the SD and the mNBI methods, the stopping criterion is defined as the fixed number of iterations N_{iter} chosen as the number of iterations taken for SDNBI to reach a pre-defined error tolerance for each test problem.

5.   Results and Discussions

The performance of the SD, mNBI, and SDNBI methods for all test problems is summarised in Table 1 and Figure 1. For SCH2, the Pareto-optimal set consists of one point and one continuous region, in which a large nonconvex and a disconnected area are present. As is apparent from Table 1, the highest HV value and the lowest DM value are achieved when using SDNBI. The performance of mNBI is similar to that of SDNBI in terms of HV and DM, but fewer points are identified within the fixed number of iterations. This is mainly because some iterations using mNBI fail to identify new points in the region where Pareto points do not exist. The strong performance of SDNBI is further highlighted in test problem ZDT5, where the true Pareto front is a set of 31 integer Pareto points. The use of SDNBI guarantees the identification of the complete set of solutions for a given fixed number of iterations, while the mNBI and SD methods appear to be relatively ineffective in achieving high accuracy in HV and N_{unq}. After iterating 40 sub-problems, all 31 Pareto points are generated by SDNBI, confirming its reliability in finding a diverse and reliable Pareto approximation, i.e., the highest HV, N_{unq}, and the lowest DM. It is noticeable that all regions where Pareto points do not exist are removed from the search space after 61 iterations, which allows the search procedure within SDNBI to terminate the algorithm, even though the stopping criteria are not satisfied.

The similar trends of the performance for all algorithms are evident for the CS1 where three nonconvex and two disconnected parts are potentially involved. By analysing the results shown in Table 1 and Figure 1, we can conclude that the SDNBI outperforms the SD and mNBI methods in all comparison criteria, with the exception of the CPU time. The SDNBI method is capable of recognising the region where no additional Pareto points are placed (see the two disconnect regions near $0.8 \leq f_2 \leq 0.85$ and $0.58 \leq f_2 \leq 0.62$

Table 1: Performance metrics for problems SCH2, ZDT5 and CS1 using SD, mNBI and SDNBI. Each test problem is evaluated for a fixed number of iterations N_{iter}=27 for SCH2, 40 for ZDT5 and 61 for CS1, respectively.

	SCH2			ZDT5			CS1		
	SD	mNBI	SDNBI	SD	mNBI	SDNBI	SD	mNBI	SDNBI
N_{unq}	26	25	26	23	23	31	59	58	60
HV / 10^{-2}	53.09	62.70	62.94	89.46	89.48	89.57	91.23	91.47	91.44
DM	0.2512	0.0998	0.0910	0.1377	0.1230	0.0944	0.1130	0.0472	0.0387
$t_{CPU,a}$ / s	9.35	9.46	9.41	73.40	52.86	51.92	12.41	20.26	29.07
$t_{CPU,t}$ / s	2.43×10^2	2.35×10^2	2.44×10^2	1.69×10^3	1.22×10^3	1.61×10^3	7.21×10^2	8.21×10^2	9.04×10^2

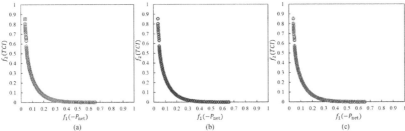

Figure 1: Pareto points in a bi-objective space generated by the (a) SD ($\times$), mNBI ($\diamond$), and SDNBI ($\triangle$) methods for CS1. Grey markers ($\circ$) indicate best-known Pareto points.

in Figure 1), making it possible to improve the Pareto approximation efficiently. The higher CPU time with the SDNBI and mNBI can be attributed to the fact that additional constraints are used in their sub-problems and so it is difficult to find feasible regions that satisfy all the constraints.

6.   Conclusions

We have proposed a novel algorithm applicable to nonconvex and discrete bi-objective problems. The algorithm is based on the combination of features from the SD algorithm and the mNBI method. It has been tested on two benchmark functions and one CAMPD application to assess its performance in approximating the Pareto front. The comparative results have highlighted the robustness of the SDNBI algorithm in terms of generating a more diverse and better-distributed set of Pareto points. Future work will involve testing the proposed approach on more case studies to derive general conclusions on its performance on MINLP problems, and the extension of the algorithm to solve optimisation problems with more than two objectives.

Acknowledgements

YSL gratefully acknowledges financial support from the British Federation of Women Graduates, and the Department of Chemical Engineering at Imperial College London for a Roger Sargent scholarship.

References

Bowskill, D.H., Tropp, U.E., Gopinath, S., Jackson, G., Galindo, A., Adjiman, C.S., 2020. Beyond a heuristic analysis: integration of process and working-fluid design for organic rankine cycles. Mol. Syst. Des. Eng. 5, 493–510. doi:10.1039/C9ME00089E.

Das, I., Dennis, J.E., 1998. Normal-boundary intersection: A new method for generating the pareto surface in nonlinear multicriteria optimization problems. SIAM J. on Optim. 8, 631–657. doi:10.1137/S1052623496307510.

Lee, Y.S., Graham, E.J., Galindo, A., Jackson, G., Adjiman, C.S., 2020. A comparative study of multi-objective optimization methodologies for molecular and process design. Comput. Chem. Eng. 136, 106802. doi:10.1016/j.compchemeng.2020.106802.

Luenberger, D.G., 1997. Optimization by vector space methods. John Wiley & Sons.

Marler, R.T., Arora, J.S., 2004. Survey of multi-objective optimization methods for engineering. Struct. Multidiscip. O 26, 369–395. doi:10.1007/s00158-003-0368-6.

Natarajan, S.K., 2003. Test Suite for Multiobjective Optimization and Results Using Normal Boundary Intersection (NBI) in Design Explorer. Utah State University.

Rennen, G., Van Dam, E.R., Den Hertog, D., 2011. Enhancement of sandwich algorithms for approximating higher-dimensional convex pareto sets. INFORMS J. Comp. 23, 493–517. doi:10.1287/ijoc.1100.0419.

Shukla, P.K., 2007. On the normal boundary intersection method for generation of efficient front, in: Procedia. Comput. Sci., Springer. pp. 310–317.

Sobol', I.M., Asotsky, D., Kreinin, A., Kucherenko, S., 2011. Construction and Comparison of High-Dimensional Sobol' Generators. Wilmott 2011, 64–79. doi:10.1002/wilm.10056.

Proceedings of the 14th International Symposium on Process Systems Engineering – PSE 2021+
June 19-23, 2022, Kyoto, Japan © 2022 Elsevier B.V. All rights reserved.
http://dx.doi.org/10.1016/B978-0-323-85159-6.50205-0

Data-driven scenario generation for two-stage stochastic programming

Georgios L. Bounitsis[a], Lazaros G. Papageorgiou[a], Vassilis M. Charitopoulos[a*]

[a]Department of Chemical Engineering, Centre for Process Systems Engineering, University College London, Torrington Place, London WC1E 7JE, UK
v.charitopoulos@ucl.ac.uk

Abstract

The efficient exploitation of large amount of data for the uncertain parameters constitutes a crucial condition for effectively handling stochastic programming problems. In this work we propose a novel data-driven mixed-integer linear programming (MILP) model for the Distribution Matching Problem (DMP). In cases of multiple uncertain parameters, sampling using copulas is conducted as preliminary step. The integration of clustering methods and DMP in the proposed model is proven to improve the computational efficiency. For the evaluation of the performance of the proposed scenario generation approaches several case studies of a two-stage stochastic programming problem are examined. Compared with state-of-the-art scenario generation (SG) approaches the proposed model is shown to achieve consistently the lowest errors regarding the expected values when compared to full-space stochastic solutions as well as manages to preserve good accuracy in the resulting probabilistic and statistical qualities of the reduced generated sets.

Keywords: Scenario Generation; Stochastic Programming; Distribution Matching; Mixed-Integer Linear Programming (MILP).

1. Motivation

The increasing volatility in modern-day process industries and the access to large amounts of historical data have led to an intensive study of optimisation problems under uncertainty (Li and Grossmann, 2021). Among the various optimisation-based approaches, these problems can be solved as two-stage or multi-stage stochastic programming problems, in which the uncertain parameters are considered though a discrete number of their possible realisations. These realisations are also referred to as scenarios. Although such stochastic programming models can be easily formulated, their ability to capture the uncertainty relies on the number of scenarios considered which in turn tends to grow exponentially with the number of parameters under study. To this end, there has been an increasing interest from the research community, aiming at either the reduction of the uncertainty set or the generation of a representative and smaller in size set of scenarios to be implemented in the problem (Römisch, 2009).

OSCAR (Li and Floudas, 2014) and SCANCODE (Medina-González et al., 2020) are two recently presented methods for scenario aggregation which employ clustering techniques and distance metrics to preserve the quality of the stochastic solution whilst minimizing the number of required scenarios. With respect to scenario generation approaches, a nonlinear programming-based moment and distribution matching method was presented by Calfa et al. (2014). In this work, we employ an initial uncertain sample and select a reduced set which matches optimally the statistical moments and the cumulative distribution functions of the marginal distributions. In case of multiple uncertain parameters, preliminary copula-based sampling is employed to account for correlations among multiple parameters. The remainder of the article is organised as follows: in Section 2 a brief literature review and problem statement are outlined while key methodological contributions are outlined in Section 3. In Section 4, we employ the proposed model and compare its performance with state-of-the-art models for scenario generation. Finally, conclusions are drawn in Section 5.

2. Literature review

Optimisation problems under uncertainty are dealt in the open literature with a wide range of mathematical techniques including stochastic programming (Sahinidis, 2004). The most common version of the risk-neutral stochastic programming is the two-stage stochastic programming, in which the target is to optimise the objective function of the first-stage costs while optimizing the expected value of the second-stage costs when uncertainty is revealed. The second stage expected value, when there are known probability distributions of the uncertain parameters, i.e., scenarios $\xi_1,\ldots,\xi_k$, with respective probabilities $p_1,\ldots,p_k$, is formulated as:

$$\mathbb{E}[F(x,\xi)] = \sum_{k=1}^{K} p_k \cdot F(x,\xi_k) \tag{1a}$$

and analogously the two-stage stochastic programming problem (TSSP) is modelled as:

$$\begin{aligned} \min_{x,y_1,\ldots,y_k} \quad & c^\top \cdot x + \sum_{k=1}^{K} p_k \cdot q_k^\top \cdot y_k \\ s.t. \quad & T_k \cdot x + W_k \cdot y_k = h_k, \quad y_k \geq 0, \quad k = 1,\ldots,K \\ & A \cdot x = b, \quad x \geq 0 \end{aligned} \tag{1b}$$

In the above formulation, every scenario $\xi_k = (q_k, T_k, W_k, h_k), k = 1,\ldots,K$, results to a two-stage decision vector y_k and by solving the two-stage problem an optimal first-stage solution $\bar{x}$ is obtained (Shapiro et al., 2014). The existence of a very large number of possible realisations could render the problem computationally intractable and motivates the use of scenario generation and/or reduction techniques. These methods aim at the creation of a smaller in size set of scenarios for the uncertain parameters, with certain values and probabilities which are representative of the original uncertainty set (Li and Grossmann, 2021).

Moment Matching Problem (MMP) constitutes a well-known scenario tree generation approach (Høyland et al., 2003). It is based on the minimisation of the errors regarding the statistical moments between the original uncertain set and the final reduced set. In general, MMPs are modelled as nonlinear programming (NLP) problems. Moreover, the parallel matching of the stochastic distribution of the uncertain parameter (DMP), by minimizing the errors regarding the cumulative density function, has been proposed and enhances the effectiveness of the approach (Calfa et al., 2014). Recently an MMP MILP model for scenario selection from an original scenario set was proposed in the literature (Kaut, 2021).

Copula based capture of the multivariate structure of data and dependence between marginal distributions constitutes another concept for the scenario generation methods (Kaut and Wallace, 2011).

3. Methodology and mathematical developments

MMP constitutes an error minimisation problem where the errors regarding the first four statistical moments, e.g. mean, variance, skewness, and kurtosis are considered. In particular, the errors between the values of the moments calculated from the data and the ones computed by the final reduced set are minimised. Finally, the errors can be quantified by various distances such as the Euclidean distance (L^2-norm), Manhattan distance (L^1-norm) or the Chebyshev distance (L$^\infty$-norm) and weights may be considered for the errors of different moments (Calfa et al., 2014). An extended version of the MMP, referred as Distribution Matching Problem (DMP), matches additionally the marginal Empirical Cumulative Distribution Function (ECDF) between the reduced and the original dataset. Calfa et al. (2014) employed a nonlinear approximation of the ECDF using simplified Generalised Logistic Function.

The proposed MILP model considers the original distributions of the uncertain parameters to generate discrete original scenarios as input for the model. Considering multidimensional data sets, copula-based sampling is implemented, generating tuples as original scenarios. Theoretically, an n-dimensional copula expresses the joint cumulative distribution function (CDF) for which the marginal distributions of each variable are uniform on the interval [0,1]. Denoting multivariate CDF as F and marginal distributions as $F_1, \ldots, F_n$, the copula C is defined as (Kaut and Wallace, 2011):

$$F(x_1, \ldots, x_n) = C(F_1(x_1), \ldots, F_n(x_n)) \tag{2}$$

The dependence between two variables can be captured by various parametric bivariate copula families, e.g. Gaussian, Archimedean and Student t. For multivariate cases, appropriate pairwise copula families along with the structure of the data set can be considered leading to a vine copula.

For each uncertain parameter $i \in I$ let us consider a set of equiprobable original scenarios $n \in N$ with values denoted as $\tilde{x}_{i,n}$ and ECDF as $ECDF_{i,n}$. In a pre-processing step k-means clustering is utilised to cluster the original set into as many clusters as the desirable size of the reduced set $c \in C$. Hence, we introduce a set $CL_{c,n}$, which maps each scenario $n \in N$ to one $c \in C$. From the original scenarios only one is selected at each prespecified cluster $c \in C$, through binary variables $y_{c,n}$. The corresponding probabilities of occurrence are denoted as $p_{c,n}$ and the cumulative probability sums up to 1. The latter are imposed by Eqs. (4)-(7). For the presented models only L^1-norm or L$^\infty$-norm are used to quantify the errors. The objective function in the following formulation contains the errors regarding the statistical moment using L^1-norm and the summation of the maximum errors of the selected scenarios regarding the ECDF.

$$\min_{y_{c,n}, p_{c,n}} \quad \sum_{i \in I, m \in M} W_m^{sm} \cdot (d_{i,m}^+ + d_{i,m}^-) + \sum_{i \in I} W_i^{prob} \cdot ed_i \tag{3}$$

s.t.

$$\sum_{n \in CL_{c,n}} y_{c,n} = 1 \qquad \forall \, c \in C \tag{4}$$

$$\sum_{c \in CL_{c,n}} y_{c,n} \leq 1 \qquad \forall n \in N \tag{5}$$

$$P^{min} \cdot y_{c,n} \leq p_{c,n} \leq P^{max} \cdot y_{c,n} \qquad \forall c \in C, n \in N \tag{6}$$

$$\sum_{c,n \in CL_{c,n}} p_{c,n} = 1 \tag{7}$$

$$\sum_{c,n \in CL_{c,n}} \tilde{x}_{i,n} \cdot p_{c,n} + d_{i,m}^+ - d_{i,m}^- = \widetilde{M}_{i,m} \qquad \forall i \in I, m = 1 \tag{8}$$

$$\sum_{c,n \in CL_{c,n}} \left(\tilde{x}_{i,n} - \widetilde{M}_{i,1}\right)^k \cdot p_{c,n} + d_{i,m}^+ - d_{i,m}^- = \widetilde{M}_{i,m} \qquad \forall i \in I, m > 1 \tag{9}$$

$$\sum_{c \in C} y_{c,n} \cdot ECDF_{i,n} - \sum_{c,n' \in CL_{c,n'} \wedge x_{i,n'} \leq x_{i,n}} p_{c',n} = \Phi_{i,n} \qquad \forall i \in I, n \in N \tag{10}$$

$$ed_i \geq \Phi_{i,n} - \left(1 - \sum_{c \in CL_{c,n}} y_{c,n}\right) \qquad \forall i \in I, n \in N \tag{11}$$

$$ed_i \geq -\Phi_{i,n} - \left(1 - \sum_{c \in CL_{c,n}} y_{c,n}\right) \qquad \forall i \in I, n \in N \tag{12}$$

$$-1 \leq \Phi_{i,n} \leq 1 \qquad \forall i \in I, n \in N \tag{13}$$

$$ed_i \geq 0 \qquad \forall i \in I \tag{14}$$

$$0 \leq p_{c,n} \leq 1 \qquad \forall c \in C, n \in N \tag{15}$$

$$y_{c,n} \in \{0,1\} \qquad \forall c \in C, n \in N \tag{16}$$

$$d_{i,m}^+, d_{i,m}^- \geq 0 \qquad \forall i \in I, m \in M \tag{17}$$

Eqs. (8)-(9) calculate the moments of the selected scenarios and the corresponding errors. Eq. (10) defines to variables $\Phi_{i,n}$ the deviations regarding the ECDF curve till the occurrence of each data point $n \in N$ of each uncertain parameter $i \in I$. However, Eqs. (11)-(12) are implemented, along with the minimization objective function Eq. (3), to define the maximum absolute errors regarding each parameter $i \in I$ to variables ed_i.

For the case of one uncertain parameter ($|I| = 1$) and sorted original data points, the computational efficiency is drastically enhanced by substituting $\Phi_{i,n}$ to $\bar{\Phi}_{i,c}$ and Eq. (10)-(13) to the following ones:

$$\sum_{n \in N} y_{c,n} \cdot ECDF_{i,n} - \sum_{n,c' \in CL_{c',n}} p_{c',n} = \bar{\Phi}_{i,c} \qquad \forall i \in I, c \in C \tag{18}$$

$$ed_i \geq \bar{\Phi}_{i,c} \qquad \forall i \in I, c \in C \tag{19}$$

$$ed_i \geq -\bar{\Phi}_{i,c} \qquad \forall i \in I, c \in C \tag{20}$$

$$\sum_{n \in CL_{c,n}} y_{c-1,n} \cdot \tilde{x}_{i,n} \leq \sum_{n \in CL_{c,n}} y_{c,n} \cdot \tilde{x}_{i,n} \qquad \forall i \in I, c > 1 \tag{21}$$

$$-1 \geq \bar{\Phi}_{i,c} \geq 1 \qquad \forall i \in I, c \in C \tag{22}$$

Weights of the errors regarding the moments are calculated as $W_{i,m}^{sm} = \bar{w}_{i,m}/|\widetilde{M}_{i,m}|$, where $\bar{w}_{i,m}$ is chosen arbitrarily equal to 1 in this report. W_i^{prob} is also considered equal to 1. The presented formulation will be denoted as DMP MILP using L^1-norm. When the model is reformulated to minimise the summation of the maximum absolute errors regarding the moments (of all $i \in I, m \in M$) and the maximum absolute ECDF error (of all $i \in I$), we refer to it as DMP MILP using L^∞-norm.

4. Case studies – Capacity Planning under uncertainty

In this section, a capacity planning problem under uncertainty is studied. The mathematical model along with the process description, data and different uncertain cases can be found in Li and Floudas (2014). Briefly, 5 products are produced by 5 raw materials using 11 candidate processes. The objective function aims at the maximisation of profit. We consider endogenous uncertainty, regarding production yields of processes. For case study 1 is considered only one uncertain parameter and the scenario set is reduced from 1,000 data points of the original uncertain distribution to 5 selected scenarios. For case studies 2 and 3 we consider 2 and 4 uncertain parameters, generating 20 scenarios by an initial set of 1,000 and 2,000 copula-based generated scenarios respectively. Regarding the computational efficiency of the SG approaches, in the first case study the presented models are solved to optimality after short execution times (<10 seconds) using GUROBI 9.1 in GAMS 30.3. As far as case studies are considered, a time limit of 1,800s and an optimality gap tolerance of 5% are set.

To evaluate the quality of the scenarios generated by the different algorithms the expected value of the two-stage stochastic program is computed using the reduced and the full-space set of scenarios. The results regarding the errors for each case study are summarised in Figure 1.

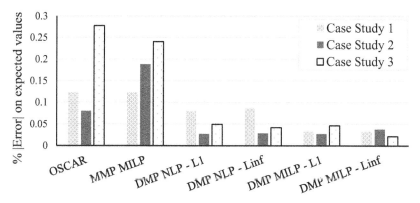

Figure 1: *Errors on expected values of the TSSP problem for each case study.*

The scenarios of the proposed DMP MILP model consistently result to the lowest errors. The second case study considers a reduction from 1000 original sets to 20 and DMP models seem to behave similarly. However, DMP MILP using L^1-norm results to the lowest error. For the third case study with four uncertain parameters DMP MILP using L^∞-norm leads to the lowest error.

The proposed approach integrating clustering and distribution matching resolves the issue of under-specificity of original MMP (Calfa et al., 2014). The combined impact prevents the assignment of a value to multiple scenarios and/or zero probabilities for scenarios regardless of the number of the prespecified scenarios/clusters. Overall, although higher total error regarding the moments may be obtained, the ECDF is matched properly and the results indicate enhanced performance of the reduced sets.

The impact of ECDF matching through this approach on the reduced set is visualised in Figure 2. For instance, in case study 2 and the uncertain parameter regarding Process "7", the reduced set of 20 final scenarios obtained by the proposed model matches the ECDF of the original marginal distribution remarkably better than the set obtained by using OSCAR. It is noted that for OSCAR the explicit ECDF marching is not considered.

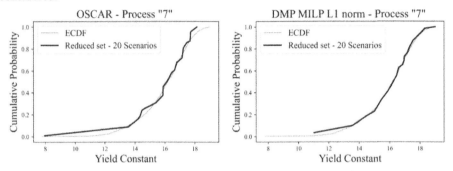

Figure 2: *ECDF matching comparison on case study 2.*

5. Conclusions and future work

The proposed MILP model is proven to be competitive to the existing scenario generation/reduction approaches in terms of errors regarding TSSP problems and statistical properties matching. The integration of copula-based simulation in the framework constitutes a crucial asset as this is not feasible for NLP formulations which also suffer from numerical and under-specificity issues. Future work within our group focuses on the use of decomposition techniques to enhance the computational performance of the proposed model.

References

B. Calfa, A. Agarwal, I. Grossmann & J. Wassick, 2014. Data-driven multi-stage scenario tree generation via statistical property and distribution matching, Comput. Chem. Eng., 68, 7–23.

K. Høyland, M. Kaut & S. Wallace, 2003. A heuristic for moment-matching scenario generation, Comput. Optim. Appl., 24(2–3), 169–185.

M. Kaut, 2021. Scenario generation by selection from historical data, Computational Manag. Sci., 18(3), 411–429

M. Kaut & S. Wallace, 2011. Shape-based scenario generation using copulas, Comput. Manag. Sci., 8(1), 181–199.

C. Li & I. Grossmann, 2021. A Review of Stochastic Programming Methods for Optimization of Process Systems Under Uncertainty, Front. Chem. Eng., 2, 34.

Z. Li & C. Floudas, 2014. Optimal scenario reduction framework based on distance of uncertainty distribution and output performance: I. Single reduction via mixed integer linear optimization, Comput. Chem. Eng., 70, 50–66.

S. Medina-González, I. Gkioulekas, V. Dua & L. G. Papageorgiou, 2020. A graph theory approach for scenario aggregation for stochastic optimisation. Comp. Chem. Eng., 137, 106810.

W. Römisch, 2009. Scenario reduction techniques in stochastic programming. In Stochastic Algorithms: Foundations and Applications, 5, 1–14.

N. Sahinidis, 2004. Optimization under uncertainty: State-of-the-art and opportunities. Comput. Chem. Eng., 28(6–7), 971-983.

A. Shapiro, D. Dentcheva & A. Ruszczyński, 2014. Lectures on stochastic programming: modeling and theory. Philadelphia, Pennsylvania: SIAM.

Proceedings of the 14th International Symposium on Process Systems Engineering – PSE 2021+
June 19-23, 2022, Kyoto, Japan © 2022 Elsevier B.V. All rights reserved.
http://dx.doi.org/10.1016/B978-0-323-85159-6.50206-2

Joint Chance Constrained Process Optimization through Neural Network Approximation

Shu-Bo Yang[a], Jesús Moreira[b], Zukui Li[a*]

[a]*Department of Chemical and Materials Engineering, University of Alberta, 9211 116 St, Edmonton T6G1H9, Canada*
[b]*Imperial Oil, 505 Quarry Park Blvd SE, Calgary, T2C5N1, Canada*
zukui@ualberta.ca

Abstract

A neural network-based approach is proposed in this work for joint chance-constrained optimization (JCCP) problems. In the proposed approach, a joint chance constraint (JCC) is first reformulated as a quantile-based inequality to reduce the complexity in approximation. Then, the quantile function (QF) in the inequality is replaced by an empirical QF through sample average approximation. The empirical QF is further approximated by a ReLU artificial neural network (ANN). Afterwards, the ReLU ANN is incorporated into the optimization model that enables the JCCP to be solved as a deterministic optimization problem. To demonstrate the proposed approach, a case study on ethylene glycol (EG) production process yield maximization is studied. The results show that the proposed approach can efficiently solve a nonlinear JCCP problem with non-conservative constraint satisfaction.

Keywords: Machine Learning and Big Data; Artificial Neural Network; Joint Chance Constrained Optimization; Stochastic Optimization; Sample Average Approximation

1. Introduction

Practical process optimization often faces uncertainties. Chance constrained optimization is a popular technique for addressing uncertainty (Wendt et al., 2002). It enforces that the optimal solution should satisfy the uncertain constraint with a certain probability level. There are two types of chance constraint: the individual chance constraint (ICC) and the joint chance constraint (JCC). The JCC is more general in engineering applications than the ICC since the JCC ensures that all constraints are satisfied simultaneously to a certain confidence level, which is more natural in many applications (You et al., 2021). However, the JCC is generally difficult to solve as it requires dealing with multidimensional distributions. Thus, joint chance-constrained optimization problems (JCCP) are generally solved through approximations. There are two main approximation methods: analytical approximation methods and sampling-based methods (Yuan et al., 2017).

We focus on sampling-based methods in this work because they can avoid overly conservative solutions occurring in analytical approximation methods (van Ackooij et al., 2014). Among all sampling-based methods, the sample average approximation (SAA) is a powerful and widely used method (Pagnoncelli et al., 2009). While adopting the SAA to address a JCCP problem, the empirical joint constraint satisfaction probability is enforced to be greater than or equal to the required value. In this work, we extend the concept of the SAA to construct the empirical quantile function (QF) in the proposed approach. The key contributions of the proposed approach are as follows: The presented approach involving the empirical QF and ReLU artificial neural network (ANN) approximations can generate a solution without over-conservatism for a JCCP. Also, the presented method can be widely applied to different problems, including those with black-box functions. Finally, the proposed approach can make a stochastic JCCP deterministically solvable.

2. Problem formulation

The general formulation of a JCCP problem is given as:

$$\min_x f(x)$$
$$\text{s.t.} \quad \Pr(g_i(x,\xi) \le 0, \ i = 1, \dots, p) \ge 1 - \varepsilon \tag{1}$$

where x represents the decision variable. $f(x)$ and $g(x,\xi)$ are the objective and constraint functions. ξ is the uncertain parameter vector. $\Pr(\cdot)$ is the probability measure. The JCCP shown above enforces that all constraints $g_{i=1,\dots,p}(x,\xi)$ are satisfied simultaneously to a certain confidence level $1 - \varepsilon$.

The above JCC can be rewritten as the following individual chance constraint form:

$$\Pr(\bar{g}(x,\xi) \le 0) \ge 1 - \varepsilon, \quad \text{with} \quad \bar{g}(x,\xi) = \max_{i=1,\dots,p} g_i(x,\xi) \tag{2}$$

which can be further reformulated as the following equivalent constraint:

$$Q^{1-\varepsilon}\big(\bar{g}(x,\xi)\big) \le 0 \tag{3}$$

where $Q^{1-\varepsilon}(\bar{g}(x,\xi))$ is the $1 - \varepsilon$ quantile of $\bar{g}(x,\xi)$. The benefit of rewriting the JCC as the quantile-based form is shown through Figure 1: $Q^{1-\varepsilon}(\bar{g}(x,\xi))$ has better convexity property than $1 - \varepsilon - \Pr(\bar{g}(x,\xi) \le 0)$. Accordingly, $Q^{1-\varepsilon}(\bar{g}(x,\xi))$ will be used for surrogate modelling in the proposed work.

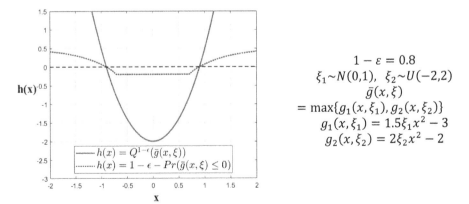

$$1 - \varepsilon = 0.8$$
$$\xi_1 \sim N(0,1), \quad \xi_2 \sim U(-2,2)$$
$$\bar{g}(x,\xi)$$
$$= \max\{g_1(x,\xi_1), g_2(x,\xi_2)\}$$
$$g_1(x,\xi_1) = 1.5\xi_1 x^2 - 3$$
$$g_2(x,\xi_2) = 2\xi_2 x^2 - 2$$

Figure 1. Comparison between $Q^{1-\varepsilon}(\bar{g}(x,\xi))$ and $1 - \varepsilon - \Pr(\bar{g}(x,\xi) \le 0)$.

The quantile $Q^{1-\varepsilon}(\bar{g}(x,\xi))$ in Eq.(3) can be approximated by the empirical QF value $\tilde{Q}^{1-\varepsilon}(\bar{g}(x,\xi))$ given as:

$$\tilde{Q}^{1-\varepsilon}\big(\bar{g}(x,\xi)\big) = \inf\Big\{\gamma \big| \tfrac{1}{N}\sum_{j=1}^{N} \mathbb{I}\big(\bar{g}(x,\xi_j)\le\gamma\big) \ge 1-\varepsilon\Big\} = \bar{g}_{[M]}(x) \tag{4}$$

where M equals to $N(1-\varepsilon)$, and N is the number of collected samples of ξ. $\mathbb{I}$ is the indicator function defined as $\mathbb{I}\big(\bar{g}(x,\xi_j)\le\gamma\big) = \begin{cases} 0, & \text{for } \bar{g}(x,\xi_j) > \gamma \\ 1, & \text{for } \bar{g}(x,\xi_j) \le \gamma \end{cases}$. $\bar{g}_{[M]}(x)$ represents the M-th smallest component of $\{\bar{g}(x,\xi_1),\dots,\bar{g}(x,\xi_N)\}$.

3. Neural network approximation-based optimization

The quantile term $\tilde{Q}^{1-\varepsilon}\big(\bar{g}(x,\xi)\big)$ in Eq.(4) can be further approximated by an ANN which is essentially a nonlinear function of x. The max operator for defining $\bar{g}(x,\xi_j)$ and the indicator function involved in Eq.(4) can be well approximated through ANN.

The ReLU ANN is one type of fully connected feed-forward neural network which is shown in Figure 2. In Figure 2, layer 0 and layer K are the input and output layers, respectively. The rest of the layers are namely hidden layers. $x_1,\dots,x_l$ and $\hat{Y}$ are the inputs and output (predicted QF value). Besides the input layer, all the neurons in each layer are fully connected with all the neurons in the previous layer. The output of one neuron in each layer (except the input layer) is computed using the following equation:

$$o_s^k = \sigma\big(\sum_{r=1}^{R} W_{rs}^k o_r^{k-1} + b_s^k\big), \quad k = 1,\dots,K \tag{5}$$

where k, r, and s are the indices of each layer, each neuron in the previous layer, and each neuron in the current layer, respectively. o, W, b, and R represent the output of the neuron, weights between the current and previous layers, the bias for each neuron in the current layer, and the number of neurons in the previous layer, respectively. σ represents the ReLU activation function given as: $\sigma(y) := \max\{0, y\}$.

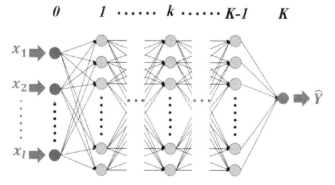

Figure 2. Schematic diagram of fully connected feed-forward neural network

The ReLU ANN for approximating the empirical QF is incorporated into the optimization model in Eq.(1) to predict the quantile value for the quantile-based inequality reformulated from the original JCC. Since the ReLU ANN model can be written as a mixed-integer linear program (MILP), the optimization model involving the ReLU ANN can be written as the formulation shown in Eq.(6).

$$\min_x f(x)$$

s.t. $\hat{Y} \le 0$

$\quad o_l^0 = x_l, \quad l = 1, \dots, L$

$$a_s^k = \sum_{r=1}^R W_{rs}^k o_r^{k-1} + b_s^k, \qquad s = 1, \dots, S, \qquad k = 1, \dots, K-1 \qquad (6)$$

$\quad 0 \le o_s^k \le H(1 - z_s^k)$

$\quad a_s^k \le o_s^k \le a_s^k + H z_s^k$

$\quad z_s^k \in \{0,1\}$

$\quad \hat{Y} = \sum_{r=1}^R W_r^K o_r^{K-1} + b^K$

In the above formulation, $\hat{Y}$ is the quantile value predicted from the embedded ReLU ANN. The embedded ReLU ANN is described by the second to the last constraints. The second and last constraints represent input and output layers, respectively. l is the index of each neuron in the input layer. L is the number of neurons in the input layer. S and R are the numbers of neurons in the current layer and in the previous layer, respectively. a_s^k is the linear combination of outputs from the previous layer. H is a big number. z_s^k is a binary variable. The third to the sixth constraints represent the hidden layer model. The fourth to sixth constraints are for the ReLU activation function. The proposed approach for solving JCCP is based on the solution of the above deterministic problem.

Notably, since $\bar{g}(x, \xi) = \max_{i=1,\dots,p} g_i(x, \xi)$ is used in the quantile-based reformulation, the proposed approach can be applied to the problem with any number of constraints in the JCC. In addition, the proposed method is applicable to different problems, including those with black-box functions.

4. Case Study

This case study is the yield maximization of the EG production process shown in Figure 3. According to Figure 3, ethylene oxide (EO) and water are fed into the CSTR to produce EG. The following reactions occur in the CSTR:

$$EO + H_2O \to EG$$
$$EG + EO \to DEG \qquad\qquad (7)$$
$$DEG + EO \to TEG$$

DEG and TEG are diethylene glycol and triethylene glycol, respectively, which are undesirable by-products. The output of the CSTR is connected to the flash separator, and the product (EG) is collected from the bottom of the flash separator. Meanwhile, 97 % of the top flash vapor stream is recycled to mix with the feed flow. The vapor-liquid equilibrium in this process is assumed as ideal phase behaviour. More details about this process can be found in (Kahrs et al., 2007). In this case study, the entire EG production process is simulated as a nonlinear black-box model using Aspen Plus.

In this problem, the objective is to maximize the EG molar flowrate ($\dot{F}_{EG}$, unit: kmol/h) in the bottom of the flash separator. The decision variables $\dot{F}_w$, V_{CSTR}, and T_f are the water feed flowrate (unit: kmol/h), the CSTR volume (unit: m^3), and the temperature in the flash separator (unit: K), respectively. The pressure inside the flash separator is fixed at 30 kPa. X_{EO} and x_{EG} are the EO conversion rate and the mole fraction of EG in the bottom flow of the flash separator, respectively. $\xi_{X_{EO}}$ and $\xi_{x_{EG}}$ are uncertain parameters following Gaussian distributions $N(0,0.03)$ and $N(0,0.015)$, respectively.

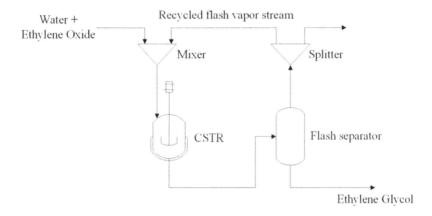

Figure 3. Flowsheet of the studied EG production process

The optimization problem of this case study is given as:

$$\max_{\dot{F}_w, V_{CSTR}, T_f} \dot{F}_{EG}$$
$$\text{s.t.} \quad \Pr\begin{pmatrix} -X_{EO} - \xi_{X_{EO}} + 0.5 \leq 0 \\ -x_{EG} - \xi_{x_{EG}} + 0.5 \leq 0 \end{pmatrix} \geq 1 - \varepsilon$$
$$700 \leq \dot{F}_w \leq 5000$$
$$221 \leq V_{CSTR} \leq 321$$
$$300 \leq T_f \leq 390$$

(8)

We first gather 2000 samples of $\dot{F}_{EG}$, X_{EO}, and x_{EG} corresponding to different sets of decision variables, from the Aspen Plus simulator. Then, we collect 1000 samples of $[\xi_{X_{EO}}, \xi_{x_{EG}}]$ from the assumed distributions. The 2000 samples of $\dot{F}_{EG}$ corresponding to different decision variables are used to train the first ReLU ANN to predict $\dot{F}_{EG}$ in the objective function. For addressing the JCC in the above optimization, based on a confidence level $1 - \varepsilon$, the 2000 samples of X_{EO} and x_{EG} are combined with 1000 samples of $[\xi_{X_{EO}}, \xi_{x_{EG}}]$ to generate 2000 quantile values based on Eq.(4). Then, we use the 2000 quantile values paired with different decision variables to train the second ReLU ANN to predict the quantile value for the quantile-based inequality reformulated from the JCC. Finally, the two mentioned ReLU ANNs are incorporated into the above optimization to form a MILP problem based on the optimization model shown in Eq.(6). The MILP problem is solved by using CPLEX in GAMS. The attained results are shown in Table 1.

Table 1. Optimization results

$1 - \varepsilon$	$\dot{F}_w$	V_{CSTR}	T_f	$\hat{F}_{EG} / \dot{F}_{EG}$	$\Pr(\bar{g} \leq 0)$
0.8	1048.887	321	365.415	427.134 / 426.261	0.8006
0.95	916.229	321	368.191	396.610 / 395.247	0.9508

[a] $\hat{F}_{EG}$ is computed by the first ReLU ANN. $\dot{F}_{EG}$ is from the Aspen Plus simulator.

[b] $\bar{g} = \max \{-X_{EO} - \xi_{X_{EO}} + 0.5, \ -x_{EG} - \xi_{x_{EG}} + 0.5\}$ in the last column.

[c] The probabilities in the last column are based on 10^6 samples of uncertain parameters.

According to Table 1, the joint chance constraint satisfaction probabilities of the optimal solutions (in the last column) are very close to the required probability targets (in the first column). Also, the $\hat{F}_{EG}$ computed from the first ReLU ANN are very close to the corresponding $\dot{F}_{EG}$ computed from the true model (Aspen Plus simulation). Therefore, by using the presented method, the JCCP in this case study can be reliably handled without over-conservatism.

5. Conclusions

A novel method involving the empirical quantile reformulation of JCC and the ReLU ANN approximation is proposed in this work to address JCCP problems. The presented method relies on the sampled data of objective and constraint function values, which can be obtained from explicit process model equations or black-box process simulators. Hence, the method can be used for different process optimization problems, such as problems with explicit model or black-box constraint functions. In the meantime, there is no restriction on the number of constraints in the JCC. The problem is finally converted to the solution of a deterministic MILP problem. Through a case study, it is shown that the developed method can efficiently solve a nonlinear joint chance-constrained process optimization problem without over-conservatism.

References

O. Kahrs, and W. Marquardt, 2007, The validity domain of hybrid models and its application in process optimization, Chemical Engineering and Processing: Process Intensification, 46(11), 1054-1066

B. K. Pagnoncelli, S. Ahmed, and A. Shapiro, 2009, Sample average approximation method for chance constrained programming: theory and applications, Journal of optimization theory and applications, 142(2), 399-416

W. van Ackooij, R. Henrion, A. Möller, and R. Zorgati, 2014, Joint chance constrained programming for hydro reservoir management, Optimization and Engineering, 15(2), 509-531

M. Wendt, P. Li, G. Wozny, 2002. Nonlinear chance-constrained process optimization under uncertainty. Industrial & engineering chemistry research, 41(15), 3621-3629.

B. You, E. Esche, J. Weigert, and J.-U. Repke, 2021, Joint Chance Constraint Approach based on Data-Driven Models for Optimization Under Uncertainty applied to the Williams-Otto Process, Computer Aided Chemical Engineering, Vol. 50, pp. 523-528, Elsevier.

Y. Yuan, Z. Li, and B. Huang, 2017, Robust optimization approximation for joint chance constrained optimization problem, Journal of Global Optimization, 67(4), 805-827

Proceedings of the 14th International Symposium on Process Systems Engineering – PSE 2021+
June 19-23, 2022, Kyoto, Japan © 2022 Elsevier B.V. All rights reserved.
http://dx.doi.org/10.1016/B978-0-323-85159-6.50207-4

Gaussian Processes for Simulation-Based Optimization and Robust Design

Alex Durkin[a], Marcos Millan-Agorio[a], Miao Guo[a,b*]

[a]*Department of Chemical Engineering, Imperial College London, London SW7 2AZ, UK*
[b]*Department of Engineering, King's College London, London WC2R 2LS, UK*
miao.guo@imperial.ac.uk

Abstract

Gaussian Processes present a versatile surrogate modeling toolbox to address simulation-based optimization and uncertainties arising from non-converged simulations. In this work we present a black-box optimization methodology framework in which Gaussian Process Regression is used to model complex underlying process performance models and Gaussian Process Classification is used to model feasibility constraints based on converged and non-converged simulations. Additionally, we present a conservativeness parameter to enable tuning of the feasible region based on the trade-off between process performance and the risk of infeasibility due to non-converged simulations.

Keywords: Gaussian Processes, Optimization, Surrogate Modeling.

Introduction

Modeling complex process systems has long been of interest in industry and the research community (Sahinidis, 2004). As a result, commercial simulation software has been developed, enabling engineers to quickly evaluate process designs without the capital costs associated with pilot studies (Cozad et al., 2014). Such simulation-based process design can be categorised into decomposition techniques (Douglas, 1988) and optimization methods (Bhosekar and Ierapetritou, 2018). The former involves sequentially designing each stage of the process using design heuristics to obtain a quick solution. Conversely, optimization methods simultaneously design stages of the process, offering guarantees of optimality at the expense of computational cost.

Simulation-based optimization is also known as black-box optimization where the simulator is treated as a black-box, embedding complex underlying functions not accessible to the user. Black-box optimization is widely used for the optimization of complex systems and generally follows either an evolutionary approach or a surrogate-based approach. The former uses heuristics to select subsequent samples in the search space until convergence, however, this approach has problems finding globally optimal solutions. In surrogate-based optimization, sampled data is used to fit a surrogate model, representative of the underlying complex model, and then rigorous optimization methods are used on the surrogate (Jones et al., 1998). However, fitting a surrogate model introduces additional uncertainty to be considered, between surrogate model predictions and the true underlying function.

Surrogate modeling can be partitioned into 2 stages: sampling and surrogate model fitting. The former aims to sample input-output information from the black-box function whilst minimising function evaluations (Sacks et al., 1989). A trade-off between homogenous coverage of the design space and non-correlated input variables has led to quasi-random sampling techniques being developed such as Latin Hypercube Sampling (LHS) (McKay et al., 1979). For the choice of surrogate model, the trade-off between model accuracy and computational tractability within an optimization problem must be considered. Whilst linear and polynomial models offer computationally tractable surrogate models, they can fail to accurately represent non-linearities in the underlying complex model. Conversely, Gaussian Process Regression (GPR) or "kriging" has gained popularity as a more robust surrogate modeling framework, albeit with reduced computational tractability within optimization problems (Caballero and Grossmann, 2008).

An additional challenge of black-box optimization is addressing the fact that not all samples within the search space are guaranteed to return a converged result when evaluated by the simulator. In response to this problem, feasibility constraints can be constructed to confine the optimization search space to a region where designs are more likely to have converged during sampling, and therefore are more likely to represent a feasible design. To build such feasibility constraints, classification machine learning models, such as support vector machines or Gaussian Process Classification (GPC), can be trained on the binary classification data from converged/non-converged simulations (Ibrahim et al., 2018).

In this work, we present a computational modeling framework harnessing GPR and GPC for simulation-based optimization and robust design against uncertainties in infeasibility due to non-converged simulations. Specifically, GPR was used to represent process performance in the optimization objective function, whilst GPC was used to represent process feasibility constraints. Additionally, we introduce a "conservativeness" parameter to enable tuning of the process robustness. The GPR and GPC models were embedded in an optimization problem to determine minimum cost solutions that are robust to the uncertainty from non-converged simulations.

This article proceeds with an overview of Gaussian Processes. We then present the methodology framework developed in this study followed by a demonstrative application. Finally, we discuss the results and make some concluding remarks on the implications of this work.

Gaussian Processes

Gaussian Processes (GPs) provide a framework for modeling complex black-box functions. By not assuming any model characteristics, GPs are not restricted to a fixed (and potentially incorrect) functional form, nor a finite set of parameters. Instead, GPs assume a prior probability distribution over an effectively infinite number of functions, where certain characteristics can be favored, and expert knowledge can be incorporated (for example favor smooth/periodic/noisy functions). The combination of the prior with some observed data yields a posterior distribution over functions, from which it is possible to extract a mean function and the variance in these functions. For the modeling of black-box functions, the GP posterior mean function can be used for predictive purposes whilst the GP posterior variance provides the uncertainty in these predictions.

The GP prior is defined via the specification of a covariance function of the GP which fixes some properties of the functions in the distribution and defines a set of hyperparameters that enable learning based on observed data. For a stochastic GP, $Z(\cdot)$, Eq.(1) shows the covariance function (**R** between two points x_i, x_j), for the squared exponential correlation function containing the tuneable parameter l_k, scaled by the tuneable process variance, σ_z^2. Specifically, l_k represents the sensitivity of the covariance function to dimension k, where a smaller value of l_k represents higher sensitivity, ensuring that even two points far away are correlated. Additionally, Eq.(1) has the property that if two points are very close, the covariance approaches the process variance, and as the distance between two points increases, the covariance approaches zero.

$$\mathbf{R}\Big(Z(x_i), Z(x_j)\Big) = \sigma_z^2 \exp\left(-\sum_{k=1}^{m} l_k \big(x_{i,k} - x_{j,k}\big)^2\right) \tag{1}$$

GPR models process input-output relationships, $y(x)$, by utilising a stochastic GP with covariance given by Eq.(1) and with expected value equal to zero, $E\big(Z(x)\big) = 0$, to model the deviations from a constant term, μ (Eq.(2)).

$$y(x) = \mu + Z(x) \tag{2}$$

Modeling the deviations from a constant term in this way, after optimizing the fit of hyperparameters (μ, σ_z^2, l_k) to observed data via Maximum Likelihood Estimation (MLE), it can be shown that the GPR posterior mean function (used for surrogate model predictions, $\hat{y}(x^{\text{new}})$) and variance (used to quantify uncertainty in predictions, $s^2(x^{\text{new}})$) are given by Eq.(3) and Eq.(4), respectively, where r is the vector of covariances between x^{new} and training data, obtained by evaluating Eq.(1) at $\mathbf{R}(x^{\text{new}}, x)$, y is the vector of observations, and $\mathbf{1}$ is a vector of ones (6).

$$\hat{y}(x^{\text{new}}) = \mu + r^T R^{-1}(y - \mathbf{1}\mu) \tag{3}$$

$$s^2(x^{\text{new}}) = \sigma_z^2(\mathbf{1} - r^T R^{-1} r) \tag{4}$$

Eq.(3) and Eq.(4) have properties such that a new sample taken at the same point as a training observation results in a prediction equal to the value of that observation and a variance equal to zero. In other words, the GPR predictive function passes through all observations with no uncertainty. For new samples further away from training observations, the prediction approaches the constant term μ, influenced only by the nearest observations, and the prediction variance approaches the process variance.

GPC predicts the probability that a new sample x^{new} is feasible. To achieve this, the GPC model is trained on classification data such that a feasible converged simulation is labelled 1, whilst an infeasible non-converged simulation has class label 0. The prediction equation for GPC can then be generalised by Eq.(5) where the term on the left is the probability that a new sample, x^{new}, has class label $t^{\text{new}} = 1$ (i.e. is feasible) given training data x, t. The term on the right of Eq.(5) is a latent function $f(\cdot)$, over which a GP prior is placed, "squashed" through the sigmoid logistic function $\sigma(\cdot)$ so that the outputs are probabilities between 0 and 1.

$$p(t^{\text{new}} = 1 \mid x^{\text{new}}, x, t) = \sigma\big(f(x^{\text{new}}, x, t)\big) \tag{5}$$

To determine the analytical form of the GPC predictive function requires the approximation of analytically intractable integrals. Eq.(6) shows the predictive form used in this work, where the Laplace approximation and probit approximation have been used, and where v is the latent predictive variance, itself a function of x^{new}, x, t and the latent posterior mode $\hat{f}$ which was obtained numerically (Rasmussen and Williams, 2006).

$$p(t^{\text{new}} = 1) = \sigma\left(r^T\left(t - \sigma(\hat{f})\right)\left(1 + \frac{\pi}{8}v\right)^{-\frac{1}{2}} \right) \tag{6}$$

Method

Figure 1 shows the methodology framework developed in this study. Black-box simulation software was used to perform computer experiments. Samples were taken from the black-box simulations by varying input process design variables, x, representing design decisions to optimize process performance. Output variables sampled were continuous process performance variables, y, and binary classification targets representing converged/non-converged simulations, t. The sampling strategy to produce these samples was "maximin" optimized LHS which ensures improved homogenous space-filling properties compared to traditional LHS (Johnson et al., 1990).

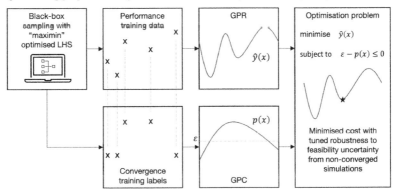

Figure 1. The methodology framework developed in this study for simulation-based optimization under uncertainty due to non-converged simulations. Computer experiments used an optimized Latin Hypercube Sampling (LHS) strategy. Gaussian Process Regression (GPR) and Gaussian Process Classification (GPC) formed process performance functions and feasibility constraints, respectively, in the resulting optimization problem.

Table 1. Optimization problem statement.

Given...	Samples	$i = 1, ..., n$
	Converged samples	$j = 1, ..., m$
	Input dimensionality	$k = 1, ..., q$
	Process cost training data for GPR	$x_{j,k}^{GPR}, y_j$
	Convergence target labels for GPC	$x_{i,k}^{GPC}, t_i$
	Fitted GPR parameters	$\mu, l_k^{GPR}, R_{j,j'}^{-1}$
	Fitted GPC parameters	$l_k^{GPC}, \hat{f}_i, P_{i,i'}^{-1}$
	Conservativeness parameter	ε
Determine...	Process design variables	x_k^{new}
	Intermediate GPC variables	α_i, v
	GPC probability of feasibility	p
To optimize...	GPR predicted process cost	$\hat{y}$

Using sampled performance data and convergence target labels from computer experiments, GPR and GPC models were fitted by MLE, respectively. Specifically, only converged samples were used to train the GPR to obtain an accurate model within the feasible region without influence from non-converged samples. In this way, the complex black-box functions could be represented functionally within a mathematical optimization formulation whilst simultaneously restricting the search space to more probable feasible designs.

The functional predictive forms of the GPR and GPC models were embedded within a Non-Linear Programming (NLP) optimization problem. The matrix algebra of the GPR and GPC models, spanning vectors over training samples and input dimensions, were expanded into summation notation to ensure compatibility with NLP solver IPOPT (Wächter and Biegler, 2006), using Pyomo (Bynum et al., 2021). The optimization problem statement can be written as shown in Table 1 whilst the generalised NLP formulation is shown by Eq.(7) to Eq.(11).

Eq.(7) represents the GPR predictive function in Eq.(3) expanded into summation notation for use as the optimization objective function. Eq.(8) is the feasibility constraint where the probability of process feasibility, predicted by GPC, must be greater than the given conservativeness parameter. Eq.(9) is the implementation of Eq.(6) for the GPC predictions, expanded into summation notation for use as an optimization constraint. Eq.(10) and Eq.(11) are constraints to calculate intermediate variables within the optimization implementation of GPC.

$$\min \quad \hat{y} = \mu + \sum_{j=1}^{m} \sum_{j'=1}^{m} R_{j,j'}^{-1}(y_{j'} - \mu) \exp\left(-\sum_{k=1}^{q} l_k^{GPR}\left(x_k^{new} - x_{j,k}^{GPR}\right)^2\right) \tag{7}$$

$$\text{s.t.} \quad \varepsilon - p \leq 0 \tag{8}$$

$$p = \sigma\left(\frac{\sum_{i=1}^{n}\left(t_i - \sigma\left(\hat{f}_i\right)\right)\alpha_i}{\left(1 + \frac{\pi}{8}v\right)^{\frac{1}{2}}}\right) \tag{9}$$

$$v = 1 - \sum_{i=1}^{n} \alpha_i \sum_{i'=1}^{n} P_{i,i'}^{-1}\alpha_{i'} \tag{10}$$

$$\alpha_i = \exp\left(-\sum_{k=1}^{q} l_k^{GPC}\left(x_k^{new} - x_{i,k}^{GPC}\right)^2\right) \tag{11}$$

Results

Figure 2 shows the results of a demonstrative application of the presented methodology framework as a proof of concept. Specifically, Figure 2A shows data points sampled using "maximin" LHS from an underlying black-box function, where converged samples are shown by squares, non-converged samples are shown by circles, and the underlying function is shown (for demonstrative purposes) by the dashed line.

Figure 2B shows the trained GPR model exhibits a good fit over the feasible region, with GPR uncertainty increasing with increasing distance from converged training samples (shown by the shaded region). Figure 2B exhibits the GPR characteristic that predictions pass exactly through training samples. Additionally, as the distance from training samples increases, the GPR model predictions regress to the fitted constant term μ.

Figure 2C shows the training labels for GPC and Figure 2D shows the resulting GPC predictions used in the optimization problem feasibility constraints. A GPC prediction greater than 0.5 predicts a feasible design, whereas a GPC output less than 0.5 predicts an infeasible design. In this way, there exists a separating hyperplane where the GPC predictions are equal to 0.5 – the region separated in this way is shown by the color of the solid line in Figure 2B. Tuning the conservativeness parameter enables tightening/relaxation of the feasible region, for example, only allowing designs with a probability of feasibility greater than 0.8 or relaxing the feasible region to include all designs with a probability of feasibility greater than 0.1.

NLP solver IPOPT was used to solve the 3 optimization problems with different conservativeness parameters. For $\varepsilon = 0.5$, the GPR objective function was minimised and the solution $\hat{y} = -1.05$ (absolute uncertainty $s^2 = \pm 0.087$, relative uncertainty ± 8.3 %) found at $x = 2.52$ with predicted probability of feasibility at the $p = 0.50$ boundary (CPU time 1.45 s). For a stricter $\varepsilon = 0.8$, the solution was a more conservative $\hat{y} = -0.37$ (absolute uncertainty $s^2 = \pm 0.012$, relative uncertainty ± 3.2 %) found at $x = 1.54$ with predicted probability of feasibility at the $p = 0.80$ boundary (CPU time 3.91 s). Finally, by relaxing the feasible region with $\varepsilon = 0.1$, the solution space included the global optimum $\hat{y} = -1.47$ (absolute uncertainty $s^2 = \pm 0.75$, relative uncertainty ± 51 %) which was found at $x = 3.74$ with predicted probability of feasibility of $p = 0.19$ (CPU time 1.69 s).

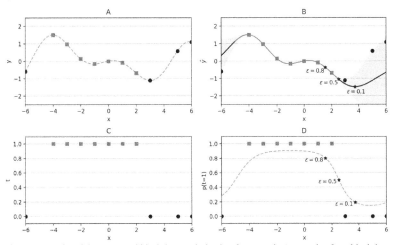

Figure 2. Results of the presented black-box optimization framework. A: samples from black-box simulations where the dashed line is the underlying function, squares show converged simulations, and circles show non-converged simulations. B: 3 optimization solutions superimposed on the GPR predictions (solid line) and uncertainty (shaded region) over the design space for 3 different conservativeness parameter values (where the solid line color shows the feasible region for conservativeness equal to 0.5). C: target values from black-box simulations. D: GPC prediction of probability of feasible designs with the 3 solutions superimposed.

Conclusions

In this work, we presented a GP-based optimization methodology framework embedding GPR for process performance and uncertainty predictions, and GPC for tuneable feasibility constraints for robust design. GPR has previously been shown to be an effective surrogate model for simulation-based optimization (Caballero and Grossmann, 2008), but we couple this, for the first time (to the best of our knowledge), with GPC feasibility constraints. We show that the probabilistic predictions from trained GPC models enable the definition and tuning of a conservativeness parameter depending on process infeasibility risk and process performance tolerances. Ongoing research includes incorporation of the GP uncertainty into a robust optimisation framework, and applications of the developed methodology to simulation-based superstructure optimization problems, formulated as mixed integer non-linear programs, for the optimization of integrative processes to recover resources from wastewater. This work contributes process systems engineering knowledge to other interesting applications of GPs to wastewater treatment research such as (Kocijan and Hvala, 2013; Oyebamiji et al., 2017).

Acknowledgements

The authors would like to acknowledge the UK Engineering and Physical Sciences Research Council (EPSRC) for providing financial support for research under the DTP "Systems modelling design for waste resource recovery" [2194316].

References

Bhosekar, A., Ierapetritou, M., 2018. Advances in surrogate based modeling, feasibility analysis, and optimization: A review. Computers & Chemical Engineering 108, 250–267.

Bynum, M.L., Hackebeil, G.A., Hart, W.E., Laird, C.D., Nicholson, B.L., Siirola, J.D., Watson, J.-P., Woodruff, D.L., 2021. Nonlinear Programming with Pyomo, in: Bynum, M.L., Hackebeil, G.A., Hart, W.E., Laird, C.D., Nicholson, B.L., Siirola, J.D., Watson, J.-P., Woodruff, D.L. (Eds.), Pyomo — Optimization Modeling in Python. Springer International Publishing, Cham, pp. 91–109.

Caballero, J.A., Grossmann, I.E., 2008. An algorithm for the use of surrogate models in modular flowsheet optimization. AIChE Journal 54, 2633–2650.

Cozad, A., Sahinidis, N.V., Miller, D.C., 2014. Learning surrogate models for simulation-based optimization. AIChE Journal 60, 2211–2227.

Douglas, J.M., 1988. Conceptual Design of Chemical Processes, Chemical engineering series. McGraw-Hill.

Ibrahim, D., Jobson, M., Li, J., Guillén-Gosálbez, G., 2018. Optimization-based design of crude oil distillation units using surrogate column models and a support vector machine. Chemical Engineering Research and Design 134, 212–225.

Johnson, M.E., Moore, L.M., Ylvisaker, D., 1990. Minimax and maximin distance designs. Journal of Statistical Planning and Inference 26, 131–148.

Jones, D.R., Schonlau, M., Welch, W.J., 1998. Efficient Global Optimization of Expensive Black-Box Functions. Journal of Global Optimization 13, 455–492.

Kocijan, J., Hvala, N., 2013. Sequencing batch-reactor control using Gaussian-process models. Bioresource Technology 137, 340–348.

McKay, M.D., Beckman, R.J., Conover, W.J., 1979. A Comparison of Three Methods for Selecting Values of Input Variables in the Analysis of Output from a Computer Code. Technometrics 21, 239–245.

Oyebamiji, O.K., Wilkinson, D.J., Jayathilake, P.G., Curtis, T.P., Rushton, S.P., Li, B., Gupta, P., 2017. Gaussian process emulation of an individual-based model simulation of microbial communities. Journal of Computational Science 22, 69–84.

Rasmussen, C.E., Williams, C.K.I., 2006. Gaussian Processes for Machine Learning. The MIT Press.

Sacks, J., Welch, W.J., Mitchell, T.J., Wynn, H.P., 1989. Design and Analysis of Computer Experiments. Statist. Sci. 4, 409–423.

Sahinidis, N.V., 2004. Optimization under uncertainty: state-of-the-art and opportunities. Computers & Chemical Engineering 28, 971–983.

Wächter, A., Biegler, L.T., 2006. On the implementation of an interior-point filter line-search algorithm for large-scale nonlinear programming. Mathematical Programming 106, 25–57.

Proceedings of the 14th International Symposium on Process Systems Engineering – PSE 2021+
June 19-23, 2022, Kyoto, Japan © 2022 Elsevier B.V. All rights reserved.
http://dx.doi.org/10.1016/B978-0-323-85159-6.50208-6

Machine Learning-Enabled Optimization of Force Fields for Hydrofluorocarbons

Bridgette J. Befort[a], Ryan S. DeFever[a], Edward J. Maginn[a], Alexander W. Dowling[a*]

[a]*Department of Chemical and Biomolecular Engineering, University of Notre Dame, Notre Dame, Indiana 46556, United States*
adowling@nd.edu

Abstract

In this work surrogate assisted optimization is utilized to calibrate predictive molecular models, called force fields, used in molecular simulations to reproduce the liquid density of a hydrofluorocarbon refrigerant molecule. A previous calibration workflow which relied on Gaussian process regression models and large Latin hypercube samples to screen force field parameter space is extended to include Bayesian optimization methods to efficiently guide the search for force field parameters. In comparison to the previous work, the Bayesian-based calibration workflow finds a parameter set which results in a lower objective function value than the original workflow after evaluating approximately 50% fewer parameter sets. It is envisioned that this updated workflow will facilitate rapid force field optimization enabling screening of vast molecular design space.

Keywords: Bayesian optimization, Gaussian process regression, Molecular simulation

1. Introduction

Molecular simulation is a powerful tool for studying the thermodynamic and dynamic properties of materials. For example, molecular simulation shows great promise for screening vast molecular design spaces which could be expensive or infeasible to probe experimentally. However, to utilize molecular simulation in this capacity requires accurate predictive molecular models, called force fields. Force fields use a functional form and parameters to describe the potential energy of a system and are utilized in classical molecular simulations to model intra- and intermolecular interactions. Developing generalized, or transferable, force fields to describe large swaths of chemical space has historically been a laborious endeavour, often taking months to years to complete. Though these off-the-shelf force fields offer accurate predictions for some systems, they inevitably lack accuracy across the extraordinary range of molecules found in the natural and synthetic world. Further optimization of force field parameters is often necessary to ensure the model has the required accuracy for the molecules and properties of interest (Wang and Kollman, 2001). Thus, force field optimization represents a bottleneck to applying molecular simulation to new systems.

Emerging computational frameworks promise to greatly accelerate the calibration of highly accurate, physics-based force fields from experimental data. Efforts to calibrate force fields encompass gradient-based, stochastic search, analytical, and *ad hoc* optimization approaches (Befort et al., 2021). Often, a barrier to efficiently calibrating force fields is the expense of calculating the objective function, which quantifies the difference between the simulation prediction and experimental value of a property of interest. The time requirement of simulations, ranging from minutes-to-hours (*e.g.,* liquid density calculations) to days-to-weeks (*e.g.,* vapor-liquid equilibrium), often makes the objective function calculation cost prohibitive. This cost only increases as more objectives, state points (*e.g.,* temperatures, pressures), and parameters are incorporated in the optimization procedure. Recently, machine learning (ML) methods have been harnessed to address this challenge by mapping microscopic coordinates to a microscopic potential. This functionality enables ML force fields (Unke et al., 2021), but their black box nature often prevents physical insights that can be gained from a physics-based functional form and parameters of a traditional force field.

ML techniques also facilitate surrogate-assisted optimization. Recently, we developed Gaussian process regression (GPR) and support vector machine models to emulate molecular simulations to calibrate force fields (Befort et al., 2021), hereafter referred to as the JCIM workflow. Our surrogate-assisted optimization JCIM workflow successfully screened millions of potential parameter sets, generated through iterative batches of space filling Latin hypercube sampling (LHS). Compared to a force field calibrated via hand-tuning, our workflow enabled the screening of $\mathcal{O}(10^3)$ times more parameter sets while requiring five times fewer simulations. However, this semi-automated workflow required generating large parameter set samples each iteration as well as user input to select which parameter sets to consider in the next iteration (*i.e.,* batch of molecular simulations).

In this work, we explore automating our ML-enabled force field calibration framework by leveraging Bayesian optimization (BO) (Wang and Dowling, 2022) to intelligently propose new parameter sets. Instead of relying on large $\mathcal{O}(10^5 - 10^6)$ LHS batches of parameter sets and user-driven decisions to screen parameter space, BO automatically balances the search for optimal parameter sets between regions which improve the molecular simulation agreement with experimental data (exploitation) and regions which, if sampled, will reduce the uncertainty of the ML model (exploration). As a demonstration case, we optimize force field parameters for a hydrofluorocarbon (HFC) refrigerant molecule, difluoromethane (HFC-32). HFCs are a motivating application because they are subject to recent mandates which require the phaseout of high global warming potential (GWP) materials. Molecular simulation can aid in the sustainable implementation of this phaseout, but this is contingent upon highly accurate force field models for HFCs. Here, we consider optimization of a force field for HFC-32 which is widely used in many refrigerants and will play a significant role in the transition to next-generation refrigerants due to its low GWP relative to other commonly used HFCs.

2. Methods

2.1. Force Field Model
This work calibrates a classical molecular mechanics force field for HFC-32 with the functional form:

$$U(\boldsymbol{r}) = \sum_{\text{bonds}} k_r (r - r_0)^2 + \sum_{\text{angles}} k_\theta (\theta - \theta_0)^2 + \sum_{\text{dihedrals}} v_n [1 + \cos(\eta\phi - \gamma)]$$
$$+ \sum_i \sum_{j>i} \frac{q_i q_j}{4\pi\epsilon_0 r_{ij}} + \sum_i \sum_{j>i} 4\varepsilon_{ij} \left[\left(\frac{\sigma_{ij}}{r_{ij}}\right)^{12} - \left(\frac{\sigma_{ij}}{r_{ij}}\right)^6 \right]$$

Here, U is the potential energy and $\boldsymbol{r}$ is the vector of position coordinates within the configuration space. The first three terms in this equation represent intramolecular

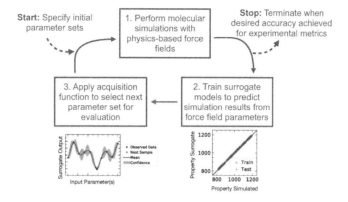

Figure 1: Overview of the proposed BO-enabled force field calibration workflow.

interactions and the fourth term represents Coulombic intermolecular interactions. The parameters in these terms are not calibrated and are reported in Befort et al. (2021). The final term of this force field functional form contains σ_{ij} and ε_{ij} which parameterize the Lennard-Jones potential describing the van der Waals repulsion-dispersion intermolecular interactions between atoms i and j. Here, we focus on rapidly generating an accurate force field, *i.e.*, improving $U(\mathbf{r})$, for HFC-32, by calibrating the like-interaction Lennard-Jones parameters, σ_{ii} and ε_{ii}, to reproduce experimental HFC-32 liquid density. These parameters are calibrated for the three atom types (C, F, and H) of HFC-32, resulting in six total fitting parameters. A description of the model, parameters, and general system setup can be found in Befort et al. (2021). System changes in this work include: first, performing simulations using the LAMMPS molecular dynamics package and, second, expanding the parameter bounds as follows (σ in Å, ε in kcal/mol): $3.0 \leq \sigma_C \leq 4.0, 2.5 \leq \sigma_F \leq 3.5, 1.7 \leq \sigma_H \leq 2.7, 0.06 \leq \varepsilon_C \leq 0.16, 0.04 \leq \varepsilon_F \leq 0.14, 0.0 \leq \varepsilon_H \leq 0.05$. While this paper only focuses on optimizing the intermolecular Lennard-Jones parameters, which are the least accurate when force fields are traditionally parameterized using quantum calculations, we emphasize the proposed BO calibration workflow is applicable to any parameters in the force field.

2.2. Bayesian Optimization Workflow

The goal of this work is to refine $U(\mathbf{r})$ by optimizing force field parameters, ζ, such that the objective function, $f(\zeta)$, is minimized. For this case study, $\zeta = (\sigma_C, \sigma_F, \sigma_H, \varepsilon_C, \varepsilon_F, \varepsilon_H)$. Figure 1 shows the BO-enabled force field calibration workflow. First, ten initial parameter sets are generated via LHS. In step one, molecular simulations compute the liquid density, $\mathbf{y}^{sim}$, of HFC-32 from $U(\mathbf{r})$ at multiple state points of interest. Depending upon the quality of $U(\mathbf{r})$, $\mathbf{y}^{sim}$ may or may not be close to the experimental values, $\mathbf{y}^{exp}$, and this discrepancy is quantified as the mean squared error objective function, $f(\zeta) = \sum_{i=1}^{n}\left(y_i^{sim}(\zeta) - y_i^{exp}\right)^2$, where n is the number of state points considered. After the initial molecular simulations, for each parameter set, $\mathbf{y}^{sim}$ and the subsequent objective function $f(\zeta)$ are computed from the simulation output. At some state points the parameters used in the simulation are so poor that the vapor, not liquid, density of HFC-32 is the simulation result, leading to a discontinuity in objective function value that may be difficult for a surrogate model to capture. To prevent this discontinuity, if a simulation outputs a density lower than the critical density of HFC-32, the simulation density is reported as the critical density. This formulation results in a sufficiently poor objective function value, indicating

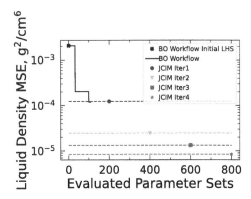

Figure 2: Comparison of the best objective function value after evaluating a certain number of parameter sets using the proposed BO workflow (black **x**, black line) versus our prior JCIM workflow (colored markers, dashed lines).

a poor parameter set, while preventing a discontinuity. In step two, a GPR model is trained to predict $f(\zeta)$ as a function of calibrated parameters ζ (Befort et al., 2021). In step three a BO acquisition function is optimized to determine the next parameter set to evaluate. Here, the expected improvement (EI) acquisition function is used to select the next optimal parameter set for simulation (Wang and Dowling, 2022). Upon applying the EI acquisition function, a new parameter set is generated which is used in new simulations, and the workflow continues iteratively until the desired simulation accuracy is reached or no improvement can be achieved in the objective function.

3. Results

We begin by comparing our automated BO workflow to our prior semi-automated JCIM workflow. Figure 2 plots the best (lowest) objective function value found after simulating 110 trial parameter sets (*i.e.,* initial ten LHS parameter sets plus one hundred EI-generated samples) in the BO workflow compared to the best objective function values found after evaluating 200, 400, 600, and 800 total parameter sets in the JCIM workflow. Figure 2 shows the improvement in objective function value for both workflows as more parameter sets are evaluated and the surrogate models are trained on more data. After 101 parameter sets are evaluated in the BO-based workflow, the objective function is 1.20×10^{-4} g^2/cm^6 while the lowest objective function for the JCIM workflow's initial 200 parameter sets, which were generated via LHS, was 1.24×10^{-4} g^2/cm^6. This indicates that the BO workflow can achieve a lower objective function value after evaluating approximately 50% fewer parameter sets, and therefore performing less simulations, than a space filling sample of parameter space. We hypothesize this is the result of the adaptive nature of BO acquisition function, which can effectively explore and exploit parameter space to more efficiently find optimal parameter sets. We expect that as more simulations are performed, the GPR models in the BO workflow will improve such that this workflow will additionally require fewer simulations to surpass the objective function values found after evaluating 400, 600, and 800 samples in the JCIM workflow.

GPR model improvement for the BO workflow is seen in Figure 3, which shows the absolute error between the GPR model prediction of the objective and the actual simulation result for each trial parameter set. The standard deviation in the GPR model prediction is plotted and shows a decreasing trend. The discrepancy between the GPR model prediction and actual simulation result also shows a decreasing, although less obvious, trend. This indicates GPR model improvement as more training data and regions of parameter space are sampled via the guidance of BO. Figure 4 compares the GPR model predictions and the actual simulation results of the objective for each evaluated parameter set, with the GPR model uncertainty plotted as error bars. This figure provides an example of how the BO-based workflow balances exploration and exploitation, showing how GPR model predictions for certain trial parameter sets result in objectives very close to simulation results (exploitation) while other predictions are significantly different than simulations and have high uncertainty, indicating exploration. Thus, instead of relying on GPR models to generate batches of new trial parameter sets in the original workflow, the BO-based workflow systematically samples parameter sets to gain information about the parameter regions which result in the lowest objective function values. We believe this approach both reduces the burden of the user by automatically selecting new parameter sets to sample and improves the efficiency of the workflow by decreasing the number of parameter set samples and subsequent simulations required to calibrate force fields.

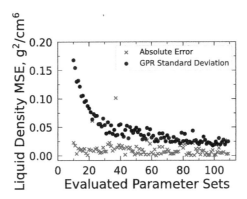

Figure 3: Absolute error between GPR model and simulation (green x) and GPR prediction uncertainty (black •) change as more parameter sets are evaluated.

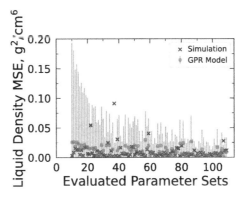

Figure 4: Comparison of GPR model prediction mean (red •) and standard deviation (red |, error bar) versus molecular simulation results (blue x) as more parameter sets are evaluated.

Further analysis is required to benchmark the BO-based calibration workflow. The BO results shown in Figure 2 were generated using the gradient based L-BFGS (scipy) optimizer to calibrate the GPR model hyperparameters for the first 80 iterations. Then, the hyperparameter optimization failed due to a Cholesky factorization error (the GP kernel became negative semi-definite) and was switched to an ADAM (BOTorch) optimizer. Reproducing this result using only the BOTorch optimizer is a work in progress; with only the BOTorch optimizer, the GPR model error remains $\mathcal{O}(10^{-2})$ whereas the JCIM workflow was $\mathcal{O}(10^{-4})$ after 200 samples. Ongoing work is investigating the differences in trained GP hyperparameters and overall BO performance using these two optimizers. Additional opportunities for further improving this framework include determining the minimum amount of data and initial parameter set samples necessary for efficient GPR model improvement, exploring various formulations for the objective function, kernel function, and the vapor-liquid density discontinuity, and evaluating the capabilities of various GPR model optimizers. We expect these analyses to improve the overall efficiency of the BO calibration workflow.

4. Conclusions

In this paper, we prototype a fully automated BO framework for force field calibration. Results show that after evaluating 101 parameter set samples with the BO workflow, the lowest mean squared error between simulation and experimental values for the liquid density of HFC-32 is 1.20 x 10^{-4} g^2/cm^6. This objective was 0.04 x 10^{-4} g^2/cm^6 smaller than the best objective found in the initial 200 parameter set LHS used in our prior JCIM workflow. This result suggests the BO techniques enhance the efficiency of force field calibration. Additionally, BO has enabled automated sampling of parameter space removing the need for user decisions for generating trial parameter sets. We expect that as more parameter sets are sampled, improvement within the GPR models will continue to show that fewer simulations will yield equally accurate force fields as the original workflow. Ultimately, this framework can be used to develop accurate force fields for multiple HFCs and other classes of molecules for which accurate molecular models are lacking.

5. Acknowledgements

We acknowledge support from the National Science Foundation grant CBET-1917474 and the University of Notre Dame. BB acknowledges support from the Richard and Peggy Notebaert Premier Fellowship.

6. References

Befort, B. J., DeFever, R. S., Tow, G. M., Dowling, A. W., & Maginn, E. J. (2021). Machine Learning Directed Optimization of Classical Molecular Modeling Force Fields, *J. Chem. Inf. Model*, 61(9), 440-4414.

Unke, O. T., Chmiela, S., Sauceda, H. E., Gastegger, M., Poltavsky, I., Schütt, K. T., Tkatchenko, A., & Müller, K. R. (2021). Machine learning force fields. *Chemical Reviews*.

Wang, J., & Kollman, P. A. (2001). Automatic parameterization of force field by systematic search and genetic algorithms. *J. Comp. Chem.*, 22(12), 1219-1228.

Wang, K., & Dowling, A. W. (2022). Bayesian optimization for chemical products and functional materials. *Current Opinion in Chemical Engineering*, 36, 100728.

Proceedings of the 14th International Symposium on Process Systems Engineering – PSE 2021+
June 19-23, 2022, Kyoto, Japan © 2022 Elsevier B.V. All rights reserved.
http://dx.doi.org/10.1016/B978-0-323-85159-6.50209-8

Design of an Event-Driven Rescheduling Algorithm via Surrogate-based Optimization

Teemu J. Ikonen[a,*], Keijo Heljanko[b,c], Iiro Harjunkoski[a,d]

[a]Aalto University, Department of Chemical and Metallurgical Engineering, PO Box 16100, 00076 Aalto, Finland
[b]University of Helsinki, Department of Computer Science, PO Box 68, 00014 University of Helsinki, Finland
[c]Helsinki Institute for Information Technology (HIIT), Helsinki, Finland
[d]Hitachi Energy Research, Kallstadter Strasse 1, 68309 Mannheim, Germany
teemu.ikonen@aalto.fi

Abstract

In event-driven rescheduling, new re-optimization procedures are triggered when obtaining new information that indicates the current schedule to be outdated. Critical design aspects of such an algorithm are the definition of the trigger event and the allocated computing time for a new rescheduling procedure. We treat both of these design aspects as continuous control parameters. Nevertheless, finding the best-suited control parameter combination for a given operating environment may be computationally expensive, as it requires simulating the process with many candidate combinations. We use surrogate-based optimization to reduce the computing cost of optimizing the control parameters. We demonstrate the method on real-time rebalancing of a bike sharing system and investigate the sensitivity of the optimized parameters to changes in the operating environment.

Keywords: optimization, event-driven rescheduling, surrogate modelling, logistics, bike sharing rebalancing.

1. Introduction

Online process scheduling is real-time decision-making of operational decision, such as the set of tasks to be executed, their timing and resource allocation. As processes are inherently stochastic, reaction or anticipation is required to deviations (e.g., in batch durations and material yields), disturbances and new orders. Gupta et al. (2016) review the literature of online scheduling and propose a framework for the classification of the online scheduling design aspects. One of the design aspects is the *re-computation trigger*, which is also referred to as the *when-to-schedule decision* (Sabuncuoglu and Kizilisik, 2003). Commonly used methods to trigger a re-computation procedure are *periodic* and *event-driven* (also *event-triggered*) *rescheduling*, and their hybrids.

In this work, our focus is on event-driven rescheduling. In the literature, Touretzky et al. (2017) propose a framework where process level deviations and disturbances trigger re-computing procedures at the scheduling level. Katragjini et al. (2013) investigate heuristic schedule repair algorithms on flow shop scheduling problems. New rescheduling procedures are triggered if new events (e.g., a machine disruption, a new order, or a deviation in a task processing time) affect the current schedule. Gupta et al. (2016) demonstrate a case where a rescheduling procedure is needed even if a trigger event is not present. Pattison et al. (2017) propose a closed-loop production rescheduling framework combining the two categories of re-optimization triggers. Periodic rescheduling is conducted when receiving updates of price and demand forecasts, whereas event-driven rescheduling is conducted in the case of a market or process disturbance.

The design of an event-driven rescheduling algorithm requires a definition of *an event* that triggers a re-optimization procedure. One approach is to define a quantitative metric for the importance of the event, such that when this metric exceeds a given threshold a re-optimization is triggered. Typically, event-driven rescheduling involves also other continuous control parameters, such as the allocated computing time and the used prediction horizon length. The evaluation of the closed-loop performance of just one control parameter combination requires simulation of the process and repeatedly performed optimization procedures. Thus, optimization of these control parameters may require a long computing time, as many candidate combinations need to be evaluated.

In our earlier work, we propose surrogate-based optimization to be used to reduce the computational cost of optimizing (continuous) control parameters of a periodic rescheduling algorithm (Ikonen et al., 2021). In this paper, we extend the work to the design of an event-driven rescheduling algorithm. We investigate three continuous control parameters, including the threshold of event importance and the allocated computing time. Further, we investigate how sensitive the optimized parameters are to small changes in the operating environment.

2. Bike sharing rebalancing

Urban bike sharing systems are expanding in cities around the world. The users of the system can pickup a bike for a short-term use from (typically fixed location) stations and return them to a station in the same system after cycling. As the pickup and return rates at different stations are asymmetric, the operators of the system need to rebalance the distribution of bikes by, e.g., trucks.

We investigate event-driven rescheduling on the dynamic bike sharing rebalancing problem (BRP), in which the rebalancing actions are performed during the day when the system is in use. We have chosen the application because in it new information of the state of the system is obtained frequently and it (like typical online production scheduling) involves solving mixed-integer programming (MIP) problems within a limited time. Last but not least, real process data of the bike sharing systems is publicly available.

We use the framework by Schuijbroek et al. (2017) to optimize the rebalancing actions. The framework consists of 1) a prediction model for the bike levels at different stations, 2) a MIP model to decompose the routing problem into smaller problems, each of which includes only one vehicle, and 3) an MIP model for optimization of the rebalancing actions of a vehicle. In this work, we formulate the dynamic BRP for only a single vehicle. Thus, we use the probabilistic prediction model and the MIP model for rebalancing operations from the framework by Schuijbroek et al. (2017).

The prediction model for the bike inventory at station $i \in S$ is based on the $M_t/M_t/1/K$ queuing system, where the arrivals of new 'customers' (here: bikes) and their service are both non-stationary Markovian processes. Both events are assumed to be exponentially distributed with time-dependent rates, which are determined based on historical data. One machine is serving the 'customers' and there is a total of K waiting spaces (here: the capacity C_i of station i). The transient probabilities for the bike levels can be solved by the Kolmogorov forward equations and the fourth order Runge-Kutta method. Figure 1 shows the predictions of the bike levels at a station, located in a residential area, in the Helsinki bike sharing system in the morning and afternoon of August 5, 2020. The predictions are based on the data recorded in June 2020. The white path shows the actual realization of the bike level on August 5, 2020.

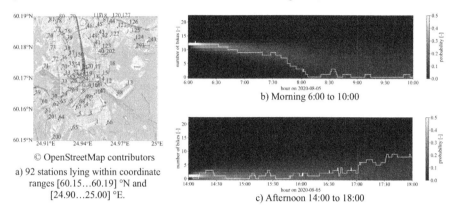

© OpenStreetMap contributors

a) 92 stations lying within coordinate ranges [60.15…60.19] °N and [24.90…25.00] °E.

b) Morning 6:00 to 10:00

c) Afternoon 14:00 to 18:00

Figure 1: The selected stations from the Helsinki bike sharing system, Finland, (Subfigure **a**) and four-hour probabilistic predictions (**b** and **c**) made at 6:00 and 14:00 on August 5, 2020 at the Toinen Linja bike sharing station (number 149 in Subfigure **a**) (Helsinki Region Transport, 2016) (Kainu, 2017). The white paths show the actual bike levels.

The MIP model for the rebalancing actions minimizes the rebalancing time to bring the system to a state where all stations fulfil a given *service level requirement* (SLR) β for both pickup and return demand during a predefined prediction horizon T. The service level is the fraction of satisfied pickup/return demand. It can be determined based on the probabilistic prediction for the station levels. For detailed descriptions of the prediction and MIP model, the reader may consult the papers by Schuijbroek et al. (2017) and Ikonen et al. (2021).

We trigger a new rebalancing procedure when the service level of a station, having no scheduled visit, drops below a certain threshold β_{trig} (abbreviated as SL trigger). This value, as well as the SLR β and the allocated computing time t_c for solving the MIP model, are the continuous control parameters of our event-driven rescheduling algorithm. The objective is to minimize the total time the stations in the system, S, are either empty of full, $\Sigma_{i \in S} t_i^{\text{ef}}$, where t_i^{ef} is the time station i is empty/full. The next section introduces surrogate-based optimization, which we use to optimize the control parameters.

3. Surrogate-based optimization

Surrogate-based optimization is a sample efficient search method, suitable for black box type objective functions that are expensive to evaluate. Figure 2 shows a generic illustration of surrogate-based optimization. First, after identifying important decision variables, the initial sampling plan is generated using a design of experiment method. Second, each candidate solution is evaluated and used to construct a surrogate of the

objective function in the search space. Third, an
iterative process is started where new candidate
solutions (also referred to as *infill points*) are
identified based on an infill criterion and evaluated.
The obtained data is used to update the surrogate.
The iterative process is continued until a predefined
termination criterion. We refer the reader to the
paper by Forrester and Keane (2009) for a review of
surrogate-based optimization and to that by McBride
and Sundmacher (2019) for review of surrogate
modelling in chemical process engineering.

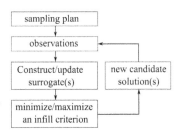

Figure 2: An illustration of
surrogate-based optimization.

In this work, we use the efficient global optimization (EGO) algorithm by Jones et al.
(1998). We generate the initial sampling plan with n_0 points using Latin hypercube
sampling. We then identify the first n_{ei} infill points by maximizing the expected
improvement and the following $n_{\hat{y}}$ points by seeking the point where the predicted
value from the surrogate is the smallest. We use the implementation of the EGO method
by Bouhlel et al. (2019).

4. Results

We evaluate the proposed method on optimization problems formulated based on real
process data recorded in Helsinki bike sharing system (Helsinki Regional Transport,
2016, Kainu, 2017). We consider a subset of the stations (92), the coordinates of which
lay within [60.15...60.19] °N and [24.90...25.00] °E (see Figure 1a), the rebalancing of
which is to be conducted by one vehicle. The predictions of station levels are based on
data recorded in June 2020. When optimizing the control parameters, we evaluate each
control parameter combination on 9 to 10 weekdays in August-September 2020. The
objective function value is the average of the obtained results. Each day, the rebalancing
is conducted from 6:00 to 15:00. We evaluate the objective $\Sigma_{i \in S} t_i^{\mathrm{ef}}$ from 6:00 to 22:00.

In order to investigate also the sensitivity of the results, we consider three different time
windows (TW1: August 3 - 14 (data from August 11 is missing), TW2: August 17 - 28,
TW3: August 31 - September 11). Weekends are excluded. TW2 is comparable to the
case studied by periodic rescheduling in Section 4.1 of Ikonen et al. (2021). We use the
prediction horizon of $T = 1.738$ h, which was the optimized value with the periodic
rescheduling algorithm. Further details of the test case are given in Ikonen et al. (2021).

The search space is defined by the following bounds: SL trigger $\beta_{\mathrm{trig}} \in [0.2 \dots 0.9]$,
SLR $\beta \in [0.2 \dots 0.9]$, computing time $t_c \in [0.05 \dots 3.0]$ h. We allocate a total of 32
evaluations for each optimization procedure by the EGO method ($n_0 = 15$, $n_{\hat{y}} = 15$,
$n_{\hat{y}} = 2$). We use full factorial sampling as a reference method, for which we allocate 64
evaluations (a $4 \times 4 \times 4$ grid). The evaluations were performed on a high-performance
computing facility, such that each run was allocated one thread of an Intel Xeon E5
2680/2690 v3 node with 4 GB of memory. We solve the MIP models using Gurobi
9.1.2.

Figure 3 visualizes the obtained results by the EGO method and full factorial sampling
for TW2. Table 1 shows the numerical results for all three time windows. On the
studied time windows, EGO method yields 1.2 to 5% smaller objective function values
than full factorial sampling. In the optimized parameter combinations, obtained by the

EGO method, the SLR β has the smallest variation (all values are within 1.3% from each other). The optimized SL trigger β_{trig} and allocated computing time t_c have more variation depending on the time window. Figure 4 shows the realized and planned route of the vehicle at the first two time points it receives operations updates on August 17, 2020 (TW2). The used parameters are those obtained by the EGO method.

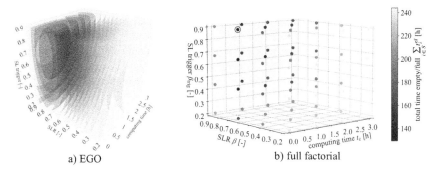

a) EGO   b) full factorial

Figure 3: Optimization results by the EGO method and the full factorial sampling for TW2. Subfigure (**a**) shows isosurfaces obtained from a surrogate that is trained with all observed data. In Subfigure (**b**), the best parameter combination is circled.

Table 1: The optimized control parameters (i.e., service level trigger β_{trig}, service level requirement β, computing time t_c) for the three time windows by EGO the method and full factorial sampling.

time window	days	method	evals.	objective $\Sigma_{i \in s} t_i^{\text{ef}}$ [h]	β_{trig} [-]	β [-]	t_c [h]
TW1	9	EGO	32	120.62	0.701	0.730	0.050
		full factorial	64	125.54	0.667	0.667	0.050
TW2	10	EGO	32	127.75	0.722	0.732	0.420
		full factorial	64	129.33	0.900	0.667	0.050
TW3	10	EGO	32	95.53	0.810	0.739	0.370
		full factorial	64	100.63	0.667	0.667	0.050

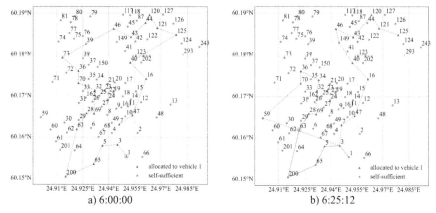

a) 6:00:00   b) 6:25:12

Figure 4: Realized (solid line) and planned route (dashed line) of the vehicle when obtaining the first two operations updates on August 17, 2020.

5. Conclusions

In this work, we investigated surrogate-based optimization of three parameters of an event-driven rescheduling algorithm, using the EGO method. On the three tested time windows, the EGO method yielded 1.2 to 5% smaller objective function values than full factorial sampling, when allocated 50% fewer function evaluations. The optimized service level requirement β has only small variation between the tested time windows, whereas the other two optimized parameters have larger variation.

Acknowledgement: Financial support from the Academy of Finland is gratefully acknowledged (project RELOOP, decision number 330388). The calculations presented in this work were performed using computer resources within the Aalto University, School of Science, "Science-IT" project.

References

M. A. Bouhlel, J. T. Hwang, N. Bartoli, R. Lafage, J. Morlier, & J. R. Martins, 2019, A Python surrogate modeling framework with derivatives, *Advances in Engineering Software*, 135, 102662.

A. I. Forrester, & A. J. Keane, 2009, Recent advances in surrogate-based optimization. *Progress in aerospace sciences*, 45(1-3), 50-79.

D. Gupta, C. T. Maravelias, and J. M. Wassick, 2016, From rescheduling to online scheduling, *Chemical Engineering Research and Design*, 116:83–97.

Helsinki Region Transport, 2016, City bike stations' Origin-Destination (OD) and location data [accessed on November 3, 2020], https://www.avoindata.fi/data/en_GB/organization/helsingin-seudun-liikenne.

T. J. Ikonen, K. Heljanko, I. Harjunkoski, 2021, Surrogate-based optimization of a periodic rescheduling algorithm, *AIChE Journal* (submitted).

D. R. Jones, M. Schonlau, and W. J. Welch, 1998, Efficient global optimization of expensive black-box functions, *Journal of Global Optimization*, 13(4):455–492.

M. Kainu, 2017, City bikes of Helsinki: Open data of bike levels at stations during seasons 2017, 2018, 2019, 2020 ja 2021 (translated from Finnish) [accessed on February 22, 2021], https://data.markuskainu.fi/opendata/kaupunkipyorat/.

K. Katragjini, E. Vallada, and R. Ruiz, 2013, Flow shop rescheduling under different types of disruption, *International Journal of Production Research*, 51(3):780–797.

K. McBride and K. Sundmacher, 2019, Overview of surrogate modeling in chemical process engineering, *Chemie Ingenieur Technik*, 91(3):228–239.

R. C. Pattison, C. R. Touretzky, I. Harjunkoski, and M. Baldea, 2017, Moving horizon closed-loop production scheduling using dynamic process models, *AIChE Journal*, 63(2):639–651.

I. Sabuncuoglu and O. B. Kizilisik, 2003, Reactive scheduling in a dynamic and stochastic FMS environment, *International Journal of Production Research*, 41(17):4211–4231.

J. Schuijbroek, R. C. Hampshire, and W.-J. Van Hoeve, 2017, Inventory rebalancing and vehicle routing in bike sharing systems, *European Journal of Operational Research*, 257(3):992–1004.

C. R. Touretzky, I. Harjunkoski, and M. Baldea, 2017, Dynamic models and fault diagnosis-based triggers for closed-loop scheduling, *AIChE Journal*, 63(6):1959–1973.

Proceedings of the 14th International Symposium on Process Systems Engineering – PSE 2021+
June 19-23, 2022, Kyoto, Japan © 2022 Elsevier B.V. All rights reserved.
http://dx.doi.org/10.1016/B978-0-323-85159-6.50210-4

A two-stage network optimization for sustainable treated wastewater planning

Fatima-zahra Lahlou[a], Sarah Namany[a], Hamish Mackey[a], Tareq Al-Ansari[a,b]

[a]Divison of Sustainable Development, College of Science and Engineering, Hamad Bin Khalifa University, Qatar Foundation, Doha, Qatar
[b]Divison of Engineering Management and Decision Sciences, College of Science and Engineering, Hamad Bin Khalifa University, Qatar Foundation, Doha, Qatar
*talansari@hbku.edu.qa

Abstract

The current global availability of water resources is able to sustain human activities, however, its uneven distribution causes scarcities in some regions of the world, leading to the hindrance of industrial and agricultural operations. In addition to that, water undergoes multiple volatilities and dynamics owing to its dependence on precipitations and weather conditions which are now accentuated due to climate change. To overcome water shortage, water scarce countries have deployed tremendous efforts in enhancing their water sectors by developing novel technologies substituting the renewable water base. Wastewater reuse represents a sustainable opportunity to alleviate water scarcity in arid regions by providing additional reserves. Nevertheless, public perception is the major obstacle to implement such practices due to social constraints. This study presents a two-stage methodology to evaluate the socio-economic and environmental aspects of reusing treated wastewater (TW) generated from different municipal wastewater treatment plants in an arid climate country. The first step consists of assessing the social acceptance of TW use in different applications to preselect the highly socially welcomed ones. Selected uses are then assessed economically and environmentally using a multi-objective network optimization model that aims to reduce the cost associated with the treatment process and the transportation of TW, and to minimize the engendered environmental burden. The TW allocation is constrained by the social acceptance, the capacity of treatment and production along with the quality of the TW. Firefighting, athletic fields irrigation and street cleaning were the uses that obtained the highest social acceptance amongst the studied sample. As for the environmental and economic aspects, the network involving a high contribution of treated municipal wastewater represents the optimum plan.

Keywords: Treated wastewater, social acceptance, multi-objective network optimization, sustainability.

1. Introduction

1.1 Background

Water security is the ability to maintain a continuous access to sufficient and safe water resources to preserve ecosystems and humans' wellbeing for a guaranteed social development and economic prosperity. While water is the backbone of all the vital industrial and economic activities and processes such as agriculture and power generation, it represents a threatened commodity due to several factors. In fact, the ever-increasing population, along with its associated growing demand for water resources, induce tremendous pressure on the water base leading to scarcities in many regions, particularly the arid ones. Climate change is also another issue that further intensifies water scarcity leading to water insecurity. It is, indeed, the direct cause of volatile rainfall patterns, droughts, floods, and many sudden environmental events that reduce the replenishment of renewable water sources. As a response to the multiple risks governing water security, alternative water sources have been introduced to ensure the satisfaction of the current and future water demands. Desalination is one of the exhaustively deployed technologies to provide water in water-scarce regions. For instance, the Golf Cooperation Council Countries (GCC) which suffers from very limited water reserves, are principally adopting desalination to cover most of their water needs. Although this technique is efficient in alleviating water insecurity, it represents an energy intensive option that engenders significant environmental impact. As part of the efforts to shift to more sustainable water provision technologies, wastewater reuse represents a promising substitute to reduce the environmental and economic costs of desalination methods. In fact, producing water from a treatment facility can cost nine times less that providing it from a thermal desalination plant. However, social perception is still a hinder hampering the deployment of this technology in all domains, counting agriculture and drinking, and the usage is only restricted to activities not including direct human consumption or involvement such as landscaping and firefighting.

1.2 Literature review

The investigation of the potential of utilising TW as an alternate water source was significantly investigated in literature. Studies have addressed the topic from different perspectives representing the three sustainability pillars, counting economic, social and environmental aspects (Lahlou et al., 2021). Considering the economic viewpoint, works have mainly shed the light on the feasibility analysis and the economic benefits of wastewater use in different domains. In this regard, Lahlou et al. (2020a; 2020b), with a focus on agricultural activities, have examined the potential of utilising TW for irrigation purposes such that the nutritional intake of the crops and their water requirement are both satisfied simultaneously. Minhas et al. (2015) have also proven the efficiency of using TW in minimising fertilisers in agriculture through supplying sufficient amounts of Nitrogen and Phosphorus(Minhas et al., 2015). Wang et al. (2020) suggested two-stage model based on a genetic algorithm that optimises the efficiency of a system integrating wastewater reuse and power generation. Adopting an environmental perspective, Canaj et al. (2021) conducted a Life Cycle Analysis (LCA) to assess the environmental viability of the adoption of TW for irrigation purposes. Similarly, Almanaseer et al. (2020) investigated the impact of the wastewater treatment and reuse on water basins by quantifying the microbial biological of the surrounding environment of the plant. As for the social aspect, the focus of TW studies was mainly to assess the social perception and acceptance of adopting TW in certain applications. For instance, Lahlou et al. (2021) examined through a survey analysis, the social perception on TW usage generated from oil and gas industries, in addition to the impact of newly-identified factors on the reuse acceptance. All these studies have looked at the TW utilisation from a single perspective or considering the combination of two sustainability pillars, however, in order to holistically assess the sustainability performance of wastewater reuse, there is a need to aggregate the three aspects in one model. In this paper, a two-stage approach is adopted to determine the optimal allocation of wastewater from different sources into diverse sectors considering economic and environmental constraints and relying on the social perception.

2. Methodology

2.1 Problem Formulation

The two-stage methodology consists first of conducting a survey to assess the acceptance level of reusing treated sewage effluent generated from municipal WWTPs. The results from the social study can then feed into the second stage of the methodology which is based on a multi-objective optimization model. The first objective of the model is represented by equation 1. It aims at reducing the cost associated with the transportation of the TW from the different sources to the different sinks which were identified during the initial stage. The second objective is the minimization of the global warming potential which is engendered by moving the water. If one of the applications requires N fertilization, the amount of carbon footprint offset using the TW for fertigation is taken into consideration in the carbon footprint calculation. The second objective is formulated in equation 2. Finally, the last objective, equation 3, is to maximize the total nitrogen uptake by the sinks that require this resource in order to reduce the material and environmental costs associated with the energy intensive commercial fertilizers.

$$Cost = \sum_{i=1}^{I}\sum_{j=1}^{J} x_{ij}\, d_{ij}\partial \tag{1}$$

$$CF = \sum_{i=1}^{I}\sum_{j=1}^{J} x_{ij}d_{ij}\zeta E - \sum_{i=1}^{I}\sum_{z=1}^{Z} x_{ij}n_i\, N_\zeta \tag{2}$$

$$N_T = \sum_{i=1}^{I}\sum_{z=1}^{Z} x_{ij}n_{ij} \tag{3}$$

Where:

- x_{ij} is the decision variable such that i and j are the indices for the source and the sink, respectively;
- R_j is the total water requirement for sink j [m^3];
- I and J represent the total number of sources and sinks, respectively;
- d_{ij} represents the distance from course i to sink j [km];
- ∂ is the average price to transport 1 m^3 of water across 1 km using a pipeline [USD.m^{-3}km^{-1}];
- E is the energy required to transport 1 m^3 of water across 1 km using a pipeline [kWh.m^{-3}km^{-1}];
- ζ represents the carbon footprint associated with producing 1kWh of energy [CO$_2$-eq.kWh^{-1}];
- n_i represents the N concentration in source N [kg/m3];
- N_ζ represents the carbon footprint associated with the production packaging and transportation of 1kg of N fertilizer [CO$_{2\text{-eq}}$.kg$_N$];
- z represents the indices of the sinks which require N fertilization.

Subject to the following set of constraints:

$$\sum_{j}^{J} x_{ij}R_j \leq \xi_i\,, \;\; \forall i \in (1,I)$$

$$\sum_{j}^{J} x_{ij} = 1\,, \;\; \forall i \in (1,I)$$

Where ξ_i is the total capacity of the source i.

2.2 Case study

The State of Qatar is one of the most water scarce countries in the world, thereafter, effort is required to develop water resources management while respecting the triple bottom line of sustainable development. In the context of Qatar, developing such water planning framework involving the reuse of alternative water resources as a function of social acceptance represents an opportunity for water stress alleviation at reduced environmental and economic costs.

The public acceptance for TW reuse was assessed using a survey which initial purpose was to investigate newly identified factors, mainly maternal altruism, and their association with the public acceptance of reusing treated industrial wastewater and bio-solids generated from oil and gas industries (F.Z. Lahlou et al., 2021). The findings of part of the survey which focused on the willingness to use TW from municipal WWTPs will feed into this paper. In this study, Doha and Um-Salal municipalities are chosen which are two of the most populated ones in the State of Qatar. There are three different WWTP in the chosen municipalities. While two of them perform tertiary treatment with N and P removal, the third WWTP performs tertiary treatment without N and P removal. Hence, the N concentration is higher in the latter.

Table 1: Water requirements of different wastewater applications (sinks) and their distances from WWTPs (sources). [1]Price, 2019; [2]Bauer et al., 2020; [3]Clark Tanks, n.d.; [4]Shublaq and Sleiti, 2020

Sinks	Water Requirements	Distances from		
		Doha North WWTP	Lusail WWTP	Doha south WWTP
	$(m^3.year^{-1})$	(km)		
Athletic fields irrigation	1,664[1]			
Al Tamama Stadium		43.2	27.9	4.5
Ras Abu Abud Stadium		45.3	28.8	19.3
Street Cleaning	927,465[2]			
Ministry of Municipality and Environment		37.9	16.9	22.5
Firefighting	290,400[3]			
Fire Station		36.3	16.9	23.2
District Cooling	8,486,200[4]			
Plant P1		36.3	18.7	25.9
Plant P2		40.2	18.4	21.4
Plant P3		36.5	20.4	19.7
Plant Pearl		37.4	15.6	33.3

3   Results

The survey was answered by 1040 respondents which socio-demographic characteristics are significantly representative of the population of the state of Qatar in terms of gender and age group. The applications which scored the highest public acceptance for TW are athletic fields irrigation, street cleaning, firefighting, and district cooling as at least 70% declared to be willing to use TMW for these applications.

Water requirements of the different sinks considered and their distances from the three various sources of WWTP are listed in Table 1. The sinks that require the highest amount of water are the district cooling plants of which each uses over 8 million m^3 of water per year.

The results of the developed multi-objective optimization model are illustrated in Figure 1. The optimum solution comes at low economic and environmental cost as opposed to the current scenario which involves the use of energy intensive desalinated water in some of the applications. The optimum solution allocates TMW to the eight different sinks for a yearly cost of 71 thousand USD. The associated carbon footprint emissions is equivalent to less than 3700 t-CO_{2-eq}.$year^{-1}$. This optimum solution also allocates almost 10% of the nitrogen fertilization requirements of the stadium (Taylor et al., n.d.). In order to achieve these results, only two WWTP's water resources are required which are Doha South and

Doha North. As a matter of fact, the produced water of Lusail WWTP is not required as the two other plants provide sufficient water resources at lower economic and environmental costs. Figure 2 illustrates the distribution of water from the different sources to the different sinks. Most of the water comes from Doha South due to its location which happens to be closer to all the sinks considered in this study. For the case of Doha North, it is the major contributor for District cooling plant P2 and Al-Tammama Stadium.

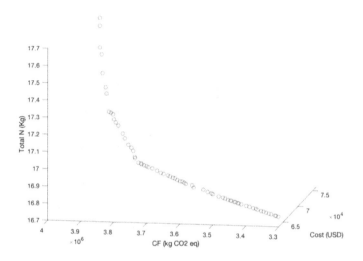

Figure 1: Three-dimensional pareto front water allocation model.

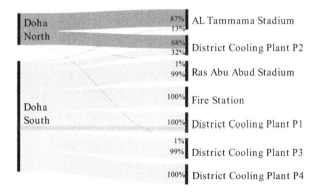

Figure 2: Summary of resource allocation to the different sinks.

4   Conclusions

In the light of the ever-increasing socio-economic and environmental stressors that threaten the availability of the renewable water base and considering the environmental burden associated with some alternative energy-intensive sources such as desalination, there is an imminent need to consider other sustainable options that can meet the demand while reducing the emissions. In this paper, the usage of TW as an alternate water supplier is investigated using a two-stage method. First, the acceptance of utilising TW in different domains was assessed by means of a survey analysis. Afterwards, a multi-objective optimisation model was conducted to optimally allocate water between different accepted water sources and multiple application sinks counting firefighting, district cooling, street cleaning and stadiums' irrigation. The optimal solution generated exhibits relatively reduced economic and environmental costs which do not exceed 71 thousand USD and 3700 $t\text{-}CO_{2\text{-}eq}.year^{-1}$ while supplying the stadiums with over 10% of their nitrogen requirements.

5   References

N. Almanaseer, M. Hindiyeh, R. Al-assaf, 2020, Hydrological and environmental impact of wastewater treatment and reuse on Zarqa river basin in Jordan, Environ., MDPI, 7.

S. Bauer, H.J. Linke, M. Wagner, 2020, Optimizing water-reuse and increasing water-saving potentials by linking treated industrial and municipal wastewater for a sustainable urban development, Water Sci. Technol., 81, 1927–1940,

K. Canaj, A. Mehmeti, D. Morrone, P. Toma, M. Todorović, 2021, Life cycle-based evaluation of environmental impacts and external costs of treated wastewater for irrigation: A case study in southern Italy, J. Clean. Prod., 293, 126142,

C Tanks, n.d. Water Storage Requirements for Fire-Fighting Services [WWW Document].

F. Lahlou, H. R. Mackey, T. Al-Ansari, 2021, Wastewater reuse for livestock feed irrigation as a sustainable practice: A socio-environmental-economic review, J. Clean. Prod., 294, 126331,

F. Lahlou, H. R. Mackey, G. McKay, T. Al-Ansari, 2021, Reuse of treated industrial wastewater and bio-solids from oil and gas industries: Exploring new factors of public acceptance, Water Resour. Ind., 26, 100159,

F. Lahlou, H.R. Mackey, G. McKay, U. Onwusogh, T. Al-Ansari, 2020a, Water planning framework for alfalfa fields using treated wastewater fertigation in Qatar: An energy-water-food nexus approach, Comput. Chem. Eng. 141, 106999

F. Lahlou, S. Namany, H.R. Mackey, T. Al-Ansari, 2020b, Treated Industrial Wastewater as a Water and Nutrients Source for Tomatoes Cultivation: an Optimisation Approach, Computer Aided Chemical Engineering, 48, 1819–1824

P .S. Minhas, Khajanchi-Lal, R.K. Yadav, S.K. Dubey, R.K. Chaturvedi, 2015, Long term impact of waste water irrigation and nutrient rates: I, Performance, sustainability and produce quality of peri urban cropping systems. Agric. Water Manag,

M. Price, 2019, Irrigation Fundamentals, Water Well J

M. Shublaq, A.K. Sleiti, 2020, Experimental analysis of water evaporation losses in cooling towers using filters, Appl. Therm. Eng. 175, 115418,

G.R. Taylor, R.H. White, S. Abernathy, D. Smith, n.d., Athletic fields and water conservation.

Y. Wang, J. Li, S. Wang, J. Yang, C. Qi, H. Guo, X. Liu, H. Zhang, 2020. Operational optimization of wastewater reuse integrated energy system. Energy 200.

Proceedings of the 14th International Symposium on Process Systems Engineering – PSE 2021+
June 19-23, 2022, Kyoto, Japan © 2022 Elsevier B.V. All rights reserved.
http://dx.doi.org/10.1016/B978-0-323-85159-6.50211-6

Surrogate Modeling for Superstructure Optimization with Generalized Disjunctive Programming

H. A. Pedrozo[a,b]; S. B. Rodriguez Reartes[a,b]; A. R. Vecchietti[c],

M. S. Diaz[a,b,*], I. E. Grossmann[d]

[a]*Planta Piloto de Ingeniería Química (PLAPIQUI CONICET-UNS), Camino La Carrindanga km. 7, Bahía Blanca, Argentina*
[b]*Departamento de Ingeniería Química, Universidad Nacional del Sur (UNS), Bahía Blanca, Argentina*
[c]*Institute of Design and Development (INGAR CONICET-UTN), Avellaneda 3657, Santa Fe, Argentina*
[d]*Department of Chemical Engineering, Carnegie Mellon University, 5000 Forbes Avenue, Pittsburgh, PA 15213, USA*
sdiaz@plapiqui.edu.ar

Abstract

In this work, we propose an iterative framework to solve superstructure design problems, which includes surrogate models, with a custom implementation of the Logic-based Outer- Approximation algorithm (L-bOA). We build surrogate models (SM) using the machine learning software ALAMO exploiting its capability for selecting low-complexity basis functions to accurately fit sample data. To improve and validate the SM, we apply the Error Maximization Sampling (EMS) strategy in the exploration step. In this step, we formulate mathematical problems that are solved through Derivative Free Optimization (DFO) techniques. The following step applies the L-bOA algorithm to solve the GDP synthesis problem. As several NLP subproblems are solved to determine the optimal solution in L-bOA in the exploitation step, the corresponding optimal points are added to the SM training set. In case that an NLP subproblem turns out to be infeasible, we solve the Euclidean Distance Minimization (EDM) problem to find the closest feasible point to the former infeasible point. In this way, the entire information from NLP subproblems is exploited. As original model output variables are required, we solve EDM problems using DFO strategies. The proposed methodology is applied to a methanol synthesis problem, which shows robustness and efficiency to determine the correct optimal scheme and errors less than 0.2% in operating variables.

Keywords: superstructure optimization; surrogate models; disjunctive programming; derivative free optimization

1. Introduction

Advances in computers and mathematical modeling have enabled the detailed representation of process systems, and thus, the development of fundamental tools for decision making in process design. This scenario also presents new challenges. In mathematical programing, the standard method to formulate a problem is to declare all process unit equations to perform the optimization. However, when formulating highly accurate models, some constraints or even the objective analytic function may not be available if they are evaluated through simulators or special programs. These functions that are not analytically available, are referred to as black-box models. When a mathematical problem includes both, explicit and black-box equations, it is referred to as hybrid or grey box model. A common approach to address this kind of problems includes building surrogate models (SMs) to replace the black-box models. SMs are simplified functions that can estimate output data from a set of input variables, requiring small CPU times.

When working with surrogate models, there is a trade-off between exploration and exploitation steps. Exploration strategies improve the global performance of the SM in the entire feasible region to reduce the probability of excluding the global optimum. On the other hand, exploitation-based methods refine the SM in regions where optima could be potentially found.

The interest of the Process Systems Engineering (PSE) community in developing efficient methods to address the formulation and solution of black/grey box problems has increased significantly in recent years (Bhosekar and Ierapetritou, 2018). Kim and Boukouvala (2020) developed a surrogate-based optimization procedure to solve mixed-integer nonlinear problems focused on avoiding the binary variable relaxation. Pedrozo et al. (2021a) proposed an iterative framework to address hybrid problems, replacing highly nonlinear equations for SM in order to reduce problem complexity. Thus, it was assumed that the analytic function was available for the exploration and exploitation steps.

In this work, we include Derivative Free Optimization (DFO) techniques (Zhao et al., 2021) in the exploration and exploitation steps to avoid using the analytic functions. Numerical results show that the strategy is efficient and accurate to address the synthesis problems and the generation and refinement of SMs.

2. Methodology

The proposed optimization framework is outlined in Fig. 1. Initially, lower and upper bounds are set for the input variables of each SM. The Latin Hypercube Sampling (LHS) technique is employed in MATLAB to generate sampling data. Output variables corresponding to each sampling point are obtained by performing simulations of the true or original model. When working with hybrid problems, a filtering step is required to discard infeasible sample points. Then, an initial SM is built in the machine learning software ALAMO (Wilson and Sahinidis, 2017) considering simple algebraic regression functions (SARFs).

Since the accuracy of this initial SM may not be good enough in all sampling points, we evaluate the corresponding relative errors, and we add Gaussians Radial Basis Functions (GRBFs) to represent those points whose errors are greater than a tolerance. In this way, we build the first SM based on both, SARFs and GRBFs, and then, we carry out the first exploration step. The Error Maximization Sampling (EMS) (Wilson and Sahinidis, 2017) strategy is applied in the exploration step. This method consists of maximizing the relative error of the SM in the feasible region. In this work, this optimization is performed through the DFO solver (Powell, 2009), which makes use of black-box simulation models. As a result, low-accuracy points of the domain are identified, and then interpolated by means of GRBF to improve the SM performance in that region, until the relative error is less than a tolerance or a maximum number of EMS problems is solved.

In the following step, we solve the hybrid model-based Generalized Disjunctive Programming (GDP) problem in GAMS. A custom implementation of the Logic-based Outer-Approximation (L-bOA) algorithm is employed (Pedrozo et al., 2021b, Pedrozo et al., 2020). We exploit the information of the L-bOA subproblems to refine the SM in the exploitation step. The feasible NLP subproblem solutions are compared to the rigorous black-box simulations to assess the SMs accuracy in that region. As some NLP subproblems or black-box simulations might be infeasible due to the performance of the SMs, we formulate an optimization problem to determine the feasible sampling point that minimizes the Euclidean distance to the NLP subproblem solution, and this point is then added to the training set. This optimization problem is also solved using DFO solvers (Powell, 2009).

The iterative algorithm, which is shown in Fig. 1, stops when the specified convergence criterion is met. Otherwise, the exploration step is carried out again (the number of major iterations of the algorithm is equal to the times the GDP problem is solved).

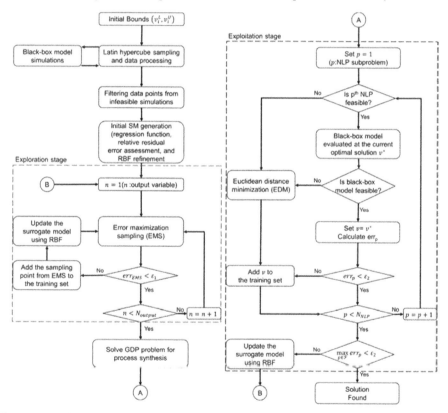

Figure 1: Iterative optimization framework

2.1. Software resources

The solution procedure is automated using MATLAB as a core for data transferring (see Fig. 2). In this way, ΛLAMO is run from MATLAB to generate the corresponding initial SMs. These functions and their derivatives are transferred to GAMS to formulate the hybrid GDP problem for process synthesis, and to solve it with the custom implementation of the L-bOA algorithm. To improve the SMs, we solve DFO problems for black-box models in the exploration and exploitation steps. In these cases, we employ the algorithms developed by Powell (2009), through the package provided by Ragonneau and Zhang (2021). Since these algorithms do not explicitly handle constraints, the Bound Optimization BY Quadratic Approximation (BOBYQA) algorithm is used.

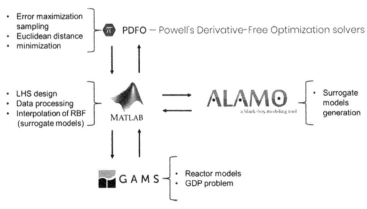

Figure 2: Software integration

3. Case Study

The methanol synthesis problem (Chen and Grossmann, 2019) is used as case study to test the proposed iterative algorithm. Figure 3 shows the process superstructure, where discrete decisions are represented using dashed lines for both, equipment and streams. The objective function is profit maximization.

In order to illustrate the algorithm, reactor models (units 9 and 10) are replaced by surrogate models to calculate conversion in each reactor. In this way, a hybrid formulation, which includes first principles and two SMs, is obtained.

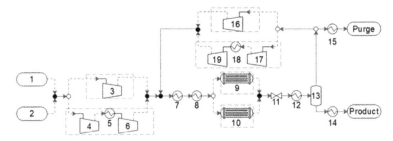

Figure 3: Superstructure for methanol synthesis (Chen and Grossmann, 2019)

4. Results

In order to show the robustness of the method and to consider the random component of the sampling technique, the problem is solved using ten different initial sampling data sets. In addition, we test 100 and 1,000 initial sampling points to assess the impact of the initial SM in the algorithm performance.

We observe that the iterative algorithm of Fig. 1 determines the optimal solution of the problem in each run (1,840 M$/y), and the error in the objective value is less than 0.2 % even in the worst case. Moreover, we observe that for the runs with 100 initial sampling points, the algorithm generally requires two major iterations (in 7 runs of 10, Fig.4) to satisfy the convergence criterion. Thus, these SMs are refined only one time in the neighbourhood of the optimal solution during the exploitation step to make them accurate enough. However, in the worst case, four major iterations are required to meet the convergence criterion. On the other hand, considering large initial sampling data (1,000 points), the proposed method generally converges in one iteration (in 5 runs of 10, Fig.4).

Accordingly, the initial SM after exploration step has enough accuracy, so no data points are included in the exploitation step. In the worst cases, four iterations are also required. This analysis indicates that we cannot guarantee the quality of the initial SM. Even working with a large initial sampling data set, SM refinement during the exploration and exploitation steps can be required to achieve the desired accuracy of the generated SMs. Regarding the algorithm performance, Fig. 5 shows the corresponding CPU time distributions. On average, 11.9 and 2.5 minutes are the total CPU time for 100 and 1,000 initial sampling points, respectively. The exploration step is the most time consuming, followed by the exploitation step, while CPU times associated with the initial fit and the GDP problem solution are negligible. These results are related to the use of DFO strategies in the refinement steps. Solving either an optimization problem for the exploration or exploitation step with DFO methods, requires 40 s approximately. Thus, the quality of initial SMs strongly influences the method's performance. When the algorithm is run with a large initial sampling data set (1000 points), the SMs require less refinement, and consequently, fewer problems must be solved using DFO strategies, as compared to the case of using 100 initial sampling points. These results are in agreement with those from Wilson and Sahinidis (2017).

When comparing this strategy with the case of using NLP solvers (CONOPT) for the exploration and exploitation steps (Pedrozo et al. 2021a), there is a significant increase in CPU time, i.e., 15 s vs. 2.5 min for 1,000 initial sampling points on average.

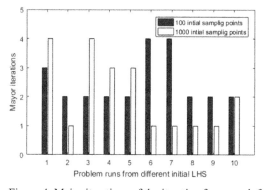

Figure 4: Major iterations of the iterative framework from different initial LHS sets

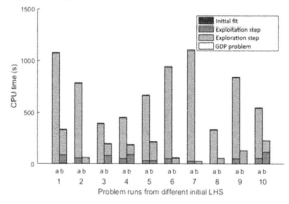

Figure 5: CPU time distribution. a) 100 initial sampling points. b) 1000 initial data sampling points. CPU times corresponding to initial fit and GDP problem solution are less than six seconds, so they are not easily distinguishable in the figure

5. Conclusions

In this work, we propose an algorithm for SMs generation and refinement using DFO strategies in the exploration and exploitation steps for the synthesis of process flowsheets using Generalized Disjunctive Programming with surrogate models. The algorithm has been tested with a methanol synthesis case study. The optimization tool has been proven to be robust and effective in generating solutions with relative errors lower than 0.2 % for the objective function in the worst cases, and obtaining the same optimal flowsheet as the rigorous model. The CPU time can be reduced by using a larger initial sampling point set. This strategy paves the way to efficiently refine SMs by the use of black-box models and DFO solvers.

References

Bhosekar, A., & Ierapetritou, M. (2018). Advances in surrogate based modeling, feasibility analysis, and optimization: A review. Comp. & Chem. Eng., 108, 250-267.

Chen, Q., & Grossmann, I. (2019). Modern modeling paradigms using generalized disjunctive programming. Processes, 7(11), 839.

Kim, S. H., & Boukouvala, F. (2020). Surrogate-based optimization for mixed-integer nonlinear problems. Comp. & Chem. Eng., 140, 106847.

M. J. D. Powell, The BOBYQA algorithm for bound constrained optimization without derivatives, Technical Report DAMTP 2009/NA06, Department of Applied Mathematics and Theoretical Physics, Cambridge University, Cambridge, UK, 2009

Pedrozo, H. A., Reartes, S. R., Bernal, D. E., Vecchietti, A. R., Díaz, M. S., & Grossmann, I. E. (2021a). Hybrid model generation for superstructure optimization with Generalized Disjunctive Programming. Comp. & Chem. Eng., 154, 107473.

Pedrozo, H. A., Reartes, S. R., Vecchietti, A. R., Díaz, M. S., & Grossmann, I. E. (2021b). Optimal design of ethylene and propylene coproduction plants with generalized disjunctive programming and state equipment network models. Comp. & Chem. Eng., 149, 107295.

Pedrozo, H. A., Rodriguez Reartes, S., Diaz, M. S., Vecchietti, A. R., Grossmann, I. E. (2020), Coproduction of ethylene and propylene based on ethane and propane feedstocks, Computer Aided Chemical Engineering, 48, 907-912. https://doi.org/10.1016/B978-0-12-823377-1.50152-X

T. M. Ragonneau and Z. Zhang, PDFO: Cross-Platform Interfaces for Powell's Derivative-Free Optimization Solvers (Version 1.1), available at https://www.pdfo.net

Wilson, Zachary T., and Nikolaos V. Sahinidis. "The ALAMO approach to machine learning." Comp. & Chem. Eng., 106 (2017): 785-795.

Zhao, F., Grossmann, I. E., García-Muñoz, S., & Stamatis, S. D. (2021). Flexibility index of black-box models with parameter uncertainty through derivative-free optimization. AIChE Journal, 67(5), e17189.

Proceedings of the 14th International Symposium on Process Systems Engineering – PSE 2021+
June 19-23, 2022, Kyoto, Japan © 2022 Elsevier B.V. All rights reserved.
http://dx.doi.org/10.1016/B978-0-323-85159-6.50212-8

Educational computer-aided tools towards Industry 4.0: recommendations and BioVL

Carina L. Gargalo[a], Simoneta Caño[a], Fiammetta Caccavale[a], Krist V. Gernaey[a], Ulrich Krühne[a*]

[a]*Process and Systems Engineering Centre (PROSYS), Department of Chemical and Biochemical Engineering, Technical University of Denmark, Søltofts Plads, Building 228 A, 2800 Kgs. Lyngby, Denmark*
ulkr@kt.dtu.dk

Abstract

Industry 4.0 is no longer a distant concept but an ongoing paradigm shift. Thus, it seems essential to prepare future engineers by fine-tuning our current educational approach. For example, advanced modelling, programming, and data analysis are now becoming fundamental skills. Therefore, it is essential to integrate these elements/subjects in the graduate and undergraduate curriculums. For a dynamic and active experience, educational computer-aided tools could be an excellent platform to teach fundamental engineering concepts and other essential tools for digitalization.

In this work, we propose the customization of the current curriculum and introduce those prerequisites for Industry 4.0's realization through an on-line and open-source educational computer-aided platform/simulator (BioVL). Hence, BioVL is built upon: (i) the identification of learning requirements; (ii) a learning design; and, (iii) a motivation strategy that includes gaming elements and an agile microlearning approach. BioVL (available at www.biovl.com) is in its prototype stage and under continuous development and refinement. Some of the ongoing and future steps include implementing AI-powered adaptive learning so that the students can receive immediate feedback and prevent error propagation.

To conclude, we encourage building on the pillars of a successful transition towards a digitalized industry by upgrading the curriculum and integrating on-line educational computer-aided tools to prepare future engineers to be fluent in data analysis and process modelling.

Keywords: biomanufacturing, digital models, digital platform, BioVL, education

1. Introduction

Industry 4.0, also frequently referred to as the Industrial Internet of Things or smart manufacturing, is no longer a distant concept but an ongoing paradigm shift. Among other processing industries, the biomanufacturing/biochemical industry now has the opportunity to adopt the technologies supporting smart manufacturing and intelligent automation. This leads increasingly to the introduction of digital solutions that focus on data communication/transfer, process modelling, and AI to predict and optimize the behavior of the process at all life cycle stages in real-time (Gargalo et al., 2021).

Henceforth, for this to be a reality, there is a high demand for qualified engineers. Today's engineers need to be ready for such developments, which poses a challenge since the typical engineering undergraduate and graduate curriculum is not yet ready. There is a need to fine-tune the current educational approach in order to prepare engineers for a digitalized industry (Cameron et al., 2019; Narayanan et al., 2020). However, existing studies in the PSE field do not present neither propose a comprehensive perspective on how and what needs to change regarding education. Thus, we must answer a critical question: what do (bio)chemical engineers need to learn to contribute positively to making Industry 4.0 a reality?

Industry 4.0 entails implementing the concept of digital twins, which is, in a perfect world, a flawless digital replica of the physical process (Figure 1). It is a cyber-physical loop system where the different units in a manufacturing process interact with one another, share information, simulate outcomes that strengthen decision-making, and thus make adaptive decisions without, or with minimal, human intervention Presently in its prototype stage, BioVL (www.biovl.com, Figure 2) has been built to support blended learning. The main intention of this software platform is to provide more modelling and programming exercises to graduate and undergraduate students in the chemical and biochemical engineering study line. It focuses on explaining, solving, and enabling the modification of conditions and parameters in mechanistic models for bioprocesses-focused education (Deloitte, 2021; Gargalo et al., 2021; Narayanan et al., 2020; Udugama et al., 2021). Some of its enabling tools and methods are big data, data sharing, the Internet of Things, artificial intelligence (AI), and the development of process models, among many others. All the tools mentioned above share a common element: the demand for a computer platform/approach. Hence, we are convinced that educational computer-aided tools have the potential to become the preferred platform to teach, through an active experience, not only engineering fundamental concepts but also the essential tools for digitalization such as data analysis and basic and advanced modelling. For example, in a smart factory, engineers must now know how to combine process knowledge with the benefits brought by advanced data analysis (i.e., big data analytics). Big data analytics allows examining large data sets to uncover hidden patterns and trends and quickly identify a faulty batch or any other process faults in order to make informed decisions.

Although the available methods and tools for data analysis and other digitalization enablers are numerous and highly complex, they are not different among fields (e.g., mechanical engineering, business). However, process models are system-specific and highly depend on conditions and process boundaries. Therefore, the teaching of basic and advanced modelling should be rigorous and requires the selection and proper implementation of process models. This entails that, firstly, the students must understand the system and its requirements, as well as the adequate modelling strategy (e.g., first principles, hybrid model, surrogate model, etc.). Thus, when the appropriate model is chosen (depending on the complexity level required), it can be derived and described through a set of mathematical expressions to be further applied for process control and optimization, among other tasks. Therefore, for future engineers to be an active part of the Industry 4.0 movement and implementation, it is essential that there is a detailed understanding of process modelling and more complex computer-aided methods. In this study, we recommend and propose that the students acquire practical experience throughout their curriculum in order to be able to: (i) observe and recognize trends and patterns in the data; (ii) propose a model; (iii) implement it; (iv) test it; and finally, (v) use the model (e.g., for optimization purposes). Consequently, an educational computer-aided platform can be used which embeds these steps and provides a structural and theoretical frame for learning the needed methods and tools (e.g., big data, AI, etc.). Thus, the authors have developed *BioVL* (**Bio**process **V**irtual **L**aboratory), an educational platform whose goal is to tackle these challenges (Figure 1) and train the users in applied modelling and programming (Caño De Las Heras et al., 2019). *BioVL*, presently in its prototype stage, is an open-source online simulator that aims to explain, solve, and modify bioprocess models and support the users in creating their own models. Features, as well as software design and targets, are discussed at length in the following sections. We believe this is a valuable tool to face the knowledge needs and challenges for the transition and continuous operation of smart biomanufacturing facilities.

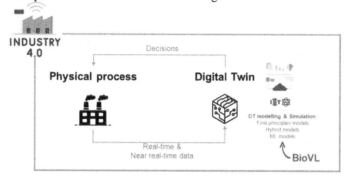

Figure 1: Industry 4.0 and the simplified relationship between the physical process and its Digital Twin. Orange: Knowledge gap in the (bio)chemical engineering curriculum (modelling and programming). Blue: BioVL contribution. Graphic illustration used elements from www.flaticon.com.

2. Methodology

As previously stated, educational platforms must become active enablers of the ongoing digital transformation (Caño De Las Heras et al., 2021b; Gargalo et al., 2021; Narayanan et al., 2020). To develop such a platform, as detailed in (Caño de las Heras et al., 2021), there are three main steps: identification of learning requirements, formulation and implementation of the learning design, and validation. The educational platform developed in this work is based on the mentioned steps, as described in the following sub-sections.

2.1. Identification of Learning requirements
Previous studies by the authors (Caño De Las Heras et al., 2021b, 2021c), as well as others (Balamuralithara & Woods, 2009; Dyrberg et al., 2017; Feisel & Rosa, 2005), have collected and quantified the students' perception on building on essential skills (e.g., programming) and on the use of simulators in their education. The study by (Caño De Las Heras et al., 2021b, 2021c) has revealed that, according to the students' opinion, the programming content in the curriculum is not sufficient to cover the industry's future needs. Furthermore, (Caño De Las Heras et al., 2021b) also reported that Python is the preferred language for modelling and optimization subjects. Further, based on the students' and teachers' perceptions, other topics are lacking, such as the use of collaborative learning; the students miss the social elements of traditional education (Caño de Las Heras et al., 2020) and/or wish for a more dynamic and iterative simulator for open-ended exploration/investigation.

The mentioned learning needs are used as the foundation for the learning design definition.

2.2. Learning Design formulation
A learning design is developed to overcome the mentioned pedagogical needs. It is built upon the (i) learning goals, (ii) background describing how the learning will occur, (iii)

learning content, theory and methods used, (iv) evaluation method, and (v) learning prerequisites (Caño de las Heras et al., 2021; Caño De Las Heras et al., 2021b; Hiim, H and Hippe, 1997). This didactic framework was first proposed (Hiim, H and Hippe, 1997) and later expanded (Weitze, 2016). Besides, the learning goals include the higher levels of the Bloom taxonomy associated with meta-cognitive knowledge (Caño De Las Heras et al., 2021b; Krathwohl, 2002).

The learning design is embedded in our educational computer-aided platform (BioVL). A central objective of BioVL is to teach applied modelling and programming in Python to graduate and undergraduate (bio)chemical students/engineers and potentially technicians. Hence, BioVL has several features such as multimedia resources, questionnaires, and activities described in detail in the Results and Discussion section.

2.3. Learning Design verification

Learning design is mostly based on "if…, then…" rules (Berggren et al., 2005) and commonly requires verification that it is valuable for the students. Therefore, many validation strategies have been previously proposed. However, in this work, we decided to intrinsically involve the students during different steps of the process. This strategy, known as co-participatory design, integrates the students as co-designers for content and platform development. It has also been proven that students can develop a sense of ownership and empowerment, while misunderstandings, confusions, and false impressions are minimized (Yamauchi, 2012).

3. Results & discussion: BioVL

Presently in its prototype stage, BioVL (www.biovl.com, Figure 2) has been built to support blended learning. The main intention of this software platform is to provide more modelling and programming exercises to graduate and undergraduate students in the chemical and biochemical engineering study line. It focuses on explaining, solving, and enabling the modification of conditions and parameters in mechanistic models for bioprocesses-focused education (Caño De Las Heras et al., 2021b). BioVL includes the following features: (a) collaborative learning through a chatbot; (b) information about bioprocess model formulation; (c) a simulator where realistic operational problems might occur requiring the student to propose a solution (Caño De Las Heras et al., 2019, 2021b); (d) a library of mechanistic models in the form of a functional database (Caño De Las Heras et al., 2021a); and, (e) a set of coding tasks in Python specifically related to bioprocess problems. Furthermore, to make the software engaging and easy to use, it employs gamification elements and agile microlearning (learning content is broken down into smaller segments that can be achived in minutes). In addition, students are active agents in the design of the content and layout of the software through co-participatory design. Due to the highlighted collaboration with students and teachers to make the best possible software, BioVL is far from finished. Future steps for BioVL's continuous improvement include introducing and teaching the students (i) more advanced modelling strategies by including optimization exercises; (ii) to develop a suitable control strategy for the system; and (iii) data analysis and its practical aspects by, for instance, introducing small experiments for the development of hybrid models. Furthermore, we are in the first stages of implementing AI-powered adaptive learning so that the students can receive immediate feedback and prevent error propagation.

Figure 2: BioVL welcome screen. More at www.biovl.com.

4. Conclusions & Future perspectives

Educational computer-aided tools should be the preferred platform to teach, through an active experience, not only engineering fundamental concepts but also the essential tools for digitalization such as data analysis and advanced modeling. Engineers need to combine their process knowledge with the benefits of advanced data analysis to actively and dynamically contribute to the ongoing digitalization efforts and effective operation. Although AI methods do not vary among fields, process models are system-specific. Thus, background knowledge is essential for the successful selection, implementation/formulation, and use of process models (e.g., for advanced control and optimization purposes). Therefore, it is fundamental to integrate the teaching of basic and advanced modeling, as well as programming, in the graduate and undergraduate curriculums. To tackle the mentioned prerequisites of Industry 4.0-related activities, in this work, we propose to expand/customize the current curriculum (learning requirements), customize it to the current needs (learning design), and dynamically include the students in the process (learning verification). To achieve this, the authors have developed an online and open-source educational platform (BioVL) that, among other strategies, integrates gamification elements and an agile microlearning as a motivation approach. BioVL is in its prototype stage and under continuous development and refinement. Some of the ongoing and future steps include implementing AI-powered adaptive learning so that the students can receive immediate feedback and prevent error propagation. To conclude, we encourage building on the pillars of a successful transition towards a digitalized industry by upgrading the curriculum by integrating online educational computer-aided tools to empower future engineers to be fluent in data analysis and process modelling.

References

Balamuralithara, B., & Woods, P. C. (2009). Virtual laboratories in engineering education: the simulation lab and remote lab. *Computer Applications in Engineering Education*, *17*(1), 108–118.

Berggren, A., Burgos, D., Fontana, J. M., Hinkelman, D., Hung, V., Hursh, A., & Tielemans, G.

(2005). Practical and Pedagogical Issues for Teacher Adoption of IMS Learning Design Standards in Moodle LMS. *Journal of Interactive Media in Education*, *2005*(1), 3.

Cameron, I. T., Engell, S., Georgakis, C., Asprion, N., Bonvin, D., Gao, F., Gerogiorgis, D. I., Grossmann, I. E., Macchietto, S., Preisig, H. A., & Young, B. R. (2019). Education in Process Systems Engineering: Why it matters more than ever and how it can be structured. *Computers and Chemical Engineering*, *126*, 102–112.

Caño de las Heras, S., Gargalo, C. L., Weitze, C. L., Mansouri, S. S., Gernaey, K. V., & Krühne, U. (2021). A framework for the development of Pedagogical Process Simulators (P2Si) using explanatory models and gamification. *Computers and Chemical Engineering*, *151*.

Caño de Las Heras, S., Jones, Mark Nicholas Gernaey, K. V., Krühne, U., & Mansouri, S. S. (2020). An E-learning Bot for Bioprocess Systems Engineering. *Computer Aided Chemical Engineering*, *48*, 2023–2028.

Caño De Las Heras, S., Kensington-Miller, B., Young, B., Gonzalez, V., Krühne, U., Mansouri, S. S., & Baroutian, S. (2019). Facilitating learning by failure through a pedagogical model-based tool for bioprocesses. In *29th European Symposium on Computer Aided Process Engineering* (Vol. 46). Elsevier Masson SAS.

Caño De Las Heras, S., Kensington-Miller, B., Young, B., Gonzalez, V., Krühne, U., Mansouri, S. S., & Baroutian, S. (2021a). Minerva: a non-relational bioprocesses modeling database supportedby an ontology. *Submitted to Chemical Engineering Journal*.

Caño De Las Heras, S., Kensington-Miller, B., Young, B., Gonzalez, V., Krühne, U., Mansouri, S. S., & Baroutian, S. (2021b). Programming skills across the (bio)engineering curriculum – a students' perspective. *Computer Aided Chemical Engineering*, *50*, 2039–2044.

Caño De Las Heras, S., Kensington-Miller, B., Young, B., Gonzalez, V., Krühne, U., Mansouri, S. S., & Baroutian, S. (2021c). Benefits and Challenges of a Virtual Laboratory in Chemical and Biochemical Engineering: Students' Experiences in Fermentation. *Journal of Chemical Education*, *98*(3), 866–875.

Deloitte. (2021). *Tech Trends 2021 | Deloitte Insights*. https://www2.deloitte.com/us/en/insights/focus/tech-trends.html

Dyrberg, N. R., Treusch, A. H., & Wiegand, C. (2017). Virtual laboratories in science education: students' motivation and experiences in two tertiary biology courses. *Journal of Biological Education*, *51*(4), 358–374.

Feisel, L. D., & Rosa, A. J. (2005). The role of the laboratory in undergraduate engineering education. *Journal of Engineering Education*, *94*(1), 121–130.

Gargalo, C. L., de Las Heras, S. C., Jones, M. N., Udugama, I., Mansouri, S. S., Krühne, U., & Gernaey, K. V. (2021). Towards the Development of Digital Twins for the Bio-manufacturing Industry. *Advances in Biochemical Engineering/Biotechnology*, *176*, 1–34.

Hiim, H and Hippe, E. (1997). Learning through experience, understanding and action. *Gyldendal Uddannelse*.

Krathwohl, D. R. (2002). A revision of bloom's taxonomy: An overview. *Theory into Practice*, *41*(4), 212–218.

Narayanan, H., Luna, M. F., von Stosch, M., Cruz Bournazou, M. N., Polotti, G., Morbidelli, M., Butté, A., & Sokolov, M. (2020). Bioprocessing in the Digital Age: The Role of Process Models. *Biotechnology Journal*, *15*(1), 1–10.

Udugama, I. A., Lopez, P. C., Gargalo, C. L., Li, X., Bayer, C., & Gernaey, K. V. (2021). Digital Twin in biomanufacturing: challenges and opportunities towards its implementation. *Systems Microbiology and Biomanufacturing*, *1*(3), 257–274.

Weitze, C. L. (2016). Designing for learning and play: The smiley model as a framework. *Interaction Design and Architecture(S)*, *29*(1), 52–75.

Yamauchi, Y. (2012). Participatory Design. In *Field Informatics* (pp. 123–138). Springer Berlin Heidelberg.

Proceedings of the 14th International Symposium on Process Systems Engineering – PSE 2021+
June 19-23, 2022, Kyoto, Japan © 2022 Elsevier B.V. All rights reserved.
http://dx.doi.org/10.1016/B978-0-323-85159-6.50213-X

Process Superstructure Optimization through Discrete Steepest Descent Optimization: a GDP Analysis and Applications in Process Intensification

David E. Bernal[a*], Daniel Ovalle[a,c*], David A. Liñán[b], Luis A. Ricardez-Sandoval[b], Jorge M. Gómez[c], and Ignacio E. Grossmann[a]

[a] *Department of Chemical Engineering, Carnegie Mellon University, 5000 Forbes Avenue, Pittsburgh PA 15213, United States of America*
[b] *Department of Chemical Engineering, University of Waterloo, Ontario N2L 3G1, Canada*
[c] *Departamento de Ingeniería Química y de Alimentos, Universidad de Los Andes, Bogotá 111711, Colombia*
These authors contributed equally to this work.
grossmann@cmu.edu

Abstract

This manuscript introduces a Logic-based Discrete-Steepest Descent Algorithm (LD-SDA) to tackle problems arising from process superstructure optimization. These problems often appear in Process Systems Engineering and become challenging when addressing Process Intensification applications. The current algorithm considers a disjunctive interpretation of these optimization problems through Generalized Disjunctive Programming (GDP). This formulation allows further analysis of the solution method as a tailored approach for GDP and results in a general open-source implementation of the method relying on the modeling paradigm Pyomo.GDP. Complementing our previous studies in the subject, we compare the LD-SDA against other well-known GDP solution methods and a D-SDA that does not consider the disjunctive nature of these problems. The results showcase the advantages of LD-SDA when dealing with superstructure problems arising from process intensification.

Keywords: superstructure optimization; process intensification; convex discrete analysis.

1. Introduction

The optimal design of processes is a challenge the Process Systems Engineering (PSE) community faces. Chemical processes require a systematic procedure to find optimal designs to remain competitive. Recent developments from Process Intensification (PI) have shown to be promising alternatives to traditional processes by integrating and interconnecting units and achieving superior processes in terms of economic, environmental, and efficiency objectives (Sitter et al., 2019). Different process flowsheets can be integrated into a single process superstructure, where potential units and interconnections are considered. Superstructure models allow the units and interconnections' equations to be constraints in optimization problems.

Since these equations can involve nonlinear functions and depend on both continuous (e.g., flowrates or temperatures) and discrete variables (e.g., equipment choice, interconnection location), the mathematical models become Mixed-Integer Nonlinear Programs (MINLP). The solution to these optimization problems is challenging given their combinatorial and nonconvex nature. Generalized Disjunctive Programming (GDP) has been proposed to tackle specific modeling and solution challenges of MINLP. In GDP, the modeling capabilities of traditional mathematical programming are extended by introducing Boolean variables involved in propositions and disjunctions.

The novelty of this work is to frame a Discrete-Steepest Descent Algorithm (D-SDA) for the solution of discrete nonlinear problems within the scope of GDP and use it to address process superstructure problems with ordered interconnections. Such problems arise in PI applications, such as studying a series of units with interunit refluxes, e.g., tray-by-tray distillation column models.

2. Generalized Disjunctive Programming

In general, a GDP problem can be written as

$$
\begin{aligned}
&\min_{\mathbf{x}, \mathbf{Y}, \mathbf{z}} f(\mathbf{x}, \mathbf{z}) + \sum_{k \in K} c_k \\
&\text{s.t. } \mathbf{g}(\mathbf{x}, \mathbf{z}) \leq 0; \ \Omega(\mathbf{Y}) = \text{True} \\
&\bigvee_{i \in D_k} \begin{bmatrix} Y_{ik} \\ \mathbf{r}_{ik}(\mathbf{x}, \mathbf{z}) \leq 0; \ c_k = \gamma_{ik} \end{bmatrix} \forall k \in K \\
&\mathbf{x} \in X \subseteq \mathbb{R}^{n_x}; \mathbf{Y} \in \{\text{True}, \text{False}\}^{n_y}; \mathbf{z} \in Z \subseteq \mathbb{Z}^{n_z}; \mathbf{c} \subseteq \mathbb{R}^{|K|}
\end{aligned} \tag{1}
$$

Where the continuous variables are denoted by the n_x-dimensional vector $\mathbf{x}$ bounded by the finite set X, and the discrete variables are denoted by the n_z-dimensional vector $\mathbf{z}$, bounded by the finite set Z. The function $f: \mathbb{R}^{n_x} \times \mathbb{R}^{n_z} \to \mathbb{R}$ is the objective function, and the vector function $\mathbf{g}: \mathbb{R}^{n_x} \times \mathbb{R}^{n_z} \to \mathbb{R}^{n_l}$ denotes the global inequality constraints. $\mathbf{Y}$ is a n_y-dimensional vector of logic variables, where for each disjunct $i \in D_k$ of each disjunction ($\vee$) $k \in K$ the individual logic variable Y_{ik} enforce the set of inequalities $\mathbf{r}_{ik}: \mathbb{R}^{n_x} \times \mathbb{R}^{n_z} \to \mathbb{R}^{n_{ik}}$ and the fixed cost γ_{ik}. Logical constraints $\Omega: \{\text{True}, \text{False}\}^{n_y} \to \{\text{True}, \text{False}\}$ encode logical relationships among the logical variables.

Besides offering a more intuitive modeling paradigm of discrete problems through disjunctions, a GDP model can inform computational solution tools of the original problem's underlying structure of the original problem, thus leading to improved solving performance. The GDP framework has successfully addressed problems derived from process superstructure optimization (Chen et al., 2021).

GDP problems are often solved by reformulating them as MINLP problems, by adding a binary variable y_{ik} for each Boolean variable Y_{ik}, and reformulating the constraints $\mathbf{r}_{ik}$ within the disjunctions to be enforced when the corresponding variable $y_{ik} = 1$ or trivially satisfied otherwise. The two best-known cases are the Big-M and the Hull reformulation, for which the Big-M case requires fewer continuous variables while the Hull reformulation is always at least as tight as the Big-M reformulation.

The tailored solution methods for GDP are usually based on generalizing algorithms for MINLP. The optimization problems are decomposed in a way where the discrete variables are fixed into what we call a discrete combination and allow to solve the problem only in terms of the continuous variables. Different methods are used to select the combination of these discrete variables, including branching across the different values the discrete variables can take (i.e., Branch-and-Bound) or solving a linear approximation of the original problem (Kronqvist et al., 2019). For GDP algorithms, contrary to the case in MINLP, these (possibly Mixed-Integer) Nonlinear Programming (NLP) subproblems that arise when fixing a particular discrete combination, now including the logical variables, only include the constraints that concern the logical variables within each combination. Namely, for a given logical combination $\widehat{\mathbf{Y}}$ the subproblem becomes

$$
\begin{aligned}
&\min_{\mathbf{x},\mathbf{z}} f(\mathbf{x},\mathbf{z}) + \textstyle\sum_{\text{ik if }\widehat{Y}_{ik}=\text{True}} \gamma_{ik} \\
&\quad \text{s.t. } \mathbf{g}(\mathbf{x},\mathbf{z}) \le 0 \\
&\mathbf{r}_{ik}(\mathbf{x},\mathbf{z}) \le 0 \text{ if } \widehat{Y}_{ik} = \text{True } \forall i \in D_k, k \in K \\
&\quad\quad \mathbf{x} \in X \subseteq \mathbb{R}^{n_x}, \mathbf{z} \in Z \subseteq \mathbb{Z}^{n_z}
\end{aligned}
\tag{2}
$$

Notice that in the most general case, the problem in Eq.(2) is an MINLP, although in most applications, $n_z = 0$, leading to the problem being an NLP. This problem avoids evaluating numerically challenging nonlinear equations whenever its corresponding logical variables are irrelevant (i.e., "zero-flow" issues).

The different tailored algorithms for GDP are defined in the strategy to find the logical combination $\widehat{\mathbf{Y}}$ such that subproblems as in Eq.(2) solve to the optimal solution Eq.(1). One alternative is using gradient-based linearizations of the nonlinear constraints at the optimal solution of Eq.(2) to approximate the original problem feasible region. This defines a Mixed-Integer Linear Program (MILP) whose optimal solution returns values for the integer combinations. This method is known as the Logic-based Outer-Approximation (LOA) method. One can also systematically explore the values of the Boolean variables in a search tree where the nodes correspond to partial fixations of these variables, whose solutions provide bounds to the optimal solution, in a method called the Logic-based Branch-and-Bound (LBB) method (Chen et al., 2021). Both methods seek to find potentially optimal combinations of logical variables efficiently.

3. Discrete Steepest Descent Optimization

In a previous study, we presented the D-SDA (Liñán et al., 2020a) based on the theory of discrete convex analysis (Murota, 1998). The algorithm aims to solve Mixed-Binary Nonlinear Programs (MBNLP) and relies on reformulating the original discrete problem, in terms of binary variables, into a problem of integer choices, referred to as external variables. This reformulation was designed for binary variables defined in an ordered set constrained to an assignment constraint, meaning that only one of these ordered binary variables can be 1. These external variables, which are no longer representable in the original problem constraints, provide a concise representation of the discrete feasible region. This structure often appears in process superstructure optimization problems, e.g., when a set of binary variables define the location of a reflux stream within a stages sequence, implicitly defining the existence of left-over stages after them.

Exploring discrete neighborhoods of the external variables provides the D-SDA with an efficient approach to choose which combination of the discrete variables should be considered to solve the subproblems that appear by fixing such values, NLPs in this case, thus efficiently searching the combinatorial space of the discrete variables. The D-SDA uses the integrally local optimality as a termination criterion (Murota, 1998), enabling the efficient solution of process superstructure optimization problems.

When considering a series of continuously stirred tank reactors (CSTR), the D-SDA outperforms MINLP solvers in solution time and quality (Liñán et al., 2020a). Furthermore, we applied the algorithm to the optimal design of a PI application involving reactive distillation, where we tackled the production of Ethyl tert-butyl ether (ETBE) from iso-butene and ethanol through the optimal design of a catalytic distillation column.

The D-SDA revealed a better performance against MINLP solvers when optimizing an economic objective in this problem (Liñán et al., 2020b). This allowed us to consider more complex models for this system, i.e., modeling multi-scale phenomena through a rate-based model for mass and energy transfer (Liñán et al., 2021).

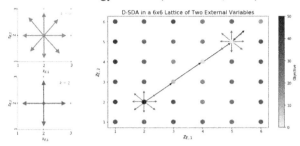

Figure 1. Pictorial representation of (a) different search neighborhoods in external variables lattice and (b) D-SDA with the neighbor and line search using $k = \infty$

4. Discrete-steepest descent optimization as a disjunctive algorithm LD-SDA

The problem in Eq. (1) suggests that the structure fitting for the D-SDA algorithm appears naturally in GDP, namely the disjunctions $\left(\vee_{i \in D_k} Y_{ik}\right)$ enforce the assignment constraint, $\text{ExactlyOne}\left(Y_{1k}, \dots, Y_{|D_k|k}\right)$, which would enable the reformulation with external variables if $\{Y_{ik} | i \in D_k\}$ represents an ordered decision. The reformulation is also possible across other ordered sets of Boolean variables, i.e., $\vee_{S(a) \in S} Y_{S(a)}$ defined over the ordered set $S = \{s_1, \dots, s_{|S|}\}$ with the element of S in its a-th position denoted $S(a)$. These sets are common within process superstructure problems and the reformulation into external variables $\mathbf{z}_E \in \{1, \dots, |S|\} \subseteq \mathbb{Z}$ becomes $Y_{S(a)} \Leftrightarrow z_E = a$. Notice that this reformulation allows the external variables to be interpreted as indicators of position within the set.

Such a reformulation allows us to map the Boolean variables into a lattice of integer variables, on which we can perform exploration based on ideas from discrete convex analysis (Murota, 1998). This leads to the Logic-based D-SDA (LD-SDA), which compares the objective function of each problem solved at a lattice site with its neighbors, defined by either a $k = 2$ or $k = \infty$ norm as seen in Fig.(1a), together with a line search along the direction provided by the best objective improvement after a complete neighbor search, as seen in Fig.(1b). The local optimality of the solution determines the stopping criterion compared to its neighbors (Murota, 1998).

From a GDP perspective, the external variables delineate a branching rule in the disjunctions, informing the problem structure. Notice that the more $\text{ExactlyOne}(Y_S)$ constraints the problem have, the more effective this reformulation is, with the limiting case of not having any other apart from the disjunctions, making it equivalent to LBB.

5. Numerical Experiments

We implement this method in open-source code using Python, available in https://github.com/bernalde/dsda-gdp. This code automatically transforms Pyomo.GDP (Chen et al., 2021) models, reformulates the disjunctions and the logical constraints $\text{ExactlyOne}\left(Y_{S(1)}, \dots, Y_{S(|S|)}\right)$ automatically and solves the models using LD-SDA. We present the following two case studies after solving these problems with the solvers in GAMS 34.2 and using an Intel Core i7-7700 @ 3.6GHz PC with 16 Gb of RAM Memory.

5.1. Continuously Stirred Tank Reactors in series superstructure

We consider a superstructure of N_T CSTR in series where its total volume is minimized given an autocatalytic reaction $A + B \rightarrow 2B$ with 1st order reaction rate. This example is generalized from the one presented in (Liñán et al., 2020a). This example is illustrative given that we have an analytical solution at the limit of $N_T \rightarrow \infty$ equivalent to the Plug Flow reactor, and that we can explore the behavior in instances varying the value of N_T. Fig.(2) presents a scheme of the problem and its GDP formulation, together with its external variables reformulation. For this problem, there is a locally optimal solution with five reactors and reflux before the first reactor, $\mathbf{z}_E = (5,1)$.

Figure 2. Scheme of (a) CSTR reactor superstructure and (b) Case with $N_T = 5$ and reformulation using external variables $z_{E,1}$ the number of reactors, $z_{E,2}$ the relative position of the reflux

We considered a set of different solver approaches to this problem with $N_T = [5, \dots, 25]$, including reformulating it into MINLP via Big-M and Hull reformulations, using LBB, LOA, and GLOA, and LD-SDA with two different norms, as seen in Fig.(3). We also include the total enumerations through the external variable reformulation.

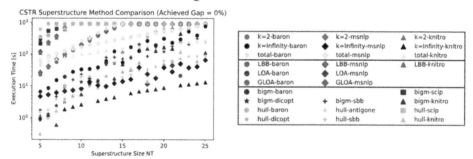

Figure 3. Execution time to achieve global minimum vs N_T for optimization of CSTR superstructure problem using different combinations of NLP solvers and reformulation methods.

From Fig.(3), one can see that LD-SDA provides the most efficient methods to solve this problem to global optimality. For this problem, the $k = 2$ norm neighborhood does not obtain the optimal solution. Notice that the external variable reformulation leads to a better search procedure, as seen when a total enumeration in the external variable space can be more efficient than other GDP solution alternatives.

5.2. Rate-based catalytic distillation column

The economic objective maximization of a catalytic distillation column to produce ETBE from butenes and methanol was solved using a D-SDA (Liñán et al., 2021). This test case is relevant since it deals with a PI design problem, where several traditional optimization methods fail even to compute feasible solutions (Liñán et al., 2021). The derivation of the D-SDA method was initially motivated to address this PI superstructure optimization problems, leading to a series of papers as seen in (Liñán et al., 2020b, 2020a, 2021).

The previous D-SDA would tackle the problem as an MBNLP, fixing and unfixing binary variables and including constraints of the form $yg(x) \leq 0$ to enforce the logic constraints.

Here we show that considering the problem from a disjunctive point of view as in LD-SDA leads to the solution of subproblems as in Eq.(2) instead of including irrelevant and numerically challenging nonlinear constraints.

Table 1. Execution time of Catalytic distillation optimal design problem from (Liñán et al., 2021)

NLP Solver	D-SDA: (Liñán et al., 2021)				LD-SDA: This work			
	CONOPT		MSNLP		CONOPT		MSNLP	
Neighborhood	k=2	k=inf	k=2	k=inf	k=2	k=inf	k=2	k=inf
Time [s]	367.1	16880.0	3626.0	102030.7	118.7	6751.1	2000.0	38532.5

As seen in Table (1), the proposed LD-SDA method leads to speedups up to 3x in this challenging PI problem. We could obtain the same solution to all subproblems more efficiently, given that only the relevant constraints were included for each problem. Adding to the fact that the previous results using the D-SDA were already beating state-of-the-art MINLP solution methods shows the advantages of the LD-SDA.

6. Conclusions

The current manuscript presents the usage of a disjunctive discrete steepest descent optimization algorithm LD-SDA to tackle process superstructure problems. This algorithm is presented from the perspective of Generalized Disjunctive Programming solution methods, showing its relationship with existing algorithms for GDP. Moreover, this allowed for the algorithm to be implemented in Python and through the modeling paradigm of Pyomo.GDP. With this implementation, we solved problems of superstructure optimization, a series of CSTR volume minimization, and a rate-based catalytic distillation column economical design more efficiently than other proposed solution methods, including MINLP reformulations, GDP-tailored algorithms, and a D-SDA aimed at MBNLP problems. The results in this manuscript show how LD-SDA becomes a valuable tool to address process superstructure problems, of which many challenges instances arise from PI applications.

References

Chen, Q., Johnson, E. S., Bernal, D. E., Valentin, R., Kale, S., Bates, J., Siirola, J. D., & Grossmann, I. E. (2021). Pyomo.GDP: an ecosystem for logic based modeling and optimization development. *Optimization and Engineering.*

Kronqvist, J., Bernal, D. E., Lundell, A., & Grossmann, I. E. (2019). A review and comparison of solvers for convex MINLP. *Optimization and Engineering,* 1–59.

Liñán, D. A., Bernal, D. E., Gómez, J. M., & Ricardez-Sandoval, L. A. (2021). Optimal synthesis and design of catalytic distillation columns: A rate-based modeling approach. *Chemical Engineering Science, 231,* 116294.

Liñán, D. A., Bernal, D. E., Ricardez-Sandoval, L. A., & Gómez, J. M. (2020a). Optimal design of superstructures for placing units and streams with multiple and ordered available locations. Part I: A new mathematical framework. *Computers & Chemical Engineering, 137,* 106794.

Liñán, D. A., Bernal, D. E., Ricardez-Sandoval, L. A., & Gómez, J. M. (2020b). Optimal design of superstructures for placing units and streams with multiple and ordered available locations. Part II: Rigorous design of catalytic distillation columns. *Computers & Chemical Engineering, 139,* 106845.

Murota, K. (1998). Discrete convex analysis. *Mathematical Programming, Series B.*

Sitter, S., Chen, Q., & Grossmann, I. E. (2019). An overview of process intensification methods. In *Current Opinion in Chemical Engineering.*

Proceedings of the 14th International Symposium on Process Systems Engineering – PSE 2021+
June 19-23, 2022, Kyoto, Japan © 2022 Elsevier B.V. All rights reserved.
http://dx.doi.org/10.1016/B978-0-323-85159-6.50214-1

Advances in Generalized Disjunctive and Mixed-Integer Nonlinear Programming Algorithms and Software for Superstructure Optimization

David E. Bernal[a], Yunshan Liu[a], Michael L. Bynum[b], Carl D. Laird[a], John D. Siirola[b], and Ignacio E. Grossmann[a]

[a]*Department of Chemical Engineering, Carnegie Mellon University, 5000 Forbes Avenue, Pittsburgh PA 15213, United States of America*
[b]*Discrete Mathematics and Optimization, Sandia National Laboratories, 1515 Eubank SE, Albuquerque NM, 87185, United States of America*
grossmann@cmu.edu

Abstract

This manuscript presents the recent advances in Mixed-Integer Nonlinear Programming (MINLP) and Generalized Disjunctive Programming (GDP) with a particular scope for superstructure optimization within Process Systems Engineering (PSE). We present an environment of open-source software packages written in Python and based on the algebraic modeling language Pyomo. These packages include MindtPy, a solver for MINLP that implements decomposition algorithms for such problems, CORAMIN, a toolset for MINLP algorithms providing relaxation generators for nonlinear constraints, Pyomo.GDP, a modeling extension for Generalized Disjunctive Programming that allows users to represent their problem as a GDP natively, and GDPOpt, a collection of algorithms explicitly tailored for GDP problems. Combining these tools has allowed us to solve several problems relevant to PSE, which we have gathered in an easily installable and accessible library, GDPLib. We show two examples of these models and how the flexibility of modeling given by Pyomo.GDP allows for efficient solutions to these complex optimization problems. Finally, we show an example of integrating these tools with the framework IDAES PSE, leading to optimal process synthesis and conceptual design with advanced multi-scale PSE modeling systems.

Keywords: superstructure optimization; generalized disjunctive programming; MINLP.

1. Introduction

Process superstructure optimization is a challenging problem within Process Systems Engineering (PSE). Using a mathematical programming formulation, the problem of superstructure optimization can be written as a set of constraints to be satisfied by selecting the values of variables while optimizing an objective function. These variables can be continuous, and represent properties of a process (e.g., temperature, pressure), or discrete, representing discrete choices (e.g., selecting a piece of given equipment). The constraints include the superstructure model equations (e.g., mass and energy balances, thermodynamic equations), and the objective function is a goal to reach by selecting the decision variables (e.g., maximize profit, minimize environmental impact). It is particularly challenging to obtain the globally optimal solutions to problems whose nonlinear constraints describe a non-convex region (Kronqvist et al., 2019).

This paper covers two different modeling paradigms for such superstructure optimization problems, Mixed-Integer Nonlinear Programming (MINLP), which relies only on algebraic functions of discrete and continuous variables, and Generalized Disjunctive Programming (GDP) that considers disjunctions, logical variables, and constraints for these problems. After mentioning the different solution methods for each paradigm, we present a set of examples of process superstructure optimization problems that have been modeled and solved using each of these approaches. The modeling has been done through the open-source software Pyomo.GDP (Chen et al., 2021), and made available as part of the problem library GDPLib. Finally, we demonstrate how these modeling tools and solution methods can be applied to a more intricate model created through the advanced modeling framework IDAES PSE (Miller et al., 2018).

2. Mixed-Integer Nonlinear Programming

The optimization models obtained from process superstructures have traditionally been written in algebraic equations and variables with both continuous and discrete domains. Mathematical optimization models with these characteristics are known as Mixed-Integer Nonlinear Programs (MINLP). The solution methods for this challenging type of optimization problem usually rely on the separate treatment of the two sources of complexity of the problem, the nonlinearity of the constraints and the integer variables' discreteness. Among the best-known deterministic solution strategies for these problems, we can count the Branch-and-Bound (BB) method and decomposition methods.

Both methods rely on finding bounds to the optimal objective function value through relaxations and restrictions of the original problem. A relaxation accounts for a different optimization problem whose feasible region is larger than the one of the original problem, whose solution is an optimistic bound of the optimal solution. Among these relaxations, the usual ones are continuous relaxations, where the discreteness of the integer variables is ignored, yielding a continuous problem, and linear relaxations, where the nonlinearities of the problems are replaced by linear feasible region that encompasses the feasible region of the original problem. These relaxations are not unique, and the successful solution of these problems can strongly depend on how close the relaxation approximates the original feasible region, known as its tightness, and other factors such as its size. The restriction of the original problem usually appears when fixing the value of some of the discrete variables, leading to a continuous problem in a lower-dimensional space. In the case that the original problem's objective is minimized, the optimal solution of a relaxation yields a lower bound of the optimal objective function, while any feasible solution to the problem, usually found through a partial or total fixing of the discrete variables and an optimization on the remaining variables, leads to an upper bound of the optimal solution.

In the BB method, starting from the solution of the continuous relaxation of the original MINLP, one systematically enforces values on the discrete variables to explore increasingly smaller and restricted subproblems. The solution of specific subproblems allows the derivation of extra inequalities that can help better approximate the original problem's feasible region, improving the quality of the lower bound obtained by solving it. Although effort has been made to derive strong inequalities, or cuts, for the nonlinear case and this can be generalized for branching on continuous variables, the BB method is better known for its highly successful implementations in modern solvers when addressing Mixed-Integer Linear Programming (MILP).

The decomposition methods for MINLP usually rely on MILP relaxations, which can be efficiently solved through BB, and continuous subproblems. As with BB, the MILP relaxations can be improved iteratively using cuts derived from the solution of the continuous restrictions. Eventually, if the relaxations are rigorous and each subproblem is solved optimally, either the decomposition methods or the BB methods will find the optimal solution in a finite number of steps/iterations. These two algorithms are the main ingredients of most known MINLP solvers (Kronqvist et al., 2019).

Considering this, a solver for MINLP is usually a meta-solver, where the solution of the original problem relies on other solvers to tackle subproblems. This observation has led us to develop the open-source Mixed-Integer Nonlinear Decomposition Toolbox in Pyomo - MindtPy (Bernal et al., 2018). This solver uses the interface that the Python-based algebraic modeling language Pyomo (Hart et al., 2017) has to solvers of continuous problems and MILP solvers and provides a flexible implementation of several of the decomposition methods known in the literature, such as the Outer-Approximation method. Furthermore, it includes implementations of heuristic techniques and enhancements such as single-tree solution methods and regularization-based algorithms. Furthermore, the derivation of strong relaxations to nonlinear terms is vital to solving these problems efficiently. We have also developed the open-source software CORAMIN (Bynum et al., 2019), which generates easily refinable relaxations of a Pyomo model's nonlinear constraints. These relaxations can be integrated within MINLP algorithms.

The convergence to the optimal solution of the MINLP is guaranteed when the relaxations are valid and can be further refined after each subsequent iteration and when the continuous subproblems are guaranteed to be solved to global optimality. This is easier to achieve when assuming well-behaved nonlinearities, e.g., convexity in the nonlinear functions. In this case, the linear relaxation can be found through the 1st-order Taylor expansions of the nonlinear functions in a method known as the Outer-Approximation (OA). When the convexity assumption is not satisfied, disciplined relaxations can still be derived as implemented in CORAMIN or through generalized McCormick relaxations (Scott et al., 2011) available in the software MC++. These allow our methods to solve even non-convex MINLP problems using a Global Outer-Approximation (GOA).

3. Generalized Disjunctive Programming

A more natural framework to represent superstructure optimization problems is Generalized Disjunctive Programming (GDP), which extends the modeling capabilities of traditional mathematical programming by incorporating logic variables involved in propositions and disjunctions. In general, a GDP problem can be written as

$$
\begin{aligned}
&\min_{\mathbf{x},\mathbf{Y},\mathbf{z}} f(\mathbf{x},\mathbf{z}) \\
&\text{s.t. } \mathbf{g}(\mathbf{x},\mathbf{z}) \leq 0; \ \Omega(\mathbf{Y}) = \text{True} \\
&\underset{i \in D_k}{V} \begin{bmatrix} Y_{ik} \\ \mathbf{r}_{ik}(\mathbf{x},\mathbf{z}) \leq 0 \end{bmatrix} \forall k \in K \\
&\mathbf{x} \in X \subseteq \mathbb{R}^{n_x}; \mathbf{Y} \in \{\text{True},\text{False}\}^{n_y}; \mathbf{z} \in Z \subseteq \mathbb{Z}^{n_z}
\end{aligned} \tag{1}
$$

where the continuous variables are denoted by the n_x-dimensional vector $\mathbf{x}$ within a bounded set X, the discrete variables are denoted by the n_z-dimensional vector $\mathbf{z}$ within a bounded set Z, the function $f: \mathbb{R}^{n_x} \times \mathbb{R}^{n_z} \to \mathbb{R}$ is the objective function, and the vector function $\mathbf{g}: \mathbb{R}^{n_x} \times \mathbb{R}^{n_z} \to \mathbb{R}^{n_g}$ denotes the global constraints. Besides, the logical structure of the problem includes $\mathbf{Y}$ as a n_y-dimensional vector of logic variables, where for each disjunct $i \in D_k$ of each disjunction $k \in K$ the set of inequalities $\mathbf{r}_{ik}: \mathbb{R}^{n_x} \times \mathbb{R}^{n_z} \to \mathbb{R}^{n_{ik}}$ are enforced by the individual logic variables Y_{ik}, and $\Omega: \{\text{True}, \text{False}\}^{n_y} \to \{\text{True}, \text{False}\}$ that encodes logical relationships among the logical variables. Notice that if the disjunctions set K is empty, Eq.(1) represents an MINLP problem.

The modeling framework of GDP allows for a more intuitive representation of the problems arising from superstructure optimization. The structure of such a representation can be exploited by a tailored solution algorithm to solve these problems more efficiently. First, reformulations can convert a GDP into MINLP, such as the Big-M and the Hull reformulations. These reformulations include all the constraints in the GDP and enforce or make trivially satisfiable constraints depending on the values of newly introduced binary variables $y_{ik} \in \{0,1\} \leftrightarrow Y_{ik} \in \{\text{True}, \text{False}\}$. The capability of writing a model directly as a GDP is included in the open-source code Pyomo.GDP (Chen et al., 2021).

We present two algorithms that generalize ideas from MINLP for GDP: the Logic-based Branch-and-Bound (LBB) and the Logic-based Outer-Approximation (LOA) algorithms. Like their MINLP counterpart, these algorithms have a search strategy for the values of the discrete variables, including the logic variables $\mathbf{Y}$, but consider the logical constraint Ω, pruning it. On the other hand, by leveraging the existing structure provided by the disjunctive formulation of the GDP, some algorithms selectively remove constraints that are not involved in each combination of the logical variables while exploring that combination. This approach is beneficial given the numerical issues that can appear from evaluating nonlinear constraints on vanishing variables, i.e., "zero-flow".

Similar to the MINLP case, if the subproblems are solved to optimality, for example, through the global solvers mentioned earlier, the relaxations of the nonlinear constraints are built rigorously, using MC++ or tailored relaxations as those in CORAMIN, these algorithms can solve non-convex problems to global optimality. We call this method Global Logic-based Outer Approximation (GLOA). These algorithms are implemented in the open-source GDP solver GDPOpt (Chen et al., 2021).

4. GDPLib, the library for GDP models

Finally, we highlight the usability of our framework and solution methods by solving different process superstructure problems. These problems have been previously presented in the literature, mainly as MINLPs. We included several instances as Pyomo.GDP problems in the repository github.com/grossmann-group/gdplib.

The library currently contains nine different examples of process or unit superstructure optimization, including a Methanol production process (Türkay & Grossmann, 1996), a Hydrodealkylation (HDA) process to produce Toluene (Kocis & Grossmann, 1989), a biofuel processing network, a heat exchanger network evaluating modular process design, a plant capacity expansion model, a synthesis gas production plant from methane, a Kaibel distillation column, and a tray distillation column design. Several examples include a few test cases leading to 25 GDP problems related to PSE. These instances range from $n_x \in [6, 31968]$, $n_y \in [2, 516]$, $n_z \in [0, 5040]$, $n_g \in [30, 14927]$.

We show two cases with more detail related to process superstructures. The first detailed case for the process superstructure optimization is the profit maximization of a methanol production process (Türkay & Grossmann, 1996). Mass balances define the global constraints of the problem, and there are 4 disjunctions in this problem as seen in Fig.(1a), one associated with the feed choice, another one choosing between a high-cost and high-conversion reactor or a low-cost and low-conversion reactor, and having a single or two-stage compression for the feed and the recycle. This problem involves 285 variables, of which 8 are Boolean and the remaining continuous. The total number of configurations is 2^4 but GDPOpt using LOA requires only two iterations to find the optimal solution.

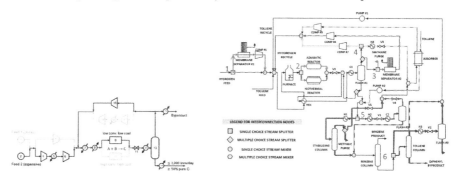

Figure 1. Flowsheet superstructure for (a) Methanol production and (b) Hydrodealkylation of Toluene. Alternatives highlighted correspond to optimal solutions.

The second example is the profit maximization of the Toluene production through the HDA process (Kocis & Grossmann, 1989). This superstructure, shown in Fig.(1b), considers 6 disjunctions: the choice to pretreat the hydrogen feed, whether to use an adiabatic or isothermal reactor, whether to purge or treat a methane stream for it to be recycled, considering the installation of an absorber or recycle a vapor stream, using a stabilizing column or a flash to remove extra methane from the process, and whether to use a distillation column to separate Toluene or a flash to obtain Diphenyl as a byproduct. There are 733 variables, with 12 being Boolean and the rest continuous, and 728 constraints, of which 12 are nonlinear. The MINLP transformation of this model is quite challenging for solvers, and both ANTIGONE and BARON fail to solve this problem to global optimality. Through LOA, GDPOpt was able to find the globally optimal solution, verified via enumeration. When using IPOPT and Gurobi as subsolvers, LOA converged to that solution in 17 iterations and 1 minute of computation in a standard desktop.

We highlight that the modeling paradigms and algorithms presented here, given their roots in Pyomo, can be used within more complicated process modeling alternatives. That is the case of the next-generation multi-scale PSE framework IDAES. By being based on Python and Pyomo, this framework leads to supporting our implementations natively. This results in the potential use of detailed process models, including property and thermodynamic packages and a disjunctive framework. We do this through the Methanol production example, which has been reimplemented as an IDAES PSE model and is available in GDPLib. The integration with IDAES PSE allows considering rigorous thermodynamic properties, resulting in more challenging optimization problems.

5. Conclusions

This paper presents two modeling paradigms for process superstructure optimization problems: Mixed-Integer Nonlinear Programming (MINLP) and Generalized Disjunctive Programming (GDP). MINLP is traditionally used and for which powerful solvers have been developed. On the other hand, GDP can be not only transformed into MINLP through different reformulations, leading to a difference in solution performance but can also be solved directly by algorithms that take advantage of the disjunctive and logical structure encoded in it. We have developed open-source software tools for such models to be implemented, as is the case for Pyomo.GDP, and solved, which is the case for MindtPy and GDPOpt, within the algebraic modeling language in Python, Pyomo.

Moreover, this paper presents process superstructure optimization problems that have been implemented using GDP. These Python implementations are available in the repository GDPLib and are freely available and installable through the package manager pip (pip install gdplib). We show two examples of flowsheet superstructure optimization, namely Methanol and Toluene production processes. Finally, we include the Methanol production process case implemented using the IDAES PSE framework. This example highlights the applicability of this paper's modeling and algorithmic ideas to an advanced process modeling framework, enabling conceptual process design through superstructure optimization integrated with rigorous property models and unit operations blocks.

We hope this library leads process designers to adopt these modeling paradigms and algorithm developers to use these examples as a testbed to improve solution methods for these optimization problems. We envision more models becoming part of GDPLib, leading to a richer resource for the process design and optimization communities.

Disclaimer: Sandia National Laboratories is a multimission laboratory managed and operated by National Technology and Engineering Solutions of Sandia, LLC., a wholly owned subsidiary of Honeywell International, Inc., for the U.S. Department of Energy's National Nuclear Security Administration under contract DE-NA-0003525. This paper describes objective technical results and analysis. Any subjective views or opinions that might be expressed in the paper do not necessarily represent the views of the U.S. Department of Energy or the United States Government.

References

Bernal, D. E., Chen, Q., Gong, F., & Grossmann, I. E. (2018). Mixed-Integer Nonlinear Decomposition Toolbox for Pyomo (MindtPy). In *Computer Aided Chemical Engineering*.

Bynum, M., Castillo, A., Laird, C., Watson, J.-P., & USDOE. (2019). *Coramin v. 0.1 Beta, Version v. 0.1*.

Chen, Q., Johnson, E. S., Bernal, D. E., Valentin, R., Kale, S., Bates, J., Siirola, J. D., & Grossmann, I. E. (2021). Pyomo. GDP: an ecosystem for logic based modeling and optimization development. *Optimization and Engineering*, 1–36.

Hart, W. E., Laird, C. D., Watson, J.-P., Woodruff, D. L., Hackebeil, G. A., Nicholson, B. L., Siirola, J. D., & others. (2017). *Pyomo-optimization modeling in Python* (Vol. 67). Springer.

Kocis, G. R., & Grossmann, I. E. (1989). Computational experience with dicopt solving MINLP problems in process systems engineering. *Computers and Chemical Engineering*, 13(3), 307–315.

Kronqvist, J., Bernal, D. E., Lundell, A., & Grossmann, I. E. (2019). A review and comparison of solvers for convex MINLP. *Optimization and Engineering*, 1–59.

Miller, D. C., Siirola, J. D., Agarwal, D., Burgard, A. P., Lee, A., Eslick, J. C., Nicholson, B., Laird, C., Biegler, L. T., Bhattacharyya, D., Sahinidis, N. V., Grossmann, I. E., Gounaris, C. E., & Gunter, D. (2018). Next Generation Multi-Scale Process Systems Engineering Framework. In *Computer Aided Chemical Engineering*.

Scott, J. K., Stuber, M. D., & Barton, P. I. (2011). Generalized McCormick relaxations. *Journal of Global Optimization*.

Türkay, M., & Grossmann, I. E. (1996). Logic-based MINLP algorithms for the optimal synthesis of process networks. *Computers & Chemical Engineering*, 20(8), 959–978.

Proceedings of the 14th International Symposium on Process Systems Engineering – PSE 2021+
June 19-23, 2022, Kyoto, Japan © 2022 Elsevier B.V. All rights reserved.
http://dx.doi.org/10.1016/B978-0-323-85159-6.50215-3

Designing Novel Structured Packings by Topology Optimization and Additive Manufacturing

Andreas Lange[a*], Georg Fieg[a]

[a]*Hamburg University of Technology, Am Schwarzenberg-Campus 4, 21073 Hamburg, Germany*
a-lange@tuhh.de

Abstract

Additive manufacturing (AM) reveals a completely new freedom in design and development of structured packings for thermal separation columns. This potential might lead to the next generation of high-performance packings, but it can only be fully used if novel design methods are developed. One of these innovative design methods is presented in this contribution. A topology optimization approach based on the coupling of a stochastic optimization algorithm and computational fluid dynamics (CFD) simulations is applied to generatively design structured packings. By its application, novel structured packing shapes may be found. Binary elements, which are either defined as packing material or as empty elements, are considered as design variables in a defined design space. A multi-objective genetic algorithm with tailored process- and manufacturing-related constraints is used to identify the best packing material distribution within the column shell, revealing minimized pressure drop and maximized surface area. In this paper, the optimization tool and CFD model are presented before selected results of an exemplary topology optimization study are given. The objective of this study is the development of a packing element for a lab scale distillation column. The promising results prove the viability of the design method, showing that it is possible to generatively design structured packings algorithm-based and without any well-defined initial packing geometries as starting point.

Keywords: Generative Design; Topology Optimization; Structured Packings; Additive Manufacturing

1. Introduction

Structured packings are column internals, which are widely applied in thermal separation apparatuses like distillation columns to intensify the mass transfer between the present fluid phases. Besides maximized separation efficiency, minimal pressure drop and maximal capacity are essential parameters in leading to a successful separation process. Improvements in these key parameters directly affect the performance of the entire column, resulting in a more efficient and sustainable separation process.

The three highlighted performance parameters are directly correlated to the flow behaviour of the fluid phases, which is in turn strongly affected by the specific shape of the structured packing. For this reason, the shape of structured packings has been of research interest for decades (Spiegel and Duss, 2014), but previous developments were restricted by the limitations of conventional manufacturing methods. Additive manufacturing as a class of innovative manufacturing processes makes it now possible to realize novel packing shapes, which are not feasible to manufacture by conventional methods due to the high complexity of the shapes. Accordingly, a new freedom in design is available, which can result in the next generation of high-performance structured packings using AM as the key technology. However, the main challenge is the identification of novel packing shapes in a systematic and targeted way. Therefore, advanced design methods based on mathematical optimization techniques and tailored computational tools for the targeted identification and systematic development of structured packings are essential. These design methods and tools need to use the potential of the high freedom in design, while simultaneously considering the specific constraints of both the additive manufacturing process and thermal separation applications.

In general, three different structural optimization approaches, classified as sizing (Neukäufer et al., 2019), shape optimization (Lange and Fieg, 2020; A. Courtais et al., 2020), or topology optimization (Rosinha et al., 2015) approaches can be applied to structurally optimize or identify novel packings. In the following, a method for the generative and hence algorithm-based design of structured packings is presented. Using a topology optimization approach, a multi-objective genetic algorithm is applied to develop novel structured packings with minimized pressure drop and maximized surface area. Rigorous CFD simulations are conducted to evaluate the key performance parameters of the packings and determine the values of the objectives. To present the design method, the optimization problem is defined and the topology optimization approach is presented in the next chapter. Then, first results of an optimization study are shown in chapter 3.

2. Generative Packing Design

For the design of structured packings several objectives and constraints need to be considered to meet the specific demands of the separation task as well as the additive manufacturing process. The minimization of the pressure drop across the packing as well as the maximization of the separation efficiency are essential objectives in packing design, especially in the case of vacuum distillation applications. This results in a complex constrained multi-objective optimization problem. To solve this task and to targeted identify novel structured packing shapes, a topology optimization algorithm and a rigorous analysis model for the evaluation of the values of the objective functions are needed. In the following the optimization problem is formulated before focussing on the optimization tool and the parametrisation of an exemplary topology optimization study.

2.1. Optimization Problem Formulation

For the formulation of the optimization problem the design variables and the design space need to be defined first, before focussing on the objective functions. The design space is defined by the given separation column diameter and the defined height of a single packing element. The resulting volume is discretized by a finite number of volume elements, where each element can either act as a packing material element or an empty element. The entirety of the material elements builds the structured packing, whereas fluid can flow through the empty elements. This behaviour is described by a binary code, defining a material element as a one and a fluid element as a zero. Then, each packing can be described by a matrix E of binary elements, where n describes the number of binary elements e_{ijk} in the direction of the cartesian coordinates of x, y and z. In turn, the matrix E can be reduced to a vector x_E.

$$E: (1, \dots, n_x) \times (1, \dots, n_y) \times (1, \dots, n_z) \rightarrow S \quad (i, j, k) \mapsto e_{ijk} \quad e_{ijk} \in [0,1] \tag{1}$$

$$x_{E_{i+(j-1) \cdot n_y + (k-1) \cdot n_x \cdot n_y}} = e_{ijk} \tag{2}$$

The resulting matrix E would describe a packing element with a squared cross-sectional area. Due to the fact that separation columns have a circular cross-sectional area, the coordinates of the packing are projected on the unit circle.

$$x_{Circ} = x \cdot \sqrt{1 - \frac{y^2}{2}}, \qquad y_{Circ} = y \cdot \sqrt{1 - \frac{x^2}{2}} \tag{3}$$

Based on the vector x_E of binary elements as design variables, the objective function is defined. Besides a minimum pressure drop across the packing, the separation efficiency should be maximized. Assuming perfect wetting of the packing surface, perfect mixing of the present phases, an infinitesimal small liquid film thickness on the packing and no dead volumes, the geometric surface area is equal to the interfacial mass transfer area. In this case, the separation efficiency of the packing is a function of the geometric surface area. Also, in the assumed case the multiphase system can be simplified as a first approximation to a single-phase vapour system. Accordingly, the objective is the minimization of the dry pressure drop $\Delta p_{P,d}$ and the reciprocal of the geometric surface area A_P of the packing.

$$f(x_{E,Opt}) = \min_{x_E} \left(\Delta p_{P,d}, \frac{1}{A_P} \right) \tag{4}$$

The geometric surface area A_P of the packing is defined as the sum of all faces of the material elements. These faces are either aligned parallelly to the main flow direction of the vapour phase or orthogonally directed to the main flow. It can be assumed, that the impact of the latter on the pressure drop is higher than the former. To consider the effect of the different face orientation of every single material element on the dry pressure drop, the objective function is complemented by a weighting factor β. This constant can take values between 0 and 1. The relevant surface area is then defined as the sum of the parallel $A_{P,par}$ and orthogonal $A_{P,orth}$ surface area weighted by β and one minus β. Accordingly, the objective function reads as follows.

$$f(x_{E,Opt}) = \min_{x_E} \left(\Delta p_{P,d}, \frac{1}{\beta \cdot A_{P,par} + (1 - \beta) \cdot A_{P,orth}} \right); \quad 0 \leq \beta \leq 1 \tag{5}$$

After defining the design space and the objective function of the optimization problem, the basic details of the optimization tool will be presented in the following.

2.2. Optimization Tool

The optimization tool is a combination of a developed modular control program implemented in MATLAB, using the PlatEMO platform (Tian et al., 2017) and OpenFOAM. The coupling between the optimization platform and the analysis model implemented in OpenFOAM is done by the tessellated packing data in STL-data format via the control program. The stochastic multi-objective genetic Strength Pareto

Evolutionary Algorithm 2 (SPEA2) is used as optimization algorithm, which was developed by Zitzler et al. (2001). As a genetic algorithm it mimics the evolutional theory by evaluating a fitness function and using the operators mutation, crossover and selection to generate a new generation of individuals. Also, process and manufacturing related constraints are considered. Every material element needs to be connected to another material element or to the boundaries of the design space, because unconnected material cannot be manufactured. Also, a minimum number of free flow channels needs to be available, because otherwise the mass transfer would be near zero. If these constraints are violated, the individual of the generation is punished.

2.3. Analysis Model

To predict the stationary flow behaviour of air flowing through the packing and to evaluate the resulting pressure drop over the created packings, rigorous CFD simulations are necessary. A laminar single-phase air flow at ambient conditions passes the packing from the lower to the upper end. Simplified Navier-Stokes equations in a finite-volume method implementation are solved using the SIMPLE-algorithm. The fluid is considered as incompressible and isothermal. No-slip condition at the surface of the packing and the column wall are assumed. A constant velocity at the inlet of the packing which correlates to a certain gas load or F-factor is defined and at the outlet a constant pressure is assumed.

The pressure drop is evaluated over the inlet and outlet of the packing as an area-averaged mean value. The total surface area of the packing as well as the surface area parallel and orthogonal to the main flow direction are also determined. OpenFOAM is used to conduct pre- and post-processing and for solving the model equations. Due to the high number of necessary CFD simulations for each evaluated generation, the simulations are performed at the North-German Supercomputing Alliance (HLRN).

2.4. Topology Optimization Study

In an exemplary optimization study, a packing for a lab scale distillation column should be generatively designed by the presented topology optimization approach. The column diameter is 54 mm and the height of a single packing element is 100 mm. The edge length of the quadratic material elements is chosen to 2.3 mm, assuming 23 elements in x- and y-direction and 43 material elements in z-direction. A preferred porosity of 0.8 for the randomly created initial generation is defined. The population size is 300 individuals per generation and the weighting factor β is 1/3. All CFD simulations are conducted at an F-factor at the inlet of the packing of 0.5 $\sqrt{Pa}$. In the following chapter, the results of the topology optimization study are presented.

3. Results

Selected results of the topology optimization study are shown in Figure 1 by plotting the specific pressure drop against the specific surface area of the evaluated packings for the three selected generations 0, 9, and 19. Having a look at the initial generation, the diversity of the individuals is quite low, due to the defined preferred packing porosity. Up to generation 20, the range of specific surface areas of the individuals rises up to a range of 370 m^2/m^3 to almost 420 m^2/m^3. Hence, the diversity also rises significantly. From generation to generation, the front is moving constantly into the lower right direction

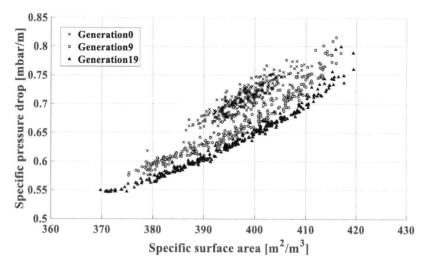

Figure 1: Specific dry pressure drop plotted against the specific surface area of the evaluated packings of the selected generations 0, 9 and 19

showing a good convergence behaviour. The best compromise individual regarding dry pressure drop and specific surface area reveals a specific dry pressure drop of 0.546 mbar/m and a specific surface area of 371.3 m^2/m^3. The appearance of this packing is shown in Figure 2 as STL-data in the side and top view. It becomes clear, that as expected, the packing consists of quite large material elements. Repetitive or regular parts are not visible yet. Hence, the optimization run needs to be continued. However, it can be stated that a packing element for the lab scale distillation column is successfully generatively designed, algorithm-based without any starting geometry.

In further studies, the edge length of the material elements will be lowered. Also, optimization studies for the development of tailored packings for specific separation tasks depending on the assumed boundary conditions and the selection procedure of the packings will be performed.

4. Conclusions

In this paper, an innovative method for the generative design of structured packings as a tool for the systematic identification of novel structured packing shapes was presented. The method is based on a topology optimization approach using the multi-objective genetic algorithm SPEA2 in combination with CFD simulations for the evaluation of the packings. A first optimization study for the development of a packing element for a lab scale distillation column was presented. First results show that it is possible to successfully design structured packings generatively without a well-performing packing as a starting point.

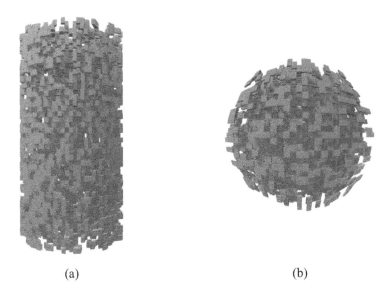

(a)   (b)

Figure 2: STL-data of the packing element which shows the best compromise between pressure drop and surface area of generation 19 shown in (a) side view and (b) top view

Acknowledgement

The authors gratefully acknowledge the support from the North-German Supercomputing Alliance (HLRN).

References

A. Lange, G. Fieg, 2020, Systematische Entwicklung von formoptimierten additiv gefertigten strukturierten Packungen, Chemie Ingenieur Technik 92, No. 9, p. 1299

A. Lange, G. Fieg, 2021, Systematische Entwicklung neuartiger strukturierter Packungen – Generatives Design neuartiger additiv fertigbarer strukturierter Packungen für thermische Trennapparate, North-German Supercomputing Alliance (HLRN), Project ID hhi00035

A. Courtais, F. Lesage, Y. Privat, C. Pelaingre, A. Latifi, 2020, Shape Optimization of a Fixed-bed Reactor using Additive Manufacturing, Computer Aided Chemical Engineering 48, p. 1939-1944

J. Neukäufer, F. Hanusch, M. Kutscherauer, S. Rehfeldt, H. Klein, T. Grützner, 2019, Methodology for the Development of Additively Manufactured Packings in Thermal Separation Technology, Chemical Engineering & Technology 42, No. 9, p. 1970-1977

I. P. Rosinha, K. V. Gernaey, J. M. Woodley, U. Krühne, 2015, Topology optimization for biocatalytic microreactor configurations, Computer Aided Chemical Engineering 37, p. 1463-1468

L. Spiegel, M. Duss, 2014, Structured Packings, p. 146-151 in Distillation: Equipment and Processes (edited by A. Gorak, Z. Olujic), Academic Press

Y. Tian, R. Cheng, X. Zhang, Y. Jin, 2017, PlatEMO: A MATLAB Platform for Evolutionary Multi-Objective Optimization, IEEE Computational Intelligence Magazine 12, No. 4, p. 73-87

E. Zitzler, M. Laumanns, L. Thiele, 2001, SPEA2: Improving the strength pareto evolutionary algorithm, TIK-Report 103, Zurich, Switzerland

Proceedings of the 14th International Symposium on Process Systems Engineering – PSE 2021+
June 19-23, 2022, Kyoto, Japan © 2022 Elsevier B.V. All rights reserved.
http://dx.doi.org/10.1016/B978-0-323-85159-6.50216-5

Multi-Objective Bayesian Optimization for Design and Operating of Fluidized Bed Reactor

Minsu Kim[a], Sunghyun Cho[b], Areum Han[c], Yoojin Han[d], Joseph Sang-Il Kwon[e], Jonggeol Na[c,*], Il Moon[a,*]

[a]Department of Chemical and Biomolecular Engineering, Yonsei University, 50 Yonsei-ro, Seodaemun-gu, Seoul, 03722, Republic of Korea

[b]Harvard John A. Paulson School of Engineering & Applied Sciences, Science and Engineering Complex 3.401, 150 Western Avenue, United States
[c]Department of Chemical Engineering and Materials Science, Ewha Womans University, Seoul 03760, Republic of Korea

[d]Graduate Institute of Ferrous & Energy Materials Technology, Postech, 77 Cheongam-Ro, Nam-Gu, Pohang, 37673, Republic of Korea

[e]Texas A&M Energy Institute, Texas A&M University, College Station, TX 77845, USA

Abstract

Treating the explosive waste using fluidized bed reactor, the design and operating conditions have highly effect to emission of pollutants (e.g. nitrogen oxides). Although it is possible to reduce the amount of pollutants through additional unit processes and extreme design and operating conditions, there are many practical difficulties because it causes an increase in cost. In addition, because of the explosive properties of waste, designing the process through actual experiments has many risks. Therefore, computational fluid dynamics (CFD) is used to simulate the reactor with high accuracy and to observe the internal temperature characteristics. While CFD shows high accuracy, it is difficult to obtain sufficient data for optimization because it requires a long computation time. Bayesian optimization repeats surrogate model optimization and infill criteria optimization and adaptively constructs the surrogate model. It shows good performance for time-consuming or expensive experiments. This study is to identify the design and operating conditions that minimize nitrogen oxides and cost through multi-objective Bayesian optimization. Multi-objective optimization problems generally do not have a single global optimization solution, but multiple solutions. This set of solutions forms a pareto front, which derives various solutions and gives decision-makers many options.

Keywords: explosive waste, nitrogen oxides, Bayesian optimization, multi-objective

1. Introduction

Explosive waste is treated via fluidized bed reactors. In this process, major air pollutant(e.g. nitrogen oxides, NOx) such as nitrogen oxides are generated. Taking environmental benefits through extremely high costs may present impractical solution. The fluidized bed reactor has the advantage of being easy to control the temperature of the reactor, so it was judged to be suitable for the incineration process of explosive waste. In addition, a hot spot with a rapid increase in temperature causes a significant amount of nitrogen oxide to occur instantaneously, and computational fluid dynamics was used to simulate this phenomenon with high accuracy. It aims to minimize the emission of nitrogen oxides and the cost of the process by optimizing the design of the reactor as well as the operating conditions of the incineration process. In the case of changing the design of the reactor, it takes a lot of time to set up the mesh of the system a new, so there are many practical difficulties in optimization. The surrogate model is widely used in the engineering field as a method of simulating the underlying function inherent in an actual system with high accuracy through data. However, the surrogate model, whose accuracy is determined by the quality and quantity of data, has many difficulties in the data collection stage when sufficient data are not secured. Therefore, the importance of the design of experiment is further emphasized in this case. Adaptive sampling is a suitable method when it is difficult to obtain high-quality data due to cost and time issues. Bayesian optimization is a method that simultaneously performs adaptive design of experiment and optimization. In the case of multi-objective optimization that minimizes NOx emission and cost at the same time, the next experiment point is allocated through optimization of filling criteria, and a pareto front composed of a set of points that maximizes (or minimizes) the value of the Gaussian process-based surrogate model is drawn. Through this, several optimal solutions can be obtained, and it can help a lot in decision-making in real-world problem.

2. Mathematical model : Fluidized Bed Reactor

2.1. Governing equation

The mass and momentum transport phenomenon is based on Eq. (1) (mass transport) and Eq. (2) (momentum transport).

$$\frac{\partial \theta_f \rho_f}{\partial t} + \nabla \cdot \left(\theta_f \rho_f \boldsymbol{u}_f \right) = \delta \dot{m}_p \tag{1}$$

$$\frac{\partial (\theta_f \rho_f \boldsymbol{u}_f)}{\partial t} + \nabla \cdot \left(\theta_f \rho_f \boldsymbol{u}_f \boldsymbol{u}_f \right) = -\nabla p + \boldsymbol{F} + \theta_f \rho_f \boldsymbol{g} + \nabla \cdot \left(\theta_f \boldsymbol{\tau}_f \right) \tag{2}$$

In case of Newtonian fluid, the stress is calculated by Eq. (3) and the acceleration of the particle is calculated by Eq. (4).

$$\tau_{f,ij} = 2\mu S_{ij} - \frac{2}{3} \mu \delta_{ij} \frac{\partial u_k}{\partial x_k} \tag{3}$$

$$\frac{d\boldsymbol{u}_p}{dt} = D_p \left(\boldsymbol{u}_f - \boldsymbol{u}_p \right) - \frac{1}{\rho_p} \nabla p + \boldsymbol{g} - \frac{1}{\theta_p \rho_p} \nabla \tau_p + \frac{\bar{\boldsymbol{u}}_p - \boldsymbol{u}_p}{\tau_D} \tag{4}$$

The drag function D_p is expressed by Eq. (6) and it is calculated using drag coefficient C_d(Eq. (7))and the Reynold number Re.

$$D_p = \frac{3}{8} C_d \frac{\rho_f \left| \boldsymbol{u}_f - \boldsymbol{u}_p \right|}{\rho_p r_p}, \qquad Re = \frac{2\rho_f r_p \left| \boldsymbol{u}_f - \boldsymbol{u}_p \right|}{\mu_f} \tag{5}$$

To calculate the drag coefficient, the Wen-Yu/Ergun blend model that combines the Wen-Yu model and the Ergun model is used and the specific information about these models is explained in (*C. Wen et al., S. Ergun et al.*). Several gas phase pollutants such as NOx and CO occur through a complex mechanism consisting of 131 reactions and a total of 25 components(*N. E. Ermolin et al, S. Cho et al(2020).*).

2.2. Cost estimation

In order to adjust the temperature of the air flowing into the fluidized bed reactor, a compressor and a heater are additionally needed in front of the fluidized bed reactor. The cost according to the operating conditions of the heater and the compressor and the gas mixture (oxygen/nitrogen) was considered. Each compressor is an isentropic type, with isentropic efficiency of 0.72 and mechanical efficiency of 1.0. It operates on electricity and is 0.0775 \$/kWh. The heater is a fired heater operated at a cost of 0.0153\$/kWh. The cost is calculated via Aspen Plus and the specific information about cost estimation is described in (*S. Cho et al(2021).*)

3. Methodology : Multi-objective Bayesian optimization

3.1. Gaussian process

The Gaussian Process(GP) is a Bayesian regression approach that predicts a system value by quantifying uncertainty of data. Let $x_n = \{x_i | i = 1, 2, \cdots, n\}$ be the input of the training set, and $y_n = \{y_i | i = 1, 2, \cdots, n\}$ the output of the training set. If we do not know the Bayesian statistics of a certain system, it is assumed that x_n, and y_n are randomly selected from a specific prior probability distribution. GP regression is a non-parametric approach that assumes the prior probability distribution as a multivariate normal distribution (N), and the mean (μ) and variance (=*Kernel, K*) are expressed as functions. Therefore, it is possible to calculate the distribution $p(\mathcal{F})$ of the function $\mathcal{F}$ through GP. A detailed description of GP is described in (*Rasmussen and Williams*).

$$p(\mathcal{F}) = N(\mu(x), K(x, x'))$$ (8)

3.2 Multi-objective Bayesian optimization : q-Expected Hypervolume Improvement

Multi-objective optimization does not have only one global optimum but forms a set of several global optimums, which is called a pareto front. Bayesian optimization consists of two stages, and it proceeds while optimizing a certain function in each stage. First, a surrogate model is generated by quantifying uncertainty through the GP model. The maximum value of the objective function is implemented through GP optimization.

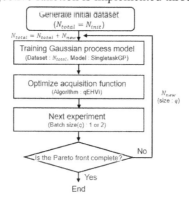

Figure 1. Multi-objective Bayesian optimization loop

The key to Bayesian optimization is to know the next design of experiment. The Nadir point (=Reference point) gives information about the range of objectives in the Pareto front stage in multi-objective optimization (Fig.2.(b)). These are the worst objective values determined by the decision maker, and since it is difficult to determine compared to the ideal point (=Utopia), it must be decided by domain knowledge (*Kalyanmoy Deb et al*).

Optimize the infill criteria that determine the next design of experiment and receive feedback on the next experiment with the most information. q-Expected Hypervolume Improvement (q-EHVI) (*Samuel Daulton et al*) is shown in Fig. 2. Find the experiments that maximizes the hypervolume in the initial objective function scatter (Fig.2.(a)) constructed as shown in Fig.2.(c) and repeat the optimization loop as shown in Fig.1. to maximize the hypervolume. As a result, when a part of the pareto front appears as shown in Fig.2.(e), the loop is terminated.

The number of next experiments has a trade-off between the quality of the data and the overall research time and cost. As the number increases, the research process time decreases, but the quality of the data decreases, so more experiments may be required than the optimal design of experiment. On the other hand, if the number of experiments is reduced, the sampling time increases, but the cost can ultimately be reduced because the data quality is good. Therefore, one or two experiment(s) is preferred.

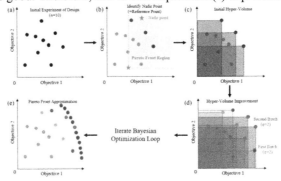

Figure 2. Sequence of q-EHVI algorithm and pareto front

4. Results

The reference point was selected based on domain knowledge among the factors that have a huge influence on the quality of the solution set identified through multi-objective Bayesian optimization. Based on Republic of Korea's air pollutant emission standard of 90 ppm, 100 ppm was selected with a margin of 10 ppm, and the cost standard was assumed to be 8,000,000 dollars. 100 initial data sets for GP model generation were selected, and the distribution of two objective values in the initial dataset is shown in Fig. 3. The reactor was a cylinder-type fluidized bed reactor, and 3 variables related to reactor design were selected and 7 variables related to operating were selected (Table 1.). In addition, although the objective is to minimize both NOx emission and cost, it has been transformed into a maximization problem by applying a negative sign for the efficient application of the optimization algorithm.

Figure 3. Reference point and Pareto front region

Through iteration of the Bayesian optimization loop, the maximum value of each objective function value farther from the reference point can be obtained compared to the initial dataset, and it shows a convex shape. Also, except for some points, a solution set is obtained within the preset reference point range.

Category	Parameter (Unit)	Lower bound	Upper bound
Operating parameter	Inlet gas velocity(m/s)	1	3.5
	Temperature(K)	400	800
	Pressure(bar)	2	4
	Particle radius(mm)	2	4
	Particle mass ratio	0.25	0.75
	Filled sand ratio	0.1	0.7
	O2 composition ratio in inlet gas	0.1	0.8
Design parameter	Fluidized bed diameter(m)	0.2	1
	Fluidized bed height(m)	1	5
	Sparger area/Fluidized bed cross sectional area(m²)	0.1	4

Table 1. Operating and Design parameters

The objective function values for 40 dataset extracted through Bayesian optimization excluding the initial dataset are shown in Fig. 4. In order to make the range of the two objective functions the same, it was converted through a standard score (Z score). Most of the two objective function values show a trade-off relationship. However, in the 31st experiment (Red mark), it can be seen that both values are high. This can be seen as a stage of exploration to reduce the uncertainty of the surrogate model rather than performing exploitation that maximizes the values of the two objective functions. Also, for various solution sets, the particle radius is mostly calculated as the lower bound of 2 mm. That is, when minimizing both cost and NOx emission, the smaller the particles of explosive waste, the better.

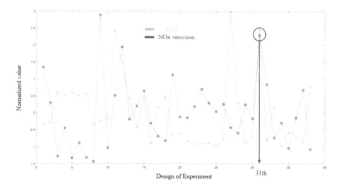

Figure 4. Trade-off between cost and NOx emission

5. Conclusions

Here, we optimize the amount of NOx emission and the cost of operation and design simultaneously to identify the practical reactor design and operating conditions. When the design of the reactor is changed, it is necessary to reconfigure and execute the mesh of the CFD structure, which is a highly time-consuming task. To overcome this problem, the GP model was adaptively improved through Bayesian optimization. This can be used very efficiently not only in CFD but also in actual experimental situations.

6. Acknowledgement

This research was supported by the MOTIE (Ministry of Trade, Industry, and Energy) in Korea, under the Fostering Global Talents for Innovative Growth Program (P0008747) supervised by the Korea Institute for Advancement of Technology (KIAT)

References

Robert Durichen, 2019, Multi-task Gaussian process models for biomedical applications, IEEE-EMBS International Conference on Biomedical and Health Informatics

Samuel Daulton, 2020, Differentiable Expected Hypervolume Improvement for Parallel Multi-Objective Bayesian Optimization, *NeurIPS 2020*

Kaifeng Yang, 2019, Multi-Objective Bayesian Global Optimization using expected hypervolume improvement gradient, *Swarm and Evolutionary Computation*, 44, 945-956

Eric Brochu, 2010, A Tutorial on Bayesian Optimization of Expensive Cost Functions, with Application to Active User Modeling and Hierarchical Reinforcement Learning, *arXiv*

C. Wen et al., 1966, Mechanics of fluidization, *Chem. Eng. Prog. Symp.*, 62, 100-111

S.Ergun et al., 1949, Fluid Flow through Randomly Packed Columns and Fluidized Beds, *Ind. Eng. Chem.*, 41, 1179-1184

S. Cho et al., 2020, Finding the best operating condition in a novel process for explosive waste incineration using fluidized bed reactors, *Comput. Chem. Eng.*, 142, 107054

Carl E. Rasmussen and Christopher Williams, Gaussian Processes for Machine Learning. *MIT press*, 2006.

Proceedings of the 14th International Symposium on Process Systems Engineering – PSE 2021+
June 19-23, 2022, Kyoto, Japan © 2022 Elsevier B.V. All rights reserved.
http://dx.doi.org/10.1016/B978-0-323-85159-6.50217-7

Analysis of Optimization Algorithms for Real-Time Optimization Applied on the Model of a Fluid Catalytic Cracking Unit

Adriana L. Rodríguez[a], Carlos A. M. Riascos[a]*

[a]*Univesidad Nacional de Colombia, Chemical and Environmental Department, Group of Process System Engineerig, Avenida Carrera 30, 45-03, Bogotá 111321, Colombia.
camartinezri@unal.edu.co*

Abstract

On-line optimization of Fluid Catalytic Cracking Units (FCCU) is essential in modern refineries, because of high commercial value of cracking products. Within Real-Time Optimization (RTO) the on-line optimization module plays a fundamental role since operational conditions must be frequently adjusted. The performance of this module must guarantee good solutions in a sufficiently short time to allow on-line implementation.

This work presents an assessment of some deterministic and stochastic optimization algorithms into a three-layer RTO strategy for a virtual FCCU. The implementation begins with definition of an economic objective function, a sensitivity analysis to evaluate how profit is affected by variations on operational variables and concludes with a performance comparison of some algorithms.

Results from deterministic algorithms confirm that there are multiple local solutions in FCCU optimal operation problem, and deterministic search methods could be trapped in these solutions. On the other hand, GA allowed to obtain satisfactory solution, but with the default values for stopping parameters, it doesn´t generate the solution in the available time for an RTO implementation. As alternative to obtain good solution in a reasonable time, some GA parameters were adjusted and a hybrid strategy was assessed. With these approaches, execution time was satisfactorily reduced, and the hybrid strategy was confirmed as an interesting option for optimization modules in on-line applications.

Keywords: On-line Optimization; Optimization Methods Assessing; GA Parameter Adjusting; Hybrid Algorithms.

1. Introduction

Optimization has received important attention as a tool for increasing competition, reducing production costs, improving quality, and satisfying environmental requirements and regulations. The use of optimization has been extended in the engineering of process systems since it is not easy to find an optimal solution that leads to more profitable and competitive operating conditions (Biegler and Grossmann, 2004).

Optimization in process design and equipment specification is usually performed prior to the implementation of the process (off-line). On the other hand, optimization of operating conditions is carried out monthly, weekly, daily, hourly, or even, in the extreme, every minute. In that way, on-line optimization makes decisions in different levels of the organization for improving the performance of industrial processes during their execution. RTO is an on-line optimization executed at an intermediate level, between the production scheduling and the control system (Rodríguez, 2019). While scheduling defines detailed programming to fulfill the strategic planning, the RTO defines the operational conditions that provide the highest performance of the process, and the control system must adjust the operation of the process to these optimal conditions.

Since disturbances affect the process performance, RTO develops a continuous reevaluation of any alteration on operating conditions, so that the economic productivity of the process is maximized. RTO cycle starts as soon as a steady state is detected after an external disturbance or a control action and, because of new disturbances could affect the process at any time, this cycle needs to be concluded as fast as possible.

In oil and gas industry, Fluid Catalytic Cracking (FCC) optimization has led to a significant increase in the performance. In FCCU applications, the on-line optimization problem usually comprises the maximization of the operational profit subject to a set of constraints and a non-linear programming problem (NLP), with additional complexity generated by a strong interaction between riser and regenerator (Fernández et al., 2007). Therefore, FCCU is a good candidate for RTO applications. This work presents a brief analysis of some optimization algorithms as candidates for implementing the optimization module into an RTO.

2. Methodology

This study was developed on the MATLAB platform, taking advantage of its toolboxes (MathWorks, 2018), optimization runs were developed on an Intel® Xeon® CPU E3-1241 v3 @ 3.5GHz. The FCCU model is presented with detail in Rodriguez (2019). A sensitivity analysis allowed selecting the optimization variables, as well as their limits and an approximate value for the objective function. The objective function in Eq.(1) is the FCCU profit (US$/s), it includes prices for products, feed and utilities used in the unit for the gas oil conversion. Additionally, a penalty factor considering the Lyapunov stability criterion (Torgashov et al., 2003) was added to punish unstable points, allowing to discard them, as it is shown in Eq.(2).

$$max \quad FCCU_{prof} = f(F_{air}, F_{cat}, F_{feed}, T_{feed}, T_{air})$$
$$s.t. \quad \begin{cases} FCCU\ Model\ equations \\ upper\ and\ lower\ bounds \end{cases} \tag{1}$$

$$where\ FCCU_{prof} = \left(\sum P_{products} - \sum P_{feedstock} - \sum P_{utilities}\right) * penalty \tag{2}$$

As candidates, two deterministic algorithms (SQP and Interior Point), a metaheuristic algorithm (Genetic Algorithm) and a Hybrid strategy were analyzed. These algorithms were selected because of their proven capacity to solve NLP problems, and their availability in MATLAB, these and other analysis on the RTO modules implementation are presented in our complementary works (Reyes et al., 2015; Rodríguez, 2019).

3. Results and analysis

Results from a previous work (Rodríguez, 2019) revealed that product value as a function of its quality (octane number) is fundamental for the estimation of the optimal operational conditions, and the significance order of the variables for this purpose is:

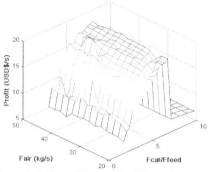

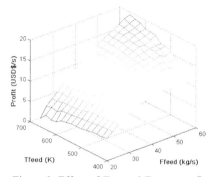

Figure 1. Effect of F_{air} and F_{cat}/F_{feed} ratio on profit.　　Figure 2. Effect of F_{feed} and T_{feed} on profit.

ratio catalyst flow/feed flow (F_{cat}/F_{feed}) > feed flow (F_{feed}) > feed temperature (T_{feed}) > air flow (F_{air}) > air temperature (T_{air}).

3.1. Sensitivity analysis

From this analysis, optimization variables and their limits were stablished, some key effects of optimization variables on objective function are shown in Figures 1 and 2. The effect of F_{cat}/F_{feed} on FCCU profit is the strongest, when this ratio goes from 2 to 6.8 a high increase on profit is observed; however, beyond 6.8 the profit drastically falls. This is mainly due to the fact that the increment in the F_{cat}/F_{feed} ratio generates a continuous increase in temperature at the riser outlet, a high riser temperature favours cracking but an over cracking diminishes the gasoline fraction (results not shown).

Effects of T_{feed} and F_{feed} on profit are important too and the variables F_{air} and T_{air} have smaller, but not insignificant, effect on profit. These analyses show the high non-linearity of the FCCU system, which generates local optima as observed in next results.

3.2. Assessment of optimization algorithms

In a comparative assessment of some optimization algorithms, it was observed that Genetic Algorithm (GA) allows to obtain satisfactory operational conditions, but it does not generate the solution in the available time for an RTO implementation. In contrast, the assessed deterministic algorithms (Interior Point, and SQP) generated solutions in short calculation time but with worse objective function values (Table 1).

Table 1. Performance of standard optimization algorithms

	Lower bound	Upper bound	Initial Point	Method		
				Int. Point	SQP	G A
F_{cat} (kg/s)	115.0	390.0	294.0	290.7	294.0	385.3
F_{feed} (kg/s)	20.0	60.0	40.6	58.8	40.6	59.6
F_{air} (kg/s)	20.0	46.0	25.4	45.9	25.4	37.6
T_{feed} (K)	400.0	670.0	434.6	448.5	434.7	656.8
T_{air} (K)	310.0	525.0	360.0	373.8	360.0	360.0
T_{ris} (K)	755.0	840.0	779.2	753.8	779.2	833.5
T_{rgn} (K)	810.0	1090.0	972.0	1006.6	972.0	1001.3
Octane Number	85.0	100.0	91.7	89.0	91.7	97.3
Profit (US$/s)	-	-	9.7	12.1	9.9	19.9
Run time (s)	-	-	-	148	185	13,932

Results from each algorithm propose operational conditions with remarkable differences, e.g. conditions obtained by GA include high flow of catalyst, feed and air, and high feed temperature; in other way, IP suggests medium catalyst flow, high feed and air flow and low feed temperature, and SQP suggests medium catalyst and feed flow, low air flow and feed temperature. These results confirm the complexity and high non-linearity of this optimization problem which is a challenge for on-line applications.

Analysing the performance of GA with default parameters, the hypothesis that it is possible to obtain a satisfactory optimization for on-line implementation by adjusting the stopping parameters is formulated. A satisfactory optimization implies to reduce the convergence time without damaging the quality of the solution. Results obtained for several GA runs (Figure 3 shows two of these) were used to analyse the performance and the confidence of the GA. Evolution of Best and Mean fitness shows that the diversity of the population is highly reduced by the 10th generation, and after the 20th generation, no significant change in the profit function value was observed.

From this analysis, *Generation* and *Stall Generations* were selected as adjustable stopping parameters. GA stops when the total number of evaluated generations reaches the value of *Generations*, as on the right side in Figure 3 or when the improvement in the fitness over *Stall Generations* is less than a tolerance (MathWorks, 2018). Analysing these criteria and the evolution of the best and mean fitness, the number of stall generations was adjusted to 10 and the maximum of generations to 20, this generates a reduction from 3.9 to 0.5 hours in the average computation time.

Optimization results with the adjusted value for stopping parameters are presented in Figure 4 and Table 2. This figure shows that improvement in best fitness was very modest since 4th generation. Analysing values for operational variables from GA with default values (Table 1) and adjusted values (Table 2), it can be observed that both solutions propose similar operational conditions: high values (near or on the upper limit) for the flows of catalyst, feed and air, as well as high and medium values for temperatures of feed and air, respectively. Therefore, calculates values for riser and regenerator temperatures are similar (883.5 vs 829.4 and 1001.3 vs 996.3 K). These results suggest that a deterministic search starting on the best point identified by GA algorithm must be considered as an alternative to improve the whole optimization procedure.

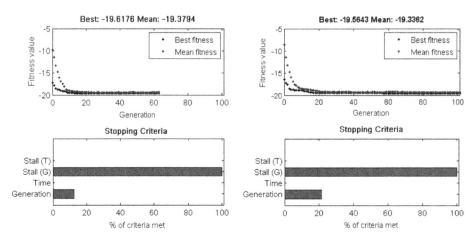

Figure 3. Convergence in two GA runs with default parameters.

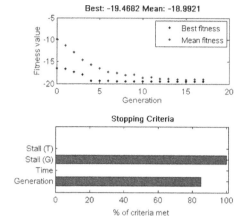

Figure 4. GA convergence with adjusted parameters.

Table 2. Solution from adjusted GA.

Variable	Value
F_{cat} (kg/s)	388.7
F_{feed} (kg/s)	60.0
F_{air} (kg/s)	43.6
T_{feed} (K)	651.7
T_{air} (K)	360.0
T_{ris} (K)	829.4
T_{rgn} (K)	996.3
Octane Number	97.3
Profit (US$/s)	19.8
Run time (s)	1,800

3.3. Hybrid optimization strategy

The hybrid strategy considers a first step with GA and a second one with a deterministic algorithm (Interior Point or SQP). Initial search with GA must allow identifying the region where the global solution is in, and final search with deterministic algorithm must allow to reach the optimal point. To confirm the viability and robustness of this strategy multiple hybrid runs were developed changing the number of total GA generations and the deterministic algorithm.

In general, operational conditions obtained from hybrid runs are similar to the ones previously obtained only by GA (section 3.2). To analyse the ability to identify the global solution, Figure 5 shows the profit obtained after the GA step and after the complete hybrid run, employing 10 GA generations and IP. Some important characteristics of these results are: i) only in 50% of runs deterministic step generates a significant improvement in profit, and ii) the performance of deterministic step does not depend on the results generated from GA: in run 3, instead of the relatively low profit from GA, IP didn´t improve the solution.

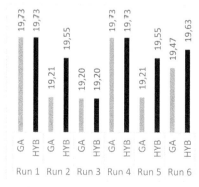

Figure 5. Profit obtained from hybrid strategy: 10 GA Gen + IP.

Table 3. Solutions from hybrid strategy

Variable	Mean / MAPD (%)		
	10GA+IP	**5GA+IP**	**5GA+SQP**
F_{cat} (kg/s)	378.0 / 2.8	381.8 / 1.5	374.4 / 3.7
F_{feed} (kg/s)	59.3 / 0.9	58.4 / 1.2	57.4 / 2.8
F_{air} (kg/s)	40.8 / 5.6	39.8 / 7.2	37.9 / 6.8
T_{feed} (K)	659.5 / 1.2	651.3 / 2.1	651.7 / 1.2
T_{air} (K)	412.7 / 9.1	391.1 / 12.9	386.1 / 11.0
Profit (US$/s)	19.6 / 0.7	19.2 / 1.4	18.8 /2.7
AvImpPro	0.14	0.32	0.19

Table 3 presents average values and the mean absolute percentage deviations (MAPD) for some operational variables and the final profit from hybrid strategy with 10 and 5 GA generation and IP or SQP, as well as the average improvement in profit (AvImpPro) obtained in the deterministic step. These results show that this hybrid strategy doesn´t rigorously guarantee to reach the global optimum because of differences in operational variables values are small but not negligible. The average and the mean absolute percentage deviation (MAPD) show that characteristics of feed (flow and temperature) are the most stable, while characteristics of air have the biggest variation. Improvement in profit obtained with IP and SQP have not significant differences.

Results from hybrid strategy and GA with adjusted parameters show that both strategies could be good alternatives for on-line optimization, and inspirate new studies to analyse their advantages and the challenge to reach, with confidence, the global solution. Additional results, not showed, suggest that stopping criteria for GA must guarantee a minimum number of generation and that iteration time is not a good stopping criterion.

4. Conclusions

Optimization allows to identify optimal operational conditions for a FCCU which improves its profit, and the algorithm choice is key in the success of this search, especially for on-line implementations.

Results from studied algorithms propose operational conditions with remarkable differences and show the complexity and high non-linearity of the FCCU optimization problem, this non-linearity generates local solutions in which deterministic algorithm could stop.

Operational conditions proposed from GA with default and adjusted stopping parameter values confirm that execution time can be reduced in GA, when stopping parameters are adjusted. However, a minimum of generations must be guaranteed to do not reduce the quality of the solution.

Performance of hybrid strategy shows that it isn´t easy to reach the global convergence, and that new studies are necessary to generates reliable strategies.

References

L.T. Biegler, I.E. Grossmann, 2004, Retrospective on optimization, Comput. & Chem. Eng., 28, 8, 1169–1192.

J.L. Fernández, C.I.C. Pinheiro, N. Oliveira, A.I. Neto, F.R. Ribeiro, 2007, Multiplicity of steady states in an UOP FCC unit with high efficiency regenerator, Chemical Eng. Science, 62, 22, 6308–6322.

MathWorks, 2018, How the Genetic Algorithm Works, *Genetic Algorithm*, Available at: https://www.mathworks.com/help/gads/how-the-genetic-algorithm-works.html.

J.D. Reyes, A.L. Rodríguez, A.L., C.A.M. Riascos, 2015, Data Analysis and Modelling of a Fluid Catalytic Cracking Unit (FCCU) for an Implementation of Real Time Optimization, Computer Aided Chem. Eng., 37, 611-616.

A.L. Rodríguez, 2019, Implementation and performance assessment of a real-time optimization system on a virtual fluidized-bed catalytic-cracking plant, MSc Thesis, Universidad Nacional de Colombia.

A.Y.Torgashov, K.C. Park, H.C. Choi, Y.K. Choe, 2003, Stability analysis of distillation control using vector Lyapunov function, Computer Aided Chem. Eng., 15, 1058-1063.

Proceedings of the 14th International Symposium on Process Systems Engineering – PSE 2021+
June 19-23, 2022, Kyoto, Japan © 2022 Elsevier B.V. All rights reserved.
http://dx.doi.org/10.1016/B978-0-323-85159-6.50218-9

Scalable Stochastic Programming with Bayesian Hybrid Models

Jialu Wang[a], Elvis A. Eugene[a], Alexander W. Dowling[a*]

[a]Department of Chemical and Biomolecular Engineering, University of Notre Dame, Notre Dame, IN 46556, USA
adowling@nd.edu

Abstract

Bayesian hybrid models (BHMs) fuse physics-based insights with machine learning constructs to correct for systematic bias. In this paper, we demonstrate a scalable computational strategy to embed BHMs in an equation-oriented modelling environment. Thus, this paper generalizes stochastic programming, which traditionally focuses on aleatoric uncertainty (as characterized by a probability distribution for uncertainty model parameters) to also consider epistemic uncertainty, i.e., mode-form uncertainty or systematic bias as modelled by the Gaussian process in the BHM. As an illustrative example, we consider ballistic firing using a BHM that includes a simplified glass-box (i.e., equation-oriented) model that neglects air resistance and a Gaussian process model to account for systematic bias (i.e., epistemic or model-form uncertainty) induced from the model simplification. The gravity parameter and the GP hypermeters are inferred from data in a Bayesian framework, yielding a posterior distribution. A novel single-stage stochastic program formulation using the posterior samples and Gaussian quadrature rules is proposed to compute the optimal decisions (e.g., firing angle and velocity) that minimize the expected value of an objective (e.g., distance from a stationary target). PySMO is used to generate expressions for the GP prediction mean and uncertainty in Pyomo, enabling efficient optimization with gradient-based solvers such as Ipopt. A scaling study characterizes the solver time and number of iterations for up to 2,000 samples from the posterior.

Keywords: Hybrid model; Bayesian uncertainty quantification; Optimization; Gaussian process; Pyomo

1. Introduction

Predictive models play a key role in control and decision-making (Adjiman et al., 2021). While the glass-box models are constructed from scientific principles and have a deeper understanding of the underlying processes, they are often complex to form and solve. Many glass-box models contain unknown parameters that are inferred from experimental data. These data are often subject to random phenomena such as variability between experiments or observation noise (Kalyanaraman et al., 2015), which gives rise to aleatory (i.e., parametric) uncertainties. Stochastic programming and robust optimization are routinely used to directly incorporate parametric uncertainty into decision-making frameworks. However, to maintain computational tractability, glass-box models are often simplified or replaced with surrogate models in multiscale engineering frameworks (Biegler et al., 2014). The systematic bias from model inadequacy arising from such simplifications is often referred to as model-form or epistemic uncertainty (McClarren, 2018).

Bayesian hybrid models (BHM) offer a principled framework to quantify, propagate, and mitigate aleatoric and epistemic uncertainties by combining physical glass-box models with black-box surrogate models. In their seminal work, statisticians Kennedy and O'Hagan (2001) proposed a (Bayesian) hybrid modelling framework using Gaussian process models:

$$y = \eta(\boldsymbol{x}|\boldsymbol{\theta}) + \delta(\boldsymbol{x}|\boldsymbol{\phi}, \boldsymbol{D}) + \varepsilon \tag{1}$$

The prediction y consists of three components: the inadequate (simplified or reduced order) glass-box model $\eta(\boldsymbol{x}|\boldsymbol{\theta})$ which depends on the state variables $\boldsymbol{x}$ and model parameters $\boldsymbol{\theta}$; the Gaussian process discrepancy $\delta(\boldsymbol{x}|\boldsymbol{\phi}, \boldsymbol{D})$ which models epistemic uncertainty as a function of the state variables $\boldsymbol{x}$, hyperparameters $\boldsymbol{\phi}$, and data $\boldsymbol{D} = [\boldsymbol{x_{obs}}, \boldsymbol{y_{obs}}]$; and, finally, the observation error ε which is modeled as a random variable with known probability distribution. Unlike other hybrid model architectures, such as a neural differential equation, the probabilistic nature of the GP enables the use of Bayesian calibration (Higdon et al., 2004) to infer the model parameters and hyperparameters and provides readily interpretable uncertainty information. The joint posterior distribution of model parameters resulting from Bayesian model calibration informs the uncertainty in the models; specifically, the distribution of model parameters $\boldsymbol{\theta}$ and observation error ε quantifies aleatory uncertainty while the GP output quantifies epistemic uncertainty. We emphasize that prior applications of the Kennedy-O'Hagan framework in chemical engineering (Mebane et al., 2013, Kalyanaraman et al., 2015, Kalyanaraman et al., 2016, Bhat et al., 2017) predominately considers model calibration and uncertainty propagation and not decision-making under uncertainty.

2. Methods

2.1 Stochastic Programming Formulation

In this work, we develop and implement a single-stage stochastic program formulation in Pyomo (Hart et al., 2017) to optimize decisions using BHMs by minimizing the expected values of an arbitrary objective function $u(y)$ in the form of Eqs. (2a):

$$\min_{\boldsymbol{x}} \mathop{\mathrm{E}}_{\boldsymbol{\theta},\boldsymbol{\phi}}[u(y)] \approx \frac{1}{\sqrt{\pi}} \sum_{s \in S} \sum_{j \in J} w_s w_j u_{s,j} \tag{2a}$$

$$\delta_j = \mu(\boldsymbol{x}|\boldsymbol{\phi}, \boldsymbol{D}) + \sqrt{2} z_j \, \sigma(\boldsymbol{x}|\boldsymbol{\phi}, \boldsymbol{D}), \qquad \forall j \in J \tag{2b}$$

$$\eta_s = \eta(\boldsymbol{x}|\boldsymbol{\theta}_s), \ \forall s \in S \tag{2c}$$

$$y_{s,j} = f(\eta_s, \delta_j), \forall s, j \in S \times J \tag{2d}$$

$$u_{s,j} = u(y_{s,j}), \forall s, j \in S \times J \tag{2e}$$

In Eq. (2a), the expectation E of $u(y)$ is approximated using scenario weights $w_s = 1/|S|$. Set S contains samples from the posterior distribution (trace) of $\boldsymbol{\theta}$. Set J contains Gauss-Hermite quadrature nodes z_j and weights w_j, which are used in Eq. (2b) to approximate the GP output distribution characterized by GP prediction mean μ and standard deviation σ. In Eq. (2c), the glass-box model is evaluated at samples θ_s. In Eqs.

(2d) and (2e), the BHM output y and objective function $u(y)$ are evaluated over the set $S \times J$. This formulation is computationally attractive because the highly nonlinear GP prediction mean and standard deviation are evaluated only once, while the glass-box model, and the objective function are evaluated $|S|$, and $|S| \times |J|$ times, respectively.

2.2 Ballistics Firing Example

We apply the stochastic program to the ballistics example from Eugene et al. (2020):

$$\eta_s = \frac{2v_0^2}{g_s} \cdot \sin \psi \cdot \cos \psi, \forall s \in S \tag{3a}$$

$$y_{s,j} = \eta_s + \delta_j, \forall s, j \in S \times J \tag{3b}$$

$$y_{s,j} - \bar{y} = u_{s,j}^+ - u_{s,j}^-, \ u_{s,j} = u_{s,j}^+ + u_{s,j}^-, \ u_{s,j}^+, u_{s,j}^- \geq 0, \forall s, j \in S \times J \tag{3c}$$

Eqs. (3a, b) describe the BHM. The state variables are $x = [v_0, \psi]$, where v_0 (m/s) is the firing velocity and ψ (°) is the firing angle. The glass-box model has one uncertain parameter, the acceleration due to gravity g. y (m) is the distance to the impact location of the projectile measured horizontally from $y=0$ which is the firing location of the projectile. We seek to predict the optimum conditions x to hit a target a fixed distance $\bar{y} = 100$ m away, despite neglecting air resistance (epistemic uncertainty) in the glass-box model. The objective function $u(y) = |y - \bar{y}|$ is reformulated using slack variables in Eq. (3c) to provide differentiable constraints for gradient-based optimization. By combining Eqs. (2) and (3), the expectation of u is minimized to find the optimum $x = [v_0, \psi]$ to hit the target.

The observed data $D = [x_{obs}, y_{obs}]$ is generated from the true physical model which includes the effects of air-resistance on the projectile resulting in its non-parabolic trajectory as described by Eugene et al. (2020). Six data points corresponding to observations from experiments 1 to 5 and 6c in Table 1 of Eugene et al., 2020 were used for the *sequential Bayesian calibration* of the hybrid model. First, the glass-box model is calibrated using the data D, a likelihood function, and priors (see Eugene et al. 2020 for details) via Hamiltonian Monte Carlo in PyMC3 (Salvatier et al., 2016) which returns a trace of 2,000 samples from the posterior distribution of the glass-box model parameter g. Next, using the mean value of g from the trace, $\bar{g}$, we compute the residuals $y_{obs} - \eta(x_{obs}, g)$ which represents the systematic bias in the model due to epistemic uncertainty. These residuals are used to train a discrepancy function for which we assume a Gaussian process with kriging kernel:

$$y_{obs} - \eta(x_{obs}, \bar{g}) = \delta(x|\phi, D) \sim \mathcal{GP}(\mu, k(\cdot, \cdot)) \tag{4a}$$

$$k(x_j, x_k) = \sigma_f^2 \exp\left(-\sum_{i=1}^n \beta_i |x_{ij} - x_{ik}|^2\right), \ j, k \in 1, \dots, m, \ \beta_i \geq 0 \tag{4b}$$

where μ and σ_f^2 are the prediction mean and the variance of the GP model, respectively and β_i is the kriging weight. $n=2$ denotes the number of input dimensions for $x = [v_0, \psi]$, and m = 6 is the number of observations in the training data set for the GP. The GP model hyperparameters $\phi = [\mu, \sigma_f^2, \beta_1, \beta_2] = [-0.68, 2.28, 1.53, 0.13]$ are trained using maximum likelihood estimation (MLE) (Forrester et al., 2008) implemented in the

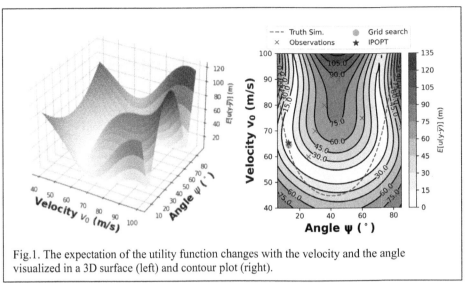

Fig.1. The expectation of the utility function changes with the velocity and the angle visualized in a 3D surface (left) and contour plot (right).

PySMO toolbox of IDAES (Lee et al., 2021). We do not explicitly model aleatory uncertainty due to observation noise in this study.

3. Results

The optimization problem in Eqs. (2, 3) is constructed in Pyomo and solved using IPOPT and the linear solver MA57 (HSL, 2007) using $|S| = 1000$ and $|J|=10$. To visualize the objective function surface and contours in Fig. 1, square instances of Eqs. (2,3), i.e., x is fixed such that there are no degrees of freedom, are evaluated using a grid of 2750 uniformly space samples over $v_0 \in [40, 100]$ (m/s) and $\psi \in [5.7, 85.5]$ (°). Fig. 1 (left) shows that firing at large angles (near vertical orientation) with large velocities results in undesirably high objective values with expected miss distances over 120 m. In contrast, firing at shallower angles (near horizontal orientation) and modest velocities results in expected miss distances less than 15 m. The dashed blue line in Fig. 1 (right) shows the combinations of angles and velocities that result in a direct hit based on simulations of the true physical model. The optimum calculated by the gradient-based solver Ipopt (purple star), and the grid search optimum (yellow dot), are nearly identical and both close to the direct hit line, indicating Bayesian hybrid model and stochastic programming formulation accurately account for epistemic uncertainty. The optimization problem is reliably solved by Ipopt in approximately 4 s on a MacBook with a 2.6 GHz Intel Core i7 CPU, finding an optimal solution as $v_0 = 65.34$ m/s, $\psi = 12.99$ ° and an objective function value of 5.07 m. The optimum found by the grid search is $v_0 = 64.49$ m/s, $\psi = 13.1$ °, and the optimized expectation value is 5.14 m. As expected, the gradient-based solver outperforms the grid search.

Next, we demonstrate the scalability of the proposed stochastic programming formulation. Fig. 2 shows the variation in CPU time and the number of Ipopt iterations as the number of scenarios $|S|$ increases. For each value of $|S|$, Eqs. (2, 3) are resolved 50 times using samples randomly drawn from the posterior distribution trace. For $|S| = 2000$, Eqs. (2, 3) are solved once using the entire trace. The dots represent the medians for both metrics, while the error bar represents the 75th and 25th percentiles. Fig. 2 (left) shows that as $|S|$ increases, the median CPU time increases from 0.03 s with 10 scenarios, to 4.8 s with

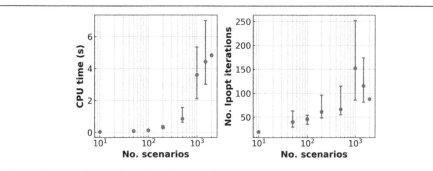

Fig.2. The CPU time and number of IPOPT iterations increase with the number of samples $|S|$. The dots represent the median and the error bars denote the 25%-ile and 75%-ile for 50 random samples except for $|S| = 2,000$.

2000 scenarios. Likewise, Fig. 2 (right) shows median of the number of Ipopt iterations increases from 19 with 10 scenarios, achieving a peak at 152.5 with 1,000 scenarios, and decreases to 88 with 2,000 scenarios. We hypothesize the large variability in metrics for a given $|S|$ is due to the different scenario data considered for each of the 50 replicates. The problem considering 2,000 scenarios can be solved in less than 4.8 s and 88 iterations with 82,014 variables and 62,012 equality constraints, showing that this stochastic program can be reliably solved by gradient-based solvers with small computational burden. It is also noted that the optimum decisions are practically the same as $|S|$ increases. This highlights the potential to accommodate larger problems with multiple sources of model-form uncertainty, i.e., multiple GP discrepancy functions, by using only a modest number of posterior scenarios, e.g., $|S|$ is 10 or 50. Likewise, we hypothesize this formulation can scale to a large number of glass-box parameters $\boldsymbol{\theta}$ using a modest number of posterior samples and approaches such as sample average approximation. Systematic study of these scaling properties is left as future work.

4. Conclusions

In this paper, we demonstrate a scalable stochastic programming formulation for optimization under both aleatoric (i.e., parametric) and epistemic (i.e., model-form) uncertainties using Bayesian hybrid models (BHMs). By leveraging both Gaussian quadrature rules and PySMO, we demonstrate efficient optimization using the equation-oriented Pyomo modeling environment and gradient-based Ipopt nonlinear programming solver. Through an illustrative ballistics example, we show the Kennedy-O'Hagan inspired BHMs effectively capture epistemic uncertainty; their predictions are consistent with the full-physics true model. Moreover, accounting for epistemic uncertainty in the stochastic programming formulation may be accomplished using as little as 10 samples. As future work, we plan to explore the application of optimization-supported decision-making with hybrid models for diverse applications in process system engineering and adjacent domains. We are especially interested in using BHMs to account for information-loss from model simplified in molecular-to-systems engineering frameworks.

Acknowledgement

This project was funded by NSF CBET Award CBET-1941596. E. A. E. gratefully acknowledges partial support from the Patrick and Jana Eiler's Graduate Fellowship. J.W. gratefully acknowledges partial support from the Carbon Capture Simulation for Industry

Impact ($CCSI^2$), funded through the U.S. DOE office of Fossil Energy by the Lawrence Berkeley National Laboratory through contract #DE-AC02-05CH11231.

References

C.S. Adjiman, N.V. Sahinidis, D.G. Vlachos, B. Bakshi, C.T. Maravelias and C. Georgakis, 2021, Process systems engineering perspective on the design of materials and molecules, Ind. Eng. Chem. Res, 60, 14, 5194-5206, 10.1021/acs.iecr.0c05399

K.S. Bhat, D.S. Mebane, P. Mahapatra and C.B. Storlie, 2017, Upscaling uncertainty with dynamic discrepancy for a multi-scale carbon capture system, Journal of the American Statistical Association, 112, 520, 1453-1467,

L.T. Biegler, Y.-d. Lang and W. Lin, 2014, Multi-scale optimization for process systems engineering, Computers & chemical engineering, 60, 17-30, 10.1016/j.compchemeng.2013.07.009

E.A. Eugene, X. Gao and A.W. Dowling, 2020, Learning and optimization with bayesian hybrid models, 2020 American Control Conference (ACC), 3997-4002, 10.23919/ACC45564.2020.9148007

A. Forrester, A. Sobester and A. Keane, 2008, Engineering design via surrogate modelling: A practical guide, John Wiley & Sons,

W.E. Hart, C.D. Laird, J.-P. Watson, D.L. Woodruff, G.A. Hackebeil, B.L. Nicholson and J.D. Siirola, 2017, Pyomo-optimization modeling in python, Springer, 67,

D. Higdon, M. Kennedy, J.C. Cavendish, J.A. Cafeo and R.D. Ryne, 2004, Combining field data and computer simulations for calibration and prediction, SIAM journal on scientific computing, 26, 2, 448-466, 10.1137/s1064827503426693

HSL, 2007, Collection of fortran codes for large-scale scientific computation, http://www. hsl. rl. ac. uk,

J. Kalyanaraman, Y. Fan, Y. Labreche, R.P. Lively, Y. Kawajiri and M.J. Realff, 2015, Bayesian estimation of parametric uncertainties, quantification and reduction using optimal design of experiments for CO_2 adsorption on amine sorbents, Computers & chemical engineering, 81, 376, 10.1016/j.compchemeng.2015.04.028

J. Kalyanaraman, Y. Kawajiri, R.P. Lively and M.J. Realff, 2016, Uncertainty quantification via bayesian inference using sequential monte carlo methods for CO_2 adsorption process, AIChE Journal, 62, 9, 3352-3368,

M.C. Kennedy and A. O'Hagan, 2001, Bayesian calibration of computer models, Journal of the Royal Statistical Society. Series B, Statistical methodology, 63, 3, 425-464, 10.1111/1467-9868.00294

A. Lee, J.H. Ghouse, J.C. Eslick, C.D. Laird, J.D. Siirola, M.A. Zamarripa, D. Gunter, J.H. Shinn, A.W. Dowling, D. Bhattacharyya, L.T. Biegler, A.P. Burgard and D.C. Miller, 2021, The idaes process modeling framework and model library—flexibility for process simulation and optimization, Journal of advanced manufacturing and processing, 3, 3, 10.1002/amp2.10095

R.G. McClarren, 2018, Uncertainty quantification and predictive computational science : A foundation for physical scientists and engineers, Cham : Springer International Publishing : Imprint: Springer,

D.S. Mebane, K.S. Bhat, J.D. Kress, D.J. Fauth, M.L. Gray, A. Lee and D.C. Miller, 2013, Bayesian calibration of thermodynamic models for the uptake of CO_2 in supported amine sorbents using ab initio priors, Physical Chemistry Chemical Physics, 15, 12, 4355-4366,

J. Salvatier, T.V. Wiecki and C. Fonnesbeck, 2016, Probabilistic programming in python using PyMC3, PeerJ. Computer science, 2, e55, 10.7717/peerj-cs.55

A. Wächter and L.T. Biegler, 2006, On the implementation of an interior-point filter line-search algorithm for large-scale nonlinear programming, Mathematical programming, 106, 1, 25-57

Proceedings of the 14th International Symposium on Process Systems Engineering – PSE 2021+
June 19-23, 2022, Kyoto, Japan © 2022 Elsevier B.V. All rights reserved.
http://dx.doi.org/10.1016/B978-0-323-85159-6.50219-0

A Combined Particle Swarm Optimization and Outer Approximation Optimization Strategy for the Optimal Design of Distillation Systems

Fanyi Duanmu, Dian Ning Chia, and Eva Sorensen[*]

Department of Chemical Engineering, University College London (UCL), Torrington Place, London WC1E 7JE, United Kingdom

*Corresponding author: e.sorensen@ucl.ac.uk

Abstract

Distillation is by far the most important separation process in the chemical industries, but is also one of the most energy intensive units, thus significant efforts are being placed on optimizing the design and operation of both new and existing distillation systems to achieve potentially significant energy and/or capital savings. This work introduces an optimization strategy based on combining a preliminary stochastic optimization method, either Particle Swarm Optimization (PSO) or Genetic Algorithm (GA), which is used to perform a global search, with a deterministic optimization method, Outer Approximation method (OAERAP), for the local search. A dividing wall distillation column and a hybrid distillation/pervaporation superstructure is used to illustrate the methodology. The performance of stand-alone PSO, stand-alone GA, combined PSO/OAERAP and combined GA/OAERAP, are compared and it is shown that the PSO/OAERAP combination provides the optimal design in a significantly shorter time and can also optimize a superstructure efficiently. This work also presents the use of a parallel computing function when performing stochastic optimization, which significantly speeds up the optimization.

Keywords: Particle Swarm Optimization, Parallel Computing, Distillation, Dividing Wall Column, Hybrid Distillation

1. Introduction

The optimization of a distillation system is a highly non-convex Mixed Integer Nonlinear Programming (MINLP) problem due to the tight coupling between different parts of the mathematical model (thermodynamic equations, MESH equations, etc.) and the existence of discrete (number of stages, feed location, existence of a unit in the superstructure, etc.) and continuous variables (reflux ratio, heat input, flowrates, etc.). The solution is thus is a very challenging task, not only from a computational point of view, particularly for initialization, but also due to the existence of multiple local optima (Javaloyes-Anton et al., 2013). In a previous work (Chia et al., 2021), a combined approach between stochastic (Genetic Algorithm, GA) and deterministic (Outer Approximation / Equality Relaxation / Augmented Penalty, OAERAP) methods was proposed where the preliminary optimal design obtained from the stochastic method acts as the initial values in the deterministic method. It was found that the combined approach can effectively reduce the optimization difficulty, the computational effort, and the overall CPU time.

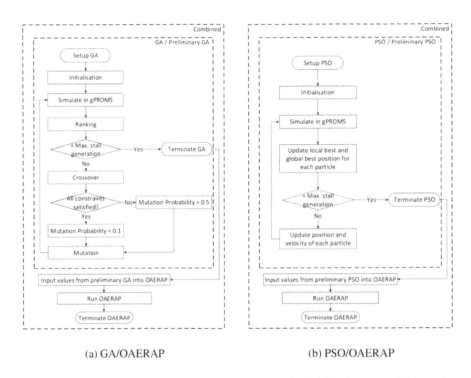

(a) GA/OAERAP   (b) PSO/OAERAP

Figure 1: Flowcharts of the optimization procedures for (a) GA/OAERAP strategy (Chia et al., 2021), and (b) PSO/OAERAP strategy.

In this work, the GA/OAERAP approach is extended, replacing the GA with a Particle Swarm Optimization (PSO) which has a faster convergence speed than GA (Mesloub and Mansour, 2009). Two case studies will be used to illustrate the strategy, including a dividing wall column (DWC) and a hybrid distillation/pervaporation process.

2. Methodology

The combined optimization strategy starts with the stochastic optimization method for the global search, followed by the deterministic optimization method for the local search. Figure 1a shows the GA/OAERAP strategy also studied in a previous work (Chia et al., 2021), where the concept of a preliminary stochastic optimization was initially proposed. A looser fitness tolerance (10^{-2}) is utilized in the preliminary stochastic optimization (preliminary GA) while a tighter fitness tolerance (10^{-4}) is used in the deterministic optimization (OAERAP). In this work, another stochastic optimization (Particle Swarm Optimization, PSO) is also considered in order to evaluate the relative optimization performances of the different methods and method combinations.

The flowsheet of the PSO/OAERAP strategy is shown in Figure 1b and the inner box is the procedure for (preliminary) PSO. The PSO is developed in MATLAB (The MathWorks Inc., 2019), and several classical mathematical functions (Schwefel function and constrained Rosenbrock function) and literature (Deb, 2000; Deep et al., 2009) have been used for validation (not shown).

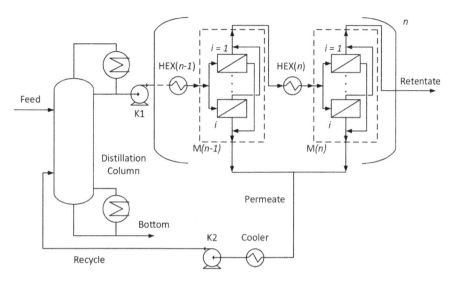

Figure 2: Superstructure of the hybrid distillation/pervaporation process.

The swarm size in PSO and the population size in GA are set to be the same, which is five times the optimization variables, for fair comparison. For the stopping criteria, both PSO and GA are terminated once the fitness value stays constant within the fitness tolerance for 20 consecutive iterations. Other settings of GA can be found in Chia et al. (2021), while the other settings for PSO are given below. The inertia is dynamically varied by randomly choosing a value from a Gaussian distribution of $w \sim N (0.72, \sigma)$ at each iteration (the "random adjustments" method by Engelbrecht (2007), where σ should be small enough to prevent w predominantly larger than one) with $\sigma = 1$ used in this work. The two acceleration coefficients, c_1 (cognitive) and c_2 (social), are linearly changed between 0.5 and 2.5, where c_1 decreases while c_2 increases (Engelbrecht, 2007). All particle locations are initialized using uniform randomization and all particle velocities are initially set as zero. The boundary handling method used in this work is the random forth method (Gandomi and Kashani, 2018) and the penalty function utilized is as proposed by Deb (2000). Moreover, the dynamic bound proposed in Chia et al. (2021) is also applied in PSO to reduce the chance of infeasible designs and simulations. For example, the feed location can never exceed the total number of stages in a column, so the upper bound of the feed location is dynamically changed to be equal to the total number of stages. The outer box in Figure 1b shows the OAERAP procedure. The results from the preliminary PSO are used as initial values in OAERAP. The constraint tolerances in both preliminary PSO and OAERAP, and the fitness tolerance in OAERAP, are set as 10^{-4}, although the fitness tolerance in preliminary PSO is set as 10^{-2}.

The GA and PSO are developed in MATLAB, and OAERAP is built-in in gPROMS ProcessBuilder (Process Systems Enterprise, 2020). All rigorous simulations are performed in gPROMS ProcessBuilder, and gO:MATLAB (Process Systems Enterprise, 2019) is used to transfer data between gPROMS ProcessBuilder and MATLAB. Moreover, the parallel computing function is activated in MATLAB to use 18 workers while doing the stochastic optimization to speed up the optimization.

Table 1: Case Study 1, Dividing Wall Column - Comparison between optimization methods

Items	GA	PSO	GA/OAERAP		PSO/OAERAP	
			Prelim.	Final	Prelim.	Final
Prefractionator						
Total stages	23	24	22	23	21	23
Feed stage	12	14	13	14	12	12
Main Column						
Total stages	42	44	41	42	42	43
Feed stages	8/32	8/33	8/31	7/31	9/31	7/31
Liq. sidedraw stages	18/8	18/8	18/6	19/7	18/9	19/7
Vap. sidedraw stage	32	33	31	31	31	31
Liq. side [†] ($kmol\ h^{-1}$)	332/178	332/176	330/183	330/182	332/186	330/173
Vap. side [†] ($kmol\ h^{-1}$)	614	627	632	641	645	623
Distillate ($kmol\ h^{-1}$)	333	333	334	336	333	336
Molar reflux ratio	2.29	2.24	2.30	2.22	2.38	2.22
Fitness and Time						
TAC ($M\ \$\ y^{-1}$)	6.0374	5.9924	6.0646	5.9852	6.0206	5.9879
Generation/Iteration	190	97	86	-	61	-
Unparallel CPU time (s)	20346	25704	15764	128	14746	117
Parallel CPU time* (s)	2052	2341	1697	-	1465	-
Total CPU time* (s)	2052	2341	1825		1582	

* Parallel computing used, number of workers/cores = 18

† Liquid/vapor side draw from the main column to the prefractionator

3. Case Studies

The proposed PSO/OAERAP optimization strategy is compared with stand-alone GA, stand-alone PSO, and a GA/OAERAP optimization strategy using two different distillation structures including a dividing wall column (DWC) and a hybrid distillation/pervaporation process. In the stand-alone GA and PSO, the tolerance of both constraints and fitness is set as 10^{-4}. All optimization tasks are repeated several times and the designs with the most common fitness and CPU time are chosen for comparison. All calculations are performed using a desktop with an AMD Ryzen 9 3900X CPU (24 logical processors) with 3.79 GHz and 64 GB memory.

3.1. Description

Case study 1 is the separation of equi-molar benzene/toluene/o-xylene (UNIQUAC as thermodynamic model) in a dividing wall column. The feed flowrate is 1000 $kmol\ h^{-1}$ and the feed condition is saturated liquid at 0.37 *bar*. The column is operated at 0.37 *bar*, and pressure drop is neglected. Since there is no commercially available DWC library in gPROMS ProcessBuilder, a thermodynamically equivalent Petlyuk structure is used instead. Case study 2 is a hybrid distillation/pervaporation process (Figure 2) and the membrane model is a user-defined lumped hollow fiber model (validated against the experimental data by Tsuyumoto et al. (1997), not shown) to separate a feed of 200 *kmol* h^{-1} saturated liquid ethanol/water mixture at 1 *bar* with 10 *mol %* ethanol (UNIQUAC as thermodynamic model). The membrane network allows optimization of number of membrane stages in series, number of membrane modules in parallel at each stage, and the existence of membrane stage feed heaters. Due to computational limitations, a simplified optimization method proposed by Marriott and Sorensen (2003) is used, with the upper bound of the number of membrane stages studied set as eight stages. The

Table 2: Case Study 2, Hybrid Distillation - Comparison between optimization methods

Items	GA	PSO	GA/OAERAP		PSO/OAERAP	
			Prelim.	Final	Prelim.	Final
Column						
Total stages	21	21	20	19	21	21
Feed stages	17/17	17/18	17/17	16/18	17/17	17/20
Distillate (*kmol h*$^{-1}$)	23	23	23	23	23	23
Molar reflux ratio	1.15	1.19	1.45	1.34	1.19	1.16
Membrane Network *						
No. membrane stages	5	5	5	5	5	5
No. modules in stage 1	8	7	8	8	9	7
No. modules in stage 2	11	9	11	10	13	8
No. modules in stage 3	9	11	8	8	12	12
No. modules in stage 4	17	14	14	15	14	15
No. modules in stage 5	18	20	19	20	15	20
Total membrane area (*m^2*)	378	366	360	366	378	372
Fitness and Time						
TAC (*M $ y^{-1}*)	0.7575	0.7506	0.7690	0.7606	0.7593	0.7527
Generation/Iteration	93	86	45	-	34	-
Unparallel CPU time (*s*)	7308	9082	4140	22	4303	9
Parallel CPU time † (*s*)	813	828	433	-	371	-
Total CPU time † (*s*)	813	828	455		380	

* Existence of membrane stage feed heater is not shown due to space limit, but all the optimization results show that feed heaters exist for all stages except for stage 1
† Parallel computing used, number of workers/cores = 18

number of membrane stages is first fixed, with all the other variables optimized simultaneously. This procedure is then repeated for each number of membrane stages that are being studied and the optimized total annualized costs (TACs) are recorded. Finally, the structure which gives the lowest TAC is considered as the optimal design, and its optimized variables, CPU time, and TAC are shown in the Results section.

3.2. Results and Discussion

The optimized designs of each case study using the different optimization methods are shown in Tables 1 and 2, respectively. The TAC and CPU time are chosen as the main performance indicators. The optimization is significantly sped up with the use of parallel computing with 18 workers, where it is up to 11 times and 12 times faster for the two case studies, respectively. Comparing stand-alone GA and PSO, and preliminary GA and PSO, it shows that PSO and preliminary PSO usually require fewer iterations but a longer CPU time per iteration than GA. GA requires lesser time per iteration due to its algorithm where a few chromosomes in the current generation will appear in the next generation (elite parents and low mutation probability at the end), leading to a higher rate of feasible simulation and lower CPU time for each generation, owing to the "sequential initialization" algorithm in gPROMS ProcessBuilder (subsequent simulation is initialized using the results from the previous simulation, and the simulation will be easier with similar initial values). However, by considering the parallel CPU time, PSO and preliminary PSO show similar CPU times with GA and preliminary GA, indicating a better paralleling computing performance than PSO and preliminary PSO. Comparison between stand-alone GA and PSO shows that PSO can yield a better design. However, for GA/OAERAP and PSO/OAERAP, the final TACs are similar. The comparison between combined optimization strategies and their corresponding stand-alone methods shows that the combined optimization strategies can achieve good optimal designs in a shorter CPU time, where the time savings for GA/OAERAP and PSO/OAERAP are up to 44 % and 54 %, respectively. The PSO/OAERAP is even faster than GA/OAERAP with time saving up to 16 % for the combined PSO strategy compared to the GA strategy. In our experience, the optimization of distillation using PSO and preliminary PSO also has a much higher chance to converge into a good optimal design and the results from several repeated optimizations are close.

4. Conclusions

This work considers a combined optimization strategy of a stochastic optimization method (GA or PSO) followed by a deterministic optimization method (OAERAP) for the optimisation of different distillation systems, implemented using parallel computing. The comparison between stand-alone stochastic methods (GA and PSO) and the combined strategy (GA/OAERAP and PSO/OAERAP) shows that PSO/OAERAP can yield an optimal design within a significantly shorter CPU time. With the help of the parallel computing function (18 workers), the optimization speed can be about 11 times faster and the effect is even better for PSO than for GA. Moreover, a simple superstructure optimization of a hybrid distillation/pervaporation process (case study 2) showed that the combined optimization strategy is also capable of handling superstructure optimization of distillation systems.

References

Chia, D. N., Duanmu, F., and Sorensen, E. (2021). Optimal Design of Distillation Columns Using a Combined Optimisation Approach. In Turkay, M. and Gani, R., editors, 31st European Symposium on Computer Aided Process Engineering, pages 153–158. Elsevier B.V.Y.

Deb, K. (2000). An efficient constraint handling method for genetic algorithms. Computer Methods in Applied Mechanics and Engineering, 186(2-4):311–338.

Deep, K., Singh, K. P., Kansal, M., and Mohan, C. (2009). A real coded genetic algorithm for solving integer and mixed integer optimization problems. Applied Mathematics and Computation, 212(2):505–518.

Engelbrecht, A. (2007). Computational intelligence: An introduction. John Wiley&Sons Ltd, 2 ed.

Gandomi, A. H. and Kashani, A. R. (2018). Probabilistic evolutionary bound constraint handling for particle swarm optimization. Operational Research, 18(3):801–823.

Javaloyes-Anton, J., Ruiz-Femenia, R., and Caballero, J. A. (2013). Rigorous Design of Complex Distillation Columns Using Process Simulators and the Particle Swarm Optimization Algorithm. Industrial & Engineering Chemistry Research, 52(44):15621– 15634.

Marriott, J. and Sorensen, E. (2003). The optimal design of membrane systems. Chemical Engineering Science, 58(22):4991–5004.

Mesloub, S. and Mansour, A. (2009). Hybrid PSO and GA for global maximization. International Journal of Open Problems in Computer Science and Mathematics, 2(4):597– 608.

Process Systems Enterprise (2019). gO:MATLAB.

Process Systems Enterprise (2020). gPROMS ProcessBuilder version 1.4.

The MathWorks Inc. (2019). MATLAB R2019b version 9.7.

Tsuyumoto, M., Teramoto, A., and Meares, P. (1997). Dehydration of ethanol on a pilotplant scale, using a new type of hollow-fiber membrane. Journal of Membrane Sci., 133(1):83–94.

Proceedings of the 14th International Symposium on Process Systems Engineering – PSE 2021+
June 19-23, 2022, Kyoto, Japan © 2022 Elsevier B.V. All rights reserved.
http://dx.doi.org/10.1016/B978-0-323-85159-6.50220-7

A semantic based decision support framework to enable model and data integration

Edlira Vakaj*, Linsey Koo[b], Franjo Cecelja[b]

[a]*Department of Computing and Data Science, Brimingham City University, Birmingham, UK*
[b]*Centre for process & Information Systems Engineering, University of Surrey, Guildford GU2 7XH, UK*

Edlira.vakaj@bcu.ac.uk

Abstract

Model reusability and integration with datasets are major contributors towards their interoperability, the concepts that follows process established by computer aided process engineering (CAPE) community (Belaud & Pons 2002). This paper proposes a semantic approach which enables model/data registration, their discovery and concomitantly model their integration. The functionality of the process is fully controlled by a biorefining domain ontology implemented using Ontology Web Language (OWL) and tested using biorefining related scenarios.

Keywords: biorefining, semantic repository, model integration, OWL-S.

1. Introduction

Significant efforts are applied on modelling to support synthesis and design, planning and scheduling, process monitoring and control in biorefining. Modelling addresses the complexity in characteristics of various types of feedstock and associated processing technologies and respective pathways, including thermochemical, chemical, biochemical and hybrid conversion routes, among other aspects. As a result, there are many contributions from modelling and experimental prospective and a large number of custom-made models and data are available to be used and hence reused. Integrating existing models and data developed/generated by different tools and processes, sharing and reusing them towards a common aim is still a challenge. To address this problem, we introduce a semantic approach towards model and data integration, all coordinated by a biorefinery ontology. The concept follows on the principle of service integration which in consequence benefits from respective Ontology Web Service (OWL-S) framework.

2. Theoretical formulation of model/data integration

A superstructure approach is used to represent models by their functionality, inputs, outputs and auxiliary inputs (Figure 1a), whereas datasets are characterised by their functionality in relation to what they describe, outputs representing actual data and auxiliary inputs (Figure 1b). The model inputs and the model and data outputs and auxiliary inputs are characterised by n_I input properties $P_i^{n_I}$, n_O output properties $P_i^{n_O}$ and n_E auxiliary properties $P_i^{n_E}$ as shown in (Figure 1) (Koo at al, 2017).

The whole process of matching and then model and data integration is coordinated by the InterCAPEmodel ontology defined as a 6-tuple structure $O = \langle H^I, H_C, R_i^C, R^C, E^C, S_i^I \rangle$ of i) instances s_j formed of n_M models and n_D datasets, organised into classes S_i^I with N_i^I distinct names representing concepts, ii) a graph $H_C = (S_i^I, is - a)$ forming a subsumption hierarchy in ontology sense, iii) class relationships R_i^C which form a set of bijective relationships $r_{i,j}$ between all the elements of domain classes, iv) a subsumtion R^C of properties R_i^C, and v) extension E^C of a class S_i^I which is defined by the relationship R_i^C profiling the structural properties of the class by its relations with other classes.

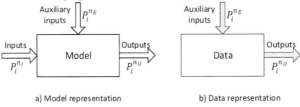

a) Model representation   b) Data representation

Figure 1 Model and data representation

Model and data matching is performed on the request of the user for model/data discovery or formed by the input properties of requesting model for model/data integration. The matching process is based on i) metrics defined over model/data output properties $P_i^{No} = \{p_{i,j} | p_{i,j} \in \mathbb{R}, \ i = 1, \cdots, n_C\}_{j=1}^{No}$ characterising them (only numerical output properties are taken into account) and representing the domain explicit knowledge, and ii) metrics defined over mutual position (distance measured in number of edges) of respective classes in the domain ontology, the InterCAPEmodel ontology, and representing the domain tacit knowledge. For matching the properties $\mathbf{p}_n$, we define h-metric h_k^V as

$$h_k^V = \left\{ \frac{\mathbf{p}_i \cdot \mathbf{p}_j}{\|\mathbf{p}_i\| \|\mathbf{p}_j\|} \right\}_{i,j=1}^{n}, \quad k = 1,2, \cdots, 2^n \qquad (1)$$

representing the measure known as the **vector similarity**. For metrics measuring the mutual position of respective S_i^I and S_j^I classes in the ontology, we define h-metric h_k^C as

$$h_k^C = \min_{S_C^I \in H^I} \left[\delta(S_i^I, S_C^I) + \delta(S_j^I, S_C^I) \right] \qquad (2)$$

where $\delta(S_i^I, S_C^I)$ $(\delta(S_j^I, S_C^I))$ is the distance between classes S_i^I (S_j^I) and another class S_C^I measured in number of intermediate edges in graph sense along subsumption H_C and along selected R_i^C relationships. Final match is obtained as an aggregated similarity measure h_k as

$$h_k = \frac{\alpha h_k^V + \beta h_k^C}{\alpha + \beta} \qquad (3)$$

where α and β are weighting factors deepening the semantics of the ontology similarity and their values are dictated by the application. The similarity h_k is then used to support decision in model and data integration and/or reuse.

3. Implementation

The semantic based decision support platform was implemented using semantic web technologies and knowledge graphs. The core functionalities include: i) *Model/data Registration* for registering a model with their Inputs, Outputs, Preconditions and Effects, ii) *Model/data Publishing* for sharing models and data, iii) *Model/data Discovery* for creating a set of candidate models and data for integration and/or reuse, iv) *Model/data Selection* towards most appropriate integration, and v) *Model composition* for integration and data exchange between the selected models and datasets. The architecture (Figure 1) of the platform follows the semantic web application principles in which various and heterogeneous data sources are considered, their mapping to the corresponding schema or ontology for providing a knowledge graph of concepts and associated instances (Kalemi et al. 2017). The platform is organised around the InterCAPEmodel domain ontology and well established OWL-S ontology. The InterCAPEmodel ontology defines a common vocabulary to capture the knowledge of various biorefining models or the supply chain network using taxonomy, attributes, and relations of the models and datasets. OWL-S framework (Martin et al. 2007), is a set of interlinked ontologies used to semantically describe web services. In the approach proposed in this paper, each model or dataset is considered as a web service and hence making use of OWL-S which semantically describes them in terms of their functionality, inputs required for successful execution, outputs generated in the course and after the execution, and preconditions (auxiliary inputs) needed for models to run. The model/data knowledge is acquired through the registration phase and concomitant assigning as ontology instances.

The *Model/data Discovery* module is a core part of the platform based on the match-making process. We have adopted a semantic matching which follows the three-stage input/output matching approach: i) elimination, where all datasets and models which do not satisfy the critical criteria are excluded from the selection list, ii) semantic matching by calculating similarity measures which defines the level of compatibility between the requested model/data and the candidate models/data as defined by eq. (3), and iii) ranking of the candidate models/data by similarity measure. The critical criteria is defined by the user during the formulation of the requesting model. Semantic matching process calculates the semantic relevance between the requesting model and all the models published in the repository. This is calculated as an aggregated value of distance measure (eq. (2)) signifying semantic similarity and property similarity (eq. (1)) (Koo et al., 2017).

JAVA programming language and GraphDB in the form of a native RDF graph database are the key technologies used to implement this platform. The interfaces are designed using Bootstrap and Java Server Pages technologies and can be accessed through web browsers. OWLAPI, a Java library for manipulating OWL ontologies is used to verify the consistency of the knowledge base, perform reasoning and disseminate queries to the knowledge base via SPARQL Protocol. In collaboration with the reasoner (Pellet) and other supporting Java classes, OWLAPI, are checking the domain knowledge for consistency, parsing the inferred ontology for passing it to further elaboration from the front end, expanding the knowledge base with new instances of models or integrated models.

Figure 4 demonstrates the platform interface for model/data discovery and concomitant integration. As the first step, the user defines the request, which contains the functionality of the requesting model, the characteristics and the inputs that it needs. In Step 2 a list of most suitable candidate models/data is provided ranked according to the matching level with justification of the match level.

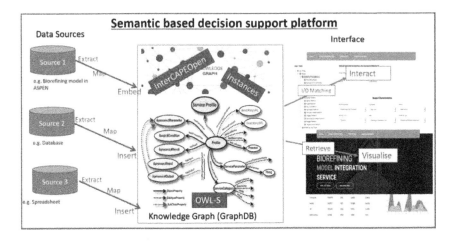

Figure 2 Semantic based decision platform architecture.

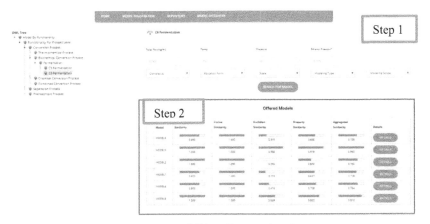

Figure 4 Model/data discovery interface

4. Demonstration

The performance of the proposed model and data integration is demonstrated by a commercial scale process flowsheet for biodiesel production from virgin vegetable oil and waste cooking oil (Zhang *et al.*, 2003; Nguyen and Demirel, 2011). Each stage of the process, such as i) transesterification reaction, ii) methanol recovery, iii) glycerol separation and (iv) fatty acid methyl esters (FAME) purification, are separately registered as an instance in the repository to demonstrate the possible discovery of the models. Here, the model representing FAME purification is the last in chain and therefore identified as a requesting model. The required input component of this model is FAME, hence, the models that have FAME as an output are discovered as a potential match to the FAME purification model. The discovery process was performed by backward matching process and the profiles of discovered models are listed in Table 1. The restriction to the FAME purification process is the presence of glycerol, therefore, the streams that contain glycerol are eliminated, as illustrated in Figure 5. Therefore, the user is presented with three models that have FAME as an output stream without the presence of glycerol in the stream. The combination of hexane extraction, water washing and glycerol separation processes represents a glycerol separation process. The second stage of backward matching is conducted to run the discovered models, which requires FAME and glycerol as inputs in the stream. As a result, a model representing methanol recovery process that obtains a good separation of methanol from FAME and glycerol was identified. In addition, as a final stage of matching, transesterification models using four different catalysts were discovered as potential matches to the methanol recovery model to form a network of process models representing biodiesel production from feedstock to final product.

Table 1 Profile of processes offering potential match

Process Model	# Input Stream	Input components per stream	# Output Stream	Output components per stream
Hexane Extraction	2	S1. FAME, Glycerol S2. Hexane	2	S1. FAME S2. Glycerol
Water Washing	2	S1. FAME, Glycerol S2. Water		
Glycerol Separation	1	S1. FAME, Glycerol		
Methanol Recovery	1	S1. Methanol, FAME, Glycerol	2	S1. Methanol (Recycle) S2. FAME, Glycerol
Transesterification 1 Transesterification 2	3	S1. Waste Oil S2. Methanol S3. Catalyst: T1 - H_2SO_4 T2 - H_2SO_4, NaOH	2	S1. FAME, Glycerol, Methanol S2. Catalyst (Recycle)
Transesterification 3 Transesterification 4	3	S1. Virgin Oil S2. Methanol S3. Catalyst: T1 - NaOH T2 - Ca_3La_1		

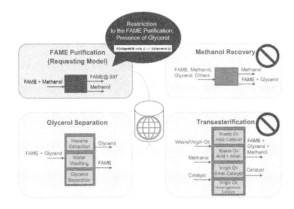

Figure 5 Process of Elimination of the Models with Glycerol

5. Conclusion

The concept of using ontology in model and data integration was introduced to improve upon previous research with particular focus on i) flexibility (partial matching) and reusability (reuse of existing models and data), ii) coordination of every step in the process of model and data integration starting with model and data registration up to their invocation and execution. The semantic algorithm for establishing interoperability between the models and data is presented to reflect the knowledge based on technical compatibility and functional feasibility. The domain ontology embeds both tacit and explicit knowledge in the domain of biorefining modelling. Process models and data are semantically annotated in terms of input(s), output(s), precondition(s), the software environment in which they operate, as well as the functionality they perform. The ma5tching concept is fully justified and its implementation explained.

References

Jean-Pierre Belaud, Michel Pons, Open Software Architecture For Process Simulation: The Current Status of CAPE-OPEN Standard, Computer Aided Chemical Engineering,Volume 10,2002,Pages 847-852,

Kalemi, E., L. Koo, et al. (2017). "A Semantic Repository for Model Integration in Biorefining." Computer Aided Chemical Engineering 40: 2323-2328

Koo, L., N. Trokanas, et al. (2017). "A semantic framework for enabling model integration for biorefining." Computers & Chemical Engineering **100**: 219-231

Nguyen, N. T. and Demirel, Y. (2011) 'A Novel Biodiesel and Glycerol Carbonate Production Plant', International Journal of Chemical Reactor Engineering, 9(1), pp. 5–7.

Zhang, Y. et al. (2003) 'Biodiesel production from waste cooking oil: 1. Process design and technological assessment', Bioresource Technology, 89(1), pp. 1–16

Proceedings of the 14th International Symposium on Process Systems Engineering – PSE 2021+
June 19-23, 2022, Kyoto, Japan © 2022 Elsevier B.V. All rights reserved.
http://dx.doi.org/10.1016/B978-0-323-85159-6.50221-9

Design of Non-Redundant Sensor Networks for Reliable Estimation in Nonlinear Systems

Garima Patel[a], Mani Bhushan[a]*

[a]*Department of Chemical Engineering, Indian Institute of Technology Bombay, Mumbai 400076, India*
mbhushan@iitb.ac.in

Abstract

In this work, we focus on the problem of designing non-redundant sensor network for steady state nonlinear processes where minimum number of sensors are placed to ensure reliable estimation of all process variables. We propose to use an equation-variable matching approach as the basis for designing sensor networks. This approach is based only on the structural information of the system of equations and hence can be used for nonlinear systems without requiring any linearization or knowledge of operating values of the process variables and process parameters. Based on the obtained equation-variable matching, a signal flow graph which represents the sequence of computation of various variables is constructed. Reliability of estimating each variable is then computed based on information extracted from the signal flow graph. The approach is applied to a nonlinear process case study to design optimal sensor network.

Keywords: Reliability, Equation variable matching, Structural equations, Optimization.

1. Introduction

In a typical chemical process, it is generally not possible to measure each and every variable due to technical and economic issues, as well as due to complexities associated with collecting, and processing a large amount of data in real-time. Choosing appropriate variables to be measured in a process, is the sensor network design problem and is the focus of this work. Sensor networks can be designed to ensure satisfaction of various requirements such as those related to observability, estimability, reliability, etc [Bagajewicz and Sanchez, 1999]. For a well-designed sensor network, it is important to be able to estimate all the variables with high reliability, either based on their direct measurement or relationships with other variables as captured by a process model, given that sensors are prone to failure. The current work focuses on this aspect of reliable estimation. For linear flow processes, many graph-theoretic concepts based on spanning trees, cycles, cutsets, chord sets, etc. have been used to aide in the design of sensor networks for reliable estimation [Ali and Narasimhan, 1993, Prakash et. al., 2020].

Most of the real-world systems are nonlinear in nature. For nonlinear processes, the literature is comparatively scarce. While an approach to design sensor network based on cost and precision is available [DuyQuang and Bagajewicz, 2008], there is no reported work on ensuring reliable estimation for nonlinear processes. In this work, we focus on the problem of designing non-redundant sensor network for steady state nonlinear processes where minimum number of sensors are placed to ensure reliable estimation of all process variables.

We propose to use equation-variable matching approach as the basis for designing sensor networks. Equation-variable matching approach is widely used in flowsheeting (process design) literature [Stadtherr et. al., 1984]. This approach is based only on the structural matrix of the system of equations and hence can be used for nonlinear systems without requiring any linearization or even the knowledge of operating values of the process variables and process parameters. Given a set of variables on which sensors have been placed, we propose to use equation-variable matching approach to match unmeasured variables to equations. A full matching ensures that based on the structural relationships amongst variables, the unmeasured variables can be estimated with the given set of sensors. Based on the obtained matching, a signal flow graph capturing the sequence of computation of various variables is constructed. This in turn allows us to compute the reliability of estimation of each variable given the failure probabilities of sensors on the measured variables. The optimal sensor network design then corresponds to the set of measurements which maximize the minimum reliability of estimation amongst all variables. The proposed approach is generic in the sense that it can be applied to any nonlinear process as it does not make any assumption about the form of the equations.

The rest of the paper is organized as follows. The sensor network design problem for reliable estimation in nonlinear systems is discussed in Section 2. The proposed approach to compute reliability of estimation is discussed in Section 3. An example based on proposed approach is shown in Section 4. Further, case study is presented in Section 5., followed by conclusions and discussions in Section 6.

2. Problem Definition

Consider a nonlinear steady state process modeled as:

$$f(x) = 0 \tag{1}$$

where $x \in R^n$ are the process variables, and $f : R^n \rightarrow R^m$ represents the model equations which are nonlinear in nature. Further it is assumed that $n \geq m$. Given the model equations as Eq.(1), the sensor network design problem is to choose $n - m$ variables to be measured so as to maximize the minimum reliability of estimation amongst all variables. This is stated as:

$$\max_{q_1, q_2, \dots, q_n} \quad \min_{1 \leq i \leq n} R_i : s.t. \ \sum_{i=1}^{n} q_i = n - m, \text{ with } q_i \in \{0, 1\}, \ i = 1, 2, \dots, n \tag{2}$$

where, R_i is the reliability of estimation of variable x_i and q_i is a binary variable indicating if variable x_i is measured ($q_i = 1$) or unmeasured ($q_i = 0$). For linear mass flow system, computation of R_i is well understood using graph theoretic concepts [Ali and Narasimhan, 1993, Prakash et. al., 2020]. However, for nonlinear systems this issue has not been addressed in literature and is the focus of the current work.

3. Proposed Methodology

Given a set of $n - m$ measurements in a nonlinear process, we now propose an equation variable matching followed by depth-first search of a signal flow graph to compute reliabilities of estimation of all variables. These ideas are discussed next. Let M be the set of measured variables $m_j \in M, j = 1, 2, \ldots, n - m$, and U be the set of unmeasured variables $u_i \in U, i = 1, 2, \ldots, m$.

3.1. Equation-Variable Matching

As a first step in the proposed approach, each equation is matched to one of its incident unmeasured variable, i.e. to an unmeasured variable which occurs in that equation. This matching is done such that no two equations are matched to the same unmeasured variable, and similarly no two unmeasured variables are matched to the same equations. Matching problem is a well studied problem in literature with several applications and several tools to obtain maximum cardinality matchings [Hopcroft and Karp, 1973, Irving et. al., 2006]. The equation variable matching is based on structural matrix $\mathbf{Z}$ representation of the system of equations in the form of Eq.(1), such that $Z_{i,j} = 1$ if variable x_j appears in equation f_i, and is 0 otherwise. A full equation-variable matching where all the m equations are matched ensures that the system of equations is structurally solvable to yield the values of the unmeasured variables. Lack of full matching implies that at least one unmeasured variable cannot be estimated. For the given set of measurements, to simplify the notation, assume that equation f_i is matched to unmeasured variable $u_i, i = 1, 2, \ldots, m$. The reliability of estimation of each variable can now be computed as discussed next.

3.2. Reliability Computation

The equation-variable matching information provides a sequence in which the variables can be estimated. In particular, variable u_i can be estimated by solving f_i for u_i. This in turn will need estimates of all other variables appearing in equation f_i and thus reliability of estimation of u_i can be obtained in principle by knowing the reliabilities of estimation of other variables occurring in f_i. However, the other unmeasured variables are also computed from their corresponding matched equations using similar concept and their reliabilities are dependent on the variables appearing in those equations. Only the measured variables are not matched to any equation. This sequential nature of variable computation can be represented by a signal flow graph [Robichaud et. al., 1962] $G = (V, E)$. A signal flow graph G is a digraph, with V being the set of vertices, and E being the set of directed edges. Each vertex corresponds to a variable in the original system. An edge from node v_i (corresponding to variable x_i) to v_j (corresponding to variable x_j) exists if variable x_i appears in the equation which is used to compute variable x_j. Since measured variables are not computed from the equations, they will be the root nodes [Cormen et. al., 2001] (nodes with only output edges) in the signal flow graph.

Depth first search based graph traversal [Reif, 1985] from a root node corresponding to measured variable m_i in the signal flow graph is now performed to obtain the set of nodes which can be reached from this root node. The unmeasured variables belonging to this set of reachable nodes are the ones which require the value of m_i for their computation. This depth first search traversal is performed from each root node. The reliability of estimation of any unmeasured variable u_i is then simply the product of reliabilities of sensors of those measured variables from where u_i is reachable, i.e.

$$R_{u_i} = \prod_{m_j \in S_i} R_{m_j}, \qquad u_i \in U \tag{3}$$

where, S_i is the set of measured variables from which there is a path to variable u_i in the signal flow graph. For the measured variables, the reliability of estimation is simply the reliability of the corresponding sensor being in working condition, i.e.

$$R_{m_j} = (1 - s_j), \qquad m_j \in M \tag{4}$$

with s_j being the failure probability of sensor used to measure variable m_j. For the given set of measurements, the system reliability is then the minimum reliability amongst all measured and unmeasured variables. We now present an example to illustrate the proposed ideas.

Remark 1: In the above discussion, it has been assumed that the sensor failure events across different sensors are independent events.

Remark 2: If full equation-variable matching is not obtained in the equation-variable matching step, then system reliability can be directly assigned a value of 0 without any further processing.

4. Example

Consider ammonia flow process [Ali and Narasimhan, 1993] for illustration here. The process is a mass flow process consisting of eight variables (flow rates) and five process units- each corresponding to a mass balance. The process graph is shown in Figure 1(a). The structural matrix of the system of equations is:

$$\mathbf{Z} = \begin{bmatrix} 1 & 0 & 0 & 0 & 0 & 1 & 0 & 1 \\ 1 & 1 & 0 & 0 & 0 & 0 & 0 & 0 \\ 0 & 1 & 1 & 0 & 0 & 0 & 0 & 0 \\ 0 & 0 & 1 & 1 & 1 & 0 & 0 & 0 \\ 0 & 0 & 0 & 1 & 0 & 0 & 1 & 1 \end{bmatrix} \tag{5}$$

This process has eight variables and five equations, and hence three variables need to be measured for a non-redundant sensor placement. For illustration let the measurements be of variables $\{x_1, x_4, x_6\}$. Equation-variable matching is then performed using Dulmage-Mendelsohn decomposition (dmperm function in Matlab) [Dulmage and Mendelsohn, 1958]. The signal flow graph corresponding to this matching is shown in Figure 1(b). In particular, unmeasured variables x_2, x_3, x_5, x_7, x_8 can be matched to equations 2, 3, 4, 5, and 1, respectively. Depth first search traversal is now performed on this graph to compute the set S_i of measured variables from which there is a path to unmeasured variable i in the signal flow graph. For example, set S_8 for unmeasured variable x_8 is $S_8 = \{x_1, x_6\}$ and thus the reliability of estimation of variable x_8 is $R_8 = R_1 R_6 = (1 - s_1)(1 - s_6)$. Similarly, the reliability expressions for all other variables can be computed and are listed as:

$$R_2 = R_1, \; R_3 = R_1, \; R_5 = R_1 R_4, \; R_7 = R_1 R_4, \; R_8 = R_1 R_6 \tag{4}$$

where, $R_1 = (1 - s_1)$, $R_4 = (1 - s_4)$, $R_6 = (1 - s_6)$ with s_1, s_4, s_6 being the failure probabilities of sensors used to measure variables x_1, x_4 and x_6, respectively.

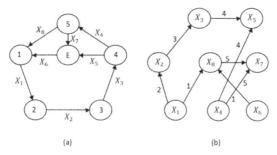

(a)   (b)

Figure 1: (a) Ammonia process graph [Ali and Narasimhan, 1993] (b) The signal flow graph with sensors on $\{x_1, x_4, x_6\}$

We now present a case study of a nonlinear system to perform optimal sensor placement for reliable estimation.

5. Case Study

Consider a steady state nonlinear process shown in Figure 2(a) explained by [Maurya et. al., 2003]. The variables considered in the process are $f, v, w, T, P, m, x_{d1}, x_{d2}, x_{w1}, x_{w2}$ with the sensor failure probabilities as 0.11, 0.12, 0.14, 0.21, 0.24, 0.32, 0.35, 0.38, 0.30, 0.37, respectively. The mathematical model describing the process is given in Figure 2(b).

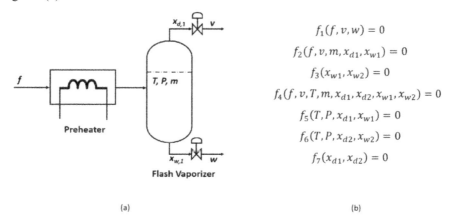

$$f_1(f, v, w) = 0$$
$$f_2(f, v, m, x_{d1}, x_{w1}) = 0$$
$$f_3(x_{w1}, x_{w2}) = 0$$
$$f_4(f, v, T, m, x_{d1}, x_{d2}, x_{w1}, x_{w2}) = 0$$
$$f_5(T, P, x_{d1}, x_{w1}) = 0$$
$$f_6(T, P, x_{d2}, x_{w2}) = 0$$
$$f_7(x_{d1}, x_{d2}) = 0$$

(a)   (b)

Figure 2: (a) Flash Vaporizer [Maurya et. al., 2003] (b) Mathematical Model

This process has ten variables and seven equations, hence the minimum number of measured variables is three. Thus, there are a total of $\binom{10}{3} = 120$ choices. For each choice, the reliabilities of all the variables are computed using the equation-variable matching and signal flow graph traversal approach discussed in section 3. The minimum reliability across all the variables is the system reliability for that measurement combination. By solving the problem given in Eq.(2), the optimal reliability of system, R_{sys} is 0.266. The variables chosen for optimum sensor placement are $\{m, x_{d2}, x_{w2}\}$.

6. Conclusions

A method to design non-redundant sensor network for reliable estimation for nonlinear processes has been proposed in the current work. Based on the concept of equation variable matching, the approach utilizes only structural information about the nonlinear equations and is hence applicable at the design stage as well. The utility of the approach was demonstrated by applying it to a nonlinear case study. Extension of the approach to optimally design redundant sensor networks is being currently investigated.

References

Y. Ali, S. Narasimhan, 1993, Sensor network design for maximizing reliability of linear processes, *AIChE J., 39*, 820

M. J. Bagajewicz, M. C. Sanchez, 1999, Design and upgrade of nonredundant and redundant linear sensor networks, *AIChE J., 45*, 1927

T. H. Cormen, C. E. Leiserson, R. L. Rivest, C. Stein, 2001, Introduction to algorithms, *MIT Electrical Engineering and Computer Science*, The MIT Press, 253

A. Dulmage, N. Mendelsohn, 1958, Coverings of Bipartite Graphs, *Canadian Journal of Mathematics, 10*, 517

N. DuyQuang, M. Bagajewicz, 2008, Design of Nonlinear Sensor Networks for Process Plants, *Ind. Eng. Chem. Res., 47*, 5529

J. E. Hopcroft, R. M. Karp, 1973, An $n^{5/2}$ Algorithm for Maximum Matchings in Bipartite Graphs, *SIAM J. Comput., 2*, 225

R. W. Irving, T. Kavitha, K. Mehlhorn, D. Michail, K. Paluch, 2006, Rank-Maximal Matchings, *ACM Transactions on Algorithms, 2*, 601

M. R. Maurya, R. Rengaswamy, V. Venkatasubramanian, 2003, A Systematic Framework for the Development and Analysis of Signed Digraphs for Chemical Processes. 2. Control Loops and Flowsheet Analysis, *Ind. Eng. Chem. Res., 42*, 4811

O. Prakash, M. Bhushan, S. Narasimhan, R. Rengaswamy, 2020, Sensor Network Design based on System Wide Reliability Criteria: 1. Objetive, *Journal of Process Control, 93*, 66

J. H. Reif, 1985, Depth-First Search is Inherently Sequential, *Inf. Process. Lett., 20*, 229

L. P. A. Robichaud, M. Boisvert, J. Robert, 1962, Signal flow graphs and applications, Englewood Cliffs, N.J., *Prentice Hall*, 214

M. Stadtherr, E. Wood, 1984, Sparse Matrix Methods for Equation-Based Chemical Process Flowsheeting-I, *Comput. Chem. Engng., 8*, 9

Proceedings of the 14th International Symposium on Process Systems Engineering – PSE 2021+
June 19-23, 2022, Kyoto, Japan © 2022 Elsevier B.V. All rights reserved.
http://dx.doi.org/10.1016/B978-0-323-85159-6.50222-0

A Novel Global-Local Feature Preserving Projection Method Based on Adaptive Linear Local Tangent Space Alignment for Process Monitoring

Yang Li, Cheng Ji, Jingde Wang*, Wei Sun*

College of Chemical Engineering, Beijing University of Chemical Technology, North Third Ring Road 15, Chaoyang District, Beijing, 100029, China
sunwei@mail.buct.edu.cn

Abstract

Due to the rapid increase of complexity in industrial process, feature extraction plays an important role in process monitoring. In conventional process monitoring methods, represented by multivariate statistical process monitoring (MSPM) method, global feature of process data is mainly considered, such as variance information. By contrast, the local feature of process data, obtained by preserving neighbourhood information, is preferred in newly emerging manifold learning method. Process monitoring methods with both global and local features of data were then proposed. Theoretically, better monitoring results can be expected with the consideration of both global and local features, but methods can be significantly different for the extraction of global or local feature, which requires better mathematical description of the global and local features ahead. However, there is no specific discussion on this topic in literature yet. To address this issue, A novel global-local feature preserving projection (NGLFPP) method based on adaptive linear local tangent space alignment is proposed. The neighbourhood of each sample is given adaptively by considering the local distribution of data. The local feature of data is obtained by modified tangent estimation. On the basis of the adaptive neighbourhood, geodesic distance is introduced to represent global feature of data. In order to extract global and local features of data simultaneously, a dual objective optimization function is constructed. Tennessee Eastman (TE) process is employed to validate the proposed method.

Keywords: Global local feature preserving projection; Feature extraction; Local tangent space alignment; Adaptive neighbourhood; Geodesic distance.

1. Introduction

With the increase in the scale and complexity of industrial processes, process safety has become more and more important than ever. Process monitoring technologies, which aim at early detection of process faults, are attracting further attention. Due to the extensive use of distributed control system and advanced measuring instruments, large amounts of operational data were collected, which provides a foundation for data-driven process monitoring technology (Qin and Chiang, 2019). MSPM methods, represented by principal component analysis (PCA) and its variants, are the most intensively and widely studied data-driven process monitoring technique. However, the MSPM methods only focus on the global feature of the data represented by variance information and high-order statistics, while ignoring the local feature of the data expressed by neighbourhood information. In recent years, the emergence of manifold learning makes it possible to preserve the local feature of data. Many manifold learning methods were first proposed for pattern recognition and their linear variants are further applied for process monitoring, such as local preserving projection (LPP) and neighbourhood preserving embedding (NPE). However, the global feature of data is not explicitly considered by the aforementioned methods.

In view of the above problems, several monitoring methods were proposed, which can preserve the global and local features of data simultaneously. A unified framework namely global-local preserving projection (GLPP) was built based on LPP and it relies on a heat kernel function to provide neighbourhood information based on distance (Luo, 2014). From another perspective, NPE based on neighbourhood reconstruction weights is also extended to preserve both global and local features of the data (Ma et al., 2015). As an effective local feature extraction method, linear local tangent space alignment (LLTSA) has rarely been extended to global-local feature extraction for process monitoring (Zhang et al.,2007). The main reason is that the performance of LLTSA is closely related to the accuracy of local tangent space estimation. PCA-based tangent space estimation in LLTSA assumes that the data are uniformly distributed, and that the neighbourhood space is locally linear. However, the above assumptions are often violated in real data. In addition, LLTSA only relies on the alignment of the neighbourhood tangent space to extract data feature, ignoring global feature of the data.

To further improve the performance of methods in this category, a novel global-local feature preserving projection method is proposed. The adaptive neighborhood based on distribution density is first constructed. Weight based on distance and manifold curvature is introduced to improve PCA-based neighborhood tangent space estimation. With LLTSA, local feature of the data is obtained by aligning the tangent space coordinates. Based on the constructed adaptive neighborhood, geodesic distance is introduced to obtain the global feature of data. A dual-objective optimization function is constructed to fully retain the global and local features of data. Process monitoring method based on NGLFPP is then built for real-time process monitoring.

2. NGLFPP Algorithm

2.1. Neighbourhood Construction

Among monitoring methods that preserve global and local features simultaneously, the k nearest neighbour (KNN) method is most commonly used to construct a neighbourhood for each sample. Since the local density distribution of data is usually different in real process, it is hard to describe the nearest neighbour for any data sample by a universal k. In addition, global feature represented by non-neighbourhood relations also depends on neighbourhood construction. Therefore, a density-based adaptive neighbourhood construction method is introduced to describe neighbourhood information of data (Ji and Yang, 2019). Given a data set $X = [x_1, x_2, \cdots, x_n] \in R^{m \times n}$, initial value k of the nearest neighbor is selected. The local density of sample x_i is defined as follows:

$$D_{ld}(i) = \frac{1}{d_{i1} + d_{i2} + \cdots + d_{ik}} \tag{5}$$

where d_{ij} denotes the Euclidean distance between data sample x_i and its jth nearest neighbour. The average local density is calculated by the mean of local density as Eq.(6).

$$D_{ald} = \frac{1}{n}(D_{ld}(1) + D_{ld}(2) + \cdots + D_{ld}(n)) \tag{6}$$

As shown in Eq.(7), the coefficient derived from the ratio of the local density to the average local density is calculated to adjust the initial number of nearest neighbors. The number of the nearest neighbor for data sample x_i is computed as Eq.(8). The ceil function in Eq.(8) indicates that the number in the parentheses is rounded upward.

$$D_{ef}(i) = exp\left((D_{ld}(i) - D_{ald})/D_{ald}\right) \tag{7}$$

$$k_i = ceil\left(k \times D_{ef}(i)\right) \tag{8}$$

2.2. Local Feature Extraction

Based on the above method, the local distribution of data has been considered. Further considering the inconsistent contribution of samples in the neighbourhood to the tangent space estimation, Zhang *et al.* (2011) proposed an improved local tangent space alignment (ILTSA) method based on distance weights. In addition, the assumption of local linearity for PCA-based local tangent space estimation will be violated when the curvature of the data manifold in the neighbourhood is large. So, weights based on distance and curvature in the neighbourhood are employed simultaneously to improve the accuracy of local tangent space estimation. The weight w is defined as Eq.(9).

$$w_{ij} = w_{ij}^D \times w_{ij}^C = exp\left(-D_E(x_i, x_{ij})^2/t\right) \times exp\left(-\frac{D_G(x_i, x_{ij}) - D_E(x_i, x_{ij})}{D_E(x_i, x_{ij})}\right) \tag{9}$$

where w_{ij}^D and w_{ij}^C denote the weight based on distance and manifold curvature. $D_E(x_i, x_j)$ and $D_G(x_i, x_{ij})$ represent the Euclidean distance and geodesic distance between x_i and its jth nearest neighbour x_{ij}. The value of the t is identified as the average value of the Euclidean distance between x_i and its k_i nearest neighbor samples. The optimization objective in tangent space estimation can be reformulated as follows:

$$\begin{cases} \underset{Q}{argmin} \sum_{j=1}^{k_i} W_{ij} \|x_{ij} - x_i - Q^T Q(x_{ij} - x_i)\|_2^2 \\ s.t. \quad Q^T Q = I \end{cases} \tag{10}$$

Similar to ILSTA, Eq.(10) can be transformed into Eq.(11), and projection matrix Q can be calculated by eigenvalue decomposition for each neighborhood X_i.

$$\underset{Q^T Q=I}{argmax} \; tr(Q^T (\bar{X}_i W_i)(\bar{X}_i W_i)^T Q) \tag{11}$$

where W_i is a diagonal matrix and $W_i(j,j)=w_{ij}$. $\bar{X}_i$ is defined as $[x_{i1} - x_i, x_{i2} - x_i, \cdots, x_{ik} - x_i]$. Consistent with the LTSA, the alignment of local tangent coordinates is calculated by minimizing global reconstruction error. The objective function of local feature extraction can be further represented as follows:

$$J_{local} = min \sum_{i=1}^n \|E_i\|_2^2 = min \; tr(YSWW^T S^T Y) = min \; tr(A^T XBX^T A) \tag{12}$$

where $S = [S_1, S_2, \cdots, S_n]$ and $YS_i = Y_i$. W is a diagonal matrix consisting of W_i and A is a projection matrix which is defined as $Y = A^T X$.

2.3. Global Feature Extraction

Inspired by GLPP, the distance between non-neighbouring samples is retained as a representation of global feature. Compared to Euclidean distance, geodesic distance is introduced due to its more accurate estimation of the non-neighbouring distance on the data manifold. Dijkstra algorithm is used to estimate the geodesic distance by calculating the shortest path distance based on the adjacency graph. The objective function of global feature extraction is constructed as follows:

$$J_{global} = max \sum_{i,j}^{n} \|y_i - y_j\|^2 \bar{W}_{ij} = max \, tr(A^T X L X^T A) \tag{13}$$

$$\bar{W}_{ij} = exp\left(-D_G\left(x_i, x_j\right)^2 / t\right) \quad if \; x_j \notin \Omega\left(\vec{x}_i\right) \; and \; x_i \notin \Omega\left(\vec{x}_j\right) \tag{14}$$

where $D_G(x_i, x_j)$ denotes the geodesic distance between x_i and x_j, and the value of t is given by the average value of the geodesic distance between non-neighboring samples. And L denotes a Laplacian matrix, which can be calculated as $L = \bar{D} - \bar{W}$. $\bar{D}$ represents the diagonal matrix, which can be calculated by $\bar{D}(j, j) = \sum_j^n \bar{W}_{ij}$.

2.4. Unified Objective for NGLFPP

In order to preserve both local and global features of the data, a dual-objective optimization function is constructed as Eq.(15):

$$J_{NGLFPP} = min \, \eta J_{local} - (1 - \eta) J_{global} = min \, tr(A^T X M X^T A) \tag{15}$$

where $M = \eta X B X^T - (1 - \eta) X L X^T$, η is a tradeoff parameter which can be determined adaptively by the spectral radius of the matrix. The orthogonal constraint $A^T A = I$ is introduced due to its computational advantages in the statistics and residual space. The above-mentioned optimization problem can be transformed into solving of the eigenvalue problem by the Lagrange multiplier method, and projection matrix A consists of the eigenvectors corresponding to the d smallest eigenvalues.

3. NGLFPP-Based Process Monitoring

As training dataset, normalized normal condition data set X is applied to NGLFPP algorithm so as to obtain the projection matrix A. In online monitoring, according to F-distribution and χ^2-distribution, two popular monitoring statistics of new sample x_{new} and their control limits are calculated as follows:

$$T_{new}^2 = x_{new}^T A \Lambda^{-1} A^T x_{new} \leq \frac{d(n-1)}{n-d} F_\alpha(d, n-d) \tag{16}$$

$$Q_{new}^2 = \|(I - AA^T) x_{new}\|^2 \leq g \chi_{h,\alpha}^2 \tag{17}$$

where $\Lambda = X^T AA^T X / (n-1)$ denotes the covariance matrix of Y. The complete procedure of NGLFPP-based monitoring method is presented as Figure 1.

4. Case Study

TE process is a well-known benchmark test for evaluating monitoring performance of different methods, and more details on TE process can be found in (Downs and Vogel, 1993). 33 variables, including 22 measurement variables and 11 operation variables, are selected for monitoring purpose. Training dataset with 960 normal samples is used for model construction. The test dataset includes 21 fault types, and each test data contains 960 samples. The performance of the proposed NGLFPP-based method is compared with PCA-based and GLPP-based monitoring methods. For PCA, nine latent variables are selected by cross validation (Lee et al., 2006). For a fair comparison, the same number of latent variables is chosen for GLPP and NGLFPP. The same number of nearest neighbors $k=10$ is determined for GLPP and NGLFPP. The confidence level for control limits of T^2 and Q statistics are set as 99 % for three monitoring methods.

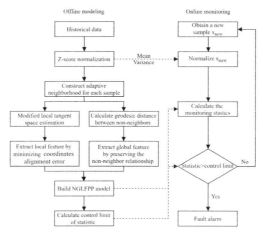

Figure 1 Monitoring diagram based on NGLFPP algorithm

Table 1 FDRs (%) of different method on TE process

	NGLFPP		GLPP		PCA	
Fault num	T^2	Q	T^2	Q	T^2	Q
1	**99.75**	99.5	**99.75**	99.5	99.125	**99.75**
2	97.25	**98.5**	94	**98.5**	**98.5**	96.125
3	1.75	11.875	1.75	11.5	1.625	1.375
4	**84.25**	96.625	41.375	96.625	6.5	**99.875**
5	**100**	34.375	99.75	**34.5**	24.75	17.5
6	**100**	99.625	**100**	99.5	99.25	**100**
7	**100**	**100**	67.875	**100**	42.125	**100**
8	96.125	**98.625**	79.375	**98.625**	96.75	89.25
9	1.25	8.875	0.875	8.875	1.625	1.375
10	72.375	54.375	80.875	54.875	31.875	16.75
11	**56.625**	71.625	28	71.625	22.125	**72.25**
12	**99.125**	99.375	94.75	**99.375**	97.25	89.75
13	**94.5**	94.625	94.125	94.625	93.375	**95.25**
14	**99.875**	**100**	92.5	**100**	81	**100**
15	2.5	14.25	1.5	14	1.125	1.625
16	78	**39.875**	87.875	38.75	13.75	16.375
17	**93**	91.75	90.125	91.625	74	**93.125**
18	**90**	90.625	89.875	**90.75**	89.125	89.75
19	66.125	14.25	89.25	12.875	0.5	**29.375**
20	**81.75**	**58**	73.875	57.125	32	44.875
21	**36.5**	46.75	8.75	**47.75**	33.625	45.75
Average	**85.847**	**77.139**	78.451	77.035	57.535	71.986

Table2 Average FAR (%) of different method on TE process

	NGLFPP		GLPP		PCA	
Fault num	T^2	Q	T^2	Q	T^2	Q
Average	0.625	4.028	0.729	4.097	0.486	0.833

The fault detection rates (FDRs) of three monitoring methods for TE process are shown in Table1. Previous studies have shown that faults 3, 9 and 15 are difficult to detect because of their small magnitudes. The monitoring performances of the rest 18 faults is compared and their average values are calculated. The bolded numbers in Table1 represent the best FDR for the corresponding statistic under each fault condition. For T^2 statistics, the proposed method gives the highest detection rate for 13 of 18 faults, and significant improvement for fault 4, 7 and 14. For Q statistics, the proposed method gives similar FDRs to GLPP-based method and higher FDRs compared to the PCA-based method on 10 of 18 faults, especially on faults 8,10,12. The performance of the proposed method can be further seen by the average FDR of 18 faults given in Table 1. False alarm rate (FAR) is also an important indicator for evaluating the monitoring performance, and average FARs of three methods for 18 faults are shown in Table2. Obviously, the proposed method has a lower average FAR for T^2 statistics. Similar to GLPP-based method, the proposed method has a slightly higher average FAR for Q statistics compared with PCA-based method. In general, the proposed method has better performance than PCA-based and GLPP-based methods.

5. Conclusion

In this paper, a novel global-local feature preserving projection method is proposed. Considering the difference of local distribution, the density-based adaptive neighbourhood construction method is applied to determine local and global scopes of data. On this basis, a modified neighbourhood tangent estimation method is integrated into LLTSA to preserve the local feature of the data accurately. Furthermore, global feature of data based on geodesic distance is obtained. The above features of data are extracted simultaneously by constructing a dual objective optimization function. Therefore, the proposed method is more comprehensive in feature extraction of data, and gives better performance in process monitoring on TE process, compared to PCA-based and GLPP-based monitoring methods.

References

J. J. Downs, E. F.Vogel, 1993, A plant-wide industrial process control problem, Computers & chemical engineering, 17, 3, 245-255.

W. Ji, H. Yang, 2019, Soft sensor modeling based on adaptive Isomap algorithm, Journal of Nanjing University of Science and Technology, 43, 3, 269-274.

L. Luo, 2014, Process Monitoring with Global–Local Preserving Projections, Industrial & Engineering Chemistry Research,53, 18, 7696-7705.

J. M. Lee, S. J. Qin, I. B. Lee, 2006, Fault detection and diagnosis based on modified independent component analysis, AIChE Journal, 52, 3501–3514.

Y. Ma, B. Song, H. Shi, Y. Yang, 2015, Fault detection via local and nonlocal embedding, Chemical Engineering Research and Design, 94, 538-548.

S. J. Qin, L. H. Chiang, 2019, Advances and opportunities in machine learning for process data analytics, Computers & Chemical Engineering, 126, 465-473.

P. Zhang, H. Qiao, B. Zhang, 2011, An improved local tangent space alignment method for manifold learning, Pattern Recognition Letters, 32, 2, 181-189.

T. Zhang, J. Yang, D. Zhao, X. Ge, 2007, Linear local tangent space alignment and application to face recognition, Neurocomputing, 70, 7-9, 1547-1553.

Proceedings of the 14th International Symposium on Process Systems Engineering – PSE 2021+
June 19-23, 2022, Kyoto, Japan © 2022 Elsevier B.V. All rights reserved.
http://dx.doi.org/10.1016/B978-0-323-85159-6.50223-2

Prognostics on Noisy and Uncertain Dynamic Systems using Cumulative Sum Chart of Inferential Sensors

Efi Safikou[a], and George M. Bollas[b*]

[a] Department of Electrical & Computer Engineering, University of Connecticut, 371 Fairfield Way, Unit 4157, Storrs, CT, 06269, USA
[b] Department of Chemical & Biomolecular Engineering, University of Connecticut, 191 Auditorium Road, Unit 3222, Storrs, CT, 06269, USA, george.bollas@uconn.edu

Abstract

Inferential sensing techniques have been proven very successful in the field of fault detection and isolation, as they yield robust outcomes in a cost-effective and reliable manner. Herein, we propose a framework that deploys inferential sensors in the presence of noise and uncertainty, while focusing on the detection time and early sensitivity to faults. The most informative inferential sensor is derived through symbolic regression with an objective function that uses optimality criteria from information theory, wherein the sensitivity of the inferential sensors with respect to faults and uncertainty is estimated using the system digital twin. For deployment of the inferential sensors, the Cumulative Sum Control Chart method is employed and tuned to monitor deviations from the anticipated system performance. The proposed method is applied for the detection of faults in a crossflow plate-fin heat exchanger, at various levels of measurement noise and uncertainty, under transient operation. When compared to existing (hard) sensors, the inferential sensor provides intelligible deviations from the "fault-free" system response, thus enabling accurate and robust estimates for the initiation and progression of faults.

Keywords: symbolic regression; inferential sensing; prognostics; diagnostics.

1. Introduction

Diagnostics and prognostics are key components of cyber-physical system digital twins to enable effective system monitoring and ensure safety (Vogl et al., 2019). The former encapsulates the process of fault detection and isolation based on prior knowledge of the entire system operation, thus generating an anticipated response that can be attributed to the failure mode. The latter, provides a forecast of future system conditions and potential failure timelines, given only present or historic information (Biggio et al., 2020). While diagnostics is an extensively studied field with a plethora of documented analyses and methods (Palmer & Bollas, 2019), research on prognostics coupled with inferential sensing techniques is limited and more challenging (Adams, 2019). Typically, inferential sensors combine available system inputs and outputs in either analytical expressions, or empirical relationships based on data (Hale & Bollas, 2020). Herein, we employ inferential sensing for the diagnosis and prognosis of faults in the presence of noise and uncertainty, focusing on the time for detection and early sensitivity to faults. The Cumulative Sum Control Chart (CUSUM; Montgomery, 2009) method is used and tuned to monitor present and future deviations from the anticipated system performance to determine potential failure initiation instances.

2. Methods

2.1. System model representation

We assume the existence of an accurate dynamic system model for the system, expressed as a set of differential algebraic equations that are based on physical system knowledge or semi-empirical correlations:

$$\mathbf{f}(\dot{\mathbf{x}}(t), \mathbf{x}(t), \mathbf{u}(t), \boldsymbol{\theta}, t) = 0, \tag{1}$$

where $\mathbf{f}$ is the system governing equations, $\mathbf{x}(t)$ the vector of state variables, $\dot{\mathbf{x}}(t)$ the time derivatives, $\mathbf{u}(t)$ are the admissible inputs, $\boldsymbol{\theta}$ the model parameters, and t denotes the time. All model parameters remain invariant for a timespan, $\boldsymbol{\tau}$, within which Eq.(1) is accurate for steady-state and dynamic operation. Let $\hat{\mathbf{y}}$ be the measured outputs of the system as a function of states, inputs, and parameters, whose N_y components correspond to the available hard sensors: $\hat{\mathbf{y}} = \mathbf{h}(\mathbf{x}(t), \mathbf{u}(t), \boldsymbol{\theta}, t)$. We define the inferential sensors, $\hat{\mathbf{z}}$, as standardized functions of $\hat{\mathbf{y}}$ and $\mathbf{u}(t)$ based on the nominal value, $\hat{\mathbf{z}}_{\mathrm{nom}} = \mathbf{g}(\bar{\mathbf{y}})$, with $\bar{y} = \hat{y}/\hat{y}_{\mathrm{nom}}$. The vector of nominal values for the system outputs, $\hat{\mathbf{y}}_{\mathrm{nom}}$, contains output values corresponding to predetermined values for the admissible system inputs, $\mathbf{u}$. A $(N_y + N_z)$-dimensional binary vector, $\mathbf{a}$, can be introduced to define active and inactive sensors, depending on their use for a particular diagnostics or prognostics test. Note that N_z denotes the number of inferential sensors. For inactive sensors the respective index in $\mathbf{a}$ is equal to 0, while the positions of active sensors correspond to elements equal to 1. The vector of the system inputs $\mathbf{u} = \left[\mathbf{u}_p(t), \mathbf{u}_q\right]$ contains the uncertain inputs, $\mathbf{u}_q$, as well as the controllable system inputs, $\mathbf{u}_p(t) = \left[\mathbf{u}_p^1, \mathbf{u}_p^2, \ldots, \mathbf{u}_p^{N_k}\right]$, with N_k denoting the number of changes in u_p during the examined period (i.e., the number of tests). Considering $\mathbf{u}_p^{[k]}$ that obtains acceptable values from a continuous test design space, $\mathbf{U}_p$, we can design tests $k \in \{1, \ldots, N_k\}$. The vector of system parameters, $\boldsymbol{\theta}$, can be divided in three components, $\left[\boldsymbol{\theta}_f, \boldsymbol{\theta}_q, \boldsymbol{\theta}_p\right]$, where $\boldsymbol{\theta}_f$ are the parameters that represent faults, $\boldsymbol{\theta}_q$ the parameters related to system uncertainty, and $\boldsymbol{\theta}_p$ the known and invariant parameters that symbolize the system design. It follows that the faults, the parameters related to uncertainty, as well as the system inputs, are concatenated into a N_ξ-dimensional vector, $\boldsymbol{\xi} = \left[\boldsymbol{\theta}_f, \boldsymbol{\theta}_q\right] \cup \left[\mathbf{u}_q\right] = \left[\boldsymbol{\xi}_f, \boldsymbol{\xi}_q\right]$, whose elements are separated into faults, $\boldsymbol{\xi}_f$, and uncertainty, $\boldsymbol{\xi}_q$. Note that $\boldsymbol{\xi}$ is later employed during the optimization of the test design. We assume that the anticipated fault parameter values, $\tilde{\boldsymbol{\xi}}_f$, can be acquired from historical data of system components or are simply known a priori from past system operation. Moreover, faults are considered the only indicators of undesirable system performance, with the uncertainty parameters being part of the normal operation that should not lead to false alarms. Let $l \in \{1, \ldots, N_l\}$ denote the faults scenarios, with N_l being the total number, and $\tilde{\boldsymbol{\xi}}_f^{[l]}$ the anticipated fault scenarios. Then, each fault scenario, l, corresponds to a different fault level in $\boldsymbol{\xi}_f$, with the uncertainty vector $\boldsymbol{\xi}_q$ remaining constant and containing the mean values of the uncertain system parameters and inputs.

2.2. Active FDI test design optimization

Consider a vector $\boldsymbol{\phi}^{[k]}$ that contains a set of continuous variables $\mathbf{u}_p^{[k]}$, and a binary vector $\mathbf{a}$ related to sensor selection. Then, for all N_k, this design vector can be formulated as $\boldsymbol{\phi} = \left[\mathbf{u}_p^1, \ldots, \mathbf{u}_p^{N_k}, \mathbf{a}\right]$. The optimal FDI test design, $\boldsymbol{\phi}^*$, is the product of a mixed-integer nonlinear optimization program, which is founded on the maximization of the estimability of the faults as functions of the sensitivity of active sensors with respect to faults (Palmer et al., 2016) and, specifically, the minimization of the joint confidence between faults and faults with uncertain parameters. For dynamic tests (in which the system transient is monitored and used for FDI), the optimization problem is then as shown in Eq.(2):

$$\boldsymbol{\phi}^* = \left[\mathbf{u}_p^*(\boldsymbol{\tau}_1), \ldots, \mathbf{u}_p^*(\boldsymbol{\tau}_{N_k}), \mathbf{a} \right] \in \arg\max_{\boldsymbol{\phi} \in \Phi} \ln \Psi_{\mathrm{D_S}}$$

s.t.

$$\mathbf{f}\big(\dot{\mathbf{x}}(t), \mathbf{x}(t), \mathbf{u}_p(t), \boldsymbol{\theta}_p, \widetilde{\boldsymbol{\xi}}, t\big) = \mathbf{0},$$

$$\hat{\mathbf{y}} = \mathbf{h}\big(\mathbf{x}(t), \mathbf{u}_p(t), \boldsymbol{\theta}_p, \widetilde{\boldsymbol{\xi}}, t\big),$$

$$\mathbf{x}^L \leq \mathbf{x} \leq \mathbf{x}^U, \forall\, t \in \boldsymbol{\tau},$$

$$\mathbf{u}_p \subset \mathbf{U}_p, \forall\, t \in \boldsymbol{\tau},$$

(2)

where $\mathbf{u}_p^*(\boldsymbol{\tau}_k)$ denotes the optimal inputs for each test of timespan $\boldsymbol{\tau}_k$. The objective function selected for the optimization problem is the $\mathrm{D_s}$-optimality criterion, $\Psi_{\mathrm{D_s}}$, that is based on the Fisher Information Matrix (FIM), which encapsulates the existing knowledge about the faults and system uncertainty; see Eq.(3). The FIM, $\mathbf{H}_\xi$, can be evaluated as the resultant of three secondary matrices that correspond to $\boldsymbol{\xi}_f$ and $\boldsymbol{\xi}_q$; see Eq.(4). The foregoing submatrices $\mathbf{H}_{ff}$, $\mathbf{H}_{fq}$, and $\mathbf{H}_{qq}$, represent the covariance between (i) faults, (ii) faults and system uncertainty, and (iii) system uncertainty, respectively.

$$\mathbf{H}_\xi^{[l]}\big(\boldsymbol{\phi}, \widetilde{\boldsymbol{\xi}}\big) = \begin{bmatrix} \mathbf{H}_{ff}^{[l]} & \mathbf{H}_{fq}^{[l]} \\ \mathbf{H}_{qf}^{[l]} & \mathbf{H}_{qq}^{[l]} \end{bmatrix} = \frac{\sum_{k=1}^{N_k} \sum_{i=1}^{N_y + N_z} a_i \sigma_i^{-2} Q_i^{[k,l]^T} Q_i^{[k,l]}}{\sum_{i=1}^{N_y + N_z} a_i}$$

(3)

$$\mathbf{H}_{ff}^{[l]} \in \mathrm{R}^{N_f \times N_f}, \ \mathbf{H}_{fq}^{[l]} \in \mathrm{R}^{N_f \times (N_\xi - N_f)}, \ \mathbf{H}_{qf}^{[l]} = \big(\mathbf{H}^{[l]}\big)_{fq}^T, \ \mathbf{H}_{qq}^{[l]} \in \mathrm{R}^{(N_\xi - N_f) \times (N_\xi - N_f)}$$

(4)

where N_f denotes the number of fault parameters, and σ_i^2 is the measurement variance of the ith output. The sensitivity matrix, $\mathbf{Q}$, consists of the partial derivatives of the active hardware or/and inferential sensors, with respect to ξ (Palmer & Bollas, 2019). In more detail, the $\mathrm{D_s}$-optimality criterion of Eq.(5), minimizes the covariance between the entire set of fault parameters, uncertain parameters, and inputs, towards increased fault isolation. Enhanced detection is achieved through the neglection of the covariance between the elements of ξ_q. Note that summation over all possible fault scenarios N_l enables designs for different faults or fault severity levels, including the healthy state.

$$\Psi_{\mathrm{D_s}}\big(\mathbf{H}_\xi\big) = N_l^{-1} \sum_{l=1}^{N_l} \ \log \left| \mathbf{H}_{ff}^{[l]} - \mathbf{H}_{fq}^{[l]} \big(\mathbf{H}_{qq}^{[l]}\big)^{-1} \mathbf{H}_{qf}^{[l]} \right|^{1/N_\xi}.$$

(5)

2.3. Cumulative Sum control chart

The CUSUM is a type of control chart, which constitutes a particularly effective tool when small process shifts are of interest. It calculates the cumulative sums of the sample values deviations, by taking into consideration all the information in the respective sequence (Montgomery, 2009). The cumulative sums of deviations from a target are plotted in the CUSUM chart, which can be represented in a tabular form that provides an ease of interpretation and a robust control limit setting. Two statistics, namely the upper, C_i^+, and the lower, C_i^-, CUSUM charts, are constructed in the tabular CUSUM; see Eq.(6). Deviations above the target are accumulated in the C_i^+ statistic, while sub-target inconsistencies are collected in the C_i^- statistic. Along these lines, we have:

$$C_i^- = \min\{0, C_{i-1}^- + x_i - \mu + K\}, \text{ and } C_i^+ = \max\{0, C_{i-1}^+ + x_i - \mu - K\}, \tag{6}$$

where μ denotes the target value, while the starting values C_0^- and C_0^+ are equal to 0. In case one of the C_i^+ and C_i^- violates the control limits set by the decision interval, H, the process is assumed out-of-control. Additionally, the reference value, K, must be selected properly to achieve an adequately quick detection, based on the respective out-of-control value (i.e., fault). It is worth mentioning that the critical tuning parameters H and K regulate the sensitivity of the CUSUM chart. Herein, the target value μ corresponds to the fault-free condition of the system, and K is set equal to σ, where σ is the standard deviation of the incorporated sensors. For H we assume a typical value equal to 5σ.

2.4. Genetic Programming

Genetic Programming (GP) is employed to discover functional relationships between the incorporated variables (i.e., symbolic regression). In each generation, the most informative inferential sensor is pursued and then maintained until a better one is derived. The D_s-optimality criterion incorporating solely inferential sensors was selected as the objective function in this study, although fusion of hard and inferential sensors is also feasible. In that sense, the program of Eq. (3) is updated to include the inferential sensors as the optimization variables, $\boldsymbol{\phi}_{\mathbf{GP}} = \mathbf{z}$, which is solved for the FDI test design calculated from Eq. (3). After the most informative inferential sensor is obtained, it is employed in Eq. (3) as a new sensor and the FDI test design $\mathbf{u}_p$ is re-optimized. This operation iterated between FDI test design optimization and inferential sensor evolution (with D_s-optimality being the consistent objective) until the test design and functional form of the inferential sensor remain the same in consecutive iterations, when the process is terminated. Otherwise, the GP algorithm is trained with the new optimal system input, until convergence is achieved. For the calculation of the sensitivities of the inferential sensors, the chain rule of partial derivatives of automatic differentiation is applied, making the calculation of D_s-optimality in the symbolic regression step computationally inexpensive.

3. Case Study

The proposed framework was applied on a crossflow plate-fin heat exchanger (PFHE) system (Palmer et al., 2016), where the measured outputs correspond to temperatures and pressures of the outlet streams, $\mathbf{y} = [T_c, T_h, P_c, P_h]$, and the system admissible input is the mass flow rate of the hot stream, $u_p = \dot{m}_{h,i}$ (kg/s). The PFHE fault studied is thermal fouling resistance in the cold stream side of the PFHE, $\theta_{f=1} = R_f$, subject to uncertainty that includes the cold air inlet stream moisture content, $\omega_{H2O} \sim N(7, 4)$, and the cold air inlet temperature, $T_{in}^{cold} \sim N(35, 25)$. The FDI test design and inferential sensors were optimized for three fault scenarios; namely: (i) a fault free case ($R_f = 0.4$), (ii) 20% blocked fouling ($R_f = 1.6$), (iii) 50% blocked fouling without error ($R_f = 4$). The FDI design is aware of the model parameters that represent uncertainty and the standard deviation of the hard sensors, but not the exact instantiations of uncertainty and noise that the system may exhibit. In non-exact terms, the goals of FDI test design and inferential sensor optimization are to minimize the covariance between fault parameters, and fault parameters and uncertainty. Then, to investigate system performance in various operating scenarios, we examine two cases of PFHE performance, in which we injected uncertain parameters $[\omega_{H2O}, T_{in}^{cold}] = [5.6, 46]$, and $[\omega_{H2O}, T_{in}^{cold}] = [12, 35]$, respectively. In both, we also inject a linear increase in the PFHE fouling that starts at $t = 100$ s ($R_f = 0.4$) and lasts for $\Delta t = 360$ s ($R_f = 4$).

4. Results – Discussion

For brevity, in Fig. 1 we present the outcomes of the CUSUM chart for a single hard sensor (i.e., T_c). As illustrated in Figs. 1a and 1c, for the first case described in Section 3, a fault is erroneously detected by CUSUM at time $t = 3$ s, due to the instantiation of uncertainty and noise. Figs. 1b and 1d (i.e., for the second case) show that in a different uncertainty scenario, the system is out-of-control at $t = 288$ s, when the fouling level is close to 20% - blocked. The required time for fault detection is 188 s. The foregoing observations manifest that CUSUM is unpredictable when employed solely with hard sensors to detect system faults in the presence of noise and uncertainty.

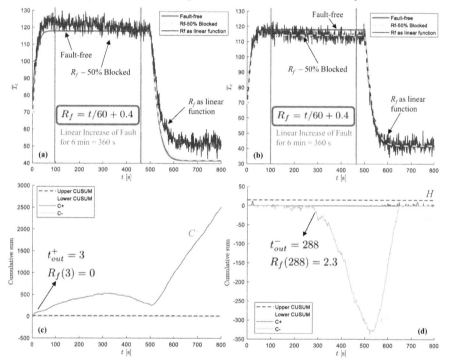

Figure 1. Hard sensor timeseries for linearly increasing fault, in the cases of (a) $[\omega_{H2O}, T_{in}^{cold}] = [5.6, 46]$, and (b $[\omega_{H2O}, T_{in}^{cold}]$–) [12, 35], with (c, d) the respective results of the CUSUM chart.

The first examined case seems more challenging for CUSUM, thus is adopted for the implementation of the optimal inferential sensor, obtained by using the same system outputs as the independent variables of symbolic regression. The functional form of the D_s-optimal inferential sensor is shown in Eq.(7) and it is notably simple and explainable. The inferential sensor uses the ratio of outlet temperatures as the key driver to decrease the evidence of uncertainty and improve the estimability of the fault:

$$Z_{Ds} = [(T_c - 4.7440)/T_c + (T_c/2)/T_h]/1.6556 \tag{7}$$

In Fig. 2, we can observe that the inferential sensor detects the existence of a fault at time $t = 362$ s (i.e., after 262 s). The value of the fault at that time is $R_f = 3$ (see Fig.2b), which is slightly larger than 20% blocking of the PFHE (i.e., $R_f = 1.6$), but smaller than the value of 50% blocked that constitutes the maximum assessed fault level (i.e., $R_f = 4$). While there is noise in its sequence (see Fig. 2a), the inferential sensor reduces the deviations induced by epistemic uncertainty, thus enabling the robust and effective detection of faults in the dynamic test. It is important to note that the CUSUM chart method is more effective when small shifts in the sensor sequence take place. However, the fluctuations when using solely hard sensors are erratic; see also Fig. 1a. In contrast, the incorporation of an inferential sensor provides much smoother deviations (see Fig. 2a), thus making them particularly suited for use along with CUSUM charts. This was also consistent for the fault and uncertainty scenario studied in Figs. 1b and 1d, where the inferential sensor produced no false alarms and detected the PFHE fouling at $t = 200$ s, (fouling level under 20%), earlier than the most informative hard sensor, T_c.

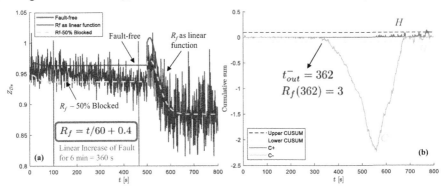

Figure 2. (a) The timeseries of the inferential sensor, with a linearly increasing fault. (b) The respective tabular form of the CUSUM chart.

5. Conclusions

We showed that the CUSUM chart method is effective for FDI when small deviations from the target sequence (i.e., fault-free scenario) occur. The use of CUSUM, however, solely with hard sensors induces erratic sequence fluctuations, thus hindering accurate fault detection. On the other hand, the employment of inferential sensors via the proposed framework, was shown to mitigate such issues. Therefore, we argue that the combination of CUSUM charts and inferential sensing techniques can constitute a robust tool for fault diagnosis and prognosis.

References

Biggio, L., & Kastanis, I. (2020) Prognostics and Health Management of Industrial Assets: Current Progress and Road Ahead, *Front Artif Intell*, **3**, 10.3389/frai.2020.578613.

Vogl, G.W., Weiss, B.A., & Helu, M. (2019) A review of diagnostic and prognostic capabilities and best practices for manufacturing, *J Intell Manuf*, **30**, 79-95, 10.1007/s10845-016-1228-8.

Hale, W.T., & Bollas, G.M., (2020) Least-squares- and information-theory-based inferential sensor design for fault diagnostics, *ACC 2020*, 3182–3187.

Adams, Van H. (2019) Data Prognostics Using Symbolic Regression, engrXiv, 10.31224/osf.io/fq8ze.

Palmer, K.A., Hale, W.T., Such, K.D., Shea, B.R., & Bollas, G.M. (2016) Optimal design of tests for heat exchanger fouling identification, *Appl Therm Eng*, **95**, 382-393, 10.1016/j.applthermaleng.2015.11.043.

Montgomery, D.C. (2009) *Introduction to Statistical Quality Control*, 6th edition, Wiley & Sons, 9780470169926.

Palmer, K.A., & Bollas, G.M. (2019) Sensor selection embedded in active fault diagnosis algorithms, 505 IEEE Trans Control Syst Technol, 1–14.

Proceedings of the 14th International Symposium on Process Systems Engineering – PSE 2021+
June 19-23, 2022, Kyoto, Japan © 2022 Elsevier B.V. All rights reserved.
http://dx.doi.org/10.1016/B978-0-323-85159-6.50224-4

Quantifying Subsea Gas Leakages using Machine Learning: a CFD-based study

Gustavo L.R. Caldas[a*], Thiago F.B. Bento[b], Roger M. Moreira[b], Maurício B. de Souza Jr.[a]

[a] *Escola de Química, Universidade Federal do Rio de Janeiro, Rio de Janeiro 21941-909, Brazil*
[b] *Escola de Engenharia, Universidade Federal Fluminense, Niterói 24210-240, Brazil*
gustavo.caldas@eq.ufrj.br

Abstract

Subsea images captured on-site can be used to quantify gas leakage in the subsea environment. In this work, gas leakage in reduced conditions was simulated by Computational Fluid Dynamics (CFD). The aim is to develop a computational vision tool to quantify the leakage. The images generated from CFD simulations were processed by a convolutional neural network (CNN) structure, the U-Net. A class is attributed to each image pixel, and a post-processing algorithm computes the corresponding bubble area. Two cases were carried out: image segmentation into two (water and bubble) and three classes (bubble interface included). The multi-class U-Net shows a good agreement with CFD results compared to the binary one because separating the pixels into just two categories leads to bubble diameter overestimation. Hence, this method is of potential use in fault detection and diagnosis and could support the decision-making process on deepwater leakage remediation.

Keywords: gas leakage; machine learning; convolutional neural network; process safety.

1. Introduction

Subsea oil and gas activities demand safety procedures and constant monitoring to prevent impact on marine ecosystems and financial losses for the operating companies (Figueredo et al., 2022). Several resources might take hold for this purpose. For instance, real-time leakage filming is possible with the Remotely Operated Vehicles (ROV) equipped with a camera onboard. These images, however, provide information only on whether the leak is occurring. For a better assessment, it is of great interest to develop a quantitative tool to support the decision-making process of intervention.

A possible parameter for the leak estimation is the bubble diameter (Jamialahmadi et al., 2001), which could be computed using image processing techniques. More recently, convolutional neural networks (CNN) - a type of Machine Learning (ML) algorithm – became part of these techniques (Goodfellow et al., 2016). CNNs are sparsely connected neural networks, i.e., not all neurons are connected to the ones of the subsequent layers. As a result, it saves plenty of computational resources when dealing with tensor data such as images and sounds (Krizhevsky et al., 2012). In a CNN structure, the first argument is the input, and the second one, the kernel (filter). Typically, the input is a tensor containing the image height, width, and input channels (colors). The output is called the feature map, which stores the characteristics of the input data and simultaneously reduces its size by using a kernel smaller than the matrix – this is the reason for the sparse connectivity. The kernels' number, shape, and activation function are hyper-parameters defined by the user (Goodfellow et al., 2016).

Convolutional neural networks have already been applied to fault detection and diagnosis problems. Wu and Zhao (2018) verified its usefulness on the Tennessee Eastman process. The relation between different process variables and sampling time is concatenated into two-dimensional matrices, adequate for CNN computing. The fault diagnosis rate scored 88.2 %. Li et al. (2018) proposed a CNN to detect chemical leakage in hydrocarbon tanks based on image recognition. They obtained 85.82 % accuracy. Bai et al. (2021) developed a real-time classifier of gas dispersion state in a bubble column using a novel CNN architecture named BubbleNet. It differentiated flow conditions according to bubbles' size and shape after being trained to a labeled dataset. It scored 97.8 % and 97.5 % of the performance for the training and test, respectively.

In some chemical engineering applications with multi-phase flows, e.g., liquid-liquid extraction, it is fundamental to know the particle size distribution, a variable of interest for the transport phenomena control. Schäfer et al. (2019) investigated it using a particular convolutional neural network, the U-Net. This network was designed for image segmentation (Ronneberger et al., 2015), an application interested in localizing objects and boundaries by partitioning the image pixels into various segments. Thus, the U-Net permits phase fractions distinction. Another advantage is that post-processing enables the calculation of the droplet size distributions from the U-Net output. Therefore, the present study aims to develop a system capable of quantifying leakages in subsea processes employing the U-Net convolutional neural network.

2. Methodology

We carried out reduced model simulations of gas leakages employing Computational Fluid Dynamics (CFD). Reduced model is a technique that is used to save computational costs by downscaling the original phenomenon. For instance, it reproduces an event from the subsea scale to the laboratory. Gas leakages are released with different velocities (v) and from different orifice diameters (d). The initial value problem is solved via a finite volume method. The Volume of Fluid (VoF) method is employed to model the two-phase gas-liquid flow. Continuity and the unsteady RANS (Reynolds-Averaged Navier-Stokes) equations are satisfied in the fluid domain, with the classical κ-ε turbulence model being used. The CFD results are being validated with experiments and semi-empirical models. They agree on the trend found in the literature (Jamialahmadi et al., 2001). The simulation was carried out in ANSYS Fluent software, producing videos that represent the leakage. Each video frame generated an image set, totalizing 3159 images from the different conditions.

In a second step, the images are forwarded to a CNN model, called the U-Net structure. The main goal of this architecture is to classify each pixel individually as belonging to some class. The images are the input for training this network, and the targets are the masks created by a segmentation method. The CNN was developed in Keras environment employing Python with Tensorflow as backend. The segmentation was carried out using the unsupervised Otsu's methodology (Otsu, 1979) in the Scikit Image library written in Python. It is an algorithm whose aim is to find a threshold that can divide the pixels of a grayscale image into two clusters (classes): foreground f and background b. A threshold t is searched, such that the intra-class variance, represented in Eq. 1, is minimized (and the inter-class is maximized as well). The weights ω calculated contain the probabilities of a pixel to belong to one of the classes. In this case, classes are water (label zero) and bubble (label one). Given the importance of phase fraction when accounting bubble diameter, the problem was extended to multi-segmentation, in which the interface is labeled as number two. Multi-level thresholding can be performed as described by Otsu (1979).

$$\sigma^2_{w(t)} = \omega_b(t)\sigma^2_b(t) + \omega_f(t)\sigma^2_f(t) \tag{1}$$

The U-Net structure is shown in Figure 1. It is composed of a down-sampling part: successive blocks of convolutional 2D layers with filters of window dimension 3x3 and initialization "He" followed by 20 % dropout; a second convolutional layer; and a max pooling layer, which takes the maximum value over the window 2x2. In the next block, the number of filters is doubled (starting with 32). The second part comprises the up-sampling operations: transposed convolution (deconvolution) layers with filters 2x2 and stride 2x2. Information is concatenated from the corresponding feature maps of convolutional and deconvolutional layers. Another two convolutional layers are present on each block with half of the filters from the previous up-sampling block. The batch size is 128.

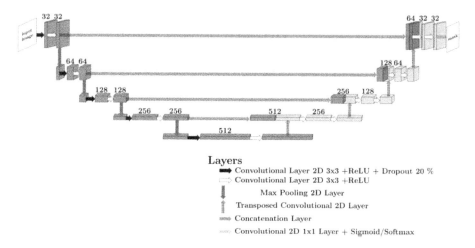

Layers
➡ Convolutional Layer 2D 3x3 +ReLU + Dropout 20 %
⇨ Convolutional Layer 2D 3x3 +ReLU
↓ Max Pooling 2D Layer
↑ Transposed Convolutional 2D Layer
〰 Concatenation Layer
〰 Convolutional 2D 1x1 Layer + Sigmoid/Softmax

Figure 1: The U-Net architecture.

The total number of parameters for the binary class and the multi-label segmentation problems are 7,759,521 and 7,759,587, respectively. The metric used in this case was the Dice-Sørensen coefficient (Eq. 2a), which computes the similarity between the actual and predicted samples in relation to the group. It is important to use one-hot encoding format for the multi-class problem. Thus, the dice coefficient is extended for each class C (Eq. 2b). For the one-hot encoding format, the categorical cross-entropy (Eq. 3) was employed as a loss function to be minimized.

$$DSC = \sum_{n=1}^{N} \frac{2 \sum_{j=0}^{128} \sum_{i=0}^{48} \hat{y}_{ij,n} * y_{ij,n}}{\sum_{j=0}^{128} \sum_{i=0}^{48} \hat{y}_{ij,n} + \sum_{j=0}^{128} \sum_{i=0}^{48} y_{ij,n}} \tag{2a}$$

$$DSC = \sum_{c=1}^{C} \frac{DSC_c}{C} \tag{2b}$$

$$CCE = -\frac{1}{N} \sum_{n=1}^{N} \sum_{j=0}^{128} \sum_{i=0}^{48} \sum_{c=1}^{C} y_{c,ij,n} \, log \, \hat{y}_{c,ij,n} \tag{3}$$

3. Results and Discussion

Figure 2 shows an image sample (U-Net input), the corresponding binary segmentation mask, and the mask predicted. Bubble statistics are presented in Table 1.

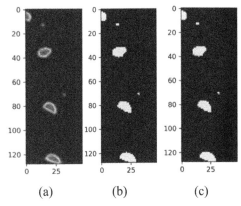

     (a)   (b)   (c)

Figure 2: Snapshot of a sample: (a) U-Net input. (b) Mask generated by the binary Otsu's thresholding (U-Net target). (c) Mask predicted by the binary U-Net.

Table 1: Binary U-Net: predicted $\hat{d}_b$ against expected numerical diameter d_b.

d (mm)	v (m/s)	d_b (mm)	count	$\hat{d}_b$ (mm) mean	$\hat{d}_b$ (mm) std. dev.
0.5	0.25	6.45	350	7.82	0.36
0.5	0.625	7.22	369	9.79	1.16
0.5	1.0	7.69	374	10.19	1.95
1.0	0.24	6.37	317	9.44	0.94
1.0	0.37	6.46	311	9.95	1.72
1.0	0.5	7.28	377	11.74	2.01
5.0	0.02	6.70	373	8.67	0.37
5.0	0.055	8.05	308	10.51	0.96
5.0	0.09	8.11	380	12.14	2.30

The U-Net output is very similar to the target as the Dice-Sørensen coefficients for training and validation imply: 0.9915 and 0.9888, respectively. An overestimation is reported when comparing the expected numerical diameter d_b with the predicted one ($\hat{d}_b$). The reason is that the binary Otsu's thresholding does not set apart the interface and the bubble. This factor influences the area for calculation.

Due to the overestimation, it was decided to investigate further and add a phase fraction, turning the problem into a multi-class one. Figure 3 shows the analog result to Figure 2. The resulting mask resembles much more to the original image when compared to the previous case. The training was also successful. The multi-dice coefficient for training and validation reported 0.9507 and 0.9573, respectively. Similarly, the categorical cross-entropy loss found was 7.14 x 10^{-3} (training) and 5.34 x 10^{-3} (test). The predicted diameter by the multi-class U-Net shows a good agreement with the expected numerical diameter, as statistics shown in Table 2. Low standard deviations suggest that the biggest bubbles are relatively uniform for each dataset. Deviations from the actual values do not exceed 10 %, except for the 1.0 mm diameter crack cases.

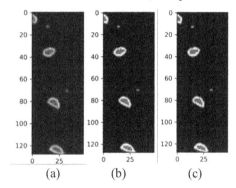

(a) (b) (c)

Figure 3: Snapshot of a sample: (a) U-Net input. (b) Mask generated by the multi-label Otsu's thresholding (U-Net target). (c) Mask predicted by the multi-class U-Net.

Table 2: Multi-class U-Net: predicted $\hat{d}_b$ against expected numerical diameter d_b.

d (mm)	v (m/s)	d_b (mm)	count	$\hat{d}_b$ (mm) mean	$\hat{d}_b$ (mm) std. dev.
0.5	0.25	6.45	350	6.13	0.34
0.5	0.625	7.22	369	7.23	0.90
0.5	1.0	7.69	374	7.41	1.23
1.0	0.24	6.37	317	7.13	0.73
1.0	0.37	6.46	311	7.34	1.22
1.0	0.5	7.28	377	8.39	1.37
5.0	0.02	6.70	373	6.67	0.32
5.0	0.055	8.05	308	7.68	0.69
5.0	0.09	8.11	380	8.66	1.74

Regarding the model convergence, each model's total training time lasted around 1h30 min (2.5 - 3 min/epoch) in an Intel Core i5-10210. It has achieved less than 0.10 of loss in the fifth epoch, and after 15 epochs, more than 0.90 of Dice similarity coefficient.

4. Conclusions

A novel methodology was presented to quantify gas leakages that can be applied in a subsea environment, combining convolutional neural networks and a segmentation tool. The U-Net enabled the multi-segmentation post-processing to reach good predictability of the bubble diameter (less than 10 % deviation in general, the worst case was 15.24 % deviation). It is noteworthy that this performance was achieved with a relatively low amount of data (3159). For future works, the validation of the methodology is in progress by exposing the CNN to experimental data.

Acknowledgments

[a]Financial support from the Human Resources Program of the National Agency of Petroleum, Natural Gas, and Biofuels – PRH-ANP, funded by oil companies qualified in the R&D and Innovation clause from ANP Resolution 50/2015 (process no. 041319). [b]Financial support from PETROBRAS (process no. PETROBRAS/UFF/FEC 5900.0113248.19.9).

References

C. Bai, H. Park, Yong, C.Y. Ng, L. Wang, 2021, Classification of gas dispersion states via deep learning based on images obtained from a bubble sampler, Chemical Engineering Journal Advances, 5, 100064

A. K. M. Figueredo, M. B.de Souza, P. F. F. Frutuoso e Melo, C. A. Vaz Junior, J. Di Domenico, 2022, How does subsea processing safety policy impact safety? Lessons learned from the Brazilian experience, Journal of Loss Prevention in the Process Industries, 74, 104668

I. Goodfellow, Y. Bengio, A. Courville, 2016, Deep Learning, MIT Press, 775p.

M. Jamialahmadi, M.R. Zehtaban, H. Müller-Steinhagen, A. Sarrafi, J.M. Smith, 2001, Study of Bubble Formation Under Constant Flow Conditions, Chemical Engineering Research and Design, 79, 5, 523-532

A. Krizhevsky, I. Sutskever, G.E. Hinton, 2012, Image net classification with deep convolutional neural networks, Advances in Neural Information Processing Systems, 25, 1097–1105

L. Li, X. Jia, W. Tian, S. Sun, W. Cao, 2018, Convolution Neural Network based Chemical Leakage Identification, Computer Aided Chemical Engineering, 44, 2329 – 2334.

N. Otsu, 1979, A Threshold Selection Method from Gray-Level Histograms. In: IEEE Transactions on Systems, Man, and Cybernetics, 62, 2168-2909.

O. Ronneberger, P. Fischer, T. Brox, 2015, U-Net: Convolutional networks for biomedical image segmentation, In: Medical Image Computing and Computer-Assisted Intervention – Lecture Notes in Computer Science, 9351, 234–241, Springer

J. Schäfer, P. Schmitt, M.W. Hlawitschka, H. Bart, 2016, Measuring particle size distributions in multiphase flows using a convolutional neural network, Chemie Ingenieur Technik, 91, 11, 1688–1695

H. Wu, J. Zhao, 2018, Deep convolutional neural network model based chemical process fault diagnosis, Computers & Chemical Engineering, 115, 185-197

Proceedings of the 14th International Symposium on Process Systems Engineering – PSE 2021+
June 19-23, 2022, Kyoto, Japan © 2022 Elsevier B.V. All rights reserved.
http://dx.doi.org/10.1016/B978-0-323-85159-6.50225-6

Dynamic Risk Analysis for Process Safety

Yuchen Wang[a,b] , Zuzhen Ji[a] , Shuanghua Yang[a,b], and Yi Cao[a,b*]

[a] *Department of Chemical Engineering, Zhejiang University, Hangzhou, 310000, China*
[b] *Institute of Zhejiang University-Quzhou, 78 Jiuhua Boulevard North, Quzhou, China 32400*
caoyi2018@zju.edu.cn

Abstract

Successful implementation of chemical production systems requires an effective mechanism to assess dynamic risk quantitatively. Existing works of dynamic risk analysis are based on mechanism examination and probability estimation. Complexity arises due to the difficulty while collecting historical accident data. Also utilizing the indicators obtained from the combination of multivariate variables cannot clearly represent the relationship between physical components and safety. To address the shortcomings of the existing methods, this paper proposed a dynamic risk analysis method for process safety. This is achieved by firstly using canonical variable analysis (CVA) to monitor the system, and then computing the remaining useful life (RUL) from simulation as the indicator representing the dynamic risk. A coal slurry gasification process is applied to illustrate the effectiveness of the proposed method. The method has the potential for the industry to understand how a failure occurred and at what time to prevent.

Keywords: Fault detection; Failure prognosis; Safety prediction; Dynamic risk analysis

1. Introduction

Modern chemical processes are becoming complex, which further arises the challenges to the safety of chemical production. The traditional chemical safety assessment is mostly subjective associated with risk analysis, while many risk methods are based on the knowledge and experience of the experts who conduct the analysis. No doubt, this would cause deviations among different experts. Although the ISO31000 has addressed a standard way to analyse risk by including experts from different perspectives to compromise the deviations, there are still weakness, for example, time-consuming.

Risk is used to represent the safety of a process. Recent studies were focused to develop quantitative or dynamic methods to analyse the risk for the chemical process. An efficient process monitoring scheme is able to capture the complex relationships among the interacting process variables and also to estimate the risk of the process continually (Amin et al.,2020). The current dynamic risk methods are often developed based on historical data or operation data (Zio, 2018). Historical statistics data is also known as Accident Sequence Precursor (ASP) data, which refers to the data recorded via historical accidents. Amin et al. (2020) used a combination of the naïve Bayes classifier, Bayesian network, and event tree analysis to detect and diagnose the fault, and obtain the probability that indicates the dynamic failure prognosis. Alternatively, to ensure a reliable result, a large amount of ASP data is often required. Some other methods are using operational data to examine the safety risks. Zadakbar et al. (2013a) used a combination of the multivariate statistic method and probability model to assess the system dynamic risk. Other risk analysis works are using prognostic methods; however, these works are often bespoke.

Some other research has utilized the model-based method to demonstrate the development of the system to get the dynamic risk (Zadakbar et al., 2013[b]). However, it's difficult to attain the precise model for the complicated process, or the modelling cost is not acceptable. In addition, recent process monitoring methods are usually based on the indicators obtained by multivariable combinations, which cannot clearly reveal the relationship between specific physical meaning and safety indicators.

The purpose of the work is to propose a method independent of the mechanism model and probability model that analyses the evolution from fault to failure using dynamic risk analysis. The dynamic risk in this paper is the relative risk which is compared with the risk within the time series of the system itself. Canonical variables analysis (CVA) is utilized to detect the fault and identify the subspace model, then simulate the safety critical variables to get the system remaining useful life (RUL), which represents the time from fault to failure. The RUL is utilized as the metric of system dynamic risk.

The rest of the paper is organized as follows. Section 2 introduces a specific method framework, and then, the proposed approach is demonstrated to be effective through a gasification case study in Section 3. Finally, the paper is concluded in Section 4.

2. Methodology

The overall methodology has been concluded in Figure 1. We need to analyse the safety critical variables (SCVs) and their threshold values in advance. The definition of SCVs can be seen in previous work (Ji et al., 2021). And the SCVs are considered as the directed standard that assesses whether system failure occurs. Once any SCVs is out of the threshold, the system will be regarded as having a failure. Next is to monitor and identify the system using CVA method. If a fault is detected at a point in time, the identified model is used to simulate the SCVs at each point of time until any SCVs exceeds threshold. We can obtain the RUL for each point of time, which is regarded as an indicator that reveal the system relatively dynamic risk, and can provide in-time information with reference value to the operators that shows current dynamic risk and the degree of urgency to solve the fault.

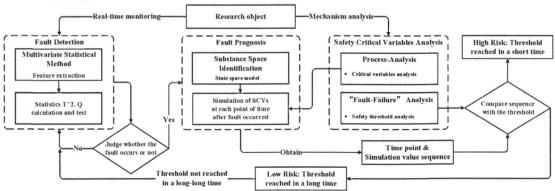

Figure 1 Research Approach

2.1. Safety critical variable analysis

There are adequate traditional methods to analyse system safety, such as event tree analysis, fault tree analysis, bow-tie analysis, and HAZOP. The above methods can be used for SCV selection.

2.2. System monitoring

The proposed process monitoring method is based on the CVA (Ruiz-Cárcel et al, 2016). It can be divided into two parts: Off-line modelling and On-line monitoring.

1) Off-line modelling

Assume y and u are the outputs and the inputs of the system after pre-processing of normal operation dataset. The past and future vectors p_t and f_t of current time point can be defined as Eq. (1), where p and f are the hysteresis.

$$p_t = [y_{t-1}^T, \dots, y_{t-p}^T, u_{t-1}^T, \dots, u_{t-p}^T]^T \qquad f_t = [y_t^T, y_{t+1}^T, \dots, y_{t+f}^T]^T \tag{1}$$

Then we get the past and future Hankel matrix P_t and F_t. And the number of columns of Hankel matrix can be calculated as $N = n - p - f + 1$, where n means the sample number.

$$P_t = [p_t, p_{t+1}, \dots, p_{t+N-1}] \qquad F_t = [f_t, f_{t+1}, \dots, f_{t+N-1}] \tag{2}$$

The solution for the optimization problem to find the linear combination that best correlates both data sets can be obtained by using the Singular Value Decomposition (SVD) of the Hankel matrix H, where $\Sigma_{A,B}$ represents the sample covariance matrix of two matrices A and B.

$$H = \Sigma_{F_t,F_t}^{-1/2} \Sigma_{F_t,P_t} \Sigma_{P_t,P_t}^{-1/2} = UDV^T \tag{3}$$

The reduced matrix V_r can be taken by selecting the columns of V related with the r highest eigenvalues from D. And the rest q columns of matrix V is recorded as V_q. Calculate state vector x_t, change vector e_t outside state space, residual vector r_t based on mapping matrix J, L, R according to Eq. (4). And $x_t = Jp_t$, $e_t = Lp_t$, $r_t = Rp_t$. Then the Hotelling and SPE statistics can be calculated as $T_s^2 = x_t^T x_t$, $T_r^2 = e_t^T e_t$, $Q = r_t^T r_t$.

$$J = V_r^T \Sigma_{P_t,P_t}^{-1/2} \qquad L = V_q^T \Sigma_{P_t,P_t}^{-1/2} \qquad R = I - J^T J \tag{4}$$

And for identification of the state space model, given a set of inputs u and outputs y, the model that represents the linear state-space can be described as Eq. (5). The system outputs y_k and inputs u_k are known and x_k can be obtained from CVA analysis, the only unknowns of the system are the matrices A, B, C, D. The multivariate regression can be used for the calculation of these matrices.

$$x_{k+1} = Ax_k + Bu_k + w \quad y_k = Cx_k + Du_k + v$$

$$\begin{bmatrix} A & B \\ C & D \end{bmatrix} = \sum \left[\begin{pmatrix} x_{k+1} \\ y_k \end{pmatrix}, \begin{pmatrix} x_k \\ u_k \end{pmatrix} \right] \cdot \sum \left[\begin{pmatrix} x_k \\ y_k \end{pmatrix}, \begin{pmatrix} x_k \\ u_k \end{pmatrix} \right]^{-1} \tag{5}$$

2) On-line monitoring

The new process data can also be organized as the form of past vector $p_{t,fault}$, and according to Eq. (4), we can obtain the state vector $x_{t,fault}$. Then we can get the SPE and Hotelling statistics of the new process data. Then the process can be monitored by comparing the statistics with the corresponding threshold. If the threshold is continuously exceeded, the system is considered being in faulty.

2.3. Dynamic risk analysis

For the new process, if a fault is detected, the state space model is updated in real time after 30 sampling intervals. In order to improve the accuracy of multi-step simulation, the model coefficient is retrained. The specific method is shown as Eq. (6-7). According to the identified model, SCV is simulated over time until one of them exceeds the threshold, and the number of steps is recorded as RUL. Take the RUL as the indicator for the relative dynamic risk and its evolution trend.

$$\hat{y}_k = Cx_k + Du_k + v$$

$$\hat{x}_{k+1} = Ax_k + Bu_k + w \qquad \hat{y}_{k+1} = C\hat{x}_{k+1} + Du_{k+1} + v \quad \dots \qquad (6)$$

$$\hat{x}_{k+n} = A\hat{x}_{k+n-1} + Bu_{k+n-1} + w \qquad \hat{y}_{k+n} = C\hat{x}_{k+n} + Du_{k+n} + v$$

$$L1(A,B,C,D) = argmin(\| \begin{bmatrix} \hat{y}_k & \hat{y}_{k+1} & \cdots & \hat{y}_{k+n} \end{bmatrix} - \begin{bmatrix} y_k & y_{k+1} & \cdots & y_{k+n} \end{bmatrix} \|_2^2) \qquad (7)$$

3. Application of the proposed methodology

3.1. Introduction of the coal slurry gasification

Coal water slurry gasification is an entrained flow gasification process for generating syngas under high temperature and high pressure with coal water slurry as raw material and oxygen or air as gasification agent. The main component of syngas is carbon monoxide, carbon dioxide and hydrogen. The gasification process applied as a case study is based on a dynamic simulation model which contains coal slurry storage tank, gasifier combustion chamber and quench chamber. Figure 2 illustrated the gasification process.

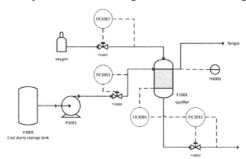

Figure 2 Coal slurry gasification process

3.2. Determine safety critical variables

There are 14 measured variables and 10 manipulated variables in the gasification process. And the SCVs are selected as gasifier combustion chamber temperature R1.T and R2.T using the method proposed previously (Ji et al., 2021). The threshold of the upper and lower temperature of combustion chamber are [920 ,1019] $\mathcal{C}$ and [1405 ,1505] $\mathcal{C}$.

3.3. Fault detection

Considering the large fluctuation of coal composition in the actual process, the component of coal is selected as the variable of fault. The fault is introduced after 3.5 hours of simulation, and the total simulation time is 13.5 hours. The response curves of oxygen flow, gasifier temperature, CO and CO_2 molar fractions are illustrated in Figure 3.

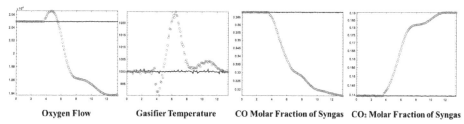

Figure 3 Response curve (Circle line: fault condition; Solid line: normal condition)

Then the CVA algorithm is used to realize the safety monitoring of gasification process. The results are shown as Figure 4. The dotted line refers to the threshold of statistics under the condition of confidence of 0.999.

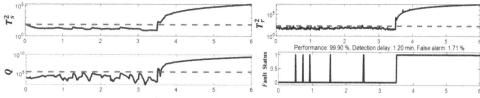

Figure 4 Fault monitoring of gasifier

From Figure 4, it can be seen that the process fault detection rate based on three statistics is 99.90%, the false alarm rate is 1.71%, and the fault detection delay time is 1.20min. According to the sampling interval of 0.01h, it is the delay of two sampling intervals.

3.4. Dynamic risk analysis for the gasification

Based on Sections 2.2 and 2.3, we obtained the identified model of the normal system, and then verify the accuracy of the model on the testing dataset sampled in normal operation. The validation results are illustrated in Figure 5, where the circle line represents simulation value, and solid line represents real value. And based on the coefficient of determination R^2, it can be seen that the accuracy is acceptable and satisfactory.

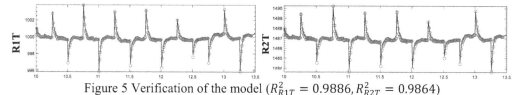

Figure 5 Verification of the model ($R^2_{R1T} = 0.9886, R^2_{R2T} = 0.9864$)

When the fault is detected, the identified model trained from the normal mode is not applicable. According to the section 2.3, the state space model is retrained using fault data and the results will be used as the initial value of multi-step regression training. Finally, the simulation of SCVs is executed for each time point. Figure 6 is an example of the 400th point of time, where the circle line represents simulation value, solid line represents real value, and black line means the threshold. Their accuracy is acceptable.

For the dynamic risk analysis, the simulation of each point has been executed until the values of SCVs are out of the threshold, and the needed time length is recoded. The variation of RUL with sampling points is shown in Figure 7. The asterisk represents RUL obtained from simulation, while circle represents real value from the dynamic model. The RUL obtained from simulation is compared with the real value of remining useful life, and their correlation coefficient is 0.999, which means that the simulation traces the real circumstance well. From Figure 7, RUL decreases continuously, hence the risk is increasing correspondingly. And with the continuous development of the fault, the RUL has been reduced to an unacceptable level, i.e., corresponding measures must be applied to the system immediately.

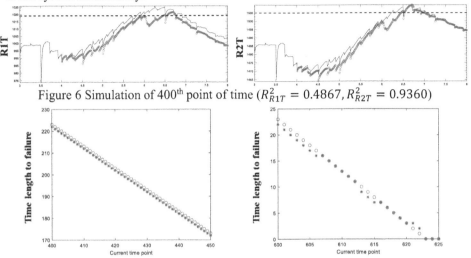

Figure 6 Simulation of 400th point of time ($R^2_{R1T} = 0.4867, R^2_{R2T} = 0.9360$)

Figure 7 Development of RUL over time

4. Conclusions

This work proposed a novel dynamic risk analysis approach that could better demonstrate the dynamicity of risk based on RUL. This would be useful for managing process risk. In this approach, the process is monitored by the CVA, and once the fault is detected, then CVA would identify a model for the simulation of SCVs analyzed from the system mechanism, and then the simulation would obtain the time RUL which indicated the dynamic risk of the system. The proposed approach was applied to a coal slurry gasification for its application and validation. The result proved the method to be effective to reveal the system dynamic risk and its evolution trend.

References

T. Amin, F. Khan, S. Ahmed, S. Imtiaz, 2020. A novel data-driven methodology for fault detection and dynamic risk assessment. The Canadian Journal of Chemical Engineering 98, 2397 – 2416.

E. Zio, 2018. The future of risk assessment. Reliability Engineering & System Safety 177, 176-190.

O. Zadakbar, S. Imtiaz, F. Khan , 2013. Dynamic risk assessment and fault detection using principal component analysis. Industrial & Engineering Chemistry Research, 52(2), 809 – 816.

O. Zadakbar, S. Imtiaz, F. Khan, 2013. Dynamic risk assessment and fault detection using a multivariate technique. Process Safety Progress 32, 365 – 375.

C. Ruiz-Cárcel, L. Lao, Y. Cao, D. Mba, 2016. Canonical variate analysis for performance degradation under faulty conditions. Control Engineering Practice, 54, 70 – 80.

Z. Ji, S.Yang, Y. Cao, 2021. Harmonizing safety and security risk analysis and prevention in cyber-physical systems. Process Safety and Environmental Protection, 148(5)

Proceedings of the 14th International Symposium on Process Systems Engineering – PSE 2021+
June 19-23, 2022, Kyoto, Japan © 2022 Elsevier B.V. All rights reserved.
http://dx.doi.org/10.1016/B978-0-323-85159-6.50226-8

Monitoring of smart chemical processes: A Sixth Sense approach

Bogdan Dorneanu[a], Mohamed Heshmat[b], Abdelrahim Mohamed[c], Harvey Arellano-Garcia[a,*]

[a]*LS Prozess- und Anlagentechnik, Brandenburgische Technische Universität Cottbus-Senftenberg, Cottbus, D-03046, Germany*
[b]*Faculty of Environment and Technology, University of the West of England, Bristol, BS16 1QY, United Kingdom*
[c]*Institute for Communication Systems, Home of 5GIC, University of Surrey, Guildford, GU2 7XH, United Kingdom*
arellano@b-tu.de

Abstract

This paper introduces the development of an intelligent monitoring and control framework for chemical processes, integrating the advantages of technologies such as Industry 4.0, cooperative control or fault detection via wireless sensor networks. The system described is able to detect faults using information on the process' structure and behaviour, information on the equipment and expert knowledge. Its integration with the monitoring system facilitates the detection and optimisation of controller actions. The results indicate that the proposed approach achieves high fault detection accuracy based on plant measurements, while the cooperative controller improves the operation of the process.

Keywords: fault detection, wireless sensor networks, cooperative control, Industry 4.0.

1. Introduction

Industry 4.0 is transforming chemical processes into complex, smart cyber-physical systems, by the addition of elements such as smart sensors, Internet of Things (IoT), big data analytics, or cloud computing. Modern engineering systems and manufacturing processes are operating in highly dynamic environments, and exhibiting scale, structure and behavior complexity. Under these conditions, plant operators find it extremely difficult to manage all the information available, infer the desired conditions of the plant and take timely decisions to handle abnormal operation (Natarajan & Srinivasan, 2014). Human beings acquire information from the surroundings through sensory receptors for vision, sound, smell, touch, and taste, the Five Senses. The sensory stimulus is converted to electrical signals as nerve impulse data is communicated with the brain. When one or more senses fail, the humans are able to re-establish communication and improve the other senses to protect from incoming danger. Furthermore, the mechanism of reasoning has been developed during evolution, which enables analysis of present data and generation of a vision of the future, which might be called the Sixth Sense.

As industrial processes are already equipped with the five senses: hearing from acoustic sensors, smelling from gas and liquid sensors, seeing from cameras, touching from vibration sensors and tasting from compositions monitors, the Sixth Sense could be achieved by forming a sensing network which is self-adaptive and self-repairing, carrying out deep-thinking analysis with even limited data, and predicting the sequence of events via integrated system modelling.

In this paper, an intelligent monitoring and control framework for chemical processes is proposed, which takes advantage of recent technological developments such as wireless sensor networks (WSNs), 5G communication, or cooperative control to ensure stable process operation.

2. System architecture

The framework consists of five main components, designed in a modular manner (Fig.1). The first one is a wireless sensor network (WSN), transmitting over a 5G communication network, that facilitates data management for improved fault detection. The second component is an efficient fault detection algorithm that can analyse the data and classify it in faulty or normal. The third component is a knowledge-based and model-based fault detection monitoring system. For the fault-detection, a two-stage method based on a hybrid learning approach is applied, which utilizes supervised and unsupervised learning. The fourth component is a cooperative model predictive control (MPC) system that takes the required measures to ensure stable process operation. Finally, the fifth component is an intelligent adaptive decision-making framework.

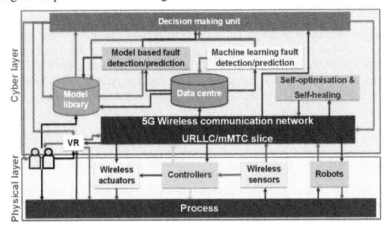

Figure 1: System structure - High level overview

The proposed architecture divides the system into a physical layer, which includes the industrial process, the wireless sensors and actuators, the controllers, and inspector robots, and a cyber layer, formed of the wireless communication network, the fault detection algorithms and the decision-making framework.

2.1. Industrial process

The application of the proposed architecture is investigated on a mini plant (Fig.2) available at the Department of Chemical and Process Engineering of the University of Surrey (Guildford, United Kingdom). The plant produces sodium ion solution for sale to fine chemical, pharmaceutical and food industry. The raw material (sodium chloride contaminated with calcium chloride) is pre-mixed with sodium bicarbonate. This feedstock is then fed into a reactor vessel charged with pre-heated water, and reacted at 65 °C. The suspension resulted from the reaction is then pumped by a positive displacement pump through a plate filter, which removes a high proportion of the calcium carbonate. The output stream splits into a product and a recycle line. The recycle line is fed back into the reactor, while the product is passed through a polishing filter, to remove any remaining solids, and then to the lot tank. The carbon dioxide resulted in the reaction is absorbed in an alkaline solution. The plant is provided with wireless sensors connected to the cellular network, that monitor process variables (e.g., temperature, pressure, processing unit level, etc.) and a distributed control system. The sensors are transmitting data every second.

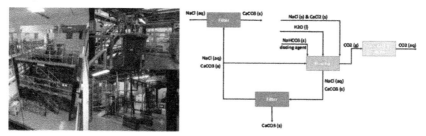

Figure 2: Mini plant and simplified process diagram

Robots are also deployed in the plant for periodic maintenance and surveillance. In the proposed framework, the mobile robots will autonomously patrol around the plant. They are equipped with sensors for recording the necessary measurements, performing the periodic inspection and surveillance, as well as acting as relays in deep fading areas. For the mobile robots exploited in this system, the navigation is achieved using standard robot operating system navigation stack.

2.2. Communication network

Legacy cellular systems have been designed primarily for human initiated mobile broadband communications, making them highly suboptimal for narrow band, short-bust, sporadic traffic (e.g., sensor measurement data) generated by sensors in chemical plants. It is envisioned that a new design paradigm is needed to support large numbers of heterogeneous sensing devices with diverse requirements and unique traffic characteristics. Comparing to sensors in traditional IoT network, those deployed in extreme environments need to operate in harsh, sometimes hazardous conditions, and are, thus, prone to wear and tear, and cannot be easily replaced, posing major challenges in designing resilient networks for reliable communication.

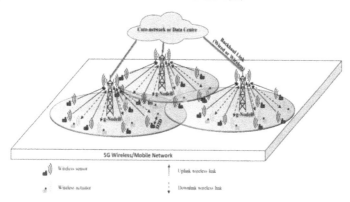

Figure 3: Communication network

For the system presented in this paper, a centralized control mechanism of the communication network is considered, where the sensors are connected to a fusion node via wireless links, as shown in Fig.3. The wireless links can also be used to send commands to the actuators within the mini plant. The resulting network consists of a heterogeneous set of periodic and event triggered sensors with mixed requirements, characteristics and traffic models.

Considering the plant and associated sensors' heterogeneity, a statistical model rather than a deterministic model is chosen for the sensor transmission events. The number of incoming packets (or events when each event generates a single packet) per unit time follows the Poisson distribution, while the packet interval is modelled as an exponential distribution. This results in probability-based transmissions that can be controlled by the arrival rate and the inter-arrival time.

2.3. Machine learning

In the machine learning model, both fault detection and prediction applications are embedded for sophisticated fault handling, as illustrated in Fig.4, and takes in online data streams and inputs to feed them to both (or either one of) the fault detection and fault prediction sub-models.

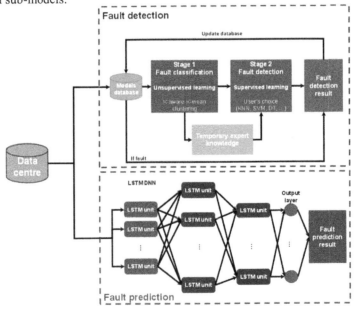

Figure 4: Fault detection and fault prediction model

In the fault detection, a batch of online data streams are checked for expert knowledge recognized types, recorded in the databases. If the streams pass this initial check, a combination of unsupervised and supervised learning algorithms are applied on the data for fault classification. The unsupervised learning algorithms, namely K-aware K-mean, are an extension of the conventional K-mean clustering algorithms with additional capacity to self-optimize the K-value (K≤1). This phase aims to acquire a temporary expert knowledge on what the minority of the current data (the smallest cluster) is like and labels them as outliers. Subsequently, a choice of the classical supervised learning algorithms is conducted based on the temporary expert knowledge to classify the new types of faults and comparing them with the expert knowledge database. Once a new type of fault is validated by the system, the database is updated.

In the fault detection sub-model, a long short-term memory (LSTM) deep neural network (DNN) is proposed to perform online fault prediction. The relationship between the elements of a single LSTM unit is described by the following relationships.

$$i_t = \sigma_g \cdot (W_i \cdot x_t + U_i \cdot h_t + b_i) \tag{1}$$

$$o_t = \sigma_g \cdot (W_o \cdot x_t + U_o \cdot h_t + b_o) \tag{2}$$

$$f_t = \sigma_g \cdot (W_f \cdot x_t + U_i \cdot h_f + b_f) \tag{3}$$

$$c_t = f_t{}^\circ c_{t-1} + i^\circ \sigma_c \cdot W_c \cdot x_t + U_c \cdot h_t + b_c \tag{4}$$

$$h_t = o_t{}^\circ \sigma_h(c_t) \tag{5}$$

With $x \in \mathcal{R}^n$ and $h \in \mathcal{R}^h$ the input and the first hidden layer output of the LSTM-DNN, respectively; t the time step; $i, o,$ and f the input gate, the output gate and the forget gate vectors, respectively; $c \in \mathcal{R}^h$ the cell state vector; W_i, U_i, W_o, U_o, W_f, U_f, W_c and U_c the weight matrices; b_i, b_o, b_f and b_c the biases; σ_g, σ_h and σ_c the activation functions. In the equations above $^\circ$ denotes the Hadamard product.

2.4. Cooperative control

A cooperative distributed MPC approach is considered to achieve highly flexible dynamic optimal control. A cooperative protocol is defined using a simple algorithm to reach an agreement regarding the state of a number of N process units (agents). The MPC controller receives information from the process unit in the form of the output process variable, y, as well as from the neighbouring units in the form of a cooperation variable, v. Based on this exchange of information, the controller will correct the input variables to the system, u).

2.5. Decision-making system

To add intelligent and adaptive decision-making capabilities, a multi-agent system (MAS) is defined to be integrated with the cooperative MPC. The MAS has two main tasks: to decide the optimal connectivity between the distributed MPCs for safer and better operation, and to monitor the system and detect any deviation in the behaviour, which is then transmitted to the controllers. The proposed MAS consists of follower agents, which keep track of equipment behaviour and its relationship with other control units, a coordinator agent, which decides the optimal connectivity between controllers, and a monitor agent, which analyses the information gathered from the coordinator agent and reports the expected failures and recommendations to the operator.

3. Results

The framework presented in the previous sections has been implemented for fault detection and prediction applications in the mini plant. A dataset was obtained from the plant during the year 2017-2018 and consists of over 10 million samples, each containing measurements for 43 variables, collected at a frequency of 1 Hz. Data types include both floating point and Boolean value data. The batch size for both fault detection, and prediction algorithms is set to 10,000. All simulations are conducted in Python and Keras application programming interface (API) with Tensorflow backend on an Intel i7-8700 CPU (6 Core/12-Thread, 12 MB cache, up to 4.6 GHz with Intel Turbo Boost

Technology) and dual Nvidia GeForce GTX 1080 Ti GPUs (with 11GB GDDR5X each). For all supervised learning algorithms, the train-test ratio is chosen at 0.75:0.25. During fault detection, the result of classifying the original high dimensional data is projected into a lower dimension (2D plane) using principal component analysis (PCA) as shown in Figure 5. Table 1 compares different supervised learning algorithms regarding fault detection accuracy.

Table 1: Complexity comparison

Supervised learning classifier	Detection accuracy, %
Logistic regression	97.5
K-nearest neighbors	100.0
Decision tree	99.4
Linear support vector machines	99.5

For fault prediction, a three hidden layer LSTM-DNN is configured to perform one time step ahead prediction for 40 dynamic variables, with 30, 50, and 30 units used, respectively. The mini-batch method is used to accelerate the stochastic gradient optimiser. Each LSTM hidden layer uses a linear activation function and the same applies for the output layer. The proposed LSTM-DNN is able to achieve a prediction accuracy of 99.7%. The train-test learning curve comparison is illustrated in Figure 6.

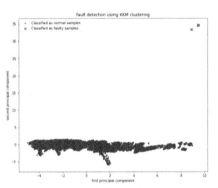

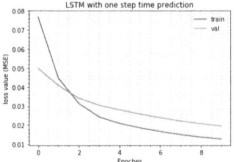

Figure 5. Fault detection   Figure 6. Train-test learning curve comparison

4. Conclusions

In this paper, a high-level interdisciplinary framework is developed for leveraging capabilities of 5G WSNs, machine learning algorithms and cooperative control to step towards the industrial Sixth Sense. Since different applications have different requirements, the proposed system is built in a modular manner. A higher decision layer is proposed for fault detection and prediction to optimise the plant operation. Focusing on a chemical process as a case study, the proposed framework has been used to control the plant. The results indicate that the proposed approach achieves high fault detection/prediction accuracies based on real plant measurements. Future work will consider the impact of mobile wireless sensors deployed in robots, as well as integrating the machine learning fault detection/prediction schemes network-specific models to achieve both network and process fault prediction.

References

Natarajan, S., & Srinivasan, R., 2014, Computers and Chemical Engineering 60, pp. 182-196

Proceedings of the 14th International Symposium on Process Systems Engineering – PSE 2021+
June 19-23, 2022, Kyoto, Japan © 2022 Elsevier B.V. All rights reserved.
http://dx.doi.org/10.1016/B978-0-323-85159-6.50227-X

Fault detection in a benchmark simulation model for wastewater treatment plants

Pedram Ramin[a]*, Xavier Flores-Alsina[a], Sebastian Olivier Nymann Topalian[a], Ulf Jeppsson[b], Krist Gernaey[a]

[a] *Process and Systems Engineering Center (PROSYS), Department of Chemical and Biochemical Engineering, Technical University of Denmark, Building 228A, DK-2800, Kgs. Lyngby, Denmark*
[b] *Division of Industrial Electrical Engineering and Automation, Department of Biomedical Engineering, Lund University, Box 118, SE-221 00, Lund, Sweden*
*Corresponding Author's E-mail: pear@kt.dtu.dk

Abstract

The International Water Association (IWA) Benchmark Simulation Models (BSM1 and BSM2) have been successfully used in both industry and academia to test and verify control strategies in wastewater treatment plants (WWTPs). In this study, a new (plant-wide) benchmark simulation model, the BSM2-LT, is developed to evaluate monitoring algorithms. This platform provides opportunities to generate various sensor/actuator and process faults. To make this realistically, different Markov-chain models are used to re-create the alternation of sensor/actuator states based on predefined occurrence probability. The same principle is used to describe the occurrence of toxic/inhibitory compounds. Using this platform, one can test the performance of a monitoring algorithm such as a fault detection method. To demonstrate this in an example, a multivariate method based on adaptive dynamic principal component analysis (dPCA) was used to detect faulty events. The performance of the monitoring algorithm is evaluated with a penalization index, scoring from 0 to 100. While the tested method had a good false alarm score, it resulted in a low false acceptance. While the results could be certainly improved, the main focus of this study is the benchmark simulation model and not presenting a well optimized monitoring algorithm. The software which will be produced and freely distributed in the near future, will allow an objective evaluation of monitoring algorithms for WWTPs for any user.

Keywords: Benchmark simulation, Fault detection, Markov chains, Monitoring algorithms, Wastewater treatment

1. Introduction

Instrumentation, control and automation for industrial chemical and biochemical processes to attain cost-effective and safe process operation are highly dependent on reliability of the real-time measurements. Despite considerable development of online sensors during the past decades, their dependability is still impaired due to various fouling and failing issues. Occasionally unsatisfactory measurement performance can prevent full instrumentation of plant-wide control systems. This is especially important for wastewater treatment plants (WWTPs) where often fault-tolerant control systems needs to be implemented. Small WWTPs generate up to 500 signals (including on-line and off-line signals), whereas larger ones typically register over 30,000 (Olsson 2012). Despite a large number of available signals, data reconciliation and validation for online instrumentation has remained a largely unexplored field with a lack of standardized approaches. Most data are stored unstructured, with lots of gaps, repetition, ambiguity and uncertainty. This has led to "data-rich, information-poor" situations in which data sets are often too large and complex for processing and analysis to be used for decision-making. To turn raw data into useful and actionable information, data need to be validated. This can be achieved through a fault detection procedure. While several advanced data validation tools have already been developed for various chemical industries, their application to wastewater treatment facilities is not straight forward. Compared to chemical industrial processes, municipal WWTPs have unique features which complicates their monitoring and control strategies: (i) Wastewater influent is characterized by short- and long-term high temporal variability in both quantity and quality. WWTPs are impacted by growing urban areas, and variable rain events; (ii) Input materials (wastewater, storm water) cannot be stored in large quantities if the supply exceeds the process capacity; (iii) Low effluent water quality cannot be discarded or ignored; (iv) Wastewater treatment processes exhibit nonlinear, nonstationary, autocorrelated, cross-correlated behavior and are characterized by changes at many different time-scales; (v) Challenging environmental conditions impose sensor impairment due to solids deposition, precipitate formation and biofilm growth.

1.1. Benchmark simulation models

Benchmark simulation models are great tools to test and evaluate different monitoring methods under various fault conditions (sensors or process faults). The Benchmark simulation for Tennessee Eastman process (TEP) (Downs and Vogel 1993) is perhaps the best known platform in chemical engineering, resembling a real-world example, to test different fault detection strategies in an industrial reaction process (Gravanis et al. 2022). Another example is the IWA Benchmark Simulation Model No. 1 (BSM1) and No. 2 (BSM2) (Gernaey et al. 2005; Jeppsson et al. 2006) describing typical biological and physico-chemical processes in WWTPs (Gernaey et al. 2014). BSM1 includes a five-reactor activated sludge plant configuration with a (non-reactive) secondary clarifier, whereas BSM2 is a plant-wide description of a typical WWTP, extending BSM1 with pretreatment and sludge treatment processes. These benchmark platforms allow simulation-based performance evaluation of process control and monitoring strategies (Gernaey et al. 2014). An extension to BSM1, named BSM1-LT, was also developed (Rosen et al. 2004) to enable long term evaluation of control strategies (e.g. sludge retention time control based on wastewater flowrate) and process monitoring performance (e.g. detecting equipment failure such as nitrate and ammonium sensors). The BSM1-LT has also been used to test different univariate fault detection methods (Corominas et al. 2011). A preliminary attempt was made to simulate different faults in BSM2 followed by detection and diagnosis using incremental principal component analysis (IPCA) (Kazemi et al. 2020).

The aim of this study is to extend BSM2 by including "realistically" different sensor/actuator and process faults which are compatible and unified with the previous developments (influent generator, process models, sensor and actuator models, simulation procedure, evaluation criteria). The final output, the BSM2-LT, will include different scenarios which will be suitable to test univariate/multivariate statistical monitoring methods as well as fault-tolerant control strategies. The final software will be freely available for any user.

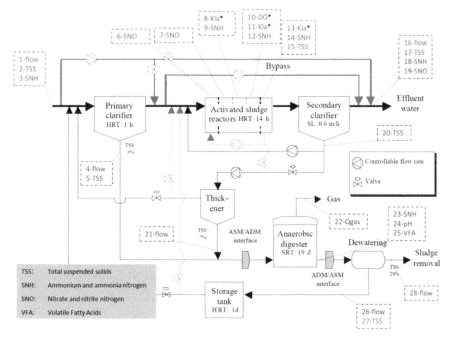

Figure 1. Layout of BSM2/ BSM2-LT. Process data for objective evaluations in this study are indicated with numbers (definition are given in the box). Controlled variable (DO) and manipulated variable (K_La), indicated with asterisks, are subject to faults in this study.

2. Methods

Two different types of faults, sensor/actuator fault and process fault were investigated.

2.1. Sensor/actuator fault generation

Faults were created only for the oxygen (DO) sensor in reactor 4 (used to control oxygen in aerated reactors 3 to 5) and for the actuator, K_La (oxygen mass transfer coefficient, equivalent to airflow in aerated reactors). Faults were modelled using a Markov-chain approach, where 7 different states were considered with a predefined occurrence probability, reported here as % for DO and K_La, respectively: (i) fully functional (93.8% and 88.3%); (ii) excessive drift (0.5% and 9.2%); (ii) shift (0.9% and 0.1%); (iv) fixed value, (1.6% and 1.6%); (v) complete failure (0.2% and 0.7%); (vi) wrong gain (2.7% and 0%); (vii) calibration (0.4% and 0%). The model was regenerated from earlier studies (Rosen et al. 2008; Corominas et al. 2011) following the same recommendations and parameters.

2.2. Process fault generation

Process disturbances were created by introducing two inhibitory or toxic substances, represented by new state variables S_{tox} and X_{tox}, in soluble and particulate form (absorbed to other particulate matters), respectively. The inhibition here is defined as the reduction in growth rate and toxicity is defined as both reduced growth rate and increased decay rate. The biological impact is defined by different inhibition/toxicity parameters using combined concentration of S_{tox} and X_{tox}. These parameters impact growth and decay of heterotrophs and autotrophs in activated sludge reactors (Gernaey et al. 2014). To generate S_{tox} and X_{tox} at the influent of BSM2-LT, two separate Markov-chain models were used to create a basic 'seed' file. Three states were used, no discharge, discharge with low amount (inhibitory discharge), discharge with high amount (toxic discharge). For S_{tox}, toxicity is assumed to occur every six months and inhibition every two weeks, with a duration of 3 hours for both. For X_{tox}, toxicity is assumed to occur every six months and inhibition once every month, with a duration of 1 hour for both. The 'seed' file was then used in the sewer model of the influent generator in a similar approach as described elsewhere (Gernaey et al. 2014).

2.3. Fault detection

An adaptive-dynamic fault detection was tested (Odom et al. 2018) using dynamic principal component analysis (dPCA) with a moving window (8 days). To take into account the correlation between sequential observations, all the data were lagged two-time steps (two samples). The first 60 days were used for training and were assumed to be a 'normal' period (all faults and toxicity were removed in this period). Two multivariate monitoring statistics, i.e. Hotelling's T^2 and the square prediction error (SPE) were used with a threshold of 0.5%. A flag was issued if this threshold was violated. Five consecutive flags would then trigger an alarm, indicating fault in the data. In total 28 variables were selected for the fault detection as presented in Fig. 1.

2.4. Performance evaluation

To evaluate the performance of the previously described fault detection method, an evaluation index was used as a measure of reliability (Corominas et al. 2011). This index is ranging from 0 (not reliable) to 100 (reliable). It is calculated by penalization points when the fault detection does not succeed. Penalizations are importantly based on: (i) late detection in which penalty points exponentially increases and reach a maximum level, (ii) extra penalizing intermittent detection for unfavorable switching from correct detection to non-detection during a fault event. Indices are defined for false alarm (J_{FAL}), and false acceptance (J_{FAC}) as well as a total index (J). Moreover, precision and accuracy were also calculated according to a calculated confusion matrix (error matrix).

3. Results

The results of fault generation, model simulation and fault detection are presented in Fig. 2. The results are only shown for reactor 4 for the tested scenarios, i.e. sensor/actuator fault (S1A to S1G) and process fault (S2A to S2G). Table 1 summarises the performance of the fault detection using different evaluation indices. This assessment is done considering T^2 alarm, SPE alarm, and the combination of both.

3.1 Sensor/actuator fault

The DO sensor in reactor 4, is connected to a feedback PI controller with a set point tracking objective. The DO signal oscillated around the set point of 2 g/m^3 (Fig. 2 S1D). A combination of drift in the K_La signal and a wrong gain for the DO sensor, caused the oxygen in reactor 4 to ramp down to almost zero. This fault was captured by T^2 and SPE with delays (Fig 2. S1C). In three occasions of fixed value faults for the DO sensor, the signal from this sensor is reduced to nearly zero, causing the oxygen in reactor 4, momentarily to reach 6 g/m^3. This was due to an overreaction of the control system, compensating for an apparent lack of oxygen. Fixed fault in the K_La signal, significantly brought down the K_La value to around 30, causing the oxygen to drop close to zero. Continuation of this scenario for 10 days, reduced the population of autotrophs by 75%

(Fig. 2 S1F). Consequently, it took nearly 100 days until the situation was brought back to normal in the absence of any other major failure. In this period, ammonium concentrations reached above 40 g/m^3 (S1G). This fault period was well detected by both T^2 and SPE. Overall, the tested fault detection showed relatively good false alarm performance but low false acceptance score (Table 1).

3.2 Process fault

While S$_{tox}$ (Fig. 2 S2A) follows the transport dynamics of the soluble species, X$_{tox}$ (Fig. 2 S2B) resembles those of particulates. This implies that S$_{tox}$ is impacted by dilution with relatively short retention time whereas the retention time for X$_{tox}$ depends on the sludge retention time. This creates different effects on the plant performance. In BSM2-LT the activated sludge system has a hydraulic retention time (HRT) of 14 hours, and the sludge retention time (SRT) in the anaerobic digester is 19 days. In case of appearance of toxic/inhibitory chemicals in reactor 4, autotrophs were in general more impacted than heterotrophs (Fig. 2, S2D and S2F). This in turn caused ammonium concentrations to rise. However, loss of heterotrophs due to high S$_{tox}$ concentration, triggered readily degradable substrate concentration to rise sharply on three occasions. T^2 statistics could capture these faulty moments. In other periods, due to frequent occurrence of toxicity, especially S$_{tox}$, both T^2 and SPE showed a high level of alarm. In general, SPE was found to be more sensitive compared to T^2 for the tested faults and generated nearly 60% more flags (Fig. 2 S1C and S2C). Better optimization of the hyper parameter, e.g. threshold for SPE and T^2 statistics and the number of flags considered before initiating an alarm, is expected to improve the results. Variable selection for fault detection is also another challenge. It was for example found that only considering the activated sludge reactors (variables 6 to 15) can improve J from 60 to 72 for the sensor/actuator faults scenario.

4. Conclusion

The BSM2-LT presented in this study provides opportunities to create realistic scenarios for both sensor/actuator and process faults. Using this platform, one can test the performance of a fault detection method. The method should ideally distinguish various faults and isolate highly consequential deviating instruments, and initiate an alarm before the system has undergone a severe disturbance. The tested fault detection method here showed good precision and false alarm scores but resulted in low accuracy and false acceptance. Further studies will focus on expanding this platform to simulate more realistic fault scenarios (e.g. for the anaerobic digester), which can occur simultaneously. A combination of both univariate and multivariate monitoring methods will be also used which is expected to improve the results.

Table 1. Evaluation indices for fault detection method tested in this study. TP: true positive, TN: true negative, FP: false positive, FN: false negative.

	Indicator	Precision (%)	Accuracy (%)	J$_{FAC}$ (0-100)	J$_{FAL}$ (0-100)	J (0-100)
	Formula	$\frac{TP}{TP+FP}$	$\frac{TP+TN}{TP+FP+FN+TN}$			
Sensor fault scenario	T2 alarm	95.4	78.2	2.3	95.4	61.9
	SPE alarm	68.2	59.4	20.8	68.2	51.0
	T2 + SPE alarm	70.4	65.1	41.8	70.4	60.0
Process fault scenario	T2 alarm	65.6	10.6	2.1	65.6	5.8
	SPE alarm	99.4	45.7	37.3	99.4	41.0
	T2 + SPE alarm	88.8	43.2	36.1	88.8	39.2

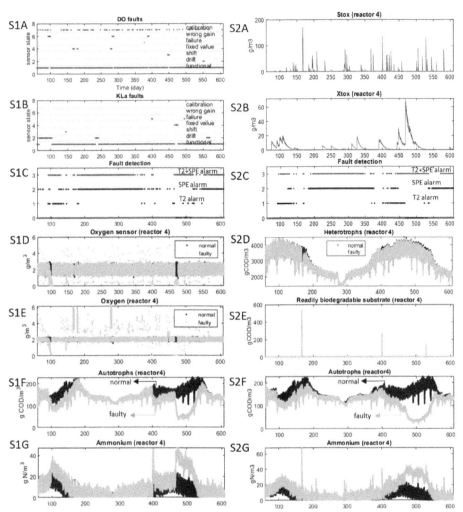

Figure 2. The fault scenarios in this study for sensor faults (S1A to S1G) and process faults (S2A to S2G). The results are shown only for reactor 4.

References

Corominas L, et al., 2011, Biotechnology & Bioengineering 108:333–344.

Downs JJ, Vogel EF, 1993, Computers & Chemical Engineering 17:245–255.

Gernaey KV, et al., 2014, IWA Scientific & Technical Report No. 23. IWA Publishing, London, UK.

Gernaey K V, et al., 2005, Industrial Electrical Engineering and Automation, Lund University, Sweden.

Gravanis G, et al., 2022, Computers & Chemical Engineering 156:107531.

Jeppsson U, et al., 2006, Water Science & Technology 53:287–295.

Kazemi P, et al., 2020, Water Science & Technology 82:2711–2724.

Odom GJ, et al., 2018, Applied Stochastic Models in Business and Industry 34:880–892.

Olsson G, 2012, Water Reseach 46:1585–1624.

Rosen C, et al., 2004, Water Science & Technology 50:41–49.

Rosen C, et al., 2008, Water Science & Technology 57:337–344.

Proceedings of the 14th International Symposium on Process Systems Engineering – PSE 2021+
June 19-23, 2022, Kyoto, Japan © 2022 Elsevier B.V. All rights reserved.
http://dx.doi.org/10.1016/B978-0-323-85159-6.50228-1

Formulation of integrated key performance indicator dashboard for chemical plants

Yasunori Kobayashi[a]*, Yoshiyuki Yamashita[a]

[a]*Department of Chemical Engineering, Tokyo University of Agriculture and Technology, Tokyo 184-8588, JAPAN*
yasunori.5ba8shi@gmail.com

Abstract

A process control system (PCS) exhibits monitoring functions that help board operators achieve safe and stable manufacturing in real time. Because of the rapid changes in the business environment, management objectives, such as carbon neutrality, energy conservation, and profitability, are required in addition to conventional objectives of safety, availability, and productivity. As additional management objectives conflict with conventional objectives, board operators need to monitor the manufacturing process from an optimization standpoint while understanding the new management strategy. New monitoring functions for the next generation of PCS were formulated in this study to help operators achieve energy-saving and profitable manufacturing.

Keywords: KPI, Dashboard, Optimization, Profit, Energy savings

1. Introduction

The monitoring functions in a general process control system (PCS) consist of process flow graphs, process trend graphs, and process alarms. Critical process variables were selected as subjects for monitoring based on a hazard and operability (HAZOP) study (from a safety standpoint) and control narratives (from a stability standpoint). Monitoring functions display these variables as key performance indicators (KPIs) for operators (operational KPIs). Process flow graphs display real-time process variables on a simplified piping and instrument diagram (P&ID) to highlight the material balance and heat balance of relevant manufacturing processes reflecting the impact of disturbance. Process trend graphs display the real-time trends of the process variables to highlight mutual correlation, propagation, and forecasting. Process alarms activate alarms when the process variable exceeds defined limits, such as high, low, deviation, and velocity, requiring manual interventions. These functions are specialized to achieve the independent management objectives of safety, availability, and productivity.

Because of management objectives, operational KPIs need to be reselected based on carbon neutrality, energy conservation, and profitability. New monitoring functions are required to comprehensively display an increased number of operational KPIs from a higher perspective. As additional management objectives conflict with conventional objectives (for example, energy savings impact productivity, and safety margin impacts profitability), new monitoring functions are required to indicate the balance in KPI achievement across multiple management objectives. In addition, because energy-saving, profitable manufacturing is still new to operators owing to a lack of practical training, new monitoring functions are required to establish the relationship between operational KPIs and management KPIs (cause and effect). Based on these considerations, we formulated new monitoring functions, including an integrated KPI, KPI tree graph, KPI balance graph, KPI trend graph, and KPI alarm.

2. Integrated KPI

The integrated KPI consists of five management objectives in three organizational roles. **Operational KPIs** are mainly used by operators. Only controllable process variables using PCS were selected. **Technical KPIs** are mainly used by the process and mechanical engineers to bridge the gap between plant management and operations. The KPIs calculated using the operational KPIs were selected from the viewpoints of chemical and mechanical engineering. **Management KPIs** are primarily used in plant management. Aggregated KPIs connected to technical KPIs were selected.

Safety-related KPIs are categorized as **safety KPIs**. Although safety KPIs have already been selected based on a HAZOP study, safety allowance can be defined as a new KPI that shows how the safety margin is sufficiently small. Asset-related KPIs are categorized as **availability KPIs**, including those related to the availability and reliability of plant assets. Productivity-related KPIs are categorized as **production KPIs**, including KPIs related to capacity utilization and throughput. KPIs related to carbon neutrality, energy savings, and product quality are categorized as **energy KPIs** because carbon emissions are linked to energy consumption, and quality giveaway increases energy consumption. Profitability-related KPIs are categorized as **profit KPIs**, including the yield of high-value products, material loss, and quality giveaways. An example of an integrated KPI for the depropanizer process is presented in Table 1. The P&ID of the target depropanizer process are shown in Figure 1.

The fractionator was controlled by two operating variables: material balance and heat balance. The change in material balance indicated a change in the cut point, and a change in the heat balance indicated a change in fractionation with variation in the reflux ratio. The material balance was controlled using the C3 flow rate. The C4 flow rate was automatically adjusted using a bottom-level controller. The heat balance was controlled using a reboiler low-pressure steam (LPS) flow rate. A condenser duty was automatically adjusted because the condenser outlet temperature was controlled by the cooling tower water flow rate. The reboiler return temperature was correlated with the C4 content in C3. The C3 flow rate was changed as needed to satisfy the specifications for C3 (that is, stabilize the reboiler return temperature). Board operators manually change the setpoints of the reboiler return temperature and reboiler LPS flow rate to prevent quality giveaway or off specifications.

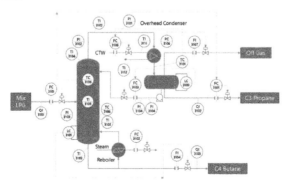

Figure 1. Depropanizer process

Table 1. Example of integrated KPI for depropanizer process

Management Objective	Management KPIs	Technical KPIs	Operation KPIs
Safety KPIs	Safety allowance	Safety allowance	Feed rate, Bottom level, Reflux rate, Reboiler return temp, Overhead drum level, Overhead drum pressure, CTW flow rate, Reflux pump inlet and outlet pressure
Availability KPIs	Availability rate Reliability rate	Availability rate Overhead dew point Dew point allowance Vapor Velocity	Feed rate Overhead dew point Overhead pressure, External reflux temp, Overhead dew point Overhead pressure, Overhead temp, C3 flow rate, Reflux rate, Off gas flow rate
Production KPIs	Capacity utilization rate Feed supply rate Total product rate	Capacity utilization rate Feed supply rate Total product rate C3 product rate C4 product rate	Demonstrated max feed rate, feed rate Planned feed rate, feed rate Planned C3 flow rate, C3 flow rate, Planned C4 flow rate, C4 flow rate Planned C3 flow rate, C3 flow rate Planned C4 flow rate, C4 flow rate
Energy KPIs	CO2 emission Energy consumption Energy efficiency Energy loss	CO2 emission Steam consumption Reboiler duty Reboiler duty ratio (Feed) Reboiler duty ratio (C3) Reboiler duty ratio (C4) Reflux ratio (Feed) Reflux ratio (C3) Reflux ratio (C4) Overhead condenser duty Feed enthalpy C3 enthalpy C4 enthalpy Off gas enthalpy	Low pressure steam flow rate, CO2 specific consumption Low pressure steam flow rate Low pressure steam flow rate, Low pressure steam condensing heat Reboiler duty, Feed rate Reboiler duty, C3 flow rate Reboiler duty, C4 flow rate Reflux rate, Feed rate Reflux rate, C3 flow rate Reflux rate, C4 flow rate Off gas latent heat, CTW flow rate, CTW inlet temp, CTW outlet temp Feed rate, Feed specific heat, Feed temp C3 flow rate, C3 specific heat, C3 temp C4 flow rate, C4 specific heat, C4 temp Off gas flow rate, Off gas specific heat, Off gas temp
Profit KPIs	Marginal profit Yield rate Material loss Quality giveaway	Marginal profit C3 yield rate C4 yield rate Material loss C3 in C4 rate C4 in C3 rate	Feed rate, C3 flow rate, C4 flow rate, Off gas flow rate, each unit price Feed rate, C3 flow rate Feed rate, C4 flow rate Feed rate, C3 flow rate, C4 flow rate, Off gas flow rate C3 content in C4 C4 content in C3

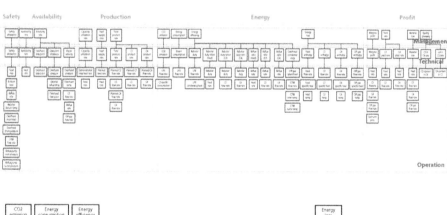

Energy KPIs

Figure 2. Design example of KPI tree graph

3. KPI tree graph

An example of the design of the KPI tree graph for the depropanizer process is shown in Figure 2. The KPI tree graph displays all the KPI information with mutual connections in a hierarchical manner. This information can help board operators understand which operational KPI impacts which management KPI and encourage board operators to take prompt action against operational KPI alarms before impacting management KPI. If the KPI alarm function is embedded in this graph (for example, the color of the box is changed during alarming), the KPI tree graph can assist board operators in solving all the KPI alarms equivalently toward total optimization.

4. KPI balance graph

An example of the design of the KPI balance graph is shown in Figure 3. This graph displays the KPI achievement scores in a pentagon for each management objective. The shape of the pentagon starts from the largest regular pentagon at the beginning of the day (the KPI score of each management objective starts at 100). The shape is deformed and small in real time when the relevant KPIs are alarming. If all the KPIs are alarming during the day, the shape disappears (the KPI score of each management objective reaches zero). The KPI balance graph helps board operators optimize KPIs across conflicting management objectives, and the scoring function motivates board operators as though it is a game. An example of the score calculation for each management objective in each organizational role (for example, profit operation) is expressed in Eq. (1):

$$\text{KPI Score (\%)} = \frac{1}{x_1} \sum_{n_1=1}^{x_1} \frac{8640 - \sum_{n_2=1}^{8640} x_2}{86.4} \tag{1}$$

where x_1 is the number of KPIs (for example, 15 in profit operation). The alarm state of each KPI was determined every 10 s periodically from the beginning to the end of the day (8640 times per day). The value of x_2 is 1(alarming) or 0 (normal).

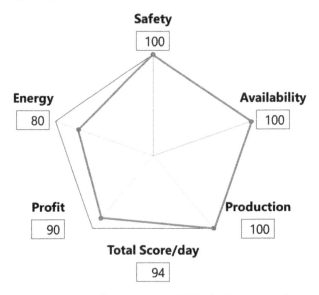

Figure 3. Design example of KPI balance graph

5. KPI trend graph

An example of the design of the KPI trend graph for the depropanizer process is shown in Figure 4. The KPI trend graph shows multiple KPI trend graphs. This graph can help board operators understand the exact propagative order and time lag among the relevant KPIs to identify the root cause. The acknowledgement function can be allocated in each graph because it is crucial to clarify human responsibility for KPI alarm recovery. The event log of the KPI alarm notification, acknowledgement, and recovery should be stored for future operation analysis. The guidance function will be valuable for junior operators to identify the root cause of the KPI alarm and adopt adequate countermeasures until they master plant operations.

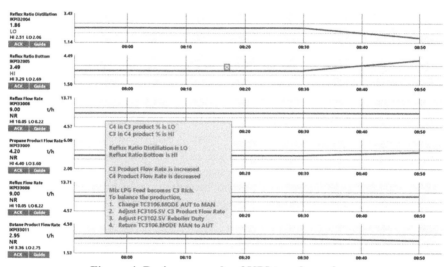

Figure 4. Design example of KPI trend graph

6. Case Study

New monitoring functions for the next generation of PCS worked satisfactorily in the following case study in the depropanizer process, while the fractionator feed (mixed LPG) became C3 rich.

- The operator identified C4 in C3 product in the **LO** alarm (this indicates that quality giveaway was losing profit), and C3 in C4 product is in the **HI** alarm (this indicates that the C4 product was going to be off the specification) on the KPI tree graph.

- Subsequently, the column temperature controller increased the C3 product flow rate to compensate for the lower column temperature. At this moment, the operator identified that the C3 product flow rate increased, the reflux flow rate decreased owing to the constant reboiler duty, and the C4 product flow rate decreased on the KPI trend graph.

- During the adjustment of the column temperature, the operator identified that the reflux ratio distillation (R/C3) was in the **LO** alarm, and the reflux ratio bottom (R/C4) was in the **HI** alarm (this indicated that the vapor and liquid balance in the fractionator shifted) on the KPI tree graph. In the relevant KPI balance graph, the shapes of the profit and energy became slightly small.

Based on the above information, the senior operator identified that the fractionator feed (mixed LPG) became C3 rich. The junior operator reached the same conclusion by checking the guidance message on the relevant KPI trend graph. The following are performed to adjust the fractionator to the optimum operation point (minimum quality giveaway within its specification for both products).

- The operator first turns off the column temperature controller TC3106 (by changing the control mode from AUT to MAN) to accelerate the adjustment.

- Next, the operator adjusts the set point of the C3 flow controller FC3105 (that is, adjusting the material balance) and the reboiler duty–steam flow controller FC3102 (this means adjusting the heat balance).

- After adjusting the column operation based on the economical guidance message, the operator turned on the column temperature controller TC3106 (changing the control mode from MAN to AUT) for stable operation.

In this case, new monitoring functions based on the integrated KPI help board operators realize energy-saving and profitable operations before impacting the relevant management KPIs.

7. Conclusion

This paper presents novel monitoring functions for an integrated KPI framework. An example formulation of the functions was demonstrated using a case study plant. We believe that these functions help process manufacturers achieve energy-saving and profitable manufacturing. Further investigations on other case study scenarios, such as the optimization of conflicting KPIs, are planned to analyze the effectiveness of the proposed functions.

References

ISO, 2014, KPIs for Manufacturing Operations Management, ISO22400.

L. Zhu, C. Johnsson, M. Varisco, M. M. Schiraldi, 2018, Key performance indicators for manufacturing operations management – gap analysis between process industrial needs and ISO 22400 standard, Procedia Manufacturing, 25, 82-88.

W. Hu, A. Almansoori, P.K. Kannan, S. Azarm, Z. Wang, 2012, Corporate dashboards for integrated business and engineering decisions in oil refineries: An agent-based approach, Decision Support Systems, 52, 729-741.

C. F. Lindberg, S.T. Tan, J. Y. Yan, F. Starfelt, 2015, Key performance indicators improve industrial performance, Energy Procedia, 75, 1785-1790.

C. Groger, M. Hillmann, F. Hahn, B. Mitschang, E. Westkamper, 2013, The operational process dashboard for manufacturing, Procedia CIRP, 205-210.

Proceedings of the 14th International Symposium on Process Systems Engineering – PSE 2021+
June 19-23, 2022, Kyoto, Japan © 2022 Elsevier B.V. All rights reserved.
http://dx.doi.org/10.1016/B978-0-323-85159-6.50229-3

Evaluation of risk in the biodiesel production process with supercritical ethanol

Diana Berenice Vega-Guerrero[a], Fernando I. Gómez-Castro [a,*], Antioco López-Molina [b]

[a]*Departamento de Ingeniería Química, División de Ciencias Naturales y Exactas, Campus Guanajuato, Universidad de Guanajuato, Noria Alta s/n Col. Noria Alta, Guanajuato, Gto. 36050, Mexico*
[b]*División Académica Multidisciplinaria de Jalpa de Méndez, Universidad Juárez Autónoma de Tabasco, Carr. Villahermosa-Comalcalco km. 27, Jalpa de Méndez, Tabasco 86205, Mexico*
fgomez@ugto.mx

Abstract

Production of biodiesel can be performed by using supercritical alcohols as reactants, avoiding the use of catalysts. Such processes show high reaction rates and have the advantage of treating raw materials with high contents of free fatty acids or water. Thus, supercritical treatments are appropriate strategies to transform low-cost raw materials. Nevertheless, one of the main concerns on these processes is related to safety issues due to the high-pressure levels required to obtain the desired yields. In this work, a process to produce biodiesel from a waste cooking oil treated with supercritical ethanol is designed using simulation tools. A strategy to assess the risk of this production scheme is developed in terms of a set of indicators. Through this strategy, the most hazardous streams in the process are detected, and the potential consequences of an accident are assessed. This information will be helpful for future work to establish strategies to reduce the risk in these high-pressure production processes and to design processes under inherent safety principles.

Keywords: biodiesel, supercritical ethanol, risk assessment, Hazard Process Stream Index.

1. Introduction

Production of biofuels has taken importance on the last years due to the continuous search for cleaner alternatives to provide energy in the transport and industrial sectors. Biodiesel is one of the most known biofuels, consisting on a mixture of alkyl esters. It can be used blended with fossil diesel to run engines, reducing emissions of CO, particulate matter, and unburned hydrocarbons (Teixeira et al., 2012). Such biofuel is traditionally produced by treating vegetable oils with a short-chain alcohol in the presence of a catalyst, commonly sodium hydroxide. Nevertheless, the main contribution to the product's final cost is the price of the raw material, representing 60-80% of the production cost (Lee et al., 2011). Thus, low-cost oils must be used as raw materials, e.g. waste cooking oil. This represents a disadvantage for the homogeneous basic catalyst route since waste oils have high concentrations of free fatty acids, which promotes saponification when using basic catalysts. To overpass such issue, acid pretreatments have been developed, followed by basic transesterification.

Nevertheless, this implies the need for additional neutralizing and recovery steps. An alternative approach implies the use of supercritical fluids to treat the oils, as supercritical methanol (Saka and Kusdiana, 2001) and supercritical methyl acetate (Saka and Isayama, 2009). In terms of costs and emissions of carbon dioxide, the one-step supercritical methanol approach is the most promissory (Gómez-Castro et al., 2015). Ethanol can also be used as a supercritical reactant, opening the possibility of using renewable ethanol. Among the advantages of using supercritical alcohols, it can be mentioned that the formation of two liquid phases in the reaction system is avoided, increasing the reaction rate.

Moreover, transesterification and esterification occur simultaneously. Therefore, the presence of free fatty acids does not affect the performance of the reaction. Additionally, water in the feedstock has no adverse effects on the yield (Kusdiana and Saka, 2004). This turns the supercritical treatments into an appropriate strategy to transform low-cost raw materials. Nevertheless, one of the main concerns on these processes is given by safety issues due to the high-pressure levels required to obtain the desired yields.

Sometimes, process safety has been considered as a verification criterion or as a governmental requirement. However, it is important to include process safety as a design and decision criterion from the early design stages in future projects, especially for processes and technologies under development, such as high-pressure biodiesel production. There are several features in the high-pressure biodiesel technologies that make it hazardous. These processes work at high pressure (up to 20 MPa); such condition propitiates many flammable substances in case of the loss of containment scenario. Furthermore, the temperature used in these processes (270 – 380°C) increases the formation rate of the vapor cloud in case of a flammable substance's release scenario. At the same time, the hot surfaces can act as an ignition source (Gómez-Castro and López-Molina, 2020). Therefore, the identification of dangerous process streams from an early stage allows generating inherently safe designs. Currently, published indices are focused on identifying explosion scenarios. However, these indices cannot accurately identify hazards on biofuel and bioproduct production processes, where combustible or aqueous mixtures are involved. The Hazardous Process Streams Index (HPSI) is one of the alternatives to identify hazards in the early stages of process design, improving inherent safety (López-Molina et al., 2020). The information needed to estimate process hazards is obtained from process simulation software.

2. Case study

Waste cooking oil is used as raw material, which is modeled with a composition of 94% triglycerides and 6% free fatty acids, with a distribution of 12.3 wt% of palmitic acid, 24 wt% of oleic acid, 56.6 wt% of linoleic acid and 7.1 wt% of linolenic acid for each fraction (Bulla Pereira, 2014). On the other hand, ethanol is used as a supercritical reagent. This alcohol can be obtained from biomass, which contributes to reducing the environmental impact of the process (Gómez-Castro et al., 2017).

A small-scale biodiesel production plant falls into a production range of less than 10,000 t/y, while a large-scale plant is in a range of more than 50,000 t/y (Skarlis et. al., 2012). The above has been taken as a basis for defining the case studies in this work to compare the production of biodiesel at small, medium, and large scales. Thus, the process design will be carried out with three production levels: 10,000, 30,000, and 50,000 tons per year.

3. Process simulation

The process is designed and analyzed with the support of the Aspen Plus® V.8 software. First, the oil and ethanol must be conditioned to the reaction conditions, 20MPa and 300°C. Subsequently, both streams enter the reactor, where triglycerides and free fatty acids are converted to ethyl esters. After the reaction, the pressure is reduced to ambient conditions. Next, the excess ethanol is recovered. The bottoms stream has two phases: phase 1 (biodiesel mainly) and phase 2 (glycerol with a small amount of water), which are separated in a decanter. Figure 1 shows the process diagram.

The reactor is modeled using the RPlug module, using the RK-Aspen model to represent the thermodynamics in the system. The reactor dimensions are set to achieve the highest possible biodiesel yield, verifying that the BIOD stream complies with the corresponding ASTM specifications.

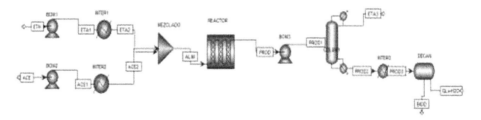

Figure 1. Biodiesel production process with supercritical ethanol in one step.

4. Risk assessment

Once the simulation has been carried out, information on the heat of combustion, molar fluxes, density, and operating pressure is extracted. Together with the flash point of the pure components, these parameters are used to determine the hazardous equipment employing the Hazardous Process Stream Index (HPSI). Once the dangerous streams are identified, it is necessary to define the consequences and process risk. The relative risk approach is used to compare and rank the risks of each alternative (López-Molina et al., 2020). The entire process relative risk (R_T) is the average of the individual risks. As such, an increase in capacity implies an increase in flow and inherently a more significant mass release in the case of loss of containment and its consequences. Therefore, the damage diameter for explosion and fire is estimated through ALOHA software.

5. Results

The results from the HPSI index calculation show the first process stages as the most dangerous due to the use of flammable substances; the same occurs in the three production scales. The analysis indicates that the hazardous streams are ETA1, ETA2, ALIM, PROD, and ETA3. This is explained in terms of the substances present in the stream; for the streams, ETA1, ETA2, and ETA3, the substance present is ethanol, while the ALIM and PROD streams carry glycerol. Table 1 shows the results of HPSI.

Table 1. HPSI results for the 10,000 ton/y scale.

Stream/index	$I_{pressure}$	$I_{density}$	I_{flow}	I_{flash}	$I_{combustion}$	HPSI
ETA	0.012	1.32	1.91	2.33	0.92	0.04
ACE	9.7E-06	0.57	0.04	0.47	1.12	3.8E-07
ETA1	2.31	1.31	1.91	2.33	0.92	7.26
ACE1	2.31	0.59	0.04	0.47	1.12	0.09
ETA2	2.31	0.64	1.91	2.33	0.92	14.88
ACE2	2.31	0.57	0.04	4.67	1.12	0.09
ALIM	2.31	0.59	1.95	4.67	0.97	3.46
PROD	2.31	0.67	1.95	4.67	0.99	3.10
PROD1	0.02	0.29	1.95	4.67	0.99	0.05
ETA3	0.02	0.003	1.79	2.37	0.92	13.78
PROD2	0.02	1.45	0.16	4.67	1.13	0.0011
PROD3	0.02	1.72	0.16	4.67	1.13	9.5E-04
BIOD	0.02	1.75	0.12	4.67	1.19	7.4E-04
GLIC-WATER	0.02	2.53	0.04	4.67	0.57	8.3E-05

The HPSI values for each scale are the same since the substances and process conditions are identical for each stream. It is worth mentioning that the HPSI does not consider the effect of production scaling. Therefore, no change in the values of this index is reflected. The pressurized reactor (REAC) and the distillation tower (COLUM) are considered as the hazardous equipment, defining an explosion as a probable accident due to the flammability of ethanol (class 3, according to NFPA). On the other hand, glycerol has low flammability (class 1, according to NFPA), so this stream has a low probability of fire.

The effect of increased production on the risk was evaluated by the relative risk of each process. Table 2 shows that the largest production scale has a high-risk level, confirming that the consequences will be more significant.

Table 2. Relative risk calculated using the HPSI index.

Production scale (t/y)	Relative total risk (R_T)	Risk level
10,000	0.2	Low risk
30,000	0.6	Medium risk
50,000	1.0	High risk

The scenario of explosion and fire for the two dangerous equipment (REAC and COLUM) shows the effect of process capacity on the consequences of an accident. Table 3 presents the affectation distance in case of explosion and fire. These distances represent values between 3.1 and 1.1 psi for explosion and the flammable area for a fire with 10 minutes of duration.

Table 3, Consequences of explosion and fire for each scale production

	10,000		30,000		50,000	
	REAC	COLUM	REAC	COLUM	REAC	COLUM
Explosion (m)	20	23	25	27	30	32
Fire length (m)	46	49	70	75	90	95
Fire width (m)	14	15	17	18	20	22

6. Conclusions

This paper presents a comparative study on the magnitude of hazard between supercritical processes and their scale of biodiesel production, applying an improved inherent safety index. This index presents a measurement-oriented approach that quantifies the safety of the process at the design stage and considers safety scores based on individual streams, providing a more intuitive and easier way to identify the hazard of each stream. Based on the results obtained, it has been observed that the most significant risk that can occur is a fire or explosion due to the inherent flammability of ethanol. The relative risk is high in the case of a production scale of 50,000 t/y. Therefore, it should be considered of vital importance to improve the safety of the process. Finally, the risk associated with the production scale is validated by the analysis of the consequences.

Acknowledgments

The authors acknowledge the support given by Universidad de Guanajuato and Universidad Juárez Autónoma de Tabasco for the development of this project.

References

F.I. Gómez-Castro, A. López-Molina, 2020, Non-catalytic production of biodiesel: energy and safety considerations, Biofuels: Advances in Research and Applications, 1-29

F.I. Gómez-Castro, J.G. Segovia-Hernández, S. Hernández-Castro, V. Rico-Ramírez, C. Gutiérrez-Antonio, A. Briones-Ramírez, I. Cano-Rodríguez, Z. Gamiño-Arroyo, 2015, Analysis of alternative non-catalytic processes for the production of biodiesel fuel, Clean Technologies and Environmental Policy, 17, 2041-2054

D. Kusdiana, S. Saka, 2004, Effects of water on biodiesel fuel production by supercritical methanol treatment, Bioresource Technology, 91, 3, 289-295

S. Lee, D. Posarac, N. Ellis, 2011, Process simulation and economic analysis of biodiesel production processes using fresh and waste vegetable oil and supercritical methanol, Chemical Engineering Research and Design, 89, 12, 2626-2642

A. López-Molina, A.A. Huerta-Martínez, F.I. Gómez-Castro, C. Conde-Mejía, 2020, A novel approach to identify hazards in non-conventional/intensified biofuels production processes, Chemical Engineering and Processing – Process Intensification, 157, 108139

S. Saka, D. Kusdiana, 2001, Biodiesel fuel from rapeseed oil as prepared in supercritical methanol, Fuel, 80, 2, 225-231

S. Saka, Y. Isayama, 2009, A new process for catalyst-free production of biodiesel using supercritical methyl acetate, Fuel, 88, 7, 1307-1313

E.C. Teixeira, C.D.P. Mattiuzi, S. Feltes, F. Wiegand, E.R.R. Santana, 2012, Estimated atmospheric emissions from biodiesel and characterization of pollutants in the metropolitan area of Porto Alegre-RS, Anais da Academia Brasileira de Ciências, 84, 3, 655-667

A.E. Bulla Pereira, 2014, "Design of the biodiesel production process from frying oils". Master's Thesis in Engineering - Mechanical Engineering, Universidad Nacional de Colombia.

F.I. Gómez-Castro, M.G. Aldana-González, C. Conde-Mejía, C. Gutiérrez-Antonio, A.G. Romero-Izquierdo, R. Morales-Rodríguez, 2017, "Process integration for the supercritical production of biodiesel and the production of lignocellulosic bioethanol", *Computer Aided Chemical Engineering*, Vol. 40, p. 931-936.

Str. Skarlis, E. Kondili, J.K. Kaldellis, 2012, "Small-scale biodiesel production economics: a case study focus on Crete Island", *Journal of Cleaner Production*, Vol. 20, No. 1, p. 20-26.

A. López-Molina, D. Sengupta, C. Shi, E. Aldamigh, M. Alandejani, M. Mahmoud El-Halwagi, 2020, "An Integrated approach to the design of centralized and decentralized biorefineries with environmental, safety, and economic objectives", *Processes*, Vol. 8, No. 12, 1682.

Proceedings of the 14th International Symposium on Process Systems Engineering – PSE 2021+
June 19-23, 2022, Kyoto, Japan © 2022 Elsevier B.V. All rights reserved.
http://dx.doi.org/10.1016/B978-0-323-85159-6.50230-X

Process Monitoring Based on Deep Neural Networks with Continuous Wavelet Transform

Chinatsu Ukawa[a*], Yoshiyuki Yamashita[a], and Seiji Hotta[a]

[a]*Tokyo University of Agriculture and Technology, 2-24-16 Naka-cho, Koganei, Tokyo 184-8588, JAPAN*
s193040z@st.go.tuat.ac.jp

Abstract

In this paper, we proposed a novel fault detection method using a three-dimensional convolutional neural network (3DCNN), and continuous wavelet transform (CWT). Multivariate time series data of a chemical plant was transformed into time-frequency scalogram using CWT, and the 3DCNN was trained with the CWT scalogram. The output obtained was a binary unit representing whether there was a fault or not. The proposed method was applied to the Tennessee Eastman process datasets for fault detection, since they are widely used for verifying the performance of fault detection methods. Our method yielded accurate results for fault detection.

Keywords: Fault Detection; Deep Neural Network; Continuous Wavelet Transform; Time Series Data

1. Introduction

Fault detection and diagnosis play an important role in monitoring chemical processes, where it is expected to prevent severe accidents that cause emergency shutdowns, financial losses, environmental disruptions, and risk to human life. Process monitoring starts with fault detection. Fault detection methods are divided into two types: model-based methods, and data-driven methods. Model-based methods depend on first-principles modelling, which is generally difficult to perform because of process complexity. However, data-driven methods are established without a large amount of process knowledge, and mathematical operations, due to which they have versatility in industrial applications. Additionally, they are quicker to implement than the model-based methods. Numerous studies on fault detection and diagnosis have been conducted so far. In the early stages of fault detection, a univariate analysis with a limit check was applied. However, fault data could not be found because of the highly correlated variables in the chemical processes. To find the buried fault data, a multivariate statistical process was adopted after the univariate analysis. For instance, Principal Component Analysis (PCA), Partial Least Squares, and Support Vector Machine, which are widely applied in industrial processes, were used. However, these methods do not consider the dynamics. Wenfu K (1995) introduced Dynamic PCA as the method which can handle process dynamics. Neural network-based methods have attracted attention in many fields because of their flexibility in modelling complex structures, and dynamics. Various neural network models have been proposed in chemical engineering fields, such as Deep Belief Networks (Zhang et al., 2017), Recurrent Neural Networks (Shaodong et al., 2020), Long Short-Term Memory (Han et al., 2020), and Convolutional Neural Network (Hao Wu et al., 2018).

An important step in the establishment of data-driven methods is pre-processing. A high detection rate cannot be achieved without an appropriate pre-processing method, even if the model possesses great ability. So far, signal processing methods, such as Fourier transform, fast Fourier transform, short-time Fourier transform, and wavelet transform have been applied to various fields, and have exhibited good performance. Short-time Fourier transform and wavelet transform generate time-frequency spectrograms from the original signal data. Wavelet transform is expected to be applicable to chemical process data as it is more suitable at handling non-steady signal analysis, when compared to the Fourier transform. Despite the aforementioned facts, the pre-processing step has not been considered in many previous methods of fault detection for chemical processes. Furthermore, they do not consider the changes in the time-frequency domain of the chemical process data.

In this paper, we proposed a novel fault detection method using a three-dimensional convolutional neural network (3DCNN), and continuous wavelet transform (CWT). We transformed multivariate time series samples into time-frequency scalogram using CWT. After this processing, we trained the 3DCNN with the scalogram as inputs. The output was a binary unit representing whether there was a fault or not.

2. Method

2.1. Continuous wavelet transforms

The CWT produces time-frequency domain information from an original time series data. It is also commonly applied to various research fields, such as transient analysis, electrocardiogram analysis, and fault detection and diagnosis of bearings (Guo. et al., 2018) (Zhang et al., 2020). Unlike the Fourier transform (FT), CWT uses a wavelet to map an objective function onto the time-frequency space. FT does not reflect the information of time and space because it assumes that the signal can be divided into infinite sine waves (Serizawa et al., 2017). This method is not suitable for the analysis of non-stationary data. Short-time Fourier transform (STFT) is an improved method that analyzes signals, using a particular window size fixed for all frequencies. Due to this property, STFT cannot analyze signals accurately if non-linearity remains in the viewing window. However, CWT is more flexible than STFT, and it does not require the definition of a window size. CWT expresses the original signal with the mother wavelet by shifting and scaling. The selection of an appropriate type of wavelet can be easily changed according to engineering conditions (Zhang et al., 2020). Accordingly, CWT is appropriate for handling non-steady time-series data such as chemical process data. Equation (1) represents the CWT of x(t). For a given mother wavelet ψ, 'a' is the scale parameter related to the frequency concept, and 'b' is the shift parameter related to position.

$$W_x(a, b) = \frac{1}{\sqrt{a}} \int_{-\infty}^{\infty} x(t)\, \psi^* \left(\frac{t-b}{a}\right) dt \qquad (1)$$

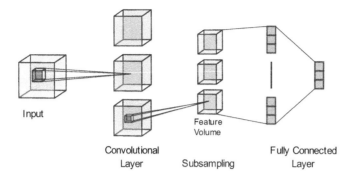

Figure 1 The simple description of 3D convolutional neural network

2.2. 3D convolutional neural network

We adopted a 3DCNN for feature extraction and classification, to handle multi-variable datasets. It is a logical extension of 2DCNN, which works with three-dimensional data such as video, and has an additional temporal dimension in addition to the X and Y coordinates. The first CNN was developed by Fukushima (1980). It could automatically complete feature learning without prior knowledge, and has an efficient recognition ability (Lu Deng, et al. 2021). 2DCNNs have been successful in image-based feature extraction and classification. A 3DCNN was proposed for activity recognition, which required a temporal domain. The basic 3DCNN architecture is illustrated in this slide (Figure 1). The 3D filter is convolved with 3D data to produce the feature volumes. After subsampling and flattening, the features are fed to a fully connected layer for classification.

2.3. Proposed model

First, the chemical process data was divided by a moving time window. In our case, the moving window width was 20 and the stride was 1. Divided data were transformed into a spectrogram using a continuous wavelet transform. We set the size of the spectrograms to (20 x 20) during transformation. We performed pre-processing for each variable. Finally, the shape of the input data was (20 × 20 × the number of variables). The dimensions of the input data were (20 × 20 × 33) because we used 22 process measurement variables, and 11 manipulated variables. Next, the input data was fed into the 3DCNN, and the model was trained. The output was a binary unit representing the existence of the fault.

3. Case study

We evaluated the ability of our proposed method using the Tennessee Eastman process datasets. The Tennessee Eastman (TE) process was first introduced by Downs et al. (2013), and is based on a real process. It is widely used as a benchmark for evaluating fault detection and diagnosis methods (Onel et al. 2018) (Rato et al. 2017). It consists of five main units: a reactor, condenser, compressor, separator, and stripper. Four reactants and two products are included. It has 52 variables, including 41 process variables, and 11 manipulated variables. In this study, the data of the TE process were obtained from the extended database published by Rieth et al. (2017). This dataset includes 500 simulation runs for the training, and testing data of the normal, and 20 fault types. Each simulation

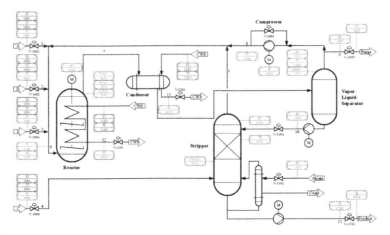

Figure 2 Process flow sheet of Tennessee Eastman process (Andreas, B., et al, 2015)

run involved 500 data samples for training, and 960 data samples for testing. The sampling period was set to 3 min (20 samples per hour). Each fault was introduced to the process after sample numbers 20, and 160 for fault training, and fault testing, respectively. The process flowsheet is shown in Figure 2. We selected this dataset because the conventional dataset was insufficient to train the CNN model. The datasets used in this study were downloaded from the Harvard database. In this study, 22 process variables and 11 manipulated variables were selected, and used to develop the fault detection model.

4. Result

4.1. Metrics for evaluation

We evaluated the proposed method and compared its performance using the fault detection rate (FDR). TP represents true positive, and FN represents false negative.

$$Fault\ Detection\ Rate = \frac{TP}{TP + FN} \tag{1}$$

4.2. Application to TEP

We compared the proposed model with PCA. PCA is the most widely used model for fault detection. The number of principal components was set to nine, and the confidence interval was set to 0.99. Hotelling T^2 and Squared Prediction Error (SPE) were calculated for each fault. A comparison of each model is presented in Table 1. The proposed method tended to improve the fault detection rate of faults in which PCA could not represent high performance.

5. Discussion

We selected fault 5 and considered the effectiveness of the CWT for feature extraction. Fault 5 was a step-like change caused by the condenser cooling water inlet temperature. It affected the variables surrounding the reactor and condenser. We selected variables 32 and 33 from the process flow. Variable 32 was the reactor cooling water flow, and variable 33 was the condenser cooling water flow. They were located around the reactor and condenser. The resultant spectrograms are shown in Figure 3. They were selected for each of the 10 steps. The spectrogram of each variable showed different characteristics between normal operating condition, and fault 5. This indicated that the change in variables appeared in the time-frequency domain. We believe that this difference implies the effectiveness of the proposed method for detecting faults.

6. Conclusions

In this paper, we proposed a fault detection model for chemical processes based on 3DCNN and CWT. 3DCNN was applied for multivariable analysis. CWT was applied for pre-processing the chemical process data because of its good performance for non-steady signal processing. First, the chemical process data were transformed to a time-frequency spectrogram using CWT. The 3DCNN model was built with convolutional layers, pooling layers, dropout layers, and fully connected layers and trained with a spectrogram. The output was a binary unit representing the normal operation, or faulty condition. The results of the case study with TEP showed that the proposed method performed well on fault detection of TEP faults. Particularly, for faults in which PCA could not show good performance, the proposed method had a better score. It represented the time-frequency domain with the feature of process data.

Table 1 Accuracy comparison of models

Status	PCA(T2)	PCA(SPE)	Proposed	Status	PCA(T2)	PCA(SPE)	Proposed
Normal	0.989	0.990	0.983				
Fault 1	0.991	0.997	0.985	Fault 11	0.255	0.755	**0.857**
Fault 2	0.985	0.949	0.964	Fault 12	0.968	0.949	**0.981**
Fault 3	0.013	0.010	**0.030**	Fault 13	0.934	0.919	0.919
Fault 4	0.086	1.000	0.997	Fault 14	0.862	1.000	0.982
Fault 5	0.245	0.114	**0.936**	Fault 15	0.015	0.012	**0.167**
Fault 6	0.989	1.000	0.989	Fault 16	0.078	0.114	**0.390**
Fault 7	0.364	1.000	0.986	Fault 17	0.719	0.897	**0.946**
Fault 8	0.955	0.861	0.934	Fault 18	0.929	0.937	**0.939**
Fault 9	0.014	0.011	**0.025**	Fault 19	0.022	0.295	0.189
Fault 10	0.210	0.172	**0.419**	Fault 20	0.263	0.460	**0.825**

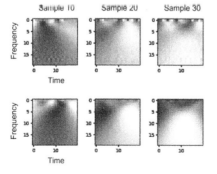 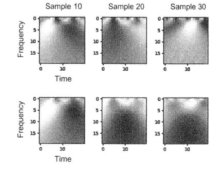

Figure 3 The spectrograms of variable 32 on normal operating condition (the first row) and fault 5 (the second row)

Figure 4 The spectrograms of variable 33 on normal operating condition (the first row) and fault 5 (the second row)

References

A. Bathelt, N. L. Ricker, M. Jelali, 2015, Revision of the Tennessee Eastman Process Model, *IFAC-PapersOnLine*, 48, Issue 8, 309-314

L. Deng, Y. Zhang, Y. Dai, X. Ji, L. Zhou, Y. Dang, 2021, Integrating feature optimization using a dynamic convolutional neural network for chemical process supervised fault classification, Process Safety and Environmental Protection, 155, 473-485

J.J. Downs, E.F. Vogel, A plant-wide industrial process control problem, 1993, Computers & Chemical Engineering, 17, 3, 245-255

K. Fukushima, 1980, Neocognitron: A Self-organizing Neural Network Model for a Mechanism of Pattern Recognition Unaffected by Shift in Position, Biological Cybernetics, 36, 193-202

S. Guo, T. Yang, W. Gao, C. Zhang, Y. Zhang, 2018, An Intelligent Fault Diagnosis Method for Bearings with Variable Rotating Speed Based on Pythagorean Spatial Pyramid Pooling CNN, *Sensors*, 18(11), 3857

Y. Han, N. Ding, Z. Geng, Z. Wang, C. Chu, 2020, An optimized long short-term memory network based fault diagnosis model for chemical processes, Journal of Process Control, 92, 161-168

M. Onel, C. A. Kieslich, Y. A. Guzman, E. N. Pistikopoulos, 2018, Simultaneous Fault Detection and Identification in Continuous Processes via nonlinear Support Vector Machine based Feature Selection, Computer Aided Chemical Engineering, Elsevier, 44, 2077-2082,

W. Ku, R. H. Storer, C. Georgakis, 1995, Disturvance detection and isolation by dynamic principal component analysis, Chemometrics and Intelligent Laboratory systems, 30, 1, 179-196

T. J. Rato, M. S. Reis, 2017, Improved Fault Diagnosis in Online Process Monitoring of Complex Networked Processes: a Data-Driven Approach, Computer Aided Chemical Engineering, Elsevier, 40, 1681-1686

C. A. Rieth, B. D. Amsel, R. Tran, M. B. Cook, 2017, "Additional Tennessee Eastman Process Simulation Data for Anomaly Detection Evaluation", https://doi.org/10.7910/DVN/6C3JR1, Harvard Dataverse, V1

T. Serizawa, T. Suzuki, S. Choi, and O. Sasaki, 2017, 3-D surface profile measurement using spectral interferometry based on continuous wavelet transform, *Optics Communication*, 396, 216-220

H. Wu, J. Zhao, Deep convolutional neural network model based chemical process fault diagnosis, 2018, Computers & Chemical Engineering, 115, 185-197

M. Zhang, M. Li, J. Zhang, L. Liu, H. Li, 2020, Onset detection of ultrasonic signals for the testing of concrete foundation piles by coupled continuous wavelet transform and machine learning algorithms, Advanced Engineering Informatics, 43, 101034

Z. Zhang, J. Zhao, A deep belief network based fault diagnosis model for complex chemical processes, 2017, Computers & Chemical Engineering, 107, 395-407

S. Zheng, H. Zhao, 2020, A new unsupervised data mining method based on the stacked autoencoder for chemical process fault diagnosis, Computers & Chemical Engineering, 135, 106755

Proceedings of the 14th International Symposium on Process Systems Engineering – PSE 2021+
June 19-23, 2022, Kyoto, Japan © 2022 Elsevier B.V. All rights reserved.
http://dx.doi.org/10.1016/B978-0-323-85159-6.50231-1

Methyl sec-butyl ether content estimation in MTBE products via clustering-based adaptive nonlinear soft sensors

Andrei Torgashov[a], Oleg Snegirev[a], Fan Yang[b*]

[a]*Process Control Laboratory, Institute of Automation and Control Process FEB RAS, 5 Radio Str., Vladivostok, Russia*
[b]*Beijing National Research Center for Information Science and Technology and Department of Automation, Tsinghua University, Beijing 100084, China*
yangfan@mail.tsinghua.edu.cn

Abstract

The problem of developing an adaptive soft sensor (SS) using clustering methods is considered to be an example of an industrial reactive distillation process for the production of methyl tert-butyl ether (MTBE). We propose the use of clustering methods to assess the feasibility of updating the model parameters. An algorithm for the functioning of an adaptive SS using a *moving window* and clustering is proposed and tested on industrial data. The reduction of the computational cost in comparison with the adaptive SS using the moving-window method with continuous updating of the model parameters is shown. The accuracy of adaptive SSs based on various nonparametric methods is compared.

Keywords: soft sensing modeling; clustering; adaptation; methyl sec-butyl ether.

1. Introduction

Currently, data from the laboratory and in-line analyzers are used to control the quality of the output products of distillation columns. However, the results of analysis obtained in laboratories do not allow quality management in real time, as they have an insufficient level of efficiency. Therefore, soft sensors are used in production to solve this problem. Soft sensing is a data analysis tool that allows one to get an estimate of a difficult-to-measure output variable using the values of variables available for measurement at any given time. In comparison with rigorous modeling methods based on physical-chemical laws, data-driven soft sensors are more flexible and can be easily implemented in the process industry.

Basically, the soft sensors used in production are usually based on linear regression models, which imply the assumption of a linear structure in the model of a plant. However, this is not always true in real conditions. The use of nonparametric regression methods is free from the requirement of knowledge of the model structure. There exist many nonparametric regression methods. The most popular methods include kernel, spline, and local polynomial kernel. Neural network-based models are also very popular (Wang et al., 2019), allowing extremely complex dependencies to be reproduced based on representative data as a result of training. In this paper, we consider soft sensors based on Alternating Conditional Expectations (ACE) (Snegirev and Torgashov, 2021), Kernel-based orthogonal projections to latent structures (K-OPLS) (Li et al., 2020), and neural networks (Zhu et al., 2018).

In real conditions, the parameters of a plant often change over time, and therefore there is a problem of the degradation of the model, which leads to a deterioration in the accuracy of the evaluation of the output variable. To solve this problem, adaptive soft sensors are used to adjust models using new measurement data. Typical adaptive soft sensors are based on methods such as just-in-time (JIT) (Guo et al., 2020), time difference (TD), and moving window (MW) approaches (Urhan and Alakent, 2020). In this paper, we consider methods for adapting soft sensors based on MW, the essence of which is to update the SS model using training samples. From these training samples, when a new observation appears, the earliest observation is removed, and a new one is added. In well-known methods, when developing an adaptive SS based on MW, clustering methods are used to divide data into clusters and build a separate model for each cluster.

This paper presents an algorithm for the operation of an adaptive soft sensor based on MW using clustering methods to determine the need to update the SS. The superiority of the algorithm in terms of reducing computational costs under the updating of model parameters is shown.

2. Industrial plant description and problem formulation

The chemical plant of research is a mass-transfer (reactive distillation) process (MTP). A specific feature of this MTP is that a reversible chemical reaction occurs simultaneously with the partial or almost complete separation of the resulting mixture by distillation. The product of MTP is methyl tert-butyl ether (MTBE), which is widely used in the production of high-octane gasolines.

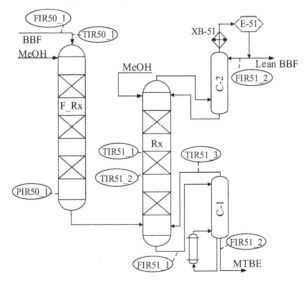

Figure 1: Flowsheet diagram of the reactive distillation process

The key indicator of the quality of the MTBE product (Fig. 1) is the concentration (wt,%) of impurity as methyl *sec*-butyl ether (MSBE). We consider the problem of developing SS for MSBE content estimation. The following measured process variables were used as regressors: u_1 – MTBE flowrate (FIR51_2); u_2 – temperature of fresh BBF in a for-contact (pre) reactor (F-Rx) (TIR50_1); u_3 – the flowrate of fresh BBF in a for-contact (pre) reactor (F-Rx) (FIR50_1); u_4 – the reflux flowrate in C-2 (FIR51_2); u_5 – the temperature of the reacting mass from the top of C-1 in Rx (TIR51_3); u_6 – the flowrate of reacting mass in C-1 (FIR51_1); u_7 – bottom pressure of F-Rx (PIR50_1); u_8 – the temperature in the top of the middle zone of the catalyst bed of Rx (TIR51_1); u_9 – the temperature in the bottom of the middle zone of the catalyst bed of Rx (TIR51_2).

3. Methods used for model evaluation

In this paper, we present a method based on the ACE in comparison with Kernel-OPLS and neural networks.

3.1. Alternating Conditional Expectation (ACE)

A nonlinear soft sensor model can be obtained using the ACE algorithm (Snegirev and Torgashov, 2021):

$$\theta(Y) = b_0 + \sum_{i=1}^{m} \phi_i(u_i),$$

Where the θ - function of output variable Y ; b_0 - bias; ϕ_i - optimal transformation of the i-th input variable u_i ; m – number of input variables.

3.2. Kernel-based Orthogonal Projections to Latent Structures (Kernel-OPLS)

The Kernel-OPLS method is a reformulation of the original OPLS method to its kernel equivalent (Li et al., 2020). A distinctive feature of kernel-based methods is the consideration of the kernel matrix as point products in a multidimensional object space.

3.3. Neural networks

Neural networks can also be used to build soft sensors. In this work, a single-hidden-layer neural network is used. The hidden layer contained $S=10$ nodes, equal to the number of input variables. A set of 300 observations of variables was used to train the neural network.

4. Description of the proposed adaptation algorithm

The proposed algorithm is based on the "Moving Window" (MW) method. The proposed algorithm differs from MW in that when a new observation appears, the need to add a new observation to the training set and to update the SS model is evaluated. In this paper, we propose clustering methods to determine the need to update the current SS model. At the initial stage, the initial set of observations is divided into K clusters. Clustering is carried out in the space of the input variables of the model. Algorithm 1 shows a pseudocode describing how the need to update the SS model is assessed when a new observation is obtained.

The Euclidean distance was used as a distance measure in the algorithm (Cardarilli et al., 2020):

$$d(p,q) = \sqrt{\sum_{i=1}^{m}(p_i - q_i)^2}$$
.

As one of the criteria for the need to update the SS, we propose a calculation of the difference in time between the appearance of a new observation and the last one in the cluster (time factor), which will allow for timely consideration of the manifestation of non-stationary properties of the object in the model.

To take into account the time factor at time t for cluster k, we propose using the following indicator: $\Delta \tau_t^k = \dfrac{\tau_t - \tau_{Q_k}^k}{\overline{T}^k}$, where τ_i is the value of the moment of the appearance of a new observation, $\tau_{Q_k}^k$ is the value of the moment of the appearance of the last element in cluster k, $T^k = (\tau_1^k - \tau_0^k, \tau_2^k - \tau_1^k, ..., \tau_Q^k - \tau_{Q-1}^k)$ is the vector of time intervals between the appearance of observations of the k-th cluster, τ_0^k is the initial moment of time, $\overline{T}^k$ is the average value of the vector T^k

---

Algorithm 1. Assessment of the need to update the SS

1. Calculate the Euclidean distance $d(u_n, \mu_j)$ from the new observation to the j-cluster center, $j = 1...K$

2. Select the cluster **k** for which $d(u_n, \mu_k)$ is minimal

3. **If** there is a small number of observations in cluster **k,** then

4.   Add a new observation to the training set. Recalculate cluster centers taking into account the new observation. **Recalculate the parameters of the SS**

5. **Else If** $d(u_n, \mu_k)$ is greater than the maximum distance from the elements of cluster **k** to its center

6.   Add a new observation to the training sample. Increase the number of clusters by 1. Recalculate the cluster centers taking into account the new observation. **Recalculate SS parameters**

7. **Else If** MAE of the estimate of the output variable taking into account the new observation are greater than the MAE at the previous time

8.   Add a new observation to the training sample. Recalculate cluster centers taking into account the new observation. **Recalculate the parameters of the SS**

9. **Else If** $\Delta \tau^k > 1$ (How long has an observation similar to the new one been encountered)

10.   Add a new observation to the training set. Recalculate cluster centers taking into account the new observation. **Recalculate the parameters of the SS**

11. **Else**

12.   The new observation should not be included in the training set. **Leave the SS model unchanged**

---

5. Results and discussion

5.1. Comparison of models accuracy

The accuracy of the soft sensor models was compared on the data of the MTBE production process plant. The mean absolute error (MAE) was used as the evaluation criterion (Wang and Lu, 2018). Table 1 shows the values of MAE at the end time. The value of MAE at the final time for the K-OPLS-based soft sensor was 52% less than that of the ACE-based soft sensor and 45% less than that of the neural network-based soft sensor for the proposed adaptation algorithm. For the moving window algorithm, the MAE value for the K-OPLS-based soft sensor was 52.3% less than that of the ACE-based soft sensor and 35.5% less than that of the neural network-based soft sensor.

Table 1. MAE at the end time

	Proposed Method	Moving Window
ACE	0.1596	0.15694
K-OPLS	0.0766	0.07485
Neural Networks	0.13945	0.11604

5.2. Comparison of computational costs for adaptive soft sensors

Figures 2 and 3 are graphs of MAE and computational time of adaptive SS based on the ACE and SS based on the K-OPLS. Table 2 presents the value of computational time spent at work adaptive soft sensors based on the ACE, the K-OPLS and of the neural network working on the proposed method and the method of MW.

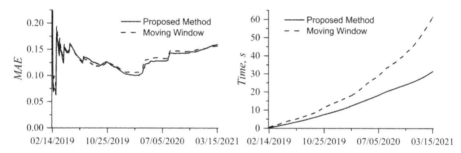

Figure 2: The change of MAE during the process (left) and the time spent on work (right) for the ACE-based soft sensor

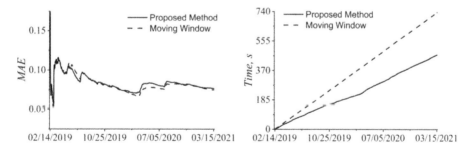

Figure 3: The change of MAE during the process (left) and computational cost (time) spent on updating (right) for the K-OPLS-based soft sensor

Table 2. Computational cost (time) of adaptive soft sensors

	Proposed method	Moving Window
ACE	31.43	61.45
K-OPLS	468.3	735.71
Neural Networks	51.77	86,1

The advantage of the proposed algorithm is to reduce the computational cost. Thus, the ACE-based SS, K-OPLS-based SS and the neural network-based SS during the process showed approximately the same values of MAE for both the proposed algorithm and the MW, but the reduction in computational time spent updating the model was 48.8% for the ACE-based SS, 36.3% for the K-OPLS-based SS and 39.8% for the neural network-based SS.

6. Conclusions

We have proposed an algorithm for the operation of an adaptive SS based on an MW using clustering methods and taking into account the time factor. During the testing of the algorithm on the data of the reactive distillation process, we have shown that the time for recalculation (updating) of the model parameters was reduced compared to the MW algorithm for the ACE-based SS by 48.8%, for the K-OPLS-based SS by 36.3% and for the neural network-based SS by 39.8%.

We have compared the use of ACE and K-OPLS algorithms and neural networks in the construction of soft sensors. The MAE value at the last moment for a soft sensor based on K-OPLS was 52% less than that of a soft sensor based on ACE, and 45% less than that of a soft sensor based on a neural network for the proposed adaptation algorithm. For the MW algorithm, the MAE value for the K-OPLS-based soft sensor was 52.3% less than that of the ACE-based soft sensor and 35.5% less than that of the neural network-based soft sensor.

7. Acknowledgements

The reported study was partially funded by RFBR and NSFC (project numbers 21-57-53005 and 62111530057).

References

Cardarilli, G.C., Nunzio, L.D., Fazzolari, R., Nannarelli, A., Re, M., Spano, S , 2020, N-Dimensional Approximation of Euclidean Distance, IEEE Transactions on Circuits and Systems II: Express Briefs, 67, 565 – 569

Guo, F., Xie, R., Huang, B., 2020, A Deep Learning Just-In-Time Modeling Approach for Soft Sensor Based On Variational Autoencoder, Chemometrics and Intelligent Laboratory Systems, 197, 103922

Li, J., Li, K., 2020, Application in Soft Sensing Modeling of Chemical Process Based on K-OPLS Method, Journal of Measurement Science & Instrumentation, 11, 17-27

Snegirev, O.Y., Torgashov, A.Y., 2021, Adaptation of the Structure and Parameters of Nonlinear Soft Sensors by the Example of an Industrial Reactive Distillation Process, Automation and Remote Control, 82, 1774–1786

Urhan, A., Alakent, B., 2020, Integrating Adaptive Moving Window and Just-In-Time Learning Paradigms for Soft-Sensor Design, Neurocomputing, 392, 23–37.

Wang, K., Shang, Ch., Lei Liu, Jiang, Y., Huang, D., Yang, F., 2019, Dynamic Soft Sensor Development Based on Convolutional Neural Networks, Industrial & Engineering Chemistry Research, 58 (26), 11521-11531

Wang, W., Lu,Y., 2018, Analysis of the Mean Absolute Error (MAE) and the Root Mean Square Error (RMSE) in Assessing Rounding Model, IOP Conference Series: Materials Science and Engineering, 324, 012049, DOI: 10.1088/1757-899x/324/1/012049

Zhu, W., Ma, Y., Zhou, Y., Benton, M., Romagnoli, J., 2018, Deep Learning Based Soft Sensor and Its Application on a Pyrolysis Reactor for Compositions Predictions of Gas Phase Components, Computer Aided Chemical Engineering, 44, 2245-2250

Proceedings of the 14th International Symposium on Process Systems Engineering – PSE 2021+
June 19-23, 2022, Kyoto, Japan © 2022 Elsevier B.V. All rights reserved.
http://dx.doi.org/10.1016/B978-0-323-85159-6.50232-3

Early identification of abnormal deviations in nonstationary processes by removing non-stationarity

Cheng Ji, Fangyuan Ma, Jingde Wang*, Wei Sun*

College of Chemical Engineering, Beijing University of Chemical Technology, North Third Ring Road 15, Chaoyang District, Beijing, 100029, China
sunwei@mail.buct.edu.cn, jingdewang@mail.buct.edu.cn

Abstract

In chemical processes, most measurements show stationary characteristic around their set points. However, the means of specific measurements are still time-varying with a wide range of variation, which makes the interval of data under normal operating conditions determined from multivariate statistics process monitoring method relatively large. In such case, the fault signal could be buried by these nonstationary features at its early stage, resulting in a long fault detection time and low fault detection rate. In this work, a process monitoring strategy dealing with nonstationary process is proposed by removing non-stationarity. Stationarity test is first applied to determine measurements with nonstationary characteristic. Support vector regression (SVR) model is then established for each nonstationary measurement using independent variables selected by mutual information. The original nonstationary measurement can be replaced by model residual, which is the difference between the regression value and the measured value, and therefore the nonstationary characteristic can be removed. When the multivariate statistical monitoring model is further established, the interval of normal operating conditions is effectively narrowed, by which the faulty deviation can be identified earlier. In order to verify the proposed method, case studies on Tennessee Eastman process (TEP) are investigated. The results demonstrate a better performance in detecting the abnormal deviations in nonstationary systems compared to other related methods.

Keywords: Chemical nonstationary process; Mutual information; Support vector regression; Process monitoring

1. Introduction

With the rapid development of data measurement and storage technology, multivariate statistical process monitoring (MSPM) methods have received considerable attention because of their unique advantages in processing highly coupled and multivariate data. However, some measurements in chemical industrial processes inevitably show a certain dynamic and nonstationary characteristic due to equipment aging or random disturbances, which violates the assumption of traditional MSPM that the process is time-independent (Li and Yan, 2019). Dynamic principal component analysis (DPCA) applies augmented matrix to describe such time-varying dynamic characteristic of data. However, the selection of lag order is limited for high-dimensional process data and all process variables have to be expended to the same level, while process dynamic has different effects on each variable (Huang et al., 2019). Slow feature analysis, as an unsupervised learning algorithm of extracting constant or slowly changing features of time series, has been applied for dynamic process monitoring (Shang et al., 2015). The process can be better described by considering both static and dynamic indices, but variances of original nonstationary data are still not processed. When applying MSPM to project high-dimensional data onto a lower dimensional feature space, the interval of normal region will be wide because the main variance of original data is preserved. The fault signal could be buried in nonstationary trends of process variables at its early stage, leading to a long fault detection time. Aiming at the process non-stationarity, cointegration theory has been developed to extract time-invariant characteristics by establishing cointegration relationship among nonstationary variables (Li et al., 2014). Process monitoring can be implemented by distinguishing between normal changes in cointegration relationships and abnormal deviations, but the application of cointegration is still relatively limited as a new method introduced to process monitoring.

In this work, a monitoring strategy for nonstationary process is proposed by removing characteristic of original nonstationary measurements. Process variables are first divided into stationary variables and nonstationary variables by stationarity test. Regression model is then established by mutual information (MI) and support vector regression (SVR) for each nonstationary variable. Model residuals of these variables, which no longer show nonstationary characteristics, are put together with stationary variables to replace the original nonstationary signals. Therefore, the variances of data under normal operating conditions are significantly reduced, the interval of normal operating conditions determined from monitoring statistics of principal component analysis model is effectively narrowed, by which the abnormal deviations can be identified at its early stage. The proposed method is employed to Tennessee Eastman process (TEP) and the performance of process monitoring is compared with related methods. The results show that the fault detection rate can be significantly improved by removing non-stationarity.

2. Methodology

In this section, the preliminaries of methods applied in the proposed process monitoring strategy are introduced.

2.1. Stationarity test

Process stationarity is an important assumption for building statistical models. Unit root test is usually used to test stationarity by judging whether the first-order difference of a time series is stable. In this work, the Kwiatkowski–Phillips–Schmidt–Shin (KPSS) test is applied to divide process measurements into stationary part and nonstationary part.

2.2. Mutual information (MI)

MI is a commonly used correlation analysis tool from the aspect of information theory. Considering two random variables X and Y, the MI value can be calculated as follows,

$$MI(X,Y) = \sum_{x,y} p(x,y) \log \frac{p(x,y)}{p(x)p(y)} \tag{1}$$

where $p(x, y)$ is the joint probability distribution function, $p(x)$, $p(y)$ are the marginal probability distribution function of x and y respectively. The probability distribution function can be calculated in Equation (2) by kernel density estimation,

$$p(x) = 1/n \sum_{i=1}^{n} K(x - x_i) \tag{2}$$

where K is the kernel function. In this work, MI is applied to select independent variables for its advantage in identifying nonlinear relationship.

2.3. Support vector regression (SVR)

SVR is a statistical machine learning method that has been applied in industrial processes. For a training set $T = \{(\mathbf{x}_i, y_i), i = 1...l\}$, where $\mathbf{x}_i \in \mathbf{R}^N$, $y_i \in \mathbf{R}$, SVR aims at finding a regression function that can fit all training samples,

$$f(x) = \mathbf{w}^T \Phi(\mathbf{x}) + b \tag{3}$$

where $\mathbf{W}$ is a coefficient vector in feature space, $\Phi(\mathbf{x})$ is a kernel function to map input $\mathbf{x}$ to a vector in feature space and b is an intercept. The solution of $\mathbf{w}$ and b can be obtained by solving the optimization problems in literature (Smola and Schölkopf, 2004). SVR has a great advantage in dealing with nonlinear processes by introducing a kernel function to project the original data into a high-dimensional linearly separable space. Therefore, SVR is selected to build regression models for nonstationary variables.

2.4. Principal component analysis (PCA)

For a high dimensional data set X, PCA can be employed to find a projection direction that maps the data into a lower dimensional space by orthogonal transformation,

$$X = TP^T + E \tag{4}$$

where T is a score matrix, P is a loading matrix, and E is a residue matrix. T^2 statistic and SPE statistic can be further established in the corresponding principal component space and residual space to realize process monitoring.

3. The proposed monitoring strategy by removing process non-stationarity

In this section, the idea of removing process non-stationarity and the implementation procedures of the proposed process monitoring framework are introduced.

3.1. Strategy for removing process non-stationarity

The main contribution of the proposed monitoring strategy is to early identify the abnormal process deviations from normal random disturbances in nonstationary process. If the process non-stationarity can be effectively removed, the fault can be early detected with traditional PCA. On this basis, SVM is applied to extract nonstationary and nonlinear relationships among variables and establish regression models for nonstationary variables. The obtained residues are used as virtual variables to replace nonstationary variables. Therefore, all process variables are processed to be stationary, and then better process monitoring results can be easily obtained with PCA.

3.2. The implementation procedures of the proposed process monitoring framework

The implementation procedures of the proposed process monitoring method are shown in Figure 1. It consists of offline training and online monitoring. For offline training, the first step is to divide training data under normal conditions into stationary part and nonstationary part by KPSS test. For nonstationary variables, MI is first calculated to select independent variables. Then SVR model is established for each nonstationary variable using corresponding independent variables. The optimal parameters are determined by grid search and cross-validation. Once the SVR models are determined, the difference between the regression value and the measured value of each nonstationary variable is applied as a virtual variable to replace original nonstationary signal. The virtual variables are put back together with original stationary variables, by which the process is converted to stationary. Therefore, a PCA model can be established and control limits of T^2 statistic and SPE statistic can be determined.

For online process monitoring, real-time data are input into the SVR models to get the regression values of nonstationary variables. Real-time virtual variables are calculated from the difference between regression values and measured values. Then virtual variables and stationary variables are put together and brought into the PCA model to calculate T^2 statistic and SPE statistic of the current sample. The monitoring results can be determined by comparing statistics with the control limits.

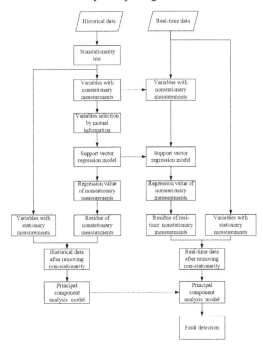

Figure 1 Procedures of the proposed process monitoring framework

4. Case studies on Tennessee Eastman process (TEP)

In this section, the proposed monitoring strategy by removing process non-stationarity is applied to TEP. The results are discussed and compared with other related methods.

4.1. Tennessee Eastman process and data description

TEP is a famous chemical benchmark simulated from an industrial plant (Downs and Vogel, 1993), and has been commonly used to test the performance of newly proposed process control and monitoring methods. The process includes five units, a total of 52 variables, and 21 pre-set faults that can be introduced. The information of the variables and the types of the faults is available in Downs and Vogel's paper (Downs and Vogel, 1993). In this work, a normal data set and 18 faulty data sets are applied. Each data set contains 960 samples and 33 variables because the component variables are excluded for their long sampling time. All the faults are introduced at the 160th sample point.

4.2. Results and discussion

KPSS test is applied to the normal data set, 7 variables are determined as nonstationary variables, which are compressor work, compressor recycle valve, condenser cooling water flow and other four variables in stripper. It is worth noting that stream 4 in TEP is directly delivered to the stripper, and most faults introduced to stream 4 cannot be early detected, which can be considered that the fault signal is buried in process non-stationarity. Independent variables are selected to train SVR models for these 7 variables respectively. Radial basis function is selected as kernel function and model parameter C is 20, gamma is 0.004 according to cross validation. The residues are used to replace original signals and the fault signal can be early identified because the process non-stationarity is removed. Taking fault 8 as an example, original normal data set and fault data set of 4 nonstationary variables are shown in Figure 2. The normal curves for certain variables show a similar nonstationary trend because they are all collected from stripper and highly correlated. The fault signal cannot be distinguished from the normal signal at its early stage because the fault is introduced to nonstationary variables. By removing non-stationarity using virtual variables in Figure 3, the interval of random disturbances under normal conditions is narrowed and the fault signal can be early identified. PCA model is then established for process monitoring, and the monitoring results of all 16 faults are shown in Table 1. It can be obtained that the proposed method shows the best performance in fault detection rate. It is worth noting that the proposed method shows obvious advantages in fault 5, 10, 12, 20, and 21 because these faults are introduced into nonstationary variables. For fault 5, fault detection rate obtained by the comparison methods is low because the response of the control system reduces the fault signal, but the fault signal can still be obviously distinguished by proposed method. For other faults, the proposed method also shows better performance in fault detection time. It is proved that this method provides a feasible idea for monitoring nonstationary processes.

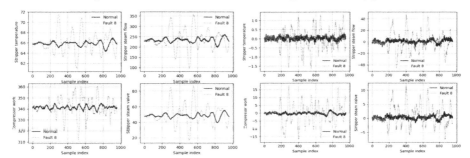

Figure 2 Original data of nonstationary variables   Figure 3 Data of virtual variables in this work

5. Conclusions

In this work, a monitoring strategy for chemical process with nonstationary measurements is proposed. The original signals of nonstationary variables are replaced by virtual variables, which are residues obtained by MI-based SVR models. The process non-stationarity has been removed because the nonstationary and nonlinear feature can be extracted by SVR. Therefore, the interval of normal operating conditions determined from PCA model can be effectively narrowed, by which the faulty deviation can be identified earlier. Case studies on TEP illustrate the effectiveness of this method in nonstationary processes. The proposed method provides a brand-new way to deal with nonstationary measurements in nonstationary process monitoring.

Table 1 Fault detection rates of different methods

Fault	PCA		DPCA		DICA		KSFA		Proposed method	
No.	T^2	SPE	T^2	SPE	T^2	SPE	S^2	SPE	T^2	SPE
1	0.99	1	0.99	1	1	1	0.99	0.99	0.99	**1**
2	0.98	0.99	0.99	0.99	0.99	0.98	0.99	0.99	0.98	**1**
4	0.54	0.96	0.12	1	1	1	0.96	0.99	0.57	**1**
5	0.23	0.25	0.27	0.53	1	1	0.93	0.95	1	**1**
6	0.99	1	0.99	1	1	1	0.99	0.99	0.99	**1**
7	1	1	1	1	1	1	1	1	1	**1**
8	0.98	0.98	0.97	0.97	0.98	0.98	0.99	0.99	0.98	0.98
10	0.33	0.34	0.36	0.57	0.88	0.88	0.78	0.71	0.77	0.84
11	0.21	0.64	0.20	0.83	0.80	0.76	0.87	0.80	0.58	0.82
12	0.97	0.98	0.99	0.97	1	1	0.99	0.99	1	**1**
13	0.94	0.96	0.95	0.96	0.95	0.95	0.95	0.97	0.95	0.96
14	1	0.99	1	1	1	1	1	1	1	**1**
16	0.16	0.25	0.18	0.59	0.89	0.75	0.50	0.70	0.87	0.87
17	0.74	0.89	0.78	0.97	0.97	0.96	0.94	0.96	0.84	**0.97**
18	0.89	0.9	0.90	0.90	0.91	0.91	0.91	0.92	0.91	0.91
19	0.14	0.28	0.20	0.56	0.91	0.9	0.14	0.36	0.78	0.82
20	0.32	0.60	0.36	0.70	0.89	0.81	0.67	0.78	0.61	**0.81**
21	0.26	0.43	0.44	0.60	0.44	0.37	0.536	0.47	0.51	**0.65**
Average	0.648	0.747	0.649	0.841	0.923	0.903	0.841	0.864	0.852	**0.924**

References

J. J. Downs and E. F. Vogel, 1993, A plant-wide industrial process control problem, Computers & chemical engineering, 17, 3, 245-255.

J. Huang, O. K. Ersoy, and X. Yan, 2019, Fault detection in dynamic plant-wide process by multi-block slow feature analysis and support vector data description, ISA transactions, 85, 119-128.

G. Li, S. J. Qin, and T. Yuan, 2014, Non-stationarity and cointegration tests for fault detection of dynamic processes, IFAC Proceedings Volumes, 47,3, 10616-10621.

Z. Li, and X. Yan, 2019, Complex dynamic process monitoring method based on slow feature analysis model of multi-subspace partitioning, ISA transactions, 95, 68-81.

C. Shang, F. Yang, X. Gao, X. Huang, A. K. Suykens, and D. Huang, 2015, Concurrent monitoring of operating condition deviations and process dynamics anomalies with slow feature analysis, AIChE Journal, 61, 11, 3666-3682.

A. J. Smola, and B. Schölkopf, 2004, A tutorial on support vector regression, Statistics and computing, 14, 3, 199-222.

Proceedings of the 14th International Symposium on Process Systems Engineering – PSE 2021+
June 19-23, 2022, Kyoto, Japan © 2022 Elsevier B.V. All rights reserved.
http://dx.doi.org/10.1016/B978-0-323-85159-6.50233-5

AI System for Substance Identification Based on Chemical Substance-Symptom Knowledge Graph

Sangwoo Yoo[a], Hunggi Lee[a], Juri Lim[b], Dongil Shin[a,b*]

a Department of Disaster and Safety, Myongji University, Yongin, Gyeonggido 17058, Korea
b Department of Chemical Engineering, Myongji University, Yongin, Gyeonggido 17058, Korea
dongil@mju.ac.kr

Abstract

Current chemical safety management technology is focused on detecting and responding to leaks based on sensors installed in the field, so it is difficult to respond appropriately in case of sensor failure or unexpected accidents. In a laboratory or a site where various chemical substances are irregularly handled, the accuracy of judging exposed substances based on bias is low, especially if prior risk analysis or sensor installation is insufficient. Therefore, loss can be minimized by providing quick and accurate initial response information at the accident site as well as support for accident material identification using the symptoms expressed by the exposed person, which can be viewed as one of the biosensors. Accordingly, this study supported the establishment of a substance-symptom knowledge base and developed a real-time exposure substance identification AI system based on the manifestation symptoms.

This study developed a system that identifies chemicals exposed from symptoms expressed to the exposed person in unexpected chemical leakage accidents and supports response information of determined substances for preemptive response in dangerous situations. In the development, in addition to knowledgeing exposure symptoms and chemical information, a knowledge base (KB) was established in the form of a knowledge graph using AllegroGraph. In order to determine whether knowledge within the established KB is true, knowledge demonstration was conducted through a knowledge graph embedding technique. Based on the established KB, material discrimination was conducted using SPARQL knowledge query inference. In addition, in the case of new substances with insufficient symptom knowledge, it is difficult to support with the KB-based inference system proposed in this study, so a structure-based symptom prediction DNN model using the fingerprint technique (MACCS Keys, Mordred) was proposed, showing high accuracy of 81.82.

Keywords: chemical incident, exposure symptom knowledge, chemical identification, deep learning, artificial intelligence

1. Introduction

In the production, handling, distribution, storage and use of chemical substances, unexpected chemical leakage accidents at the site can cause enormous damage such as personal injury and property damage if the initial response is not appropriate. In the event of a chemical leakage accident, early identification of the leaked material and prompt initial response are essential in minimizing the loss caused by the accident.

Existing chemical detection technology lacks smart technology for detecting and discriminating contact chemicals essential for initial response in the event of an unexpected chemical leakage accident. When an exposure accident occurs, it is difficult to accurately identify the leaked chemical if it is not filtered in the prior risk analysis based only on sensor information. Compared to research on leak response technology and sensor-based abnormal detection and monitoring technology, research on chemical substance diagnosis considering symptoms is very insufficient. If a sensor is not installed at the accident site, an initial estimate must be made based on qualitative exposure symptoms, but the knowledge service on hazardous chemicals considering human bio-sensing information (symptoms) is also relatively insufficiently developed.

This study proposed a knowledge service-based AI system that identifies chemicals exposed from symptoms expressed to the exposed person in unexpected chemical leakage accidents and supports response information of determined substances for preemptive response in dangerous situations.

2. Proposed System: SEARCH

A Symptom-based Expert for Advanced Response (SEARCH) system was proposed and established to provide real-time exposure substance identification support and initial response information based on symptoms of expression when an unexpected chemical accident occurs at the chemical handling site (see Fig. 1). In this paper, we intend to deal only with the knowledge base construction, knowledge verification, exposure substance identification, and knowledge expansion based on predictive models, which are the key issues in the operation of SEARCH.

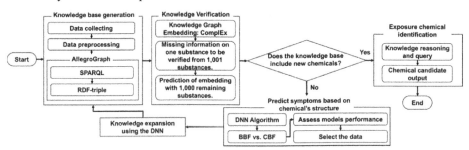

Figure 1. SEARCH system flow chart

3. Chemical-symptom knowledge base generation

A knowledge base was established to support symptom-based exposure substance identification and to verify knowledge using knowledge graph embedding (see Fig. 2). In the case of symptom-based exposure substance identification support, it is not possible to support substances not equipped with a knowledge base, so it is essential to expand knowledge based on predictive models for continuous support. To secure the ease of knowledge expansion, a graph database-based knowledge base that is easy to add/delete/change was built.

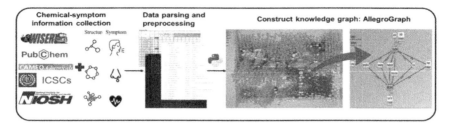

Figure 2. Framework of constructing knowledge graph

3.1. Chemical and symptom data collection

The collected chemicals were collected from 1,001 chemicals, including 499 core substances commonly used in industrial sites mounted on National Institutes of Health (NIH)'s Wireless Information System for Emergency Responders (WISER) and 502 substances provided by PubChem, Camo Chemicals, ICSCs, and NIOSH, which are open chemical databases. Exposure symptom knowledge of chemicals was based on NIH's WISER-mounted information, and symptom knowledge contains 79 symptom information (high body temp, blood noise, etc.) divided into 10 categories such as temperature, nervous system, oral cavity, and skin (Hochstein, C., 2008). In addition, RDKit, a Python package (provided by name, substructure and similarity of chemical substances, SMILES, InChI, etc.), was used to collect additional chemical information.

3.2. Chemical information and molecular structure preprocessing

In order to predict the symptoms of new substances not mounted on the knowledge base, the collected chemical information and molecular structure information were pre-processed using the fingerprint technique. To further confirm which method of bits based fingerprint (BBF) or count based fingerprint (CBF) shows better prediction performance in predicting symptoms, BBF-based MACCS keys and CBF-based Mordred fingerprint methods were used (see Fig. 3).

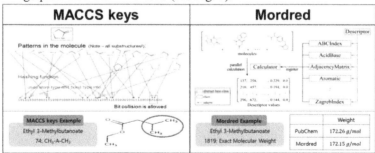

Figure 3. MACCS keys vs. Mordred

MACCS keys convert SMILES into MACCS keys with the most commonly used structural key (Anju Sharma, 2021). Using RDKit, a Python package, it was converted to 166 bits of structural keys of 960 bits and 166 bits. Mordre is a molecular descriptor calculator (Hirotomo Moriwaki, 2018). From various experiments, the chemical information of the molecule is converted into standardized experimental results (real numbers), which are 1825 expressors. RDKit, a Python package, was used for conversion.

3.3. Chemical substance-symptom knowledge base construction

AllegroGraph, a knowledge graph tool, was used to build a knowledge base. AllegroGraph is a triple store system designed to store knowledge in the form of Resource Description Framework (RDF) triple, available through Common Lisp, Python, and other APIs, and supports knowledge graph queries and reasoning such as SPARQL, RDFS+ (Gundla & Chen, 2016). Therefore, AllegroGraph, which can be linked to Python and supports knowledge graph construction, query, and reasoning, was selected as a knowledge graph tool. The previously collected and extracted 1,001 chemical substances, 79 symptom knowledge information, and preprocessed data were saved in Excel and XML format, and converted into RDF triple, one of the knowledge expression methods, to build a knowledge base in AllegrpGraph. For the construction, agraph-python, a Python package provided by AllegroGraph, was used in a Linux environment.

4. Knowledge verification using knowledge graph embedding

Although several DBs have been cross-verified for the expression of chemicals, it is difficult to secure data, and errors may exist because people directly intervene in building knowledge graphs to add knowledge and data, so knowledge graphs were embedded.

4.1. Adaptation of KB embedding algorithm

In this study, the ComplEx model, a knowledge graph embedding model, was used to demonstrate knowledge within the knowledge graph. The formula for the Score Function of the ComplEx model is as follows (T. Trouillon et al., 2016):

$$Score\ Function: RE\left(< v_s, v_p, \overline{v_o} >\right) \tag{1}$$

The data were set to triple 73,692 cases including exposed material-expression symptoms, exposed material-MACCS key, train/test set ratio was 8:2, and parameters were set to k=150, epochs=20, optimizer=adam, batch_count=100, eta=5. For knowledge verification, information on one substance to be verified was omitted from 1,001 substances mounted on the knowledge graph, and then embedding prediction was conducted with the remaining 1,000 substances. In prediction, if the prob value of the missing substance was greater than 0.98, it was accepted as True.

4.2. Knowledge verification results

As a result of knowledge verification through knowledge graph embedding, the results of knowledge verification of substances with less than 10 (Cuminaldehyde), 10 or more and less than 30 (isoamyl acetate), and 30 or more and less than 79 (benzene) among 1,001 substances can be found in Table 1 below. The average FP rate of 1,001 materials, including the three specified materials, was very low at 0.19, confirming the demonstration of triple mounted in the knowledge graph.

Table 1. Result of knowledge verification of Cuminaldehyde, Isoamyl Acetate, Benzene

	FN Rate	FP Rate
Cuminaldehyde	0.0	0.0
Isoamyl Acetate	0.1	0.06
Benzene	0.12	0.07

5. Identification of symptom-based exposure substances

Using SPARQL provided by AllegroGraph, symptom-based exposure substance discrimination was performed by knowledge query reasoning. As a case study, case 1 entered five symptom information (Nose_sneezing, chills, chest pain, eye swelling, tinnitus). In addition, if there are unconfirmed symptoms in the knowledge query inference process, the speed and accuracy of inference may be increased by excluding the symptoms, and case 2 is an example: Case 2 entered five symptom information (Nose_sneaking, chills, chest pain, eye swelling, tinnitus), and added skin swelling to the symptom information to enter five expression symptoms and one non-expression symptom, where skin swelling is a non-expression symptom.

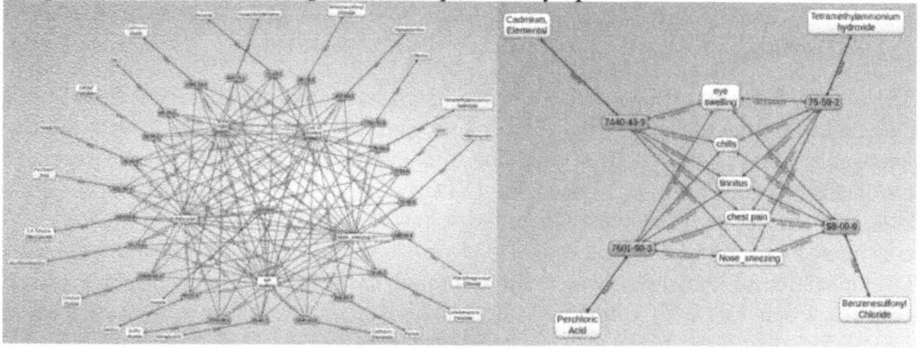

Figure 4. (a) Case 1; (b) Case 2.

As a result of inference, it can be seen that 11 chemicals were inferred in case 1, and 4 chemicals were inferred in case 2. Case 1 showed the same performance as the result of substance estimation only with symptoms among WISER's identity compound function. However, WISER must enter an average of 40 or more symptoms when only symptoms are entered to identify one substance (Bhavnani et al., 2007). Therefore, there is a limit to rapid chemical identification. Case 2 is a symptom exclusion function through unconfirmed symptoms that are not present in WISER. Using SPARQL conditional statements, unconfirmed symptoms were excluded from material estimation, showing that certain substances could be identified with less information input (see Fig. 4).

6. Symptom knowledge expansion using DNN

Since symptom-based substance identification support is not possible in the established knowledge base, a Deep Neural Network (DNN) model was developed to predict symptom knowledge from the molecular structure of the chemical as one of the ways to expand knowledge in the future. In order to compare and analyze the effective fingerprint method in predicting symptoms, it was divided into MACCS keys and mordred. In case 1, MACCS keys are added as input values, and in case 2, mordred is added as input values, and one chemical comes out as output values, resulting in the accuracy of predicting 79 detailed symptoms.

6.1. Adaptation of DL algorithm

In this study, the DNN model was used as a DL method for knowledge expansion. The data is 482 substances except WISER's solid, 502 substances in PubChem, 79 sub-symptoms, 166 MACCS keys, 1,825 mordred, the train/test set ratio is 8:2, parameters were set as hidden layer=3, activation function=Relu, softmax, optimizer=adam.

6.2. Result of model performance assessment

As a result of the DNN model performance according to Fingerprint, the accuracy of the prediction model using mordred as input was about 10%. The reason Mordred has high performance is that mordred has about 11 times more data than MACCS keys, while MACCS keys only have binary bits of 0 and 1, while mordred contains real information obtained through various experiments.

Table 2. Model accuracy according to two fingerprints

	MACCS keys	Mordred
Accuracy	70.24	81.82

7. Conclusions

The starting point of a response to a chemical exposure incident is the identification of a potential exposure substance. To this end, a total of 1,001 chemical-symptom-based knowledge bases were built by adding the symptoms provided by WISER and chemicals provided in the open chemical DB targeting high-risk substances at industrial sites or chemical accident sites. ComplEx, a knowledge graph embedding model, was constructed to demonstrate knowledge in the established knowledge base. Demonstration of knowledge was verified through case studies. The average FP rate of 1,001 materials was 0.19, which was very low. Based on the proven knowledge base, a system for identifying exposure substances that receives symptom information in real time and presents candidates for exposure substances was designed, and its effectiveness was verified through case studies. The case study showed the same results as WISER, the existing standard system, and showed that the speed and accuracy of discrimination can be increased through material discrimination that reflects the conditions that WISER does not have. In addition, since it is difficult to support new substances with little symptom knowledge with the KB-based reasoning system proposed in this study, a structure-based symptom prediction DNN model using the fingerprint method (MACCS Keys, Mordred) was proposed. The DNN model using Mordred as input showed the best performance with an accuracy of 81.82.

References

Anju Sharma, Rajnish Kumar, Shabnam Ranjta and Pritish Kumar Varadwa, 2021, "SMILES to Smell: Decoding the Structure–Odor Relationship of Chemical Compounds Using the Deep Neural Network Approach", *J. Chem. Inf. Model*, 61, 676-688.

Garrett B. Goh, 2017, "Chemception: A Deep Neural Network with Minimal Che mistry Knowledge Matches the Performance of Expert-developed QSAR/QSPR Models", *arXiv preprint arXiv:1706.06689.*

Gundla, N. K., & Chen, Z., 2016, "Creating NoSQL biological databases with ontologies for query relaxation", *Procedia Computer Science*, 91, 460-469.

Hirotomo Moriwaki, Yu-Shi Tian, Norihito Kawashita and Tatsuya Takagi, 2018, "Mordred: a molecular descriptor calculator", *Journal of Cheminformatics*.

Suresh K Bhavnani, 2007, "Network Analysis of Toxic Chemicals and Symptoms: Implications for Designing First-Responder Systems", *AMIA Annual Symposium Proceedings*, 51-55.

T. Trouillon, J. Welbl, S. Riedel, E. Gaussier and G. Bouchard, 2016, "Complex embeddings for simple link prediction", *Proc. 29th Int. Conf. Mach. Learn.*, pp. 2071-2080.

Proceedings of the 14th International Symposium on Process Systems Engineering – PSE 2021+
June 19-23, 2022, Kyoto, Japan © 2022 Elsevier B.V. All rights reserved.
http://dx.doi.org/10.1016/B978-0-323-85159-6.50234-7

Model-based monitoring of an intensified unit for continuous pharmaceutical filtration-drying

Francesco Destro[a], Massimiliano Barolo[a], Zoltan K. Nagy[b,*]

[a]*CAPE-Lab, University of Padova, 35131 Padova, PD, Italy*
[b]*Purdue University, West Lafayette, IN 47906, USA*
znagy@purdue.edu

Abstract

Active pharmaceutical ingredient (API) separation from synthesis and crystallization mother liquors is typically carried out in pharmaceutical manufacturing through filtration and drying. These steps are of utmost importance, as impurities herein retained will inevitably end up in the drug product. Recently, a novel carousel has been developed for carrying out filtration and drying in a continuous intensified fashion. The unit represents a step forward with respect to traditional batch filtration and drying, as continuous operation can reduce the variability of the product quality. However, the occurrence of faults compromising product compliance can be assessed only upon discharge of the final cake of API crystals, when its purity can be measured. In this work, we develop a model-based monitoring system for the unit, based on state and parameter estimation. The implemented monitoring system succeeds in tracking the product critical quality attributes (CQAs), and in detecting common faults for the carousel, such as sudden variations of the feed attributes.

Keywords: Process monitoring, State estimation, Quality-by-Design, Continuous pharmaceutical manufacturing, Fluid-solid separation

1. Introduction

In response to the recently registered alarming numbers of drug shortages and recalls, pharmaceutical regulators are encouraging the transition to the so-called "six sigma quality" (Yu and Kopcha, 2017). Under a six sigma quality system, there are six standard deviations between the process mean of each quality variable and the relevant nearest specification limit. Albeit six sigma quality is established in many manufacturing industries (e.g., the semiconductors one), the pharmaceutical industry is still lagging behind, at a two-three sigma quality standard. Among the pharmaceutical emerging technology needed to achieve six sigma quality, a pivotal role is assumed by the transition to continuous processing, and by the implementation of an advanced monitoring system. Such monitoring system should include process analytical technology or soft sensors for directly monitoring the product critical quality attributes (CQAs), and suitable routines for automatic detection of faults that might compromise the product quality.

In this study, we present a monitoring system for a novel continuous carousel for intensified filtration-drying of crystallization slurries (Destro et al., 2021). The carousel is an enabler for end-to-end continuous pharmaceutical processing, as it is one of the few technologies on the market that can connect the upstream and downstream sections of pharmaceutical processes in a continuous fashion. The unit features multiple processing stations embedded in a main cylindrical body, which rotates at every given time interval (cycle duration), transferring the material from one station to the subsequent one. In the first station, the crystallization slurry is loaded, and the first processing cycle starts. At the end of every cycle, the material is transferred to the following station, until it reaches the final one, and it is discharged in the form of a dry crystals cake. The rotation mechanism enables continuous operation, as different batches of slurry are processed simultaneously in the stations. The CQA of the process is the purity of the discharged crystals cake, which must respect tight solvent and impurity content constraints. However, the composition of the cake being dried cannot be directly measured through sensors during carousel operation. At the same time, other parameters strictly related to the occurrence of disturbances that might compromise the product quality (e.g., abnormal filter mesh fouling or critical change of physical properties of the cake) cannot be measured in real time. Hence, in this study we propose a monitoring system comprising a state estimator (Ray, 1981) for soft-sensing the CQAs of the cakes being processed in the carousel. The monitoring system also features real time parameter estimation routines for tracking critical parameters that can indicate the occurrence of faults. Univariate charts are used on process measurements and estimated states and parameters for fault detection purposes. The monitoring system is tested on a simulated process (Destro et al., 2021) for the isolation of paracetamol crystals from a paracetamol/ethanol slurry with the carousel technology object of this study. Section 2 introduces the process and the case study. Section 3 outlines the conceived monitoring system and presents the monitoring results, before the concluding section.

2. Continuous filtration-drying of paracetamol/ethanol slurries

The carousel setup (Figure 1, equipment legend in Tables 1-2) features five cylindrical ports. In the first one (V101), a volume of paracetamol/ethanol slurry V_{slurry} (controlled by FQC-101) is loaded from a slurry tank (V106), and filtration starts under the action of the pressure P_{compr}, delivered by compressor P101 (controlled by PC-101). Simultaneously, cake deliquoring occurs in V103-V104, and cake thermal drying occurs in V105. Thermal drying is promoted by a flow of hot air, whose temperature when entering V105, $T_{in,g}$, is controlled by TC-101. After a fixed cycle duration Δt_{cycle}, controller KC-101 triggers a cycle rotation. All the material being processed in V101-V104 moves to the following station. The cake entering V105 is ejected through a piston movement, and new slurry is loaded into V101. Different disturbances affect the process in general operating conditions, such as stochastic variabilities of slurry concentration, cake porosity, cake specific resistance and drying kinetic constant, introduced to generate inter-batch variability. Filter mesh fouling also occurs during carousel operation, and must be considered when designing the control strategy of the unit. After every cycle, the meshes installed below ports V101-V104 become more and more fouled, thus increasing the filtration and drying durations. When filter mesh fouling becomes excessive (i.e., every six processing cycles in the simulator), a meshes cleaning-in-place (CIP) procedure is automatically triggered. The material already present in the carousel is processed regularly, but no more slurry is loaded into the carousel. When all the material present at the CIP triggering is discharged from the carousel, ethanol is flowed into all filter meshes, restoring clean filter mesh conditions. A new carousel processing cycle is then initiated by loading new slurry in V101. Note that in the first cycle after the process onset, and after every CIP, only V101 contains material: the remaining ports start operating gradually, cycle after cycle. The simulator is initiated by setting the following values for the controller set-points: $T_{in,g}^{sp}$=50°C (TC-101), V_{slurry}^{sp}= 6 mL (FQC-101),

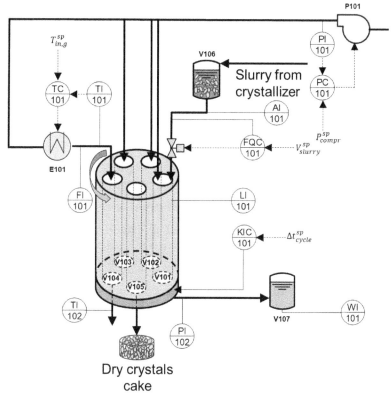

Figure 1. Schematic diagram of the carousel process. V101-V104 present a filter mesh at the bottom, while V105 is open for cake discharge. The equipment legend is given in Table 1 (unit operations and controllers) and in Table 2 (sensors).

Table 1. Legend of the diagram of Figure 1: unit operations and controllers.

Name	Description	Name	Description
P101	Compressor	VI106	Slurry tank
E101	Drying air heater	VI107	Filtrate collector
VI101	Carousel Station 1		
VI102	Carousel Station 2	FQC101	Fed slurry volume controller
VI103	Carousel Station 3	KIC101	Carousel rotation controller
VI104	Carousel Station 4	PC101	Pressure controller
VI105	Carousel Station 5	TC101	Drying air inlet temperature controller

and $P_{compr}^{sp}=1$ bar$_g$ (PC-101). The cycle duration set-point Δt_{cycle}^{sp} (KIC-101) is instead controlled at closed-loop, as outlined in Section 3. The remaining specification needed for running the simulated process is the nominal slurry concentration, which is fixed at 250 kg/m^3.

Two datasets are generated, both of 1 h duration: Dataset 0, corresponding to normal operating conditions, and Dataset 1, where a sudden 100% increase of the nominal specific cake resistance occurs in the cakes formed by the slurry loaded into the carousel, starting 5 min after the process onset. Table 2 lists the set of measurements generated for each dataset. In the remained of the paper, we use the symbol y to denote a measurement.

Table 2. Legend of the diagram of Figure 1: sensors and corresponding measurements.

Name	Measured variable	Symbol	Unit	Notes
AI-101	Slurry concentration	$y_{c_{slurry}}$	kg/m³	Ultrasonic probe
FI-101	Air flowrate	$y_{\dot{V}_{in,g}}$	NL/min	
LI-101	Cake height	$y_{H_{cake}}$	m	Camera system
	Fed slurry volume	$y_{V_{slurry}}$	m³	Camera system
PI-102	Pressure	y_P	Pa	
TI-101	Drying air inlet temperature	$y_{T_{in}}$	K	
TI-102	Drying air inlet temperature	$y_{T_{out}}$	K	
WI-101	Filtrate mass	$y_{M_{filt}}$	kg	

3. Monitoring system: implementation and proof of concept

We propose a monitoring system for the carousel of Figure 1 that features: *i)* real-time parameter estimation, *ii)* state estimation, and *iii)* univariate charts for fault detection and diagnosis, with control limits. The framework for real-time parameter and state estimation (Figure 2) features three routines.

At the end of every cycle that involves slurry processing in V101, a set of filtration-relevant parameters is estimated: the resistance of the filter mesh installed in V101 ($\hat{R}_m$), the specific cake resistance ($\hat{\alpha}$), the cake porosity ($\hat{\epsilon}$), and the filtration duration ($\Delta \hat{t}_{filt}$). The cake porosity is directly estimated through a mass balance:

$$\hat{\epsilon} = 1 - \frac{y_{V_{slurry}} y_{c_{slurry}}}{\rho_s y_{H_{cake}} A_{dryer}}, \tag{1}$$

where ρ_s is the crystals density, A_{dryer} is the filter cross-section, and the measurements legend is in Table 2. Then, $\hat{R}_m$ and $\hat{\alpha}$ are obtained through maximum likelihood estimation using a filtration model (Destro et al., 2021), P_{compr}^{sp}, $\hat{\epsilon}$, and measurements $y_{c_{slurry}}, y_{H_{cake}}, y_{V_{slurry}}$, and $y_{M_{filt}}$ (Table 2). Based on the estimated $\hat{R}_m$ and $\hat{\alpha}$, the

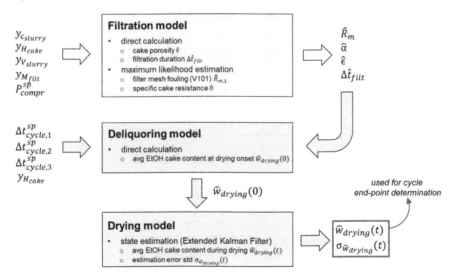

Figure 2. Framework for real-time parameter and state estimation.

filtration model is exploited again, this time for estimating the filtration duration $\Delta \hat{t}_{filt}$ of the cake that has just been processed in V101.

Before the beginning of every carousel cycle that involves cake drying, the duration $\Delta \hat{t}_{deliq}$ of the deliquoring step undergone by the cake that is about to be dried is estimated, from the previously obtained $\Delta \hat{t}_{filt}$, as:

$$\Delta \hat{t}_{deliq} = \Delta t_{cycle,1}^{sp} + \Delta t_{cycle,2}^{sp} + \Delta t_{cycle,3}^{sp} - \Delta \hat{t}_{filt} , \qquad (2)$$

where $\Delta t_{cycle,i}^{sp}$ (for i = 1, 2, 3) is the duration of the cycles during which the considered cake was, respectively, in V101, V102, and V103. From $y_{H_{cake}}$, $\hat{R}_m$, $\hat{\alpha}$, $\Delta \hat{t}_{deliq}$, and $\hat{\epsilon}$, the ethanol content of the cake entering dryer V104 ($\hat{w}_{drying}(0)$) is calculated through a deliquoring model (Destro et al., 2021).

Based on $\hat{w}_{drying}(0)$, a state estimator (an extended Kalman filter; Ray, 1981), rooted on a drying model developed for the carousel (Destro et al., 2021), is then initiated. The state estimator is used, during the following cycle, for real-time tracking of the time evolution of $\hat{w}_{drying}$ of the cake being dried in V104 (Figure 3). The state estimator also provides $\sigma_{\hat{w}_{drying}}$, the standard deviation of the estimation error of $\hat{w}_{drying}$. In addition to soft-sensing $\hat{w}_{drying}$, the CQA of the process, the state estimator is used for determining Δt_{cycle}^{sp}. When the upper confidence limit of the estimated ethanol content in the cake being dried in V104 reaches the quality threshold, a carousel rotation is triggered (Figure 3). This automated setting for cycle duration determination allows consistently obtaining cakes meeting the target quality specification, because during carousel operation Δt_{cycle}^{sp} is automatically adjusted based on the needed drying duration (Figure 4a). Note that, for processing cycles in which V104 is empty, Δt_{cycle}^{sp} is kept fixed to 30 s. In Dataset 1 (Figure 4a), a sudden increase of the average cycle duration is registered after the 13-th cycle. This cycle actually corresponds to the situation when, for Dataset 1, the first cake with an abnormally large specific resistance (cake #7) enters V104. Since the parameter estimation routine effectively tracks the specific cake resistance increase in the cakes entering V101 (Figure 4b), the state estimator allows to promptly detect the

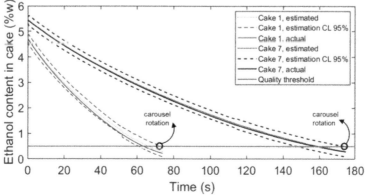

Figure 3. Dataset 1: ethanol content during drying for the first and the seventh cakes processed in the carousel: estimated value, estimation error 95% confidence limits (CL) and actual value.

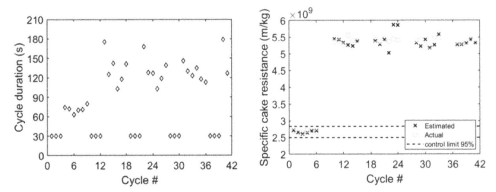

Figure 4 Dataset 1: *(a)* duration of the different processing cycles, *(b)* univariate monitoring chart for specific cake resistance of the cake in V102, reporting estimated value, actual value, and 95% control limits for fault detection, obtained from the normal operating conditions dataset (Dataset 0).

larger drying duration needed by cake #7, compared to cake #1 (Figure 3). Figure 4b also reports the 95% control limits, obtained from Dataset 0, for the estimated specific resistance of the cakes in V101. Abnormal specific cake resistance is immediately detected after cycle #10 (corresponding to when cake #7 enters V102).

Conclusions

We presented a monitoring framework for intensified filtration-drying of a paracetamol/ethanol slurry through a novel continuous carousel. The monitoring system features parameter and state estimation routines for monitoring the product CQAs and key operating parameters. The estimated CQAs are exploited for automatically determining the drying end-point. The monitoring system has successfully been tested under a set of disturbances on a simulated process. Multivariate process monitoring implementation for fault detection and diagnosis is envisioned for the future work.

Acknowledgements

Funding for this publication was made possible, in part, by the Food and Drug Administration through grant (U01FD006738). Views expressed in written materials or publications and by speakers and moderators do not necessarily reflect the official policies of the Department of Health and Human Services; nor does any mention of trade names, commercial practices, or organization imply endorsement by the United States Government. F.D. gratefully acknowledges the "CARIPARO Foundation" for his PhD scholarship and "Fondazione Ing. Aldo Gini" for the financial support.

References

Destro, F., Hur, I., Wang, V., Abdi, M., Feng, X., Wood, E., Coleman, S., Firth, P., Barton, A., Barolo, M., Nagy, Z. 2021. Mathematical modeling and digital design of an intensified filtration-washing-drying unit for pharmaceutical continuous manufacturing. Chem. Eng. Sci., 244, 116803.

Ray, W.H., 1981. Advanced process control. McGraw-Hill, New York.

Yu, L.X., Kopcha, M., 2017. The future of pharmaceutical quality and the path to get there. Int. J. Pharm. 528, 354–359

Proceedings of the 14th International Symposium on Process Systems Engineering – PSE 2021+
June 19-23, 2022, Kyoto, Japan © 2022 Elsevier B.V. All rights reserved.
http://dx.doi.org/10.1016/B978-0-323-85159-6.50235-9

Plant Fault Diagnosis System using Negative Selection Algorithm

Naoki Kimura*, Yuki Ichikawa, Kazunori Tanihara, Yuichi Makiya, Gen Inoue, Yoshifumi Tsuge

Dept. of Chemical Engineering, Kyushu University, 744 Motooka, Nishi-ku, Fukuoka, 819-0395 Japan
nkimura@chem-eng.kyushu-u.ac.jp

Abstract

Early fault detection and correct diagnosis are required for chemical plants. Therefore, the existing fault detection systems using upper/lower thresholds have difficulties to detect faults when the correlation among process variables breaks without excess of any thresholds. In our previous study, an artificial immune system—especially, negative selection algorithm— had been adopted to fault detection system. Negative selection algorithm is one of methods of artificial immune systems which imitate the vital immune system. We have built up a multiagent based fault detection system using negative selection algorithm. In our system, a set of detectors is generated in each two-dimensional variable space consists of two process variables.

In this study, we extend the system to plant fault diagnosis based on the fault detection result using negative selection algorithm. In this paper, we will illustrate our fault detection and diagnosis system using negative selection algorithm. And we will show the detection and diagnosis results when a malfunction occurs in a dynamic plant simulator of a boiler plant.

Keywords: Fault detection; Fault diagnosis; Artificial immune system; Negative selection algorithm.

1. Introduction

Chemical plants are very complicated because they composed of lots of equipment and instruments. It is an essential to keep safe and stable state in operation of chemical plant, and various countermeasures are taken. A fault detection mechanism of an existing plant protection system generally sets a threshold value for each measuring instrument, and when it exceeds the threshold value, it issues a signal and becomes an alarm. As a method of setting the threshold value, there are methods such as upper limit / lower limit, upper limit difference / lower limit difference, upper limit of change rate / lower limit of change rate. However, we thought that an abnormal condition that could not be detected by only the technique that defines these thresholds exists, and wanted to propose a new fault detection method that can detect the features of anomalies with different properties. Therefore, in our previous study (Kimura 2018), we have proposed an artificial immune system as a new fault detection method capable of detecting features of abnormalities with different properties. An artificial immune system is a system focused on the mechanism of immunity of living organisms and has been proposed in the early 1990's (Dasgupta 2006 & 2011). In the artificial immune systems, negative selection algorithms designed to imitate the mechanism of differentiation and maturation of immature T cells and the mechanism of discrimination of normality / abnormality of immune are systems specialized for fault detection of researchers attracting attention.

In this research, we aim to develop a fault diagnosis system as a extension of our previously investigated fault detection system using negative selection algorithm.

2. Methodology

2.1. Fault Detection using Negative Selection Algorithm

Negative selection algorithm is one of the fault detection methods in artificial immune systems. Artificial immune system is a mechanism to maintain the system normal, borrowed the idea from the vital immune systems. In this study, the normal operational data of the plant is regarded as 'self', and the abnormal operational data, that is 'fault', is regarded as 'non-self'. Fig.1(a)–(e) illustrates the outline of this algorithm. In our method, there are two phases—detector generation phase and detection phase.In the detector generation phase, there is a variable space consisted of plural process variables which are normalized to [0,1] range. Fig.1(a) shows two-dimensional variable space with two process variables P1 and T1. And the figure also shows there is a path which represents a normal operational data—regarded as 'self' region in this method. The remaining area is regarded as 'non-self' region.Fig.1(b) shows the way to generate detectors. The figure shows four points which are the centers of the detector candidates are generated in the variable space. If the detector candidate has a high affinity with

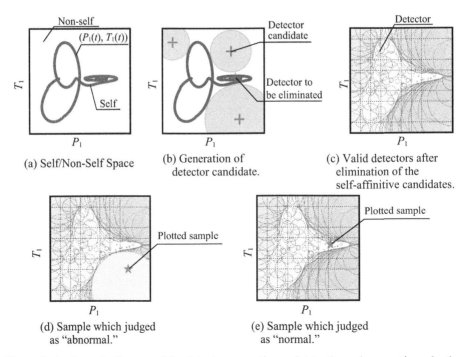

(a) Self/Non-Self Space

(b) Generation of detector candidate.

(c) Valid detectors after elimination of the self-affinitive candidates.

(d) Sample which judged as "abnormal."

(e) Sample which judged as "normal."

Figure 1: A schematic diagram of the detector generation and detection using negative selection algorithm

the self region, it will be eliminated. One of the four detector candidates in Fig.1(b) is eliminated. On the other hand, if the detector candidate has no affinity with the self region, it will be set the radius which is the shortest distance between self region and the center point and adopted as a detector. This mechanism is called negative selection. To cover the non-self region with detectors efficiently, detector candidates are firstly generated on lattice points in the process variable space, and then detector candidates are generated randomly thereafter. Fig.1(c) shows the detectors fully cover the non-self region of the variable space.

In the detection phase, the data to be subjected to abnormality detection is normalized and plotted in the process variable space. If the plot is placed inside the detector(s) or outside the range of [0, 1], the data is judged as abnormal. In Fig.1(d), a star represents the plotted data, and the data was plotted inside detectors. On the other hand, if the plot is placed without capture by any detectors the data is judge as normal, shown in Fig.1 (e).

2.2. Fault Diagnosis Method

In preparation for fault diagnosis, consideration of the impact on the process when an assumed malfunction occurs. Based on the PFD, P&ID and HAZOP study, it is considered if an assumed malfunction occurs whether the measured value of the sensor increases (denotes as "+"), decreases (denotes as "-") or no effect (denotes as "0") compared to the normal state. After consideration about all the assumed malfunctions, a sign and malfunction table is obtained.

If n variables are used, 3n kinds of sign (+/-/0) combinations can be theoretically made, and if different sign combinations are shown for each cause of malfunction, it should be used to identify the cause of malfunction. However, a variable set in which all *n* signs

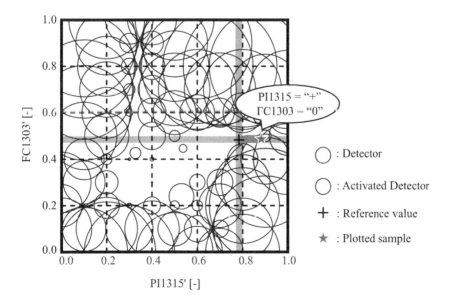

Figure 2: Current operational data plot and reference value in variable space covered by the detectors.

are 0 for a certain malfunction cause or a variable set in which different malfunction causes show the same sign combination cannot be used for fault diagnosis.

The current operation data is plotted in the variable space covered by the detectors every sampling time (Fig.2). If it was plotted in the detection area of the detector, the fault was detected. Then, the sign is judged in three stages: higher (+), no change (0), and lower (-) than the reference value of the operational condition. The sign is determined and summarized for all variable spaces in which a fault is detected, and the diagnostic sign pattern of the monitoring variable set is determined to compare with pattern table.

And then, matching rate for each assumed malfunction is calculated.

Matching rate $m = n_{match} / n$ (1)

where, n_{match} is the number of signs that match the sign of the assumed malfunction in the assumed sign pattern and the diagnostic sign pattern, and n is the number of monitoring variables. The malfunction cause(s) are presented to the operator as plausible malfunction cause candidate(s) if the rate(s) is larger than 50%.

3. Simulations Results

Table 1 shows the assumed malfunctions of boiler plant. And the table 1 also shows the diagnostic sign pattern for each malfunction.

Since there are five assumed causes, it can be identified by variables with $n = 2$ or more, but for the reason mentioned in section 2.2, there is no variable set that can be identified with $n = 2$, even though there are more than one hundred sensors in the boiler plant. However, only the combination of { PI1311, PI1315, FC1303 } became an identifiable combination with $n = 3$. Then, these sensor variables are used as a monitoring variable set.

The normal operation data and abnormal operational data was acquired by a dynamic plant simulator "VisualModeler". As for the normal operation data, a total of 12 conditions were acquired when the steam demand was stepwise changed. The abnormal operation data was acquired for a total of 30 conditions: (5 malfunctions; total steam demands: 120, 130 or 140 t/h; 2 types of fluctuation of steam demand).

Table 1: Assumed plant malfunctions

	Assumed malfunction	PI1311	PI1315	FC1303
Mal-1	Heavy oil flowmeter failure	+	+	0
Mal-2	Boiler feed water flowmeter failure	0	0	+
Mal-3	Air flowmeter failure	-	-	0
Mal-4	Boiler water pipe leakage	+	+	+
Mal-5	Burner flame-out	+	0	0

Figure 3 shows the matching rates graph when the malfunction Mal-4 was caused. In Fig.3, the matching rate of correct malfunction cause (Mal-4) shows 100% from detection time to end and the rate for other cause (Mal-1) shows 66.7%. It means that both of the causes are possible cause, because the rates are over 50%. However Mal-1's rate is always maintained at the highest level, it is judged as Mal-1 is plausible cause.

Table 2 shows the diagnosis results for 30 conditions where "Correct" denotes correct diagnosis, "Multiple" denotes that matching rates of both correct and incorrect cause(s) are the same and highest, "False" denotes that matching rate of incorrect cause is the highest, "Missed" denotes that no fault was detected. In this study, two "Multiple", one "Missed" and 27 "Correct" case was obtained.

4. Conclusions

Failure diagnosis has become possible by introducing a sign determination method into the fault detection system that uses a negative selection algorithm. It is necessary to

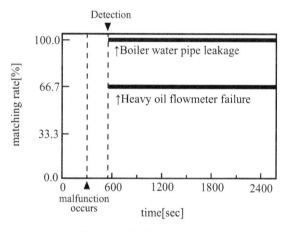

Figure 3: Matching rates after malfunction (Boiler feed water pipe leakage) was occurred.

Table 2: Diagnosis results

| | W/O change of steam demand | | | With change of steam demand | | |
| | Total steam demand | | | Total steam demad before change | | |
	140 t/h	130 t/h	120 t/h	140 t/h	130 t/h	120 t/h
Mal-1	Correct	Multiple	Correct	Correct	Multiple	Correct
Mal-2	Correct	Correct	Missed	Correct	Correct	Correct
Mal-3	Correct	Correct	Correct	Correct	Correct	Correct
Mal-4	Correct	Correct	Correct	Correct	Correct	Correct
Mal-5	Correct	Correct	Correct	Correct	Correct	Correct

improve the performance of the fault diagnosis.

References

D. Dasgupta, Advances in artificial immune systems, Computational intelligence magazine, 1, 40–49, 2006.

D. Dasgupta, S. Yu, F. Nino, Recent Advances in Artificial Immune Systems: Models and Applications, Applied Soft Computing, 11, 1574–1587, 2011.

N. Kimura, Y. Takeda, Y. Tsuge, Agent Based Fault Detection System for Chemical Processes using Negative Selection Algorithm, Advances in Science, Technology and Engineering Systems Journal, 3, 2, 90–98, 2018.

Proceedings of the 14th International Symposium on Process Systems Engineering – PSE 2021+
June 19-23, 2022, Kyoto, Japan © 2022 Elsevier B.V. All rights reserved.
http://dx.doi.org/10.1016/B978-0-323-85159-6.50236-0

Digital Twin of a pilot-scale bio-production setup

Monica Muldbak[a], Carina Gargalo[a], Ulrich Krühne[a], Isuru Udugama[a,b], Krist V. Gernaey[a]*

[a]*Process and Systems Engineering Center (PROSYS), The Department of Chemical and Biochemical Engineering, Technical University of Denmark, Kgs. Lyngby 2800, Denmark*
[b]*The Department of Chemical Systems Engineering, The University of Tokyo, Bunkyo-ku 113-8654, Japan*
kvg@kt.dtu.dk

Abstract

The term digital twin is now everywhere in the domain of bio-manufacturing. Despite this, the actual implementation of "Digital Twins" in operations is somewhat limited, and the core elements contained within such an implementation are ambiguous. A vital aspect of a fully developed digital twin is the two-way communication capability between the physical plant and the digital model. This contribution will describe the data management and modelling elements needed to achieve a full-fledged digital twin, emphasising the digital model that acts as the prediction engine of a digital twin. To this end, the overall operational workflow of developing a digital replica of a bio-based pilot process will be described. It is expected that the knowledge gained from this endeavour will enable the development of a general framework towards digital model building. Thus, it is expected to generate practical know-how for future digitalisation applications in bio-production.

Keywords: digital twin, digitalisation, modelling, implementation, bio-manufacturing

1. Introduction

Digital Twin (DT) is one of the new buzzwords within the engineering field. A simple literature search shows that the number of scientific publications containing this term has increased significantly over the last couple of years (Udugama, Lopez, et al., 2021). The term DT was first introduced by (Grieves, 2015) where it was defined as a "digital representation of a physical object". Since then, the term DT has been liberally used to describe digitalisation efforts in manufacturing and beyond (Lukowski et al., 2018). In the domain of bio-manufacturing operations, DTs are also gaining popularity. Despite this, a survey conducted with individuals involved with biotech manufacturing in Denmark found that the actual number of implementations that can be considered a DT in plant operations is limited (Udugama, Öner, et al., 2021).

The core of the DT is the digital model(s) being used to simulate the process. Still, the optimal modelling approach and required auxiliary elements to distinguish a digital model from a DT are yet to be defined with the necessary level of detail. At the beginning of 2021, (Udugama, Lopez, et al., 2021) published a five-step pathway to develop a DT for the bio-manufacturing industry. Furthermore, (von Stosch et al., 2021) published an opinion paper about the potential for integrating the DT with artificial intelligence.

In this work, we detail the development of an overall implementation framework for a pilot-scale *E. coli* based production process operated for engineering education at the Bio-manufacturing, Training and Education Center at NC State University (BTEC).

This process has been selected because it is a well-known fermentation process with great relevance in education (e.g., at the BTEC facility) and in industrial settings.. The development of a DT for this process is expected to be used as a demonstration case. The lessons learnt can be used to further the application of DTs in the bio-manufacturing industry. The remainder of this article is organised as follows: Section 2 will describe the benefits and drawbacks of choosing between mechanistic, data-driven, and hybrid options for digital model development. Section 3 gives a detailed description of the implementation framework. Section 4 summarizes the initial lessons learnt and identifies potential opportunities. Finally, conclusions are derived in Section 5.

2. Digital Models

Digital models form the core of any DT application. However, models can quickly become computationally heavy and would thus struggle with the requirement of real-time data handling of a fully realised DT. Therefore, in order to be implemented for real-time simulation, the selection of the modelling approach and the corresponding level of complexity is vital when setting up a digital model.

2.1. Data-driven vs. mechanistic models

Prior to focusing on model complexity, it is essential to select the correct strategy and modelling approach. Mathematical models can generally be divided into three main categories; mechanistic, data-driven and hybrid models. Mechanistic modelling, or parametric modelling, is theory-based modelling. This type of model often contains various parameters and constants, the value of which may be appropriately adjusted to almost any system.

Mechanistic models are widely used in modelling fermentation processes such as *E. coli* based production processes. One such example is (Anane et al., 2017), where a mechanistic approach was used to model overflow metabolism in *E. coli* at a macro-scale. This model was then validated using measurable concentrations within a fed-batch. (Millard et al., 2017) also modelled the growth of *E. coli* but at a smaller scale, which added details regarding metabolite regulation within the cells. However, the number of parameters increases drastically with the complexity of the model, adding a significant computational burden. It can be challenging for complex models to determine the value of these parameters and validate the model. Therefore, adopting a mechanistic model is not trivial and requires expert knowledge.

Data-driven models, on the other hand, tackle the system from a completely different point of view. They are, as the name implies, based on system data. This means that data-driven models can be susceptible to variance within data sets unless large amounts of data are available. However, the collection of large datasets is resource-intensive. Notwithstanding, it can be an advantage if, for model improvements, we can apply a machine learning algorithm (e.g., artificial neural networks) since these types of models usually improve with larger data sets. The advantage of the data-driven models is that they usually require less experience and expert knowledge to set up and can be easier to validate than some mechanistic models.

A disadvantage of data-driven models is related to the fact that they are limited by the type and sensitivity of the sensors available. A sensor setup composed of different sensors can be cumbersome and expensive to set up. Adding additional sensors to an existing system is not without trouble, especially when considering biopharma, where stringent documentation is, and it will always be, a requirement. Flow following sensors form a newer alternative to make use of a more comprehensive sensor setup in a bioreactor. Since they do not require physical installation to the bioreactor and can acquire data at different points in the tank, flow following sensors seem to be a promising and flexible tool.

Recent examples of flow follower studes include (Lauterbach et al., 2019), who has been working on the development of a truly miniaturised flow follower, which can measure temperature in lab-scale equipment. (Reinecke & Hampel, 2018) have developed a sensor for aerobic digesters. (Bisgaard et al., 2020) presented results on mixing studies using one of the only commercially available multi-parametric flow followers. So far, it has been demonstrated that it provides less extensive and expensive setup modifications, while still providing impactful data collection (Bisgaard et al., 2020).

2.2. Hybrid models

Hybrid models is a term used for any model, which combines the mechanistic and data-driven approaches. Many of the newer hybrid modelling approaches integrate mechanistic modelling and machine learning. There are many different ways this can be done. (von Stosch et al., 2016) have developed a strategy that couples mechanistic modelling with neural networks. Hybrid approaches are also an option when working with models integrating the effect of scale, from macromixing to cellular products. An example of such a multiscale model is the fermentation model developed by (Benalcázar et al., 2020). The issue with neural networks and other traditional machine learning algorithms is that they are discrete by nature. A potential solution to this was proposed by (Chen et al., 2018), who developed a continuous machine learning algorithm based on ordinary differential equations.

3. Proposed Framework

Bio-manufacturing processes are often not fully automated, which is a requirement for implementation of a DT where it can communicate bi-directionally with the plant. To this end, there is a need to develop concepts that can close this gap and provide the operator with actionable predictive information from the DT. The overall framework illustrated in Figure 1 suggests a potential roadmap towards realising a fully-fledged DT for bio-manufacturing processes while respecting the inherent limitations that it implies. Due to the versatile implementation and automation of bio-manufacturing processes, the framework for a DT also needs to be adaptable as well as agile. The strategy to meet this requirement is to develop a 'plug-and-play' approach. Individual unit operation models are embedded within the larger framework, allowing the framework to be configured to the DT's desired purpose and for relatively easy adaptation to other processes.

At the core of the framework is a digital model capable of bi-directional communication. Based on section 2, hybrid models are recommended as the default choice for building this crucial step of the framework. Regarding inputs into the DT, the framework identifies that information from the physical plant can be gathered in real-time as long as the relevant sensors are installed. Since bio-manufacturing processes are mainly operated as batch production processes, the information collected must contain both process data (e.g temperature, pH, flow) and scheduling information (batch sequence, runtime). The data gathered must also be stored in an accessible format so that it can be used for further model validation and improvements.

Connecting the output of the DT to the model is much more complicated. This is because many critical process operations are either carried out manually by the plant operator or require the operator to take action on a subsystem that is not configured to take external commands. Regulatory requirements and the costs of automation mean that these types of operational configurations will likely remain in bio-manufacturing processes for the foreseeable future. To this end, the action suggested by the DT must be taken by the plant operators. An effective way to communicate these actions is through the use of targeted data visualisatiuon that can provide the operator with actionable information. However, unlike an automated system, operators are susceptible to making mistakes and have individual behavioural traits. While fully describing the nature of a particular human operator is beyond the scope of this work, the framework has identified the need to develop simplified human behaviour models that can be incorporated into the DT.

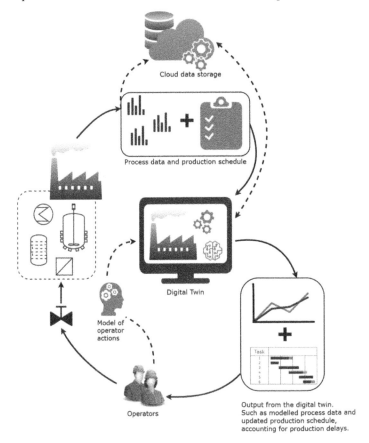

Figure 1: Conceptual framework for the development of Digital Twin for a process, which has not been automated.

4. Lessons learnt

This framework is currently applied to a pilot-scale *E. coli* fermentation, operated at the Bio-manufacturing, Training and Education Center (BTEC) at NC State University. This initial work identifies some minimum communication and modelling requirements, along with the potential for developing a fault detection algorithm for batch prediction.

4.1. Minimum Communication Requirements

For the DT to be realisable, the process in question needs to have some level of automation. If any data-driven or hybrid modelling approach is applied, the models require inputs from the sensors to operate and accurately estimate the state of the process.

To this end, there is a need to establish communication between the digital model and the physical system. Typically, the minimum requirement for bi-directional communication is a system consisting of digital actuators that a central DCS/SCADA can control. A critical constraint that has been identified in the current development process is the need for live extraction of the process data and production schedule. This requires a digital model with a fast simulation time and a high-level programming language to gather DCS/SCADA system data. This is due to the fact that acquiring process data in real-time is crucial for a fully integrated digital twin capable of two-way communication.

4.2. Minimum Modeling Requirements

An important focus area is the applicability and adaptability of the models and the overall implementation framework. The DT can be reasonably adaptable and customisable to different processes within bio-manufacturing. In addition, the overall digital model developed needs to execute in real-time under the constraints imposed by communication limitations and computational requirements. The need to move away from complete mechanistic modelling was identified as a method for fulfilling this requirement. To this end, the proposed strategy is based on hybrid modelling of key unit operations, which can run under a larger modelling framework.

4.3. Potential Fault Detection

Due to documentation requirements within the biopharmaceutical field, all the process data has to be stored. However, in many cases, the full potential of the process data is not explored. (Xu et al., 2019) presented an interesting view on the application of a DT for fault diagnosis. This is an exciting concept that could potentially be applied within bio-manufacturing where process data can be used to predict the variation for each batch and predict when a batch is at a high risk of failure due to off-specification product formation or high byproduct formation. This will allow the operators to decide whether or not to discard a batch or adjust the process conditions due to expected delays or a potential change in product quality.

5. Conclusions

This work detailed the development of a ' plug and play' framework for creating a fully-fledged DTs in the domain of bio-manufacturing. This framework is customizable to the different processes based on the unit operations involved. Sufficient communication infrastructure and appropriate model choices were identified as key requirements for successfully implementing DT in bioprocessing industries. The pros and cons of mechanistic, data-driven, and hybrid modelling approaches were identified and reviewed. Overall, it was shown that a key to successfully applying a DT is the need for robust models, which are simple enough to be run in real- time while still accurate enough to provide adequate decision support capabilities.

Acknowledgements

This work is supported by the Accelerated Innovation in Manufacturing Biologics (AIM-Bio) project funded by the Novo Nordisk Foundation (Grant number NNF19SA0035474).

References

Anane, E., López C, D. C., Ncubauer, P., & Cruz Bournazou, M. N. (2017). Modelling overflow metabolism in Escherichia coli by acetate cycling. *Biochemical*

Engineering Journal, *125*, 23–30.

Benalcázar, E. A., Noorman, H., Filho, R. M., & Posada, J. A. (2020). Modeling ethanol production through gas fermentation: A biothermodynamics and mass transfer-based hybrid model for microbial growth in a large-scale bubble column bioreactor. *Biotechnology for Biofuels*, *13*(1).

Bisgaard, J., Muldbak, M., Cornelissen, S., Tajsoleiman, T., Huusom, J. K., Rasmussen, T., & Gernaey, K. V. (2020). Flow-following sensor devices: A tool for bridging data and model predictions in large-scale fermentations. *Computational and Structural Biotechnology Journal*, *18*, 2908–2919.

Chen, R. T. Q., Rubanova, Y., Bettencourt, J., & Duvenaud, D. (2018). Neural Ordinary Differential Equations. *32nd Conference on Neural Information Processing Systems, NeurIPS 2018*, 6571–6583.

Grieves, M. (2015). Digital Twin : Manufacturing Excellence through Virtual Factory Replication. In *A Whitepaper*.

Lauterbach, T., Lüke, T., Büker, M. J., Hedayat, C., Gernandt, T., Moll, R., Grösel, M., Lenk, S., Seidel, F., Brunner, D., Bley, T., Walther, T., & Lenk, F. (2019). Measurements on the fly– Introducing mobile micro-sensors for biotechnological applications. *Sensors and Actuators, A: Physical*, *287*, 29–38.

Lukowski, G., Rauch, A., & Rosendahl, T. (2018). The Virtual Representation of the World is Emerging. In P. Krüssel (Ed.), *Future Telco* (pp. 165–173). Springer International Publishing.

Millard, P., Smallbone, K., & Mendes, P. (2017). Metabolic regulation is sufficient for global and robust coordination of glucose uptake, catabolism, energy production and growth in Escherichia coli. *PLoS Computational Biology*, *13*(2).

Reinecke, S., & Hampel, U. (2018). Investigation of bioreactors by smart sensor particles. *Chemie Ingenieur Technik*, *90*(9), 1268–1268.

Udugama, I. A., Lopez, P. C., Gargalo, C. L., Li, X., Bayer, C., & Gernaey, K. V. (2021). Digital Twin in biomanufacturing: challenges and opportunities towards its implementation. *Systems Microbiology and Biomanufacturing*, *1*(3), 257–274.

Udugama, I. A., Öner, M., Lopez, P. C., Beenfeldt, C., Bayer, C., Huusom, J. K., Gernaey, K. V., & Sin, G. (2021). Towards Digitalization in Bio-Manufacturing Operations: A Survey on Application of Big Data and Digital Twin Concepts in Denmark. *Frontiers in Chemical Engineering*, *3*.

von Stosch, M., Hamelink, J. M., & Oliveira, R. (2016). Hybrid modeling as a QbD/PAT tool in process development: an industrial E. coli case study. *Bioprocess and Biosystems Engineering*, *39*(5), 773–784.

von Stosch, M., Portela, R. M., & Varsakelis, C. (2021). A roadmap to AI-driven in silico process development: bioprocessing 4.0 in practice. *Current Opinion in Chemical Engineering*, *33*, 100692.

Xu, Y., Sun, Y., Liu, X., & Zheng, Y. (2019). A Digital-Twin-Assisted Fault Diagnosis Using Deep Transfer Learning. *IEEE Access*, *7*, 19990–19999.

Proceedings of the 14th International Symposium on Process Systems Engineering – PSE 2021+
June 19-23, 2022, Kyoto, Japan © 2022 Elsevier B.V. All rights reserved.
http://dx.doi.org/10.1016/B978-0-323-85159-6.50237-2

Plant O&M Support System Based on Supervised Data-Clustering Technology

Yoshinari Hori[a*], Takaaki Sekiai[a], Hiroto Takeuchi[b]

[a] *Research & Development Group, Hitachi, Ltd., Ibaraki 319-1292 JAPAN*
[b] *Service & Platforms Business Unit, Hitachi, Ltd., Ibaraki 319-1293 JAPAN*
yoshinari.hori.ns@hitachi.com

Abstract

We propose a plant operations and maintenance (O&M) support system that can correlate plant operational data to both key performance indicators (KPIs) and qualitative data such as plant statuses or anomaly types. The system consists of a supervised data-clustering function and a visualization function for clustered results. The supervised data-clustering function is based on the ART2 network and can correlate plant operational data to KPIs and qualitative data by classifying the operational data. Therefore, the operational data are classified into different categories when the KPIs of the operational data are the same and their qualitative data are different. The visualization function can illustrate the relation between the operational data and the KPIs and the qualitative data as a three-dimensional graph or a two-dimensional graph. An x-y plane showing the gravity centres of the categories is mapped by multidimensional scaling, and the qualitative data are displayed beside dots in both graph types. KPIs are indicated by the z-axis in the three-dimensional graph and by dot colours in the two-dimensional graph. We examined whether the system can be used to analyze plant operational data using process simulation data. The results demonstrate that our system can monitor and maintain industrial plant performance.

Keywords: Operation; Maintenance; Data clustering; Applications.

1. Introduction

To maintain high productivity at industrial plants, it is important to monitor key performance indicators (KPIs) such as plant operational efficiency.

One of the technologies for monitoring plant KPIs is soft sensors. For example, Okada et al. (2012) developed an adaptive soft sensor technique to respond to the degradation of soft sensors. Kim et al. (2013) developed an inferential control system that integrates soft sensors and model predictive control. In addition, Matsui et al. (2014) estimated product quality by using PLS in the deposition process of a thin-film solar cell and visualised the relationship between the main two variables and quality in a three-dimensional graph.

Hori et al. (2019) have developed a performance evaluation system for industrial plants that uses data clustering technology. The system can be employed to analyze plant operational data by using the KPIs and consists of a data clustering function for operational data of the KPIs and a visualisation function of clustering results. The data clustering function is based on the ART2 network (Carpenter and Grossberg, 1987), which is one of the adaptive resonance theory (ART) networks. It can correlate plant operational data to KPIs by classifying operational data. The visualisation function of clustering results illustrates the relation between operational data and KPIs by using a 3D graph with a z-axis indicating the KPIs and an x-y plane showing where the gravity centres of the categories are mapped by multidimensional scaling (MDS).

In this study, we enhance that system and propose a plant operations and maintenance (O&M) support system that can correlate plant operational data to both KPIs and qualitative data such as plant statuses or anomaly types. We also examine whether the system can be used to analyse plant operational data by using process simulation data.

2. Proposed system

2.1 Overview of the proposed system

Figure 1 shows an overview of the proposed plant O&M support system using data clustering technology.

The system consists of a supervised data clustering function and a visualisation function of clustering results. The basics of each function are described below. Hereafter, the term "qualitative data such as plant status or anomaly type", is simply referred to as "plant status" or "status".

In the supervised data clustering function, the operational data of the plant are classified into multiple categories, and the relationship between a category and a selected KPI and its status is set. The centre of Figure 1 shows the supervised data clustering results. To simplify the explanation, the operational data are two-dimensional data. The points plotted in the graph are the operational data of each time, and the colour of the point represents the KPI. Those with a high KPI value are black and those with a low KPI value are white. The circle surrounding the operational data represents a category that classifies the data. In the example in Figure 1, the operational data are classified into eight categories. The type of line drawing each circle corresponds to the plant status. Solid, dashed, and dotted lines indicate normal (Norm.), abnormal (Abnl.) A and abnormal (Abnl.) B, respectively.

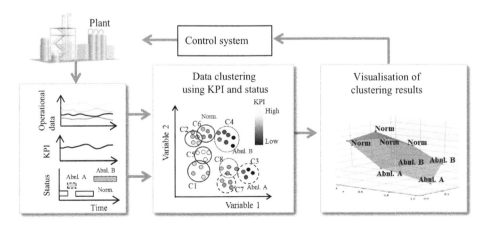

Figure 1 Schematic of the proposed system

In the visualisation function of the clustering results, the relationship between categories and KPI and plant status are visualized in three-dimensional graphs. The Z-axis, that is, the vertical axis indicates the KPI, the XY plane represents the positional relationship of the centre of gravity of the data classified into each category (hereinafter referred to as the gravity centre of the category). Since the gravity centre of the category is N-dimensional data, it is not possible to accurately represent the positional relationship on a two-dimensional plane. However, it is possible to express the approximate positional relationship by using the MDS method. Therefore, as shown in Figure 1, the function can display the positional relationship of the categories with their KPIs and plant status in a three-dimensional graph. That information is useful to support O&M of industrial plant.

In the above, a three-dimensional graph with a KPI axis has been described. However, a two-dimensional graph expressing the value of KPI in colour can be used, instead.

2.2 Data clustering algorithm

The algorithm of the supervised data clustering function is described below.

Step 1: Read multi-dimensional operational data, KPI and plant status and set the vigilance parameter ρ_j for category j to a given initial value.

Step 2: Classify the operational data by using the vigilance parameter ρ_j set in the previous step. The vigilance parameter ρ_j determines the size of category j; namely, the larger ρ_j is, the smaller the size of the category j is.

Step 3: Calculate V_j and M_j by Eqs. (1) and (2).

$$V_j = KPI\_max_j - KPI\_min_j \tag{1}$$

$$M_j = Nm_j / N_j \tag{2}$$

Herein, KPI_max$_j$ is the maximum value of KPI of the data classified into category j and KPI_max$_j$ is the minimum value of KPI of the data classified into category j. N_j is the number of data in category j, N_m is the number of data with the highest proportion of plant status.

Step 4: If the V_j calculated in step 3 is above V_{set}, the set value of V_j, or M_j is below M_{set}, the set value of M_j, or the number of calculations is less than the given value, proceed to step 5. Otherwise, proceed to step 6.

Step 5: Update the value of ρ_j by selecting the larger of ρ_{V_j} and ρ_{M_j} calculated by Eq. (3) and Eq. (4), respectively and return to step 2.

$$\rho_{V_j} = \frac{V_{set} \times \rho_j + a_V(V_j - V_{set}) \times \rho_{max}}{V_{set} + a_V(V_j - V_{set})} \tag{3}$$

$$\rho_{Mj} = \frac{M_{set} \times \rho_j + a_M(M_{set} - M_j) \times \rho_{max}}{M_{set} + a_M(M_{set} - M_j)} \tag{4}$$

Herein, in Eqs. (3) and (4) , ρ_{max} is the maximum value of ρ in this system and a_V and a_M are adjustment coefficients.

Step 6: Calculate the average value of the KPI and select the plant status and map the relationship between the categories and both the KPIs and plant status.

Figure 2 is an explanatory diagram of the above algorithm. Figure 2(a) represents an example of the initial condition of categories, or the clustering result in step 2. In step 2, ρ_j is set to an initial value, then all the categories are the same size. Therefore, a category could have data with a wide range of KPI values and it could have data with different plant status. In Figure 2(a), category C1 has data with high and middle KPI values and category C3 has data in abnormal A and in abnormal B. However, in going from step 3 to step 5, if necessary, the size of the categories gets smaller. In Figure 2(b), category C5 is created for data with high KPI value and category C8 is for data in abnormal B. In this way, each category is supposed to have data with a given range of KPI values and the same plant status.

In the situation where two operational data are very similar and the KPI values are very different or their plant statuses are different because of noise, it is difficult to classify the data into different categories and the category sizes can become very small for such categories. In this case, the value of V_{set} must be made larger or the value of M_{set} must be made smaller. For example, if the value is set to 0.9, 10 % of the data classified in each category can be for another plant status, which can avoid creating categories that are too small.

As described above, the relationship between the multi-dimensional operational data and KPIs and plant status is learned by the proposed algorithm

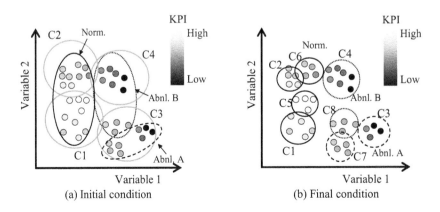

Figure 2 Explanatory diagram of proposed algorithm

3. Data analysis and results

We examined whether the system can be utilised to analyse plant operational data by using Tennessee Eastman process data, which are commonly used as benchmark data for evaluating anomaly detection technology (Downs and Vogel,1993). Several variations of data sets of Tennessee Eastman process data are open to the public. The data used in this study contained 15 data sets with different disturbances: IDV(1) to IDV(15)(N. L. Ricker, 1996). Each data set had time series data which consisted of 41 measured variables, 12 manipulated variables and 10 calculated variables including operational cost, 63 variables in total. The sampling interval was 10 min and each data set contained 301 samples (data covering 50 h). We chose operational cost as the KPI and disturbance as plant status and made test data for the data analysis.

In particular, we chose three data sets IDV(1), IDV(2) and IDV(6) shown in Table 1 for the test data because of their large change in operational cost. Time series data of operational cost for these IDVs are shown in Figure 3. We also chose 9 manipulated variables and for operational data from the 63 variables. The variables whose value were constant in the data sets were not used for the test data. Data analysis was conducted using the test data where V_{set} was 0.4 and M_{set} was 0.9. The results are shown in Figure 4.

Figure 4 is a two-dimensional MDS graph. Each dot indicates the gravity centre of each category and the colour of each dot indicates the KPI value. The legend of each dot indicates plant status. Areas A, B, and C were seen in Figure 4. Operational data of IDV(1) with low KPI values were classified into the categories in area A, operational data of IDV(1) data with high KPI values were classified into the categories in area B, and operational data of IDV(6) with high KPI values were classified into the categories in area C. Then, the KPI value and plant status can be assumed from the area where the category is located.

Table 1 Analysis data

Disturbance	Description	Type
IDV (1)	A/C feed ratio, B composition constant (stream 4)	Step
IDV (2)	B composition, A/C ratio constant (stream 4)	Step
IDV (6)	A feed loss (stream 1)	Step

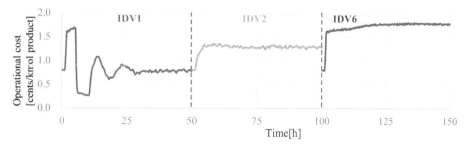

Figure 3 Operational cost of test data

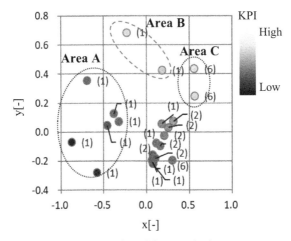

Figure 4 Results of data analysis

4. Conclusions

We proposed the plant O&M support system that can correlate plant operational data to both KPIs and plant statuses. The system consists of a supervised data-clustering function and a visualisation function for clustered results, and it learns the relationship between the multi-dimensional operational data and both KPI and plant statuses.

We examined whether the system was applicable to analysis of plant operational data by using Tennessee Eastman process data sets and setting the operational cost as the KPI and the disturbance as plant status.

The results showed the proposed algorithm classified the operational data into categories according to their KPI values and plant status and our system was demonstrated as useful to support O&M of industrial plants.

References

G. Carpenter and S. Grossberg, 1987, "ART2:Self-Organization of Stable Category Recognition Codes for Analog Input Patterns," *Applied Optics*, 26, 23, 4919–4930

Y. Hori, T. Shiraishi, and S. Hasebe, 2019 "Performance Evaluation System for Industrial Plants Using the ART2 Network That Considers Cluster Size," *Kagaku Kogaku Ronbunshu,* 35, 127-132

S. Kim, M. Kano, S. Hasebe, A. Takinami, and T. Seki, 2013, "Long-Term Industrial Applications of Inferential Control Based on Just-In-Time Soft-Sensors: Economical Impact and Challenges," *Ind. Eng. Chem. Res.*, 52-35, 12346-12356

T. Matsui, K. Murakami, and S. Suzuki; 2014, "Data Analysis Technology in Plant Control," *Fuji Denki Gihoh*, 87, 33-37

T. Okada, H. Kaneko, and K. Funatsu, 2012,"Development of An Adaptive Soft Sensor Method Considering Prediction Confidence of Models," *J. Comput. Chem. Jpn.*, 11, 24-30

N. L. Ricker, 1996, "Decentralized control of the Tennessee Eastman Challenge Process," *J. Proc. Cont.*, 6, 205-221

Proceedings of the 14th International Symposium on Process Systems Engineering – PSE 2021+
June 19–23, 2022, Kyoto, Japan ©2022 Elsevier B. V. All rights reserved.
http://dx.doi.org/10.1016/B978-0-323-85159-6.50238-4

A Novel Cycle Partitioning Approach to Reliability Based Optimal Sensor Placement for Linear Flow Processes

Om Prakash[a*] and Mani Bhushan[a]

[a]*Department of Chemical Engineering, Indian Institute of Technology Bombay, Mumbai 400076, India*

prakash.om@iitb.ac.in

Abstract

In literature, system reliability for sensor placement design for linear mass flow processes has been defined in terms of cycles (Prakash et al., 2020a). The computation of system reliability involves computation of probability of a union of a set of events, which is NP-hard, thereby limiting its applicability to large processes. To reduce this computational complexity, in the current work, we propose to partition the set of cycles, instead of partitioning the original process. Thus, our approach involves approximating the system reliability function of the original process, rather than approximating the original process. Towards this end, we use a bipartite spectral graph partitioning algorithm to obtain the partitions of cycles. The resulting sensor placement design approach is applied to a case study to show its efficacy.

Keywords: Bipartite graph, Estimation of variables, Graph partitioning

1. Introduction

Sensor placement design (SPD) is the problem of selecting key variables to be measured in the process, so as to maximize some performance criteria while satisfying various design constraints (Ali and Narasimhan, 1995; Bhushan and Rengaswamy, 2002). The focus of the current work is on sensor placement design for the application in estimation of variables in a steady state linear flow process. A pure mass flow process, e.g., water distribution network, is known as a linear flow process, where linear mass balances can be written to describe the process model (Ali and Narasimhan, 1995). Linear flow process is conveniently modeled as a directed graph (process graph) with edges in the graph representing the flow variables (process variables), and vertices representing the process units. SPD is to then appropriately select a set of flow variables to be measured. In the current work, we focus on system reliability based criteria for SPD given that sensors are prone to failure with known probabilities.

The area of SPD for ensuring reliable estimation for linear flow processes has received considerable attention in literature. Most of the works in literature have defined system reliability as the minimum reliability of estimation of individual variables (Ali and Narasimhan, 1995; Bagajewicz and Sánchez, 2000; Kotecha et al., 2008). Recently, for use in SPD, Prakash et al. (2020a) defined the system reliability as the probability of estimating all variables. This definition captures the interacting nature of reliabilities, which was missing in the previous definitions. Prakash et al. (2020a) used the result that all variables in a steady state linear flow process can be estimated if the unmeasured variables do not form a cycle (Mah et al., 1976). Prakash et al. (2020a) expressed system reliability as one minus probability of having at least one cycle with all unavailable variables. They defined an unavailable variable as a variable which is either not measured by any sensor, i.e., the variable is unmeasured, or all sensors measuring that variable have failed. In their work (Prakash et al., 2020a), the computation of system reliability involves computation of probability of a union of a set of events, which is NP-hard (Veeraraghavan and Trivedi, 1991). (Prakash et al., 2020b) proposed a sum of disjoint product based approach to systematically compute this probability. However, the number of terms in the expression of system reliability exponentially grows with the number of cycles. To illustrate, Prakash et al. (2020b) have considered steam metering process for sensor placement design, which has 12 units, 28 variables, and 3209 cycles. The system reliability expression consisted of 334630 terms. For larger case studies, the number of terms will be even more, and thus will pose challenges related to: (a) computation, (b) storage, and (c) quick evaluation, of the system reliability expression. These challenges limit the applicability of system reliability based SPD for large processes.

Addressing these issues is the motivation for our current work. A traditional heuristic to deal with large processes is to partition the original graph into several disconnected subgraphs by removing a set of edges (Rajeswaran et al., 2018), and then performing SPD in each of these subgraphs. However, this will lead to loss of edges (process variables), and loss of cycles in general as the collection of cycles in the two resulting subgraphs will not lead to the cycles in the original graph. In the current work, we propose a novel approach that partitions the set of cycles and not the original process. Our approach ensures that the collection of cycles in the partitions is equal to the set of cycles in the original graph. Towards this end, we propose to compute the approximated system reliability which is maximized to obtain SPD. Further, we present a case study to demonstrate its efficacy.

The rest of the paper is organized as follows. Relevant existing information is presented in Section 2.. Section 3. presents the novel approach of partitioning cycles, and SPD formulation. Section 4. presents a case study. Finally, Section 5. concludes the work.

2.   Preliminaries related to reliability based sensor placement design

For a steady state linear flow process, reliability based SPD for the application in estimation of variables is posed as (Prakash et al., 2020b),

$$\max_{\{q_i\}_{i=1}^{n_v}} R_{sys} = 1 - P\left(\bigcup_{k=1}^{n_c} \mathcal{S}_k\right); \text{ s.t., } \sum_{i=1}^{n_v} c_i q_i \leq C^*, \text{ and, } q_i \in \mathbb{Z}_{\geq 0}, i = 1, ..., n_v \quad (1)$$

where c_i and q_i are cost of a sensor and number of sensors placed to measure the ith variable, respectively, C^* is the total cost available for SPD, and n_v is the number of process variables that can be measured in the process. The system reliability objective R_{sys} in Eq. (1) is the probability of estimating all variables in the process and is defined in terms of cycles. S is the set of cycles in the process graph, and n_c is its cardinality. $\mathcal{S}_k$ denotes the event that kth cycle (S_k) in the process graph has all unavailable variables. Probability that the ith variable is unavailable is $s_i^{q_i}$, where s_i is the failure probability of the sensor measuring the ith variable, provided full active redundant configuration is followed. The SPD formulation given in Eq. (1) is a non-linear integer programming problem owing to the nature of R_{sys}. Computation of R_{sys} in Eq. (1) involves computation of probability of a union of a set of events, which is NP-hard (Veeraraghavan and Trivedi, 1991). Prakash et al. (2020b) proposed a sum of disjoint product based approach to systematically compute R_{sys}.

3. Proposed cycle partitioning based sensor placement design

The length of expression of R_{sys} which is the optimization objective in SPD (Eq. (1)), grows exponentially with the number of cycles. This poses significant difficulties in solving the SPD for a large scale problem, since computation, storage and quick evaluation of R_{sys} become a challenge. One intuitive heuristic to overcome this issue would be to partition the process graph into several disjoint subgraphs by removing edges in the graph. Subsequently, SPD can be solved for each of these subgraphs. But, this approach suffers from two drawbacks: (a) removing edges in the graph eliminates the corresponding process variables from process graph, and (b) it leads to a loss of cycles in general as the collection of cycles in the subgraphs does not recreate the cycles in the original graph. Thus, this approach involves approximating the process, i.e., solving SPD for different (simpler) processes instead of the original process.

In the current work, we propose to approximate the objective function R_{sys} in the SPD (Eq. (1)) without modifying the process. Towards this end, we propose a novel idea to partition the set of cycles S into two disjoint partitions S^a and S^b, where $S^a \cap S^b = \emptyset$, and $S^a \cup S^b = S$. Thus, we do not eliminate any process variables from process graph, and the cycles are also preserved. The system reliability is then approximated as the product of reliabilities corresponding to these two partitions. To ensure that this approach leads to computational benefits for SPD, the partitions S^a, S^b have to be appropriately chosen. To discuss this issue, let us consider that we have the partitions. Then, we can write the system reliability R_{sys} as (Eq. (1)),

$$R_{sys} = 1 - P\left(\underbrace{\left(\bigcup_{k_a=1}^{n_{c_a}} \mathcal{S}_{k_a}^a \right)}_{\alpha} \bigcup \underbrace{\left(\bigcup_{k_b=1}^{n_{c_b}} \mathcal{S}_{k_b}^b \right)}_{\beta} \right) = 1 - (P(\alpha) + P(\beta) - P(\alpha|\beta)P(\beta)) \qquad (2)$$

where $\mathcal{S}_{k_a}^a$ and $\mathcal{S}_{k_b}^b$ denote the event that k_ath and k_bth cycle in S^a and S^b have all unavailable variables, respectively, and n_{c_a} and n_{c_b} are cardinalities of S^a and S^b, respectively. In Eq. (2), $P(\alpha)$ and $P(\beta)$ denote the probability of having at least one cycle in S^a and S^b with all unavailable variables, respectively. Now, consider, $R^a = 1 - P(\alpha)$ and $R^b = 1 - P(\beta)$ as the reliabilities corresponding to the partitions. The product $R^a R^b = 1 - (P(\alpha) + P(\beta) - P(\alpha)P(\beta))$ can be thought of as the approximation of R_{sys}. However, it will be exactly equal to R_{sys} only when the partitions are such that $P(\alpha|\beta) = P(\alpha)$ in Eq. (2). This equality will not hold in general, because many process variables are common to the cycles in partitions S^a and S^b, leading to dependent nature of α and β. Also, note that $P(\alpha|\beta) \geq P(\alpha)$, as the occurrence of β increases the probability of occurrence of α. This gives rise to the following criteria of partitioning the cycles,

$$\min_{S^a, S^b \subseteq S} P(\alpha|\beta) - P(\alpha), \quad \text{and} \quad \min_{S^a, S^b \subseteq S} \text{abs}(|S^a| - |S^b|) \qquad (3)$$

where abs($\cdot$) denotes the absolute value. First criteria of Eq. (3) maximizes the independence of α and β, while the second criteria of Eq. (3) ensures that the obtained partitions are balanced. It is required because we do not want length of the reliability expression (R^a or R^b) corresponding to one of the partitions to increase significantly. Note that characterizing independence of the partitions involves computation of $P(\alpha|\beta)$, which is equivalent to computing R_{sys}. One heuristic to maximize independence is to minimize the number of process variables that are common to the partitions. This has to be achieved while ensuring that the partitions are balanced (second criteria in Eq. (3)). This is a well studied problem in graph partitioning literature, and is known to be NP-complete (Dhillon, 2001). Spectral graph partitioning algorithm is a widely used heuristic to effectively solve this problem. In this work, we adapt the bipartite spectral graph partitioning algorithm (Dhillon, 2001) to solve our cycle partitioning problem. It is to be noted that we are not partitioning the original process graph, instead we are partitioning the set of cycles using the graph partitioning algorithm. Next, we formally propose this algorithm in the context of our application.

3.1.   Cycle-variable bipartite graph partitioning algorithm and SPD formulation

We propose to model the cycle-variable relationship with an undirected bipartite graph $G = (S, V, E)$. $S = \{S_1, \ldots, S_{n_c}\}$ and $V = \{v_1, \ldots, v_{n_v}\}$ denote the set of vertices, and $E = \{\{S_i, v_j\}, \forall S_i \in S$ and $v_j \in V\}$ denotes the set of undirected edges. In our work, S is the set of cycles, V is the set of all process variables, and edge $\{S_i, v_j\}$ exists if the process variable v_j is contained in cycle S_i. The partitioning problem is to find balanced partitions P_1^* and P_2^* of $S \cup V$ such that the number of common edges $\{S_i, v_j\}$ between these partitions is minimized. Consider the following terminologies related the graph. The adjacency matrix $\mathbf{A} \in \mathbb{R}^{(n_c+n_v) \times (n_c+n_v)}$ of the bipartite graph G is given as, $\mathbf{A} = \begin{bmatrix} [\mathbf{0}] & \mathbf{C} \\ \mathbf{C}^\top & [\mathbf{0}] \end{bmatrix}$, where $\mathbf{C} \in \mathbb{R}^{n_c \times n_v}$ represents the cycle by variable matrix with $C_{i,j} = 1$ if $\{S_i, v_j\}$ exists, and is 0 otherwise. First n_c rows and columns in $\mathbf{A}$ corresponds to the cycles, and last n_v rows and columns corresponds to the process variables. The diagonal degree matrix $\mathbf{D} \in \mathbb{R}^{(n_c+n_v) \times (n_c+n_v)}$ is the matrix with its element $D_{l,l} = \sum_k A_{l,k}$. $\mathbf{D}$ is written as, $\mathbf{D} = \begin{bmatrix} \mathbf{D}_1 & \mathbf{0} \\ \mathbf{0} & \mathbf{D}_2 \end{bmatrix}$, where $\mathbf{D}_1$ and $\mathbf{D}_2$ matrices correspond to the block matrices in $\mathbf{A}$. The spectral partitioning heuristic given in Dhillon (2001) which is used to solve our cycle partitioning problem is now presented as a theorem.

Theorem 1 (Dhillon (2001)) *Given a bipartite graph G, $\mathbf{x}_2 = \mathbf{D}_1^{-1/2}\mathbf{u}_2$ is the partition vector, where $\mathbf{u}_2$ is the left singular vector corresponding to the second largest singular value of $(\mathbf{D}_1^{-1/2}\mathbf{C}\mathbf{D}_2^{-1/2})$. Partitioning of cycles is obtained by assigning $\mathbf{x}_2$ to bi-modal values.*

Theorem 1 presents an efficient heuristic to obtain the partitions S^a and $S^b \subseteq S$. Having these partitions, we propose the SPD as follows,

$$\max_{\{q_i\}_{i=1}^{n_v}} \widehat{R}_{sys} = (1 - P(\alpha))(1 - P(\beta)); \text{ s.t., } \sum_{i=1}^{n_v} c_i q_i \leq C^*, \text{ and, } q_i \in \mathbb{Z}_{\geq 0} \qquad (4)$$

where $\widehat{R}_{sys}$ is the approximated system reliability. Next, we present a case study, where we have applied the proposed SPD (Eq. (4)) to obtain the sensor placement.

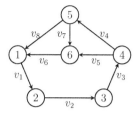

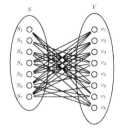

Figure 1: Ammonia process graph (Prakash et al., 2020a)

Figure 2: Ammonia bipartite graph G

4. Case Study

We present the Ammonia process case study which has been widely used for data reconciliation and gross error detection (Ali and Narasimhan, 1995). It has 6 nodes including the environmental node and 8 flow variables where sensors can be placed to measure the flow rates. There are 7 cycles in the process graph (Prakash et al., 2020a). The process graph and its cycle-variable bipartite graph are presented in Figures 1 and 2, respectively. The sensor failure probabilities are taken from Prakash et al. (2020a), and unit cost is considered for all sensors. The set of cycles are partitioned using the algorithm presented in Section 3.1., and then sum of disjoint product based approach is applied to compute $P(\alpha)$ and $P(\beta)$. The resulting expressions are,

$$P(\alpha) = s_6^{q6} s_7^{q7} s_8^{q8} + (1 - s_6^{q6} s_8^{q8}) s_4^{q4} s_5^{q5} s_7^{q7} + (1 - s_7^{q7}) s_4^{q4} s_5^{q5} s_6^{q6} s_8^{q8} \tag{5}$$

and, $P(\beta) = s_1^{q1} s_2^{q2} s_3^{q3} s_5^{q5} s_6^{q6} + (1 - s_5^{q5} s_6^{q6}) s_1^{q1} s_2^{q2} s_3^{q3} s_4^{q4} s_8^{q8} + (1 - s_6^{q6})(1 - s_4^{q4})$

$$s_1^{q1} s_2^{q2} s_3^{q3} s_5^{q5} s_7^{q7} s_8^{q8} + (1 - s_5^{q5})(1 - s_8^{q8}) s_1^{q1} s_2^{q2} s_3^{q3} s_4^{q4} s_6^{q6} s_7^{q7} \tag{6}$$

Now, we compute the approximated system reliability $\widehat{R}_{sys}$ (Eq. (4)). To compare, we also compute the exact expression of system reliability R_{sys} to be:

$$R_{sys} = 1 - \left[s_6^{q6} s_7^{q7} s_8^{q8} + (1 - s_6^{q6} s_8^{q8}) s_4^{q4} s_5^{q5} s_7^{q7} + (1 - s_7^{q7}) s_4^{q4} s_5^{q5} s_6^{q6} s_8^{q8} + \right.$$

$$((1 - s_4^{q4} s_8^{q8})(1 - s_7^{q7}) + s_7^{q7}(1 - s_4^{q4})(1 - s_8^{q8})) s_1^{q1} s_2^{q2} s_3^{q3} s_5^{q5} s_6^{q6} +$$

$$((1 - s_5^{q5} s_6^{q6})(1 - s_7^{q7}) + s_7^{q7}(1 - s_5^{q5})(1 - s_6^{q6})) s_1^{q1} s_2^{q2} s_3^{q3} s_4^{q4} s_8^{q8} +$$

$$\left. (1 - s_6^{q6})(1 - s_4^{q4}) s_1^{q1} s_2^{q9} s_3^{q0} s_5^{q5} s_7^{q7} s_8^{q0} + (1 - s_8^{q8})(1 - s_5^{q5}) s_1^{q1} s_2^{q2} s_3^{q3} s_4^{q4} s_6^{q6} s_7^{q7} \right] \tag{7}$$

It can be noted that the total number of terms in R_{sys} is 9, while $P(\alpha)$ and $P(\beta)$ have 3 and 4 terms only. Thus, there is an overall reduction in the length of combined expressions of $P(\alpha)$ and $P(\beta)$. Further, we apply the proposed SPD (Eq. (4)) on the Ammonia process to obtain the sensor placement. We also maximize the exact system reliability R_{sys} (Eq. (1)) to enable comparison with the proposed SPD formulation. Enumeration is used to solve these problems. It is observed that for each C^* (Table 1), the solution is same for both the problems thereby validating the utility of the proposed approach.

5. Conclusions

In the current work, we propose a novel cycle partitioning approach to solve SPD for large processes. To achieve this, we model the cycle-variable relationship as a bipartite

Table 1: SPD results for ammonia process

C^*	Exact R_{sys} (Eq. (1))		Proposed SPD formulation (Eq. (4))	
	Selected vars.	R_{sys}	Selected vars.	$\hat{R}_{sys}$
3	$\{v_1, v_4, v_7\}$	0.4909	$\{v_1, v_4, v_7\}$	0.4909
4	$\{v_1, v_4, v_6, v_7\}$	0.6894	$\{v_1, v_4, v_6, v_7\}$	0.6777
5	$\{v_1, v_4, v_5, v_7, v_8\}$	0.8124	$\{v_1, v_4, v_5, v_7, v_8\}$	0.8083

graph. We then apply a bipartite spectral graph partitioning algorithm to obtain the cycle partitions. The resulting partitions are used to approximate system reliability objective for SPD. The approach is demonstrated on a case study.

References

Ali, Y., Narasimhan, S., 1995. Redundant sensor network design for linear processes. AIChE Journal 41, 2237–2249.

Bagajewicz, M., Sánchez, M.C., 2000. Cost-optimal design of reliable sensor networks. Computers & Chemical Engineering 23, 1757–1762.

Bhushan, M., Rengaswamy, R., 2002. Comprehensive design of a sensor network for chemical plants based on various diagnosability and reliability criteria. 1. Framework. Industrial & Engineering Chemistry Research 41, 1826–1839.

Dhillon, I.S., 2001. Co-clustering documents and words using bipartite spectral graph partitioning, in: Proceedings of the seventh ACM SIGKDD international conference on Knowledge discovery and data mining, pp. 269–274.

Kotecha, P.R., Bhushan, M., Gudi, R., Keshari, M., 2008. A duality based framework for integrating reliability and precision for sensor network design. Journal of Process Control 18, 189–201.

Mah, R.S., Stanley, G.M., Downing, D.M., 1976. Reconciliation and rectification of process flow and inventory data. Industrial & Engineering Chemistry Process Design and Development 15, 175–183.

Prakash, O., Bhushan, M., Narasimhan, S., Rengaswamy, R., 2020a. Sensor network design based on system-wide reliability criteria. Part I: Objectives. Journal of Process Control 93, 66–82.

Prakash, O., Bhushan, M., Narasimhan, S., Rengaswamy, R., 2020b. Sensor network design based on system-wide reliability criteria. Part II: Formulations and applications. Journal of Process Control 93, 14–27.

Rajeswaran, A., Narasimhan, S., Narasimhan, S., 2018. A graph partitioning algorithm for leak detection in water distribution networks. Computers & Chemical Engineering 108, 11–23.

Veeraraghavan, M., Trivedi, K.S., 1991. An improved algorithm for symbolic reliability analysis. IEEE Transactions on Reliability 40, 347–358.

Proceedings of the 14th International Symposium on Process Systems Engineering – PSE 2021+
June 19-23, 2022, Kyoto, Japan © 2022 Elsevier B.V. All rights reserved.
http://dx.doi.org/10.1016/B978-0-323-85159-6.50239-6

The impact of sampling frequency on chemical process monitoring

Tingting Tao, Jiatao Wen, Yang Li, Cheng Ji, Jingde Wang*, Wei Sun*

College of Chemical Engineering, Beijing University of Chemical Technology, North Third Ring Road 15, Chaoyang District, Beijing, 100029, China
sunwei@mail.buct.edu.cn

Abstract

Data-driven process monitoring technology, which is generally realized by extracting data feature under normal operating conditions, has been developed rapidly to ensure operation safety. Correlation analysis, including auto-correlation and cross-correlation, plays an important role in these feature extraction algorithms. In chemical industrial processes, auto-correlation and cross-correlation in process measurements are always dynamic and could be greatly affected by sampling frequency. The extraction of these features directly determines the generalization ability of the process monitoring model. Therefore, it is important to study the influence of different sampling frequencies on the auto-correlation and cross-correlation of process variables. With the rapid development of data acquisition technology, data of multiple sampling frequencies can be flexibly acquired from distributed control system (DCS), which provides a basis for this research. The aim of this work is to build a process monitoring method by using the optimal sampling strategy and dynamic principal component analysis (DPCA). Time series analysis is first applied to check the degree of auto-correlation of sequence data at different scales according to industrial data with different sampling frequencies. It can be concluded that process dynamic has different effects on different variables. Dynamic principal component analysis is then used for feature extraction and process monitoring. Monitoring results under different sampling frequencies are compared and analysed to obtain an optimal process monitoring method. The research is implemented on Tennessee Eastman Process (TEP). The method shows better results than other methods without the consideration of sampling strategies and dynamic characteristics.

Keywords: Correlation analysis; Feature extraction; Dynamic principal component analysis; Optimal sampling strategy.

1. Introduction

With the development of process industry, chemical production has been gradually getting larger scale and more complicated operation, which is accompanied by a great potential safety hazard. Once a safety accident occurs, it will not only cause economic losses, but also threaten human safety. To avoid safety accidents, process monitoring technology has been developed in chemical processes to assist operators to detect abnormal changes in a process plant timely. With the wide application of distributed control system (DCS), data-driven process monitoring technology has been extensively studied in order to ensure production safety. Whether it is the commonly used multivariate statistical method or recently proposed deep learning-based methods, the main aim is to extract data feature under normal operating conditions by projecting or mapping high-dimensional process data into low-dimensional space. A conventional multivariate statistical procedure: Principal Component Analysis (PCA), assuming that the observations are static and independent of each other, can simplify and improve process monitoring procedures (MacGregor, et al., 1995). Dynamic principal component analysis (DPCA) was proposed with the adoption of augment matrix to describe the dynamic characteristics of data (Ku, et al., 1995). The data matrix of DPCA contains hysteresis information, which makes it more suitable for monitoring of sequence-related data. Deep learning-based methods, such as neural networks and autoencoder, also achieved good results on simulation data of Tennessee Eastman Process (Cheng, et al., 2019). However, auto-correlation and cross-correlation of industrial process data measurements are always dynamic and could be greatly affected by sampling frequency. The extraction of these features directly determines the generalization ability of the process monitoring model, but the impact of sampling frequency on process monitoring results is hardly investigated. Although dynamic PCA has certain advantages in extracting the dynamic features from process data, the selection of key lag order is generally limited to a low value, which will lead to the loss of auto-correlation features of time series data. With the rapid development of data acquisition technology, data of multiple sampling frequencies can be flexibly acquired from distributed control system (DCS). Data features under different sampling frequencies can be studied at different scales, which provides a basis for studying the impact of sampling frequency on process monitoring results.

The aim of this paper is to extract data features for process monitoring under the premise of considering the data dynamic relevance. When analyzing data with different sampling frequencies, it can be found that process dynamic has different effects on different variables. On this basis, an optimal sampling strategy is proposed to characterize auto-correlation. For the extraction of dynamic cross-correlation features, the statistics of Hotelling-T^2 (T^2) and squared prediction error (SPE) are obtained by PCA and DPCA methods. The alarm point and false alarm rate, obtained from the built statistics, are employed for comparison. The research is implemented on Tennessee Eastman Process (TEP). The results show that DPCA combined with the best sampling strategy could give an earlier alarming with a lower false alarm rate compared with other methods without the consideration of dynamic correlation. It can provide a new idea for the selection of sampling frequency on industrial time series data.

2. Methodology

In this section, the methods applied in this work are introduced.

2.1. The auto-correlation functions

Auto-correlation coefficient is an important index for time series analysis, which can reflect the dynamic characteristics of the process to a certain extent. It is assumed that data have been regularly sampled from a time series $\{X\}$, where $\{x_t, t = 1, 2, ..., n\}$ is a set of observation samples from $\{X\}$. The mean of samples is given as

$$\bar{\mu} = \frac{1}{n} \sum_{t=1}^{n} x_t, \tag{1}$$

For the given samples $\{x_t\}$, the auto-covariance function $\widehat{\gamma_k}$ at the delay number k is given as

$$\widehat{\gamma_k} = \frac{1}{n-k}\sum_{t=1}^{n-k}\left(x_t - \widehat{\mu}\right)\left(x_{t+k} - \widehat{\mu}\right), 1 \le k < n, \tag{2}$$

And when k=0, the corresponding auto-covariance function can be simplified as

$$\widehat{\gamma_0} = \frac{1}{n-1}\sum_{t-1}^{n}\left(x_t - \widehat{\mu}\right)^2 \tag{3}$$

Based on Eq. (2) and (3), the auto-correlation function of the samples $\{x_t\}$ at the delay number k can be defined as follows,

$$\widehat{\rho_k} = \frac{\widehat{\gamma_k}}{\widehat{\gamma_0}}, 1 \le k < n, \tag{4}$$

2.2. Principal component analysis (PCA)

PCA, a classical technique for feature extraction and dimension reduction (MacGregor, et al., 1995), has been widely used in process monitoring with T^2 and SPE statistics. Given n observations of m measurement variables $X_{n\times m}$ after normalization, the covariance matrix of X can be calculated as follows,

$$Cov(X) = \frac{X^T X}{n-1} \tag{5}$$

Then singular value decomposition is employed to $Cov(X)$. The obtained eigenvalues and eigenvectors are sorted according to the size of the eigenvalues. On this basis, a score matrix T and a loading matrix P can be determined by retaining the first k features that contain the most information. The original matrix X can be decomposed as follows,

$$X = TP^T + E = t_1 p_1^T + \cdots + t_k p_k^T + E \tag{6}$$

where p, t are the loading vector and score vector, and E is the residual matrix. T^2 and SPE statistics can be calculated in the principal component space and residual space respectively and the corresponding control limits can be used for process monitoring. PCA has a good performance in the monitoring of stationary process, but the dynamic characteristics of the data cannot be extracted.

2.3. Dynamic principal component analysis (DPCA)

To extract the dynamic characteristics of the data, the DPCA was proposed with a stack of data matrixes as follows,

$$X = \begin{bmatrix} x_t^T & x_{t-1}^T & \cdots & x_{t-l}^T \\ x_{t-1}^T & x_{t-2}^T & \cdots & x_{t-l-1}^T \\ \vdots & \vdots & \ddots & \vdots \\ x_{t+l-n}^T & x_{t+l-n-1}^T & \cdots & x_{t-n}^T \end{bmatrix} \tag{7}$$

where x_t^T is the observation vector in the training set at time t. If enough lags are included in Eq. (7), the serial correlations can be considered in further PCA calculation. However, for high-dimensional data, a large lag order will lead to high computational loads for further matrix decomposition and the process dynamic has a different effect on different variables. Therefore, considering the limited lag order, it is necessary to select an optimal sampling frequency to consider the process dynamic better.

3. Selection of optimal sampling frequency and its application on Tennessee Eastman Process (TEP)

In this chapter, the implementation procedures of the proposed research on the selection of optimal sampling frequency are introduced with the case study of TEP.

3.1. Tennessee Eastman Process (TEP) and data description

TEP is a chemical process benchmark simulated by the Eastman Chemical Company (Downs and Vogel, 1993), which has been widely used by researchers in the field of process control, monitoring and fault diagnosis to validate their newly proposed methods. The revision version of TEP by university of Washington is applied in this work because data of different sampling frequencies and operating conditions can be easily simulated by Simulink (Bathelt, et al, 2015). 50 hours of data are simulated in normal data set and each fault data set. The fault in each fault data set is introduced in the 25th hour. The sampling frequency is set from 1 second to 3 minutes by down sampling. A total of 31 variables are selected in this work. The component variables are not considered here because such variables cannot be measured in real time in chemical operation.

3.2. Determination of the optimal sampling frequency in this work

In this work, two factors are considered to determine the best sampling frequency for chemical process monitoring. On the one hand, the dynamic characteristics of the process should be fully extracted. If the sampling frequency is too high, the dynamic characteristics of time series cannot be extracted by dynamic monitoring methods for the balance of the lag order and computational loads. On the other hand, sufficient process intermediate information has to be retained. If the sampling frequency is too low, the useful information in the process data will be lost and the fault information cannot be obtained in time. Therefore, there is an optimal sampling frequency that can be determined by striking a balance between these two aspects. Early fault detection time (FDT) and low false alarm rate (FAR) are of great significance for measuring the performance of process monitoring models. Therefore, these two factors are used as the standard to find the optimal sampling frequency in this study.

3.3. Selection of optimal sampling frequency in TEP

In this section, the procedures of this work are introduced. As mentioned before, the auto-correlation coefficient can be used to test the stationarity of time series and reflect the dynamic characteristics of data. Therefore, the auto-correlation diagrams are first applied to show the auto-correlation relationship of each variable in TEP, and then a sampling range can be initially obtained. However, it is difficult to directly determine the optimal sampling frequency, because the process dynamic characteristics have different effects on different variables. Different sampling frequencies within the range are selected and the data are brought into the PCA and DPCA models respectively to compare the monitoring results. The FDT and FAR are calculated to select the optimal sampling frequency.

4. Results and discussion

Auto-correlation diagrams of different types of variables in TEP are shown in Figure 1 and 2. It can be seen that most variables show a dynamic characteristic and the process dynamic has different effects on different variables. Therefore, the optimal sampling frequency cannot be directly determined, but it can be obtained from Figure 2 that the auto-correlation order can be effectively reduced by reducing the sampling frequency. Next, data of sampling frequencies from 1 second to 3 minutes are respectively brought into the PCA and DPCA models to compare the monitoring results.

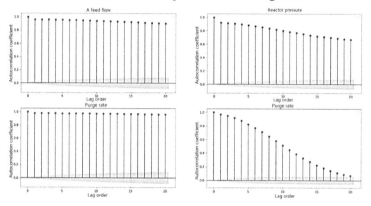

Figure 1 Autocorrelation diagrams of variables with a sampling frequency of 10s

Process monitoring results for fault 1 by PCA and DPCA are shown respectively in Figure 3 and 4. The results of FDT under different sampling frequencies are unified as second-level data. The sampling frequency is 1 second. It's obvious that DPCA has a better performance than PCA because the dynamic characteristics of the data are considered to a certain extent. In addition, the statistics fluctuate around the control limit at the early stage of the fault, making it difficult to determine whether it is a true alarm or not because the sampling frequency is too high. Monitoring results of fault 8 at different sampling frequencies are shown in Table 1. It can be concluded that fast sampling frequency is beneficial to improve FDT to a certain extent, but corresponds to high FAR. When the sampling frequency is at an appropriate value, the FAR is significantly reduced, and the fault can be also detected earlier than other sampling frequencies. Therefore, 60 seconds can be determined to be the optimal sampling frequency for TEP, which can be also validated by other faults in TEP. When the sampling frequency is further reduced, the useful feature information in the process data is lost, resulting in a late FDT. It is worth noting from Table 1 that the process dynamic characteristics will be removed if the sampling frequency is too late, which leads to similar monitoring results of PCA and DPCA.

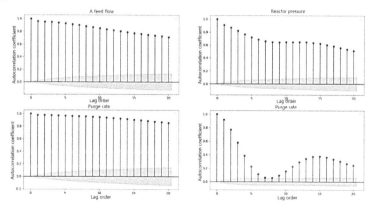

Figure 2 Auto-correlation diagrams of variables with a sampling frequency of 60s

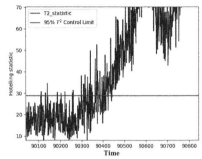
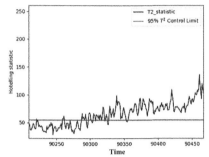

Figure 3 Monitoring result for fault 1 by PCA   Figure 4 Monitoring result for fault 1 by DPCA

Table 1 Process monitoring results for fault 8 at different sampling frequencies

Sampling frequency	1s	10s	15s	20s	30s	40s	60s	90s	180s
FDT by PCA	94650	94720	94725	94680	94740	94680	94680	94500	94500
FAR by PCA	0.0128	0.011	0.0105	0.0102	0.0093	0.0138	0.0067	0.009	0.006
FDT by DPCA	94441	94460	94455	94460	94530	94520	**94380**	94500	94680
FAR by DPCA	0.0130	0.01	0.0097	0.0084	0.0067	0.0089	**0.0033**	0.006	0

5. Conclusions

In this work, auto-correlation of variables in chemical process at different sampling frequencies is analysed by the auto-correlation diagrams. Considering the dynamic correlations of process, different sampling frequencies are used to establish process monitoring models by DPCA. A strategy for the selection of optimal sampling frequency is then proposed by comparing FDR and FAR, which are two important indicators of process monitoring. Through the case study on TEP, it can be concluded that there is an optimal sampling frequency corresponding to the best process monitoring results. Compared with other studies focusing on feature extraction, the impact of data sampling rate on process monitoring performance is discussed in detail in this work, which can provide a reference for initial data acquisition in industrial practice.

References

A. Bathelt, N. L. Ricker, and M. Jelali, 2015, Revision of the Tennessee Eastman Process Model, IFAC-PapersOnLine, 48, 8, 309-314.

F. F. Cheng, Q. P. He, and J. S. Zhao, 2019, A novel process monitoring approach based on variational recurrent autoencoder, Computers & Chemical Engineering, 129, 4, 106515-106546.

J. J. Downs and E. F. Vogel, 1993, A plant-wide industrial process control problem, Computers & chemical engineering, 17, 3, 245-255.

J. F. MacGregor and T. Kourtl, 1995, Statistical process control of multivariate processes, Control Engineering Practice, 3, 3, 403-414.

W. Ku, R. H. Storer, and C. Georgakis, 1995, Disturbance detection and isolation by dynamic principal component analysis, Chemometrics and Intelligent Laboratory Systems, 30, 1 , 179-196.

Proceedings of the 14th International Symposium on Process Systems Engineering – PSE 2021+
June 19-23, 2022, Kyoto, Japan © 2022 Elsevier B.V. All rights reserved.
http://dx.doi.org/10.1016/B978-0-323-85159-6.50240-2

Autoregressive Distributed Lag Model Based Cointegration Analysis for Batch Process Monitoring

Jiatao WEN, Cheng Ji, Jingde Wang*, Wei Sun*

College of Chemical Engineering, Beijing University of Chemical Technology, North Third Ring Road 15, Chaoyang District, Beijing, 100029, China
sunwei@mail.buct.edu.cn

Abstract

Batch processes have been widely applied in pharmaceutical and chemical industry. Variables in batch process exhibit obvious nonstationary and nonlinear characteristics, which brings challenges to process monitoring. Recently, cointegration theory gets more attention for its applications on the analysis of multivariate nonstationary time series. According to the cointegration theory, if the nonstationary random sequences in a system containing a cointegration relationship, there is at least one stable long-term dynamic equilibrium relationship among these nonstationary variables. Such dynamic equilibrium relationship can also be found in variables in industrial processes, since the nonstationary variables are controlled by physics, chemistry, and other internal mechanisms within a system. For multivariate variables system, Johansen test is a commonly used method to test cointegration relationship and estimate the cointegration vectors, which is based on the multivariate unconstrained vector autoregressive (VAR) model, in which all variables are assumed as indifferent endogenous variables. However, certain variables in real process, such as control variables, is not affected by such long-term equilibrium and is governed by external conditions, which is called a weakly exogenous variable. When there are weak exogenous variables in a system, the cointegration test based on the VAR model needs to be improved, as the impact of exogenous variable is neglected. In this work, considering the impact of weak exogenous variables, autoregressive distributed lag (ADL) model is adopted for cointegration test and parameters estimation. The penicillin fermentation process is presented to illustrate the effectiveness of the proposed method, in which many control parameters exert a significant impact on the state of fermentation. The monitoring results show that the interaction among variables can be better characterized, and abnormal behavior of the process can be correctly detected by proposed cointegration testing method based on autoregressive distributed lag model.

Keywords: Cointegration analysis; Exogenous variable; Batch process; Dynamic equilibrium relationship.

1. Introduction

Batch and semi-batch processes are widely applied in modern industries due to its flexibility. However, product quality can be easily affected by environment conditions, equipment conditions, and raw material quality, which may lead to the waste of raw materials or cause an accident. Thus, it is essential to monitor the batch process to avoid quality loss and potential accidents. However, batch process data present complex characteristics, which brings challenge to process monitoring. Many approaches have been proposed to monitor batch process in the view of complex data characteristics.

To consider the time series nature of multivariable data, VAR models have been applied to batch process monitoring. Choi et al. (2008) first used VAR models to remove the auto and cross correlation within batch data, and then principal component analysis (PCA) was applied to the residuals obtained from VAR model. Based on their work, Filho and Valk (2020) proposed a new monitoring scheme by estimating coefficients of VAR model, which was proved to hold more information on the variable dynamics than the residual-based method.

However, the VAR model is more appropriate for stationary data, while the variables in batch process exhibits obvious nonstationary characteristics. In recent years, the cointegration theory in time series analysis proposed by Engle and Granger (1987), which is applied to analyze multivariate nonstationary time series, has been introduced to the monitoring of nonstationary processes. Chen et al. (2009) applied the cointegration theory to monitor industrial distillation units and established a monitoring model by extracting the most significant cointegration relationship among variables. To improve the effect of nonstationary process monitoring, Lin et al. (2017) adopted the common trend model for nonstationary process monitoring by eliminating the influence of nonstationary common factors, so that the classic multivariate statistics method is applicable to non-stationary process monitoring. However, cointegration test and cointegration vector estimation are always complemented by Johansen test, which is based on the multivariate unconstrained VAR model where each variable is assumed as undifferentiated endogenous variables. Since weak exogenous variables in a system do not respond to long-term equilibrium, it is not appropriate to estimate the cointegration vector based on VAR model. Pesaran (1995) examined the long-term run relationship among variables based on ADL model, which indicated that ADL cointegration test is proper for a system that contains exogenous variables.

To address the limitation of previous methods, a new batch process monitoring strategy that based on ADL cointegration test is proposed. Considering the impact of weak exogenous variables, ADL cointegration test is first adopted on historical batches to determine if long term equilibrium relationship exists among variables and estimate the cointegration parameters by ordinary least squares. After that, the deviation of the stable relationship among variables of each historical batch can be obtained, which obeys the specific trajectory. Thus, online monitoring can be implemented by judging if the value of deviation is out of the specified range of the trajectory. The monitoring result of the penicillin fermentation process is presented to illustrate the effectiveness of proposed batch process monitoring strategy, which shows that abnormal behavior of the process can be detected accurately with better characterization of the interaction among variables.

2. ADL model based cointegration analysis

According to the cointegration theory, if nonstationary variables in a system contain a common stochastic trend, a stable long-term dynamic equilibrium relationship exists among these variables. The basic idea is that the common random stochastic trend can be eliminated by linear combination of these variables if multiple nonstationary sequences have a common stochastic trend. But an exogenous variable is not affected by the long-term equilibrium deviation in a cointegration system, while an endogenous variable, which is also known as dependent variable, is determined by the system.

For a system with an endogenous variable y_t and two exogenous variables z_{1t} and z_{2t}, the ADL model can be established as follow:

$$\Delta y_t = \alpha_1 (y_{t-1} - \beta_1 z_{1t-1} - \beta_2 z_{2t-1}) + \beta_3 \Delta z_{1t} + \beta_4 \Delta z_{2t} + u_t \tag{1}$$

And the long-term equilibrium relation can be represented as

$$\xi_t = y_t - \beta_1 z_{1t} - \beta_2 z_{2t} \tag{2}$$

In equation (2), ξ_t is the equilibrium error sequence which represents the series where the common linear trend is eliminated, and it is assumed that $B = (1, -\beta_1, -\beta_2)$ is the cointegration vector.

To estimate the cointegration parameters, equation (1) is transformed into the following form:

$$\Delta y_t = \alpha_1 y_{t-1} + b_1 z_{1t-1} + b_2 z_{2t-1} + \beta_3 \Delta z_{1t} + \beta_4 \Delta z_{2t} + u_t \tag{3}$$

in which $\alpha_1, b_1, b_2, \beta_3, \beta_4$ are model coefficients which can be estimated by ordinary least squares, and u_t denotes model residual. A common way to test whether there is a cointegration relationship among variables is to test the null hypothesis $\alpha_1 = 0$ with t statistics. If $\alpha_1 = 0$, there is no long-term equilibrium relationship among variables, else if $\alpha_1 \neq 0$, cointegration parameters β_1 and β_2 can be obtained by $\beta_1 = -\frac{b_1}{\alpha_1}$, $\beta_2 = -\frac{b_2}{\alpha_1}$.

3. ADL cointegration test based batch process monitoring approach

CA is an effective way to analyse nonstationary variables with common trend. For nonstationary process monitoring, monitoring index is required to indicate whether current status is abnormal. Considering the existence of endogenous variables, a monitoring strategy for batch process is proposed based on ADL cointegration test. The diagram of proposed method is shown in Figure 1.

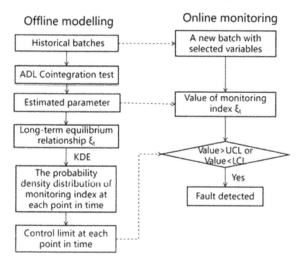

Figure 1 The diagram of proposed monitoring method

Several normal batches containing different initial conditions are labelled as training data. All exogenous variables and a key endogenous variable are selected as model variables. ADL cointegration test is applied to the training batch to determine if cointegration relationship exist among variables. Then the parameters of ADL model are estimated by ordinary least squares (OLS), and the long-term equilibrium error ξ_t which is assumed as monitoring index can be obtained as shown in equation (2). For normal batches, ξ_t present similar trajectory over time, which means that the value of ξ_t is in a certain range at every point of time. When the fault occurs, the original dynamic equilibrium relationship among variables is violated, thus ξ_t will deviate from its original range of value. Kernel density estimation is applied to training batches to estimate the probability density distribution of monitoring index at each point in time, and the upper control limits (UCL) and lower control limits (LCL) are obtained.

For a new batch which is regarded as testing data, monitoring index is calculated with parameters obtained from the training data. For each point of time t, it is assumed as normal status if the value of ξ_t is within the range of lower control limits and under upper control limits, while it is considered as abnormal condition if the value of monitoring index is over upper control limits or under lower control limits with a confidence coefficient of 99%.

4. Case study on penicillin process

4.1. Process description and data preparation

Penicillin fermentation process is a typical batch process. The initial stage of fermentation is intermittent operation, in which many cells are produced. After the glucose substrate is consumed by the cells, it comes into semi-intermittent feeding stage where glucose is continuously added into the fermentation cylinder. During fermentation, the concentration of penicillin will be affected by environment change, initial condition adjustment, and variable fluctuation. It is difficult to measure penicillin concentration online, thus real-time monitoring is required to ensure that the fermentation process runs under normal trajectory. In this work, Pensim software developed by Birol, Ündey, and Cinar (2002) is adopted to simulate the process.

4.2. Batch process monitoring based on proposed method

Ten batches of data under normal condition with different initial conditions are simulated as training data. The information of process variables is listed in Table 1. The reaction time ranges from 395 h to 405 h, and the sampling frequency is 0.1 h. Four exogenous variables and a key endogenous variable are selected as modelling variables that is shown in Table 1, of which ventilation rate is an endogenous variable and the others are exogenous variables.

Table 1 Variables in penicillin fermentation process

Variables	Units
Ventilation rate	L/h
Agitator power	W
Substrate feeding rate	L/h
Substrate feeding temperature	K
Penicillin concentration	g/L

Table 2 Faults information introduced in this work

Fault number	Fault type
1	Step decrease in aeration rate
2	Ramp decrease in agitator power
3	Ramp decrease substrate feed rate

To illustrate the effectiveness of the proposed monitoring strategy, three common faults are set on Pensim simulation platform. The faults are introduced to three different batches separately from 100 h to the end and the information of the faults is available in Table 2. At the same time, a normal batch data is supplied to test the monitoring effect on normal condition of the proposed method as comparison.

4.3. Monitoring result analysis and discussion

Three fault batches and a normal batch are set as testing data to verify the effectiveness of the proposed mothed.

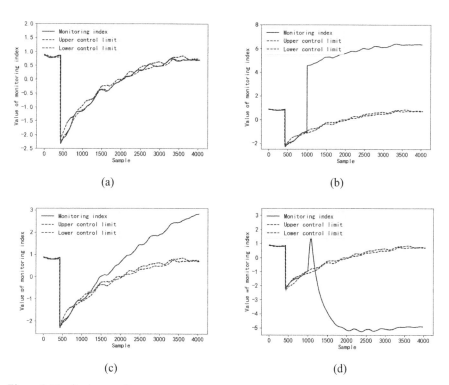

Figure 2 Monitoring results

The monitoring results are shown in Figure 2. For the normal batch as shown in (a), the value of monitoring index remains within the control limits, indicating that the data are under normal conditions and the model has a low false alarm rate that barely exceeds the control limits. For step fault monitoring result as shown in (b), the value of monitoring index exceeds the upper control limit at the first time when fault occurs, which shows that the abnormal condition can be detected in time by applying the proposed monitoring method. For slope faults as shown in (c) and (d), there is a delay to detect the fault 2 while the fault 3 is detected timely, which indicates that the sensitivities to different fault are distinct. The results show that the proposed method can effectively extract the complex dynamic and nonstationary characteristics in the batch process and monitor the faults in real time.

5. Conclusion

In this work, a new monitoring strategy based on ADL cointegration analysis for batch process is proposed. Taking the complex characteristics of batch process data into consideration, cointegration analysis is applied to the data to eliminate the common stochastic trend and obtain long-term equilibrium relationship of nonstationary variables. In the view of the exogenous variables in process which is not affected by other endogenous variables as well as the equilibrium relationships, ADL cointegration test is used to test if long term equilibrium relationship exists among nonstationary variables, and the model parameters is estimated by ordinary least squares. By considering the impact of exogenous variables, the interaction among variables is better described. On this basis, real-time monitoring of the fermentation process is implemented by monitoring the trajectory of the equilibrium error. In the end, process monitoring results on a benchmark penicillin fermentation data indicate the effectiveness of proposed monitoring strategy.

Acknowledgements

The authors gratefully acknowledge the team of Professor Cinar (Illinois Institute of Technology) for providing the source program of Pensim software which is applied to generate the experimental data in this research.

References

G. Birol, C. Ündey, and A. Cinar. "A modular simulation package for fed-batch fermentation: penicillin production." Computers & Chemical Engineering 26.11(2002):1553-1565.

Q. Chen, U. Kruger, and A. Leung. "Cointegration Testing Method for Monitoring Nonstationary Processes." Industrial & Engineering Chemistry Research 48.7(2009):3533-3543.

R. F. Engle, and C. Granger. "Cointegration And Error-Correction: Representation, Estimation and Testing." Econometrica 55.2(1987):251-276.

D. M. Filho, and M. Valk. "Dynamic VAR model-based control charts for batch process monitoring." European Journal of Operational Research 285(2020).

Y. Lin, U. Kruger, and Q. Chen. "Monitoring Nonstationary Dynamic Systems Using Cointegration and Common Trends Analysis." Industrial & Engineering Chemistry Research (2017): acs. iecr.7b00011.

M. H. Pesaran, "An autoregressive distributed lag modelling approach to cointegration analysis." Cambridge Working Papers in Economics (1995):134--150.

W. C. Sang, J. Morris, and I. B. Lee. "Dynamic model-based batch process monitoring." Chemical Engineering Science 63.3(2008):622-636.

Proceedings of the 14th International Symposium on Process Systems Engineering – PSE 2021+
June 19-23, 2022, Kyoto, Japan © 2022 Elsevier B.V. All rights reserved.
http://dx.doi.org/10.1016/B978-0-323-85159-6.50241-4

A Data-Driven Fault Detection and Diagnosis by NSGAII-t-SNE and Clustering Methods in the Chemical Process Industry

Nahid Raeisi Ardali[a], Reza Zarghami[a*], Rahmat Sotudeh Gharebagh[a], and Navid Mostoufi[a]

[a] *Process Design and Simulation Research Centre, School of Chemical Engineering, College of Engineering, University of Tehran, P.O. Box 11155-4563, Tehran, Iran.*
rzarghami@ut.ac.ir

Abstract

This study aims to illustrate a novel unsupervised learning method for fault detection and diagnosis of chemical processes. The data-driven fault detection and diagnosis contains two main steps. a) data preparation and feature selections as preprocessing step and b) fault detection and diagnosis for fault indication. In this study, a non-dominated sorting genetic algorithm (NSGAII) was utilized for selecting the most relevant variables from the measured variables for each fault. The t-distributed stochastic neighbor embedding (t-SNE) algorithm was used for information extraction from the selected variables which will lead to visualization of extracted features. Meanwhile, fault detection was performed by k-means and density-based spatial clustering of applications with noise (DBSCAN) clustering algorithms. The Tennessee Eastman benchmark process and faults of process variation were applied to validate the proposed method. Results show that the combination of NSGAII, t-SNE, and clustering methods is an efficient method for Tennessee Eastman process fault detection and diagnosis. And the proposed method could be used in chemical processes for early fault detection.

Keywords: Process Monitoring; Fault Detection; Tennessee Eastman Process; NSGAII; t-SNE.

1. Introduction

Early fault detection and diagnosis play a critical role in managing abnormal circumstances in dynamic processes (Md Nor et al., 2020). Fault detection and diagnosis methods are mainly divided into three categories as quantitative, qualitative, and data-driven. Quantitative models need an accurate process model based on system governing equations such as momentum, energy, and mass conservation equations, chemical kinetics, and thermodynamic equations. In such models, fault detection and diagnosis are based on the residuals of real process data and the predicted data at normal conditions (Elhsoumi et al, 2017). Qualitative models are based on the causal models and the knowledge of experts about the process such as fault trees (Venkatasubramanian et al., 2003). Due to the complexities and difficulties in obtaining variables needed for quantitative and qualitative modeling, these models could not be practically applied (Ziaei-Halimejani et al., 2021). Meanwhile, by the availability of large volumes of data, data-driven methods for fault detection and diagnosis (supervised and unsupervised) have been considered by many researchers. In industrial plants, historical data are mostly available without labels. In start-up conditions, faults could not be detected clearly, so unsupervised data-driven methods are more suitable to be applied. Therefore, the purpose of this study is to develop an unsupervised learning method for fault detection and diagnosis of chemical processes. In this paper, a non-dominated sorting genetic algorithm (NSGAII) was used for feature selection and the t-SNE algorithm was used for feature extraction and visualization. Then fault detection and the diagnosis were done by clustering algorithms.

2. Theory

2.1 Data Pre-processing

Basically, a good feature in data-driven models should be informative, discriminative, and independent. Meanwhile, by selecting appropriate features the computation time and overfitting error will be reduced. The NSGAII algorithm was introduced in 2002 by Deb et al. and it is a multi-objective genetic algorithm for non-dominated sorting that includes crossover, mutation, merge, non-dominated sorting, crowding distance calculation, and population sorting functions as shown in Figure 1. Therefore, in this paper NSGAII algorithm was utilized for multi-objective feature selection. And classification error and the number of features were determined as objectives that should be minimized. But it is worth noting that both of these parameters could not be minimized simultaneously, and by decreasing the number of features the classification error will increase. Thus a trade-off between these parameters should be done.

After feature selection, t-distributed stochastic neighbor embedding (t-SNE) was utilized for feature extraction. t-SNE is a nonlinear statistics method for data dimension reduction to two or three dimensions and it is an efficient method for data visualization that was proposed by van der Maaten (2008). The t-SNE algorithm consists of two main steps. First, data transformation from high dimension space to a low dimensional space by probability distribution calculation. Somehow similar points have a high probability and dissimilar points have a low probability of being selected. Then, in low dimension space, a possible distribution is created and the Kullback–Leibler divergence is minimized between the two distributions according to the position of the points.

$$P_{j|i} = \frac{\exp(-\|X_i - X_j\|^2 / 2\sigma_i^2)}{\sum_{k \neq i} \exp(-\|X_i - X_k\|^2 / 2\sigma_i^2)} \tag{1}$$

$$P_{ij} = \frac{P_{j|i} + P_{i|j}}{2N} \tag{2}$$

$$q_{ij} = \frac{(1 + \|y_i - y_j\|^2)^{-1}}{\sum_{k \neq i}(1 + \|y_i - y_j\|^2)^{-1}} \tag{3}$$

$$KL(P\|Q) = \sum_{i \neq j} P_{ij} \log \frac{P_{ij}}{q_{ij}} \tag{4}$$

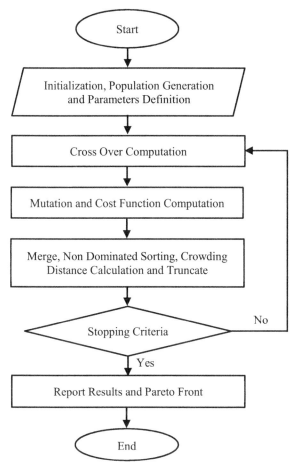

Figure 1: Flowchart of NSGAII Algorithm

2.2 Clustering

Data clustering methods are categorized in unsupervised learning methods whereas these methods don't need datasets labels and training phase. In this paper, data clustering was performed by using k-Means and DBSCAN algorithms. In the k-Means method, cluster centres are chosen based on the predetermined cluster numbers. And cluster members will be assigned to the nearest cluster, then in each iteration, the cluster centres and cluster members will be updated. DBSCAN method is a density-based method that cloud de utilized under noisy conditions. Epsilon and min points number are two main parameters that should be adjusted for each problem. In the DBSCAN Method data points will be categorized as cluster members, cluster borders, and noise depending on their spatial density. The main difference between the k-Means and the DBSCAN algorithm is that DBSCAN could be utilized in nonconvex geometries (Ziaei-Halimejani et al., 2021).

3. Results and discussion

The case study of this paper is the Tennessee Eastman benchmark process. In this process, four main reactants A, C, D, and E react in the gas phase in the presence of B as inert, to produce G and H main products and F as a by-product. The unit operations of the Tennessee Eastman process are a reactor, a condenser, a gas-liquid separator, a stripper, and a compressor. The Tennessee Eastman process contains 12 manipulated variables and 41 measurement variables (Downs and Vogel, 1993). In this paper, 19 flow component analyses were not considered. Tennessee Eastman Process Simulink model (https://depts.washington.edu/control/ *LARRY/TE/download.html*) is used for data generation, there are 20 faulty conditions and one normal condition. This paper included conditions 0, 1, 2, 4, 6, 7, 13, and 14, as normal, 5 step faults,1 slow drift, and 1 sticking valve fault. The datasets contain 480 samples for each condition.

3.1. Data normalization
Measured data in the chemical processes have different operating ranges, hence by using Eq.5 and dividing by their standard deviation the measured data have been normalized. The normalized data are between -1 and 1.

$$\hat{X}_s^{fn} = \frac{X_s^{fn} - \mu}{\sigma} \tag{5}$$

3.2. Feature selection

As mentioned in section 2, the NSGAII algorithm was utilized for feature selection. The parameters of the algorithm were adjusted as presented in Table 1. And for the 8 conditions dataset, the optimum number of selected features and classification errors is shown in Figure 2. As illustrated, 8 optimum solutions were provided with different numbers of features and classification errors. Therefore, 9 cases for all features and 8 NSGAII, N_F were tested (Table 2).

Table 1: NSGAII Algorithm Parameters

Maximum Iterations	Number of Populations	Crossover	Mutation	Mu
50	20	0.7	0.4	0.1

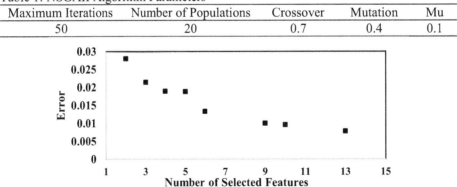

Figure 2: Error of feature selection using NSGAII algorithm versus number of selected features

3.3. Feature extraction

After the feature selection step, t-SNE as a nonlinear dimension reduction method was utilized to extract three features from selected features and feature visualization as shown in Figure 3.a. In Figure 3.b Feature extraction results of the PCA method are shown.

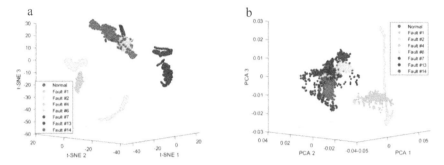

Figure 3: Feature Extraction, a) t-SNE method and b) PCA method

3.4. Fault detection and diagnosis

Fault detection and diagnosis have profited from clustering algorithms. In this research k-Means and DBSCAN methods were utilized. In Figures 4.a and 4.b the results of test 5 are illustrated.

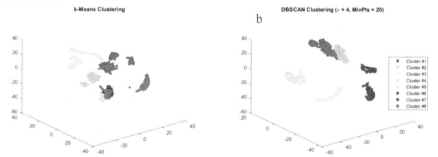

Figure 4: Fault Detection and Diagnosis, a) k-Means method and b) DBSCAN method

3.5. Evaluation

To validate the results of clustering methods, four indexes including adjusted rand index (ARI), adjusted mutual information (AMI), V-Measure, and accuracy have been used. The evaluation results are reported in Table 2. As shown, in all tests, the t-SNE method obtained better results than the PCA method. In test numbers 8 and 9, the t-SNE-k-Means provided better results and in the rest of the tests, DBSCAN results are more accurate. It is worth noting that test number 5 was the best test. In this case, 6 Features included XMEAS (21), XMV (3), XMV (4), XMV (5), XMV (6), and XMV (10) were selected. The classification error and $R_F=N_F/N$ were computed as 0.0133 and 0.18, respectively. Also as shown in Table 2, the t-SNE-clustering performed better in cases with a lower number of features compared with PCA-clustering.

Table 2: Clustering Results Evaluation

	N_F	Extraction	k-Means				DBSCAN			
			ARI	AMI	V-Meas.	Acc.	ARI	AMI	V-Meas.	Acc.
1	33	t-SNE	0.35	0.51	0.64	0.45	**0.39**	**0.54**	**0.66**	**0.52**
		PCA	0.28	0.44	0.50	0.44	0.27	0.45	0.57	0.44
2	13	t-SNE	0.54	0.73	0.78	0.57	**0.64**	**0.8**	**0.84**	**0.73**
		PCA	0.35	0.54	0.66	0.50	0.35	0.56	0.65	0.49
3	10	t-SNE	0.39	0.52	0.67	0.50	**0.59**	**0.74**	**0.78**	**0.69**
		PCA	0.42	0.58	0.63	0.55	0.38	0.56	0.65	0.51
4	9	t-SNE	0.52	0.70	0.79	0.54	**0.61**	**0.75**	**0.83**	*0.96*
		PCA	0.38	0.55	0.69	0.52	0.34	0.48	0.59	0.48
5	**6**	**t-SNE**	0.64	0.76	0.81	0.69	*0.79*	*0.87*	*0.89*	0.83
		PCA	0.37	0.57	0.68	0.55	0.28	0.52	0.67	0.47
6	5	t-SNE	0.45	0.66	0.75	0.52	**0.74**	**0.82**	**0.85**	**0.82**
		PCA	0.30	0.56	0.67	0.48	0.29	0.53	0.64	0.47
7	4	t-SNE	0.58	0.70	0.77	0.69	**0.67**	**0.78**	**0.82**	**0.75**
		PCA	0.34	0.56	0.69	0.52	0.29	0.50	0.65	0.48
8	3	t-SNE	**0.62**	**0.72**	**0.76**	**0.74**	0.56	0.71	0.75	0.68
		PCA	0.35	0.55	0.64	0.51	0.35	0.56	0.63	0.48
9	2	t-SNE	**0.67**	**0.76**	**0.77**	**0.82**	0.65	0.75	0.77	0.76
		PCA	0.38	0.49	0.56	0.52	0.32	0.51	0.60	0.51

4. Conclusion

In this research, a method based on NSGAII, t-SNE, and unsupervised learning algorithms was developed for fault detection and diagnosis in chemical processes. Informative features were selected by the NSGAII algorithm and by utilizing 18 % of features, 8 conditions containing normal and 7 faults were detected and diagnosed. Results showed that the proposed method has high applicability to detect and diagnose Tennessee Eastman process faults, and could be applied for other chemical processes.

References

Deb, K., Pratap, A., Agarwal, S., and Meyarivan, T., A Fast and Elitist Multiobjective Genetic Algorithm: NSGA-II, IEEE Transactions on Evolutionary Computation, 6, 2 (2002). DOI: 10.1109/4235.996017.

Downs, J. J. and Vogel, E. F., A Plant-Wide Industrial Process Control Problem, Computers & Chemical Engineering, 17, 245-255 (1993). DOI: https://doi.org/10.1016/0098-1354(93)80018-I.

Elhsoumi, A., El Harabi, R., Hadj Ali Naoui, S. B., Abdelkrim, M. N., Luenberger Observer based Sensor and Actuator Fault Detection for Chemical Reactor, IFAC Proceedings, 42, 9, 566-571 (2009). DOI: https://doi.org/10.3182/20090921-3-TR-3005.00097.

Md Nor, N., Rosmani, C., and Azlan Hussain, M.,A review of data-driven fault detection and diagnosis methods: applications in chemical process systems, Reviews in Chemical Engineering, 36, 4, 513-553 (2020). DOI: https://doi.org/10.1515/revce-2017-0069.

van der Maaten L.J.P., and Hinton G.E., Visualizing High-Dimensional Data Using t-SNE, Journal of Machine Learning Research, 9, 2579-2605 (2008).

Venkatasubramanian, V., Rengaswamy, R., Yin, K.,,. Kavuri, S. N, A review of process fault detection and diagnosis, Part I: Quantitative model-based methods, Computers and Chemical Engineering, 27 , 293- 311 (2003). DOI: https://doi.org/10.1016/S0098-1354(02)00160-6.

Ziaei-Halimejani, H., Zarghami, R., Mansouri, S., and Mostoufi, N., Data-Driven Fault Diagnosis of Chemical Processes Based on Recurrence Plots, Industrial & Engineering Chemistry Research, 60, 3038-3050 (2021). DOI: https://doi.org/10.1021/acs.iecr.0c06307.

Proceedings of the 14th International Symposium on Process Systems Engineering – PSE 2021+
June 19-23, 2022, Kyoto, Japan © 2022 Elsevier B.V. All rights reserved.
http://dx.doi.org/10.1016/B978-0-323-85159-6.50242-6

Cyberattack Detectability-Based Controller Screening: Application to a Nonlinear Process

Shilpa Narasimhan[a], Nael H. El-Farra[a], Matthew J. Ellis[a*]

[a]*Department of Chemical Engineering, University of California Davis, Davis, CA-95616, USA*
mjellis@ucdavis.edu

Abstract

In this work, multiplicative cyberattacks targeting the sensor-controller communication link of a process control system are considered. The interdependence of detectability of an attack with respect to a general class of residual-based detection schemes and the control parameters is characterized. Exploiting this dependence, a controller screening methodology that may be used to incorporate cyberattack detectability into the standard controller design criteria is presented. Using a chemical process example, the application of the controller design screening to a nonlinear process is demonstrated.

Keywords: Multiplicative cyberattack, zero-alarm attack, controller design, cyberattack detectability

1. Introduction

Increased reliance on networked communication has rendered process control systems (PCSs) vulnerable to increasingly complex and frequent cyberattacks (Miller et al., 2018) in the past couple of decades. This has motivated an increasing body of research dedicated to the development of controller-based approaches to attack resilient controller design, cyberattack detection, identification, and mitigation schemes (Giraldo et al., 2018, and Tan et al., 2020 and references therein, Oyama et al., 2020, and Chen et al., 2021). Broadly, cyberattacks may target the PCS by compromising the data integrity of process data in the communication links or by altering the PCS logic. In this work, multiplicative zero-alarm cyberattacks compromising the data integrity of the sensor-controller communication link are considered. These attacks are modeled by a factor multiplied to the measured variable and are particularly threatening as they may be designed to evade detection by keeping the alarms in the detection scheme monitoring the process at zero, with minimal process knowledge.

The detectability of the measured states of a process may be viewed as a systems-theoretic property. In practice, the detectability of a cyberattack on the measured states of a process is dependent on the control parameters (e.g., controller gain and observer gain), and the detection scheme monitoring the process. This interdependence of the detectability of an attack and the controller design has not received much attention in the literature. In a previous work (Narasimhan et al., 2021), an approach to characterizing the interdependence of the attack detectability in terms of terminal set of residuals (a small set containing the origin within which the residual is ultimately bounded) for the attacked and the attack-free process was presented. Based on the characterization, a controller screening methodology that may be used identify and discard control parameters that mask an attack was presented for processes modeled by discrete-time linear time invariant

(LTI) dynamics. This screening may be used to incorporate cyberattack detectability into existing controller design criteria (e.g., closed loop-stability and robustness to uncertainty). The present work explores the application of the controller screening methodology to a nonlinear chemical process. To make the paper self-contained, an abridged version of the screening methodology is presented herein. Interested readers are directed to Narasimhan et al. (2021) for more information.

2. Controller Screening Methodology

Processes modeled by discrete-time linear time invariant (LTI) dynamics, and subject to bounded measurement noise and process disturbances are considered:

$$x(t + 1) = Ax(t) + B\,u(t) + Gw(t)$$

$$y(t) = \Lambda(Cx(t) + v(t))$$

(1)

where $x(t) \in \mathbb{R}^n$ is the state of the process, $u(t) \in \mathbb{R}^{n_u}$ is the control input, $y(t) \in \mathbb{R}^m$ is the output from the process, $w(t) \in W \subset \mathbb{R}^{n_w}$ and $v(t) \in V \subset \mathbb{R}^m$ are the bounded process disturbances and measurement noise. The sets W and V are compact and contain the origin in their interior. Multiplicative sensor-controller link attacks are modeled by the diagonal matrix $\Lambda = \text{diag}(\alpha_1, \alpha_2, \dots, \alpha_m)$ where $\alpha_i \neq 1$ represents attack on the ith sensor-controller communication link. To generate an estimate of the state (denoted by $\hat{x}(t) \in \mathbb{R}^n$), a Luenberger observer with gain L is used. A linear controller with gain K is used to steer the state to the origin. The eigenvalues of $A - LC$ and $A - BK$ are assumed to lie within the unit circle. For analysis, the augmented state vector is defined as $\xi(t) = [x^T(t) \quad e^T(t)]^T$, where $e(t) = x(t) - \hat{x}(t)$ is the estimation error (the dynamic model is defined in Eq. (5) of Narasimhan et al., 2021). The dynamics of the augmented state is $\xi(t + 1) = A_\xi(\Lambda, K, L)\xi(t) + B_\xi(\Lambda, L)d(t)$, where $d(t) = [w^T(t) \quad v^T(t)]^T \in F := \{\binom{w}{v}\,|\, w \in W, v \in V\}$) ($A_\xi(\Lambda, K, L)$ and $B_\xi(\Lambda, K, L)$ are given in Eq. (6) of Narasimhan et al., 2021).

Due to the presence of bounded noise in the measurement, and process disturbances, when the process is at steady state, its augmented state converges to a small set containing the origin, which is the minimum invariant set. When the closed-loop process is stable with $\max_i |\lambda_i(A_\xi(\Lambda, K, L)| < 1$ ($\lambda_i\left(A_\xi(\Lambda, K, L)\right)$ is the ith eigenvalue of $A_\xi(\Lambda, K, L)$), the minimum invariant set of the process depends upon the attack magnitude and the control parameters. It is given by the infinite Minkowski sum $D_\xi(\Lambda, K, L) = B_\xi F \oplus A_\xi B_\xi F \oplus A_\xi^2 B_\xi F \oplus \dots$ (Kuntsevich et al., 1996). The residual vector is defined as $r(t) = y(t) - \hat{y}(t)$. Writing the residual in terms of the augmented state and the disturbance gives $r(t) = [(\Lambda - I)C \quad C]\xi(t) + [0 \quad \Lambda]d(t) = A_r(\Lambda)\xi(t) + B_r(\Lambda)d(t)$. Thus, the terminal set of residuals for the process may be computed as $D_r(\Lambda, K, L) = A_r(\Lambda)D_\xi(\Lambda, K, L) \oplus B_r(\Lambda)F$.

A general class of residual-based detection schemes using the 2-norm of the residual vector as the detection metric is considered. Elaborate discussion on these detection schemes may be found in Section 2.3-2.4 of Narasimhan et al., 2021. With respect to the class of detection schemes considered, a closed-loop stability preserving attack of magnitude $\Lambda \neq I$ is defined as undetectable if the radius of the 2-norm ball enclosing the terminal residual set of the process under an attack is less than or equal to the radius of the 2-norm ball enclosing the terminal residual set of the attack-free process, i.e, $R(\Lambda, K, L) \leq R(I, K, L)$, where $R(\Lambda, K, L) := \max_{r' \in D_r(\Lambda, K, L)} ||r'||$. Similarly, any closed-loop stability preserving attack of magnitude $\Lambda \neq I$ on the process is defined as a potentially detectable attack if the radius of the 2-norm ball enclosing the terminal set of the attack-free process is less than the radius of the 2-norm ball enclosing the terminal set of the process under an attack, i.e., $R(I, K, L) < R(\Lambda, K, L)$. Finally, an attack of magnitude $\Lambda \neq I$ is said to be detectable if it renders the closed-loop system in Eq.(1) unstable. Interested readers are directed to Section 3.1 of Narasimhan et al., 2021, for more discussions.

To derive numerically verifiable conditions for characterizing attack detectability, invariant outer polytopic approximation of the minimum invariant set of the augmented states of the stable process is computed as $D_\xi^{est}(\Lambda, K, L)$ (see Raković et al., 2005 for method), such that $D_\xi(\Lambda, K, L) \subseteq D_\xi^{est}(\Lambda, K, L) \subseteq D_\xi(\Lambda, K, L) \oplus B_\infty^{2n}(\epsilon)$ $(B_\infty^{2n}(\epsilon) :=$ $\{\xi' \in \mathbb{R}^{2n} \mid \parallel \xi' \parallel_\infty \leq \epsilon \})$, where ϵ is the error bound. Then, the inner polytopic approximations of the terminal residual sets for the attack-free and the attacked process are computed as $D_{r_e}^{est}(I, K, L)$ and $D_{r_{a,e}}^{est}(\Lambda, K, L)$, respectively. These inner approximations satisfy $D_{r_j}^{est}(\Lambda, K, L) = D_r^{est}(\Lambda, K, L) \ominus A_r(\Lambda) B_\infty^{2n}(\epsilon) \subseteq D_r(\Lambda, K, L)$ $(j = e$ or $j = a, e)$, where, $D_r^{est}(\Lambda, K, L)$ is the outer polytopic approximation of $D_r(\Lambda, K, L)$.

With the disturbance set F, the attack magnitude of interest Λ, the controller gain K, and the observer gain L as the input, the controller screening algorithm is as follows. First, it is checked if $\max_i |\lambda_i(A_\xi(\Lambda, K, L)| \geq 1$. If this is true, the choice of K and L under a multiplicative attack with attack matrix Λ will render the closed-loop process unstable and the attack is detectable. The screening algorithm is terminated in this case. However, if $\max_i |\lambda_i(A_\xi(\Lambda, K, L)| < 1$, then the outer polytopic approximations of the residual sets are computed using the method described in Section 3.2 of Narasimhan et al., 2021. From the outer approximations, the inner approximations of the residual sets are computed. Then, the radii of the 2-norm balls enclosing the sets $(R^{est}(I, K, L)$, $R^{est}(\Lambda, K, L)$, $R_e^{est}(\Lambda, K, L)$, and $R_{a,e}^{est}(\Lambda, K, L))$ are computed. If $R^{est}(\Lambda, K, L) < R_e^{est}(I, K, L)$, the attack is classified as an undetectable attack, else, if $R_{a,e}^{est}(\Lambda, K, L) > R^{est}(I, K, L)$, then the attack is classified as a potentially detectable. However, if it is found that $R^{est}(\Lambda, K, L) > R_e^{est}(I, K, L)$ or $R_{a,e}^{est}(\Lambda, K, L) > R^{est}(I, K, L)$, the test is inconclusive. This may occur when the numerical approximations of the terminal sets satisfy $|R_{a,e}^{est}(\Lambda, K, L) - R^{est}(I, K, L)| \leq \beta$ or $|R_e^{est}(\Lambda, K, L) - R^{est}(I, K, L)| \leq \beta$ where $\beta > 0$ is a small number, implying that the radius estimates are close to each other.

3. Application to a Nonlinear Chemical Process

A chemical process example consisting of a continuously stirred tank reactor (CSTR) with a second-order reaction occurring is considered. The process is subject to bounded process disturbances and measurement noise. In the real-time control of chemical processes, the control actions are usually applied to the nonlinear continuous-time process at discrete time instances. To simulate this, the nonlinear ordinary differential equation model describing the CSTR process is integrated with the linear controller generating a new control action at every 10^{-2} h. To apply the screening methodology, a discrete-time LTI process model is needed. To generate the model, a continuous-time LTI model is first obtained by linearizing the nonlinear model about its open-loop stable steady state. The discrete-time LTI process model is then obtained by applying a zero-order hold discretization. The process models, and process parameter values are given in Narasimhan et al., 2021.

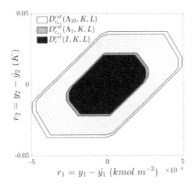

Figure 1. Outer approximation of the terminal residual set for the attack-free process ($D_r^{est}(I, K, L)$), and the inner approximations of the terminal sets for the attacked process ($D_{r_{n_e}}^{est}(\Lambda_i, K, L)$).

In this study, the control parameters are to be chosen such that they do not mask multiplicative attacks of magnitude in this range $[1.1, 2]$ on the concentration sensor-controller link. Since there are infinitely many attack magnitudes in the range, the screening algorithm is carried out with ten values from the range, i.e., with values $\Lambda_i = \mathrm{diag}(\alpha_i, 1)$ where $\alpha_i = 1.1 + 0.1(i - 1)$, $i = 1, 2, \dots, 10$. Using pole placement, the controller and observer gains are selected with the controller poles at $[0.5 - 0.1]$ and observer poles at $[-0.3 \, 0.4]$. The screening algorithm is applied to the chosen controller design over all Λ_i. The attacked closed-loop process is stable with $\max_j \left| \lambda_j \left(A_{\xi_a}(\Lambda_i, K, L) \right) \right| < 1$ for all $i = 1, 2, \dots 10$. The polytopic approximations of the minimum invariant sets of the attacked process over all attack magnitudes, and for the attack-free process are computed with an error bound of $\epsilon = 5 \times 10^{-5}$. Then, the polytopic approximations of terminal residual sets are computed (Figure 1). The size of the terminal residual set for the attacked process increases with α_i. For all cases, $R^{est}(I, K, L) < R_{a,e}^{est}(\Lambda_i, K, L)$, $i = 1, 2, \dots 10$, with $R^{est}(I, K, L) = 0.0207$, $\min_i R_{a,e}^{est}(\Lambda_i, K, L) = 0.0222$ for $\Lambda_1 = \mathrm{diag}(\alpha_1, 1) = \mathrm{diag}(1.1, 1)$ and $\max_i R_{a,e}^{est}(\Lambda_i, K, L) = 0.0375$ for $\Lambda_{10} = \mathrm{diag}(2, 1)$. Thus, all the attacks in the range of interest are potentially detectable. To verify the potential detectability of each attack magnitude, two sets of simulations of the process are performed, using the (1) discrete-time LTI process model and (2) nonlinear continuous-time process model. One thousand closed-loop simulation pairs of the attacked process are performed with various realizations of the measurement noise and the process disturbance. For each simulation pair, the same realization was applied. For both sets of simulations, the state is estimated using a Luenberger observer designed based on the discrete-time LTI process model. To monitor the process, a CUSUM detection scheme described by Eq. (12) in Narasimhan et al., 2021 is used. The detection scheme is tuned with the choice of $b = R^{est}(I, K, L) = 0.0207$ and an alarm threshold of $\tau = 0.01$ to guarantee a zero-false alarm rate in the absence of an attack.

For attacks with $\alpha_i \in [1.6, 2]$, the attack is detected over most simulations with the LTI and the nonlinear models. Results from simulating an attack of magnitude $\Lambda_{10} = \mathrm{diag}(2, 1)$ on the nonlinear process model are presented in Figure 2. The attack is detected in 969 out of 1000 simulations with the nonlinear continuous-time process model. Of these 969 simulations, the attack is not detected in the corresponding linear model simulation in 4 simulations. Similarly, during the simulations with the discrete-time LTI process model, the attack is detected in 970 out of 1000 simulations. For 5 of the 970 simulations, the attack is not detected for the

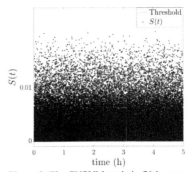

Figure 2. The CUSUM statistic $S(t)$ over 1000 simulations of the closed-loop process under an attack of magnitude $\Lambda_{10} = \mathrm{diag}(2, 1)$.

corresponding nonlinear model simulation. In most of the simulation pairs where a discrepancy between attack detection is observed, the difference in the maximum CUSUM statistic value between the two cases was small, meaning that in one case, the value exceeded the threshold by a small amount and in the other, the statistic value was close to the other, but did not exceed the threshold. For example, an attack is detected in the linear case with a CUSUM statistic value of 0.0101, and for the corresponding nonlinear case, the statistic value at the same time is 0.0095, and the attack is not detected. Finally, for the same realization of random variables applied to the nonlinear case and linear case, except for 174

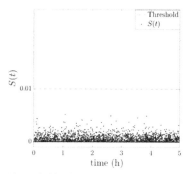

Figure 3. The CUSUM statistic $S(t)$ over 1000 simulations of the closed-loop process under an attack of magnitude $\Lambda_4 = \mathrm{diag}(1.4,1)$.

simulations, the time at which the attack is first detected is the same for both process models. Over most of these 174 simulations, the attack detection time for the two process models differed by a single time step.

For attacks with magnitude in range $\alpha_i \in [1.2, 1.5]$, while the CUSUM statistic never breaches the threshold, it is found to be a non-zero value over most simulations for both the nonlinear case and the linear case. The CUSUM statistic resulting from simulating an attack of magnitude $\Lambda_4 = \mathrm{diag}(1.4, 1)$ (with $R^{est}_{a,e}(\Lambda_4, K, L) = 0.027$) on the nonlinear model are given in Figure 3. It is also found that the maximum realization of the CUSUM statistic over each simulation of the nonlinear model is of the same order of magnitude as the maximum realization of the statistic over the corresponding simulation of the linear model. In one case, the maximum CUSUM statistic in simulations with the nonlinear case is 0, however, the maximum statistic for corresponding simulations with the linear case is 3.1×10^{-5}. The mean of the 2-norm of the residual vector over 1000 simulations is 0.0081 with a variance of 2.4563×10^{-5} for the nonlinear case. The mean of the 2-norm of the residual vector over 1000 simulations with the linear case is 0.0081 (same as that for the nonlinear case) and the variance is 2.4553×10^{-5}. While not shown here, statistical distribution of the 2-norm of the residual indicates that tuning the CUSUM detection scheme with a lower alarm threshold may enable the detection of this attack. Note that with the tuning approach adopted in this work, the CUSUM statistic remains at zero for the attack-free process, and any non-zero CUSUM statistic value would indicate an attack. Furthermore, with a decrease in α_i, the total number of simulations with non-zero realizations of the CUSUM statistic decrease, indicating that the attack becomes more difficult to detect.

During closed-loop simulations with an attack of magnitude $\Lambda_1 = \mathrm{diag}(1.1,1,1)$, the CUSUM statistic remains at zero over all the 1000 simulations for both the linear case and the nonlinear case. Thus, the attack goes undetected, despite the control parameters satisfying $R^{est}(I, K, L) < R^{est}_{a,e}(\Lambda_1, K, L)$. This does not contradict the screening algorithm, as the attack is only potentially detectable. The fact that the attack went undetected may be because $R^{est}(\Lambda_1, K, L) - R^{est}(I, K, L) = 0.0015$ is small. While further analysis is required, for this attack magnitude, a different set of control parameters with a larger separation between the sets $D^{est}_r(I, K, L)$ and $D^{est}_r(\Lambda_1, K, L)$ may enable attack detection. Moreover, for this case, the performance degradation resulting from this attack is small.

The applicability of the controller screening algorithm to the nonlinear case is verified for other control designs and attacks. For example, when the controller screening algorithm predicts that (1) an attack $\Lambda = \text{diag}(0.5,1)$ with control and observer gains selected by placing the poles at $[0.3\ 0.1]$ and $[-0.4\ 0.3]$, respectively, and (2) an attack $\Lambda = \text{diag}(1,0.9)$ for control and observer gains selected by placing poles at $[0.5 - 0.1]$ and $[0.4\ 0.4]$, respectively, are undetectable. During the closed-loop simulations with the nonlinear case and the linear case, the CUSUM statistic remains at zero, and the attacks are not detected. When the controller screening predicts that an attack $\Lambda = \text{diag}(1,1.2)$ is potentially detectable for control and observer gains with poles placed at $[0.5 - 0.1]$ and $[0.2\ 0.2]$, respectively, the CUSUM statistic has non-zero realizations over most simulations. However, it never breaches the threshold (similar to Figure 3). Thus, the controller screening algorithm based on the discrete-time LTI model of the process is applicable to the continuous-time nonlinear model of the process. This may be because the linear process model adequately represents the dynamics of the nonlinear process near the operating steady-state.

4. Conclusions

In this work, the application of a detectability-based controller design screening methodology for a multiplicative sensor-controller link cyberattacks to a nonlinear chemical process example was demonstrated. Future work will focus on controller-based approaches that enable the detection of a multiplicative sensor-controller link attack.

References

T. Miller, A. Staves, S. Maesschalck, M. Sturdee, B. Green, 2021, Looking back to look forward: Lessons learnt from cyber-attacks on industrial control systems, International Journal of Critical Infrastructure Protection, vol. 35, pp. 100464.

J. Giraldo, D. Urbina, Á.A. Càrdenas, J. Valente, M. Faisal, J. Ruths, N.O. Tippenhauer, H. Sandberg, R. Candell, 2018, A Survey of Physics-Based Attack Detection in Cyber-Physical Systems, ACM Computing Surveys, vol. 51, issue 4, article 76, pp. 1–36.

S. Tan, J.M. Guerrero, P. Xie, R. Han, J.C. Vasquez, 2020, Brief survey on attack detection methods for cyber-physical systems. IEEE Systems Journal, vol. 14(4), pp. 5329–5239.

H. Oyama, H. Durand, 2020, Integrated cyberattack detection and resilient control strategies using Lyapunov-based economic model predictive control, AIChE Journal, vol. 66, issue 12, pp. e17084.

S. Chen, Z. Wu, P.D. Christofides, Cyber-security of centralized, decentralized, and distributed control-detector architectures for nonlinear processes, 2021, Chemical Engineering Research and Design, vol. 165, pp. 25–39.

V.M. Kuntsevich, B.N. Pshenichnyi, 1996, Minimal invariant sets of dynamic systems with bounded disturbances, Cybernetics and Systems Analysis, vol. 32(1), pp. 58–64.

S.V. Raković, E.C. Kerrigan, K.I. Kouramas, D.Q. Mayne, 2005, Invariant approximations of the minimal robust positively invariant set, IEEE Transactions on Automatic Control, vol. 50, no. 3, pp. 406–410.

S. Narasimhan, N.H. El-Farra, M.J. Ellis, 2021, Detectability-based controller design screening for processes under multiplicative cyberattacks, AIChE Journal, vol. 68, issue 1, pp. e17430.

Proceedings of the 14th International Symposium on Process Systems Engineering – PSE 2021+
June 19-23, 2022, Kyoto, Japan © 2022 Elsevier B.V. All rights reserved.
http://dx.doi.org/10.1016/B978-0-323-85159-6.50243-8

OPC UA information transfer via unidirectional data diode for ICS cyber security

Toshiaki Honda[a], Takashi Hamaguchi[a], Yoshihiro Hashimoto[a]

[a]*Nagoya Insititute of Technology, Nagoya 466-8555 Japan*
h.toshiaki.377@nitech.jp

Abstract

Cyber attacks on critical infrastructure pose serious threats. When industrial control systems (ICS) are targeted by cyber attacks, the resulting incidents cause not only security problems but also safety and pestilence issues. Encrypting the communication data passing through the data diode with OPC UA will further improve the security of the communication in ICS. In this paper, we propose a method to establish both a data diode that prevents intrusion and an OPC UA encrypted communication that prevents interception and tampering.

Keywords: OPC UA; Client/Server; PubSub; Key exchange; Data diode.

1. Improved security by combining data diode and OPC UA

Cyber attacks on critical infrastructure pose serious threats. If an industrial control system (ICS) is the target of a cyber-attack, the incidents it causes are not only security issues but also safety and serious pestilence issues. For example, the negative impact of a cyber-attack can be extraordinary, such as an explosion at a manufacturing site, damage to customers or the environment due to improper shipment of products, or the negative impact on customers and society due to temporary suspension of manufacturing services.

If a controller such as a DCS (Distributed Control System) or PLC (Programmable Logic Controller) behaves improperly, it can cause a serious accident. Unfortunately, the controller is unable to determine whether it is under a cyber attack, so even if it receives a malicious command, it will do as it is told. There are many machines that can obtain controller commands and information about the target of the attack and send commands to the controller, such as operational support systems, advanced control systems, MES (Manufacturing Execution System) servers, and SCADA (Supervisory Control And Data Acquisition) system engineering workstations. If the attacker can obtain information about the controller commands and the target of the attack and hijack these devices to send dangerous commands, a serious accident may occur even if the communication protocol is secure OPC UA.

Therefore, we want to monitor what kind of commands are being communicated, even if they are encrypted. We have already proposed and developed a monitoring system that can manage encrypted communications [1]. This monitoring system will be installed close to the controllers. Since there are many controllers, the monitored command information is aggregated and stored in a separate location. If the location is hijacked by an attacker, the controller can be attacked through the monitoring system installed near the controllers. To solve this problem, we thought of installing the unidirectional data diode in the aggregation path so that even if the aggregation system is hijacked, the attack cannot reach the controller [2].

OPC UA was developed in 2006 as a communication protocol that considers security at the time of design and has been selected as a standard protocol for Industry 4.0, etc. However, since it is a one-to-one communication standard, the engineering cost when setting up communication between many devices has been an issue. The introduction of Publishers and Subscribers (PubSub) communication in addition to Client/Server was announced in 2018 and implemented starting with OPC UA v1.04, released in 2021 PubSub supports UDP, MQTT, and AMQP and can send data to many subscribers at once. Since the flow of data is one-way in PubSub UDP, data diodes can be used in conjunction with it. It can also be used as a network infrastructure able to route datagram-based messages in a broker-less form [3]. Nuclear power plants require the use of unidirectional data diodes when disclosing data. By using unidirectional data diodes to prevent an attacker's invasion and by encrypting the communication data that passes through them with OPC UA, interception and tampering can be prevented, further improving the security of the communication [4] [5].

In this paper, we propose a method for using both data diodes and OPC-UA encrypted communication because security for industrial control systems is an important issue in process system engineering.

2. OPC UA secure communication via the unidirectional data diode

2.1. Basic OPC UA Client/Server models encryption key exchange

The OPC UA's client/server is implemented at the top of the TCP/IP (Transmission Control Protocol/Internet Protocol) stack. The security architecture of OPC UA is a hybrid of the PKI (Public Key Infrastructure) and symmetric key cryptography. The symmetric key cryptosystem is used for encrypting the data, and PKI is used for encrypting the exchange information necessary for authenticating the application and generating the symmetric key. The symmetric key is not reused because it is updated every time the communication connection of OPC UA is started. Moreover, in OPC UA, the confidentiality of the data is improved by using two or more common keys for encryption.

2.2. Basic OPC UA PubSub models encryption key exchange

The OPC Foundation has added the SKS (Security Key Services) specification for use with OPC UA PubSub to the OPC UA PubSub Part 14 specification. SKS is a key exchange architecture. Specifically, SKS is an architecture that provides a common key that publishers can use to sign and encrypt data and subscribers can use to verify and decrypt data signatures. Figure 1 shows the basic key management pattern for OPC UA PubSub. The OPC UA server should support SKS for key exchange. Then, the Publisher should install the encryption key on the SKS. Since SKS is a key management function supported by the OPC UA server, the OPC UA Client/Server model is used for key exchange. Therefore, if the Subscriber obtains the key from SKS, it needs to support the OPC UA client. Furthermore, the key exchange takes place with an authenticated OPC UA client [6].

2.3. Encryption key exchange via the unidirectional data diode

The use of unidirectional data diodes improves security because they can completely block incoming packets. However, since bidirectional communication is not possible, key exchange using SKS through unidirectional data diodes is not possible. Here, we propose a key exchange that can be used when using unidirectional data diodes.

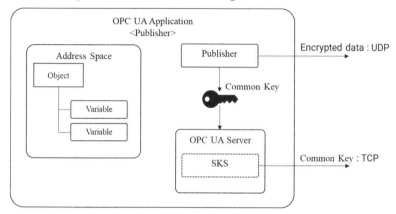

Figure 1 SKS architecture

● Publisher physically hands the key to the Subscriber

A Publisher has multiple topics, and each topic has multiple subscribers. Each topic has a different common key for reading it but the same common key for subscribers of the same topic. Since the subscription period of a topic may be different for each Subscriber, the subscription for each Subscriber needs to be confirmed at the time of registration, and as shown in the arrow at the bottom of Figure 1, different communication is inevitably required than when reading the topic.

The subscription is cross-confirmed through a channel that allows mutual communication, which is opened only during registration, and the Subscriber passes the public key corresponding to his private key to the Subscriber. When the Subscriber is allowed to register, the information needed to synthesize the symmetric key information for the subscription is encrypted by the public key and sent to the Subscriber

This information can only be decrypted by the Subscriber, so confidentiality is ensured. This procedure corresponds to steps (1) through (6) in Figure 2.

To ensure security by switching the common key, the common key information received as described above is not the value of a single common key but contains multiple common keys, and during communication, the subscriber switches which of these keys to use.

● Encrypted communication to switch the common key to be used

The Publisher randomly selects a symmetric key to be used for encryption from the set of symmetric keys exchanged in the first step and sends the ID of the key used in addition to the encrypted communication data. The received Subscriber uses the key ID information to identify the common key for decryption and decrypts the communication data. This procedure corresponds to which of the keys from (7) in Figure 2 is used for decryption.

We propose the above two hybrids. The concept of key exchange is based on PKI. However, as mentioned earlier, only UDP can be used for communication when communicating with unidirectional data diodes. Also, it is a broker-less form of communication.

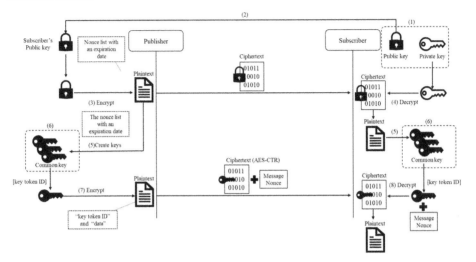

Figure 2 Encryption key exchange sequence

Figure 2 shows the Publisher and Subscriber sequence. It communicates via UDP between Publisher and Subscriber. Figure 2 also shows the key exchange between Publisher and Subscriber. In Figure 2, two pieces of data are sent from Publisher to Subscriber.

The first sequence sends the information needed to generate the common key from the Publisher to the subscribers. The Publisher is required to obtain the public key generated by the Subscriber in advance. The public key cannot be exchanged via the unidirectional data diode, so the public key will need to be physically passed to the Publisher. This can be very laborious and is open to human error, but the public key is safe to send because the Publisher can determine that only the Subscriber with the private key paired with the public key can decrypt it. Subscribers can also specify that the transmission is from an authorized publisher because the encrypted data can be decrypted with their own private key. When exchanging public keys, they need to be carefully exchanged.

The second sequence uses the generated common key to encrypt the data and sends the encrypted data and the key token ID together from Publisher to Subscriber. In OPC UA PubSub, a key token ID can assign to the common key, and the expiration date can be set for the common key. Therefore, OPC UA PubSub can manage multiple common keys and randomly use the common key to encrypt data when sending. The Subscribers can decrypt the encrypted data on the basis of the received key token ID.

2.4. OPC UA PubSub Data encryption and signature

This section describes what encryption OPC UA PubSub does when sending data after key exchange. OPC UA PubSub supports data encryption and signing. The security modes are:

● No security

- Signing but no encryption

- Signing and encryption

Message security is end-to-end security (from Publisher to Subscriber). "No security" means that the message is plain text. "Signing but no encryption" means that the message is only signed. "Signing and encryption" means signing and encrypting a message.

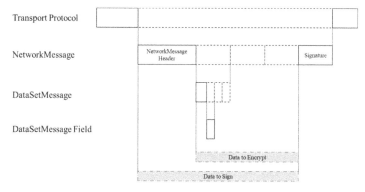

Figure 3 Scope of data signing and encryption

Figure 3 shows the extent of data signing and encryption. The Transport Protocol layer means packets of the protocol. The dashed line in the Transport Protocol layer is the protocol payload. The next layer is the layer defined by OPC UA:

- NetworkMessage

- DataSetMessage

- DataSetMessage Field

NetworkMessage is a container for DataSetMessages that contain information for exchanging data. It also contains security information. The Security information includes signature and encryption processing information. DataSetMessage and DataSetMessage Field are encrypted. DataSetMessage is a collection of DataSetMessage Fields. DataSetMessage Field is the actual value. The scope of encryption is DataSetMessage and DataSetMessage Field.

OPC UA PubSub uses Advanced Encryption Standard Counter Mode (AES-CTR) for data encryption and requires a common key and Message Nonce to decrypt the data. Figure 4 shows the security information contained in NetworkMessage. AES-CTR provides encryption and decryption with pre-exchanged keys and Message Nonce contained in the message. Therefore, data encryption can be more complex, and we can further strengthen our defense against attacks and threats [7].

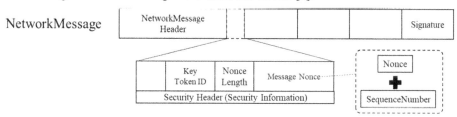

Figure 4 Security information structure

3. Conclusions

This paper proposed a key exchange used when transmitting encrypted data via the unidirectional data diode by OPC UA PubSub. Key exchange does not exchange the common key. The publisher and subscriber exchange randomly generated nonces to generate a common key. Furthermore, OPC UA PubSub uses AES-CTR for data encryption and requires a common key and the Message Nonce to decrypt the data. This can further strengthen our defense against attacks and threats.

Since we have already achieved plaintext communication of OPC UA PubSub, we plan to implement encrypted data via the unidirectional data diode on the basis of this design.

References

[1] W. Machii, I. Kato, M. Koike, M. Matta, T. Aoyama, H. Naruoka, I. Koshijima and Y. Hashimoto, "Dynamic zoning based on situational activitie for ICS security" 10th Asian Control Conference (ASCC), May 2015, pp.1242-1246

[2] T. Honda, Y. Shimazawa, T. Hamaguchi and Y. Hashimoto, "Development of a monitoring system for encrypted data by OPC UA," IIAI 2021 10th International Congress on Advanced Applied Informatics, 2021, pp. 731-736

[3] A. Eckhardt, S. Müller and L. Leurs, "An Evaluation of the Applicability of OPC UA Publish Subscribe on Factory Automation use Cases," 2018 IEEE 23rd International Conference on Emerging Technologies and Factory Automation (ETFA), 2018, pp. 1071-1074

[4] IAEA, "IAEA Nuclear Security Series No. 17," 2011

[5] B. Jeon and J. Na, "A study of cyber security policy in industrial control system using data diodes," 2016 18th International Conference on Advanced Communication Technology (ICACT), 2016, pp. 314-317

[6] OPC Foundation, "OPC Unified Architecture Specification Part 14: PubSub," 2018

[7] IETF, "AES Counter Mode Cipher Suites for TLS and DTLS", 2006

Proceedings of the 14th International Symposium on Process Systems Engineering – PSE 2021+
June 19-23, 2022, Kyoto, Japan © 2022 Elsevier B.V. All rights reserved.
http://dx.doi.org/10.1016/B978-0-323-85159-6.50244-X

Study on Device Authentication System for Dynamic Zoning of Industrial Control Systems

Takanori Miyoshi[a], Shota Shimizu[a], Kanata Nishida[a], Masato Izawa[a], and Isao Kato[a*]

[a]*Cyber-Security R&D Office, Sumitomo Electric Industries, Ltd., 1-1-3, Shimaya, Konohana-ku, Osaka 554-0024, Japan*
kato-isao@sei.co.jp

Abstract

In industrial control systems (ICSs) used in critical infrastructure (CI) such as substations and chemical plants, measures are needed to prevent serious physical damage caused by cyber attacks. This is because high volume simultaneous cyber attacks on CI may lead to complete system malfunction and a chain of serious accidents. For example, if a large-scale power outage occurs due to an accident at a substation, it may affect other CI such as transportation facilities and hospitals. In this paper, we propose a new dynamic zoning method for making system functions redundant and connecting communication paths between functions only when communication is required.

Keywords: Dynamic Zoning; Safety and Security; Device Authentication.

1. Introduction

The number of reports of cyber incidents related to ICSs used in electric power plants and chemical plants has been increasing in recent years (NCCIC, 2016) (Symantec, 2019). The purpose and target of cyber attacks are also changing to geopolitical ones (such as political use, a religious issue or terrorism) (Kaspersky, 2019). A different approach is needed because control systems differ in the assets and features to be protected from traditional information systems. In order to ensure safety, ICSs require measures to increase the probability that the system will move to a state without a possibility of physical damage, assuming that a threat that cannot be completely removed may intrude (Safety-II (Hollnagel, 2014)). Cyber security standards for ICSs (e.g. IEC-62443) recommend isolation of threats and blocking of unnecessary communication paths by defense in depth (DiD) using zones and conduits to improve the security of control systems (Knapp, 2011) (IEC62443-3-2, 2020).

To achieve DiD for control systems, types of fixed and dynamic zoning techniques have been proposed (Hashimoto et al., 2013) (Morita et al., 2013) (Moritani et al., 2014). Since the assets to be protected in the control system change over time, it is necessary to switch the focus of zone on a time axis. Therefore, a dynamic zoning method has been proposed in which zones are dynamically switched according to the operating status of the control system (Machii et al., 2014) (Machii et al., 2015). In a system in which activated functions and assets to be protected change over time, communication between devices should be normally-off and connected only when necessary.

In previous studies (Machii et al., 2014) (Machii et al., 2015), the dynamic zoning method was a software based method to control the logical disconnection of communication channels. As such, the communication channel between devices remains physically connected, and the risk of cyber-attacks on the control system using this communication channel is not completely eliminated. In addition, in the communication control function, the code data used for authentication in device authentication when allowing communication between devices is usually stored and protected in a single location, and a single successful attack could result in the theft of the code data, which could completely hijack the communication control function.

Therefore, for the ideal realization of DiD, the requirements of the communication control function for dynamic zoning include physical connection blocking control of communication paths and distributed management of authentication codes used by the communication control function for device authentication.

The purpose of our study is to implement a more robust dynamic zoning system that detects unauthorized devices on the network and blocks communication on the network to protect society such as a stakeholder's safety and company viability. We proposed a device authentication system that consists of multiple devices with logically independent communication lines (such as separate lines or an aggregation of multiple communication lines). By using our authentication system, when an abnormality in the system due to a cyber-attack is confirmed, it is possible to isolate the threat without stopping the entire system by physically disconnecting the power supply and communication path leading to the connected devices that are in an abnormal state.

2. Device Authentication System for Dynamic Zoning

In this section, we describe the concepts for two types of device authentication systems for dynamic zoning that we are currently developing.

2.1. Device Authentication System with Authentication Switch for ICSs

The concept of this system is shown in Figure 1. This system is a device authentication system using an authentication switch, which has both an authentication function to determine whether or not communication is possible between connected devices, and a communication control function to physically block or switch the connection of communication paths. This system consists of networks (communication lines, power supply lines, and authentication lines), a state control agent in MRP (Manufacturing

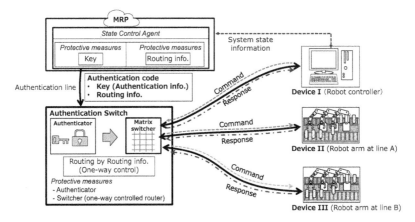

Figure 1: Concept of Device Authentication for ICSs

Resource Planning), an authentication switch, and devices (a robot controller and two robot arms).

The authentication code, which contains authentication information (Key) to verify legitimacy and routing information between connected devices to determine if they can connect to the network, is entered into the authentication switch. After determining the communication availability of the connected devices using the Key in this authentication code, the communication path between the devices is selected using the routing information.

This authentication code can include not only spatial routing information, but also state information of the equipment or control system itself (System state information). By using the system state information, it is possible to dynamically switch the communication route according to the state of the equipment or the operating status of the factory system.

The device authentication procedure for ICSs is as follows:

1. The state control agent in MRP sends the authentication code to the authentication switch via the authentication line.
2. The authentication switch uses the Key to authenticate the device.
3. If the authentication is successful, the authentication switch uses the system state information and the routing information to determine the route between the connected devices by the matrix switcher.

It is also possible to divide and manage this authentication code, and the authentication and routing information of the authentication switch is determined when all of the divided codes are collected. This segmented authentication code is stored in multiple locations that are spatially independent and separated from each other, and each of these locations is protected using different protection methods. Even if a cyber attack is successful and the attacker is able to steal part of the authentication code, the required attack cost is higher than usual because the attacker has to also successfully attack other protection measures that protect the split code to obtain all the segmented codes in order to successfully authenticate.

2.2. Device Authentication System with Security Unit for Mobility Network Systems

Figure 2 shows the concept of device authentication system for mobility network systems that manages automated guided vehicles (AGVs) and other mobility devices in a factory.

This system authenticates devices before they are connected to the network and provides power and a physical connection to the network only to those devices that have successfully authenticated. This system is intended to be used mainly in bus-type networks, and since it only performs connection blocking control of communication, the system can be built with a simpler functional configuration than the device authentication system for ICSs.

Specifically, a physical switch, called a security unit, is used to physically connect the network and devices only after successful authentication. This will prevent unauthorized devices from physically connecting to the network. This system consists of networks (communication lines, power supply lines, and authentication lines), security units, and connected devices. The security unit is a device that has physical network switches for communication and power supply lines and authentication function.

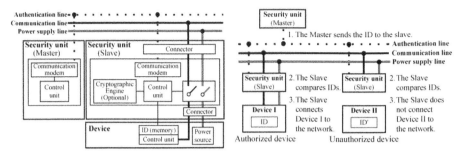

Figure 2: Concept of Device Authentication for Mobility Network Systems

Figure 3: Device Authentication Procedure for Mobility Network Systems

This system uses a Master-Slave type authentication method comprising a security unit, and devices are connected to the network through this security unit (Slave). The security unit consists of a control unit, a physical switch, and a communication modem. The control unit authenticates the connected devices and controls the physical switches. The physical switch connects the device to the communication and power supply lines of the network only if authentication is successful. This makes it possible to prevent unauthorized devices from physically connecting to the network. The communication modem communicates authentication information between security units via the authentication line. Authentication is performed via independent signal lines, which are different from the communication and power supply lines of the network, just like the device authentication system for ICSs. The device has a unique device ID that is used for authentication.

Device authentication procedures using a security unit are shown in Figure 3. The authentication procedure is as follows:

1. The Master sends the ID to the Slave.
2. The Slave compares received ID with the ID held by the connected device.
3. If the IDs match, the Slave will connect the device to the network.

In addition to ID authentication, this system can perform cryptographic authentication between Slave-connected devices using a cryptographic engine, thus enhancing security functions through two-step authentication (Option).

3. System Implementation and Results

To show that our proposed dynamic zoning scheme is feasible using realistic implementation costs and devices available in the market, we have developed a prototype authentication system using a security unit that controls the connection between the CAN bus and the device.

The control unit of the security unit uses an 8-bit microcontroller EFM8BB3 with an operating frequency of 22 MHz. The communication modem uses FSK modulation, and the communication speed can be switched from 4.8 kbps to 22.8 kbps. The ID of the device can be read out between the security unit and the device via 1-wire communication at 16 kbps serial communication.

In our prototype system, we assumed that the devices will be authenticated in a harness network for mobility devices, and that up to 8 devices will be connected to the harness.

Table 1: Evaluation Results and Estimated Time of Device Authentication

	One-to-one (Measured value)	One-to-eight (Estimated value)			
Communication speed [kbps]	19.2	4.8	9.6	19.2	22.8
Authentication time [ms]	34.5	580.8	296.9	163.0	116.5

Assuming that the allowable processing time of an application is 300 ms from the powering-on of a device to the completion of the start-up of all devices, we aimed to keep the authentication time of all devices in this system to within 150 ms, half of that time.

In order to evaluate performance, we confirmed on the actual security unit that the authentication of multiple devices (1-3 devices) connected to the network can be performed successfully. In addition, we calculated the estimated authentication processing time for 8 devices based on the results of this actual measurement, and confirmed that the estimated value could meet the target.

The evaluation included an evaluation of authentication and communication functions and a measurement of authentication time. We checked operation when authentication succeeded and when it failed in order to evaluate the authentication function. In the authentication time measurement evaluation, we measured the time from powering-on until all devices were fully booted after authentication was completed.

Table 1 shows the evaluation results for the authentication time of the prototype system. Using these actual measurements, we estimated the total processing time required for 1-to-8 authentication between Master and Slave. From this estimate, we confirmed that our target time can be met when the communication speed is 22.8 kbps.

4. Discussion

From the performance evaluation results, we have shown that it is possible to construct our proposed device authentication system using small and inexpensive devices. To further reduce the authentication time, it is effective to increase the communication speed in the authentication lines and to reduce the amount of communication data used for authentication.

However, the device authentication system implemented this time does not use two-step authentication with cryptographic authentication using an optional cryptographic engine. Therefore, if the cryptographic strength of the cryptographic engine is high, the processing time of the entire device authentication will increase due to the increase in the processing time of the cryptographic engine. In addition, circuit size may be larger if tamper resistance of the cryptographic engine is included. In environments where communication lines are susceptible to noise, the communication method and speed may be limited to guarantee noise immunity of the authentication lines.

5. Conclusions

In this paper, we proposed a new device authentication system that decentralizes and manages the authentication codes used for device authentication, and controls the physical connection and disconnection of communication and power supply lines. We also developed a prototype and evaluated the performance of the device authentication system for mobility devices, and showed that our proposed method can be realized with realistic implementation costs and devices available in the market. We also plan to conduct the experiments for the device authentication system for ICSs to show that this system can also be realized using devices that are available in the market and have realistic implementation costs.

In an always-on system, isolation of threats by dynamic zoning is an effective means against threats from cyber attacks. Threat isolation using dynamic zoning allows us to remove threats while the system is running, and at worst, safely shut down the system. This enables early restoration of the system, so our study on dynamic zoning implementation can contribute to the enhancement of resilience for business continuity.

References

Y. Hashimoto, T. Toyoshima, S. Yogo, M. Koike, T. Hamaguchi, S. Jing, & I. Koshijima, 2013, Safety securing approach against cyber-attacks for process control system, Computers & Chemical Engineering, Volume 57, 181-186.

E. Hollnagel, 2014, Safety-I and Safety-II, Routledge, ISBN-13: 978-1472423085.

IEC62443-3-2, 2020, Security for industrial automation and control systems - Part 3-2: Security risk assessment for system design, 1st ed.

Kaspersky, 2019, Kaspersky Security Bulletin 2019. Advanced threat predictions for 2020, Retrieved from https://securelist.com/advanced-threat-predictions-for-2020/95055/, (accessed 2022-01-14).

E. D. Knapp, 2011, Industrial Network Security, Syngress, ISBN-13: 978-0124201149.

W. Machii, I. Kato, M. Koike, M. Matta, T. Aoyama, I. Koshijima, & Y. Hashimoto, 2014, Dynamic Zoning of the Industrial Control System for Security Improvement, The 5th World Conference of Safety of Oil and Gas Industry (WCOGI 2014), Paper No. 1065756.

W. Machii, I. Kato, M. Koike, M. Matta, T. Aoyama, H. Naruoka, I. Koshijima, & Y. Hashimoto, 2015, Dynamic Zoning Based on Situational Activitie for ICS Security, The 10th Asian Control Conference (ASCC 2015), 1242-1246.

T. Morita, S. Yogo, M. Koike, T. Hamaguchi, S. Jung, I. Koshijima, & Y. Hashimoto, 2013, Detection of Cyber-attacks with Zone Dividing and PCA, Procedia Computer Science, Volume 22, 727-736.

H. Moritani, S. Yogo, T. Morita, M. Kojima, K. Watanabe, J. Sun, I. Koshijima, & Y. Hashimoto, 2014, Development of cad for zone dividing of process control networks to improve cyber security, 2014 14th International Conference on Control, Automation and Systems (ICCAS 2014), 1311-1316.

National Cybersecurity and Communications Integration Center (NCCIC), 2016, ICS-CERT Year in Review 2016, Retrieved from https://us-cert.cisa.gov/sites/default/files/Annual_Reports/Year_in_Review_FY2016_Final_S508C.pdf, (accessed 2022-01-14).

Symantec, 2019, Symantec 2019 Internet Security Threat Report, Volume 24. Retrieved from https://docs.broadcom.com/docs/istr-24-2019-en, (accessed 2022-01-14).

Proceedings of the 14th International Symposium on Process Systems Engineering – PSE 2021+
June 19-23, 2022, Kyoto, Japan © 2022 Elsevier B.V. All rights reserved.
http://dx.doi.org/10.1016/B978-0-323-85159-6.50245-1

Designing Framework for Tabletop Exercise to Promote Resilience Against Cyber Attacks

Yuitaka OTA[a*], Haruna ASAI, Shiho TANIUCHI, Erika Mizuno[a], Tomomi AOYAMA[a], Yoshihiro HASHIMOTO[a,] and Ichiro KOSHIJIMA[a]

aNagoya Institute of Technology, Nagoya 466-8555, JAPAN
cjr17009@nitech.ac.jp

Abstract

In recent years, there has been an increase in the number of cyber-attacks targeting ICS (Industrial Control System), also used in the critical infrastructure that supports our daily lives. As a result, companies using ICS need to improve their ability to respond to cyber incidents to ensure business continuity. Cyber incidents at ICS require an enterprise-wide response, as they have a significant impact on IT system security issues, plant safety, and the company's business. For this company-wide response to proceed smoothly, it is essential to create a response plan in advance and create an environment that allows for an instant response when an incident occurs. Many companies do not have enough experience with ICS-targeted incident response to develop this plan. In this study, we developed an exercise to simulate an incident and improve response to a cyber-attack.

Keywords: Cyber Security, Exercise, Cyber-Resilience

1. Introduction

Since controllers installed in a uranium enrichment plant were cyber-attacked in 2010[1], we must recognize that cyber-attacks have become a real threat to our production plants. It is fresh in our memory that in May 2021, the US pipeline [2] interrupted its service due to a cyber-attack by ransomware. In addition, HatMan[3] has been reported as malware that targets "safety instrumentation systems" that protect plant safety.

Until now, companies have created and operated Safety-Response Plans for safety incidents such as equipment failure and natural disasters on the ICS side, and Security-Response Plans for security incidents such as information leakage on the IT side. We have created and implemented. The authors believe it is essential to consider and prepare a business continuity plan (BCP) to ensure the plant's safety and business even in a cyber-attack on the ICS network. In addition, we believe that it is necessary to understand how cyber-attacks affect plants to consider countermeasures against cyber-attack-targeting plants (ICS BCP). However, many companies have experience with cyberattacks on IT systems, but not on OT systems. (They may be under cyber-attack but may not be able to detect them).

Therefore, we need a mechanism to gain experience with ICS cyber incidents to plan ICS-BCP. Hence, we are developing an exercise that allows to experience a simulated cyber incident to solve this problem. New exercises were developed to compensate for the improvements identified in other exercises designed and implemented.

In this paper, we describe the previous and newly developed exercises.

2. Exercises for improving resilience developed

We have been developing discussion-based ICS security exercises to recognize that hard skills such as control equipment operation and IT forensics and soft skills such as organizational cooperation and information sharing are essential in dealing with cyber incidents.

2.1. Type1: Roleplay based Cyber Defense Exercise [4]

Through this exercise, it is intended that the exercise participants will be able to discuss and learn about communication during incidents, their roles as incident response commanders, and the capabilities (communication and information gathering) required to fulfill their roles properly.

The field exercises simulate cyber incident management and require participants to respond to incidents by assessing the situation according to scenarios that play out in real-time. Figure 1 shows an exercise scenario as a communication path.

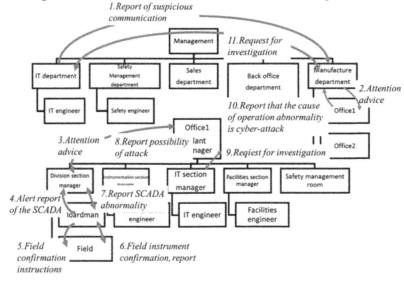

Figure1 Type1 exercise based on emergency communication management

This exercise is a simulation-type exercise based on a scenario that has been prepared in advance. Each exercise participant uses a computer in the exercise, and each is given a unique role in the scenario. There are two roles in the exercise: the role played by the exercise participants (Assigned Role) and the automatic response role (Virtual Role), which is the department or person in charge required to proceed with the exercise scenario. Each role is limited in the actions it can choose and the information it can know. Sharing the correct information at the right moment increases the number of actions available for selection.

As a result, by simulating a real-time accident response, the exercise participants will understand the importance of speed in decision-making when an accident occurs and that decisions can only be made if the proper information is conveyed to the right people at the right time.

2.2. Type2: Workflow Based Cyber Defense Exercise [5]

In this exercise, the following discussions will take place.
1. the actions and inter-organizational coordination required to ensure the safety of the factory where the incident occurred
2. the actions and communication required to suspect that the cause of the incident is a cyber attack
3. actions and communication required to eliminate the cause of the incident.

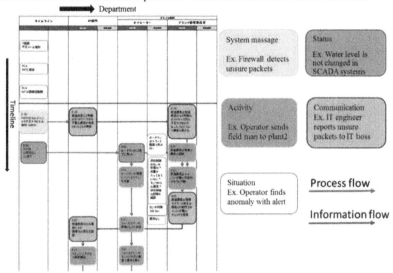

Figure2 Type2 exercise based on emergency workflow

The exercise participants will do the action the following:

1) The exercise participants are given the following information: "An alarm indicating a sudden operational abnormality is triggered, but the instruments are normal on the HMI" and "A security tool has detected an abnormality.

2) Describe the actions to be taken in the appearance where only the swim lane is shown, imagining what may happen as time passes.

3) Add a communication path for information sharing between the described actions.

The exercise participants will create a workflow by performing the tasks 1)-3), as shown in Figure 2. The exercise participants will understand the required organizational structure and information control that is the core of the response by expressing a department that needs to understand both the cyber incident signal and the process event signal on the OT side in each phase (1-3). Such a department should be the leading actor between the IT and OT sides by expressing the departments responsible for actions on the IT and OT sides and the duties involved in decision-making through communication.

These two exercises were conducted at a workshop organized by the Nagoya Institute of Technology and at the ICSCoE (Industrial Cyber Security Center of Excellence) [6] of the Ministry of Economy, Trade and Industry of Japan. As a result, the following results were obtained.

- In the Type 1 exercise, some participants said they understood the importance of an environment where communication is necessary for incident response and where rules can be established in advance so that actions can be taken before thinking.

- However, in Type1 exercise, the scenario proceeds simply by the exercise participants deciding on their actions. As a result, the exercise participants may only enjoy the exercise as a game and may not achieve the meta-learning envisioned in the exercise.

- In the Type 2 exercise, the students must imagine and respond to an incident situation in a plant or network based on the given conditions. Therefore, some say they could enhance their ability to set up temporary structures, which is necessary for formulating ICS-BCP. However, since this imagining is based on what the exercise participants have experienced so far, if they have little experience in planning the organization's incident response, they may not know what to do and may not be able to grasp the whole picture of the reaction, making the exercise less effective.

- Furthermore, since the two types of exercise focuses on organizational coordination and communication in a cyber incident, there were many cases where exercise participants who had no experience with cyber incidents could not envision the actions to be taken. In this situation, the exercise participants focused on the hard skills that they could understand or imagine, such as checking the IT system's log or the PLC's logic, and sometimes failed to achieve the essence of the exercise.

3. Card-Type Incident Response Exercise

The authors developed an exercise based on the results of our exercises described in Chapter 2 that does not depend on the experience of the exercise participants, focuses more on communication, and allows discussion of the concept of what is needed for communication, inter-organizational collaboration, and planning during an incident.
In this new exercise, participants will be given a worksheet as shown in Figure 3 and several cards with the actions taken on the front and the action's results on the back.
1)   Cards
The cards are categorized into four types: action cards, situation awareness cards, information sharing cards, and attack cards, as shown below.

- Action cards:
  This card is to ensure plant safety and to continue the corporate business.
- Situation defining cards:
  This card is for recognizing the situation to select an action.
- Information sharing cards:
  This card is for thinking about information sharing that should be done when an incident occurs.
- Attack cards:
  This card is not presented during the exercise, but it is essential for the exercise's progress. This card needs to be aligned with the cyber kill chain.

In addition, to measure the exercise participants' lack of knowledge and misunderstanding, we also prepared cards with unnecessary actions in the scenario in question.

2)   Worksheet
As in the Type-2 circumference, the swim lane lists the departments directly or indirectly related to the ICS-BCP, from the person in charge of the on-site operation in

an emergency to the sales and public relations departments. Exercise participants can add departments as needed. (Action cards related to that department can also be added.) However, some departments do not have a card with actions to be taken.

Exercise participants will perform the following actions:

(1) Based on the given information, infer a possible situation in the plant and ICS network.
(2) Select the actions that may be necessary as cards.
(3) Place the cards on the worksheet.

By performing the tasks (1)-(3), the incident response process is examined.

By having the actions presented in advance, the exercise participants do not have to discuss the details of the actions but rather.

The discussion can now focus on the communication content and inter-organizational collaboration required along the incident response process.

- What information is needed to initiate and implement the action and where it originates from
- The information needed to share the results of the action and its source
- Who acts and who directs organizers?

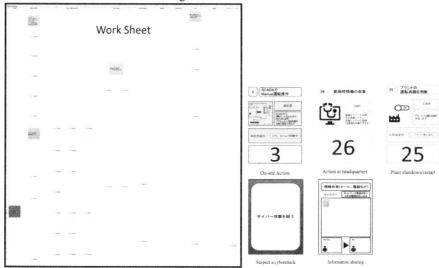

Figure3 Exercise worksheet developed on Microsoft Excel

4. Pilot Exercise

The pilot exercise using newly method was evaluated at ICSCoE. For this trial, over 100 students participated in this trial. Here are some of their comments:

- The visualization of activities by the action cards made it easier to promote discussions around the need for inter-organizational collaboration.
- I was able to think more deeply about incident response by explaining the need for adding selected action card in a logical (5W1H) manner.
- Considering the division of duties in my company, I cannot image of any action to request to the "Safety Management Department" in case of a cyber-attack. I could understand the necessity of revising the internal rules because safety measures are essential.

- The swim lanes in the worksheet included customers, control equipment vendors, and government agencies, which made me realize that incident response is not only for internal use but also for external stakeholders.
- I recognized the need to review the current safety response to recover from cyber incidents.
- The response workflow could be configured with almost the same cards regardless of the method of cyber-attack. This fact helped me to understand the effectiveness of the Consequence-driven Cyber-informed Engineering proposed by INL [7].
- This new exercise method can be customized by your company with little effort, such as changing card contents, modifying swim lanes, and adding cards.

5. Conclusions

In this paper, the authors have described the exercises we have developed to increase the pseudo experience of cyber incidents. We believe that this exercise is essential for companies to plan their ICS-BCP to mitigate damage and recover the current situation as soon as possible in the event of a cyber incident.

In the future, we will introduce a method to make people aware of possible risks due to failure to act [8] to improve resiliency to cyber incidents.

References

[1]SECURELIST by Kaspersky, Stuxnet: Zero victims, https://securelist.com/stuxnet-zero-victims/67483/

[2]BBC NEWS, US fuel pipeline hackers 'didn't mean to create problems', https://www.bbc.com/news/business-57050690

[3]CYBERSECURITY & INFRASTRUCTURE SECURITY AGENCY, MAR-17-352-01 HatMan – Safety System Targeted Malware(Update B), https://us-cert.cisa.gov/ics/MAR-17-352-01-HatMan-Safety-System-Targeted-Malware-Update-B

[4]H. Hirai, Y. Takayama, T. Aoyama, Y. Hashimoto, and I. Koshijima, 2018, Development of the Cyber Exercise for Critical Infrastructures Focusing on Inter-Organization Communication, 13th International Symposium on Process Systems Engineering(PSE 2018) (pp. 1669-1674)

[5]Y. Ota, T. Aoyama, D. Nyambayar, and I. Koshijima, Cyber Incident Exercise for Safety Protection in Critical Infrastructure, Int J. Saf. Secure. Eng. 8,246-257(2018)

[6]Information-technology Promotion Agency (IPA), Industrial Cyber Security Center of Excellence (ICSCoE), https://www.ipa.go.jp/icscoe/english/index.html

[7]Idaho National Laboratory, CONSEQUENCE-DRIVEN CYBER-INFORMED ENGINEERING, https://inl.gov/cce/

[8]E. Mizuno, Y. Saito, T. Hamaguchi, and Y. Hashimoto, 2021, Cyber Incident Response Tabletop Exercise to Raise Ownership, Proceeding of the Japan Joint Automatic Control Conference 64

Proceedings of the 14th International Symposium on Process Systems Engineering – PSE 2021+
June 19-23, 2022, Kyoto, Japan © 2022 Elsevier B.V. All rights reserved.
http://dx.doi.org/10.1016/B978-0-323-85159-6.50246-3

Self-Organizing Map Based Approach for Assessment of Control Room Operator Training

Mohammed Aatif Shahab[a*], Babji Srinivasan[b,c*], Rajagopalan Srinivasan[b,c**]

[a]Department of Applied Mechanics, Indian Institute of Technology Madras, Chennai, Tamil Nadu, 600036, India
[b]Department of Chemical Engineering, Indian Institute of Technology Madras, Chennai, Tamil Nadu, 600036, India
[c]American Express Lab for Data Analytics, Risks and Technology, Indian Institute of Technology Madras, Chennai, Tamil Nadu, 600036, India
*babji.srinivasan@iitm.ac.in, **raj@iitm.ac.in

Abstract

Operators' knowledge during abnormal situations that are faced in chemical process industries is critical to ensure safety. Operators expand their knowledge base through training programmes that assess their comprehension and skills using simple success and failure criteria, process-based measures, and operator actions. However, these assessment techniques often overlook factors relevant to the evaluation of their cognitive capabilities such as information acquisition pattern, cognitive workload and decision-making strategy. In this work, we present a methodology for evaluating operators' performance during training that blends process-based measurements with eye-tracking-derived cognitive behaviour. Our methodology is based on Self-Organizing Map (SOM), an unsupervised neural network that allows optimum visualization of complex data. Accordingly, we trained two different SOM networks, one using the process data and the other using eye-tracking data to obtain information about operators' performance during training. Results indicate that when operators learn the process dynamics, the number of neuronal clusters hit by the process as well as operators' eye gaze trajectory decrease. The decrease in the number of clusters on SOM trained using process data indicates improved operator performance in terms of successful completion of the task and correct control action with appropriate magnitude. On the other hand, the decrease in the number of clusters hit on SOM trained using eye gaze data signifies that the operator attends to only a few regions on HMI that are critical to the current disturbance/abnormality in the process. Thus, the proposed methodology can be used to gauge the operators' learning progress during training to understand the transition from novice to expert.

Keywords: Operator Training, Self-Organizing Map, Eye-Tracking, Cognitive Behavior

1. Introduction

Control room operators are responsible for monitoring the state of the process and intervene when abnormal situations occur. This requires in-depth knowledge of the process dynamics, and therefore, operators' understanding of the process is crucial to ensure safe plant operation, higher throughput and optimal product quality. However, the complex automation and control techniques have made it challenging for the operators to understand causal relationships related to process behavior (Liu et al., 2012).

Process industries have resorted to operator training programs that aim to impart operators with the knowledge of process dynamics. Process industries widely use operator training simulators (OTS) to train operators. An OTS provides a credible simulation of the process along with the automation systems. Various studies have sought to evaluate operator performance using OTS. In these studies, the assessment of operators' performance is primarily based on subjective evaluation and/or process and operator actions. Subjective measures are based on expert's opinions and are vulnerable to confirmation biases (Nazir and Manca, 2015). Approaches based on process and action-based metrics usually rely on metrics derived from process behavior (alarm information, deviation of process from steady-state) and operator responses (completion time, sequence of actions). However, there are hardly any approaches that focus on understanding the cognitive workload of operators, crucial to enhancing operators' abilities. Further, existing studies do not focus on the evolution of the operator performance during training. Therefore, it is necessary to develop an approach that can: provide information about the evolution of operators' performance and the cognitive workload of operators during training (Das et al., 2017).

Recent advancements in sensor technology have made it possible to objectively assess human cognitive behavior in high-risk industries (Srinivasan et al., 2019). In our previous works, we have used physiological sensors like eye tracking (Das et al., 2017) and electroencephalography (Iqbal et al., 2020) to study the cognitive components of operators' performance. For instance, we found that gaze entropy can distinguish between expert and novice operators (Bhavsar et al., 2017). Gaze entropy quantifies the spatial distribution of eye gaze on the HMI. Gaze transition entropy was found to be lower for expert operators indicating that they attend only a few regions on Human-Machine Interface, which are critical for dealing with process abnormality. Recently, Shahab et al. (2021) found that the fixation transition entropy decreases and remains at lower values when operators have learned to control the disturbance. This is because operators initially explore the state space of the process. Then, with learning, they understand causal relationships, which manifests in ordered eye gaze transitions between important regions on HMI. With the experience from our previous works, in this study, we propose to evaluate the evolution of operators' performance during training using process data, operator actions and eye-tracking data. Unlike our prior research in which specific regions on the HMI were pre-defined, this study employs an unsupervised neural network called the Self-Organizing Map (SOM) to visualize changes in operator performance with learning. Thus, the application of SOM can help eliminate human interference in operator performance analysis, and provide insights into human operator performance solely based on the process and eye-tracking information.

2. Experimental Studies and Methodology

The experimental study consisted of operators interacting with the Human Machine Interface (HMI) of an in-house chemical process simulator. The operators were asked to monitor the process and intervene during process abnormalities (using sliders provided on the HMI). Failure on the part of operators results in an automatic shutdown of the plant. The study lasted for 24 days, during which ten participants performed several repetitions of process control tasks, henceforth called as trials. Each trial involves six different scenarios (disturbance rejection tasks). In total, these ten participants performed 81 trials for each scenario leading to a total of 486 tasks. The reader is referred to Iqbal et al. (2021) for more details on the experimental protocol. We recorded process data, alarm information, and operator action data during all these trials. In addition to these measurements, we also recorded eye-gaze data obtained from Tobii TX 300 eye tracker, at a sampling rate of 120 Hz.

We used Self-Organizing Map as a tool to dynamically assess the improvement in operators' performance with the repetition of trials. SOM can project high-dimensional data to a low dimensional space and therefore can serve as a visualization tool to observe the changes in process and operator cognitive behavior. SOMs use an unsupervised learning neural network trained with a competitive learning algorithm to create smaller subspaces. The number of neurons selected for training SOM network is given by $8\sqrt{I}$, where I is the number of samples available for training. For every sample input, "winning" neurons (i.e., neurons that most closely resemble the sample input) are identified. The winning neuron for a sample point is the one which minimizes the Euclidian distance between the neuron and the sample input. Neuronal weights are then adjusted according to the location of "winning" neuron. After several iterations of input data sets, similar neurons come closer to each other based on their weights. A suitable clustering algorithm is then applied to group the neurons into clusters. The SOM can be used for visualization using Unified Distance Matrix (U-matrix). U-matrix depicts the boundary between each pair of neurons by calculating the distance between a neuron and its neighbour. Similar group of neurons are indicated by "Valleys" which are separated by "Mountains" from dissimilar group of neurons. Interested readers are referred to Ng and Srinivasan (2008) for more details on the SOM implementation. We trained two different SOM networks, one using the process data consisting of eleven process variables (data set of size 30781 × 11) described as M^{SOM} and the other using eye-tracking data consisting of eye gaze coordinates on the HMI and gaze duration (dataset of size 97531 × 3) described as N^{SOM}. The data to train SOM networks consists of all the available data from all the tasks (486 tasks). Next, we applied a K-means clustering algorithm to group similar neurons together. The neuronal clusters on M^{SOM} represent different process operating conditions while these represent different regions of HMI on the N^{SOM}.

To assess a particular operator's performance during a task, their process and eye gaze data is projected to the SOM space. The operators' performance during the task can be visualized by the number of neuronal clusters hit by the process and the eye gaze trajectory on M^{SOM} and N^{SOM}, respectively. We hypothesize that the number of neuronal clusters hit by the process trajectory on M^{SOM} (N_{C_P}) should decrease with repetition of trials. This is because when the operator develops an understanding of the process dynamics, they use the correct control strategy to deal with the process abnormalities. Thus, the process trajectory should end in a steady-state cluster without any hit on other process operating states. Hits on additional neuronal clusters indicate incorrect control action from the operator. Similarly, it is expected that number of neuronal clusters hit by the eye gaze trajectory on N^{SOM} (N_{C_F}) should decrease owing to the attention to only a few regions on HMI related to the process abnormality. In addition to these measures, we also evaluated operators' proactive monitoring strategy, crucial for enhancing operators' ability to deal with process abnormalities. Accordingly, we identified neuronal clusters belonging to the trend panel (area on the HMI where process variables trend is displayed). It is expected that the percentage hits on the neuronal clusters belonging to the trend panel should increase with repetition of trials. This indicates operators' ability to take time-dependent information and foresee the direction of the process. Next, we demonstrate the applicability of the proposed methodology using experimental studies.

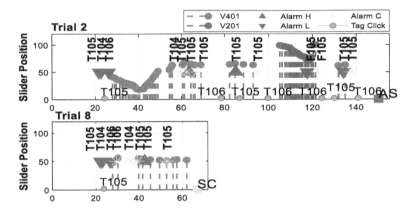

Figure 1: Operators actions with alarm information during trials 2 and 8.

3. Results and Discussion

In this section, we demonstrate the potential of the proposed methodology in capturing operators' learning progress during training using an illustrative example. Consider an operator who performed eight trials of a scenario involving a disturbance in the reflux ratio of the distillation column. The disturbance can be rectified by opening the reflux valve V401 (at least 53% open) provided on the HMI. Operator actions in the second and the last trial are shown in Fig. 1. Consider trial 2 (Fig. 1), at around 22 s, low T104, and low T105 alarms occur, followed by low T106 alarm in distillation column. Operator clicks on the tag of T105 to observe the trend of the process variable T105 and takes the first control action at around 28 s by manipulating V401; however, in the wrong direction. At around 41 s, the operator changes the direction of V401 which clears low T104 and low T105 alarms, but not T106, which results in automatic shutdown of the process. In the same trial, the operator also manipulates feed flow to the distillation column valve (V201) later, depicting that the operator keeps on exploring the possible actions which can clear the disturbance in the process. The use of multiple control actions indicates that the operator is unaware of the root cause of the disturbance. During the last trial (trial 8), as shown in Fig. 1, the operator manipulates the valve V401 by watching T105 (as shown in Fig. 1 by clicking on T105 which opens its trend) and able to clear all the alarms in the process. The manipulation of the valve V401 was very precise, and the participant increased slider opening to a maximum of 3 % during each manipulation, unlike trial 2 where the operator manipulates the slider abruptly (25% increase within short interval of time). The smooth movement of the valve in the eighth trial is an indication that the operator now understands the time constant of the process variables. Thus, with the repetition of trials, the operator learns the root cause of the disturbance along with appropriate amount of manipulation required.

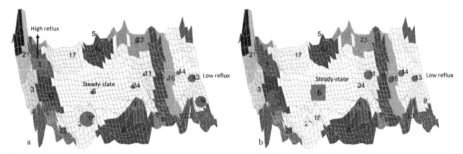

Figure 2: Process trajectory represented on SOM space during (a) Second trial (b) Eighth trial. Cluster hits are depicted by circles.

The process behavior and operator's eye gaze behaviour for the second and eighth trials are depicted in the SOM space in Fig. 2 and Fig. 3. During these trials, the process behavior and effect of control actions on the process can be observed by hits of process trajectory on neuronal clusters. The hits of the process trajectory on the neuronal clusters on M^{SOM} during the second and the eighth trial is shown in Fig. 2 (a) and Fig. 2 (b) respectively, using circles on the clusters. Rectangles on the neuronal cluster represent the end of the process trajectory. During trial 1, it can be observed that the operator's poor control action strategy leads the process to cluster 23 and 18 and further ends the process in cluster 1 (as depicted by a rectangle in Fig. 2 (a)). The total number of cluster hits by the process trajectory (N_{C_P}) during the second trial is 11. However, from Fig. 2 (b), it can be observed that in the eighth trial, the N_{C_P} decreases to 8, and the process trajectory ends in cluster 6 (steady state cluster). This indicates improved operator performance in terms of successful completion of the task and correct control action with appropriate magnitude. Fig. 3 shows operator's eye gaze behavior projected to SOM space during the second and eighth trials. It can be observed that the number of clusters hits by the operator's eye gaze trajectory (N_{C_F}) decreases to 7 in the last trial as compared to the first trial. This signifies that the operator has oriented their eye gaze pattern as per the demands of the task and directed their attention to critical information sources related to the process abnormality. The percentage of hits on neuronal clusters belonging to the trend panel cluster (clusters 4, 5 and 7) also increases from 40% in the second trial to 54 % in the last trial. This indicates operator develops a proactive monitoring strategy with learning. Thus, the proposed SOM based operator performance assessment methodology can act as a powerful technique to evaluate the effectiveness of operator training programs.

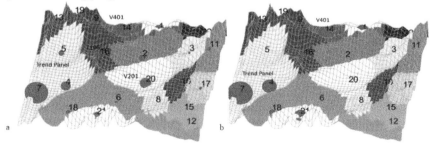

Figure 3: Operator's eye gaze trajectory represented on SOM space during (a) Second trial (b) Last trial. Clusters hits are represented by red circles.

4. Conclusions

The present work proposes an integrated process-based and operator cognitive behavior based methodology to assess operators' performance during training. The approach uses eye-tracking to obtain a trace of attention allocation of operators on the HMI. Self-Organizing Map is used to analyze the process and eye-tracking data. The evolution of cluster hits by the process, and the eye gaze trajectory on SOM can be used to track the learning progress of operators. When the operators develop correct understanding of the process dynamics, the number of clusters hit by process trajectory (N_{C_P}) and eye gaze trajectory decreases. This reflects the development of correct process comprehension and eye gaze orientation in accordance with task demands. Further, our methodology also evaluates operators' proactive monitoring strategy indicated by the percentage of hits by the eye gaze trajectory on the neuronal cluster belonging to trend panel. Our future work is intended to develop an expert operators' model using cognitive markers so as to use that as a benchmark to evaluate the performance of novice operators. The expert model can also be used to transfer knowledge to novices, thus reducing the time of training programs. Finally, a SOM can be trained using multivariate data from several physiological sensors to get deeper insights into the cognitive behavior underlying operators' expertise level.

Acknowledgments: This work is partially funded by American Express Lab for Data Analytics, Risk and Technology, Indian Institute of Technology Madras

References

Bhavsar, P., Srinivasan, B., & Srinivasan, R. (2017). Quantifying situation awareness of control room operators using eye-gaze behavior. Computers & chemical engineering, 106, 191-201.

Das, L., Srinivasan, B., & Srinivasan, R. (2017). Cognitive behavior based framework for operator learning: knowledge and capability assessment through eye tracking. In Computer Aided Chemical Engineering (Vol. 40, pp. 2977-2982). Elsevier.

Iqbal, M. U., Srinivasan, B., & Srinivasan, R. (2020). Dynamic assessment of control room operator's cognitive workload using Electroencephalography (EEG). Computers & Chemical Engineering, 141, 106726.

Iqbal, M. U., Shahab, M. A., Choudhary, M., Srinivasan, B., & Srinivasan, R. (2021). Electroencephalography (EEG) based cognitive measures for evaluating the effectiveness of operator training. Process Safety and Environmental Protection, 150, 51-67.

Liu, X.-W., Shen, X.-W., Fan, D., & Noda, M. (2012) ACP Approach-Based Plant Human–Machine Interaction Evaluation. Service Science, Management, and Engineering:, 247–264

Nazir, S., & Manca, D. (2015). How a plant simulator can improve industrial safety. Process Safety Progress, 34(3), 237-243.

Ng, Y. S., & Srinivasan, R. (2008). Multivariate temporal data analysis using self-organizing maps. 1. Training methodology for effective visualization of multistate operations. Industrial & engineering chemistry research, 47(20), 7744-7757.

Shahab, M. A., Srinivasan, B., & Srinivasan, R. (2021). Evaluating Control Room Operator Training Outcomes Through Eye Gaze Augmented Multi-Scale Data. In Computer Aided Chemical Engineering (Vol. 50, pp. 1307-1312). Elsevier.

Srinivasan, R., Srinivasan, B., Iqbal, M. U., Nemet, A., & Kravanja, Z. (2019). Recent developments towards enhancing process safety: Inherent safety and cognitive engineering. Computers & Chemical Engineering, 128, 364-383.

Proceedings of the 14th International Symposium on Process Systems Engineering – PSE 2021+
June 19-23, 2022, Kyoto, Japan © 2022 Elsevier B.V. All rights reserved.
http://dx.doi.org/10.1016/B978-0-323-85159-6.50247-5

Digital Twin of Alkaline Water Electrolysis Systems for Green Hydrogen Production

Yongbeom Shin[a], Jongyeon Oh[a], Dongkuk Jang[b], Dongil Shin[a,b*]

[a]*Dept. of Chemical Engineering, Myongji University, Yongin, Gyeonggido 17058, Korea*
[b]*Dept. of Disaster and Safety, Myongji University, Yongin, Gyeonggido 17058, Korea*
dongil@mju.ac.kr

Abstract

The digital twin which supports data-based decision making, optimization, control and anomaly detection and diagnosis, can contribute to the improvement of sustainability, agility and productivity in water electrolysis system, which is expected to provide to reduce green hydrogen production cost. In this study, we propose a digital twin for a 500kW alkaline water electrolysis (AWE) to be built at the Saemangeum Renewable Energy National Demonstration Complex in Korea to reduce green hydrogen production cost through optimal operation of AWE system. A simulation model, which is the basis of the digital twin, was developed with Python and gPROMS, and the system efficiency of the AWE process according to pressure was analyzed comparing between excluding the compression process and including the process of hydrogen compression to 200 bar. The optimum operating pressure with the compression showed at 10-30 bar. At high pressure, process equipment cost becomes higher, therefore, it is essential to consider hydrogen compression to the storage pressure in order to decide the optimal operating conditions.

Keywords: Alkaline water electrolysis, digital twin, optimal operating conditions.

1. Introduction

As the spread of renewables, it is required to increase the storage capacity of surplus energy due to intermittent characteristics, and a technology with low energy loss and high efficiency in the storage is required. Green hydrogen (by P2G) is an important eco-friendly energy source for storing surplus energy. However, its production cost is about five times higher than hydrogen produced by other methods (natural gas reforming), and alkaline water electrolysis (AWE) systems which have the highest technological maturity still have high hydrogen production costs.

Many researchers have interest of methods for reducing green hydrogen production cost included scale-up of water electrolysis system, development of high-efficiency electrode or separator material, and operation optimization. Ulleberg (2003) developed a mathematical model of an AWE system and demonstrated it for the photovoltaic-hydrogen energy plant in Julich, and Jang (2021a) proposed high-pressure operation to reduce the energy consumption of the process because hydrogen produced from the AWE system is compressed to high pressure for storage. Energy consumption and efficiency were analyzed through a model developed by Aspen Plus. Then, Jang (2021b) tried to optimize the operating conditions by analyzing the effect of temperature on the system using the developed Aspen Plus model.

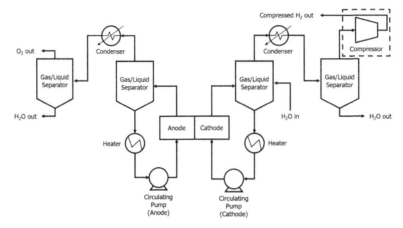

Figure 1. Diagram of the AWE system including the compressor

In this study, we propose a digital twin that integrates functions, water electrolysis process simulation, control, monitoring, optimization, to reduce green hydrogen production cost. A digital twin will be built for a 500kW AWE to be built at the Renewable Energy National Demonstration Complex in Saemangeum, Korea.

In this study, a simulation model, which is the basis of the digital twin, was developed in Python and gPROMS, and the system efficiency of the AWE process according to pressure was analyzed. For the simulation, gPROMS' gML Process and Electrochemical Cell Reactor (ECR) module are used, but the ECR module does not reflect the characteristics of the liquid electrolyte of the AWE, so the cell model in Python is developed. The process simulation model is proposed using custom modeling template of gPROMS to apply the AWE cell model. The process of compression to 200 bar, the load pressure of the trailer truck, is considered as a part of the water electrolysis system. To analyze the impact of the compression to the system efficiency, the optimal operating conditions of the AWE system are compared with the results of excluding compression.

2. Alkaline Water Electrolysis System

Figure 1 is a process diagram of an alkaline water electrolysis system for green hydrogen production. The alkaline water electrolysis system consists of a water electrolysis stack, gas/liquid separator, condenser, heater, pump, and compressor. Oxygen is generated at the anode, hydrogen is generated at the cathode, and the amount of water consumed to maintain the electrolyte concentration is supplied to the separator on cathode side. The generated gas is separated through a gas/liquid separator, and water is removed in the condenser. The hydrogen produced is then compressed to a pressure of 200 bar for loading into a trailer truck.

3. Model Description

3.1. AWE cell model in Python

The electrochemical reaction module of gPROMS, ECR, does not reflect the effects of liquid electrolytes, such as the bubble effect of AWE systems. An AWE cell model to apply in gPROMS is required, cell modeling is performed using Python.

3.1.1. Reversible voltage

Water electrolysis is a non-spontaneous reaction and requires the supply of electrical energy. The reversible voltage, which is the theoretical electrical energy required for the electrolysis of water, can be calculated by the Nernst equation, and is as follows:

$$V_{rev} = V_{rev}^{\circ} + \frac{RT}{2F}\ln\left(\frac{(P-P_{H_2O})^{1.5}P_{H_2O}^*}{P_{H_2O}}\right) \tag{2}$$

where V_{rev}° is the reversible voltage at the standard conditions, P_{H_2O} is the vapor pressure of the KOH solution, $P_{H_2O}^*$ is the vapor pressure of pure water, $P, T, R, and\ F$ are the operating pressure, temperature, gas constant, and Faraday constant.

The first term represents reversible voltage at the standard conditions can be expressed as temperature (Hammoudi, 2012):

$$V_{rev,T}^{\circ} = 1.50342 - 9.956 \times 10^{-4}T + 2.5 \times 10^{-7}T^2 \tag{3}$$

where T is the operating temperature, m is the molar concentration, w is the w weight percent concentration of KOH solution.

3.1.2. Activation overvoltage

For the water electrolysis reaction of an actual alkaline water electrolysis cell, electrical energy above the reversible voltage is required due to resistance, and it can be expressed as follows:

$$V_{cell} = V_{rev} + V_{act} + V_{ohm} \tag{4}$$

where V_{act} is the activation overvoltage, V_{ohm} is the ohmic overvoltage.

Activation overvoltage the energy loss due to the decrease of the electrochemical reaction rate at the anode and cathode, which can be expressed by the Butler-Volmer equation:

$$V_{act} = \frac{RT}{zF\alpha_{an}}\ln\left(\frac{i}{i_{o,an}}\right) + \frac{RT}{zF\alpha_{ca}}\ln\left(\frac{i}{i_{o,ca}}\right) \tag{5}$$

where α is the charge transfer coefficients, i is the current density (A/cm^2), i_0 is the exchange current density.

When hydrogen and oxygen gases are generated, the effect of gas bubble coverage in the liquid electrolyte can be expressed in terms of temperature and pressure as follows (Jang, 2021a):

$$\theta = 0.23(i)^{0.3}\left(\frac{T}{T_{ref}}\frac{P_{ref}}{P}\right)^{\frac{2}{3}} \tag{6}$$

Activation overvoltage can be calculated by applying the bubble coverage coefficient of Eq.(6) to Eq.(5).

3.1.3. Ohmic overvoltage

Ohmic overvoltage is energy loss due to resistance and can be expressed through Ohm's law as follows (Jang, 2021a):

$$V_{ohm} = I \times (R_{ca} + R_{an} + R_{KOH} + R_{Sep}) \tag{7}$$

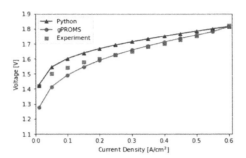

Figure 2. Model validation results by cell voltage

where I is the current of the electrolysis, $R_{ca}, R_{an}, R_{KOH}, R_{Sep}$ are the resistance of the cathode, anode, KOH solution, and separator.

The electrode resistance and electrolyte resistance are calculated based on the conductivity.

3.1.4. Hydrogen production rate

Hydrogen production can be expressed as follows:

$$\dot{n}_{H_2} = \eta \frac{I}{zF} N_{cell} \tag{8}$$

where η is the Faraday efficiency, z is the number of electrons transferred per reaction ($z=2$), N_{cell} is the number of cells in the stack.

3.2. AWE system modelling in gPROMS

The AWE cell model is integrated into the ECR module of gPROMS using a custom model template, and a simulation of the AWE system is constructed using the gML Process module. The energy consumption, stack power and balance of plant (BOP), of the AWE system is:

$$W_{System} = W_{Stack} + W_{Heater\_an} + W_{Heater\_ca} + W_{Condenser\_O2} + W_{Condenser\_H2} +$$
$$W_{pump\_an} + W_{pump\_ca} + W_{Compressor} \tag{9}$$

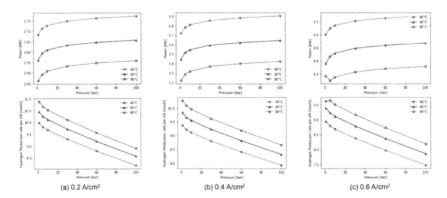

Figure 3. Power and hydrogen production efficiency without compression

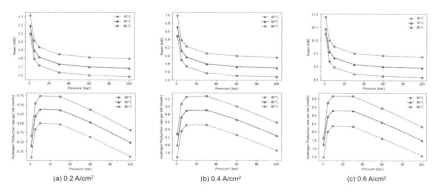

Figure 4. Power and hydrogen production efficiency with compression

4. Simulation Results

4.1. Model validation

The developed model was verified through cell voltage according to current density for AWE cells developed by Korea Institute of Energy Research (KIER), Figure 2 is the results of model validation. The Python-based cell model showed high accuracy ($R^2=0.813$). gPROMS utilized the cell model also indicated high accuracy ($R^2=0.8$), and revealed an R-squared of 0.985 at a current density of 0.2-0.6 A/cm².

4.2. AWE system simulation

Assuming that the hydrogen produced from the AWE system is compressed to 200 bar, 3 current densities (0.2, 0.4, 0.6 A/cm²), 3 temperatures (40, 60, 80 ℃), 6 pressures (1, 5, 10, 30, 60, 100 bar), a total of 54 cases were simulated.

4.2.1. Without compressor power

Figure 3 shows the total power consumption and hydrogen production efficiency when the compression process of produced hydrogen is not considered. At 0.2, 0.4 A/cm², as the pressure increases, the power consumption increases and the hydrogen production efficiency decreases. At 0.6 A/cm², when the pressure increases from 1 bar to 5 bar, the power consumption decreases, which is a phenomenon that temporarily decreases because the decrease effect of the bubble effect is greater than the increase of the reversible voltage caused by the increase in pressure.

Table 1. Stack, total BOP, compressor, and total power consumption at 0.6 A/cm², 80 ℃

Pressure [bar]	Stack Power [kW]	Total BOP [kW]	Comp. Power [kW]	Total Power [kW]	Hydrogen Production [mol/h]	Hydrogen Production per kW
1	7.893	0.470	1.892	10.255	80.493	7.849
5	7.879	0.422	0.900	9.201	80.043	8.700
10	7.934	0.418	0.619	8.971	79.482	8.860
30	8.016	0.414	0.289	8.719	77.262	8.861
60	8.067	0.412	0.157	8.636	74.001	8.569
100	8.105	0.408	0.077	8.591	69.775	8.122

4.2.2. With compressor power

Figure 4 indicates the total power consumption and hydrogen production efficiency with the compression power consumption. In all cases, at the higher pressure, the lower power consumption is indicated because the power consumption for compression up to 200 bar occupies a high proportion in the total power. The hydrogen production per kW of energy consumption presented optimal values at 10 to 30 bar, as shown in Table 1. Compared with the case with no compression at design condition (0.6 A/cm^2, 80 °C), the optimum operating pressure is increased by 6 times from 5 bar to 30 bar.

5. Conclusions

The digital twin supports data-based decision making, optimization, control, and anomaly detection and diagnosis, so it will contribute to the improvement of sustainability, agility and productivity in chemical plant. In this study, a AWE simulation model was developed using Python and gPROMS, which is basis of the development of digital twin, it is expected to improve the productivity of the AWE system resulting in reducing green hydrogen production cost.

The effect of pressure on the performance was evaluated by the developed model. The optimal operating conditions of the AWE system were compared between excluding the compression and including the compression to 200 bar to analyze the impact of the compression process. When excluding the process of compression, it showed the optimal operating pressure range of 1 to 5 bar, and including compression demonstrated the optimal range of 10 to 30 bar. However, process equipment cost becomes higher at high pressure, therefore, it is essential to consider hydrogen compression to the storage pressure, including the equipment cost, in order to decide the optimal operating conditions.

References

M. Hammoudi, C. Henao, K. Agbossou, Y. Dube, M. L. Doumbia, (2012), "New multi-physics approach for modelling and design of alkaline electrolyzers", *Int. J. Hydrog. Energy*, **37**, 13895-13913

D. Jang, H. Cho, S. Kang, (2021a), "Numerical modeling and anlaysis of the effect of pressure on the performance of an alkaline water electrolysis system", *Appl. Energy*, **287**, 116554

D. Jang, W. Choi, H. Cho, W. C. Cho, C. H. Kim, S. Kang, (2021b), "Numerical modeling and analysis of the temperature effect on the performance of an alkaline water electrolysis system", *J. Power Sources*, **506**, 230106

O. Ulleberg, (2003), "Modeling of advanced alkaline electrolyzers: a system simulation approach", *Int. J. Hydrog.*, **28**, 21-33

Acknowledgements

This research was partly supported by Korea Institute for Advancement of Technology(KIAT) grant funded by the Korea Government(MOTIE)(P0008475, Development Program for Smart Digital Engineering Specialist) and Korea Institute of Energy Technology Evaluation and Planning(KETEP) grant funded by the Korea government(MOTIE)(20207200000070, Development of performance standardization and operation risk estimation for renewable energy-linked alkaline water electrolysis hydrogen production systems using digital twins).

Proceedings of the 14th International Symposium on Process Systems Engineering – PSE 2021+
June 19-23, 2022, Kyoto, Japan © 2022 Elsevier B.V. All rights reserved.
http://dx.doi.org/10.1016/B978-0-323-85159-6.50248-7

Cyber Security Risks of aspects of operations of OPC Unified Architecture

Mariko FUJIMOTO[a], Takuho MITSUNAGA[b], Tatsuki MATSUZAWA[a], Yoshihiro HASHIMOTO[a]

[a] *Nagoya Institute of Technology, Aichi 466-8555, JAPAN*
[b] *Toyo University, Tokyo 115-0053, JAPAN*
m.shigemori.037@stn.nitech.ac.jp

Abstract

OPC Unified Architecture (OPC UA) is a new OPC standard that is the successor of OPC Classic, and it has various security features. Generally, OPC UA is considered to be secure, but if it is not appropriately implemented or configured, there might be cyber risks. In this research, evaluate the cyber risks of OPC UA using several OPC UA products. We focus on security features of OPC UA: application authentication, user Authentication, encryption, and signing. We will show the evaluation result under each typical security configuration in several OPC UA products, then introduce points of attention for OPC UA security configurations and operations based on the evaluation result. Cyber risks and corresponding measures described in this research should be conscious by OPC UA product venders, system integrators and operators of Industrial Control System.

Keywords: OPC UA, Cyber security, Penetration test, Operational Technology

1. Introduction

OLE[1] for Process Control (OPC)[2] is the interoperability standard for reliable data exchange in industrial automation. It ensures the seamless flow of information among devices from multiple vendors. OPC Classic (OPA Data Access) is a legacy OPC standard, and its security has been under discussion. Although a new OPC standard OPC Unified Architecture (OPC UA) was released in 2016, OPC Classic is still widely used.

OPC UA is a recommended communication standard in Reference Architecture Model Industrie 4.0 (RAMI4.0)[3], and all devices will be connected through OPC UA. Since OPC UA has many security features, it is recommended to migrate to OPC UA as early as possible. However, since OPC UA has also potential security risks if it is not appropriately configured and operated, recognizing security risks and corresponding measure of OPC UA are very important. In this research, we introduce the flexibility of OPC UA security settings and cyber risks in aspects of operation under each security setting. We prove cyber risks through penetration tests against several OPC UA

---

[1] Object Linking and Embedding: A technology that allows embedding and linking to documents and other objects, developed by Microsoft

[2] OLE for Process Control: A set of standards developed by a joint collaboration of leading automation industry suppliers

[3] A three-dimensional consolidation of the most important aspects of Industrie 4.0, ensuring that all participants in Industrie 4.0 share a common perspective and build a common understanding

commercial products, then propose recommended OPC UA security configurations and operations. We focus on the following security features of OPC UA.

-Application authentication: Authentication of OPC UA client application using application certificates

-User Authentication: Authentication of users of OPC UA clients using passwords or user certificates

-Encryption and signing of OPC UA communication

2. Related Research

R. Huang et al. (2010) discussed OPC UA system security issues from the views of the OPC UA application environment and OPC UA communication security. L. Roepert et al. (2020) discuss methods to discover OPC UA servers, test their authentication, obtain their configuration, and check for vulnerabilities. Both R. Huang et al. (2010) and L. Roepert et al. (2020) did not focus on cyber risks and potential attack scenarios. J. Polge, et al. (2019) identified the threats and countermeasures that may occur/be applied when using OPC-UA and proved the impact of the eavesdropping and message flooding attacks on an OPC-UA application using a real testbed. However, they evaluated an encryption suite that has average security strength. W. Matsuda et al. (2021) proved cyber risks of OPC UA using the strong encryption suite, but they evaluated only one product, detailed consideration on the result is not conducted. For the above reasons, we evaluate the cyber risks of OPC UA including strong security features through penetration tests using several OPC UA products and discuss the result.

3. Proposed approach

We evaluate the security features (authentication and encryption) of OPC UA through penetration tests using several OPC UA products and introduce security practices based on the test result.

3.1. Attack scenarios

The purpose of the attack scenario is to prove the cyber risks of attacks inappropriate implementation of OPC UA. We assume that the pentesters have been intruded into the legitimate OPC UA client PC and started attacks from the legitimate OPC UA client PC assuming that the PC had been infected with the malware. We make the hypothesis that if security configurations of OPC UA are not appropriately implemented, there could be the following security risks.

1. **Unauthorized connection**: If attackers can get information to connect OPC Server, they could connect to the OPC Server from an unauthorized client.

2. **The decryption of OPC UA message**: Forward security is a feature of specific key agreement protocols that gives assurances that session keys will not be compromised even if long-term secrets used in the session key exchange are compromised. According to W. Matsuda et al. (2021) OPC UA specification

does not refer to forward security. Therefore, if attackers could steal secret keys for OPC UA, they could decrypt the encrypted communication of OPC UA.

3.2. Evaluation environment

Table 1 shows the evaluation target OPC UA products, and Table 2 shows used tools for evaluation. For security and privacy reasons, we do not describe each product name and vendor used in the evaluation. Table 3 and Table 4 show evaluation target OPC UA security features.

Table 1 OPC UA server products for evaluation

Product	Product usage
A	PLC with OPC UA server unit
B	OPC server software including OPC UA server
C	An industrial middleware including OPC UA server

Table 2 Tools used for evaluation

Product name	Description	Purpose
UaExpert	Free OPC UA client application	For legitimate OPC UA client
Python OPC-UA	Open source OPC UA server and client application	For malicious OPC UA client (attacker)
Wireshark	Network protocol analyser	For snooping communications

Table 3 Security Mode of OPC UA

Mode name	Description
None	Setting which does not need any message signature and encryption
Sign *1	Setting which generates message signature using the private key of senders
Sign & Encrypt *1	Setting which generates message signature using the private key of senders, and encrypts messages using the private key of receivers

*1: We evaluate a strongest policy, "Basic256Sha256".

Table 4 User authentication type of OPC UA

Setting	Description
Anonymous	Setting which does not need any user authentication
ID and password (ID / pass)	Setting which authenticates the client using the password
User certificate	Setting which authenticates client using user certificate

4. Evaluation Result

4.1. Unauthorised connection to OPC UA server

Table 5 shows the result of the unauthorized connection to the OPC UA Server for each security setting condition. Without depending on products, it was possible to connect OPC servers from computers and applications that are not used in legitimate operations if attackers were able to get the necessary information. After the successful unauthorized connection, pentesters succeeded to read and changing each parameter value of the OPC servers.

Table 5 Result of unauthorized connection to OPC UA servers

OPC UA server setting		Conditions for success of attack		Encryption
Security mode	User authentication	Client private key & certificate	Client credential	
None	Anonymous	Unnecessary	Unnecessary	No
	ID / pass	Unnecessary	Mandatory (ID / pass)	No
	User certificate*2	Unnecessary	Mandatory (User certificate)	No
Sign	Anonymous	Mandatory	Unnecessary	No
Sign& Encrypt	Anonymous	Mandatory	Unnecessary	Yes
	ID / pass	Mandatory	Mandatory (ID / pass)	Yes
	User certificate	Mandatory	Mandatory (User certificate)	Yes

*2: Evaluated only for 1 product that supports user certificate.

The followings are discussions on the result.

- When security mode is None and Anonymous is allowed, pentesters can connect to the OPC server without any condition.

-If user authentication is enabled, pentesters need a legitimate user ID and password or certificate. Note that user ID is sent in plain text when the security mode is None, and some products do not support user certificates.

When security mode is "Sign" or "Sign&Encrypt", pentesters need the application certificate and corresponding private key of the legitimate OPC UA client. Note that communication is not encrypted when the security mode is "Sign".

- Application certificates and corresponding private keys are located in the installation directory of the OPC UA client application. Thus, pentesters who intruded into the OPC UA client computers could easily obtain them.

4.2. Decryption of OPC UA message

Table 6 shows the result of the decryption of the OPC UA message. Without depending on products, it was possible to decrypt OPC UA messages if attackers were able to get the client's and server's private keys. After the success of decryption and decoding, pentesters succeeded to extract the parameter values and node IDs of the OPC servers.

Table 6 Result of decryption of OPC UA message

OPC UA server setting		Conditions for success of attack			Decryption
Security mode	User authentication	Client private key	Server private key	Client credential	
Sign&	Anonymous	Mandatory	Mandatory	Unnecessary	Success
Encrypt	ID / pass	Mandatory	Mandatory	Unnecessary	Success

The followings are the decryption procedures.

1. Snoop communications between OPC UA clients and servers.

2. Stole OPC server private keys stored in the products installation directory.

3. Stole OPC client private keys stored in the legitimate OPC UA client PCs.

4. Extract and decrypt clients' and servers' nonce from snooped messages. nonces are included in the Open Secure Channel request and response, and they were encrypted by the server's / client's secret keys.

5. Make symmetric keys from clients' and servers' nonce.

6. Decrypt OPC UA Secure Conversation messages using the symmetric keys.

7. Decode parameter values from decrypted messages.

The followings are discussions on the result.

If attackers can obtain secret keys of the OPC UA server and client, they could decrypt OPC UA messages. However, since the message is encoded, attackers should get information about the OPC UA message structures and decode data.

5. Recommendation for secure practice using OPC UA

This section describes OPC UA security practices based on the evaluation result.

- Set Security Mode to Sign & Encrypt to enable digital signature and encryption for OPC UA messages. "Sign" reduces the risk of unauthorized connection but note that communication is not encrypted.

-Even if the OPC server does not configure with "Sign and encrypt", it might be possible to encrypt messages if the client connects with "Sign and encrypt" in some products.

- Disable anonymous access and enable user authentication for OPC UA. Then use supported user authentication methods (ID and password, certificate, etc.) The ID and password, user certificate should be managed in a secure way.

- Many OPC UA applications provide functions to export private keys and certificates and change the security level of the OPC UA. Thus, access control or authentication of OPC UA applications and configuration tools of OPC UA should be enabled to prevent attackers to steal sensitive information or changing security configuration maliciously.

- Manage private keys and certificates of both OPC UA servers and clients in a secure way. For instance, private keys should be protected with passwords. OPC server and client application vendors should support private keys protected by passwords.

 If disclosure of private keys is suspected, security risks can be reduced by invalidating the corresponding certificate in OPC UA client and server applications.

 - When the OPC UA server and client firstly communicate, operators should carefully confirm each certificate is issued by a trusted host. That is because once certificates are trusted, they are used until certificates are regenerated or revoked. Some OPC UA products provide options to skip the verification or automatic acceptance of certificates, but they should not be enabled.

- The cipher suites for signature and encryption depend on security policy. Use the recommended security policy in the OPC UA specification.

- Many OPC UA applications store certificates and private keys as files without protection. Thus, computers that run OPC UA servers and clients should be protected in OS level and network-level security in addition to the application security.

6. Conclusions

In this paper, we evaluated the cyber risks of OPC UA through penetration tests against several OPC UA products. OPC UA is useful for improving security, but there could be cyber risks if security features are not configured appropriately. We introduced the security practice in aspects of operations of OPC UA based on the penetration test result.

References

R. Huang, F. Liu and D. Pan, 2010, "Research on OPC UA security," 2010 5th IEEE Conference on Industrial Electronics and Applications, pp. 1439-1444

W. Matsuda, M. Fujimoto, Y. Hashimoto and T. Mitsunaga, 2021, "Cyber Security Risks of Technical Components in Industry 4.0," 2021 IEEE International Conference on Omni-Layer Intelligent Systems (COINS), pp. 1-7

B. Mihir and Y. Bennet, 2003, Forward-Security in Private-Key Cryptography, Springer Berlin Heidelberg

J. Polge, J. Robert and Y. L. Traon, 2019, "Assessing the impact of attacks on OPC-UA applications in the Industry 4.0 era," 2019 16th IEEE Annual Consumer Communications & Networking Conference (CCNC), pp. 1-6

L. Roepert, M. Dahlmanns, I. Berenice Fink, J. Pennekamp, M. Henze, 2020, Assessing the Security of OPC UA Deployments, the 1st ITG Workshop on IT Security (ITSec)

Z. Veichtlbauer, Armin and Ortmayer, Martin and Heistracher, Thomas, 2017, OPC UA integration for field devices, 2017 IEEE 15th International Conference on Industrial Informatics (INDIN)

Proceedings of the 14th International Symposium on Process Systems Engineering – PSE 2021+
June 19-23, 2022, Kyoto, Japan © 2022 Elsevier B.V. All rights reserved.
http://dx.doi.org/10.1016/B978-0-323-85159-6.50249-9

Managing Experimental-Computational Workflows in Robotic Platforms using Directed Acyclic Graphs

Federico M. Mione[a], Alexis N. Silva[a], Martin F. Luna[a], M. Nicolas Cruz B.[b,c], Ernesto C. Martinez*[a]

[a]INGAR (CONICET-UTN), S3002GJC Santa Fe, Argentina
[b]KIWI-biolab, Bioprocess Engineering, TU Berlin, Ackerstrasse 76, 13355 Berlin, Germany
[c]DataHow AG, Zürichstrasse 137, 8600 Dübendorf, Switzerland
ecmarti@santafe-conicet.gov.ar

Abstract

Robotic platforms can gather informative data sets to accomplish different modeling or optimization goals for bioprocess development by resorting to on-line redesign of multiple parallel experiments. For reproducible data analysis is key to formally represent and manage experimental-computational workflows in high-throughput experimentation by enforcing FAIR principles. To represent workflows of a robotic platform, directed acyclic graphs (or DAGs) are proposed. Computational implementation of DAGs using open-source software (Apache Airflow) not only helps FAIRizing data and experimental protocols but also obliges making explicit all methods, models, assumptions and hyperparameters used to carry out modeling and optimization tasks. Model-based productivity optimization of a bioprocess based on data from nine fed-batch parallel cultivations is used as an example. Data generated in the parallel experiments are first used to re-estimate online the model parameters and the updated model is used to optimize the feeding profile. Managing experimental-computational workflows as DAGs in the Airflow ecosystem using containers is key to foster the use of FAIR principles in modeling and optimization, and to facilitate access/reuse of costly experimental data.

Keywords: bioprocess development, FAIR principles, high-throughput experimentation, online experimental redesign, workflow automation.

1. Introduction

Reproducible results are key to compare computational methods and validate experimentally solutions found and their related models. However, in the recent survey work of Baker (2016) it was revealed that more than 70% of researchers have been unsuccessful in reproducing the outcomes of research experiments made by others and more than 50% cannot reproduce solutions and data obtained by their own research studies. For reproducible bioprocess development, experimental data used for predicting the dynamic behaviour of genetically modified microorganism and the effect of different combinations of process parameters on the productivity levels must be obtained using FAIR principles (Celebi et al., 2021). To this aim, these principles must be accounted for in the specification of all protocols and workflows used to generate data sets for different modeling or optimization goals by resorting to on-line (re)design of parallel experiments (Haby et al., 2019). This work deals with FAIRizing experimental workflows involving tasks such as feeding, sampling, at-line analytical processing, etc., which generates data. These workflows are intertwined with data processing pipelines for (re)estimating model parameters, experimental execution monitoring and on-line redesign which must also be FAIR. For widespread usage of FAIR principles in bioprocess development, experimental-computational workflows are represented here as directed acyclic graphs (DAGs) that make experimental protocols reproducible within the Apache Airflow environment (Harenslak and de Ruiter, 2021) using software containers (Dockers) that foster portability and reusability of data, methods and experimental protocols.

2. Experimental-computational Workflows

The FAIR principles (Wilkinson et al., 2016), describe a set of requirements for data management and stewardship to make research data **F**indable, **A**ccessible, **I**nteroperable, and **R**eusable. The FAIR principles are a set of guidelines that aim to maximize the value and usefulness of experimental data and highlight the importance of making experimental protocols and workflows digital objects findable and reusable by others. To this aim, the combination of DAGs with a Common Workflow Language in the Apache Airflow ecosystem is an appealing alternative for introducing FAIR principles in high-throughput experimentation facilities for bioprocess development.

Experimental-computational workflows describe the complex multi-step methods that are used for experimental design, data sampling, data preparation, model building, and active learning that led to new data products with maximum information content. Thus, this type of workflows describes a process (a set of activities) for computational or physical tasks, where different parts of the process (the tasks) are interdependent, e.g., a task can start processing after its predecessors have been (partially) completed and where data flows between tasks define the synchronization constraints. In robotic platforms for high-throughput experimentation, experimental protocols (feeding, sampling, at-line sample processing, etc.) which generates data are intertwined with computational tasks involving update of model parameters using new data and online redesign of the parallel asynchronous experiments to make the resulting data more informative for a given purpose, such as productivity optimization, strain screening or model selection.

In Fig. 1, an abstract DAG for parallel experimentation in a robotic platform involving several mini bioreactors (MBRs) arranged as subsets (columns) is shown. Cultivations can run asynchronously, but sampling must comply with some precedence constraints due to robot operation limitations. Also, for model update and online redesign data from samples for all MBRs or a group thereof must be known (a synchronization constraint). Depending on the robotic facility, the overall experiment structure can be represented at different abstraction levels using DAGs that account, to the desired level of detail, for all precedence and synchronization constraints between macro-tasks such as sample collection or liquid handling blocks at a more abstract level. Each macro-task is also internally described by a DAG where simple tasks are related to liquid handling for substrate/medium feeding or pH/Dissolved Oxygen Tension (DOT) control (see Haby et al., 2019, for details).

To guarantee FAIR data and experimental-computational workflows, a shared database is proposed for interfacing a computational pipeline that manages the parallel experiments in the robotic platform (bottom) with a pipeline of physical macro-tasks for sample collection and liquid handling (top) as it is show in the DAG of Fig. 2. Once the dummy node "Start" triggers both "parallel cultivations" and "experiment execution" nodes, the sampling times are calculated in the "Get Sample" node, which in turn triggers the execution of both the "sample collection" node and the sensing node "Get Sample Results". Once samples taken have been analysed, resulting experimental data as well as experimental design parameters related to sampling times and liquid handling tasks are saved in a local database. As soon as sampled data can be retrieved from the shared database, the "Parameter Update" node is executed followed by the node "Online Redesign," which in turn triggers the "Liquid Handling" macro-task that executes liquid handling tasks as a macro-action or block until the next change to the experimental planned tasks in the remaining part of the experiment based on new data.

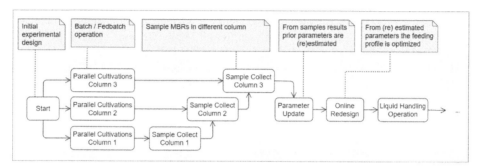

Fig. 1. Simple DAG to represent macro-tasks precedence/synchronization constraints

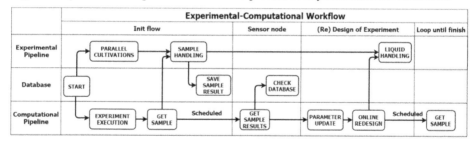

Fig. 2. An abstract DAG that integrates experimental and computational pipelines

3. Case study

To illustrate the advantages of the proposed approach, a simple robotic platform made up of nine MBRs involving the fed-batch cultivations of a microorganism are simulated using the pyFOOMB package (Hemmerich et al., 2021). More specifically, the Example 7 in the repository at https://github.com/MicroPhen/pyFOOMB will be used. As there exist uncertainty in the value of two model parameters μ_{max} and $Y_{P/X}$, the objective is to generate data which is maximally informative to define an optimal exponential feeding profile of the substrate S which is parameterized by t_F and μ_{Set} as follows:

$$F = \begin{cases} 0 & t < t_F \wedge V_L > V_{L,max} \\ \dfrac{c_{s,0} \cdot V_{L,0} \cdot \mu_{set}}{c_{S,F} - c_S} \cdot e^{\mu_{set}(t-t_F)} & t \geq t_F \end{cases} \quad (1)$$

Thus, there is an initial batch phase until t_F which is followed by a fed-batch mode of operation where the substrate exponential feeding rate is defined by μ_{Set}. The concentration parameters in Eq. (1) are related to the initial, in the feed stream and current substrate concentrations, respectively, whose values are assumed constant as well as the initial volume of each bioreactor. The model parameters for the *in-silico* simulator used for generating sampled data are given in Table 1. Also, in Table 1 are the assumed *a priori* values for model parameters before collecting any new data in the simulated parallel experiments. The goal of the experimental design is to generate data to estimate the optimal feeding profile for maximizing the final concentration of the product once the maximum volume is reached. Initial conditions are chosen the same for all MBRs as follows: X(biomass)=0.1 g/L, S(substrate)=40 g/L, P (product)= 0 g/L, V(volume)=1.0 L.

The *a priori* parameters in Table 1 are used to define the initial design of the nine parallel experiments. Firstly, the estimated optimal values of the feeding parameters are obtained: t_F=8 min   and μ_{Set}= 0.2 min⁻¹ . To start with, for all MBRs the same value for t_F is used. Secondly, the feed rate parameter for each MBR will be defined based on the (re)estimated optimal μ_{Set} (in percentages of it) as detailed in Table 2. The chosen parallel experiment design aims to introduce arbitrarily a certain degree of exploration by biasing data gathering towards a region of operating conditions that are most informative for maximizing the final concentration of the product P.

No samples will be taken from any of the bioreactors during the batch phase. During the fed-batch phase, sampling is organized by columns of bioreactors. Simultaneous sampling is only feasible for MBRs in the same column. Accordingly, after four minutes in fed-batch operation, the three bioreactors in column 1 are sampled. After another minute, the MBRs in column 2 and, one minute later the MBRs in column 3 are sampled.

For the sake of simplicity, let's assume that the time for analytical processing of the samples taken is negligible. Thus, 7 min after t_F, the two uncertain model parameters μ_{max} and $Y_{P/X}$ are re-estimated using new sampled data. On this basis, online experimental redesign is carried out and an updated value for μ_{Set} is obtained, Then, the substrate feeding profile in each MBR is changed accordingly based on the percentages of the re-estimated optimal feeding rates as detailed in Table 2. This procedure is repeated until volumetric capacities of all MBRs are full. Please refer to the repository at:

https://git.tu-berlin.de/bvt-htbd/kiwi/tf2/experimental-computational-workflows

for details about all methods used and their hyper-parameters. Note that the *a posteriori* model parameters over-estimate the product formation rate from biomass (see values for $Y_{P/X}$ in Table 1). As new data are sampled, μ_{max} and $Y_{P/X}$ have much closer values to those of the *in-silico* model. Results obtained for the optimal feeding profiles are summarized in Table 3 and Fig. 3. As shown in Fig. 3, the predicted dynamics of product formation resembles the evolution of the *in-silico* model reasonably well.

Table 1. Model parameters

Parameter	*In-silico*	*A priori*	*A posteriori*
K_S	0.02	0.02	0.02
μ_{max}	**0.4**	**0.3**	**0.398**
$Y_{X/S}$	0.5	0.5	0.5
$Y_{P/X}$	**0.2**	**0.35**	**0.203**
$C_{S,F}$ [g/L]	500.0	500.0	500.0
V_0 [L]	1.0	1.0	1.0
V_{max} [L]	2.5	2.5	2.5

Table 2. Updated feeding rates

MBR	Col 1	Col 2	Col 3
Top	102 %	101 %	103 %
Centre	96 %	100 %	104 %
Bottom	97 %	99 %	98 %

4. Airflow-based implementation environment

4.1. Architecture of the workflow manager

The overall architecture for the workflow manager in the Apache Airflow environment is shown in Fig. 4. In the schema, the interaction between the experiment execution manager (administration console) and the Airflow environment for DAGs management using projects (experiments in the robotic platform) is depicted. From this console, the execution manager completely specifies the structure and parameters of an experiment and triggers its execution. To oversee a project execution, the project manager also has at its disposal the Airflow ecosystem made up of three main components. Firstly, a PostgreSQL database to archive execution details of DAGs scheduled in the project alongside with results obtained, and the defined user preferences. Secondly, the "scheduler" which is the core of the Airflow environment that manages the resources available for parallel processing of tasks and enforces precedence and synchronization constraints. Finally, the web services which provide a user-friendly interface to monitor the execution of DAGs and micro-services to archive results obtained in a local memory.

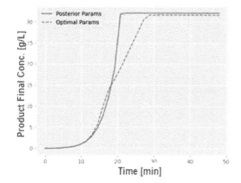

Table 3. Optimized policies compared

	In Silico	*A Posteriori*
μ_{Set}	**0.150**	**0.230**
t_F [min]	**8.0**	**8.0**
P_{final}[g/L]	**31.59**	**32.07**

Fig. 3. Final product concentrations compared

4.2. Project workflow manager

Each project in the Airflow DAGs execution environment is organized using nodes as shown in Fig. 5. The structure of files (left) is composed using Docker (centre) which are eventually managed as specific nodes in the DAGs used to execute an experiment. Each node is individually executed using a Docker container. At the end of each node script execution, its corresponding container is automatically destroyed.

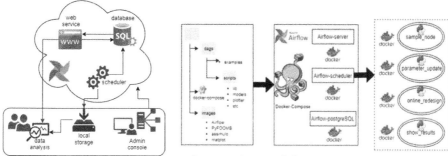

Fig. 4. Architecture   Fig. 5. Project workflow manager

4.3. Airflow ecosystem

Each project in the Airflow DAGs execution environment is organized using nodes as shown in Fig. 5. The structure of files (left) is composed using Docker containers (centre) which are eventually managed as specific nodes in the pipelines used to execute an experiment and build models from data (see Fig. 6). Each node is individually executed using a Docker container. This is necessary to transform a detailed experimental protocol into a workflow which can be understood by other modelers and experimenters. At the end of each node script execution, its corresponding container is automatically destroyed.

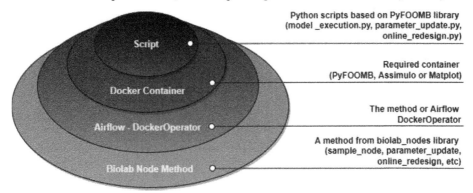

Fig. 6. Layered structure of the Airflow ecosystem

5. Concluding remarks

Simulation results demonstrate that DAGs and the Apache Airflow ecosystem are key enablers for enforcing FAIR principles in bioprocess development. The open-source nature of the software used for modeling and optimization makes experimental-computational workflows reproducible, methods transparent, and data accessible.

Acknowledgments–This work was supported by the German Federal Ministry of Education and Research through the Program "International Future Labs for Artificial Intelligence" (Grant number 01DD20002A).

References

M. Baker, 2016, 1,500 scientists lift the lid on reproducibility, Nature, 533, 7604, 452–454.

R. Celebi, J. R. Moreira, A. Hassan, S. Ayyar, L. Ridder, T. Kuhn, M. Dumontier, 2020, Towards FAIR protocols and workflows: the OpenPREDICT use case. Peer J Comput. Sci. 6:e281.

B. Haby, S. Hans, E. Anane, A. Sawatzki, N. Krausch, P. Neubauer, M. N. Cruz B., 2019, Integrated Robotic Mini Bioreactor Platform for Automated, Parallel Microbial Cultivation With Online Data Handling and Process Control, SLAS Technology, 24, 6, 569–582.

B. Harenslak, J. de Ruiter, 2021, Data Pipelines with Apache Airflow. Manning Publications.

J. Hemmerich, N. Tenhaef, W. Wiechert, S. Noack, 2021, pyFOOMB: Python framework for object oriented modeling of bioprocesses, Engineering in the Life Sciences, Eng Life Sci., 1–16. DOI: 10.1002/elsc.202000088.

M. D. Wilkinson, et al., 2016, The FAIR guiding principles for scientific data management and stewardship. Nature 3:160018 DOI 10.1038/sdata.2016.18.

Proceedings of the 14th International Symposium on Process Systems Engineering – PSE 2021+
June 19-23, 2022, Kyoto, Japan © 2022 Elsevier B.V. All rights reserved.
http://dx.doi.org/10.1016/B978-0-323-85159-6.50250-5

Development of cyber incident exercise to be widely adopted in supply chains

Yukiya Saito[a*], Erika Mizuno[a], Tetsushi Miwa[a], Koki Watarai[a], Yukino Suzuki[a], Midori Sumi[a], Takashi Hamaguchi[a], Yoshihiro Hashimoto[a]

aNagoya Insititute of Technology, Nagoya 466-8555 Japan
clf19018@nitech.jp

Abstract

Industrial control systems (ICSs) are used for various kinds of social infrastructure, and these ICSs play important roles in achieving their control functions and in ensuring safety. Therefore, the cyber security of the ICSs needs to be improved. To mitigate the success of cyber-attacks on ICSs, we need to take into account suitable cooperation not from just one organization but from multiple organizations, including the companies in their supply chains. Therefore, incident response exercises require cooperation among multiple organizations. However, some hurdles related to participation in exercises are a major obstacle to improving the resilience of incident response exercises. The hurdles for participating in such exercises must be lowered. This paper focuses on this point and on the online IMANE Card we developed.

Keywords: Cyber security; Exercise; Control systems; Card game; Incident response

1. Introduction

Industrial control systems (ICSs) are used for various kinds of social infrastructure, and these ICSs play important roles in achieving their control functions and in ensuring safety. Therefore, the cyber security of the ICSs needs to be improved. Ordinarily, ICS networks have been isolated in factories. However, the ICS networks tend to connect to external networks, because a connection between the information technology (IT) system and operational technology (OT) system is required for business. Therefore, the number of cyber threats to the ICSs is increasing, and successful cyber-attacks against the ICSs can directly affect physical objects. Blout (2021) testified, a top oil company in the United States was hit by a ransomware attack in May 2021. The attack caused an incident in which the pipeline was shut down for six days, and it had a great impact on various types of fuel transport and storage. Discontinuation of services by such incidents can cause a great deal of damage to citizens' lives, companies' business, government services, and so on [1]. Cyber security for supply chains is important for our lives. However, eliminating system vulnerabilities is difficult. In addition, cyber-attacks are caused by maliciousness. Therefore, the effects of cyber-attacks are difficult to prevent even when using countermeasures. When an incident occurs due to cyber-attacks, the entire organization is required to take prompt action under limited time, cost, and resources. Moreover, safety management, business continuity management, and issue solutions must be undertaken to respond with organizational cooperation, too. Cyber-attacks are cleverly hidden and quickly spread through IT-OT networks. Therefore, identifying the intruded and attacked zone is very difficult. Even if the malware can be removed once, reinfection can occur when the countermeasures are insufficient. Suitable cooperation from not only one organization but multiple organizations, including the companies in their supply chains, is necessary to counter such cyber-attacks. Therefore, incident response exercises require cooperation among multiple organizations, and Hashimoto et al. (2019) have developed systems for incident response exercises. They are called the IMANE (short for Incident MANagement Exercise) series, and they were designed to improve resiliency against cyber-attacks. The IMANE series has been used for exercises in workshops with various people. To improve the resiliency of multiple organizations, we need to assume that various people, such as those from group companies including superiors and subordinates, will participate. As a result, another problem may arise regarding participation in the exercises. For example, people in organizations that may have their supply chain contracts terminated may be considered risky and may hesitate to participate in the exercises. Such hurdles related to participation are major obstacles to improving resilience. The hurdles for participating in such exercises must be lowered. This paper focuses on this point and improvement one of the exercises we developed, the IMANE Card.

2. IMANE CARD

2.1 Components of the IMANE Card

The IMANE Card exercise is card-based and discussion-based. We positioned the exercise as an introduction to an incident response exercise for cyber-attacks. The participants are divided into several groups with facilitators. The participants surround one worksheet and conduct an incident response to cyber-attacks while discussing the matter with all the participants in each group.

In the IMANE Card exercise, exercise planners prepare a situation such as a virtual company and business content, plants, an organization chart and contact network, an incident scenario, etc., for the incident response exercise. In this paper, we use an example situation where one electric power company uses a hot water supply system. All the participants fully grasp the situation as a constraint and work together as a member of the company. The worksheet, milestones, and action cards of the IMANE Card are as shown in the Figure 1. This worksheet is divided into swim lanes for the actors' roles in the incident scenario. The swim lanes are presented vertically in chronological order. This example includes the computer security incident response team (CSIRT) staff and managers, who are people working in the head office, and the staff and managers of the operation section and information section, who work in the factory.

In the swim lanes, two types of boxes, called milestones, are printed such as events and target situations related to the incident scenario. This example includes the following three events as incident scenario as constraints. CSIRT checks for an increase in junk email at the head office. The information section detects suspicious signal communication on the factory. The operation section notices a change in the water level of the tank on a supervisory control and data acquisition (SCADA) display in the factory. This example features the following two target situations in the incident scenario as constraints: the recovery of abnormal water level in the tank and the resumption of the hot water supply. The participants put action cards on the worksheet. As shown in Figure 2, the action cards have card a number and name on both sides. The front side of the action card describes the concrete action as to what the card is for and the card user as to which roles the card can be used for, and some action cards have requirement states listed such as a plant stoppage. The back side of the card describes the results of the card usage in the incident scenario. The participants can imagine what kinds of roles will do what in these cards.

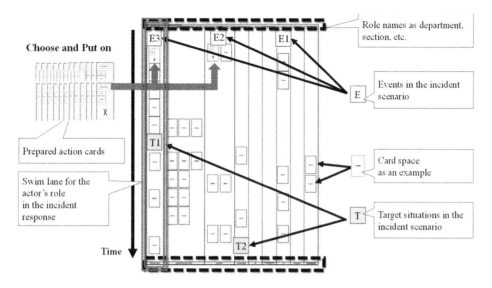

Figure 1: Worksheet, milestones, and action cards of the IMANE Card

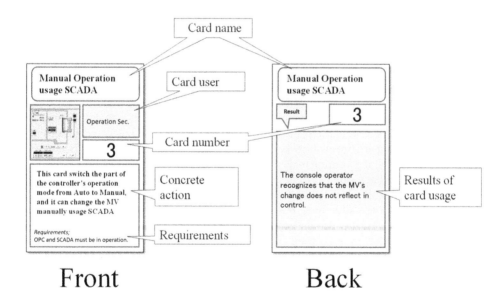

Figure 2: Action card content

For example, when the participants want to use the 17th card, the 17th card describes the situation when the 28th card is used as a prerequisite. The card arrangement order is as shown in Figure 3. As mentioned, the participants choose the suitable incident response from the prepared action cards while discussing the situation within the group. Therefore, the participants can work on exercises even if they do not have specialized knowledge about the activities of roles and cyber-attacks.

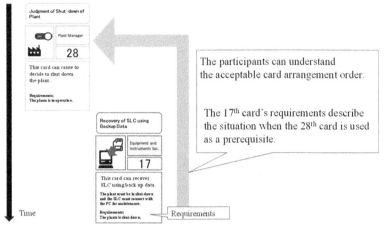

Figure 3: Card arrangement order

2.2 Procedure for the IMANE Card exercise

The IMANE Card exercise is carried out in the following phases.

     Phase 1: The participants from each organization gather at the exercise place.
     Phase 2: They receive some explanations about the exercise during a briefing.
     Phase 3: They make a workflow and start a discussion during the exercise.
     Phase 4: They review the exercise during the debriefing.
     Phase 5: The exercise is declared over. The participants go back to work.

In phase 1, the participants gather at the exercise place. In phase 2, they must learn various information and knowledge about the exercise system and procedures, the virtual company, and so on prior to the exercise in phase 3. In phase 3, they make a workflow and start a discussion. The participants fully grasp the worksheet and the incident scenario as constraints. The participants browse the action cards, check the role of each card and the person in charge of execution in the virtual company, flip the cards over, read the new situation from the back side as needed, and put the suitable action cards in the correct position of the suitable swim lanes. In this way, they think about what to do next as part of the incident response. Moreover, they also consider the information linkage with other roles as suitable information for the appropriate timing as necessary, and they must show the communications with arrows and description across the swim lanes. In this way, they can discuss and consider what communications between different roles are needed to enable suitable organizational cooperation. Each facilitator supports the progress by asking the participants what they have decided and why and by answering questions from the participants. In phase 4, they review and discuss their own worksheet as a deliverable. After that, for the debriefing, the participants compare the worksheet and other groups' worksheets and discuss the incident response to deepen their awareness. The feedback is very important to improve the resiliency. In phase 5, they return to each workplace.

3. Online IMANE Card

3.1 The hurdles to improve for the incident response exercise

The following three hurdles are the focus to make it easier for various people to participate. The first hurdle is caused from a loss to the own organization due to failure in the incident response exercise. For example, the contract may be terminated by the contractor as mentioned. Therefore, the planner must improve the exercise to enable participants to disclose as little information as necessary about themselves online in order not to have a negative impact on the working relationships when participating in the exercise. The second hurdle is the time and cost needed for the incident response exercise. For example, the physical distance to the venue can also be a major factor of this hurdle. Therefore, the planner must reduce the total time for the incident response exercise. The final hurdle is the anxiety about the lack of expertise in cyber-attacks and so on. For example, the participants may be unfamiliar with the terminology. Therefore, the planner must improve to supply the needed information to the participants on demand. In this paper, we present the online IMANE Card we developed to mitigate the impact of these three hurdles.

3.2 Components of the online IMANE Card

The online IMANE Card is based on a cloud-based online whiteboard. The online whiteboard can update the changes in real time among the participants. The necessary information required for the exercises, worksheet, card storage area, mouse pointers of other participants, overall view, and so on is in the online whiteboard of Figure 4.

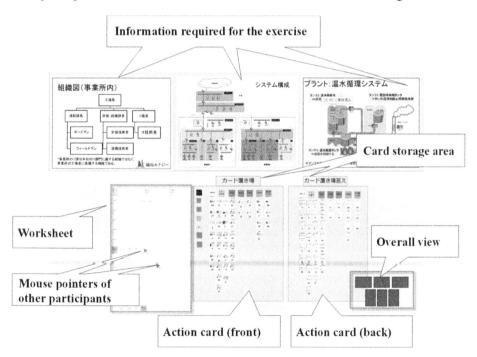

Figure 4: Online IMANE Card

The information required for the exercises such as a virtual company, business contents, the plant, organization chart and contact network, and so on are included. Action cards with a front and back are located separately in the card storage area. These are the master cards. The participants must copy the front action card and put it in the swim lane, respectively. The icons of the mouse pointers of other participants show the movement of the other participants. Each participant and facilitator can see what the other participants are focusing on, which cards they are controlling, etc. The overall view shows the participants screen's area in the overall whiteboard. This view should make it easy to move and zoom in and out for the participants and facilitator. In addition, an online meeting tool is used for discussions that are necessary during the exercises.

3.3 Procedure for the online IMANE Card exercise

In phase 1 and 5, the participants do not have to gather in one place. The participants need to prepare a PC and have an environment where they can connect to the online whiteboard. If the participants prepare such an environment, they are able to participate in the exercise from anywhere. In phase 2, the exercise planner can use a variety of information to explain the exercises as a feature of the online whiteboard, e.g., URLs, images, and videos. The planner can attach to the online whiteboard not only the actual content needed to perform the exercises, such as the swim lane and action cards, but also the additional information that the participants feel they need such as the imagination of the equipment that appears in the exercise. Also, how to use the online tools is explained in this phase, and icebreaking among the participants is done after that. In phase 3, the participants basically only need to copy and paste and write additional characters when the participants make a worksheet. Each participant can request information that they feel necessary at any time without being aware of the other participants. After putting the card there, the facilitator and the participants read the results of the back card from the card storage area. Exercise planners may have to add new rules when conducting exercises online. The same action card may be put on more than once because the participants place cards using copy and paste. If multiple same action cards are in the swim lanes, the participants have room for further discussion, and only one of them is used at the end of the exercise. In phase 4, not only has the hurdle of participating in the exercise been lowered, but effective aspects to the output have also been revealed. The output is stored as data, making it easier to share, so the participants can expect to get more notices from some other groups and past outputs.

4. Conclusions

In this paper, we focused on the hurdles and presented the online IMANE Card we developed. It can enable more efficient conduct of discussion-based exercises where distance, cost, time, and knowledge associated with exercises for multi-organization participation may be a barrier. To improve resiliency, we need to make a system that enables more people to participate in incident response exercises as many times as possible. As in the proposed method, introducing an exercise that lowers the hurdles to participants also helps to increase the frequency of exercises.

References

J. Blout, 2021, Hearing before the United States Senate Committee on Homeland Security & Governmental Affairs, https://www.hsgac.senate.gov/imo/media/doc/Testimony-Blount-2021-06-08.pdf

Y. Hashimoto, et al., 2019, Proposal for an exercise system for achieving highly resilient organization collaboration for response to unexpected and unavoidable cyber incidents, https://www.nedo.go.jp/content/100907027.pdf

Proceedings of the 14th International Symposium on Process Systems Engineering – PSE 2021+
June 19-23, 2022, Kyoto, Japan © 2022 Elsevier B.V. All rights reserved.
http://dx.doi.org/10.1016/B978-0-323-85159-6.50251-7

Requirements to a digital twin-centered concept for smart manufacturing in modular plants considering distributed knowledge

Jonathan Mädler[a*], Isabell Viedt[a], Julius Lorenz[a], Leon Urbas[a]

*aChair of Process Control Systems & Process Systems Engineering Group,
TU Dresden, 01062 Dresden, Germany*
jonathan.maedler@tu-dresden.de

Abstract

Modular plants are an essential step towards agile production via smart manufacturing in the process industry. An important challenge, however, is that they represent an ecosystem with distributed knowledge between process equipment assembly (PEA) manufacturers and owner/operators (O/Os). This complicates the application of familiar simulation methods. To address this issue, this paper reviews typical simulation tasks in the plant life cycle and investigates the distribution of knowledge in modular plants. While the O/O typically has extensive knowledge about the physical property system of a process, a PEA manufacturer can be expected to develop high equipment related expertise. It is suggested to use a digital twin (DT) to integrate these knowledge parts considering intellectual property concerns. The DT will be provided by the PEA-manufacturer, must be customizable through standardized interfaces, and should be applicable to different simulation tasks in the plant life cycle. To realize this concept, quality requirements specifications for DTs related to these simulation tasks must be developed. In addition, standardized interface specifications for the integration of physical property packages, the communication between different DTs and the simulation of DTs must be matured. Furthermore, hierarchical and horizontal DT structures are required to foster re-use of sub-models for different simulation tasks.

Keywords: digital twin, smart manufacturing, cyber-physical systems, modularization

1. Introduction

The process industry is facing increasing requirements to product individualization and time-to-market. Smart manufacturing is recognized as a concept to promote agile production across manufacturing and process industries and can therefore provide a solution to these challenges. Lu et al. (2020) distinguish four key features of smart manufacturing systems: (1) context- and self-awareness, (2) modularity, (3) self-organization, and (4) data-driven decision-making. Modular plants (MPs) built from process equipment assemblies (PEAs) (VDI, 2020) provide a promising solution for the feature (2) 'modularity' of smart manufacturing systems for the process industry. However, the features (1), (3) and (4) have virtually not yet been addressed for the MP concept.

The process systems engineering (PSE) community developed powerful methods and tools for modelling, simulation and control which are suitable to promote these features but due to the expectable knowledge distribution between PEA manufacturers and owner/operators (O/O) in smart MPs, adaptations to these methods and tools will be required. Current publications of the process engineering community like Radatz et al. (2019) and Schindel et al. (2021) did not acknowledge this challenge.

Thus, the remainder of this paper is structured as follows: firstly, simulation tasks in the life cycle of conventional and MPs are reviewed; afterwards the digital twin (DT) and the distribution of knowledge in MPs are investigated. Based on the gained insights, requirements to a DT-based concept for smart manufacturing in MPs are derived, and finally a conclusion is provided discussing further research needs.

2. Simulation in the life cycle of conventional and modular plants

Modelling, simulation, and control are key tools to provide the features (3) 'self-organization' and (4) 'data-driven decision-making' for smart manufacturing systems. Oppelt et al. (2015) define four typical simulation tasks: 'design simulation and optimization', 'virtual commissioning', 'operator training' and 'plant and online optimization', which can be assigned to different phases in the life cycle of conventional plants. The goal and utilized methods differ between these tasks. The goal of (1) **design simulation and offline optimization** is to design and layout a process plant. In conceptual design, abstract unit operations are used to derive requirements to the equipment. In basic engineering, concrete equipment is designed based on these requirements. Finally, their models are combined for process simulation and optimization to find the best operating point. Applying (2) **virtual commissioning**, the automation system including the control code is tested. For this purpose, the automation system is coupled to a dynamic simulation model that mimics the behavior of the real plant. (3) **Operator training** is used to train the plant's operating staff. Simulation models are applied to mimic the real plants behavior in regular operation and failure scenarios. Finally, (4) **plant and online optimization** summarizes a broad variety of model-based support methods and tools applied during the operation phase. E.g., model predictive controllers (MPCs) are used to calculate the best operation trajectory.

In MPs, the life cycle is divided into a PEA and a MP lifecycle (see figure 1). PEA design and engineering should rely on a PEA-type specification predefined by one or more O/Os. In this phase, **design simulation & offline optimization** as well as **virtual commissioning** can be applied similar to conventional plants. Afterwards, the PEA will be fed into the plant life cycle. On the plant level, the basic engineering and detailed engineering are combined under the term orchestration by the modularization community. **Design simulation and offline optimization** change due to the transition of plant design from a sequence of equipment design tasks to a sequence of PEA selection tasks.

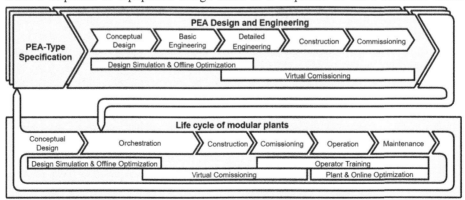

Figure 1: Simulation tasks in the life cycle of modular plants

Schindel et al. (2021) describe a general approach for technology and PEA matching in MPs. In their workflow, simulation is suggested to be used to support technology and PEA match as well as more detailed process design after choosing relevant PEAs. Radatz et al. (2019) formulate the design problem as a multi-objective superstructure optimization problem. Both papers concur in the assumption that a PEA database with simulation models of sufficient fidelity is available to the O/O. The **virtual commissioning** of MPs has been discussed e.g. by Schenk et al. (2019). The authors suggest the virtual PEA as a container packed with all virtual commissioning relevant artifacts which are needed to support the plant engineering of MPs. These models shall be used to test recipes and interlocks on MP layer. **Operator training** and **plant & online optimization** have not been addressed in the literature before.

3. The digital twin and the distribution of knowledge in modular plants

Boschert et al. (2018) define the DT as a 'semantically linked collection of the relevant digital artefacts including design and engineering data, operational data and behavioral descriptions'. Such a collection is mandatory to provide feature (1) 'context- and self-awareness' of smart manufacturing systems. In MPs, a distribution of knowledge between PEA manufacturers of high expertise and O/Os must be expected. This distribution can be illustrated applying the **product-process-resource-model** of the digital twin by Bamberg et al. (2021) (see figure 2). In this model, the **product model** represents process engineering knowledge about physical properties of pure components and mixtures, product specification, etc. (Bamberg et al., 2021). From a process simulation point of view, the product model can be related to the physical property data. In MPs, O/Os will own this knowledge and will strive to protect it from disclosure due to intellectual property (IP) concerns. The **process model** does represent physical laws, thermodynamic models, etc. and therefore equations used for the modeling (Bamberg et al., 2021). Major parts of the process model base on publicly available knowledge and are used by O/Os and PEA manufacturers alike. The **resource model** contains the 'mechanical, functional, and operational attributes of […] all equipment elements' (Bamberg et al., 2021). Hence, it characterizes the equipment with parameters like the volume of a vessel diameter. In MPs, this knowledge will be held by PEA manufacturers. Product and process model can be combined to form the **transformation model** which is a plant-independent description of the process and can be applied to derive theoretical limits e.g. of separation steps (Bamberg et al., 2021). Furthermore, it can be used to derive requirements to a concrete plant and PEAs like residence times, through puts etc. (Bamberg et al., 2021). This type of model is strongly related to the conceptual design phase of the plant life cycle of conventional and modular plants. The **capability model** is created combining the process and the resource model. It forms a product independent description of the dynamic

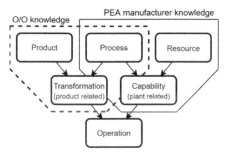

Figure 2: Knowledge distribution in MPs based on the DT structure by Bamberg et al. (2021)

behavior of a plant, equipment (Bamberg et al., 2021) or hence also a PEA. Capabilities can be estimated for ranges of material property parameters or default material system. One example are water run models, which can be applied for the purpose of virtual commissioning. Finally, the combination of transformation and capability model forms the **operation model** (Bamberg et al., 2021). This type of model is required for the optimization of process parameters and recipes for a specific product and MP. In general, this combination of information is required for the more sophisticated sub-steps in every simulation task during the plant life cycle. Therefore, a concept is required which permits to utilize the prior knowledge of both stakeholders without necessarily disclosing it.

4. A digital twin-centered concept for smart manufacturing in MPs

4.1. The smart PEA as cyber-physical system for smart manufacturing in modular plants
To address features (1), (3) and (4) of smart manufacturing systems, the modular plant concept must be extended to permit knowledge exchange and support the standard simulation tasks. At the same time, IP concerns must be considered. Thus, we suggest combining a real PEA, a digital twin of the PEA (PEA-DT), and related algorithms into a so-called smart PEA (sPEA). PEA-DTs will be composed of several information and simulation models and integrated with use case specific algorithms. In the following, requirements to PEA-DTs are discussed und R&D challenges are derived.

4.2. Simulation in the life cycle of smart modular plants

4.2.1. Design simulation and offline optimization in smart modular plants
Considering the knowledge distribution between sPEA-manufacturer and O/O, design simulation and offline optimization in smart MPs can be envisioned to split into four steps. Firstly, in a conceptual design phase the O/O will apply **transformation models** independently of specific equipment to derive requirements to the former. Based on these requirements, the O/O can find different sPEA candidates from several manufacturers or define a new PEA-type specification. The sPEA manufacturers then provide customizable **capability models** in form of downloadable or remotely accessible PEA-DTs. Hence, the PEA-DT will be used as specification of the real PEA. The O/O than must be able to customize the PEA-DTs with physical property packages to derive **operation models** from the capability model. Carrying out further process simulations using the PEA-DTs the O/O will be able to derive informed decisions which sPEAs to purchase or rent. After the physical PEA arrived, an experimentation, identification, and validation step will be necessary to reduce uncertainty of the models and validate the choice of sPEA. Finally, the identified PEA-DTs might be used to derive optimal operating points of the system. To realize this vision, PEA-DTs need to provide a sub-model describing process behavior of the PEA based on MESH equations. The external control inputs to the model should be chosen in line with the adjustable service parameters of the real PEA. The automation and control system of the sPEA itself can usually be assumed to behave ideally. The PEA-DT must provide standardized interfaces to integrate custom physical property packages, exchange mass, energy and information flows, and control the solution process. Considering model quality, the PEA-DT should provide a good accuracy, good validity around typical operation points and a high robustness. As described above, internals of simulation models might be confidential. Therefore, simulation and optimization algorithms which do not require the disclosure of the model are necessary.

4.2.2. Virtual commissioning in smart modular plants
The goal of virtual commissioning is to test the recipe with service timings and parameters, and interlocks on MP level. For this purpose, a system of PEA-DTs must be

combined in a simulation environment and coupled to the real process orchestration layer (POL), which operates the real MP afterwards. Two PEA-DTs with different levels of sophistication can be envisioned to do so. Firstly, a **capability model** considering a default material system (e.g.: water+air) and the automation system with device and I/O-models, a representation of the controller in a software-in-the-loop or model-in-the-loop configuration (cf. VDI/VDE 3693) and the OPC UA server could be used to test service sequences and interlocks. To gain a more precise picture off timings and service parameters for control loops an **operation model** will be required. Therefore, the capability model must be extendable with a physical property package. Interfaces for property packages, simulation control, and mass and energy flows can be handled like the design simulation case. The interface for information flows must be reconfigured to operate with the same service commands and data assemblies as the real PEA. The PEA-DT must provide a wide validity range, medium accuracy, and a robust numerical behavior. The simulation environment must support real time and accelerated, hybrid continuous- and discrete-time simulation since the O/O will want to test recipes and interlocks as fast as possible in a virtual environment. Accelerated simulation will require the POL to operate in a synchronized, accelerated mode as well.

4.2.3. Operator training in smart modular plants

Since, a higher fluctuation of plant configuration must be expected in MPs, operator training simulation could become a valuable tool to allow the operating staff to keep up with the changing production scenarios. Operator training does require very sophisticated process system and automation system models. In extension to 4.2.1 and 4.2.2, models must consider behavior in failure cases, which can be triggered actively and passively. Such behavior must be built in by the PEA manufacturer. The models must be combined with the POL including an operator training environment (e.g.: an app), which can be used to provide process scenarios. The interfaces of the PEA-DT are the same as in the virtual commissioning case for the most part, but an interface to actively trigger failures and provide additional feedback on failure behavior will be required. The PEA-DTs must provide a great validity range, high accuracy, high robustness, and high performance for this scenario. Simulation algorithms remain like in the virtual commissioning case.

4.2.4. Online optimization in smart modular plants

Similar to conventional plants, several different online optimization methods can be applied in smart MPs. They can be implemented on the PEA or MP level. On PEA level, the PEA-DT can be used to adjust control loops, provide MPCs, etc. In the opposite direction, the PEA-DT shall be adjusted to the state of the real PEA applying identification methods. On the plant level, PEA-DTs can be combined to e.g. provide plant wide MPCs. In most cases, the interface configuration of design simulation will be suitable for online optimization on the plant level as well. The required model quality will vary between applications. Therefore, model reduction and surrogate modeling shall be used to trade-off validity range, accuracy, robustness, and performance. The required simulation and optimization algorithms are diverse as well.

4.3. R&D challenges

Four major R&D challenges can be derived based on these requirements. Firstly, the standard simulation tasks must be related to specifiable and testable quality requirements to DTs. This is a precondition to allow certification of DTs by independent instances for specific simulation task. A promising approach is the application of quality models relying on factors, criteria and metrics (FCM) adapted from software development (Mädler et al., 2021). Secondly, standardized and open interfaces for physical property packages, flows and simulation control must be matured to allow vendor independent exchange and application of DTs. The CAPE OPEN initiative developed promising interface specifications which are a first step but currently lack support. Another promising standard is the functional mock-up interface (FMI). Thirdly, simulation and optimization algorithms which do not require disclosure of the DT internals should be further developed. Current equation-based system simulation approaches relying on equation system manipulation will sometimes be prohibited since model internals are protected due to IP concerns. Modular sequential approaches and co-simulation will be needed to simulate process systems with distributed knowledge. Surrogate modeling and simulation offer another solution approach since freely accessible surrogates could be generated of protected PEA-DTs. Finally, hierarchical and horizontal DT structures and their semantic description should be matured to foster re-use of sub-models for different simulation tasks. Currently, multiple simulation models for different purposes are developed independently during the plant life cycle. The toolchains do not support a smooth transition of valuable sub-models from phase to phase. Matured structuring and semantic enrichment could help to overcome these issues.

5. Conclusion

In this paper, we suggest a sPEA-based approach to smart manufacturing in MPs and derive requirements to this concept. Standard PSE simulation tasks can provide self-organization and data-driven decision-making capabilities to smart MPs. Context- and self-awareness can be provided by PEA-DTs. Due to the distribution of knowledge between sPEA-manufacturers and O/Os new requirements to methods and workflows arise. We identify (1) quality assurance and specification of simulation models, (2) open and standardized interfaces, (3) simulation and optimization algorithms considering IP issues and (4) model structuring and semantic description as important R&D challenges.

References

A. Bamberg, L. Urbas, S. Bröcker, M. Bortz, and N. Kockmann, 2021, The Digital Twin–Your Ingenious Companion for Process Engineering and Smart Production, Chem Eng Technol, 44, 6, 954–961

S. Boschert, C. Heinrich, and R. Rosen, 2018, Next generation digital twin, Proc. TMCE, 7–11

M. Liu, S. Fang, H. Dong, and C. Xu, 2021, Review of digital twin about concepts, technologies, and industrial applications, J Manuf Syst, 58, 346-361

J. Mädler, I. Viedt, and L. Urbas, 2021, Applying quality assurance concepts from software development to simulation model assessment in smart equipment. In Computer Aided Chemical Engineering, 50, 813-818, Elsevier

M. Oppelt, G. Wolf, and L. Urbas, 2015, Towards an integrated use of simulation within the life-cycle of a process plant, IEEE 20th Conference on Emerging Technologies & Factory Automation (ETFA), 1–8

H. Radatz, M. Schröder, C. Becker, C. Bramsiepe, and G. Schembecker, 2019, Selection of equipment modules for a flexible modular production plant by a multi-objective evolutionary algorithm. Comput Chem Eng, 123, 196–221.

T. Schenk, A. Botero Halblaub, R. Rosen, T. Heinzerling, J. Mädler, A. Klose, S. Hensel, and L. Urbas, 2019, Co-Simulation-based virtual Commissioning for modular process plants - Requirements, Framework and Support-Toolchain for a Virtual Automation Testing Environment, Automation 2019, 229–242

A.-L. Schindel, M. Polyakova, D. Harding, H. Weinhold, F. Stenger, M. Grünewald, and C. Bramsiepe, 2021, General approach for technology and Process Equipment Assembly (PEA) selection in process design, Chem Eng Process, 159, 108223

VDI 2776-1:2020-11, 2020, Modular plants – Fundamentals and planning modular plants

VDI/VDE 3693:2016-08, 2016, Virtual commissioning – Model types and glossary

Printed and bound by CPI Group (UK) Ltd, Croydon, CR0 4YY

03/10/2024

01040326-0012